ELEMENTARY LINEAR ALGEBRA

Third Edition

Roland E. Larson

The Pennsylvania State University
The Behrend College

Bruce H. Edwards

The University of Florida

D. C. Heath and Company

Lexington, Massachusetts   Toronto

Address editorial correspondence to:

D. C. Heath and Company
125 Spring Street
Lexington, MA 02173

Acquisitions: Ann Marie Jones
Development: Kathleen Sessa-Federico
Editorial Production: Rachel D'Angelo Wimberly
Design: David Ford
Art Editing: Gary Crespo
Production Coordination: Richard Tonachel

Trademark Acknowledgments: TI is a registered trademark of Texas Instruments Incorporated. Casio is a registered trademark of Casio, Inc. Sharp is a registered trademark of Sharp Electronics Corporation. *Maple* is a registered trademark of Waterloo Maple Software. *Mathematica* is a registered trademark of Wolfram Research, Inc. *Derive* is a registered trademark of Soft Warehouse, Inc. IBM PC is a registered trademark of International Business Machines Corporation. Macintosh is a registered trademark of Apple Computer, Inc. HP is a registered trademark of Hewlett Packard Company. MATLAB is a registered trademark of The MathWorks, Inc. For information on MATLAB, contact The MathWorks, Inc., 24 Prime Park Way, Natick, Massachusetts, 01760-1500.

Published simultaneously in Canada.

Printed in the United States of America.

International Standard Book Number: 0-669-39641-9 (Student Edition)

International Standard Book Number: 0-669-39917-5 (International Edition)

Library of Congress Catalog Number: 95-75260

3456789-DOC-00 99 98 97

PREFACE

Elementary Linear Algebra, Third Edition, is intended for use in an introductory course in linear algebra. Typical students in this course are sophomores or juniors majoring in engineering, computer science, mathematics, economics, statistics, science, or operations research. In writing the text, our primary goal is to present the main ideas of linear algebra clearly and concisely.

For many students, this course represents the first encounter with mathematical formalism. Hence, we have carefully balanced theory with examples, applications, and geometric intuition. We offer a wide variety of interesting, motivational material in the optional applications sections. Even if an instructor chooses not to cover applications, students will see these sections and realize that the subject has wide utility.

The order and coverage of topics were chosen for maximum efficiency, effectiveness, and balance. For example, in Chapter 4 we present the main ideas of vector spaces and bases, beginning with a brief look at R^2 and R^n and leading into the vector space concept as a natural extension of these familiar examples. This material is often the most difficult for students, but our approach to linear independence, span, basis, and dimension is carefully explained and contains many illustrative examples.

While the eigenvalue problem is developed in detail in Chapter 7, we help lay an intuitive foundation for students with earlier problems such as Exercises 55 and 56 in Section 1.2 (page 25), Exercises 43 and 44 in Section 3.1 (page 118), and Exercise 58 in the Chapter 4 Review Exercises (page 235). In addition, an optional discussion appears in Section 3.3.

As is true for most introductory college courses in mathematics, the primary prerequisite for this course is algebra. We also assume familiarity with analytical geometry and trigonometry. Calculus is not a prerequisite for this course. Although there are several examples and exercises that require calculus, these are clearly labeled and can be omitted without loss of continuity.

FEATURES OF THE THIRD EDITION

Improved Coverage   The much-appreciated suggestions of users and reviewers and the recommendations of the Linear Algebra Curriculum Study Group have been carefully considered, and many of these have been incorporated. We have included new subsections on partitioned matrices and *LU*-decomposition in Chapter 2 (Sections 2.1 and 2.4, respectively), an opportunity to discuss eigenvalues in Chapter 3 (Section 3.3), a new section on least squares and mathematical models in Chapter 5 (Section 5.4), and mathematical induction in Appendix B. In addition, throughout the text we have refined the wording of explanations, definitions, theorems, and proofs. For example, see the discussions of row equivalence in Section 2.4 (page 80), the rank and nullity of a matrix in Section 4.6 (pages 202–215), and coordinates and change of basis in Section 4.7 (pages 216–224). We have also placed a greater emphasis on vectors as column matrices.

The chapters in the text have been renumbered to fit the way most instructors use the text. Complex Vector Spaces is now covered in Chapter 8; Linear Programming (which can be covered any time after Chapter 2) is now covered in Chapter 9; and Numerical Methods is covered in Chapter 10. The topics in the numerical methods chapter can also be covered at any appropriate time in the course.

What Is Linear Algebra?   A general introduction to linear algebra now appears before the first chapter and is designed to provide students with an overview of the subject and a brief look at some of the reasons for studying it.

Theorems and Proofs   Every effort was made to state the theorems in comprehensible language—usually preceded by explanations and followed by examples. Proofs of the theorems are treated in several ways. When it is pedagogically sound to do so, proofs are presented in complete detail. Other times, proofs are given in outline form, omitting cumbersome computations. To give students practice in writing proofs, the proofs of several theorems are left as exercises. For example, see Exercises 43–50 in Section 2.2 (page 63), Exercises 39–41 in Section 4.1 (page 166), and Exercise 21 in Section 6.4 (page 358). A few of the more involved proofs are given in Appendix A, and the very few that are beyond the scope of an introductory text are omitted completely.

Graphics and Geometric Emphasis   The text contains numerous figures, including a number of new ones on quadric surfaces in Section 7.4. The text's graphics provide geometrical interpretation of problems, show how linear transformations can be used to rotate figures in two- and three-dimensional space, illustrate geometric aspects of projections and reflections, and aid in visualization of concepts. Special care has been taken to produce accurate graphs.

Applications   The last section of each of Chapters 1–7 and Chapter 10 is devoted to applications of linear algebra. Coverage of this material is left to the discretion of the instructor and is not required in subsequent chapters. We have provided a wide variety of interesting and substantive applications covering computer graphics, cryptography, differential equations, population growth, least squares approximations, and Fourier approximations. (A list of these applications is given on page ix.) In some instances, we chose to integrate applications with the presentation of a topic, as with the introduction to matrix multiplication and the development of linear programming.

Technology   Recognizing that graphing calculators, computer algebra systems, and linear algebra software such as MATLAB® (Matrix Laboratory) and MatrixPad are becoming increasingly available, the Third Edition offers the opportunity to use such technology throughout, but does not require its use. This opportunity to experience technology hands-on is achieved through a combination of optional features, including technology used as a means of discovery (see page 106), technology used to reinforce or enhance students' understanding of concepts (page 425 and Exercise 5 in the Chapter 4 MATLAB Exercises on page 237), and technology used as an efficient problem-solving tool (see the Technology Note in Section 2.1 on page 49 and Exercises 29 and 30 in Section 4.6 on pages 214–215).

Clearly labeled exercises that require the use of technology as well as specific MATLAB exercises are included. In addition, Appendix C contains information on various computer algebra systems and graphing calculators as well as a discussion of the roundoff error introduced by technology.

Technology Notes   Throughout the text, we have added Technology Notes to help students use technology appropriately in problem solving. (For instance, see pages 49 and 536.)

Examples   Numerous carefully chosen examples illustrate concepts, computational techniques, and problem-solving approaches.

Discovery   We have added Discovery features to motivate students to discover mathematical ideas and relationships on their own and to help develop an intuitive understanding of theoretical concepts. For instance, see Section 1.1, page 4, and Section 4.1, page 164.

Exercises   Hundreds of new exercises of varying difficulty, including challenging ones, have been added in the Third Edition. These include new exercises on vector spaces other than R^n, writing problems (highlighted with the symbol ▶), and conceptual exercises, proofs, and exercises requiring technology (highlighted with the symbol **C**). The text now has over 2900 problems. Each exercise set begins with skill-building problems that give practice in the computational techniques presented in the section. The problems of a more theoretical nature appear toward the end of the exercise sets. Many exercises use units of measurement from SI (metric) system, as appropriate. Some examples of the new types of problems are Exercise 28 on page 180 in Section 4.3; Exercises 43, 44, 57, and 58 on pages 191–192 in Section 4.4; Exercises 43 and 44 on page 166 in Section 4.1; Exercises 53 and 54 on page 340 in Section 6.2; Exercise 41 on page 126 in Section 3.2; Exercises 52 and 53 on page 136 in Section 3.3; and Exercises 47–50 on pages 11–12 in Section 1.1.

Review Exercises provide an extensive set of problems that summarize the important skills and concepts of each chapter. The exercises that were contained in the supplementary problem sets in the previous edition have now been incorporated into the review exercise sets.

MATLAB Exercises   One of the new kinds of exercises we have added is the optional MATLAB (Matrix Laboratory) exercises. Appearing as a special group at the end of most chapters, these exercises are designed to enhance students' understanding of concepts.

Projects   New projects appear at the end of each of the first eight chapters. These projects can serve as group activities or more extensive homework assignments. Some projects are theoretical, while others are oriented more toward applications and encourage the use of technology.

Cumulative Tests   Cumulative tests now appear after Chapters 3, 5, and 7, helping students reinforce the knowledge they have accumulated throughout the text and preparing them for exams and future courses.

Historical Notes   Each chapter begins with a biographical sketch of a mathematician who contributed to the development of linear algebra.

Flexibility   To accommodate differing emphases in teaching this course, the book allows for the following flexibility: Chapter 6 on Linear Transformations and Chapter 7 on Eigenvalues and Eigenvectors are interchangeable. There are sufficient applications to use the text in an applications-oriented course. The computational material in Chapters 9 and 10 could be emphasized for a more numerically-oriented course. The text is sufficiently rigorous for the instructor who prefers a proof-oriented course. For the computer-oriented course, computer graphics are covered in Chapter 6, and numerical methods in Chapter 10 can be presented earlier. In addition, there are new opportunities for using technology in the section exercises as well as in the MATLAB problems at the end of most chapters. Brief introductions to various computer software packages and graphing calculators are included in Appendix C. A Computer Applications supplement and MatrixPad computer software are also available. The exercise sets contain a variety of routine computational problems and problems that are more challenging and theoretical.

Enhanced Presentation   A new design improves the overall clarity of the presentation.

Mathematical Induction Appendix   A thorough presentation of mathematical induction now appears in Appendix B.

Technology Appendix   Introductions to MATLAB, MatrixPad, *Mathematica*, *Maple*, *Derive*, and graphing calculators, which are intended to help students use technology in this course, have been added as Appendix C.

Answers to Odd-Numbered Exercises   Every effort was made to provide correct answers to the exercises. Each answer has been carefully checked for accuracy.

SUPPLEMENTS

Student Solutions Guide (0-669-39643-5)

This helpful supplement contains the solutions to all of the odd-numbered section and review exercises and all of the cumulative test questions.

Instructor's Solutions Guide (0-669-39642-7)

This time-saving guide contains the solutions to all of the even-numbered section and review exercises, all of the MATLAB exercises, and all of the Projects.

Test Item File (0-669-39644-3)

This supplement contains a selection of multiple-choice and open-ended test questions. There are 500 test items, two-thirds of which are new.

Computerized Testing for the IBM (DOS and Windows) and the Macintosh

This test-generating software is the entire test item file on disk. It allows instructors to customize tests for their classes.

Technology Keystroke Guide: Elementary Linear Algebra (0-669-39645-1)

Organized by linear algebra topic and following the order of the topics in the text, specific keystroke instructions are given to assist students in working through linear algebra exercises. Coverage includes a selection of graphing calculators and MATLAB. Screen displays, step-by-step examples, and technology tips are included.

Computer Applications (0-669-21554-6)

For those instructors who are interested in additional applications of linear algebra to computer science, including homogeneous coordinates in two and three dimensions and an introduction to cubic splines, we have prepared this supplementary chapter.

MatrixPad Software

This software by Morris Orzech of Queen's University, Ontario, Canada, operates on an IBM-PC and comes with a User's Manual. The use of the disk is optional, but it can be used to great advantage by both instructors and students. This pedagogically driven software can perform basic linear algebra computations using either decimals or fractions, allows for row reduction one step at a time or automatically, provides views of more than one matrix on the screen, and handles eigenvalues and eigenvectors. A brief introduction to this software is included in Appendix C of the text.

ACKNOWLEDGMENTS

We would like to express our appreciation to the many people who helped us while this revision was being prepared. Special thanks go to the following colleagues who reviewed the manuscript and made many helpful suggestions: Glenn Adamson, Ottawa University; Paul Britt, Louisiana State University; Karabi Datta, Northern Illinois University; Julio Guillen, Jersey City State College; Robert Heller, Mississippi State University; Charles Johnson, College of William & Mary; Kirk Jones, Eastern Kentucky University; Leonard Lipkin, University of North Florida; and Robert Maynard, Tidewater Community College.

We would also like to thank the following professors who took time to review the table of contents and respond to our survey: Bruce Bukiet, New Jersey Institute of Technology;

Dietrich Burbulla, University of Toronto; John Christopher, California State University; Karabi Datta, Northern Illinois University; George DeRise, Thomas Nelson Community College; Jerome Eisenfeld, University of Texas at Arlington; William Eitemiller, Colorado Technical College; Robert Heller, Mississippi State University; David Horowitz, Golden West College; Lee Kaminetzky, CUNY-City College; Gary Ling, City College of San Francisco; Leonard Lipkin, University of North Florida; Chunqing Lu, Southern Illinois University; Louis Nachman, Oakland University; Richard Patterson, Indiana University-Purdue; Paul Phillips, Southern Illinois University; Richard Roth, University of Colorado; Ralph Steinlage, University of Dayton; Donald West, SUNY College at Plattsburgh; Pueblo Zafra, Kean College of New Jersey; and John Ziobro, Anne Arundel Community College.

Thanks go to the reviewers of the First and Second Editions: Richard C. Bollinger, Pennsylvania State University; Joseph C. Ferrar, Ohio State University; Marjorie A. Fitting, San Jose State University; David A. Horowitz, Golden West College; Roger H. Marty, Cleveland State University; and David A. Weinberg, Texas Tech University.

A special thanks goes to all of the people at D. C. Heath and Company who worked with us in the development of this text, especially Ann Marie Jones, Mathematics Acquisitions Editor; Kathy Sessa-Federico, Senior Development Editor; Rachel Wimberly, Production Editor; David Ford, Designer; Carolyn Johnson, Editorial Associate; and Richard Tonachel, Production Coordinator.

On a personal level, we are grateful to our wives, Deanna Gilbert Larson and Consuelo Edwards, for their love, patience and support. Also, a special thanks goes to R. Scott O'Neil.

If you have suggestions for improving this text, please feel free to write to us.

Roland E. Larson
Bruce H. Edwards

INDEX OF APPLICATIONS

PROJECTS

CONTENTS

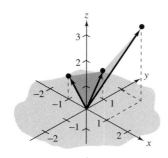

$S_2 = \{(1, 2, 3), (0, 1, 2), (-1, 0, 1)\}$
The vectors in S_2 lie in a
common plane.

Ax = λx

Addition of Complex Numbers

WHAT IS LINEAR ALGEBRA?

To answer the question "What is linear algebra?", let us take a closer look at what we will study in this course. The most fundamental theme of linear algebra, and the first topic covered in this textbook, is the theory of systems of linear equations. You have probably encountered small systems of linear equations in your previous mathematics courses. For example, suppose you travel on a plane between two cities that are 5000 kilometers apart. If the trip one way against a headwind takes $6\frac{1}{4}$ hours and the return trip the same day in the direction of the wind takes only 5 hours, can you find the ground speed of the plane and the speed of the wind, assuming that both remain constant?

If you let x represent the speed of the plane and y the speed of the wind, then the following system models the problem.

$$6.25(x - y) = 5000$$
$$5(x + y) = 5000$$

This system of two equations and two unknowns simplifies to

$$x - y = 800$$
$$x + y = 1000,$$

Original Flight

Return Flight

and the solution is $x = 900$ kilometers per hour and $y = 100$ kilometers per hour. Geometrically, this system represents two lines in the xy–plane. You can see in the figure that these lines intersect at the point $(900, 100)$, which verifies the answer we obtained.

Solving systems of linear equations is one of the most important applications of linear algebra. It has been argued that the majority of all mathematical problems encountered in scientific and industrial applications involve solving a linear system at some point. Linear applications arise in such diverse areas as engineering, chemistry, economics, business, ecology, biology, and psychology.

Of course, the small system presented in the plane example is very easy to solve. In real-world situations, it is not unusual to have to solve systems of hundreds or even thousands of equations. One of the early goals of this course is to develop an algorithm that helps solve larger systems in an orderly manner and is amenable to computer implementation.

The first three chapters of the textbook cover linear systems and two other computational areas you may have studied before: matrices and determinants. These discussions prepare the way for the central theoretical topic of linear algebra: the concept of a vector space. Vector spaces generalize the familiar properties of vectors in the plane. It is at this point in the text that you will begin to write proofs and learn to verify theoretical properties of vector spaces.

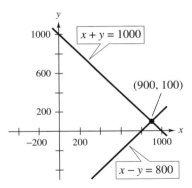

The lines intersect at (900, 100).

Vectors in the Plane

LINEAR ALGEBRA The branch of algebra in which one studies vector (linear) spaces, linear operators (linear mappings), and linear, bilinear, and quadratic functions (functionals and forms) on vector spaces. *(Encyclopedia of Mathematics, Kluwer Academic Press, 1990)*

The concept of a vector space permits us to develop an entire theory of its properties. The theorems we prove will apply to all vector spaces. For example, in Chapter 6 you will study linear transformations, which are special functions between vector spaces. The applications of linear transformations appear almost everywhere: computer graphics, differential equations, and satellite data transmission, to name just a few examples.

Another major focus of linear algebra is the so-called eigenvalue ($\bar{I}$–$g\partial n$–value) problem. Eigenvalues are certain numbers associated with square matrices and are fundamental in applications as diverse as population dynamics, electrical networks, chemical reactions, differential equations, and economics. You might want to glance at Example 5 in Section 10.4, where eigenvalues are used to model the population of human females. This model is based on actual data of birth and survival rates.

Linear algebra strikes a wonderful balance between computation and theory. As we proceed, you will become adept at matrix computations and simultaneously develop abstract reasoning skills. Furthermore, you will see immediately that the applications of linear algebra to other disciplines are plentiful. In fact, you will notice that each chapter of this textbook closes with a section of applications. You might want to peruse some of these sections to see the many diverse areas to which linear algebra can be applied. (An index of these applications appears at the front of the text.)

Linear algebra has become a central course for mathematics majors as well as students of science, business, and engineering. Its balance of computation, theory, and applications to real life, geometry, and other areas, makes linear algebra unique among mathematics courses. For many people who make use of pure and applied mathematics in their professional careers, an understanding and appreciation of linear algebra is indispensable.

1 SYSTEMS OF LINEAR EQUATIONS

Carl Friedrich
Gauss
1 7 7 7 – 1 8 5 5

*C*arl Friedrich Gauss is often ranked—with Archimedes and Newton—as one of the greatest mathematicians in history.

Gauss earned his reputation as "prince of mathematics" early. At eighteen he invented the method of least squares and at nineteen he proved that a seventeen-sided polygon is constructible using only a straightedge and compass. In his doctoral thesis Gauss proved the Fundamental Theorem of Algebra.

Gauss's landmark work in differential geometry derived from his interest in surveying and mapmaking. He also made many other contributions to algebra, complex functions, and potential theory.

Gauss wrote much more than he published. He kept files of many unpublished papers that he considered to be unfinished, inelegant, non-rigorous, or inconcise. Later readers of these papers have generally felt that Gauss was too critical of his own work. His unpublished papers covered work in two major fields: elliptic function theory and non-Euclidean geometry.

In addition to mathematics, Gauss had a keen interest in the physical sciences, especially astronomy; he held an appointment as a professor of astronomy at the University of Göttingen for nearly fifty years. One of his best-known publications in this area is *Theory of Motion of the Heavenly Bodies*, 1809. Gauss also earned great distinction for his research on theoretical and experimental magnetism. He helped improve existing techniques in telegraphy and created a new model for handling optic problems.

1.1 INTRODUCTION TO SYSTEMS OF LINEAR EQUATIONS

Linear algebra is a branch of mathematics rich in theory and applications. This text strikes a balance between the theoretical and the practical. Because linear algebra arose from the study of systems of linear equations, we shall begin with linear equations. Although some material in this first chapter will be familiar to you, we suggest that you study carefully the methods presented here. Doing so will cultivate and clarify your intuition for the more abstract material that follows.

The study of linear algebra demands familiarity with algebra, analytic geometry, and trigonometry. Occasionally you will find examples and exercises requiring a knowledge of calculus; these are clearly marked in the text.

Early in your study of linear algebra you will discover that many of the solution methods involve dozens of arithmetic steps; it is therefore essential to strive to avoid careless errors. A computer or calculator can be very useful to check your work, as well as to perform many of the routine computations in linear algebra.

Linear Equations in n Variables

Recall from analytic geometry that the equation of a line in two-dimensional space has the form

$$a_1 x + a_2 y = b, \quad a_1, a_2, \text{ and } b \text{ are constants.}$$

We call this a **linear equation in two variables** x and y. Similarly, the equation of a plane in three-dimensional space has the form

$$a_1 x + a_2 y + a_3 z = b, \quad a_1, a_2, a_3, \text{ and } b \text{ are constants.}$$

Such an equation is called a **linear equation in three variables** x, y, and z. In general, a linear equation in n variables is defined as follows.

Definition of a Linear Equation in n Variables	A **linear equation in n variables** $x_1, x_2, x_3, \ldots, x_n$ has the form $$a_1 x_1 + a_2 x_2 + a_3 x_3 + \cdots + a_n x_n = b.$$ The **coefficients** $a_1, a_2, a_3, \ldots, a_n$ are real numbers, and the **constant term** b is a real number. The number a_1 is the **leading coefficient**, and x_1 is the **leading variable**.

REMARK: We tend to use letters that occur early in the alphabet to represent constants and letters that occur late in the alphabet to represent variables.

Linear equations have no products or roots of variables and no variables involved in trigonometric, exponential, or logarithmic functions. Variables appear only to the first power. Example 1 lists some equations that are linear and some that are not.

EXAMPLE 1   *Examples of Linear Equations and Nonlinear Equations*

The following equations are linear.

(a) $3x + 2y = 7$

(b) $\frac{1}{2}x + y - \pi z = \sqrt{2}$

(c) $x_1 - 2x_2 + 10x_3 + x_4 = 0$

(d) $\left(\sin \frac{\pi}{2}\right) x_1 - 4x_2 = e^2$

The following equations are not linear.

(a) $xy + z = 2$

(b) $e^x - 2y = 4$

(c) $\sin x_1 + 2x_2 - 3x_3 = 0$

(d) $\frac{1}{x} + \frac{1}{y} = 4$

A **solution** of a linear equation in n variables is a sequence of n real numbers $s_1, s_2, s_3, \ldots, s_n$ arranged so that the equation is satisfied when the values

$$x_1 = s_1, \qquad x_2 = s_2, \qquad x_3 = s_3, \qquad \ldots, \qquad x_n = s_n$$

are substituted into the equation. For example, the equation

$$x_1 + 2x_2 = 4$$

is satisfied when $x_1 = 2$ and $x_2 = 1$. Some other solutions are $x_1 = -4$ and $x_2 = 4$, $x_1 = 0$ and $x_2 = 2$, and $x_1 = -2$ and $x_2 = 3$.

The set of *all* solutions of a linear equation is called its **solution set**, and when this set is found, the equation is said to have been **solved**. To describe the entire solution set of a linear equation, we often use a **parametric representation**, as illustrated in Examples 2 and 3.

EXAMPLE 2   *Parametric Representation of a Solution Set*

Solve the linear equation $x_1 + 2x_2 = 4$.

Solution   To find the solution set of an equation involving two variables, we solve for one of the variables in terms of the other variable. For instance, if we solve for x_1 in terms of x_2, we obtain

$$x_1 = 4 - 2x_2.$$

In this form, the variable x_2 is **free**, which means that it can take on any real value, whereas x_1 is not free, since its value depends on the value assigned to x_2. To represent the infinite number of solutions of this equation, it is convenient to introduce a third variable, t, called a **parameter**. Thus, by letting $x_2 = t$, we can represent the solution set as

$$x_1 = 4 - 2t, \qquad x_2 = t, \quad t \text{ is any real number.}$$

Particular solutions can be obtained by assigning values to the parameter t. For instance, $t = 1$ yields the solution $x_1 = 2$ and $x_2 = 1$, and $t = 4$ yields the solution $x_1 = -4$ and $x_2 = 4$.

The solution set of a linear equation can be represented parametrically in more than one way. For instance, in Example 2 we could have chosen x_1 to be the free variable. The parametric representation of the solution set would then have taken the form

$$x_1 = s, \qquad x_2 = 2 - \tfrac{1}{2}s, \quad s \text{ is any real number.}$$

For convenience, we will follow the convention of choosing as free variables those occurring last in a given equation.

EXAMPLE 3   *Parametric Representation of a Solution Set*

Solve the linear equation $3x + 2y - z = 3$.

Solution   Choosing y and z to be the free variables, we begin by solving for x to obtain

$$3x = 3 - 2y + z$$
$$x = 1 - \tfrac{2}{3}y + \tfrac{1}{3}z .$$

Letting $y = s$ and $z = t$, we obtain the parametric representation

$$x = 1 - \tfrac{2}{3}s + \tfrac{1}{3}t, \qquad y = s, \qquad z = t$$

where s and t are any real numbers. Two particular solutions are

$$x = 1, y = 0, z = 0 \qquad \text{and} \qquad x = 1, y = 1, z = 2.$$

Systems of Linear Equations

A **system of m linear equations in n variables** is a set of m equations, each of which is linear in the same n variables:

$$
\begin{aligned}
a_{11}x_1 + a_{12}x_2 + a_{13}x_3 + \cdots + a_{1n}x_n &= b_1 \\
a_{21}x_1 + a_{22}x_2 + a_{23}x_3 + \cdots + a_{2n}x_n &= b_2 \\
a_{31}x_1 + a_{32}x_2 + a_{33}x_3 + \cdots + a_{3n}x_n &= b_3 \\
&\vdots \\
a_{m1}x_1 + a_{m2}x_2 + a_{m3}x_3 + \cdots + a_{mn}x_n &= b_m.
\end{aligned}
$$

REMARK: The double-subscript notation indicates that a_{ij} is the coefficient of x_j in the ith equation.

A **solution** of a system of linear equations is a sequence of numbers $s_1, s_2, s_3, \ldots, s_n$ that is a solution of each of the linear equations in the system. For example, the system

$$
\begin{aligned}
3x_1 + 2x_2 &= 3 \\
-x_1 + x_2 &= 4
\end{aligned}
$$

has $x_1 = -1$ and $x_2 = 3$ as a solution because *both* equations are satisfied when $x_1 = -1$ and $x_2 = 3$. On the other hand, $x_1 = 1$ and $x_2 = 0$ is not a solution of the system because these values satisfy only the first equation in the system.

DISCOVERY

Graph the two lines

$$
\begin{aligned}
3x - y &= 1 \\
2x - y &= 0
\end{aligned}
$$

in the xy-plane. Where do they intersect? How many solutions does this system of linear equations have?

Repeat this analysis for the pairs of lines

$$
\begin{aligned}
3x - y &= 1 & 3x - y &= 1 \\
3x - y &= 0 & 6x - 2y &= 2
\end{aligned}
$$

In general, what basic types of solution sets are possible for a system of two equations in two unknowns?

It can happen that a system of linear equations has exactly one solution, an infinite number of solutions, or no solution. A system of linear equations is called **consistent** if it has at least one solution and **inconsistent** if it has no solution.

EXAMPLE 4   *Three Systems of Two Equations in Two Variables*

Solve the following systems of linear equations, and graph each system as a pair of straight lines.

(a) $x + y = 3$ (b) $x + y = 3$ (c) $x + y = 3$
    $x - y = -1$ $2x + 2y = 6$ $x + y = 1$

Solution   (a) This system has exactly one solution, $x = 1$ and $y = 2$. This solution can be obtained by adding the two equations to give $2x = 2$, which implies that $x = 1$ and hence $y = 2$. The graph of this system is represented by two *intersecting* lines, as shown in Figure 1.1(a).

(b) This system has an infinite number of solutions because the second equation is the result of multiplying both sides of the first equation by 2. A parametric representation of the solution set is given by

$$x = 3 - t, \qquad y = t, \quad t \text{ is any real number.}$$

The graph of this system is represented by two *coinciding* lines, as shown in Figure 1.1(b).

(c) This system has no solution because it is impossible for the sum of two numbers to be 3 and 1 simultaneously. The graph of this system is represented by two *parallel* lines, as shown in Figure 1.1(c).

Figure 1.1

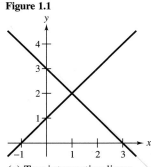

(a) Two intersecting lines:
    $x + y = 3$
    $x - y = -1$

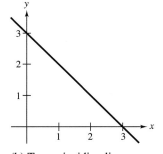

(b) Two coinciding lines:
    $x + y = 3$
    $2x + 2y = 6$

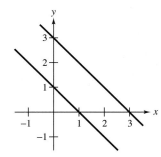

(c) Two parallel lines:
    $x + y = 3$
    $x + y = 1$

Example 4 illustrates the three basic types of solution sets that are possible for a system of linear equations. We state this result here without proof. (The proof is given later in Theorem 2.5.)

Number of Solutions of a System of Linear Equations	For a system of linear equations in n variables, precisely one of the following is true. 1. The system has exactly one solution (consistent system). 2. The system has an infinite number of solutions (consistent system). 3. The system has no solution (inconsistent system).

Solving a System of Linear Equations

Which of the following systems is easier to solve algebraically?

$$\begin{aligned} x - 2y + 3z &= 9 \\ -x + 3y &= -4 \\ 2x - 5y + 5z &= 17 \end{aligned} \qquad \begin{aligned} x - 2y + 3z &= 9 \\ y + 3z &= 5 \\ z &= 2 \end{aligned}$$

The system on the right is clearly easier to solve. We say that this system is in **row-echelon form**, which means that it follows a stair-step pattern and has leading coefficients of 1. To solve such a system, we use a procedure called **back-substitution**.

EXAMPLE 5   *Using Back-Substitution to Solve a System in Row-Echelon Form*

Use back-substitution to solve the system

$$\begin{aligned} x - 2y &= 5 \qquad && \textbf{Equation 1} \\ y &= -2. \qquad && \textbf{Equation 2} \end{aligned}$$

Solution   From Equation 2 we know that $y = -2$. By substituting this value of y into Equation 1, we obtain

$$\begin{aligned} x - 2(-2) &= 5 \qquad && \textbf{Substitute } y = -2. \\ x &= 1. \qquad && \textbf{Solve for } x. \end{aligned}$$

Thus the system has exactly one solution: $x = 1$ and $y = -2$.

The term *back-substitution* implies that we work *backward*. For instance, in Example 5 the second equation gave us the value for y. Then we substituted that value into the first equation to solve for x. Example 6 further demonstrates this procedure.

EXAMPLE 6   *Using Back-Substitution to Solve a System in Row-Echelon Form*

Solve the following system.

$$\begin{aligned} x - 2y + 3z &= 9 \qquad && \textbf{Equation 1} \\ y + 3z &= 5 \qquad && \textbf{Equation 2} \\ z &= 2 \qquad && \textbf{Equation 3} \end{aligned}$$

Solution   From Equation 3 we already know the value of z. To solve for y, we substitute $z = 2$ into Equation 2 to obtain.

$$y + 3(2) = 5 \qquad \text{Substitute } z = 2.$$
$$y = -1. \qquad \text{Solve for } y.$$

Finally, we substitute $y = -1$ and $z = 2$ in Equation 1 to obtain

$$x - 2(-1) + 3(2) = 9 \qquad \text{Substitute } y = -1, z = 2.$$
$$x = 1. \qquad \text{Solve for } x.$$

Thus the solution is $x = 1$, $y = -1$, and $z = 2$.

Two systems of linear equations are called **equivalent** if they have precisely the same solution set. To solve a system that is not in row-echelon form, we first change it to an *equivalent* system that is in row-echelon form by using the following operations.

Operations That Lead to Equivalent Systems of Equations

Each of the following operations on a system of linear equations produces an *equivalent* system.
1. Interchange two equations.
2. Multiply an equation by a nonzero constant.
3. Add a multiple of an equation to another equation.

Rewriting a system of linear equations in row-echelon form usually involves a *chain* of equivalent systems, each of which is obtained by using one of the three basic operations. This process is called **Gaussian elimination**, after the German mathematician Carl Friedrich Gauss (1777–1855).

EXAMPLE 7   *Using Elimination to Rewrite a System in Row-Echelon Form*

Solve the following system.

$$\begin{aligned} x - 2y + 3z &= 9 \\ -x + 3y \phantom{{}+ 3z} &= -4 \\ 2x - 5y + 5z &= 17 \end{aligned}$$

Solution   Although there are several ways to begin, we want to use a systematic procedure that can be applied easily to large systems. We work from the upper left corner of the system, saving the x in the upper left position and eliminating the other x's from the first column.

$$\begin{aligned} x - 2y + 3z &= 9 \\ y + 3z &= 5 \\ 2x - 5y + 5z &= 17 \end{aligned}$$
⟵ Adding the first equation to the second equation produces a new second equation.

$$\begin{aligned} x - 2y + 3z &= 9 \\ y + 3z &= 5 \\ -y - z &= -1 \end{aligned}$$
⟵ Adding -2 times the first equation to the third equation produces a new third equation.

Now that everything but the first x has been eliminated from the first column, we go to work on the second column.

$$\begin{aligned} x - 2y + 3z &= 9 \\ y + 3z &= 5 \\ 2z &= 4 \end{aligned}$$ ⟵   **Adding the second equation to the third equation produces a new third equation.**

$$\begin{aligned} x - 2y + 3z &= 9 \\ y + 3z &= 5 \\ z &= 2 \end{aligned}$$ ⟵   **Multiplying the third equation by $\frac{1}{2}$ produces a new third equation.**

This is the same system we solved in Example 6, and, as in that example, we conclude that the solution is

$$x = 1, \qquad y = -1, \qquad z = 2.$$

Each of the three equations in Example 7 is represented in a three-dimensional coordinate system by a plane. Since the unique solution to the system is the point $(x, y, z) = (1, -1, 2)$, the three planes intersect at the point represented by these coordinates, as shown in Figure 1.2.

Figure 1.2

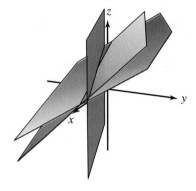

Because many steps are required to solve a system of linear equations, it is very easy to make errors in arithmetic; thus we suggest that you develop the habit of *checking your solution by substituting it into each equation of the original system*. For instance, in Example 7 we can check the solution $x = 1$, $y = -1$, and $z = 2$ as follows.

$$\begin{aligned} \text{Equation 1:} \quad & (1) - 2(-1) + 3(2) = 9 \\ \text{Equation 2:} \quad & -(1) + 3(-1) = -4 \\ \text{Equation 3:} \quad & 2(1) - 5(-1) + 5(2) = 17 \end{aligned}$$ **Check solution in each equation of original system.**

Each of the systems in Examples 5, 6, and 7 has exactly one solution. We now look at an inconsistent system—one that has no solution. The key to recognizing an inconsistent system is reaching an absurdity such as $0 = 7$ at some stage in the elimination process. This is demonstrated in Example 8.

EXAMPLE 8   *An Inconsistent System*

Solve the following system.

$$\begin{aligned} x_1 - 3x_2 + x_3 &= 1 \\ 2x_1 - x_2 - 2x_3 &= 2 \\ x_1 + 2x_2 - 3x_3 &= -1 \end{aligned}$$

Solution

$$\begin{aligned} x_1 - 3x_2 + x_3 &= 1 \\ 5x_2 - 4x_3 &= 0 \\ x_1 + 2x_2 - 3x_3 &= -1 \end{aligned}$$
⟵ Adding -2 times the first equation to the second equation produces a new second equation.

$$\begin{aligned} x_1 - 3x_2 + x_3 &= 1 \\ 5x_2 - 4x_3 &= 0 \\ 5x_2 - 4x_3 &= -2 \end{aligned}$$
Adding -1 times the first equation to the third equation ⟵ produces a new third equation.

(Another way of describing this operation is to say that we *subtracted* the first equation from the third equation to produce a new third equation.) Now, continuing the elimination process, we add -1 times the second equation to the third equation to produce a new third equation.

$$\begin{aligned} x_1 - 3x_2 + x_3 &= 1 \\ 5x_2 - 4x_3 &= 0 \\ 0 &= -2 \end{aligned}$$
Adding -1 times the second equation to the third equation ⟵ produces a new third equation.

Because the third "equation" is absurd, we conclude that this system has no solution. Moreover, because this system is equivalent to the original system, we conclude that the original system also has no solution.

As in Example 7, the three equations in Example 8 represent planes in a three-dimensional coordinate system. In this example, however, the system is inconsistent; hence the planes do not have a point in common, as shown in Figure 1.3.

Figure 1.3

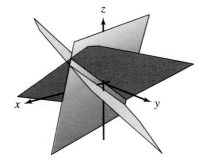

We end this section by looking at a system of linear equations that has an infinite number of solutions. We represent the solution set for such systems in parametric form, as we did in Examples 2 and 3.

EXAMPLE 9   *A System with an Infinite Number of Solutions*

Solve the following system.

$$
\begin{aligned}
x_2 - x_3 &= 0 \\
x_1 \phantom{{}+{}} - 3x_3 &= -1 \\
-x_1 + \phantom{{}3x_2{}} 3x_2 &= 1
\end{aligned}
$$

Solution   We begin by rewriting the system in row-echelon form as follows.

$$
\begin{aligned}
x_1 \phantom{{}+{}} - 3x_3 &= -1 \\
x_2 - x_3 &= 0 \\
-x_1 + 3x_2 \phantom{{}-3x_3{}} &= 1
\end{aligned}
$$
⬅ The first two equations
⬅ are interchanged.

$$
\begin{aligned}
x_1 \phantom{{}+{}} - 3x_3 &= -1 \\
x_2 - x_3 &= 0 \\
3x_2 - 3x_3 &= 0
\end{aligned}
$$
Adding the first equation to
the third equation produces
⬅ a new third equation.

$$
\begin{aligned}
x_1 \phantom{{}+{}} - 3x_3 &= -1 \\
x_2 - x_3 &= 0 \\
0 &= 0
\end{aligned}
$$
Adding −3 times the second
equation to the third equation
⬅ eliminates the third equation.

Because the third equation is unnecessary, we drop it to obtain the following system.

$$
\begin{aligned}
x_1 \phantom{{}+{}} - 3x_3 &= -1 \\
x_2 - x_3 &= 0
\end{aligned}
$$

To represent the solutions, we choose x_3 to be the free variable and represent it by the parameter t. Since $x_2 = x_3$ and $x_1 = 3x_3 - 1$, we can describe the solution set as

$$
x_1 = 3t - 1, \qquad x_2 = t, \qquad x_3 = t, \quad t \text{ is any real number.}
$$

DISCOVERY

Graph the two lines represented by the following system of equations.

$$
\begin{aligned}
x - 2y &= 1 \\
-2x + 3y &= -3
\end{aligned}
$$

You can use Gaussian elimination to solve this system as follows.

$$
\begin{aligned}
x - 2y &= 1 \\
-1y &= -1
\end{aligned}
\qquad
\begin{aligned}
x - 2y &= 1 \\
y &= 1
\end{aligned}
\qquad
\begin{aligned}
x \phantom{{}-2y} &= 3 \\
y &= 1
\end{aligned}
$$

Graph the system of equations you obtain at each step of this process. What do you observe about the lines? You are asked to repeat this graphical analysis for other systems in Exercises 73 and 74.

SECTION 1.1 ☐ EXERCISES

In Exercises 1–6, determine whether the given equation is linear in the variables x and y.

1. $2x - 3y = 4$

2. $3x - 4xy = 0$

3. $\dfrac{3}{y} + \dfrac{2}{x} - 1 = 0$

4. $x^2 + y^2 = 4$

5. $2 \sin x - y = 14$

6. $(\sin 2)x - y = 14$

In Exercises 7–12, find a parametric representation of the solution set of the given linear equation.

7. $2x - 4y = 0$

8. $3x - \frac{1}{2}y = 9$

9. $x + y + z = 1$

10. $\frac{1}{2}x - \frac{1}{3}y = \frac{1}{4}$

11. $13x_1 - 26x_2 + 39x_3 = 13$

12. $x_1 - x_2 + 2x_3 - x_4 = 14$

In Exercises 13–18, use back-substitution to solve the given system of linear equations.

13. $x_1 - x_2 = 2$
$\quad\quad\ x_2 = 3$

14. $2x_1 - 4x_2 = 6$
$\quad\quad\quad\ 3x_2 = 9$

15. $-x + y - z = 0$
$\quad\quad 2y + z = 3$
$\quad\quad\quad \frac{1}{2}z = 0$

16. $x - y \quad\ = 4$
$\quad\ 2y + z = 6$
$\quad\quad\quad 3z = 6$

17. $5x + 2y = 0$
$\quad\ - 2y = 0$

18. $x_1 + x_2 + x_3 = 0$
$\quad\quad\ x_2 \quad\quad = 0$

In Exercises 19–22, graph each system of equations as a pair of lines in the xy-plane. Solve each system and interpret your answer geometrically.

19. $2x + y = 4$
$\quad\ x - y = 2$

20. $\quad x + 3y = 2$
$\quad -x + 2y = 3$

21. $\quad x - y = 1$
$\quad -2x + 2y = 5$

22. $\frac{1}{2}x - \frac{1}{3}y = 1$
$\quad -2x + \frac{4}{3}y = -4$

In Exercises 23–46, solve the given system of linear equations.

23. $x_1 - x_2 = 0$
$\quad 3x_1 - 2x_2 = -1$

24. $3x + 2y = 2$
$\quad 6x + 4y = 14$

25. $2u + v = 120$
$\quad u + 2v = 120$

26. $x_1 - 2x_2 = 0$
$\quad 6x_1 + 2x_2 = 0$

27. $2.5x_1 - 3x_2 = 1.5$
$\quad 10x_1 - 12x_2 = 6$

28. $1.8x_1 + 1.2x_2 = 4$
$\quad 9x_1 + 6x_2 = 3$

29. $9x - 3y = -1$
$\quad \frac{1}{5}x + \frac{2}{5}y = -\frac{1}{3}$

30. $\frac{2}{3}x_1 + \frac{1}{6}x_2 = 0$
$\quad 4x_1 + x_2 = 0$

31. $\dfrac{x - 1}{2} + \dfrac{y + 2}{3} = 4$
$\quad x - 2y = 5$

32. $\dfrac{x_1 + 3}{4} + \dfrac{x_2 - 1}{3} = 1$
$\quad 2x_1 - x_2 = 12$

33. $0.02x_1 - 0.05x_2 = -0.19$
$\quad 0.03x_1 + 0.04x_2 = 0.52$

34. $0.05x_1 - 0.03x_2 = 0.21$
$\quad 0.07x_1 + 0.02x_2 = 0.17$

35. $x + y + z = 6$
$\quad 2x - y + z = 3$
$\quad 3x \quad\ - z = 0$

36. $\quad x + y + z = 2$
$\quad -x + 3y + 2z = 8$
$\quad 4x + y \quad\quad = 4$

37. $3x_1 - 2x_2 + 4x_3 = 1$
$\quad x_1 + x_2 - 2x_3 = 3$
$\quad 2x_1 - 3x_2 + 6x_3 = 8$

38. $5x_1 - 3x_2 + 2x_3 = 3$
$\quad 2x_1 + 4x_2 - x_3 = 7$
$\quad x_1 - 11x_2 + 4x_3 = 3$

39. $x_1 + 2x_2 - 7x_3 = -4$
$\quad 2x_1 + x_2 + x_3 = 13$
$\quad 3x_1 + 9x_2 - 36x_3 = -33$

40. $2x_1 + x_2 - 3x_3 = 4$
$\quad 4x_1 \quad\quad + 2x_3 = 10$
$\quad -2x_1 + 3x_2 - 13x_3 = -8$

41. $x_1 \quad\quad + 4x_3 = 13$
$\quad 4x_1 - 2x_2 + x_3 = 7$
$\quad 2x_1 - 2x_2 - 7x_3 = -19$

42. $x_1 - 2x_2 + 5x_3 = 2$
$\quad 3x_1 + 2x_2 - x_3 = -2$

43. $x - 3y + 2z = 18$
$\quad 5x - 15y + 10z = 18$

44. $x \quad\quad = 1$
$\quad x + y = 10$
$\quad 2x - y = -5$

45. $x + y + z + w = 6$
$\quad 2x + 3y \quad\ - w = 0$
$\quad -3x + 4y + z + 2w = 4$
$\quad x + 2y - z + w = 0$

46. $x_1 \quad\quad\quad + 3x_4 = 4$
$\quad 2x_2 - x_3 - x_4 = 0$
$\quad 3x_2 \quad\ - 2x_4 = 1$
$\quad 2x_1 - x_2 + 4x_3 \quad\ = 5$

C In Exercises 47–50, use a computer or graphing calculator to solve the given system of linear equations.

47. $x_1 + 0.5x_2 + 0.33x_3 + 0.25x_4 = 1.1$
$\quad 0.5x_1 + 0.33x_2 + 0.25x_3 + 0.2x_4 = 1.2$
$\quad 0.33x_1 + 0.25x_2 + 0.2x_3 + 0.17x_4 = 1.3$
$\quad 0.25x_1 + 0.2x_2 + 0.17x_3 + 0.14x_4 = 1.4$

48. $123.5x + 61.3y - 32.4z = 34.3$
$54.7x - 45.6y + 98.2z = 45.8$
$42.4x - 89.3y + 12.9z = 35.8$

49. $\frac{1}{2}x_1 - \frac{3}{7}x_2 + \frac{2}{9}x_3 = 4$
$\frac{2}{3}x_1 + \frac{4}{9}x_2 - \frac{2}{5}x_3 = 7$
$\frac{4}{5}x_1 - \frac{1}{8}x_2 + \frac{4}{3}x_3 = -5$

50. $\frac{1}{8}x - \frac{1}{7}y + \frac{1}{6}z - \frac{1}{5}w = 1$
$\frac{1}{7}x + \frac{1}{6}y - \frac{1}{5}z + \frac{1}{4}w = 1$
$\frac{1}{6}x - \frac{1}{5}y + \frac{1}{4}z - \frac{1}{3}w = 1$
$\frac{1}{5}x + \frac{1}{4}y - \frac{1}{3}z + \frac{1}{2}w = 1$

In Exercises 51–54, state why each system of equations must have at least one solution. Then solve the system and determine if it has exactly one solution or an infinite number of solutions.

51. $4x + 3y + 17z = 0$
$5x + 4y + 22z = 0$
$4x + 2y + 19z = 0$

52. $2x + 3y = 0$
$4x + 3y - z = 0$
$8x + 3y + 3z = 0$

53. $5x + 5y - z = 0$
$10x + 5y + 2z = 0$
$5x + 15y - 9z = 0$

54. $12x + 5y + z = 0$
$12x + 4y - z = 0$

55. Find a system of two equations in two unknowns, x_1 and x_2, that has the solution set given by the parametric representation $x_1 = t$ and $x_2 = 3t - 4$, where t is any real number. Then show that the solutions to your system can also be written as
$$x_1 = \frac{4}{3} + \frac{t}{3} \text{ and } x_2 = t.$$

56. Find a system of two equations in three unknowns, x_1, x_2, and x_3, that has the solution set given by the parametric representation $x_1 = t$, $x_2 = s$, and $x_3 = 3 + s - t$, where s and t are any real numbers. Then show that the solutions to your system can also be written as $x_1 = 3 + s - t$, $x_2 = s$, and $x_3 = t$.

In Exercises 57 and 58, solve the given system of equations by letting $X = 1/x$, $Y = 1/y$, and $Z = 1/z$.

57. $\dfrac{12}{x} - \dfrac{12}{y} = 7$
$\dfrac{3}{x} + \dfrac{4}{y} = 0$

58. $\dfrac{2}{x} + \dfrac{1}{y} - \dfrac{3}{z} = 4$
$\dfrac{4}{x} + \dfrac{2}{z} = 10$
$-\dfrac{2}{x} + \dfrac{3}{y} - \dfrac{13}{z} = -8$

In Exercises 59 and 60, solve the given system of linear equations for x and y.

59. $(\cos \theta)x + (\sin \theta)y = 1$
$(-\sin \theta)x + (\cos \theta)y = 0$

60. $(\cos \theta)x + (\sin \theta)y = 1$
$(-\sin \theta)x + (\cos \theta)y = 1$

In Exercises 61–66, determine the value(s) of k such that the given system of linear equations has the indicated number of solutions.

61. Exactly one solution
$4x + ky = 7$
$kx + y = 0$

62. An infinite number of solutions
$kx + y = 4$
$2x - 3y = -12$

63. Exactly one solution
$x + ky = 0$
$kx + y = 0$

64. No solution
$x + ky = 2$
$kx + y = 4$

65. No solution
$x + 2y + kz = 6$
$3x + 6y + 8z = 4$

66. Exactly one solution
$kx + 2ky + 3kz = 4k$
$x + y + z = 0$
$2x - y + z = 1$

67. Determine the values of k such that the following system of linear equations does not have a unique solution.
$x + y + kz = 3$
$x + ky + z = 2$
$kx + y + z = 1$

68. Find values of a, b, and c such that the following system of linear equations has (a) exactly one solution, (b) an infinite number of solutions, and (c) no solution.
$x + 5y + z = 0$
$x + 6y - z = 0$
$2x + ay + bz = c$

▶ **69.** Consider the following system of linear equations in x and y.
$a_1x + b_1y = c_1$
$a_2x + b_2y = c_2$
$a_3x + b_3y = c_3$
Describe the graphs of these three equations in the xy-plane when the system has (a) exactly one solution, (b) an infinite number of solutions, and (c) no solution.

▶ **70.** Explain why the system of linear equations in Exercise 69 must be consistent if the constant terms c_1, c_2, and c_3 are all zero.

71. Show that if $ax^2 + bx + c = 0$ for all x, then $a = b = c = 0$. [Hint: Choose three different values for x, and solve the resulting system of linear equations in the variables a, b, and c.]

72. Consider the following system of linear equations in x and y.
$ax + by = e$
$cx + dy = f$
Under what conditions will the system have exactly one solution?

In Exercises 73 and 74, graph the lines determined by the given system of linear equations. Then use Gaussian elimination to solve the system. At each step of the elimination process, graph the corresponding lines. What do you observe about these lines?

73. $x - 4y = -3$
$5x - 6y = 13$

74. $2x - 3y = 7$
$-4x + 6y = -14$

1.2 GAUSSIAN ELIMINATION AND GAUSS-JORDAN ELIMINATION

In Section 1.1 we introduced Gaussian elimination as a procedure for solving a system of linear equations. In this section we study this procedure more thoroughly. To begin, we present some definitions. The first is the definition of a **matrix**.

Definition of a Matrix

If m and n are positive integers, then an $m \times n$ **matrix** (read "m by n") is a rectangular array

$$\begin{bmatrix} a_{11} & a_{12} & a_{13} & \cdots & a_{1n} \\ a_{21} & a_{22} & a_{23} & \cdots & a_{2n} \\ a_{31} & a_{32} & a_{33} & \cdots & a_{3n} \\ \vdots & \vdots & \vdots & & \vdots \\ a_{m1} & a_{m2} & a_{m3} & \cdots & a_{mn} \end{bmatrix} \Biggr\} m \text{ rows}$$

$$\underbrace{\phantom{a_{11} \quad a_{12} \quad a_{13} \quad \cdots \quad a_{1n}}}_{n \text{ columns}}$$

in which each **entry**, a_{ij}, of the matrix is a number. An $m \times n$ matrix has m **rows** (horizontal lines) and n **columns** (vertical lines).

REMARK: The plural of matrix is *matrices*. If each entry of a matrix is a *real* number, then the matrix is called a **real matrix**. Unless stated otherwise, all matrices in this text are assumed to be real matrices. (Matrices with complex numbers as entries will be discussed in Chapter 8.)

The entry a_{ij} is located in the ith row and the jth column. We call i the **row subscript** because it gives the position in the horizontal lines, and j the **column subscript** because it gives the position in the vertical lines.

An $m \times n$ matrix is said to be of **size** $m \times n$. If $m = n$, the matrix is **square** of **order** n. For a square matrix, the entries $a_{11}, a_{22}, a_{33}, \ldots$ are called the **main diagonal** entries.

EXAMPLE 1   *Examples of Matrices*

The following matrices have the indicated sizes.

(a) Size: 1×1

$$[2]$$

(b) Size: 2×2

$$\begin{bmatrix} 0 & 0 \\ 0 & 0 \end{bmatrix}$$

(c) Size: 1×4

$$\begin{bmatrix} 1 & -3 & 0 & \frac{1}{2} \end{bmatrix}$$

(d) Size: 3×2

$$\begin{bmatrix} e & \pi \\ 2 & \sqrt{2} \\ -7 & 4 \end{bmatrix}$$

One very common use of matrices is to represent a system of linear equations. The matrix derived from the coefficients and constant terms of a system of linear equations is called the **augmented matrix** of the system. The matrix containing only the coefficients of the system is called the **coefficient matrix** of the system. Here is an example.

$$
\begin{array}{ccc}
\textit{System} & \textit{Augmented Matrix} & \textit{Coefficient Matrix} \\[4pt]
\begin{aligned}
x - 4y + 3z &= 5 \\
-x + 3y - z &= -3 \\
2x - 4z &= 6
\end{aligned}
&
\begin{bmatrix}
1 & -4 & 3 & 5 \\
-1 & 3 & -1 & -3 \\
2 & 0 & -4 & 6
\end{bmatrix}
&
\begin{bmatrix}
1 & -4 & 3 \\
-1 & 3 & -1 \\
2 & 0 & -4
\end{bmatrix}
\end{array}
$$

R E M A R K : Note the use of 0 to indicate that the coefficient of y in the third equation is zero. Also note the fourth column of constant terms in the augmented matrix.

When forming either the coefficient matrix or the augmented matrix of a system, you should begin by aligning the variables in the equations vertically.

$$
\begin{array}{ccc}
\textit{Given System} & \textit{Line Up Variables} & \textit{Form Augmented Matrix} \\[4pt]
\begin{aligned}
x_1 + 3x_2 &= 9 \\
-x_2 + 4x_3 &= -2 \\
x_1 - 5x_3 &= 0
\end{aligned}
&
\begin{aligned}
x_1 + 3x_2 \quad\;\; &= 9 \\
-x_2 + 4x_3 &= -2 \\
x_1 \qquad - 5x_3 &= 0
\end{aligned}
&
\begin{bmatrix}
1 & 3 & 0 & 9 \\
0 & -1 & 4 & -2 \\
1 & 0 & -5 & 0
\end{bmatrix}
\end{array}
$$

Elementary Row Operations

In the previous section we studied three operations that can be used on a system of linear equations to produce equivalent systems.
1. Interchange two equations.
2. Multiply an equation by a nonzero constant.
3. Add a multiple of an equation to another equation.
In matrix terminology these three operations correspond to **elementary row operations.** An elementary row operation on an augmented matrix corresponding to a given system of linear equations produces a new augmented matrix corresponding to a new (but equivalent) system of linear equations. Two matrices are said to be **row-equivalent** if one can be obtained from the other by a sequence of elementary row operations.

Elementary Row Operations	1. Interchange two rows. 2. Multiply a row by a nonzero constant. 3. Add a multiple of a row to another row.

Although elementary row operations are simple to perform, they involve a lot of arithmetic. Because it is easy to make a mistake, we suggest that you get in the habit of noting the elementary row operation performed in each step so that you can go back to check your work.

EXAMPLE 2   *Elementary Row Operations*

(a) Interchange the first and second rows.

Original Matrix

$$\begin{bmatrix} 0 & 1 & 3 & 4 \\ -1 & 2 & 0 & 3 \\ 2 & -3 & 4 & 1 \end{bmatrix}$$

New Row Equivalent Matrix

$$\begin{bmatrix} -1 & 2 & 0 & 3 \\ 0 & 1 & 3 & 4 \\ 2 & -3 & 4 & 1 \end{bmatrix}$$

(b) Multiply the first row by $\frac{1}{2}$

Original Matrix

$$\begin{bmatrix} 2 & -4 & 6 & -2 \\ 1 & 3 & -3 & 0 \\ 5 & -2 & 1 & 2 \end{bmatrix}$$

New Row Equivalent Matrix

$$\begin{bmatrix} 1 & -2 & 3 & -1 \\ 1 & 3 & -3 & 0 \\ 5 & -2 & 1 & 2 \end{bmatrix}$$

(c) Add -2 times the first row to the third row.

Original Matrix

$$\begin{bmatrix} 1 & 2 & -4 & 3 \\ 0 & 3 & -2 & -1 \\ 2 & 1 & 5 & -2 \end{bmatrix}$$

New Row Equivalent Matrix

$$\begin{bmatrix} 1 & 2 & -4 & 3 \\ 0 & 3 & -2 & -1 \\ 0 & -3 & 13 & -8 \end{bmatrix}$$

TECHNOLOGY NOTE

Many graphing calculators and computer software programs can perform elementary row operations on matrices. If you are using a TI-85, your screens for Example 2(c) will look like the following:

```
A

  [[1  2  -4  3  ]
   [0  3  -2  -1 ]
   [2  1  5   -2 ]]
```

```
mRAdd(-2,A,1,3)

  [[1  2  -4  3  ]
   [0  3  -2  -1 ]
   [0  -3  13  -8 ]]
```

In Example 7 in the previous section, we used Gaussian elimination with back-substitution to solve a system of linear equations. We now demonstrate the matrix version of Gaussian elimination. The two methods used in the following example are essentially the same. The basic difference is that with the matrix method we do not need to keep writing the variables.

EXAMPLE 3   *Using Elementary Row Operations to Solve a System*

Linear System	*Associated Augmented Matrix*

$$\begin{aligned} x - 2y + 3z &= 9 \\ -x + 3y &= -4 \\ 2x - 5y + 5z &= 17 \end{aligned}$$

$$\begin{bmatrix} 1 & -2 & 3 & 9 \\ -1 & 3 & 0 & -4 \\ 2 & -5 & 5 & 17 \end{bmatrix}$$

Add the first equation to the second equation.

Add the first row to the second row.

$$\begin{aligned} x - 2y + 3z &= 9 \\ y + 3z &= 5 \\ 2x - 5y + 5z &= 17 \end{aligned}$$

$$\begin{bmatrix} 1 & -2 & 3 & 9 \\ 0 & 1 & 3 & 5 \\ 2 & -5 & 5 & 17 \end{bmatrix}$$

Add -2 times the first equation to the third equation.

Add -2 times the first row to the third row.

$$\begin{aligned} x - 2y + 3z &= 9 \\ y + 3z &= 5 \\ -y - z &= -1 \end{aligned}$$

$$\begin{bmatrix} 1 & -2 & 3 & 9 \\ 0 & 1 & 3 & 5 \\ 0 & -1 & -1 & -1 \end{bmatrix}$$

Add the second equation to the third equation.

Add the second row to the third row.

$$\begin{aligned} x - 2y + 3z &= 9 \\ y + 3z &= 5 \\ 2z &= 4 \end{aligned}$$

$$\begin{bmatrix} 1 & -2 & 3 & 9 \\ 0 & 1 & 3 & 5 \\ 0 & 0 & 2 & 4 \end{bmatrix}$$

Multiply the third equation by $\frac{1}{2}$.

Multiply the third row by $\frac{1}{2}$.

$$\begin{aligned} x - 2y + 3z &= 9 \\ y + 3z &= 5 \\ z &= 2 \end{aligned}$$

$$\begin{bmatrix} 1 & -2 & 3 & 9 \\ 0 & 1 & 3 & 5 \\ 0 & 0 & 1 & 2 \end{bmatrix}$$

Here we can use back-substitution to find the solution, as in Example 6 in the last section.

The last matrix in Example 3 is said to be in **row-echelon form**. The term *echelon* refers to the stair-step pattern formed by the nonzero elements of the matrix. To be in this form, a matrix must have the following properties.

Definition of Row-Echelon Form of a Matrix

A matrix in **row-echelon form** has the following properties.
1. All rows consisting entirely of zeros occur at the bottom of the matrix.
2. For each row that does not consist entirely of zeros, the first nonzero entry is 1 (called a **leading 1**).
3. For two successive (nonzero) rows, the leading 1 in the higher row is farther to the left than the leading 1 in the lower row.

REMARK: A matrix in row-echelon form is in **reduced row-echelon form** if every column that has a leading 1 has zeros in every position above and below its leading 1.

EXAMPLE 4   *Row-Echelon Form*

The following matrices are in row-echelon form.

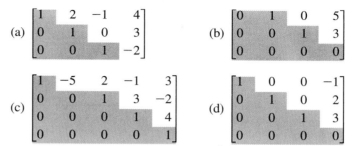

The matrices shown in parts (b) and (d) are in *reduced* row-echelon form. The following matrices are not in row-echelon form.

$$\text{(e)} \begin{bmatrix} 1 & 2 & -3 & 4 \\ 0 & 2 & 1 & -1 \\ 0 & 0 & 1 & -3 \end{bmatrix} \qquad \text{(f)} \begin{bmatrix} 1 & 2 & -1 & 2 \\ 0 & 0 & 0 & 0 \\ 0 & 1 & 2 & -4 \end{bmatrix}$$

It can be shown that every matrix is row equivalent to a matrix in row-echelon form. For instance, in Example 4 we could change the matrix in part (e) to row-echelon form by multiplying the second row in the matrix by $\frac{1}{2}$.

The method using Gaussian elimination with back-substitution to solve a system follows.

Gaussian Elimination with Back-Substitution

1. Write the augmented matrix of the system of linear equations.
2. Use elementary row operations to rewrite the augmented matrix in row-echelon form.
3. Write the system of linear equations corresponding to the matrix in row-echelon form, and use back-substitution to find the solution.

Gaussian elimination with back-substitution works well as an algorithmic method for solving systems of linear equations with a computer. For this algorithm, the order in which the elementary row operations are performed is important. We move form *left to right by columns*, changing to zero all entries directly below the leading 1's.

EXAMPLE 5   *Gaussian Elimination with Back-Substitution*

Solve the following system.

$$\begin{aligned} x_2 + x_3 - 2x_4 &= -3 \\ x_1 + 2x_2 - x_3 \quad\quad &= 2 \\ 2x_1 + 4x_2 + x_3 - 3x_4 &= -2 \\ x_1 - 4x_2 - 7x_3 - x_4 &= -19 \end{aligned}$$

Solution   The augmented matrix for this system is

$$\begin{bmatrix} 0 & 1 & 1 & -2 & -3 \\ 1 & 2 & -1 & 0 & 2 \\ 2 & 4 & 1 & -3 & -2 \\ 1 & -4 & -7 & -1 & -19 \end{bmatrix}.$$

We begin by obtaining a leading 1 in the upper left corner and zeros elsewhere in the first column.

$$\begin{bmatrix} 1 & 2 & -1 & 0 & 2 \\ 0 & 1 & 1 & -2 & -3 \\ 2 & 4 & 1 & -3 & -2 \\ 1 & -4 & -7 & -1 & -19 \end{bmatrix}$$

⟵ **The first two rows**
⟵ **are interchanged.**

$$\begin{bmatrix} 1 & 2 & -1 & 0 & 2 \\ 0 & 1 & 1 & -2 & -3 \\ 0 & 0 & 3 & -3 & -6 \\ 1 & -4 & -7 & -1 & -19 \end{bmatrix}$$

Adding −2 times the first
row to the third row
⟵ **produces a new third row.**

$$\begin{bmatrix} 1 & 2 & -1 & 0 & 2 \\ 0 & 1 & 1 & -2 & -3 \\ 0 & 0 & 3 & -3 & -6 \\ 0 & -6 & -6 & -1 & -21 \end{bmatrix}$$

Adding −1 times the first
row to the fourth row
⟵ **produces a new fourth row.**

Now that the first column is in the desired form, we change the second column as follows.

$$\begin{bmatrix} 1 & 2 & -1 & 0 & 2 \\ 0 & 1 & 1 & -2 & -3 \\ 0 & 0 & 3 & -3 & -6 \\ 0 & 0 & 0 & -13 & -39 \end{bmatrix}$$

Adding 6 times the second
row to the fourth row
⟵ **produces a new fourth row.**

To write the third column in proper form, we need only multiply the third row by $\frac{1}{3}$.

$$\begin{bmatrix} 1 & 2 & -1 & 0 & 2 \\ 0 & 1 & 1 & -2 & -3 \\ 0 & 0 & 1 & -1 & -2 \\ 0 & 0 & 0 & -13 & -39 \end{bmatrix}$$

Multiplying the third row by $\frac{1}{3}$
⟵ **produces a new third row.**

Similarly, to write the fourth column in proper form, we multiply the fourth row by $-\frac{1}{13}$.

$$\begin{bmatrix} 1 & 2 & -1 & 0 & 2 \\ 0 & 1 & 1 & -2 & -3 \\ 0 & 0 & 1 & -1 & -2 \\ 0 & 0 & 0 & 1 & 3 \end{bmatrix}$$

Multiplying the fourth row by $-\frac{1}{13}$
⟵ **produces a new fourth row.**

The matrix is now in row-echelon form, and the corresponding system of linear equations is

$$\begin{array}{rcl} x_1 + 2x_2 - x_3 \qquad\quad &=& 2 \\ x_2 + x_3 - 2x_4 &=& -3 \\ x_3 - x_4 &=& -2 \\ x_4 &=& 3. \end{array}$$

Using back-substitution, we can determine that the solution is

$$x_1 = -1, \qquad x_2 = 2, \qquad x_3 = 1, \qquad x_4 = 3.$$

When solving a system of linear equations, remember that it is possible for the system to have no solution. If, in the elimination process, you obtain a row with zeros except for the last entry, it is unnecessary to continue the elimination process. You can simply conclude that the system is inconsistent.

EXAMPLE 6   *A System with No Solution*

Solve the following system.

$$\begin{array}{rcl} x_1 - x_2 + 2x_3 &=& 4 \\ x_1 \qquad + x_3 &=& 6 \\ 2x_1 - 3x_2 + 5x_3 &=& 4 \\ 3x_1 + 2x_2 - x_3 &=& 1 \end{array}$$

Solution   The augmented matrix for this system is

$$\begin{bmatrix} 1 & -1 & 2 & 4 \\ 1 & 0 & 1 & 6 \\ 2 & -3 & 5 & 4 \\ 3 & 2 & -1 & 1 \end{bmatrix}.$$

We apply Gaussian elimination to the augmented matrix as follows.

$$\begin{bmatrix} 1 & -1 & 2 & 4 \\ 0 & 1 & -1 & 2 \\ 2 & -3 & 5 & 4 \\ 3 & 2 & -1 & 1 \end{bmatrix}$$ ⬅ **Adding -1 times the first row to the second row produces a new second row.**

$$\begin{bmatrix} 1 & -1 & 2 & 4 \\ 0 & 1 & -1 & 2 \\ 0 & -1 & 1 & -4 \\ 3 & 2 & -1 & 1 \end{bmatrix}$$ ⬅ **Adding -2 times the first row to the third row produces a new third row.**

$$\begin{bmatrix} 1 & -1 & 2 & 4 \\ 0 & 1 & -1 & 2 \\ 0 & -1 & 1 & -4 \\ 0 & 5 & -7 & -11 \end{bmatrix}$$

Adding -3 times the first row to the fourth row produces a new fourth row.

$$\begin{bmatrix} 1 & -1 & 2 & 4 \\ 0 & 1 & -1 & 2 \\ 0 & 0 & 0 & -2 \\ 0 & 5 & -7 & -11 \end{bmatrix}$$

Adding the second row to the third row produces a new third row.

Note that the third row of this matrix consists of zeros except for the last entry. This means that the original system of linear equations is *inconsistent*. You can see why this is true by converting back to a system of linear equations.

$$\begin{aligned} x_1 - x_2 + 2x_3 &= 4 \\ x_2 - x_3 &= 2 \\ 0 &= -2 \\ 5x_2 - 7x_3 &= -11 \end{aligned}$$

Since the third "equation" is absurd, it follows that the system has no solution.

Gauss-Jordan Elimination

With Gaussian elimination, we apply elementary row operations to a matrix to obtain a (row-equivalent) row-echelon form. A second method of elimination, called **Gauss-Jordan elimination** after Carl Gauss and Wilhelm Jordan (1842–1899), continues the reduction process until a *reduced* row-echelon form is obtained. We demonstrate this procedure in the following example.

EXAMPLE 7   *Gauss-Jordan Elimination*

Use Gauss-Jordan elimination to solve the system

$$\begin{aligned} x - 2y + 3z &= 9 \\ -x + 3y &= -4 \\ 2x - 5y + 5z &= 17. \end{aligned}$$

Solution   In Example 3 we used Gaussian elimination to obtain the following row-echelon form.

$$\begin{bmatrix} 1 & -2 & 3 & 9 \\ 0 & 1 & 3 & 5 \\ 0 & 0 & 1 & 2 \end{bmatrix}$$

Now, rather than using back-substitution, we apply elementary row operations until we obtain a matrix in reduced row-echelon form. To do this, we must produce zeros above each of the leading 1's, as follows.

$$\begin{bmatrix} 1 & 0 & 9 & 19 \\ 0 & 1 & 3 & 5 \\ 0 & 0 & 1 & 2 \end{bmatrix} \longleftarrow \text{Adding 2 times the second row to the first row produces a new first row.}$$

$$\begin{bmatrix} 1 & 0 & 9 & 19 \\ 0 & 1 & 0 & -1 \\ 0 & 0 & 1 & 2 \end{bmatrix} \longleftarrow \text{Adding } -3 \text{ times the third row to the second row produces a new second row.}$$

$$\begin{bmatrix} 1 & 0 & 0 & 1 \\ 0 & 1 & 0 & -1 \\ 0 & 0 & 1 & 2 \end{bmatrix} \longleftarrow \text{Adding } -9 \text{ times the third row to the first row produces a new first row.}$$

Now, converting back to a system of linear equations, we have

$$\begin{aligned} x & & & = & 1 \\ & y & & = & -1 \\ & & z & = & 2. \end{aligned}$$

The Gauss-Jordan elimination procedure employs an algorithmic approach that is easily adapted to computer use. However, this procedure makes no effort to avoid fractional coefficients. For instance, if the system in Example 7 had been listed as

$$\begin{aligned} 2x - 5y + 5z &= 17 \\ x - 2y + 3z &= 9 \\ -x + 3y &= -4 \end{aligned}$$

our procedure would have required multiplying the first row by $\frac{1}{2}$, which would have introduced fractions in the first row. For hand computations, fractions can sometimes be avoided by judiciously choosing the order in which elementary row operations are applied. Moreover, it can be shown that no matter which order you use, the reduced row-echelon form will be the same.

The next example demonstrates how Gauss-Jordan elimination can be used to solve a system with an infinite number of solutions.

EXAMPLE 8   *A System with an Infinite Number of Solutions*

Solve the following system of linear equations.

$$\begin{aligned} 2x_1 + 4x_2 - 2x_3 &= 0 \\ 3x_1 + 5x_2 &= 1 \end{aligned}$$

Solution   The augmented matrix of the system of linear equations is $\begin{bmatrix} 2 & 4 & -2 & 0 \\ 3 & 5 & 0 & 1 \end{bmatrix}$.

Using MATLAB, a graphing utility, or Gauss-Jordan elimination, you can verify that the reduced row-echelon form of the matrix is

$$\begin{bmatrix} 1 & 0 & 5 & 2 \\ 0 & 1 & -3 & -1 \end{bmatrix}.$$

The corresponding system of equations is

$$\begin{aligned} x_1 \quad + 5x_3 &= 2 \\ x_2 - 3x_3 &= -1. \end{aligned}$$

Now, using the parameter t to represent the *nonleading* variable x_3, we have

$$x_1 = 2 - 5t, \qquad x_2 = -1 + 3t, \qquad x_3 = t$$

where t is any real number.

REMARK: Note that in Example 8 an arbitrary parameter was assigned to the nonleading variable x_3. Subsequently we solved for the leading variables x_1 and x_2 as functions of t.

We have looked now at two elimination methods for solving a system of linear equations. Which is better? To some degree the answer depends on personal preference. For hand computations, Gaussian elimination with back-substitution is usually preferred because it involves fewer steps. However, we will encounter other applications in which Gauss-Jordan elimination is better. Thus you will need to know both methods.

In real-life applications of linear algebra, systems of linear equations are usually solved by computer. Most computer programs use a form of Gaussian elimination, with special emphasis on ways to reduce rounding errors and minimize storage of data. However, the examples and exercises in this text are generally much simpler, since we are focusing on the underlying concepts.

Homogeneous Systems of Linear Equations

As the final topic in this section, we look at systems of linear equations in which each of the constant terms is zero. We call such systems **homogeneous**. For example, a homogeneous system of m equations in n variables has the form

$$\begin{aligned} a_{11}x_1 + a_{12}x_2 + a_{13}x_3 + \cdots + a_{1n}x_n &= 0 \\ a_{21}x_1 + a_{22}x_2 + a_{23}x_3 + \cdots + a_{2n}x_n &= 0 \\ a_{31}x_1 + a_{32}x_2 + a_{33}x_3 + \cdots + a_{3n}x_n &= 0 \\ &\vdots \\ a_{m1}x_1 + a_{m2}x_2 + a_{m3}x_3 + \cdots + a_{mn}x_n &= 0. \end{aligned}$$

It is easy to see that a homogeneous system must have at least one solution. Specifically, if all variables in a homogeneous system have the value zero, then each of the equations must be satisfied. Such a solution is called **trivial** (or **obvious**). For instance, a homogeneous system of three equations in the three variables x_1, x_2, x_3 must have $x_1 = 0$, $x_2 = 0$, and $x_3 = 0$ as a trivial solution.

EXAMPLE 9   ***Solving a Homogeneous System of Linear Equations***

Solve the following system of linear equations.

$$x_1 - x_2 + 3x_3 = 0$$
$$2x_1 + x_2 + 3x_3 = 0$$

Solution   Applying Gauss-Jordan elimination to the augmented matrix

$$\begin{bmatrix} 1 & -1 & 3 & 0 \\ 2 & 1 & 3 & 0 \end{bmatrix}$$

yields the following.

$$\begin{bmatrix} 1 & -1 & 3 & 0 \\ 0 & 3 & -3 & 0 \end{bmatrix} \longleftarrow \text{Adding } -2 \text{ times the first row to the second row produces a new second row.}$$

$$\begin{bmatrix} 1 & -1 & 3 & 0 \\ 0 & 1 & -1 & 0 \end{bmatrix} \longleftarrow \text{Multiplying the second row by } \tfrac{1}{3} \text{ produces a new second row.}$$

$$\begin{bmatrix} 1 & 0 & 2 & 0 \\ 0 & 1 & -1 & 0 \end{bmatrix} \longleftarrow \text{Adding the second row to the first row produces a new first row.}$$

The system of equations corresponding to this matrix is

$$x_1 \qquad + 2x_3 = 0$$
$$x_2 - x_3 = 0.$$

Using the parameter $t = x_3$, we conclude that the solution set is given by

$$x_1 = -2t, \qquad x_2 = t, \qquad x_3 = t, \quad t \text{ is any real number.}$$

Therefore this system of equations has an infinite number of solutions, one of which is the trivial solution (given by $t = 0$).

Example 9 illustrates an important point about homogeneous systems of linear equations. We began with two equations in three variables and discovered that the system has an infinite number of solutions. In general, a homogeneous system with fewer equations than variables has an infinite number of solutions.

Theorem 1.1	Every homogeneous system of linear equations is consistent. Moreover, if the system has fewer equations than variables, then it must have an infinite number of solutions.
The Number of Solutions of a Homogeneous System	

SECTION 1.2 ☐ EXERCISES

In Exercises 1–6, determine the size of the given matrix.

1. $\begin{bmatrix} 1 & 2 \\ 3 & -4 \\ 0 & 1 \end{bmatrix}$

2. $\begin{bmatrix} 2 & -1 & -1 & 1 \\ -6 & 2 & 0 & 1 \end{bmatrix}$

3. $\begin{bmatrix} 1 & 2 & 3 & 4 & -10 \end{bmatrix}$

4. $\begin{bmatrix} -1 \end{bmatrix}$

5. $\begin{bmatrix} 1 \\ 2 \\ -1 \\ -2 \end{bmatrix}$

6. $\begin{bmatrix} 8 & 6 & 4 & 1 & 3 \\ 2 & 1 & -7 & 4 & 1 \\ 1 & 1 & -1 & 2 & 1 \\ 1 & -1 & 2 & 0 & 0 \end{bmatrix}$

In Exercises 7–14, determine whether the given matrix is in row-echelon form. If it is, determine whether it is also in reduced row-echelon form.

7. $\begin{bmatrix} 1 & 0 & 0 & 0 \\ 0 & 1 & 1 & 2 \\ 0 & 0 & 0 & 0 \end{bmatrix}$

8. $\begin{bmatrix} 0 & 1 & 0 & 0 \\ 1 & 0 & 2 & 1 \end{bmatrix}$

9. $\begin{bmatrix} 2 & 0 & 1 & 3 \\ 0 & -1 & 1 & 4 \\ 0 & 0 & 0 & 1 \end{bmatrix}$

10. $\begin{bmatrix} 1 & 0 & 2 & 1 \\ 0 & 1 & 3 & 4 \\ 0 & 0 & 1 & 0 \end{bmatrix}$

11. $\begin{bmatrix} 1 & 0 & 0 & 0 \\ 0 & 0 & 0 & 1 \\ 0 & 0 & 0 & 0 \end{bmatrix}$

12. $\begin{bmatrix} 0 & 0 & 1 & 0 & 0 \\ 0 & 0 & 0 & 1 & 0 \\ 0 & 0 & 0 & 2 & 0 \end{bmatrix}$

13. $\begin{bmatrix} 0 & 0 & 0 \\ 0 & 0 & 0 \\ 0 & 0 & 0 \end{bmatrix}$

14. $\begin{bmatrix} 1 & 3 & 0 & 0 \\ 0 & 0 & 1 & 0 \\ 0 & 0 & 0 & 0 \end{bmatrix}$

In Exercises 15–20, find the solution set of the system of linear equations represented by the given augmented matrix.

15. $\begin{bmatrix} 1 & 0 & 0 \\ 0 & 1 & 2 \end{bmatrix}$

16. $\begin{bmatrix} 1 & 0 & -1 & 2 \\ 0 & 1 & 1 & 3 \end{bmatrix}$

17. $\begin{bmatrix} 1 & -1 & 0 & 3 \\ 0 & 1 & -2 & 1 \\ 0 & 0 & 1 & -1 \end{bmatrix}$

18. $\begin{bmatrix} 1 & 2 & 1 & 0 \\ 0 & 0 & 1 & -1 \\ 0 & 0 & 0 & 0 \end{bmatrix}$

19. $\begin{bmatrix} 1 & 2 & 0 & 1 & 4 \\ 0 & 1 & 2 & 1 & 3 \\ 0 & 0 & 1 & 2 & 1 \\ 0 & 0 & 0 & 1 & 4 \end{bmatrix}$

20. $\begin{bmatrix} 1 & 2 & 0 & 1 & 3 \\ 0 & 1 & 3 & 0 & 1 \\ 0 & 0 & 1 & 2 & 0 \\ 0 & 0 & 0 & 0 & 2 \end{bmatrix}$

In Exercises 21–36, solve the given system of linear equations, using either Gaussian elimination with back-substitution or Gauss-Jordan elimination.

21.
$x + 2y = 7$
$2x + y = 8$

22.
$2x + 6y = 16$
$-2x - 6y = -16$

23.
$x - 3y = 5$
$-2x + 6y = -10$

24.
$2x - y = -0.1$
$3x + 2y = 1.6$

25.
$-x + 2y = 1.5$
$2x - 4y = 3$

26.
$8x - 4y = 7$
$5x + 2y = 1$

27.
$-3x + 5y = -22$
$3x + 4y = 4$
$4x - 8y = 32$

28.
$x + 2y = 0$
$x + y = 6$
$3x - 2y = 8$

29.
$x_1 - 3x_3 = -2$
$3x_1 + x_2 - 2x_3 = 5$
$2x_1 + 2x_2 + x_3 = 4$

30.
$2x_1 - x_2 + 3x_3 = 24$
$2x_2 - x_3 = 14$
$7x_1 - 5x_2 = 6$

31.
$x_1 + x_2 - 5x_3 = 3$
$x_1 - 2x_3 = 1$
$2x_1 - x_2 - x_3 = 0$

32.
$2x_1 + 3x_3 = 3$
$4x_1 - 3x_2 + 7x_3 = 5$
$8x_1 - 9x_2 + 15x_3 = 10$

33.
$x + 2y + z = 8$
$-3x - 6y - 3z = -21$

34.
$4x + 12y - 7z - 20w = 22$
$3x + 9y - 5z - 28w = 30$

35.
$3x + 3y + 12z = 6$
$x + y + 4z = 2$
$2x + 5y + 20z = 10$
$-x + 2y + 8z = 4$

36.
$2x + y - z + 2w = -6$
$3x + 4y + w = 1$
$x + 5y + 2z + 6w = -3$
$5x + 2y - z - w = 3$

C In Exercises 37–40, use a computer or graphing calculator to solve the given system of linear equations.

37. $x_1 - 2x_2 + 5x_3 - 3x_4 = 23.6$
$x_1 + 4x_2 - 7x_3 - 2x_4 = 45.7$
$3x_1 - 5x_2 + 7x_3 + 4x_4 = 29.9$

38. $23.4x - 45.8y + 43.7z = 87.2$
$86.4x + 12.3y - 56.9z = 14.5$
$93.6x - 50.7y + 12.6z = 44.4$

39. $x_1 - x_2 + 2x_3 + 2x_4 + 6x_5 = 6$
$3x_1 - 2x_2 + 4x_3 + 4x_4 + 12x_5 = 14$
$x_2 - x_3 - x_4 - 3x_5 = -3$
$2x_1 - 2x_2 + 4x_3 + 5x_4 + 15x_5 = 10$
$2x_1 - 2x_2 + 4x_3 + 4x_4 + 13x_5 = 13$

40. $x_1 + x_2 - 2x_3 + 3x_4 + 2x_5 = 9$
$3x_1 + 3x_2 - x_3 + x_4 + x_5 = 5$
$2x_1 + 2x_2 - x_3 + x_4 - 2x_5 = 1$
$4x_1 + 4x_2 + x_3 - 3x_5 = 4$
$8x_1 + 5x_2 - 2x_3 - x_4 + 2x_5 = 3$

In Exercises 41–44, solve the homogeneous linear system corresponding to the given coefficient matrix.

41. $\begin{bmatrix} 1 & 0 & 0 \\ 0 & 1 & 1 \\ 0 & 0 & 0 \end{bmatrix}$
42. $\begin{bmatrix} 1 & 0 & 0 & 0 \\ 0 & 1 & 1 & 0 \end{bmatrix}$

43. $\begin{bmatrix} 1 & 0 & 0 & 1 \\ 0 & 0 & 1 & 0 \\ 0 & 0 & 0 & 0 \end{bmatrix}$
44. $\begin{bmatrix} 0 & 0 & 0 \\ 0 & 0 & 0 \\ 0 & 0 & 0 \end{bmatrix}$

In Exercises 45 and 46, find values of a, b, and c (if possible) such that the given system of linear equations has (a) a unique solution, (b) no solution, and (c) an infinite number of solutions.

45. $x + y = 2$
$y + z = 2$
$x + z = 2$
$ax + by + cz = 0$

46. $x + y = 0$
$y + z = 0$
$x + z = 0$
$ax + by + cz = 0$

47. The following system has one solution $x = 1$, $y = -1$, and $z = 2$.

$4x - 2y + 5z = 16$ **Equation 1**
$x + y = 0$ **Equation 2**
$-x - 3y + 2z = 6$ **Equation 3**

Solve the systems given by (a) Equations 1 and 2, (b) Equations 1 and 3, and (c) Equations 2 and 3. (d) How many solutions does each of these systems have?

48. Assume that the following system has a unique solution.

$a_{11}x_1 + a_{12}x_2 + a_{13}x_3 = b_1$ **Equation 1**
$a_{21}x_1 + a_{22}x_2 + a_{23}x_3 = b_2$ **Equation 2**
$a_{31}x_1 + a_{32}x_2 + a_{33}x_3 = b_3$ **Equation 3**

Does the system composed of Equations 1 and 2 have (a) a unique solution, (b) no solution, or (c) an infinite number of solutions?

In Exercises 49 and 50, find the unique reduced row-echelon matrix that is row equivalent to the given matrix.

49. $\begin{bmatrix} 1 & 2 \\ -1 & 2 \end{bmatrix}$
50. $\begin{bmatrix} 1 & 2 & 3 \\ 4 & 5 & 6 \\ 7 & 8 & 9 \end{bmatrix}$

51. Describe all possible 2×2 reduced row-echelon matrices. Support your answer with examples.

52. Describe all possible 3×3 reduced row-echelon matrices. Support your answer with examples.

In Exercises 53 and 54, determine conditions on a, b, c, and d such that the matrix $\begin{bmatrix} a & b \\ c & d \end{bmatrix}$ will be row equivalent to the given matrix.

53. $\begin{bmatrix} 1 & 0 \\ 0 & 1 \end{bmatrix}$
54. $\begin{bmatrix} 1 & 0 \\ 0 & 0 \end{bmatrix}$

In Exercises 55 and 56, find all values of λ (the Greek letter lambda) such that the given homogeneous system of linear equations will have nontrivial solutions.

55. $(\lambda - 2)x + y = 0$
$x + (\lambda - 2)y = 0$

56. $(\lambda - 1)x + 2y = 0$
$x + \lambda y = 0$

57. Is it possible that a system of linear equations with fewer equations than variables may have no solution? If so, give an example.

58. Does a matrix have a unique row-echelon form? Illustrate your answer with examples. Is the reduced row-echelon form unique?

59. Solve the following system for α and β, $0 \le \alpha$, $\beta \le 2\pi$.

$2\cos \alpha - \sin \beta = 0$
$4\cos \alpha + 2\sin \beta = 4$

60. Solve the following system of equations for x and y.

$x^2 + 2y^3 = 2$
$3x^2 - y^3 = 13$

61. Consider the 2×2 matrix $\begin{bmatrix} a & b \\ c & d \end{bmatrix}$. Do the following sequence of row operations.

(a) Add (-1) times row 2 to the first row.
(b) Add 1 times row 1 to the second row.
(c) Add (-1) times row 2 to the first row.
(d) Multiply row 1 by (-1).

What has happened to the original matrix? Describe in general how to interchange two rows of a matrix using only the second and third elementary row operations.

1.3 APPLICATIONS OF SYSTEMS OF LINEAR EQUATIONS

Systems of linear equations arise in a wide variety of applications and are one of the central themes of linear algebra. In this section we look at two such applications, and we will see many more in subsequent chapters. The first application shows how to fit a polynomial function to a set of data points in the plane. The second application focuses on networks and Kirchhoff's laws for electricity.

Polynomial Curve Fitting

Figure 1.4

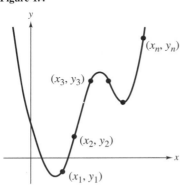

Polynomial Curve Fitting

Suppose a collection of data is represented by n points

$$(x_1, y_1), (x_2, y_2), \ldots, (x_n, y_n)$$

in the xy-plane, and you are asked to find a polynomial function

$$p(x) = a_0 + a_1x + a_2x^2 + \cdots + a_{n-1}x^{n-1}$$

of degree $n - 1$ whose graph passes through the given points. This procedure is called **polynomial curve fitting**. It can be shown that if all x-coordinates of the points are distinct, then there is precisely one polynomial function of degree $n - 1$ (or less) that fits the n points, as shown in Figure 1.4.

To solve for the n coefficients of $p(x)$, we substitute each of the n points into the polynomial and obtain n linear equations in the variables $a_0, a_1, a_2, \ldots$, and a_{n-1}:

$$a_0 + a_1x_1 + a_2x_1^2 + \cdots + a_{n-1}x_1^{n-1} = y_1$$
$$a_0 + a_1x_2 + a_2x_2^2 + \cdots + a_{n-1}x_2^{n-1} = y_2$$
$$\vdots$$
$$a_0 + a_1x_n + a_2x_n^2 + \cdots + a_{n-1}x_n^{n-1} = y_n.$$

This procedure is demonstrated with a second-degree polynomial in Example 1.

EXAMPLE 1   *Polynomial Curve Fitting*

Determine the polynomial $p(x) = a_0 + a_1x + a_2x^2$ whose graph passes through the points $(1, 4)$, $(2, 0)$, and $(3, 12)$.

Solution   Substituting $x = 1, 2,$ and 3 into $p(x)$ and equating the results to the respective y-values produces the following system of linear equations in the variables $a_0, a_1,$ and a_2.

$$p(1) = a_0 + a_1(1) + a_2(1)^2 = a_0 + a_1 + a_2 = 4$$
$$p(2) = a_0 + a_1(2) + a_2(2)^2 = a_0 + 2a_1 + 4a_2 = 0$$
$$p(3) = a_0 + a_1(3) + a_2(3)^2 = a_0 + 3a_1 + 9a_2 = 12$$

The solution of this system is $a_0 = 24$, $a_1 = -28$, and $a_2 = 8$, thus the polynomial is

$$p(x) = 24 - 28x + 8x^2.$$

The graph of p is shown in Figure 1.5. (See top of page 27.)

Figure 1.5

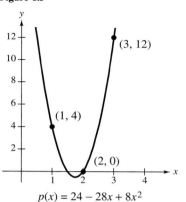

$p(x) = 24 - 28x + 8x^2$

Figure 1.6

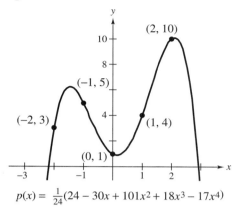

$p(x) = \frac{1}{24}(24 - 30x + 101x^2 + 18x^3 - 17x^4)$

EXAMPLE 2   *Polynomial Curve Fitting*

Find a polynomial that fits the points $(-2, 3)$, $(-1, 5)$, $(0, 1)$, $(1, 4)$, and $(2, 10)$.

Solution   Since we are given five points, we choose a fourth-degree polynomial

$$p(x) = a_0 + a_1x + a_2x^2 + a_3x^3 + a_4x^4.$$

Substituting the given points into $p(x)$ produces the following system of linear equations.

$$
\begin{aligned}
a_0 - 2a_1 + 4a_2 - 8a_3 + 16a_4 &= 3 \\
a_0 - a_1 + a_2 - a_3 + a_4 &= 5 \\
a_0 &= 1 \\
a_0 + a_1 + a_2 + a_3 + a_4 &= 4 \\
a_0 + 2a_1 + 4a_2 + 8a_3 + 16a_4 &= 10
\end{aligned}
$$

The solution of these equations is

$$a_0 = 1, \qquad a_1 = -\frac{30}{24}, \qquad a_2 = \frac{101}{24}, \qquad a_3 = \frac{18}{24}, \qquad a_4 = -\frac{17}{24}$$

which means that the polynomial is

$$
\begin{aligned}
p(x) &= 1 - \frac{30}{24}x + \frac{101}{24}x^2 + \frac{18}{24}x^3 - \frac{17}{24}x^4 \\
&= \frac{1}{24}(24 - 30x + 101x^2 + 18x^3 - 17x^4).
\end{aligned}
$$

The graph of p is shown in Figure 1.6.

The system of linear equations in Example 2 is relatively easy to solve because the x-values are small. Given a set of points with large x-values, it is usually best to translate the values before attempting the curve-fitting procedure. This approach is demonstrated in the next example.

EXAMPLE 3   ***Translating Large x-Values before Curve Fitting***

Find a polynomial that fits the points

$$(x_1, y_1) \qquad (x_2, y_2) \qquad (x_3, y_3) \qquad (x_4, y_4) \qquad (x_5, y_5)$$

$$(1986, 3), \qquad (1987, 5), \qquad (1988, 1), \qquad (1989, 4), \qquad (1990, 10).$$

Solution   Because the given x-values are large, we use the translation $z = x - 1988$ to obtain

$$(z_1, y_1) \qquad (z_2, y_2) \qquad (z_3, y_3) \qquad (z_4, y_4) \qquad (z_5, y_5)$$

$$(-2, 3), \qquad (-1, 5), \qquad (0, 1), \qquad (1, 4), \qquad (2, 10).$$

This is the same set of points as in Example 2. Thus the polynomial that fits these points is

$$p(z) = \tfrac{1}{24}(24 - 30z + 101z^2 + 18z^3 - 17z^4)$$
$$= 1 - \tfrac{5}{4}z + \tfrac{101}{24}z^2 + \tfrac{3}{4}z^3 - \tfrac{17}{24}z^4.$$

Letting $z = x - 1988$, we have

$$p(x) = 1 - \tfrac{5}{4}(x - 1988) + \tfrac{101}{24}(x - 1988)^2 + \tfrac{3}{4}(x - 1988)^3 - \tfrac{17}{24}(x - 1988)^4.$$

EXAMPLE 4   ***An Application of Curve Fitting***

Find a polynomial that relates the period of the first three planets to their mean distance from the sun, as shown in Table 1.1. Then test the accuracy of the fit by using the polynomial to calculate the period of Mars. (Distance is measured in astronomical units, and period is measured in years.)

TABLE 1.1

Planet	Mercury	Venus	Earth	Mars
Mean Distance	0.387	0.723	1.0	1.523
Period	0.241	0.615	1.0	1.881

Solution   We begin by fitting a quadratic polynomial

$$p(x) = a_0 + a_1 x + a_2 x^2$$

to the points $(0.387, 0.241)$, $(0.723, 0.615)$, and $(1, 1)$. The system of linear equations obtained by substituting these points into $p(x)$ is

$$a_0 + 0.387a_1 + (0.387)^2 a_2 = 0.241$$
$$a_0 + 0.723a_1 + (0.723)^2 a_2 = 0.615$$
$$a_0 + \quad a_1 + \quad\quad a_2 = 1.$$

The solution to the system is

$$a_0 = -0.0634, \qquad a_1 = 0.6119, \qquad a_2 = 0.4515$$

which means that the polynomial is

$$p(x) = -0.0634 + 0.6119x + 0.4515x^2.$$

Using $p(x)$ to evaluate the period of Mars produces

$$p(1.523) = 1.916 \text{ years.}$$

This estimate is compared graphically to the actual period of Mars in Figure 1.7 below. Note that the actual period (from Table 1.1) is 1.881 years.

An important lesson may be learned from the application shown in Example 4: The polynomial that fits the given data does not necessarily give an accurate model for the relationship between x and y for x-values other than those corresponding to the given points. Generally, the farther the additional points are from the given points, the worse the fit. For instance, in Example 4 the mean distance of Jupiter is 5.203. The corresponding polynomial approximation for the period is 15.343 years—a poor estimate of Jupiter's actual period of 11.861 years.

The problem of curve fitting can be difficult. Other types of functions often provide better fits than do polynomials. To see this, let's look again at the curve-fitting problem in Example 4. Taking the natural logarithm of each of the distances and periods of the first six planets produces the results shown in Table 1.2 and Figure 1.8.

TABLE 1.2

Planet	Mercury	Venus	Earth	Mars	Jupiter	Saturn
Mean Distance (x)	0.387	0.723	1.0	1.523	5.203	9.541
Natural Log of Mean	−0.949	−0.324	0.0	0.421	1.649	2.256
Period (y)	0.241	0.615	1.0	1.881	11.861	29.457
Natural Log of Period	−1.423	−0.486	0.0	0.632	2.473	3.383

Figure 1.7

Figure 1.8

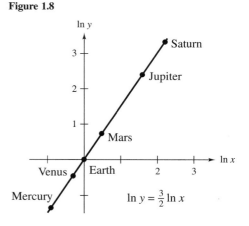

Now, by fitting a polynomial to the logarithms of the distances and periods, we obtain the following *linear relationship* between $\ln x$ and $\ln y$.

$$\ln y = \tfrac{3}{2} \ln x$$

From this equation it follows that $y = x^{3/2}$, or

$$y^2 = x^3.$$

In other words, the square of the period (in years) of each planet is equal to the cube of its mean distance (in astronomical units) from the sun. This relationship was first discovered by Johannes Kepler in 1619.

Network Analysis

Networks composed of branches and junctions are used as models in fields as diverse as economics, traffic analysis, and electrical engineering.

It is assumed in such models that the total flow into a junction is equal to the total flow out of the junction. For example, since the junction shown in Figure 1.9 has 25 units flowing into it, there must be 25 units flowing out of it. This is represented by the linear equation

$$x_1 + x_2 = 25.$$

Because each junction in a network gives rise to a linear equation, we can analyze the flow through a network composed of several junctions by solving a system of linear equations. This procedure is illustrated in Example 5.

Figure 1.9

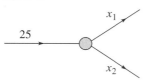

EXAMPLE 5   *Analysis of a Network*

Set up a system of linear equations to represent the network shown in Figure 1.10, and solve the system.

Figure 1.10

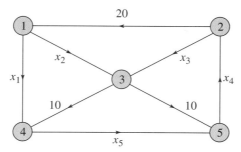

Solution   Each of the network's five junctions gives rise to a linear equation, as follows.

$$
\begin{array}{ll}
x_1 + x_2 = 20 & \text{Junction 1} \\
x_3 + 20 = x_4 & \text{Junction 2} \\
x_2 + x_3 = 20 & \text{Junction 3} \\
x_1 + 10 = x_5 & \text{Junction 4} \\
x_5 + 10 = x_4 & \text{Junction 5}
\end{array}
$$

The augmented matrix for this system is

$$\begin{bmatrix} 1 & 1 & 0 & 0 & 0 & 20 \\ 0 & 0 & 1 & -1 & 0 & -20 \\ 0 & 1 & 1 & 0 & 0 & 20 \\ 1 & 0 & 0 & 0 & -1 & -10 \\ 0 & 0 & 0 & -1 & 1 & -10 \end{bmatrix}.$$

Gauss-Jordan elimination produces the matrix

$$\begin{bmatrix} 1 & 0 & 0 & 0 & -1 & -10 \\ 0 & 1 & 0 & 0 & 1 & 30 \\ 0 & 0 & 1 & 0 & -1 & -10 \\ 0 & 0 & 0 & 1 & -1 & 10 \\ 0 & 0 & 0 & 0 & 0 & 0 \end{bmatrix}.$$

Letting $t = x_5$, we have

$$x_1 = t - 10, \qquad x_2 = -t + 30, \qquad x_3 = t - 10, \qquad x_4 = t + 10, \qquad x_5 = t$$

where t is a real number. Thus this system has an infinite number of solutions.

In Example 5, suppose that you could control the amount of flow along the branch labeled x_5. Using the solution given in Example 5, you could then control the flow represented by each of the other variables. For instance, letting $t = 10$ would reduce the flow of x_1 and x_3 to zero, as shown in Figure 1.11. Similarly, letting $t = 20$ would produce the network shown in Figure 1.12.

Figure 1.11

Figure 1.12

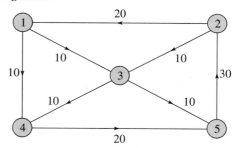

You can see how the type of network analysis shown in Example 5 could be used in problems dealing with the flow of traffic through the streets of a city or the flow of water through an irrigation system.

Another type of network to which network analysis is commonly applied is the electrical network. An analysis of such a system uses two properties of electrical networks known as **Kirchhoff's Laws**.

1. All the current flowing into a junction must flow out of it.
2. The sum of the products IR (I is current and R is resistance) around a closed path is equal to the total voltage in the path.

REMARK: A *closed* path is a sequence of branches such that the beginning point of the first branch coincides with the end point of the last branch.

In an electrical network, current is measured in amps, resistance in ohms, and the product of current and resistance in volts. Batteries are represented by the symbol ——|⊢— , where the current flows out of the terminal denoted by the larger vertical bar. Resistance is denoted by the symbol ⌁⌁⌁ .

EXAMPLE 6   *Analysis of an Electrical Network*

Determine the currents I_1, I_2, and I_3 for the electrical network shown in Figure 1.13.

Figure 1.13

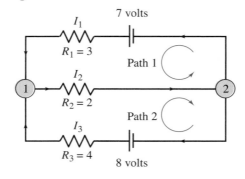

Solution   Applying Kirchhoff's first law to either junction produces

$$I_1 + I_3 = I_2 \qquad \text{Junction 1 or Junction 2}$$

and applying the second law to the two paths produces

$$R_1I_1 + R_2I_2 = 3I_1 + 2I_2 = 7 \qquad \text{Path 1}$$
$$R_2I_2 + R_3I_3 = 2I_2 + 4I_3 = 8. \qquad \text{Path 2}$$

Thus we have the following system of three linear equations in the variables I_1, I_2, and I_3.

$$\begin{aligned} I_1 - I_2 + I_3 &= 0 \\ 3I_1 + 2I_2 \quad\;\; &= 7 \\ 2I_2 + 4I_3 &= 8 \end{aligned}$$

Applying Gauss-Jordan elimination to the augmented matrix

$$\begin{bmatrix} 1 & -1 & 1 & 0 \\ 3 & 2 & 0 & 7 \\ 0 & 2 & 4 & 8 \end{bmatrix}$$

produces the reduced row-echelon form

$$\begin{bmatrix} 1 & 0 & 0 & 1 \\ 0 & 1 & 0 & 2 \\ 0 & 0 & 1 & 1 \end{bmatrix}$$

which means that $I_1 = 1$ amp, $I_2 = 2$ amps, and $I_3 = 1$ amp.

EXAMPLE 7   *Analysis of an Electrical Network*

Determine the currents I_1, I_2, I_3, I_4, I_5, and I_6 for the electrical network shown in Figure 1.14.

Figure 1.14

Solution   Applying Kirchhoff's first law to the four junctions produces

$$
\begin{aligned}
I_1 + I_3 &= I_2 & &\text{Junction 1} \\
I_1 + I_4 &= I_2 & &\text{Junction 2} \\
I_3 + I_6 &= I_5 & &\text{Junction 3} \\
I_4 + I_6 &= I_5 & &\text{Junction 4}
\end{aligned}
$$

and applying the second law to the three paths produces

$$
\begin{aligned}
2I_1 + 4I_2 &= 10 & &\text{Path 1} \\
4I_2 + I_3 + 2I_4 + 2I_5 &= 17 & &\text{Path 2} \\
2I_5 + 4I_6 &= 14. & &\text{Path 3}
\end{aligned}
$$

Thus we have the following system of seven linear equations in the variables I_1, I_2, I_3, I_4, I_5, and I_6.

$$
\begin{aligned}
I_1 - I_2 + I_3 && &= 0 \\
I_1 - I_2 &+ I_4 & &= 0 \\
I_3 &- I_5 + I_6 &= 0 \\
I_4 &- I_5 + I_6 &= 0 \\
2I_1 + 4I_2 && &= 10 \\
4I_2 + I_3 + 2I_4 + 2I_5 && &= 17 \\
2I_5 + 4I_6 &= 14
\end{aligned}
$$

Using Gauss-Jordan elimination, a calculator, or MATLAB, we solve this system:

$$I_1 = 1, \quad I_2 = 2 \quad I_3 = 1, \quad I_4 = 1, \quad I_5 = 3, \quad \text{and} \quad I_6 = 2$$

which means that $I_1 = 1$ amp, $I_2 = 2$ amps, $I_3 = 1$ amp, $I_4 = 1$ amp, $I_5 = 3$ amps, and $I_6 = 2$ amps.

SECTION 1.3 ☐ EXERCISES

Polynomial Curve Fitting

In Exercises 1–6, (a) determine the polynomial whose graph passes through the given points, and (b) sketch the graph of the polynomial showing the given points.

1. (2, 5), (3, 2), (4, 5)
2. (2, 4), (3, 4), (4, 4)
3. (2, 4), (3, 6), (5, 10)
4. (−1, 3), (0, 0), (1, 1), (4, 58)
5. (1986, 5), (1987, 7), (1988, 12) (Let $z = x − 1987$.)
6. (1986, 150), (1987, 180), (1988, 240), (1989, 360), (Let $z = x − 1987$.)
7. Try to fit the graph of a polynomial function to the given values. What happens, and why?

x	1	2	3	3	4
y	1	1	2	3	4

8. The graph of a function f passes through the points (0, 1), $(2, \frac{1}{3})$, and $(4, \frac{1}{5})$. Find a quadratic function that passes through these points.
9. Find a polynomial function p of degree 2 or less that passes through the points (0, 1), (2, 3), and (4, 5). Then sketch the graph of $y = 1/p(x)$ and compare this graph to the graph of the polynomial found in Exercise 8.
10. (Calculus) The graph of a parabola passes through the points (0,1) and $(\frac{1}{2}, \frac{1}{2})$ and has a horizontal tangent at $(\frac{1}{2}, \frac{1}{2})$. Find an equation for the parabola and sketch its graph.
11. (Calculus) A cubic polynomial has horizontal tangents at (1, −2) and (−1, 2). Find an equation for the cubic and sketch its graph.
12. Find an equation of the circle passing through the points (1, 3), (−2, 6), and (4, 2).
13. The U.S. census lists the population of the United States as 179.3 million in 1950, 203.3 million in 1960, and 226.5 million in 1980. Fit a second-degree polynomial to these three points and use your result to predict the population for 1985 and 1990.
C 14. The U.S. population for the years 1920, 1930, 1940, and 1950 is given in the following table.

Year	1920	1930	1940	1950
Population (in millions)	106	123	132	151

(a) Find a cubic polynomial that fits these data and use your result to estimate the population for 1960.
(b) How does your estimate compare with the actual 1960 population of 179 million?

15. Use $\sin 0 = 0$, $\sin(\pi/2) = 1$, and $\sin \pi = 0$ to estimate $\sin(\pi/3)$.
16. Use $\log_2 1 = 0$, $\log_2 2 = 1$, and $\log_2 4 = 2$ to estimate $\log_2 3$.
17. Prove that if a polynomial function $p(x) = a_0 + a_1 x + a_2 x^2$ is zero for $x = −1$, $x = 0$, and $x = 1$, then $a_0 = a_1 = a_2 = 0$.
18. The statement in Exercise 17 can be generalized as follows: If a polynomial function $p(x) = a_0 + a_1 x + \cdots + a_{n-1} x^{n-1}$ is zero for more than $n − 1$ x-values, then $a_0 = a_1 = \cdots = a_{n-1} = 0$. Use this result to prove that there is at most one polynomial function of degree $n − 1$ (or less) whose graph passes through n points in the plane with distinct x-coordinates. [Hint: Let
$$p_1(x) = a_0 + a_1 x + a_2 x^2 + \cdots + a_{n-1} x^{n-1}$$
and
$$p_2(x) = b_0 + b_1 x + b_2 x^2 + \cdots + b_{n-1} x^{n-1}$$
be two different polynomial functions that pass through the given points and consider $p_1(x) − p_2(x)$ at $x = x_1, x_2, \ldots, x_n$.]

Network Analysis

C 19. Water is flowing through a network of pipes (in thousands of cubic meters per hour), as shown in Figure 1.15.

(a) Solve this system for the water flow represented by x_i, $i = 1, 2, \ldots, 7$.
(b) Find the network flow pattern when $x_6 = x_7 = 0$.
(c) Find the network flow pattern when $x_5 = 1000$ and $x_6 = 0$.

Figure 1.15

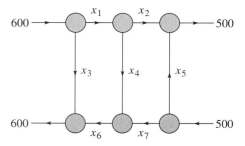

20. The flow of traffic (in vehicles per hour) through a network of streets is shown in Figure 1.16.

   (a) Solve this system for x_i, $i = 1, 2, \ldots, 5$.
   (b) Find the traffic flow when $x_2 = 200$ and $x_3 = 50$.
   (c) Find the traffic flow when $x_2 = 150$ and $x_3 = 0$.

Figure 1.16

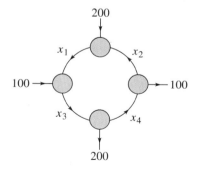

21. The flow of traffic (in vehicles per hour) through a network of streets is shown in Figure 1.17.

   (a) Solve this system for x_i, $i = 1, 2, 3, 4$.
   (b) Find the traffic flow when $x_4 = 0$.
   (c) Find the traffic flow when $x_4 = 100$.

Figure 1.17

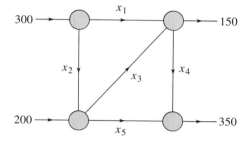

22. The flow of traffic (in vehicles per hour) through a network of streets is shown in Figure 1.18. (See top of next column.)

   (a) Solve the system for x_i, $i = 1, 2, \ldots, 5$.
   (b) Find the traffic flow when $x_3 = 0$ and $x_5 = 100$.
   (c) Find the traffic flow when $x_3 = x_5 = 100$.

Figure 1.18

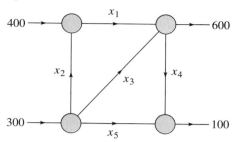

23. Determine the currents I_1, I_2, and I_3 for the electrical network shown in Figure 1.19.

Figure 1.19

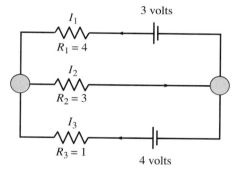

24. Determine the currents I_1, I_2, and I_3 for the electrical network shown in Figure 1.20.

Figure 1.20

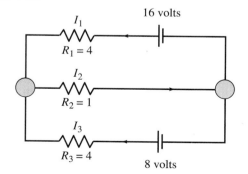

C **25.** (a) Determine the currents I_1, I_2, and I_3 for the electrical network shown in Figure 1.21.

(b) How is the result affected when A is changed to 2 volts and B is changed to 6 volts?

Figure 1.21

C **26.** Determine the currents I_1, I_2, I_3, I_4, I_5, and I_6 for the electrical network shown in Figure 1.22.

Figure 1.22

CHAPTER 1 ☐ REVIEW EXERCISES

In Exercises 1 and 2, find a parametric representation of the solution set of the given linear equation.

1. $-4x + 2y - 6z = 1$ **2.** $3x_1 + 2x_2 - 4x_3 = 0$

In Exercises 3–6, determine whether the given matrix is in row-echelon form. If it is, determine whether it is also in reduced row-echelon form.

3. $\begin{bmatrix} 1 & 0 & 1 & 1 \\ 0 & 1 & 2 & 1 \\ 0 & 0 & 0 & 1 \end{bmatrix}$ **4.** $\begin{bmatrix} 1 & 2 & -3 & 0 \\ 0 & 0 & 0 & 1 \\ 0 & 0 & 0 & 0 \end{bmatrix}$

5. $\begin{bmatrix} -1 & 2 & 1 \\ 0 & 1 & 0 \\ 0 & 0 & 1 \end{bmatrix}$ **6.** $\begin{bmatrix} 0 & 1 & 0 & 0 \\ 0 & 0 & 1 & 2 \\ 0 & 0 & 0 & 0 \end{bmatrix}$

In Exercises 7 and 8, find the solution set of the system of linear equations represented by the given augmented matrix.

7. $\begin{bmatrix} 1 & 2 & 0 & 0 \\ 0 & 0 & 1 & 0 \\ 0 & 0 & 0 & 0 \end{bmatrix}$ **8.** $\begin{bmatrix} 1 & 2 & 3 & 0 \\ 0 & 0 & 0 & 1 \\ 0 & 0 & 0 & 0 \end{bmatrix}$

In Exercises 9–30, solve the given system of linear equations.

9. $\begin{aligned} x + y &= 2 \\ x - y &= 0 \end{aligned}$

10. $\begin{aligned} x + y &= -1 \\ 3x + 2y &= 0 \end{aligned}$

11. $\begin{aligned} y &= 2x \\ y &= x + 4 \end{aligned}$

12. $\begin{aligned} x &= y + 3 \\ x &= y + 1 \end{aligned}$

13. $\begin{aligned} y + x &= 0 \\ 2x + y &= 0 \end{aligned}$

14. $\begin{aligned} y &= -4x \\ y &= x \end{aligned}$

15. $\begin{aligned} x - y &= 9 \\ -x + y &= 1 \end{aligned}$

16. $\begin{aligned} 40x_1 + 30x_2 &= 24 \\ 20x_1 + 15x_2 &= -14 \end{aligned}$

17. $\begin{aligned} 0.2x_1 + 0.3x_2 &= 0.14 \\ 0.4x_1 + 0.5x_2 &= 0.20 \end{aligned}$

18. $\begin{aligned} 0.2x - 0.1y &= 0.07 \\ 0.4x - 0.5y &= -0.01 \end{aligned}$

19. $\begin{aligned} \tfrac{1}{2}x - \tfrac{1}{3}y &= 0 \\ 3x + 2(y + 5) &= 10 \end{aligned}$

20. $\begin{aligned} \tfrac{1}{3}x + \tfrac{4}{7}y &= 3 \\ 2x + 3y &= 15 \end{aligned}$

21. $\begin{aligned} -x + y + 2z &= 1 \\ 2x + 3y + z &= -2 \\ 5x + 4y + 2z &= 4 \end{aligned}$

22. $\begin{aligned} 2x + 3y + z &= 10 \\ 2x - 3y - 3z &= 22 \\ 4x - 2y + 3z &= -2 \end{aligned}$

23. $\begin{aligned} 2x + 3y + 3z &= 3 \\ 6x + 6y + 12z &= 13 \\ 12x + 9y - z &= 2 \end{aligned}$

24. $\begin{aligned} 2x + 6z &= -9 \\ 3x - 2y + 11z &= -16 \\ 3x - y + 7z &= -11 \end{aligned}$

25. $\begin{aligned} x - 2y + z &= -6 \\ 2x - 3y &= -7 \\ -x + 3y - 3z &= 11 \end{aligned}$

26. $\begin{aligned} x + 2y + 6z &= 1 \\ 2x + 5y + 15z &= 4 \\ 3x + y + 3z &= -6 \end{aligned}$

27. $\begin{aligned} 2x + y + 2z &= 4 \\ 2x + 2y &= 5 \\ 2x - y + 6z &= 2 \end{aligned}$

28. $\begin{aligned} 2x_1 + 5x_2 - 19x_3 &= 34 \\ 3x_1 + 8x_2 - 31x_3 &= 54 \end{aligned}$

C **29.** $\begin{aligned} 2x_1 + x_2 + x_3 + 2x_4 &= -1 \\ 5x_1 - 2x_2 + x_3 - 3x_4 &= 0 \\ -x_1 + 3x_2 + 2x_3 + 2x_4 &= 1 \\ 3x_1 + 2x_2 + 3x_3 - 5x_4 &= 12 \end{aligned}$

C **30.** $\begin{aligned} x_1 + 5x_2 + 3x_3 \quad\quad\quad &= 14 \\ 4x_2 + 2x_3 + 5x_4 \quad &= 3 \\ 3x_3 + 8x_4 + 6x_5 &= 16 \\ 2x_1 + 4x_2 \quad\quad\quad - 2x_5 &= 0 \\ 2x_1 \quad\quad - x_3 \quad\quad\quad &= 0 \end{aligned}$

In Exercises 31–34, solve the given homogeneous system of linear equations.

31. $\begin{aligned} x_1 - 2x_2 - 8x_3 &= 0 \\ 3x_1 + 2x_2 \quad\quad &= 0 \\ -x_1 + x_2 + 7x_3 &= 0 \end{aligned}$

32. $\begin{aligned} 2x_1 + 4x_2 - 7x_3 &= 0 \\ x_1 - 3x_2 + 9x_3 &= 0 \\ 6x_1 \quad\quad + 9x_3 &= 0 \end{aligned}$

33. $\begin{aligned} 2x_1 - 8x_2 + 4x_3 &= 0 \\ 3x_1 - 10x_2 + 7x_3 &= 0 \\ 10x_2 + 5x_3 &= 0 \end{aligned}$

34. $\begin{aligned} x_1 + 3x_2 + 5x_3 &= 0 \\ x_1 + 4x_2 + \tfrac{1}{2}x_3 &= 0 \end{aligned}$

35. Determine the value of k such that the following system of linear equations is inconsistent.
$$\begin{aligned} kx + y &= 0 \\ x + ky &= 1 \end{aligned}$$

36. Determine the value of k such that the following system of linear equations has exactly one solution.
$$\begin{aligned} x - y + 2z &= 0 \\ -x + y - z &= 0 \\ x + ky + z &= 0 \end{aligned}$$

37. Find conditions on a and b such that the following system of linear equations has (a) no solution, (b) exactly one solution, and (c) an infinite number of solutions.
$$\begin{aligned} x + 2y &= 3 \\ ax + by &= -9 \end{aligned}$$

38. Find (if possible) conditions on a, b, and c such that the following system of linear equations has (a) no solution, (b) exactly one solution, and (c) an infinite number of solutions.
$$\begin{aligned} 2x - y + z &= a \\ x + y + 2z &= b \\ 3y + 3z &= c \end{aligned}$$

39. Describe a method for showing that two matrices are row-equivalent. Are the following two matrices row-equivalent?
$$\begin{bmatrix} 1 & 1 & 2 \\ 0 & -1 & 2 \\ 3 & 1 & 2 \end{bmatrix} \text{ and } \begin{bmatrix} 1 & 2 & 3 \\ 4 & 3 & 6 \\ 5 & 5 & 10 \end{bmatrix}$$

40. Describe all possible 2×3 reduced row-echelon matrices. Support your answer with examples.

41. Let $n \geq 3$. Find the reduced row-echelon form of the $n \times n$ matrix.

$$\begin{bmatrix} 1 & 2 & 3 & \cdots & n \\ n+1 & n+2 & n+3 & \cdots & 2n \\ 2n+1 & 2n+2 & 2n+3 & \cdots & 3n \\ \vdots & \vdots & \vdots & & \vdots \\ n^2-n+1 & n^2-n+2 & n^2-n+3 & \cdots & n^2 \end{bmatrix}$$

42. Find all values of λ for which the following homogeneous system of linear equations has nontrivial solutions.
$$\begin{aligned} (\lambda + 2)x_1 - 2x_2 + 3x_3 &= 0 \\ -2x_1 + (\lambda - 1)x_2 + 6x_3 &= 0 \\ x_1 + 2x_2 + \lambda x_3 &= 0 \end{aligned}$$

Polynomial Curve Fitting

C In Exercises 43 and 44 (a) determine the polynomial whose graph passes through the given points, and (b) sketch the graph of the polynomial showing the given points.

43. $(2, 5), (3, 0), (4, 20)$

44. $(-1, -1), (0, 0), (1, 1), (2, 4)$

C **45.** A company has sales (measured in millions) of \$50, \$60, and \$75 during three consecutive years. Find a quadratic function that fits these data, and use the result to predict the sales during the fourth year.

46. The polynomial $p(x) = a_0 + a_1 x + a_2 x^2 + a_3 x^3$ is zero when $x = 1, 2, 3$, and 4. What are the values of a_0, a_1, a_2, and a_3?

Network Analysis

C **47.** The flow through a network is shown in Figure 1.23.
   (a) Solve the system for x_i, $i = 1, 2, \ldots, 6$.
   (b) Find the flow when $x_3 = 100$, $x_5 = 50$, and $x_6 = 50$.

Figure 1.23

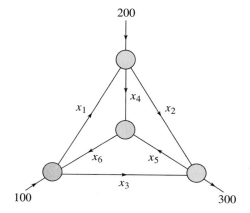

C **48.** Determine the currents I_1, I_2, and I_3 for the electrical network shown in Figure 1.24. (See right column.)

Figure 1.24

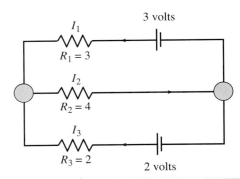

CHAPTER 1   PROJECTS

1   Graphing Linear Equations

You saw in Section 1.1 that a system of two linear equations in two unknowns x and y can be represented geometrically as two lines in the plane. These lines may intersect in a point, coincide, or be parallel.

1. Given the linear system

$$2x - y = 3$$
$$ax + by = 6$$

   find values of a and b such that the resulting system has
   (a) a unique solution,
   (b) an infinite number of solutions, and
   (c) no solution.
   Graph the lines for each of the three cases.

2. Consider a system of three linear equations in the three unknowns x, y, and z. Each equation represents a plane in the three-dimensional coordinate system. Give an example of a system represented by
   (a) three planes intersecting in a line,
   (b) three planes intersecting in a point, and
   (c) three planes with no common intersection,
   as illustrated in Figure 1.25.
   Do other configurations of three planes exist that are not covered by the three cases in the figures?

Figure 1.25

(a)   (b)   (c)

2   Underdetermined and Overdetermined Systems of Equations

A linear system of equations is said to be **underdetermined** if it has more unknowns than equations. Conversely, a system is **overdetermined** if it has more equations than unknowns. In this project, you are asked to explore whether the number of unknowns and the number of equations have any bearing on the consistency of a system of linear equations.

1. Prove (if possible) that a consistent underdetermined linear system can exist and give an example. Otherwise, explain why such a system is impossible.
2. Prove (if possible) that a consistent overdetermined linear system can exist and give an example. Otherwise, explain why such a system is impossible.
3. Prove (if possible) that an inconsistent underdetermined linear system can exist and give an example. Otherwise, explain why such a system is impossible.
4. Prove (if possible) that an inconsistent overdetermined linear system can exist and give an example. Otherwise, explain why such a system is impossible.
5. Explain why you would expect an overdetermined linear system to be inconsistent. Must this always be the case?
6. Explain why you would expect an underdetermined linear system to have an infinite number of solutions. Must this always be the case?

CHAPTER 1 ☐ MATLAB EXERCISES

1. Consider the linear system of Example 7 in Section 1.2.

$$
\begin{aligned}
x - 2y + 3z &= 9 \\
-x + 3y &= -4 \\
2x - 5y + 5z &= 17
\end{aligned}
$$

(a) Use the MATLAB command **rref** to solve the system.

(b) Let A be the coefficient matrix of the system, and B the right-hand side.

$$
A = \begin{bmatrix} 1 & -2 & 3 \\ -1 & 3 & 0 \\ 2 & -5 & 5 \end{bmatrix} \qquad B = \begin{bmatrix} 9 \\ -4 \\ 17 \end{bmatrix}
$$

Use the MATLAB command **A\B** to solve the system.

2. Enter the matrix

$$
A = \begin{bmatrix} -3 & 2 & 4 & 5 & 1 \\ 3 & 0 & 2 & -2 & 0 \\ -9 & 4 & 6 & 12 & 2 \end{bmatrix}
$$

Use the MATLAB command **rref(A)** to find the reduced row-echelon form of A. What is the solution to the linear system represented by the augmented matrix A?

3. Solve the linear system

$$
\begin{aligned}
16x - 120y + 240z - 140w &= -4 \\
-120x + 1200y - 2700z + 1680w &= 60 \\
240x - 2700y + 6480z - 4200w &= -180 \\
-140x + 1680y - 4200z + 2800w &= 140
\end{aligned}
$$

You can display more significant digits of the answer by typing **format long** before solving the system. Return to the standard format by typing **format short**.

4. Use the MATLAB command **rref(A)** to determine which of the following matrices are row-equivalent to

$$B = \begin{bmatrix} 1 & 2 & 3 & 4 \\ 5 & 6 & 7 & 8 \\ 9 & 10 & 11 & 12 \end{bmatrix}.$$

(a) $\begin{bmatrix} 1 & 1 & 1 & 1 \\ 1 & 0 & -1 & -2 \\ 0 & 1 & 2 & 3 \end{bmatrix}$ (b) $\begin{bmatrix} 1 & 3 & 2 & 4 \\ 5 & 6 & 7 & 8 \\ 9 & 10 & 11 & 12 \end{bmatrix}$ (c) $\begin{bmatrix} 12 & 11 & 10 & 9 \\ 4 & 3 & 2 & 1 \\ 8 & 7 & 6 & 5 \end{bmatrix}$

5. Let A be the coefficient matrix, and B the right-hand side of the linear system of equations

$$\begin{aligned} 3x + 3y + 12z &= 6 \\ x + y + 4z &= 2 \\ 2x + 5y + 20z &= 10 \\ -x + 2y + 8z &= 4. \end{aligned}$$

Enter the matrices A and B, and form the augmented matrix C for this system by using the MATLAB command **C = [A B]**. Solve the system using **rref**.

6. The MATLAB command **polyfit** allows you to fit a polynomial of degree $n - 1$ to a set of n data points in the plane

$$(x_1, y_1), \qquad (x_2, y_2), \qquad \ldots, \qquad (x_n, y_n).$$

Find the fourth-degree polynomial that fits the five data points of Example 2 in Section 1.3 by letting

$$x = \begin{bmatrix} -2 \\ -1 \\ 0 \\ 1 \\ 2 \end{bmatrix} \qquad y = \begin{bmatrix} 3 \\ 5 \\ 1 \\ 4 \\ 10 \end{bmatrix}$$

and entering the MATLAB command **polyfit(x,y,4)**.

7. Find the second-degree polynomial that fits the points $(1, -2), (2, 4), (-4, -6)$.

8. Find the sixth-degree polynomial that fits the seven points $(0, 0), (-1, 4.5), (-2, 133), (-3, 1225.5), (1, -0.5), (2, 3), (3, 250.5)$.

9. The following table gives the world population in billions for five different years.

Year	Population (in billions)
1960	3.0
1970	3.7
1975	4.1
1980	4.5
1985	4.8

Use **p=polyfit(x,y,4)** to fit the fourth-degree polynomial to this data. Then use **f=polyval(p,1990)** to estimate the world population for the year 1990. (The actual world population in 1990 was 5.3 billion.)

2 MATRICES

Arthur
Cayley
1 8 2 1 – 1 8 9 5

Arthur Cayley was the second son of an English merchant. Like Gauss, Cayley showed signs of mathematical genius at an early age. He attended Trinity College, Cambridge, where he soon advanced beyond his fellows. He won a series of honors culminating in his election as a Fellow of Trinity and assistant tutor, a position to which he could have been reelected had he been willing to take holy vows as a minister in the Church of England. After graduation from Cambridge, Cayley began a prolific writing career, publishing twenty-five papers in three years. The work he began in these papers directed his mathematical interest for nearly fifty years.

Cayley was unable to find a position as a mathematician, so at twenty-five he decided to enter law. For fourteen years Cayley had a modestly successful legal career, but he continued to spend considerable time on mathematics, publishing nearly 200 papers.

In 1863, Cayley was appointed professor of mathematics at Cambridge, a position he held until his death in 1895. While teaching at Cambridge, Cayley was instrumental in persuading the administration to begin accepting women as students.

Cayley's writings and mathematical creations involved many branches of mathematics, including analytic geometry. He is most remembered, however, for his work in linear algebra. He introduced matrix theory in a paper titled *A Memoir on the Theory of Matrices* (1858) and originated the theory of invariants.

2.1 OPERATIONS WITH MATRICES

In Section 1.2 we used matrices to solve systems of linear equations. Matrices, however, can do much more than that. There is a rich mathematical theory of matrices, and its applications are numerous. This section and the next introduce some fundamentals of matrix theory.

It is standard mathematical convention to represent matrices in any one of the following three ways.

1. A matrix can be denoted by an uppercase letter such as

   $A, B, C, \ldots.$

2. A matrix can be denoted by a representative element enclosed in brackets, such as

   $[a_{ij}], [b_{ij}], [c_{ij}], \ldots.$

3. A matrix can be denoted by a rectangular array of numbers

$$A = [a_{ij}] = \begin{bmatrix} a_{11} & a_{12} & a_{13} & \cdots & a_{1n} \\ a_{21} & a_{22} & a_{23} & \cdots & a_{2n} \\ a_{31} & a_{32} & a_{33} & \cdots & a_{3n} \\ \vdots & \vdots & \vdots & & \vdots \\ a_{m1} & a_{m2} & a_{m3} & \cdots & a_{mn} \end{bmatrix}.$$

As mentioned in Chapter 1, the matrices in this text are primarily *real matrices.* That is, their entries are real numbers. (Matrices whose entries are complex numbers will be discussed in Chapter 8.)

Two matrices are said to be **equal** if their corresponding entries are equal.

Definition of Equality of Matrices

Two matrices $A = [a_{ij}]$ and $B = [b_{ij}]$ are **equal** if they have the same size ($m \times n$) and

$$a_{ij} = b_{ij}$$

for $1 \le i \le m$ and $1 \le j \le n$.

EXAMPLE 1   *Equality of Matrices*

Consider the four matrices

$$A = \begin{bmatrix} 1 & 2 \\ 3 & 4 \end{bmatrix}, \qquad B = \begin{bmatrix} 1 \\ 3 \end{bmatrix}, \qquad C = \begin{bmatrix} 1 & 3 \end{bmatrix}, \qquad \text{and} \qquad D = \begin{bmatrix} 1 & 2 \\ x & 4 \end{bmatrix}.$$

Matrices A and B are **not** equal because they are of different sizes. Similarly, B and C are not equal. Matrices A and D are equal if and only if $x = 3$.

A matrix that has only one column, such as matrix B in Example 1, is called a **column matrix** or **column vector.** Similarly, a matrix that has only one row, such as matrix C, is called a **row matrix** or **row vector.** We will often use boldface lowercase letters to designate column matrices. For instance, matrix A in Example 1 can be considered to be partitioned into the two column matrices $\mathbf{a}_1 = \begin{bmatrix} 1 \\ 3 \end{bmatrix}$ and $\mathbf{a}_2 = \begin{bmatrix} 2 \\ 4 \end{bmatrix}$ as follows.

$$A = \begin{bmatrix} 1 & 2 \\ 3 & 4 \end{bmatrix} = \begin{bmatrix} 1 & \vdots & 2 \\ 3 & \vdots & 4 \end{bmatrix} = [\mathbf{a}_1 \quad \vdots \quad \mathbf{a}_2]$$

Matrix Addition

We **add** two matrices (of the same size) by adding their corresponding entries.

Definition of Matrix Addition

If $A = [a_{ij}]$ and $B = [b_{ij}]$ are matrices of size $m \times n$, then their **sum** is the $m \times n$ matrix given by

$$A + B = [a_{ij} + b_{ij}].$$

The sum of two matrices of different sizes is undefined.

EXAMPLE 2   *Addition of Matrices*

(a) $\begin{bmatrix} -1 & 2 \\ 0 & 1 \end{bmatrix} + \begin{bmatrix} 1 & 3 \\ -1 & 2 \end{bmatrix} = \begin{bmatrix} -1+1 & 2+3 \\ 0-1 & 1+2 \end{bmatrix} = \begin{bmatrix} 0 & 5 \\ -1 & 3 \end{bmatrix}$

(b) $\begin{bmatrix} 0 & 1 & -2 \\ 1 & 2 & 3 \end{bmatrix} + \begin{bmatrix} 0 & 0 & 0 \\ 0 & 0 & 0 \end{bmatrix} = \begin{bmatrix} 0 & 1 & -2 \\ 1 & 2 & 3 \end{bmatrix}$

(c) $\begin{bmatrix} 1 \\ -3 \\ -2 \end{bmatrix} + \begin{bmatrix} -1 \\ 3 \\ 2 \end{bmatrix} = \begin{bmatrix} 0 \\ 0 \\ 0 \end{bmatrix}$

(d) The sum of

$$A = \begin{bmatrix} 2 & 1 & 0 \\ 4 & 0 & -1 \\ 3 & -2 & 2 \end{bmatrix} \quad \text{and} \quad B = \begin{bmatrix} 0 & 1 \\ -1 & 3 \\ 2 & 4 \end{bmatrix}$$

is undefined.

Scalar Multiplication

When working with matrices, we usually refer to numbers as **scalars.** Unless stated otherwise, scalars will be real numbers. We multiply a matrix A by a scalar c by multiplying each entry in A by c.

Definition of Scalar Multiplication	If $A = [a_{ij}]$ is an $m \times n$ matrix and c is a scalar, then the **scalar multiple** of A by c is the $m \times n$ matrix given by $$cA = [ca_{ij}].$$

We use $-A$ to represent the scalar product $(-1)A$. If A and B are of the same size, $A - B$ represents the sum of A and $(-1)B$. That is,

$$A - B = A + (-1)B. \qquad \text{\textbf{Subtraction of matrices}}$$

EXAMPLE 3   *Scalar Multiplication and Matrix Subtraction*

For the matrices

$$A = \begin{bmatrix} 1 & 2 & 4 \\ -3 & 0 & -1 \\ 2 & 1 & 2 \end{bmatrix} \quad \text{and} \quad B = \begin{bmatrix} 2 & 0 & 0 \\ 1 & -4 & 3 \\ -1 & 3 & 2 \end{bmatrix}$$

find (a) $3A$, (b) $-B$, and (c) $3A - B$.

Solution   (a) $3A = 3\begin{bmatrix} 1 & 2 & 4 \\ -3 & 0 & -1 \\ 2 & 1 & 2 \end{bmatrix} = \begin{bmatrix} 3(1) & 3(2) & 3(4) \\ 3(-3) & 3(0) & 3(-1) \\ 3(2) & 3(1) & 3(2) \end{bmatrix} = \begin{bmatrix} 3 & 6 & 12 \\ -9 & 0 & -3 \\ 6 & 3 & 6 \end{bmatrix}$

(b) $-B = (-1)\begin{bmatrix} 2 & 0 & 0 \\ 1 & -4 & 3 \\ -1 & 3 & 2 \end{bmatrix} = \begin{bmatrix} -2 & 0 & 0 \\ -1 & 4 & -3 \\ 1 & -3 & -2 \end{bmatrix}$

(c) $3A - B = \begin{bmatrix} 3 & 6 & 12 \\ -9 & 0 & -3 \\ 6 & 3 & 6 \end{bmatrix} - \begin{bmatrix} 2 & 0 & 0 \\ 1 & -4 & 3 \\ -1 & 3 & 2 \end{bmatrix} = \begin{bmatrix} 1 & 6 & 12 \\ -10 & 4 & -6 \\ 7 & 0 & 4 \end{bmatrix}$

REMARK: It is often convenient to rewrite the scalar multiple cA by factoring c out of every entry in the matrix. For instance, in the following example, the scalar $\frac{1}{2}$ has been factored out of the matrix.

$$\begin{bmatrix} \frac{1}{2} & -\frac{3}{2} \\ \frac{5}{2} & \frac{1}{2} \end{bmatrix} = \frac{1}{2}\begin{bmatrix} 1 & -3 \\ 5 & 1 \end{bmatrix}$$

Matrix Multiplication

The third basic matrix operation is **matrix multiplication.** To see the usefulness of this operation, consider the following application in which matrices are helpful for organizing information.

A football stadium has three concession areas, located in the South, North, and West stands. The top-selling items are peanuts, hot dogs, and soda. Sales for a certain day were recorded in the first matrix below, and the price (in dollars) of each item is given in the second matrix.

	Number of items sold				*Selling Price*	
	Peanuts	*Hot dogs*	*Soda*			
South stand	120	250	305		1.00	*Peanuts*
North stand	207	140	419		2.00	*Hot dogs*
West stand	29	120	190		1.50	*Soda*

To calculate the total sales of the three top-selling items at the South stand, you can multiply each entry in the first row of the matrix on the left by the corresponding entry in the price column matrix on the right and add the results. That is, the South stand sales are

$(120)(1.00) + (250)(2.00) + (305)(1.50) = \$1077.50.$ **South stand sales**

Similarly, you can calculate the sales for the other two stands as follows.

$(207)(1.00) + (140)(2.00) + (419)(1.50) = \$1115.50$ **North stand sales**
$(29)(1.00) + (120)(2.00) + (190)(1.50) = \$554.00$ **West stand sales**

The preceding computation is an example of matrix multiplication. You can write the product of the 3×3 matrix indicating the number of items sold and the 3×1 matrix indicating the selling prices as follows.

$$\begin{bmatrix} 120 & 250 & 305 \\ 207 & 140 & 419 \\ 29 & 120 & 190 \end{bmatrix}\begin{bmatrix} 1.00 \\ 2.00 \\ 1.50 \end{bmatrix} = \begin{bmatrix} 1077.50 \\ 1115.50 \\ 554.00 \end{bmatrix}$$

The product of these matrices is the 3×1 matrix giving the total sales for each of the three stands.

The following general definition of the product of two matrices is based on the ideas just developed. Although at first glance this definition may seem unusual, you will see that it has many practical applications.

Definition of Matrix Multiplication

If $A = [a_{ij}]$ is an $m \times n$ matrix and $B = [b_{ij}]$ is an $n \times p$ matrix, then the **product** AB is an $m \times p$ matrix

$$AB = [c_{ij}]$$

where

$$c_{ij} = \sum_{k=1}^{n} a_{ik}b_{kj} = a_{i1}b_{1j} + a_{i2}b_{2j} + a_{i3}b_{3j} + \cdots + a_{in}b_{nj}.$$

This definition means that the entry in the ith row and the jth column of the product AB is obtained by multiplying the entries in the ith row of A by the corresponding entries in the jth column of B and then adding the results. The following example illustrates the process.

EXAMPLE 4   ***Finding the Product of Two Matrices***

Find the product AB, where

$$A = \begin{bmatrix} -1 & 3 \\ 4 & -2 \\ 5 & 0 \end{bmatrix} \quad \text{and} \quad B = \begin{bmatrix} -3 & 2 \\ -4 & 1 \end{bmatrix}.$$

Solution   First note that the product AB is defined because A has size 3×2, and B has size 2×2. Moreover, the product AB has size 3×2 and will take the form

$$\begin{bmatrix} -1 & 3 \\ 4 & -2 \\ 5 & 0 \end{bmatrix}\begin{bmatrix} -3 & 2 \\ -4 & 1 \end{bmatrix} = \begin{bmatrix} c_{11} & c_{12} \\ c_{21} & c_{22} \\ c_{31} & c_{32} \end{bmatrix}.$$

To find c_{11} (the entry in the first row and first column of the product), we multiply corresponding entries in the first row of A and the first column of B. That is,

$$c_{11} = (-1)(-3) + (3)(-4) = -9$$

$$\begin{bmatrix} -1 & 3 \\ 4 & -2 \\ 5 & 0 \end{bmatrix}\begin{bmatrix} -3 & 2 \\ -4 & 1 \end{bmatrix} = \begin{bmatrix} -9 & c_{12} \\ c_{21} & c_{22} \\ c_{31} & c_{32} \end{bmatrix}.$$

Similarly, to find c_{12}, we multiply corresponding entries in the first row of A and the second column of B to obtain

$$c_{12} = (-1)(2) + (3)(1) = 1$$

$$\begin{bmatrix} -1 & 3 \\ 4 & -2 \\ 5 & 0 \end{bmatrix}\begin{bmatrix} -3 & 2 \\ -4 & 1 \end{bmatrix} = \begin{bmatrix} -9 & 1 \\ c_{21} & c_{22} \\ c_{31} & c_{32} \end{bmatrix}.$$

Continuing this pattern produces the following results.

$$
\begin{aligned}
c_{21} &= (4)(-3) + (-2)(-4) = -4 \\
c_{22} &= (4)(2) \ + (-2)(1) \quad = \quad 6 \\
c_{31} &= (5)(-3) + (0)(-4) \quad = -15 \\
c_{32} &= (5)(2) \ \ + (0)(1) \quad\ = \quad 10
\end{aligned}
$$

Thus the product is

$$
AB = \begin{bmatrix} -1 & 3 \\ 4 & -2 \\ 5 & 0 \end{bmatrix} \begin{bmatrix} -3 & 2 \\ -4 & 1 \end{bmatrix} = \begin{bmatrix} -9 & 1 \\ -4 & 6 \\ -15 & 10 \end{bmatrix}.
$$

Be sure you understand that for the product of two matrices to be defined, the number of columns of the first matrix must equal the number of rows of the second matrix. That is,

$$
\underset{m \times n}{A} \quad \underset{n \times p}{B} \quad = \quad \underset{m \times p}{AB}.
$$

equal

size of AB

Thus, for instance, the product BA is not defined for matrices A and B of Example 4.

The general pattern for matrix multiplication is as follows. To obtain the element in the ith row and the jth column of the product AB, use the ith row of A and the jth column of B.

$$
\begin{bmatrix} a_{11} & a_{12} & a_{13} & \cdots & a_{1n} \\ a_{21} & a_{22} & a_{23} & \cdots & a_{2n} \\ \vdots & \vdots & \vdots & & \vdots \\ a_{i1} & a_{i2} & a_{i3} & \cdots & a_{in} \\ \vdots & \vdots & \vdots & & \vdots \\ a_{m1} & a_{m2} & a_{m3} & \cdots & a_{mn} \end{bmatrix}
\begin{bmatrix} b_{11} & b_{12} & \cdots & b_{1j} & \cdots & b_{1p} \\ b_{21} & b_{22} & \cdots & b_{2j} & \cdots & b_{2p} \\ b_{31} & b_{32} & \cdots & b_{3j} & \cdots & b_{3p} \\ \vdots & \vdots & & \vdots & & \vdots \\ b_{n1} & b_{n2} & \cdots & b_{nj} & \cdots & b_{np} \end{bmatrix}
=
\begin{bmatrix} c_{11} & c_{12} & \cdots & c_{1j} & \cdots & c_{1p} \\ c_{21} & c_{22} & \cdots & c_{2j} & \cdots & c_{2p} \\ \vdots & \vdots & & \vdots & & \vdots \\ c_{i1} & c_{i2} & \cdots & c_{ij} & \cdots & c_{ip} \\ \vdots & \vdots & & \vdots & & \vdots \\ c_{m1} & c_{m2} & \cdots & c_{mj} & \cdots & c_{mp} \end{bmatrix}
$$

$$
a_{i1}b_{1j} + a_{i2}b_{2j} + a_{i3}b_{3j} + \cdots + a_{in}b_{nj} = c_{ij}
$$

EXAMPLE 5   *Matrix Multiplication*

(a)
$$
\underset{2 \times 3}{\begin{bmatrix} 1 & 0 & 3 \\ 2 & -1 & -2 \end{bmatrix}}
\underset{3 \times 3}{\begin{bmatrix} -2 & 4 & 2 \\ 1 & 0 & 0 \\ -1 & 1 & -1 \end{bmatrix}}
=
\underset{2 \times 3}{\begin{bmatrix} -5 & 7 & -1 \\ -3 & 6 & 6 \end{bmatrix}}
$$

(b)
$$
\underset{2 \times 2}{\begin{bmatrix} 3 & 4 \\ -2 & 5 \end{bmatrix}}
\underset{2 \times 2}{\begin{bmatrix} 1 & 0 \\ 0 & 1 \end{bmatrix}}
=
\underset{2 \times 2}{\begin{bmatrix} 3 & 4 \\ -2 & 5 \end{bmatrix}}
$$

(c) $\begin{bmatrix} 1 & 2 \\ 1 & 1 \end{bmatrix} \begin{bmatrix} -1 & 2 \\ 1 & -1 \end{bmatrix} = \begin{bmatrix} 1 & 0 \\ 0 & 1 \end{bmatrix}$

$\quad\quad 2 \times 2 \quad\quad 2 \times 2 \quad\quad\quad 2 \times 2$

(d) $\begin{bmatrix} 1 & -2 & -3 \end{bmatrix} \begin{bmatrix} 2 \\ -1 \\ 1 \end{bmatrix} = \begin{bmatrix} 1 \end{bmatrix}$

$\quad\quad 1 \times 3 \quad\quad\quad 3 \times 1 \quad 1 \times 1$

(e) $\begin{bmatrix} 2 \\ -1 \\ 1 \end{bmatrix} \begin{bmatrix} 1 & -2 & -3 \end{bmatrix} = \begin{bmatrix} 2 & -4 & -6 \\ -1 & 2 & 3 \\ 1 & -2 & -3 \end{bmatrix}$

$\quad\quad 3 \times 1 \quad\quad 1 \times 3 \quad\quad\quad\quad 3 \times 3$

REMARK: Note the difference between the two products in parts (d) and (e) of Example 5. Matrix multiplication is not, in general, commutative. That is, it is usually not true that the product AB is equal to the product BA. (See Section 2.2 for further discussion of the noncommutativity of matrix multiplication.)

TECHNOLOGY NOTE

Most graphing calculators and computer software can perform matrix addition, scalar multiplication, and matrix multiplication. If you are using a TI-85, your screens for Example 5(c) will look like the following:

```
A
            [[1  2]
             [1  1]]
B

            [[-1  2 ]
             [1   -1]]
```

```
A*B
            [[1  0]
             [0  1]]
```

Systems of Linear Equations

One practical application of matrix multiplication is that of representing a system of linear equations. Note how the system

$$a_{11}x_1 + a_{12}x_2 + a_{13}x_3 = b_1$$
$$a_{21}x_1 + a_{22}x_2 + a_{23}x_3 = b_2$$
$$a_{31}x_1 + a_{32}x_2 + a_{33}x_3 = b_3$$

can be written as the matrix equation $A\mathbf{x} = \mathbf{b}$, where A is the coefficient matrix of the system, and $\mathbf{x}$ and $\mathbf{b}$ are column matrices. That is, we can write

$$\underbrace{\begin{bmatrix} a_{11} & a_{12} & a_{13} \\ a_{21} & a_{22} & a_{23} \\ a_{31} & a_{32} & a_{33} \end{bmatrix}}_{A} \underbrace{\begin{bmatrix} x_1 \\ x_2 \\ x_3 \end{bmatrix}}_{\mathbf{x}} = \underbrace{\begin{bmatrix} b_1 \\ b_2 \\ b_3 \end{bmatrix}}_{\mathbf{b}}.$$

EXAMPLE 6   *Solving a System of Linear Equations*

Solve the matrix equation $A\mathbf{x} = \mathbf{0}$, where

$$A = \begin{bmatrix} 1 & -2 & 1 \\ 2 & 3 & -2 \end{bmatrix}, \qquad \mathbf{b} = \begin{bmatrix} x_1 \\ x_2 \\ x_3 \end{bmatrix}, \qquad \text{and} \qquad \mathbf{0} = \begin{bmatrix} 0 \\ 0 \end{bmatrix}.$$

Solution   As a system of linear equations, $A\mathbf{x} = \mathbf{0}$ looks like

$$\begin{aligned} x_1 - 2x_2 + x_3 &= 0 \\ 2x_1 + 3x_2 - 2x_3 &= 0. \end{aligned}$$

Using Gauss-Jordan elimination on the augmented matrix of this system, we obtain

$$\begin{bmatrix} 1 & 0 & -\frac{1}{7} & 0 \\ 0 & 1 & -\frac{4}{7} & 0 \end{bmatrix}.$$

Thus the system has an infinite number of solutions. Here a convenient choice of parameter is $x_3 = 7t$, and we can write the solution set as

$$x_1 = t, \qquad x_2 = 4t, \qquad x_3 = 7t, \quad t \text{ is any real number.}$$

In matrix terminology, we have found that the matrix equation

$$\begin{bmatrix} 1 & -2 & 1 \\ 2 & 3 & -2 \end{bmatrix} \begin{bmatrix} x_1 \\ x_2 \\ x_3 \end{bmatrix} = \begin{bmatrix} 0 \\ 0 \end{bmatrix}$$

has an infinite number of solutions represented by

$$\mathbf{x} = \begin{bmatrix} x_1 \\ x_2 \\ x_3 \end{bmatrix} = \begin{bmatrix} t \\ 4t \\ 7t \end{bmatrix} = t \begin{bmatrix} 1 \\ 4 \\ 7 \end{bmatrix}, \quad t \text{ is any scalar.}$$

That is, any scalar multiple of the column matrix on the right is a solution.

Partitioned Matrices

The system $A\mathbf{x} = \mathbf{b}$ can be represented in a more convenient way by partitioning the matrices A and $\mathbf{x}$ in the following manner. If

$$A = \begin{bmatrix} a_{11} & a_{12} & \cdots & a_{1n} \\ a_{21} & a_{22} & \cdots & a_{2n} \\ \vdots & \vdots & & \vdots \\ a_{m1} & a_{m2} & \cdots & a_{mn} \end{bmatrix}, \quad \mathbf{x} = \begin{bmatrix} x_1 \\ x_2 \\ \vdots \\ x_n \end{bmatrix} \quad \text{and} \quad \mathbf{b} = \begin{bmatrix} b_1 \\ b_2 \\ \vdots \\ b_m \end{bmatrix}$$

are the coefficient matrix, the column matrix of unknowns, and the right-hand side, respectively, of the $m \times n$ linear system, system $A\mathbf{x} = \mathbf{b}$, then

$$A\mathbf{x} = \mathbf{b}$$

$$\begin{bmatrix} a_{11} & a_{12} & \cdots & a_{1n} \\ a_{21} & a_{22} & \cdots & a_{2n} \\ \vdots & \vdots & & \vdots \\ a_{m1} & a_{m2} & \cdots & a_{mn} \end{bmatrix} \begin{bmatrix} x_1 \\ x_2 \\ \vdots \\ x_n \end{bmatrix} = \mathbf{b}$$

$$\begin{bmatrix} a_{11}x_1 & + & a_{12}x_2 & + & \cdots & + & a_{1n}x_n \\ a_{21}x_1 & + & a_{22}x_2 & + & \cdots & + & a_{2n}x_n \\ & & & \vdots & & & \\ a_{m1}x_1 & + & a_{m2}x_2 & + & \cdots & + & a_{mn}x_n \end{bmatrix} = \mathbf{b}$$

$$x_1 \begin{bmatrix} a_{11} \\ a_{21} \\ \vdots \\ a_{m1} \end{bmatrix} + x_2 \begin{bmatrix} a_{12} \\ a_{22} \\ \vdots \\ a_{m2} \end{bmatrix} + \cdots + x_n \begin{bmatrix} a_{1n} \\ a_{2n} \\ \vdots \\ a_{mn} \end{bmatrix} = \mathbf{b}$$

In other words,

$$A\mathbf{x} = x_1\mathbf{a}_1 + x_2\mathbf{a}_2 + \cdots + x_n\mathbf{a}_n = \mathbf{b},$$

where $\mathbf{a}_1, \mathbf{a}_2, \ldots, \mathbf{a}_n$ are the columns of the matrix A. The expression

$$x_1 \begin{bmatrix} a_{11} \\ a_{21} \\ \vdots \\ a_{m1} \end{bmatrix} + x_2 \begin{bmatrix} a_{12} \\ a_{22} \\ \vdots \\ a_{m2} \end{bmatrix} + \cdots + x_n \begin{bmatrix} a_{1n} \\ a_{2n} \\ \vdots \\ a_{mn} \end{bmatrix}$$

is called a **linear combination** of the column matrices $\mathbf{a}_1, \mathbf{a}_2, \ldots, \mathbf{a}_n$ with **coefficients** $x_1, x_2, \ldots, x_n$.

In general, the matrix product $A\mathbf{x}$ is a linear combination of the column vectors $\mathbf{a}_1, \mathbf{a}_2, \ldots, \mathbf{a}_n$ that form the coefficient matrix A. Furthermore, the system $A\mathbf{x} = \mathbf{b}$ is consistent if and only if $\mathbf{b}$ can be expressed as such a linear combination, where the coefficients of the linear combination are a solution to the system.

EXAMPLE 7   The linear system

$$
\begin{aligned}
x_1 + 2x_2 + 3x_3 &= 0 \\
4x_1 + 5x_2 + 6x_3 &= 3 \\
7x_1 + 8x_2 + 9x_3 &= 6
\end{aligned}
$$

can be rewritten as a matrix equation $A\mathbf{x} = \mathbf{b}$ as follows.

$$
x_1 \begin{bmatrix} 1 \\ 4 \\ 7 \end{bmatrix} + x_2 \begin{bmatrix} 2 \\ 5 \\ 8 \end{bmatrix} + x_3 \begin{bmatrix} 3 \\ 6 \\ 9 \end{bmatrix} = \begin{bmatrix} 0 \\ 3 \\ 6 \end{bmatrix}
$$

Using Gaussian elimination, you can show that this system has an infinite number of solutions, one of which is $x_1 = 1$, $x_2 = 1$, $x_3 = -1$.

$$
1 \begin{bmatrix} 1 \\ 4 \\ 7 \end{bmatrix} + 1 \begin{bmatrix} 2 \\ 5 \\ 8 \end{bmatrix} + (-1) \begin{bmatrix} 3 \\ 6 \\ 9 \end{bmatrix} = \begin{bmatrix} 0 \\ 3 \\ 6 \end{bmatrix}
$$

That is, $\mathbf{b}$ can be expressed as a linear combination of the columns of A. This representation of one column vector in terms of others is a fundamental theme of linear algebra.

TECHNOLOGY NOTE

Many real-life applications of linear systems involve enormous numbers of equations and unknowns. For example, a flight crew scheduling problem for American Airlines required manipulating matrices with 837 rows and 12,750,000 columns! (Very Large-Scale Linear Programming: A Case Study in Combining Interior Point and Simplex Methods, Bixby, Robert E., et al., *Operations Research*, 40, no. 5, 1992.) This application of "linear programming" (see Chapter 9 for an introduction to this topic) required that the problem be partitioned into smaller pieces and then solved on a CRAY Y-MP supercomputer.

Just as we partitioned A into columns and $\mathbf{x}$ into rows, it is often useful to consider an $m \times n$ matrix as partitioned into smaller matrices. For example, the matrix

$$
\begin{bmatrix} 1 & 2 & 0 & 0 \\ 3 & 4 & 0 & 0 \\ -1 & -2 & 2 & 1 \end{bmatrix}
$$

could be partitioned as follows.

$$
\left[\begin{array}{cc|cc} 1 & 2 & 0 & 0 \\ 3 & 4 & 0 & 0 \\ \hline -1 & -2 & 2 & 1 \end{array} \right]
$$

The matrix could also be partitioned into column matrices

$$
\left[\begin{array}{c|c|c|c} 1 & 2 & 0 & 0 \\ 3 & 4 & 0 & 0 \\ -1 & -2 & 2 & 1 \end{array} \right] = \begin{bmatrix} \mathbf{c}_1 & \mathbf{c}_2 & \mathbf{c}_3 & \mathbf{c}_4 \end{bmatrix}
$$

or row matrices

$$
\left[\begin{array}{cccc} 1 & 2 & 0 & 0 \\ \hline 3 & 4 & 0 & 0 \\ \hline -1 & -2 & 2 & 1 \end{array} \right] = \begin{bmatrix} \mathbf{r}_1 \\ \mathbf{r}_2 \\ \mathbf{r}_3 \end{bmatrix}.
$$

SECTION 2.1 ☐ EXERCISES

In Exercises 1–6, find (a) $A + B$, (b) $A - B$, (c) $2A$, and (d) $2A - B$.

1. $A = \begin{bmatrix} 1 & -1 \\ 2 & -1 \end{bmatrix}$, $B = \begin{bmatrix} 2 & -1 \\ -1 & 8 \end{bmatrix}$

2. $A = \begin{bmatrix} 1 & 2 \\ 2 & 1 \end{bmatrix}$, $B = \begin{bmatrix} -3 & -2 \\ 4 & 2 \end{bmatrix}$

3. $A = \begin{bmatrix} 6 & -1 \\ 2 & 4 \\ -3 & 5 \end{bmatrix}$, $B = \begin{bmatrix} 1 & 4 \\ -1 & 5 \\ 1 & 10 \end{bmatrix}$

4. $A = \begin{bmatrix} 2 & 1 & 1 \\ -1 & -1 & 4 \end{bmatrix}$, $B = \begin{bmatrix} 2 & -3 & 4 \\ -3 & 1 & -2 \end{bmatrix}$

5. $A = \begin{bmatrix} 2 & 2 & -1 & 0 & 1 \\ 1 & 1 & -2 & 0 & -1 \end{bmatrix}$,

$B = \begin{bmatrix} 1 & 1 & -1 & 1 & 0 \\ -3 & 4 & 9 & -6 & -7 \end{bmatrix}$

6. $A = \begin{bmatrix} 3 \\ 2 \\ -1 \end{bmatrix}$, $B = \begin{bmatrix} -4 \\ 6 \\ 2 \end{bmatrix}$

7. Find (a) c_{21} and (b) c_{13}, where $C = 2A - 3B$ and

$A = \begin{bmatrix} 5 & 4 & 4 \\ -3 & 1 & 2 \end{bmatrix}$ and $B = \begin{bmatrix} 1 & 2 & -7 \\ 0 & -5 & 1 \end{bmatrix}$.

8. Find (a) c_{23} and (b) c_{32}, where $C = 5A + 2B$ and

$A = \begin{bmatrix} 4 & 11 & -9 \\ 0 & 3 & 2 \\ -3 & 1 & 1 \end{bmatrix}$ and $B = \begin{bmatrix} 1 & 0 & 5 \\ -4 & 6 & 11 \\ -6 & 4 & 9 \end{bmatrix}$.

9. Solve for x, y, and z in the matrix equation

$4\begin{bmatrix} x & y \\ z & -1 \end{bmatrix} = 2\begin{bmatrix} y & z \\ -x & 1 \end{bmatrix} + 2\begin{bmatrix} 4 & x \\ 5 & -x \end{bmatrix}$.

10. Solve for x, y, z, and w in the matrix equation

$\begin{bmatrix} w & x \\ y & x \end{bmatrix} = \begin{bmatrix} -4 & 3 \\ 2 & -1 \end{bmatrix} + 2\begin{bmatrix} y & w \\ z & x \end{bmatrix}$.

In Exercises 11–16, find (a) AB and (b) BA.

11. $A = \begin{bmatrix} 1 & 2 \\ 4 & 2 \end{bmatrix}$, $B = \begin{bmatrix} 2 & -1 \\ -1 & 8 \end{bmatrix}$

12. $A = \begin{bmatrix} 2 & -1 \\ 1 & 4 \end{bmatrix}$, $B = \begin{bmatrix} 0 & 0 \\ 3 & -3 \end{bmatrix}$

13. $A = \begin{bmatrix} 3 & -1 \\ 1 & 3 \end{bmatrix}$, $B = \begin{bmatrix} 1 & -3 \\ 3 & 1 \end{bmatrix}$

14. $A = \begin{bmatrix} 1 & -1 \\ 1 & 1 \end{bmatrix}$, $B = \begin{bmatrix} 1 & 3 \\ -3 & 1 \end{bmatrix}$

15. $A = \begin{bmatrix} 1 & -1 & 7 \\ 2 & -1 & 8 \\ 3 & 1 & -1 \end{bmatrix}$, $B = \begin{bmatrix} 1 & 1 & 2 \\ 2 & 1 & 1 \\ 1 & -3 & 2 \end{bmatrix}$

16. $A = \begin{bmatrix} 3 & 2 & 1 \end{bmatrix}$, $B = \begin{bmatrix} 2 \\ 3 \\ 0 \end{bmatrix}$

In Exercises 17–24, find (a) AB and (b) BA (if they are defined).

17. $A = \begin{bmatrix} 2 & 1 \\ -3 & 4 \\ 1 & 6 \end{bmatrix}$, $B = \begin{bmatrix} 0 & -1 & 0 \\ 4 & 0 & 2 \\ 8 & -1 & 7 \end{bmatrix}$

18. $A = \begin{bmatrix} 0 & -1 & 0 \\ 4 & 0 & 2 \\ 8 & -1 & 7 \end{bmatrix}$, $B = \begin{bmatrix} 2 \\ -3 \\ 1 \end{bmatrix}$

19. $A = \begin{bmatrix} -1 & 3 \\ 4 & -5 \\ 0 & 2 \end{bmatrix}$, $B = \begin{bmatrix} 1 & 2 \\ 0 & 7 \end{bmatrix}$

20. $A = \begin{bmatrix} 1 & 0 & 0 \\ 0 & 4 & 0 \\ 0 & 0 & -2 \end{bmatrix}$, $B = \begin{bmatrix} 3 & 0 & 0 \\ 0 & -1 & 0 \\ 0 & 0 & 5 \end{bmatrix}$

21. $A = \begin{bmatrix} 5 & 0 & 0 \\ 0 & -8 & 0 \\ 0 & 0 & 7 \end{bmatrix}$, $B = \begin{bmatrix} \frac{1}{5} & 0 & 0 \\ 0 & -\frac{1}{8} & 0 \\ 0 & 0 & \frac{1}{7} \end{bmatrix}$

22. $A = \begin{bmatrix} 0 & 0 & 5 \\ 0 & 0 & -3 \\ 0 & 0 & 4 \end{bmatrix}$, $B = \begin{bmatrix} 6 & -11 & 4 \\ 8 & 16 & 4 \\ 0 & 0 & 0 \end{bmatrix}$

23. $A = \begin{bmatrix} 6 \\ -2 \\ 1 \\ 6 \end{bmatrix}$, $B = \begin{bmatrix} 10 & 12 \end{bmatrix}$

24. $A = \begin{bmatrix} 1 & 0 & 3 & -2 & 4 \\ 6 & 13 & 8 & -17 & 20 \end{bmatrix}$, $B = \begin{bmatrix} 1 & 6 \\ 4 & 2 \end{bmatrix}$

In Exercises 25–30, write the given system of linear equations in the form $A\mathbf{x} = \mathbf{b}$ and solve this matrix equation for $\mathbf{x}$.

25. $\begin{aligned} x_1 + 3x_2 &= -1 \\ 2x_1 - x_2 &= 3 \end{aligned}$

26. $\begin{aligned} 2x_1 + 2x_2 &= 7 \\ -6x_1 - 6x_2 &= -21 \end{aligned}$

27. $8x_1 - 8x_2 = 0$
$-3x_1 + 2x_2 = 0$

28. $6x_2 + 4x_3 = -12$
$3x_1 + 3x_2 \qquad = 9$
$2x_1 \qquad - 3x_3 = 10$

29. $x_1 \qquad + 2x_3 = 5$
$3x_1 - 2x_2 + x_3 = 8$
$-2x_1 + 2x_2 - x_3 = -3$

30. $x_1 \qquad + 2x_3 = 4$
$2x_1 - 4x_2 \qquad = -6$
$3x_1 + 2x_2 + 5x_3 = 10$

In Exercises 31 and 32, solve the given matrix equation for A.

31. $\begin{bmatrix} 1 & 2 \\ 3 & 5 \end{bmatrix} A = \begin{bmatrix} 1 & 0 \\ 0 & 1 \end{bmatrix}$

32. $\begin{bmatrix} 2 & -1 \\ 3 & -2 \end{bmatrix} A = \begin{bmatrix} 1 & 0 \\ 0 & 1 \end{bmatrix}$

In Exercises 33 and 34, solve the given matrix equation for a, b, c, and d.

33. $\begin{bmatrix} a - b & 2b + c \\ c - 2d & a + d \end{bmatrix} = \begin{bmatrix} -1 & 3 \\ 5 & -2 \end{bmatrix}$

34. $\begin{bmatrix} a + b & b + c \\ c + d & a + d \end{bmatrix} = \begin{bmatrix} 2 & -1 \\ 1 & 4 \end{bmatrix}$

35. Find conditions on w, x, y, and z such that $AB = BA$ for the following matrices.

$$A = \begin{bmatrix} w & x \\ y & z \end{bmatrix} \quad \text{and} \quad B = \begin{bmatrix} 1 & 1 \\ -1 & 1 \end{bmatrix}$$

36. Verify that $AB = BA$ for the following matrices.

$$A = \begin{bmatrix} \cos \alpha & -\sin \alpha \\ \sin \alpha & \cos \alpha \end{bmatrix} \quad \text{and} \quad B = \begin{bmatrix} \cos \beta & -\sin \beta \\ \sin \beta & \cos \beta \end{bmatrix}$$

In Exercises 37 and 38, find the product AA for the given diagonal matrix. A square matrix

$$A = \begin{bmatrix} a_{11} & 0 & 0 & \cdots & 0 \\ 0 & a_{22} & 0 & \cdots & 0 \\ 0 & 0 & a_{33} & \cdots & 0 \\ \vdots & \vdots & \vdots & & \vdots \\ 0 & 0 & \cdots & 0 & a_{nn} \end{bmatrix}$$

is called a **diagonal matrix** if all entries that are not on the main diagonal are zero.

37. $A = \begin{bmatrix} -1 & 0 & 0 \\ 0 & 2 & 0 \\ 0 & 0 & 3 \end{bmatrix}$

38. $A = \begin{bmatrix} 2 & 0 & 0 \\ 0 & -3 & 0 \\ 0 & 0 & 0 \end{bmatrix}$

39. Prove that if A and B are diagonal matrices (of the same size), then $AB = BA$.

40. Let A and B be 3×3 matrices, where A is diagonal.

(a) Describe the product AB. Illustrate your answer with examples.
(b) Describe the product BA. Illustrate your answer with examples.
(c) How do the results in (a) and (b) change if the diagonal entries of A are all equal?

In Exercises 41 and 42, find the trace of the given matrix. The **trace** of an $n \times n$ matrix A is the sum of the main diagonal entries. That is, $\text{Tr}(A) = a_{11} + a_{22} + \cdots + a_{nn}$.

41. $\begin{bmatrix} 1 & 2 & 3 \\ 0 & -2 & 4 \\ 3 & 1 & 3 \end{bmatrix}$

42. $\begin{bmatrix} 1 & 0 & 0 \\ 0 & 1 & 0 \\ 0 & 0 & 1 \end{bmatrix}$

43. Prove that the following are true if A and B are square matrices of order n and c is a scalar.

(a) $\text{Tr}(A + B) = \text{Tr}(A) + \text{Tr}(B)$
(b) $\text{Tr}(cA) = c\text{Tr}(A)$

44. Prove that if A and B are square matrices of order n, then $\text{Tr}(AB) = \text{Tr}(BA)$.

45. Show that the following matrix equation has no solution.

$$\begin{bmatrix} 1 & 1 \\ 1 & 1 \end{bmatrix} A = \begin{bmatrix} 1 & 0 \\ 0 & 1 \end{bmatrix}$$

46. Show that no 2×2 matrices A and B exist that satisfy the matrix equation

$$AB - BA = \begin{bmatrix} 1 & 0 \\ 0 & 1 \end{bmatrix}.$$

47. Prove that if the product AB is a square matrix, then the product BA is defined.

48. Prove that if both products AB and BA are defined, then AB and BA are square matrices.

49. Let A and B be two matrices such that the product AB is defined. Show that if A has two identical rows, then the corresponding two rows of AB are also identical.

50. Let A and B be $n \times n$ matrices. Show that if the ith row of A has all zero entries, then the ith row of AB will have all zero entries. Give an example using 2×2 matrices to show that the converse is not true.

51. A certain corporation has four factories. Each produces two products. The number of units of Product i produced at Factory j in one day is represented by a_{ij} in the matrix

$$A = \begin{bmatrix} 100 & 90 & 70 & 30 \\ 40 & 20 & 60 & 60 \end{bmatrix}.$$

Use scalar multiplication (multiply by 1.10) to determine what the production levels would be if production were increased by 10%.

52. A company manufactures tables and chairs at two locations. Matrix C gives the total cost for manufacturing each product in each location.

$$C = \begin{matrix} Table \\ Chair \end{matrix} \begin{bmatrix} \overset{\textit{Location 1}}{627} & \overset{\textit{Location 2}}{681} \\ 135 & 150 \end{bmatrix}$$

(a) Given that labor accounts for about $\frac{2}{3}$ of the total cost, determine the matrix L that gives the labor costs for each product in each location. What matrix operation did you use?

(b) Find the matrix M that gives material costs for each product at each location. (Assume that there are only labor and material costs.)

53. A fruit grower raises two crops, which are shipped to three outlets. The number of units of Product i that are shipped to Outlet j is represented by a_{ij} in the matrix

$$A = \begin{bmatrix} 100 & 75 & 75 \\ 125 & 150 & 100 \end{bmatrix}.$$

The profit on one unit of Product i is represented by b_{1i} in the matrix

$$B = [\$3.75 \quad \$7.00].$$

Find the matrix product BA, and explain what each entry of this product represents.

54. The matrix

$$P = \begin{matrix} \textit{From R} \\ \textit{From D} \\ \textit{From I} \end{matrix} \begin{bmatrix} \overset{\textit{To R}}{0.75} & \overset{\textit{To D}}{0.15} & \overset{\textit{To I}}{0.10} \\ 0.20 & 0.60 & 0.20 \\ 0.30 & 0.40 & 0.30 \end{bmatrix}$$

represents the proportion of a voting population that changes from Party i to Party j in a given election. That is, $p_{ij}(i \neq j)$ represents the proportion of the voting population that changes from Party i to Party j, and p_{ii} represents the proportion that remains loyal to Party i from one election to the next. Find the product of P with itself. What does this product represent?

In Exercises 55 and 56, perform the indicated block multiplication of matrices A and B. If matrices A and B have been partitioned into four submatrices

$$A = \begin{bmatrix} A_{11} & A_{12} \\ A_{21} & A_{22} \end{bmatrix} \quad B = \begin{bmatrix} B_{11} & B_{12} \\ B_{21} & B_{22} \end{bmatrix},$$

then you can **block multiply** A and B provided the sizes of the submatrices are such that the matrix multiplications and additions are defined.

$$AB = \begin{bmatrix} A_{11} & A_{12} \\ A_{21} & A_{22} \end{bmatrix} \begin{bmatrix} B_{11} & B_{12} \\ B_{21} & B_{22} \end{bmatrix}$$
$$= \begin{bmatrix} A_{11}B_{11} + A_{12}B_{21} & A_{11}B_{12} + A_{12}B_{22} \\ A_{21}B_{11} + A_{22}B_{21} & A_{21}B_{12} + A_{22}B_{22} \end{bmatrix}$$

55. $A = \begin{bmatrix} 1 & 2 & 0 & 0 \\ 0 & 1 & 0 & 0 \\ 0 & 0 & 2 & 1 \end{bmatrix}$ $B = \begin{bmatrix} 1 & 2 & 0 \\ -1 & 1 & 0 \\ 0 & 0 & 1 \\ 0 & 0 & 3 \end{bmatrix}$

56. $A = \begin{bmatrix} 0 & 0 & 1 & 0 \\ 0 & 0 & 0 & 1 \\ -1 & 0 & 0 & 0 \\ 0 & -1 & 0 & 0 \end{bmatrix}$ $B = \begin{bmatrix} 1 & 2 & 3 & 4 \\ 5 & 6 & 7 & 8 \\ 1 & 2 & 3 & 4 \\ 5 & 6 & 7 & 8 \end{bmatrix}$

In Exercises 57 and 58, express the column matrix $\mathbf{b}$ as a linear combination of the columns of A.

57. $A = \begin{bmatrix} 1 & -1 & 2 \\ 3 & -3 & 1 \end{bmatrix}$, $\mathbf{b} = \begin{bmatrix} -1 \\ 7 \end{bmatrix}$

58. $A = \begin{bmatrix} 1 & 2 & 4 \\ -1 & 0 & 2 \\ 0 & 1 & 3 \end{bmatrix}$, $\mathbf{b} = \begin{bmatrix} 1 \\ 3 \\ 2 \end{bmatrix}$

59. Given an $m \times n$ matrix A and an $n \times p$ matrix B, describe step by step how you can form their product column by column.

$$AB = A[\mathbf{b}_1 \quad \mathbf{b}_2 \quad \cdots \quad \mathbf{b}_p] = [A\mathbf{b}_1 \quad A\mathbf{b}_2 \quad \cdots \quad A\mathbf{b}_p]$$

Similarly, describe how you can form their product row by row.

$$AB = \begin{bmatrix} \mathbf{a}_1 \\ \mathbf{a}_2 \\ \vdots \\ \mathbf{a}_m \end{bmatrix} B = \begin{bmatrix} \mathbf{a}_1 B \\ \mathbf{a}_2 B \\ \vdots \\ \mathbf{a}_m B \end{bmatrix}$$

2.2 PROPERTIES OF MATRIX OPERATIONS

In Section 2.1 we concentrated on the mechanics of the three basic matrix operations: matrix addition, scalar multiplication, and matrix multiplication. In this section we begin to develop an **algebra of matrices.** You will see that this algebra shares many (but not all) of the properties of the algebra of real numbers. We begin by listing several properties of matrix addition and scalar multiplication.

Theorem 2.1

Properties of Matrix Addition and Scalar Multiplication

If A, B, C are $m \times n$ matrices and c and d are scalars, then the following properties are true.

1. $A + B = B + A$ **Commutative property of addition**
2. $A + (B + C) = (A + B) + C$ **Associative property of addition**
3. $(cd)A = c(dA)$
4. $1A = A$
5. $c(A + B) = cA + cB$ **Distributive property**
6. $(c + d)A = cA + dA$ **Distributive property**

Proof   Proofs of these six properties follow directly from the definitions of matrix addition, scalar multiplication, and the corresponding properties of real numbers. For example, to prove the commutative property of *matrix addition*, we let $A = [a_{ij}]$ and $B = [b_{ij}]$. Then, using the commutative property of *addition of real numbers*, we write

$$A + B = [a_{ij} + b_{ij}] = [b_{ij} + a_{ij}] = B + A.$$

Similarly, to prove property 5, we use the distributive property (for real numbers) of multiplication over addition to write

$$c(A + B) = [c(a_{ij} + b_{ij})] = [ca_{ij} + cb_{ij}] = cA + cB.$$

The proofs of the remaining four properties are left as exercises. (See Exercises 43–46.)

In the previous section matrix addition was defined as a *binary* operation. That is, we defined only the sum of *two* matrices. The associative property for matrix addition now allows us to write expressions like $A + B + C$ as $(A + B) + C$ or as $A + (B + C)$. This same reasoning applies to sums of four or more matrices.

EXAMPLE 1   *Addition of More Than Two Matrices*

By adding corresponding entries, we can obtain the following sum of four matrices.

$$\begin{bmatrix} 1 \\ 2 \\ -3 \end{bmatrix} + \begin{bmatrix} -1 \\ -1 \\ 2 \end{bmatrix} + \begin{bmatrix} 0 \\ 1 \\ 4 \end{bmatrix} + \begin{bmatrix} 2 \\ -3 \\ -2 \end{bmatrix} = \begin{bmatrix} 2 \\ -1 \\ 1 \end{bmatrix}$$

One important property of the addition of real numbers is that the number 0 serves as the additive identity. That is, $c + 0 = c$ for any real number c. For matrices, a similar property holds. Specifically, if A is an $m \times n$ matrix and O_{mn} is the $m \times n$ matrix consisting entirely of zeros, then $A + O_{mn} = A$. We call O_{mn} a **zero matrix**, and it serves as the **additive identity** for the set of all $m \times n$ matrices. For example, the following matrix serves as the additive identity for the set of all 2×3 matrices.

$$O_{23} = \begin{bmatrix} 0 & 0 & 0 \\ 0 & 0 & 0 \end{bmatrix}$$

When the size of the matrix is understood, we may denote zero matrices simply by O.

The following properties of zero matrices are easy to prove, and we leave their proofs as exercises. (See Exercise 47.)

Theorem 2.2 Properties of Zero Matrices	If A is an $m \times n$ matrix and c is a scalar, then the following properties are true. 1. $A + O_{mn} = A$ 2. $A + (-A) = O_{mn}$ 3. If $cA = O_{mn}$, then $c = 0$ or $A = O_{mn}$.

REMARK: Property 2 can be described by saying that the matrix $-A$ is the **additive inverse** of A.

The algebra of real numbers and the algebra of matrices have many similarities. For example, compare the following solutions.

Real Numbers	$m \times n$ *Matrices*
(Solve for x.)	*(Solve for X.)*
$x + a = b$	$X + A = B$
$x + a + (-a) = b + (-a)$	$X + A + (-A) = B + (-A)$
$x + 0 = b - a$	$X + O = B - A$
$x = b - a$	$X = B - A$

The process of solving a matrix equation is demonstrated in Example 2.

EXAMPLE 2   ***Solving a Matrix Equation***

Solve for X in the equation $3X + A = B$, where

$$A = \begin{bmatrix} 1 & -2 \\ 0 & 3 \end{bmatrix} \quad \text{and} \quad B = \begin{bmatrix} -3 & 4 \\ 2 & 1 \end{bmatrix}.$$

Solution   We begin by solving the given equation for X to obtain

$$3X = B - A \quad \longrightarrow \quad X = \tfrac{1}{3}(B - A)$$

Now, using the given matrices A and B, we have

$$X = \tfrac{1}{3}\left(\begin{bmatrix} -3 & 4 \\ 2 & 1 \end{bmatrix} - \begin{bmatrix} 1 & -2 \\ 0 & 3 \end{bmatrix} \right) = \tfrac{1}{3}\begin{bmatrix} -4 & 6 \\ 2 & -2 \end{bmatrix} = \begin{bmatrix} -\tfrac{4}{3} & 2 \\ \tfrac{2}{3} & -\tfrac{2}{3} \end{bmatrix}.$$

Properties of Matrix Multiplication

In the next theorem the algebra of matrices is extended to include some useful properties of matrix multiplication. The proofs of the first two properties are given in Appendix A; the proofs of the remaining two properties are left as exercises. (See Exercise 48.)

Theorem 2.3 Properties of Matrix Multiplication	If A, B, and C are matrices (with sizes such that the given matrix products are defined) and c is a scalar, then the following properties are true. 1. $A(BC) = (AB)C$ Associative property of multiplication 2. $A(B + C) = AB + AC$ Distributive property 3. $(A + B)C = AC + BC$ Distributive property 4. $c(AB) = (cA)B = A(cB)$

The associative property of matrix multiplication permits us to write such matrix products as ABC without ambiguity, as demonstrated in Example 3.

EXAMPLE 3   *Matrix Multiplication Is Associative*

Find the matrix product ABC by grouping the factors first as $(AB)C$ and then as $A(BC)$, and show that the same result is obtained.

$$A = \begin{bmatrix} 1 & -2 \\ 2 & -1 \end{bmatrix}, \quad B = \begin{bmatrix} 1 & 0 & 2 \\ 3 & -2 & 1 \end{bmatrix}, \quad C = \begin{bmatrix} -1 & 0 \\ 3 & 1 \\ 2 & 4 \end{bmatrix}$$

Solution   Grouping the factors as $(AB)C$, we have

$$(AB)C = \left(\begin{bmatrix} 1 & -2 \\ 2 & -1 \end{bmatrix} \begin{bmatrix} 1 & 0 & 2 \\ 3 & -2 & 1 \end{bmatrix} \right) \begin{bmatrix} -1 & 0 \\ 3 & 1 \\ 2 & 4 \end{bmatrix}$$

$$= \begin{bmatrix} -5 & 4 & 0 \\ -1 & 2 & 3 \end{bmatrix} \begin{bmatrix} -1 & 0 \\ 3 & 1 \\ 2 & 4 \end{bmatrix}$$

$$= \begin{bmatrix} 17 & 4 \\ 13 & 14 \end{bmatrix}.$$

Grouping the factors as $A(BC)$, we obtain the same result.

$$A(BC) = \begin{bmatrix} 1 & -2 \\ 2 & -1 \end{bmatrix} \left(\begin{bmatrix} 1 & 0 & 2 \\ 3 & -2 & 1 \end{bmatrix} \begin{bmatrix} -1 & 0 \\ 3 & 1 \\ 2 & 4 \end{bmatrix} \right)$$

$$= \begin{bmatrix} 1 & -2 \\ 2 & -1 \end{bmatrix} \begin{bmatrix} 3 & 8 \\ -7 & 2 \end{bmatrix} = \begin{bmatrix} 17 & 4 \\ 13 & 14 \end{bmatrix}$$

Note that we did *not* list a commutative property for matrix multiplication. It can easily happen that, although the product AB is defined, A and B are not of the proper sizes to define the product BA. For instance, if A is of size 2×3 and B is of size 3×3, then the product AB is defined but the product BA is not. The next example shows that even if both products AB and BA are defined, they need not be equal.

EXAMPLE 4   *Noncommutativity of Matrix Multiplication*

Show that AB and BA are not equal for the matrices

$$A = \begin{bmatrix} 1 & 3 \\ 2 & -1 \end{bmatrix} \quad \text{and} \quad B = \begin{bmatrix} 2 & -1 \\ 0 & 2 \end{bmatrix}.$$

Solution $AB = \begin{bmatrix} 1 & 3 \\ 2 & -1 \end{bmatrix} \begin{bmatrix} 2 & -1 \\ 0 & 2 \end{bmatrix} = \begin{bmatrix} 2 & 5 \\ 4 & -4 \end{bmatrix}$

$BA = \begin{bmatrix} 2 & -1 \\ 0 & 2 \end{bmatrix} \begin{bmatrix} 1 & 3 \\ 2 & -1 \end{bmatrix} \begin{bmatrix} 0 & 7 \\ 4 & -2 \end{bmatrix}$

Note that $AB \neq BA$.

Do not conclude from Example 4 that the matrix products AB and BA are *never* the same. Occasionally they are the same. For example, try multiplying the following matrices, first in the order AB and then in the order BA.

$$A = \begin{bmatrix} 1 & 2 \\ 1 & 1 \end{bmatrix} \quad \text{and} \quad B = \begin{bmatrix} -2 & 4 \\ 2 & -2 \end{bmatrix}$$

You will see that the two products are equal. The point is this: Although AB and BA are occasionally equal, usually they are not.

Another important quality of matrix algebra is that it does not have a general cancellation property for matrix multiplication. That is, if $AC = BC$, it is not necessarily true that $A = B$. This is demonstrated in Example 5. (In the next section we will see that for some special types of matrices, cancellation is valid.)

EXAMPLE 5   *An Example in Which Cancellation Is Not Valid*

Show that $AC = BC$ for the following matrices.

$$A = \begin{bmatrix} 1 & 3 \\ 0 & 1 \end{bmatrix}, \quad B = \begin{bmatrix} 2 & 4 \\ 2 & 3 \end{bmatrix}, \quad C = \begin{bmatrix} 1 & -2 \\ -1 & 2 \end{bmatrix}$$

Solution $AC = \begin{bmatrix} 1 & 3 \\ 0 & 1 \end{bmatrix} \begin{bmatrix} 1 & -2 \\ -1 & 2 \end{bmatrix} = \begin{bmatrix} -2 & 4 \\ -1 & 2 \end{bmatrix}$

$BC = \begin{bmatrix} 2 & 4 \\ 2 & 3 \end{bmatrix} \begin{bmatrix} 1 & -2 \\ -1 & 2 \end{bmatrix} = \begin{bmatrix} -2 & 4 \\ -1 & 2 \end{bmatrix}$

Thus $AC = BC$, and yet $A \neq B$.

We now look at a special type of *square* matrix that has 1's on the main diagonal and 0's elsewhere.

$$I_n = \begin{bmatrix} 1 & 0 & 0 & \cdots & 0 \\ 0 & 1 & 0 & \cdots & 0 \\ 0 & 0 & 1 & \cdots & 0 \\ \vdots & \vdots & \vdots & & \vdots \\ 0 & 0 & 0 & \cdots & 1 \end{bmatrix}$$

For instance, if $n = 1$, 2, or 3, we have

$$I_1 = [1], \qquad I_2 = \begin{bmatrix} 1 & 0 \\ 0 & 1 \end{bmatrix}, \qquad I_3 = \begin{bmatrix} 1 & 0 & 0 \\ 0 & 1 & 0 \\ 0 & 0 & 1 \end{bmatrix}.$$

1×1 2×2 3×3

When the order of the matrix is understood to be n, we may denote I_n simply as I.

As stated in Theorem 2.4, the matrix I_n serves as the **identity** for matrix multiplication; it is called the **identity matrix of order n**. We leave the proof of this theorem as an exercise. (See Exercise 49.)

Theorem 2.4

Properties of the Identity Matrix

If A is a matrix of size $m \times n$, then the following properties are true.
1. $AI_n = A$
2. $I_m A = A$

As a special case of this theorem, note that if A is a *square* matrix of order n, then we have

$$AI_n = I_n A = A.$$

EXAMPLE 6   *Multiplication by an Identity Matrix*

(a) $\begin{bmatrix} 3 & -2 \\ 4 & 0 \\ -1 & 1 \end{bmatrix} \begin{bmatrix} 1 & 0 \\ 0 & 1 \end{bmatrix} = \begin{bmatrix} 3 & -2 \\ 4 & 0 \\ -1 & 1 \end{bmatrix}$

(b) $\begin{bmatrix} 1 & 0 & 0 \\ 0 & 1 & 0 \\ 0 & 0 & 1 \end{bmatrix} \begin{bmatrix} -2 \\ 1 \\ 4 \end{bmatrix} = \begin{bmatrix} -2 \\ 1 \\ 4 \end{bmatrix}$

For repeated multiplication of *square* matrices, we use the same exponential notation used with real numbers. That is, $A^1 = A$, $A^2 = AA$, and for a positive integer k we define A^k as

$$A^k = \underbrace{AA \cdots A}_{k \text{ factors}}.$$

It is convenient also to define $A^0 = I_n$ (where A is a square matrix of order n). These definitions allow us to establish the properties

1. $A^j A^k = A^{j+k}$ 2. $(A^j)^k = A^{jk}$

where j and k are nonnegative integers.

EXAMPLE 7   ***Repeated Multiplication of a Square Matrix***

Find A^3 for the matrix $A = \begin{bmatrix} 2 & -1 \\ 3 & 0 \end{bmatrix}$.

Solution $A^3 = \left(\begin{bmatrix} 2 & -1 \\ 3 & 0 \end{bmatrix} \begin{bmatrix} 2 & -1 \\ 3 & 0 \end{bmatrix} \right) \begin{bmatrix} 2 & -1 \\ 3 & 0 \end{bmatrix} = \begin{bmatrix} 1 & -2 \\ 6 & -3 \end{bmatrix} \begin{bmatrix} 2 & -1 \\ 3 & 0 \end{bmatrix} = \begin{bmatrix} -4 & -1 \\ 3 & -6 \end{bmatrix}$

In Section 1.1 we pointed out that a system of linear equations must have exactly one solution, an infinite number of solutions, or no solution. Using the matrix algebra developed so far, we can now prove this result.

Theorem 2.5

Number of Solutions of a System of Linear Equations

For a system of linear equations in n variables, precisely one of the following is true.
1. The system has exactly one solution.
2. The system has an infinite number of solutions.
3. The system has no solution.

Proof   We represent the system by the matrix equation $A\mathbf{x} = \mathbf{b}$. If the system has exactly one solution or no solution, there is nothing to prove. Therefore, we assume that the system has at least two distinct solutions $\mathbf{x}_1$ and $\mathbf{x}_2$. The proof will be complete if we can show that this assumption implies that the system has an infinite number of solutions. Since $\mathbf{x}_1$ and $\mathbf{x}_2$ are solutions, we have $A\mathbf{x}_1 = A\mathbf{x}_2 = \mathbf{b}$ and hence $A(\mathbf{x}_1 - \mathbf{x}_2) = O$. This implies that the (nonzero) column matrix $\mathbf{x}_h = \mathbf{x}_1 - \mathbf{x}_2$ is a solution of the homogeneous system of linear equations $A\mathbf{x} = O$. Moreover, for any scalar c, it follows that

$$A(\mathbf{x}_1 + c\mathbf{x}_h) = A\mathbf{x}_1 + A(c\mathbf{x}_h) = \mathbf{b} + c(A\mathbf{x}_h) = \mathbf{b} + cO = \mathbf{b}.$$

Therefore $\mathbf{x}_1 + c\mathbf{x}_h$ is a solution to $A\mathbf{x} = \mathbf{b}$ for any scalar c. Because there are an infinite number of possible values of c and each value produces a different solution, we conclude that the system has an infinite number of solutions.

The Transpose of a Matrix

The **transpose** of a matrix is formed by writing its columns as rows. For instance, if A is the $m \times n$ matrix given by

$$A = \begin{bmatrix} a_{11} & a_{12} & a_{13} & \cdots & a_{1n} \\ a_{21} & a_{22} & a_{23} & \cdots & a_{2n} \\ a_{31} & a_{32} & a_{33} & \cdots & a_{3n} \\ \vdots & \vdots & \vdots & & \vdots \\ a_{m1} & a_{m2} & a_{m3} & \cdots & a_{mn} \end{bmatrix}, \qquad \text{Size: } m \times n$$

then the transpose, denoted by A^T, is the $n \times m$ matrix given by

$$A^T = \begin{bmatrix} a_{11} & a_{21} & a_{31} & \cdots & a_{m1} \\ a_{12} & a_{22} & a_{32} & \cdots & a_{m2} \\ a_{13} & a_{23} & a_{33} & \cdots & a_{m3} \\ \vdots & \vdots & \vdots & & \vdots \\ a_{1n} & a_{2n} & a_{3n} & \cdots & a_{mn} \end{bmatrix}. \qquad \text{Size: } n \times m$$

EXAMPLE 8   *The Transpose of a Matrix*

Find the transpose of each of the following matrices.

(a) $A = \begin{bmatrix} 2 \\ 8 \end{bmatrix}$ (b) $B = \begin{bmatrix} 1 & 2 & 0 \\ 2 & 1 & 0 \\ 0 & 0 & 1 \end{bmatrix}$ (c) $C = \begin{bmatrix} 0 & 1 \\ 2 & 4 \\ 1 & -1 \end{bmatrix}$

Solution   (a) $A^T = \begin{bmatrix} 2 & 8 \end{bmatrix}$ (b) $B^T = \begin{bmatrix} 1 & 2 & 0 \\ 2 & 1 & 0 \\ 0 & 0 & 1 \end{bmatrix}$ (c) $C^T = \begin{bmatrix} 0 & 2 & 1 \\ 1 & 4 & -1 \end{bmatrix}$

DISCOVERY

Let $A = \begin{bmatrix} 1 & 2 \\ 3 & 4 \end{bmatrix}$ and $B = \begin{bmatrix} 3 & 5 \\ 1 & -1 \end{bmatrix}$.

Calculate $(AB)^T$, $A^T B^T$, and $B^T A^T$. Make a conjecture about the transpose of a product of two square matrices. Select two other square matrices and see if your conjecture holds.

REMARK: Note that the square matrix in part (b) of Example 8 is equal to its transpose. We call such a matrix **symmetric.** That is, a matrix A is symmetric if $A = A^T$. From this definition it is clear that a symmetric matrix must be square.

The following properties of transposes are useful. You are asked to supply the proof of Theorem 2.6 in Exercise 50.

Theorem 2.6 Properties of Transposes	If A and B are matrices (with sizes such that the given matrix operations are defined) and c is a scalar, then the following properties are true. 1. $(A^T)^T = A$ 2. $(A + B)^T = A^T + B^T$ **Transpose of a sum** 3. $(cA)^T = c(A^T)$ **Transpose of a scalar multiple** 4. $(AB)^T = B^T A^T$ **Transpose of a product**

REMARK: Remember that we *reverse the order* of multiplication when forming the transpose of a product. That is, the transpose of AB is given by $(AB)^T = B^T A^T$ and is *not* usually equal to $A^T B^T$.

Properties 2 and 4 can be generalized to cover sums or products of any finite number of matrices. For instance, the transpose of the sum of three matrices is given by

$$(A + B + C)^T = A^T + B^T + C^T,$$

and the transpose of the product of three matrices is given by

$$(ABC)^T = C^T B^T A^T.$$

EXAMPLE 9   *Finding the Transpose of a Product*

Show that $(AB)^T$ and $B^T A^T$ are equal for the following matrices.

$$A = \begin{bmatrix} 2 & 1 & -2 \\ -1 & 0 & 3 \\ 0 & -2 & 1 \end{bmatrix} \quad \text{and} \quad B = \begin{bmatrix} 3 & 1 \\ 2 & -1 \\ 3 & 0 \end{bmatrix}$$

Solution $AB = \begin{bmatrix} 2 & 1 & -2 \\ -1 & 0 & 3 \\ 0 & -2 & 1 \end{bmatrix} \begin{bmatrix} 3 & 1 \\ 2 & -1 \\ 3 & 0 \end{bmatrix} = \begin{bmatrix} 2 & 1 \\ 6 & -1 \\ -1 & 2 \end{bmatrix}$

$(AB)^T = \begin{bmatrix} 2 & 6 & -1 \\ 1 & -1 & 2 \end{bmatrix}$

$B^T A^T = \begin{bmatrix} 3 & 2 & 3 \\ 1 & -1 & 0 \end{bmatrix} \begin{bmatrix} 2 & -1 & 0 \\ 1 & 0 & -2 \\ -2 & 3 & 1 \end{bmatrix} = \begin{bmatrix} 2 & 6 & -1 \\ 1 & -1 & 2 \end{bmatrix}$

Note that $(AB)^T = B^T A^T$.

EXAMPLE 10   *The Product of a Matrix and Its Transpose*

For the matrix

$$A = \begin{bmatrix} 1 & 3 \\ 0 & -2 \\ -2 & -1 \end{bmatrix}$$

find the product AA^T and show that it is symmetric.

Solution   Since

$$AA^T = \begin{bmatrix} 1 & 3 \\ 0 & -2 \\ -2 & -1 \end{bmatrix} \begin{bmatrix} 1 & 0 & -2 \\ 3 & -2 & -1 \end{bmatrix} = \begin{bmatrix} 10 & -6 & -5 \\ -6 & 4 & 2 \\ -5 & 2 & 5 \end{bmatrix}$$

it follows that AA^T is symmetric.

REMARK: The property demonstrated in Example 10 is true in general. That is, for any matrix A, the matrix given by $B = AA^T$ is symmetric. You are asked to prove this result in Exercise 51.

SECTION 2.2   ☐   EXERCISES

In Exercises 1–6, perform the indicated operations, given that $a = 3$, $b = -4$, and

$$A = \begin{bmatrix} 1 & 2 \\ 3 & 4 \end{bmatrix}, \quad B = \begin{bmatrix} 0 & 1 \\ -1 & 2 \end{bmatrix}, \quad O = \begin{bmatrix} 0 & 0 \\ 0 & 0 \end{bmatrix}.$$

1. $aA + bB$ **2.** $(A + B)$ **3.** $ab(B)$
4. $(a + b)B$ **5.** $(a - b)(A - B)$ **6.** $(ab)O$

In Exercises 7–10, solve for X, given that

$$A = \begin{bmatrix} -4 & 0 \\ 1 & -5 \\ -3 & 2 \end{bmatrix} \quad \text{and} \quad B = \begin{bmatrix} 1 & 2 \\ -2 & 1 \\ 4 & 4 \end{bmatrix}.$$

7. $3X + 2A = B$ **8.** $2A - 5B = 3X$
9. $X - 3A + 2B = O$ **10.** $6X - 4A - 3B = O$

In Exercises 11–16, perform the indicated operations, given that $c = -2$ and

$$A = \begin{bmatrix} 1 & 2 & 3 \\ 0 & 1 & -1 \end{bmatrix}, \quad B = \begin{bmatrix} 1 & 3 \\ -1 & 2 \end{bmatrix}, \quad C = \begin{bmatrix} 0 & 1 \\ -1 & 0 \end{bmatrix},$$

$$O = \begin{bmatrix} 0 & 0 \\ 0 & 0 \end{bmatrix}.$$

11. $B(CA)$ **12.** $C(BC)$ **13.** $(B + C)A$

14. $B(C + O)$ **15.** $(cB)(C + C)$ **16.** $B(cA)$

17. If $AC = BC$, then A is *not* necessarily equal to B. (See Example 5.) Demonstrate this using the matrices

$$A = \begin{bmatrix} 1 & 2 & 3 \\ 0 & 5 & 4 \\ 3 & -2 & 1 \end{bmatrix}, \quad B = \begin{bmatrix} 4 & -6 & 3 \\ 5 & 4 & 4 \\ -1 & 0 & 1 \end{bmatrix},$$

$$C = \begin{bmatrix} 0 & 0 & 0 \\ 0 & 0 & 0 \\ 4 & -2 & 3 \end{bmatrix}.$$

18. If $AB = O$, then it is *not* necessarily true that $A = O$ or $B = O$. Demonstrate this using the matrices

$$A = \begin{bmatrix} 3 & 3 \\ 4 & 4 \end{bmatrix} \quad \text{and} \quad B = \begin{bmatrix} 1 & -1 \\ -1 & 1 \end{bmatrix}.$$

In Exercises 19–22, perform the indicated operations, given that

$$A = \begin{bmatrix} 1 & 2 \\ 0 & -1 \end{bmatrix} \quad \text{and} \quad I = \begin{bmatrix} 1 & 0 \\ 0 & 1 \end{bmatrix}.$$

19. A^2 **20.** A^4 **21.** $A(I + A)$
22. $A + IA$

In Exercises 23–26, find (a) A^T, (b) A^TA, and (c) AA^T for the given matrices.

23. $A = \begin{bmatrix} 2 & -1 & 3 \\ 4 & 3 & -5 \end{bmatrix}$ 24. $A = \begin{bmatrix} -7 & 11 & 12 \\ 4 & -3 & 1 \\ 6 & -1 & 3 \end{bmatrix}$

25. $A = \begin{bmatrix} 6 & 0 \\ 0 & -4 \\ 7 & 5 \end{bmatrix}$ 26. $A = \begin{bmatrix} 2 \\ -1 \\ -3 \end{bmatrix}$

▶ In Exercises 27 and 28, explain why the given formula is *not* valid for matrices. Illustrate your argument with examples.

27. $(A + B)(A - B) = A^2 - B^2$
28. $(A + B)(A + B) = A^2 + 2AB + B^2$
29. Verify that $(AB)^T = B^T A^T$ for the following matrices.

$$A = \begin{bmatrix} -1 & 1 & -2 \\ 2 & 0 & 1 \end{bmatrix} \quad \text{and} \quad B = \begin{bmatrix} -3 & 0 \\ 1 & 2 \\ 1 & -1 \end{bmatrix}$$

30. Verify that $(AB)^T = B^T A^T$ for the following matrices.

$$A = \begin{bmatrix} 1 & 2 \\ 0 & -2 \end{bmatrix} \quad \text{and} \quad B = \begin{bmatrix} -3 & -1 \\ 2 & 1 \end{bmatrix}$$

In Exercises 31–34, use the following matrices.

$$X = \begin{bmatrix} 1 \\ 2 \\ 3 \end{bmatrix}, \quad Y = \begin{bmatrix} 1 \\ 0 \\ 2 \end{bmatrix}, \quad Z = \begin{bmatrix} 1 \\ 4 \\ 4 \end{bmatrix}, \quad W = \begin{bmatrix} 0 \\ 0 \\ 1 \end{bmatrix}, \quad O = \begin{bmatrix} 0 \\ 0 \\ 0 \end{bmatrix}$$

31. Find scalars a and b such that $Z = aX + bY$.
32. Show that there do not exist scalars a and b such that $W = aX + bY$.
33. Show that if $aX + bY + cW = O$, then $a = b = c = 0$.
34. Find nonzero scalars a, b, and c such that $aX + bY + cZ = O$.

In Exercises 35 and 36, compute the indicated power of A for the matrix

$$A = \begin{bmatrix} 1 & 0 & 0 \\ 0 & -1 & 0 \\ 0 & 0 & 1 \end{bmatrix}.$$

35. A^{19} 36. A^{20}

In Exercises 37 and 38, find a matrix A that satisfies the given equation.

37. $A^2 = \begin{bmatrix} 9 & 0 \\ 0 & 4 \end{bmatrix}$ 38. $A^3 = \begin{bmatrix} 8 & 0 & 0 \\ 0 & -1 & 0 \\ 0 & 0 & 27 \end{bmatrix}$

In Exercises 39–42, use the following definition to find $f(A)$: If f is the polynomial function given by

$$f(x) = a_0 + a_1 x + a_2 x^2 + \cdots + a_n x^n$$

then for an $n \times n$ matrix A, $f(A)$ is defined to be

$$f(A) = a_0 I_n + a_1 A + a_2 A^2 + \cdots + a_n A^n.$$

39. $f(x) = x^2 - 5x + 2$, $A = \begin{bmatrix} 2 & 0 \\ 4 & 5 \end{bmatrix}$

40. $f(x) = x^2 - 7x + 6$, $A = \begin{bmatrix} 5 & 4 \\ 1 & 2 \end{bmatrix}$

41. $f(x) = x^3 - 10x^2 + 31x - 30$, $A = \begin{bmatrix} 3 & 1 & 4 \\ 0 & 2 & 6 \\ 0 & 0 & 5 \end{bmatrix}$

42. $f(x) = x^2 - 10x + 24$, $A = \begin{bmatrix} 8 & -4 \\ 2 & 2 \end{bmatrix}$

43. Prove the associative property of matrix addition: $A + (B + C) = (A + B) + C$.
44. Prove the associative property of scalar multiplication: $(cd)A = c(dA)$.
45. Prove that the scalar 1 is the identity for scalar multiplication: $1A = A$.
46. Prove the following distributive property: $(c + d)A = cA + dA$.
47. Prove Theorem 2.2.
48. Complete the proof of Theorem 2.3.

   (a) Prove the following distributive property: $(A + B)C = AC + BC$.
   (b) Prove the following property: $c(AB) = (cA)B = A(cB)$.

49. Prove Theorem 2.4.
50. Prove Theorem 2.6.
51. Prove that if A is an $n \times m$ matrix, then AA^T and $A^T A$ are symmetric matrices.
52. Give an example of two 2×2 matrices A and B such that $(AB)^T \neq A^T B^T$.

In Exercises 53–56, determine whether the given matrix is symmetric, skew-symmetric, or neither. A square matrix is called **skew-symmetric** if $A^T = -A$.

53. $A = \begin{bmatrix} 0 & 2 \\ -2 & 0 \end{bmatrix}$ 54. $A = \begin{bmatrix} 2 & 1 \\ 1 & 3 \end{bmatrix}$

55. $A = \begin{bmatrix} 0 & 2 & 1 \\ 2 & 0 & 3 \\ 1 & 3 & 0 \end{bmatrix}$ 56. $A = \begin{bmatrix} 0 & 2 & -1 \\ -2 & 0 & -3 \\ 1 & 3 & 0 \end{bmatrix}$

57. Prove that the main diagonal of a skew-symmetric matrix consists entirely of zeros.

58. Prove that if A and B are $n \times n$ skew-symmetric matrices, then $A + B$ is skew-symmetric.

59. If A is a square matrix of order n, then there exist a symmetric matrix B and a skew-symmetric matrix C such that $A = B + C$. Illustrate this property for

$$A = \begin{bmatrix} 2 & 5 & 3 \\ -3 & 6 & 0 \\ 4 & 1 & 1 \end{bmatrix}.$$

60. Prove that if A is an $n \times n$ matrix, then $A - A^T$ is skew-symmetric.

61. Let A and B be two $n \times n$ symmetric matrices.

    (a) Give an example to show that the product AB is not necessarily symmetric.

    (b) Prove that AB is symmetric if and only if $AB = BA$.

2.3 THE INVERSE OF A MATRIX

Section 2.2 discussed some of the similarities between the algebra of real numbers and the algebra of matrices. This section further develops the algebra of matrices to include the solution of matrix equations involving matrix multiplication. To begin, let's consider the real number equation $ax = b$. To solve this equation for x, we multiply both sides of the equation by a^{-1} (provided $a \neq 0$).

$$ax = b$$
$$(a^{-1}a)x = a^{-1}b$$
$$(1)x = a^{-1}b$$
$$x = a^{-1}b$$

The number a^{-1} is called the *multiplicative inverse* of a because $a^{-1}a$ yields 1 (the identity element for multiplication). The definition of a multiplicative inverse of a matrix is similar.

Definition of an Inverse of a Matrix

An $n \times n$ matrix A is **invertible** (or **nonsingular**) if there exists an $n \times n$ matrix B such that

$$AB = BA = I_n$$

where I_n is the identity matrix of order n. The matrix B is called the (multiplicative) **inverse** of A. A matrix that does not have an inverse is called **noninvertible** (or **singular**).

Nonsquare matrices do not have inverses. To see this, note that if A is of size $m \times n$ and B is of size $n \times m$ (where $m \neq n$), then the products AB and BA are of different sizes and therefore could not be equal to each other. Indeed, not all square matrices possess inverses. (See Example 4.) However, the following theorem tells us that *if* a matrix does possess an inverse, then that inverse is unique.

Theorem 2.7

Uniqueness of an Inverse Matrix

If A is an invertible matrix, then its inverse is unique. We denote the inverse of A by A^{-1}.

Proof   Since A is invertible, we know that it has at least one inverse B such that $AB = I = BA$. Suppose that A has another inverse C such that $AC = I = CA$. Then we can show that B and C are equal as follows.

$$AB = I$$
$$C(AB) = CI$$
$$(CA)B = C$$
$$IB = C$$
$$B = C$$

Consequently $B = C$, and it follows that the inverse of a matrix is unique.

Because the inverse A^{-1} of an invertible matrix A is unique, we can call it **the** inverse of A and write

$$AA^{-1} = A^{-1}A = I.$$

EXAMPLE 1   *The Inverse of a Matrix*

Show that B is the inverse of A, where

$$A = \begin{bmatrix} -1 & 2 \\ -1 & 1 \end{bmatrix} \quad \text{and} \quad B = \begin{bmatrix} 1 & -2 \\ 1 & -1 \end{bmatrix}.$$

Solution   Using the definition of an inverse matrix, we can show that B is the inverse of A by showing that $AB = I = BA$ as follows.

$$AB = \begin{bmatrix} -1 & 2 \\ -1 & 1 \end{bmatrix}\begin{bmatrix} 1 & -2 \\ 1 & -1 \end{bmatrix} = \begin{bmatrix} -1+2 & 2-2 \\ -1+1 & 2-1 \end{bmatrix} = \begin{bmatrix} 1 & 0 \\ 0 & 1 \end{bmatrix}$$

$$BA = \begin{bmatrix} 1 & -2 \\ 1 & -1 \end{bmatrix}\begin{bmatrix} -1 & 2 \\ -1 & 1 \end{bmatrix} = \begin{bmatrix} -1+2 & 2-2 \\ -1+1 & 2-1 \end{bmatrix} = \begin{bmatrix} 1 & 0 \\ 0 & 1 \end{bmatrix}$$

REMARK: Recall that it is not always true that $AB = BA$, even if both products are defined. However, if A and B are both square matrices and $AB = I_n$, then it can be shown that $BA = I_n$. Although we will omit the proof of this fact, it implies that in Example 1 we needed only to check that $AB = I_2$.

The following example shows how to use a system of equations to find the inverse of a matrix.

EXAMPLE 2   *Finding the Inverse of a Matrix*

Find the inverse of the matrix

$$A = \begin{bmatrix} 1 & 4 \\ -1 & -3 \end{bmatrix}.$$

Solution   To find the inverse of A, we try to solve the matrix equation $AX = I$ for X.

$$\begin{bmatrix} 1 & 4 \\ -1 & -3 \end{bmatrix} \begin{bmatrix} x_{11} & x_{12} \\ x_{21} & x_{22} \end{bmatrix} = \begin{bmatrix} 1 & 0 \\ 0 & 1 \end{bmatrix}$$

$$\begin{bmatrix} x_{11} + 4x_{21} & x_{12} + 4x_{22} \\ -x_{11} - 3x_{21} & -x_{12} - 3x_{22} \end{bmatrix} = \begin{bmatrix} 1 & 0 \\ 0 & 1 \end{bmatrix}$$

Now, by equating corresponding entries, we obtain the following two systems of linear equations.

$$\begin{array}{ll} x_{11} + 4x_{21} = 1 & x_{12} + 4x_{22} = 0 \\ -x_{11} - 3x_{21} = 0 & -x_{12} - 3x_{22} = 1 \end{array}$$

Solving the first system, we find that the first column of X is $x_{11} = -3$ and $x_{21} = 1$. Similarly, solving the second system, we find that the second column of X is $x_{12} = -4$ and $x_{22} = 1$. Therefore the inverse of A is

$$X = A^{-1} = \begin{bmatrix} -3 & -4 \\ 1 & 1 \end{bmatrix}.$$

Try using matrix multiplication to check this result.

Generalizing the method used to solve Example 2 provides a convenient method for finding an inverse. Notice first that the two systems of linear equations

$$\begin{array}{ll} x_{11} + 4x_{21} = 1 & x_{12} + 4x_{22} = 0 \\ -x_{11} - 3x_{21} = 0 & -x_{12} - 3x_{22} = 1 \end{array}$$

have the *same coefficient matrix*. Rather than solve the two systems represented by

$$\begin{bmatrix} 1 & 4 & \vdots & 1 \\ -1 & -3 & \vdots & 0 \end{bmatrix} \quad \text{and} \quad \begin{bmatrix} 1 & 4 & \vdots & 0 \\ -1 & -3 & \vdots & 1 \end{bmatrix}$$

separately, we can solve them simultaneously. We do this by **adjoining** the identity matrix to the coefficient matrix to obtain

$$\begin{bmatrix} 1 & 4 & \vdots & 1 & 0 \\ -1 & -3 & \vdots & 0 & 1 \end{bmatrix}.$$

By applying Gauss-Jordan elimination to this matrix, we can solve *both* systems with a single elimination process as follows.

$$\begin{bmatrix} 1 & 4 & \vdots & 1 & 0 \\ 0 & 1 & \vdots & 1 & 1 \end{bmatrix} \quad \longleftarrow \quad \text{Adding the first row to the second row produces a new second row.}$$

$$\begin{bmatrix} 1 & 0 & \vdots & -3 & -4 \\ 0 & 1 & \vdots & 1 & 1 \end{bmatrix} \quad \longleftarrow \quad \text{Adding } -4 \text{ times the second row to the first row produces a new first row.}$$

Thus, by applying Gauss-Jordan elimination to the "doubly augmented" matrix $[A \vdots I]$, we obtained the matrix $[I \vdots A^{-1}]$.

$$\begin{bmatrix} 1 & 4 & \vdots & 1 & 0 \\ -1 & -3 & \vdots & 0 & 1 \end{bmatrix} \longrightarrow \begin{bmatrix} 1 & 0 & \vdots & -3 & -4 \\ 0 & 1 & \vdots & 1 & 1 \end{bmatrix}$$

$\underset{A}{} \quad \underset{I}{} \qquad \underset{I}{} \quad \underset{A^{-1}}{}$

This procedure (or algorithm) works for an arbitrary $n \times n$ matrix. If A cannot be row reduced to I_n, then A is singular. We shall justify this procedure formally in the next section, after introducing the concept of an elementary matrix. For now the algorithm is summarized as follows.

Finding the Inverse of a Matrix by Gauss-Jordan Elimination

Let A be a square matrix of order n.
1. Write the $n \times 2n$ matrix that consists of the given matrix A on the left and the $n \times n$ identity matrix I on the right to obtain $[A \vdots I]$. Note that we separate the matrices A and I by a dotted line. We call this process **adjoining** the matrices A and I.
2. If possible, row reduce A to I using elementary row operations on the *entire* matrix $[A \vdots I]$. The result will be the matrix $[I \vdots A^{-1}]$. If this is not possible, then A is not invertible.
3. Check your work by multiplying to see that $AA^{-1} = I = A^{-1}A$.

EXAMPLE 3   *Finding the Inverse of a Matrix*

Find the inverse of the following matrix.

$$A = \begin{bmatrix} 1 & -1 & 0 \\ 1 & 0 & -1 \\ -6 & 2 & 3 \end{bmatrix}$$

Solution   We begin by adjoining the identity matrix to A to form the matrix

$$[A \vdots I] = \begin{bmatrix} 1 & -1 & 0 & \vdots & 1 & 0 & 0 \\ 1 & 0 & -1 & \vdots & 0 & 1 & 0 \\ -6 & 2 & 3 & \vdots & 0 & 0 & 1 \end{bmatrix}.$$

Now, using elementary row operations, we attempt to rewrite this matrix in the form $[I \vdots A^{-1}]$ as follows.

$$\begin{bmatrix} 1 & -1 & 0 & \vdots & 1 & 0 & 0 \\ 0 & 1 & -1 & \vdots & -1 & 1 & 0 \\ -6 & 2 & 3 & \vdots & 0 & 0 & 1 \end{bmatrix} \longleftarrow \begin{array}{l} \text{Adding } -1 \text{ times the first} \\ \text{row to the second row} \\ \text{produces a new second row.} \end{array}$$

$$\begin{bmatrix} 1 & -1 & 0 & \vdots & 1 & 0 & 0 \\ 0 & 1 & -1 & \vdots & -1 & 1 & 0 \\ 0 & -4 & 3 & \vdots & 6 & 0 & 1 \end{bmatrix} \longleftarrow \begin{array}{l} \text{Adding } 6 \text{ times the first} \\ \text{row to the third row} \\ \text{produces a new third row.} \end{array}$$

$$\begin{bmatrix} 1 & -1 & 0 & \vdots & 1 & 0 & 0 \\ 0 & 1 & -1 & \vdots & -1 & 1 & 0 \\ 0 & 0 & -1 & \vdots & 2 & 4 & 1 \end{bmatrix} \longleftarrow$$

Adding 4 times the second row to the third row produces a new third row.

$$\begin{bmatrix} 1 & -1 & 0 & \vdots & 1 & 0 & 0 \\ 0 & 1 & -1 & \vdots & -1 & 1 & 0 \\ 0 & 0 & 1 & \vdots & -2 & -4 & -1 \end{bmatrix} \longleftarrow$$

Multiplying the third row by -1 produces a new third row.

$$\begin{bmatrix} 1 & -1 & 0 & \vdots & 1 & 0 & 0 \\ 0 & 1 & 0 & \vdots & -3 & -3 & -1 \\ 0 & 0 & 1 & \vdots & -2 & -4 & -1 \end{bmatrix} \longleftarrow$$

Adding the third row to the second row produces a new second row.

$$\begin{bmatrix} 1 & 0 & 0 & \vdots & -2 & -3 & -1 \\ 0 & 1 & 0 & \vdots & -3 & -3 & -1 \\ 0 & 0 & 1 & \vdots & -2 & -4 & -1 \end{bmatrix} \longleftarrow$$

Adding the second row to the first row produces a new first row.

Therefore the matrix A is invertible, and its inverse is

$$A^{-1} = \begin{bmatrix} -2 & -3 & -1 \\ -3 & -3 & -1 \\ -2 & -4 & -1 \end{bmatrix}.$$

Try confirming this by multiplying A and A^{-1} to obtain I.

The process shown in Example 3 applies to any $n \times n$ matrix. If the matrix A has an inverse, this process will find it. On the other hand, if the matrix A has no inverse, the process will tell us that. The next example applies the process to a singular matrix (one that has no inverse).

EXAMPLE 4 *A Singular Matrix*

Show that the following matrix has no inverse.

$$A = \begin{bmatrix} 1 & 2 & 0 \\ 3 & -1 & 2 \\ -2 & 3 & -2 \end{bmatrix}$$

Solution We adjoin the identity matrix to A to form

$$[A \vdots I] = \begin{bmatrix} 1 & 2 & 0 & \vdots & 1 & 0 & 0 \\ 3 & -1 & 2 & \vdots & 0 & 1 & 0 \\ -2 & 3 & -2 & \vdots & 0 & 0 & 1 \end{bmatrix}$$

and apply Gauss-Jordan elimination as follows.

$$\begin{bmatrix} 1 & 2 & 0 & \vdots & 1 & 0 & 0 \\ 0 & -7 & 2 & \vdots & -3 & 1 & 0 \\ -2 & 3 & -2 & \vdots & 0 & 0 & 1 \end{bmatrix} \longleftarrow$$

Adding -3 times the first row to the second row produces a new second row.

$$\begin{bmatrix} 1 & 2 & 0 & \vdots & 1 & 0 & 0 \\ 0 & -7 & 2 & \vdots & -3 & 1 & 0 \\ 0 & 7 & -2 & \vdots & 2 & 0 & 1 \end{bmatrix} \quad \longleftarrow \quad \begin{array}{l} \text{Adding 2 times the first} \\ \text{row to the third row} \\ \text{produces a new third row.} \end{array}$$

Now, notice that adding the second row to the third row produces a row of zeros on the left side of the matrix.

$$\begin{bmatrix} 1 & 2 & 0 & \vdots & 1 & 0 & 0 \\ 0 & -7 & 2 & \vdots & -3 & 1 & 0 \\ 0 & 0 & 0 & \vdots & -1 & 1 & 1 \end{bmatrix} \quad \longleftarrow \quad \begin{array}{l} \text{Adding the second row to} \\ \text{the third row produces} \\ \text{a new third row.} \end{array}$$

Because the "*A* portion" of the matrix has a row of zeros, we conclude that it is not possible to rewrite the matrix $[A \;\vdots\; I]$ in the form $[I \;\vdots\; A^{-1}]$. This means that *A* has no inverse.

TECHNOLOGY NOTE

Most graphing calculators and computer software can calculate the inverse of a square matrix. If you are using a TI-85, your screens for Example 3 will look like the following. What happens when you try to find the inverse of the matrix from Example 4?

```
A
  [[1  -1  0 ]
   [1   0  -1]
   [-6  2   3 ]]
```

```
A-1
  [[-2 -3 -1]
   [-3 -3 -1]
   [-2 -4 -1]]
```

Using Gauss-Jordan elimination to find the inverse of a matrix works well (even as a computer technique) for matrices of size 3×3 or greater. For 2×2 matrices, however, many people prefer to use a formula for the inverse, rather than find the inverse by Gauss-Jordan elimination. This simple formula is explained as follows. If *A* is a 2×2 matrix given by

$$A = \begin{bmatrix} a & b \\ c & d \end{bmatrix}$$

then *A* is invertible if and only if $ad - bc \neq 0$. Moreover, if $ad - bc \neq 0$, then the inverse is given by

$$A^{-1} = \frac{1}{ad - bc} \begin{bmatrix} d & -b \\ -c & a \end{bmatrix}.$$

Try verifying this inverse by multiplying.

REMARK: The denominator $ad - bc$ is called the **determinant** of *A*. We will study determinants in detail in Chapter 3.

EXAMPLE 5   *Finding the Inverse of a 2 × 2 Matrix*

If possible, find the inverses of the following matrices.

(a) $A = \begin{bmatrix} 3 & -1 \\ -2 & 2 \end{bmatrix}$ (b) $B = \begin{bmatrix} 3 & -1 \\ -6 & 2 \end{bmatrix}$

Solution   (a) For the matrix A, we apply the formula for the inverse of a 2 × 2 matrix to obtain $ad - bc = (3)(2) - (-1)(-2) = 4$. Since this quantity is not zero, the inverse is formed by interchanging the entries on the main diagonal and changing the sign of the other two entries as follows.

$$A^{-1} = \frac{1}{4} \begin{bmatrix} 2 & 1 \\ 2 & 3 \end{bmatrix} = \begin{bmatrix} \frac{1}{2} & \frac{1}{4} \\ \frac{1}{2} & \frac{3}{4} \end{bmatrix}$$

(b) For the matrix B, we have $ad - bc = (3)(2) - (-1)(-6) = 0$, which means that B is not invertible.

Properties of Inverses

We now look at some important properties of inverse matrices.

Theorem 2.8 Properties of Inverse Matrices	If A is an invertible matrix, k is a positive integer, and c is a scalar, then the following are true. 1. $(A^{-1})^{-1} = A$ 2. $(A^k)^{-1} = \underbrace{A^{-1}A^{-1} \cdots A^{-1}}_{k \text{ factors}}$ 3. $(cA)^{-1} = \frac{1}{c}A^{-1}, c \neq 0$ 4. $(A^T)^{-1} = (A^{-1})^T$

Proof   Property 1 follows directly from the definition of an inverse because $AA^{-1} = I$ and $A^{-1}A = I$. To prove property 3, we use the properties of scalar multiplication given in Theorems 2.1 and 2.3. Because

$$(cA)\left(\frac{1}{c}A^{-1}\right) = \left(c\frac{1}{c}\right)AA^{-1} = (1)I = I$$

and

$$\left(\frac{1}{c}A^{-1}\right)(cA) = \left(\frac{1}{c}c\right)A^{-1}A = (1)I = I$$

it follows that $(1/c)A^{-1}$ is the inverse of cA. Properties 2 and 4 are left for you to prove. (See Exercises 43 and 44.)

For nonsingular matrices, the exponential notation used for repeated multiplication of *square* matrices can be extended to include exponents that are negative integers. This may be done by defining A^{-k} to be

$$A^{-k} = \underbrace{A^{-1}A^{-1} \cdots A^{-1}}_{k\ factors}.$$

With this convention we can show that the properties $A^j A^k = A^{j+k}$ and $(A^j)^k = A^{jk}$ hold for any integers j and k.

EXAMPLE 6   *The Inverse of the Square of a Matrix*

Compute A^{-2} in two different ways and show that the results are equal.

$$A = \begin{bmatrix} 1 & 1 \\ 2 & 4 \end{bmatrix}$$

Solution   One way to find A^{-2} is to find $(A^2)^{-1}$ by squaring the matrix A to obtain

$$A^2 = \begin{bmatrix} 3 & 5 \\ 10 & 18 \end{bmatrix}$$

and using the formula for the inverse of a 2 × 2 matrix to obtain

$$(A^2)^{-1} = \tfrac{1}{4}\begin{bmatrix} 18 & -5 \\ -10 & 3 \end{bmatrix} = \begin{bmatrix} \frac{9}{2} & -\frac{5}{4} \\ -\frac{5}{2} & \frac{3}{4} \end{bmatrix}.$$

Another way to find A^{-2} is to find $(A^{-1})^2$ by finding A^{-1}

$$A^{-1} = \tfrac{1}{2}\begin{bmatrix} 4 & -1 \\ -2 & 1 \end{bmatrix} = \begin{bmatrix} 2 & -\frac{1}{2} \\ -1 & \frac{1}{2} \end{bmatrix}$$

and then squaring this matrix to obtain

$$(A^{-1})^2 = \begin{bmatrix} \frac{9}{2} & -\frac{5}{4} \\ -\frac{5}{2} & \frac{3}{4} \end{bmatrix}.$$

Note that each method produces the same result.

DISCOVERY

Let $A = \begin{bmatrix} 1 & 2 \\ 1 & 3 \end{bmatrix}$ and $B = \begin{bmatrix} 2 & -1 \\ 1 & -1 \end{bmatrix}$.

Calculate $(AB)^{-1}$, $A^{-1}B^{-1}$, and $B^{-1}A^{-1}$. Make a conjecture about the inverse of a product of two nonsingular matrices. Select two other nonsingular matrices and see if your conjecture holds.

The next theorem gives a formula for computing the inverse of a product of two matrices.

Theorem 2.9	If A and B are invertible matrices of size n, then AB is invertible and
The Inverse of a Product	$$(AB)^{-1} = B^{-1}A^{-1}.$$

Proof   To show that $B^{-1}A^{-1}$ is the inverse of AB, we need only show that it conforms to the definition of an inverse matrix. That is,

$$(AB)(B^{-1}A^{-1}) = A(BB^{-1})A^{-1} = A(I)A^{-1} = (AI)A^{-1} = AA^{-1} = I.$$

In a similar way we can show that $(B^{-1}A^{-1})(AB) = I$ and conclude that AB is invertible and has the indicated inverse.

Theorem 2.9 says that the inverse of a product of two invertible matrices is the product of their inverses taken in the *reverse* order. This can be generalized to include the product of several invertible matrices:

$$(A_1A_2A_3 \cdots A_n)^{-1} = A_n^{-1} \cdots A_3^{-1}A_2^{-1}A_1^{-1} \ .$$

EXAMPLE 7   *Finding the Inverse of a Matrix Product*

Find $(AB)^{-1}$ for the matrices

$$A = \begin{bmatrix} 1 & 3 & 3 \\ 1 & 4 & 3 \\ 1 & 3 & 4 \end{bmatrix} \quad \text{and} \quad B = \begin{bmatrix} 1 & 2 & 3 \\ 1 & 3 & 3 \\ 2 & 4 & 3 \end{bmatrix}$$

using the fact that A^{-1} and B^{-1} are given by

$$A^{-1} = \begin{bmatrix} 7 & -3 & -3 \\ -1 & 1 & 0 \\ -1 & 0 & 1 \end{bmatrix} \quad \text{and} \quad B^{-1} = \begin{bmatrix} 1 & -2 & 1 \\ -1 & 1 & 0 \\ \frac{2}{3} & 0 & -\frac{1}{3} \end{bmatrix}.$$

Solution   Using Theorem 2.9 produces the following.

$$(AB)^{-1} = \overset{B^{-1}}{\begin{bmatrix} 1 & -2 & 1 \\ -1 & 1 & 0 \\ \frac{2}{3} & 0 & -\frac{1}{3} \end{bmatrix}} \overset{A^{-1}}{\begin{bmatrix} 7 & -3 & -3 \\ -1 & 1 & 0 \\ -1 & 0 & 1 \end{bmatrix}} = \begin{bmatrix} 8 & -5 & -2 \\ -8 & 4 & 3 \\ 5 & -2 & -\frac{7}{3} \end{bmatrix}$$

R E M A R K : Note that we *reverse the order* of multiplication to find the inverse of AB. That is, $(AB)^{-1} = B^{-1}A^{-1}$, and the inverse of AB is usually *not* equal to $A^{-1}B^{-1}$.

One important property in the algebra of real numbers is the cancellation property. That is, if $ac = bc$ ($c \neq 0$), then $a = b$. *Invertible* matrices have similar cancellation properties.

Theorem 2.10

Cancellation Properties

If C is an invertible matrix, then the following properties hold.
1. If $AC = BC$, then $A = B$.   **Right cancellation property**
2. If $CA = CB$, then $A = B$.   **Left cancellation property**

Proof   To prove property 1, we use the fact that C is invertible and write

$$AC = BC$$
$$(AC)C^{-1} = (BC)C^{-1}$$
$$A(CC^{-1}) = B(CC^{-1})$$
$$AI = BI$$
$$A = B.$$

The second property can be proved in a similar way; we leave that to you. (See Exercise 46.)

Be sure to remember that Theorem 2.10 can be applied only if C is an *invertible* matrix. If C is not invertible, then cancellation is not usually valid. For instance, Example 5 in Section 2.2 gives an example of a matrix equation $AC = BC$ in which $A \neq B$.

Systems of Equations

In Theorem 2.5 we were able to prove that a system of linear equations can have exactly one solution, an infinite number of solutions, or no solution. For *square* systems (those having the same number of equations as variables), we can use the following theorem to determine whether the system has a unique solution.

Theorem 2.11

Systems of Equations with Unique Solutions

If A is an invertible matrix, then the system of linear equations $A\mathbf{x} = \mathbf{b}$ has a unique solution given by

$$\mathbf{x} = A^{-1}\mathbf{b}.$$

Proof   Since A is nonsingular, the following steps are valid.

$$A\mathbf{x} = \mathbf{b}$$
$$A^{-1}A\mathbf{x} = A^{-1}\mathbf{b}$$
$$I\mathbf{x} = A^{-1}\mathbf{b}$$
$$\mathbf{x} = A^{-1}\mathbf{b}$$

This solution is unique because, if $\mathbf{x}_1$ and $\mathbf{x}_2$ were two solutions, we could apply the cancellation property to the equation $A\mathbf{x}_1 = \mathbf{b} = A\mathbf{x}_2$ to conclude that $\mathbf{x}_1 = \mathbf{x}_2$.

Theorem 2.11 is important theoretically, but it is not very practical for solving a system of linear equations. That is, it would be more work to find A^{-1} and then multiply by **b** than simply to solve the system using Gaussian elimination with back-substitution. A situation in which you might consider using Theorem 2.11 as a computational technique would be one in which you had *several* systems of linear equations, all of which had the same coefficient matrix A. In such a case, you could find the inverse matrix once and then solve each system by computing the product A^{-1}**b.** This is demonstrated in Example 8.

EXAMPLE 8   *Solving a System of Equations Using an Inverse Matrix*

Use an inverse matrix to solve the following systems.

(a) $2x + 3y + z = -1$ (b) $2x + 3y + z = 4$ (c) $2x + 3y + z = 0$
      $3x + 3y + z = \ \ \ 1$ $3x + 3y + z = 8$ $3x + 3y + z = 0$
      $2x + 4y + z = -2$ $2x + 4y + z = 5$ $2x + 4y + z = 0$

Solution   We first note that the coefficient matrix for each system is

$$A = \begin{bmatrix} 2 & 3 & 1 \\ 3 & 3 & 1 \\ 2 & 4 & 1 \end{bmatrix}.$$

Using Gauss-Jordan elimination, we find A^{-1} to be

$$A^{-1} = \begin{bmatrix} -1 & 1 & 0 \\ -1 & 0 & 1 \\ 6 & -2 & -3 \end{bmatrix}.$$

To solve each system, we use matrix multiplication as follows.

(a) $\mathbf{x} = A^{-1}\mathbf{b} = \begin{bmatrix} -1 & 1 & 0 \\ -1 & 0 & 1 \\ 6 & -2 & -3 \end{bmatrix} \begin{bmatrix} -1 \\ 1 \\ -2 \end{bmatrix} = \begin{bmatrix} 2 \\ -1 \\ -2 \end{bmatrix}$

The solution is $x = 2$, $y = -1$, and $z = -2$.

(b) $\mathbf{x} = A^{-1}\mathbf{b} = \begin{bmatrix} -1 & 1 & 0 \\ -1 & 0 & 1 \\ 6 & -2 & -3 \end{bmatrix} \begin{bmatrix} 4 \\ 8 \\ 5 \end{bmatrix} = \begin{bmatrix} 4 \\ 1 \\ -7 \end{bmatrix}$

The solution is $x = 4$, $y = 1$, and $z = -7$.

(c) $\mathbf{x} = A^{-1}\mathbf{b} = \begin{bmatrix} -1 & 1 & 0 \\ -1 & 0 & 1 \\ 6 & -2 & -3 \end{bmatrix} \begin{bmatrix} 0 \\ 0 \\ 0 \end{bmatrix} = \begin{bmatrix} 0 \\ 0 \\ 0 \end{bmatrix}$

The solution is trivial: $x = 0$, $y = 0$, and $z = 0$.

SECTION 2.3 ☐ EXERCISES

In Exercises 1–6, show that B is the inverse of A.

1. $A = \begin{bmatrix} 1 & 2 \\ 3 & 4 \end{bmatrix}$, $B = \begin{bmatrix} -2 & 1 \\ \frac{3}{2} & -\frac{1}{2} \end{bmatrix}$

2. $A = \begin{bmatrix} 1 & -1 \\ 2 & 3 \end{bmatrix}$, $B = \begin{bmatrix} \frac{3}{5} & \frac{1}{5} \\ -\frac{2}{5} & \frac{1}{5} \end{bmatrix}$

3. $A = \begin{bmatrix} -2 & 2 & 3 \\ 1 & -1 & 0 \\ 0 & 1 & 4 \end{bmatrix}$, $B = \frac{1}{3}\begin{bmatrix} -4 & -5 & 3 \\ -4 & -8 & 3 \\ 1 & 2 & 0 \end{bmatrix}$

4. $A = \begin{bmatrix} 2 & -17 & 11 \\ -1 & 11 & -7 \\ 0 & 3 & -2 \end{bmatrix}$, $B = \begin{bmatrix} 1 & 1 & 2 \\ 2 & 4 & -3 \\ 3 & 6 & -5 \end{bmatrix}$

5. $A = \begin{bmatrix} 2 & 0 & 0 \\ 0 & -3 & 0 \\ 0 & 0 & 4 \end{bmatrix}$, $B = \begin{bmatrix} \frac{1}{2} & 0 & 0 \\ 0 & -\frac{1}{3} & 0 \\ 0 & 0 & \frac{1}{4} \end{bmatrix}$

C 6. $A = \begin{bmatrix} 1 & 2 & 0 & 0 \\ 2 & 1 & 2 & 0 \\ 0 & 2 & 1 & 2 \\ 0 & 0 & 2 & 1 \end{bmatrix}$, $B = \frac{1}{5}\begin{bmatrix} -7 & 6 & 4 & -8 \\ 6 & -3 & -2 & 4 \\ 4 & -2 & -3 & 6 \\ -8 & 4 & 6 & -7 \end{bmatrix}$

In Exercises 7–30, find the inverse of the matrix (if it exists).

7. $\begin{bmatrix} 1 & 2 \\ 3 & 7 \end{bmatrix}$

8. $\begin{bmatrix} 1 & -2 \\ 2 & -3 \end{bmatrix}$

9. $\begin{bmatrix} -7 & 33 \\ 4 & -19 \end{bmatrix}$

10. $\begin{bmatrix} -1 & 1 \\ 3 & -3 \end{bmatrix}$

11. $\begin{bmatrix} 2 & 4 \\ 4 & 8 \end{bmatrix}$

12. $\begin{bmatrix} 11 & 1 \\ -1 & 0 \end{bmatrix}$

13. $\begin{bmatrix} 2 & 3 \\ 1 & 4 \end{bmatrix}$

14. $\begin{bmatrix} 2 & 7 \\ -3 & -9 \end{bmatrix}$

15. $\begin{bmatrix} 1 & 1 & 1 \\ 3 & 5 & 4 \\ 3 & 6 & 5 \end{bmatrix}$

16. $\begin{bmatrix} 1 & 2 & 2 \\ 3 & 7 & 9 \\ -1 & -4 & -7 \end{bmatrix}$

17. $\begin{bmatrix} 1 & 2 & -1 \\ 3 & 7 & -10 \\ 7 & 16 & -21 \end{bmatrix}$

18. $\begin{bmatrix} 10 & 5 & -7 \\ -5 & 1 & 4 \\ 3 & 2 & -2 \end{bmatrix}$

C 19. $\begin{bmatrix} 1 & -2 & -1 & -2 \\ 3 & -5 & -2 & -3 \\ 2 & -5 & -2 & -5 \\ -1 & 4 & 4 & 11 \end{bmatrix}$

C 20. $\begin{bmatrix} 4 & 8 & -7 & 14 \\ 2 & 5 & -4 & 6 \\ 0 & 2 & 1 & -7 \\ 3 & 6 & -5 & 10 \end{bmatrix}$

21. $\begin{bmatrix} 1 & 1 & 2 \\ 3 & 1 & 0 \\ -2 & 0 & 3 \end{bmatrix}$

22. $\begin{bmatrix} 3 & 2 & 5 \\ 2 & 2 & 4 \\ -4 & 4 & 0 \end{bmatrix}$

23. $\begin{bmatrix} 0.1 & 0.2 & 0.3 \\ -0.3 & 0.2 & 0.2 \\ 0.5 & 0.5 & 0.5 \end{bmatrix}$

24. $\begin{bmatrix} 2 & 0 & 0 \\ 0 & 3 & 0 \\ 0 & 0 & 5 \end{bmatrix}$

C 25. $\begin{bmatrix} 1 & 0 & 3 & 0 \\ 0 & 2 & 0 & 4 \\ 1 & 0 & 3 & 0 \\ 0 & 2 & 0 & 4 \end{bmatrix}$

C 26. $\begin{bmatrix} 1 & 3 & -2 & 0 \\ 0 & 2 & 4 & 6 \\ 0 & 0 & -2 & 1 \\ 0 & 0 & 0 & 5 \end{bmatrix}$

27. $\begin{bmatrix} 1 & 0 & 0 \\ 3 & 4 & 0 \\ 2 & 5 & 5 \end{bmatrix}$

28. $\begin{bmatrix} 1 & 0 & 0 \\ 3 & 0 & 0 \\ 2 & 5 & 5 \end{bmatrix}$

29. $\begin{bmatrix} -8 & 0 & 0 & 0 \\ 0 & 1 & 0 & 0 \\ 0 & 0 & 0 & 0 \\ 0 & 0 & 0 & -5 \end{bmatrix}$

30. $\begin{bmatrix} \frac{1}{a} & 0 \\ a & a \end{bmatrix}$, $a \neq 0$

In Exercises 31–34, use an inverse matrix to solve the given systems of linear equations.

31. (a) $\begin{aligned} -x + y &= 4 \\ -2x + y &= 0 \end{aligned}$

(b) $\begin{aligned} -x + y &= -3 \\ -2x + y &= 5 \end{aligned}$

(c) $\begin{aligned} -x + y &= 0 \\ -2x + y &= 0 \end{aligned}$

32. (a) $\begin{aligned} 2x + 3y &= 5 \\ x + 4y &= 10 \end{aligned}$

(b) $\begin{aligned} 2x + 3y &= 0 \\ x + 4y &= 0 \end{aligned}$

(c) $\begin{aligned} 2x + 3y &= 1 \\ x + 4y &= -2 \end{aligned}$

33. (a) $\begin{aligned} 3x + 2y + 2z &= 0 \\ 2x + 2y + 2z &= 5 \\ -4x + 4y + 3z &= 2 \end{aligned}$

(b) $\begin{aligned} 3x + 2y + 2z &= -1 \\ 2x + 2y + 2z &= 2 \\ -4x + 4y + 3z &= 0 \end{aligned}$

(c) $\begin{aligned} 3x + 2y + 2z &= 0 \\ 2x + 2y + 2z &= 0 \\ -4x + 4y + 3z &= 0 \end{aligned}$

C 34. (a) $\begin{aligned} x_1 - 2x_2 - x_3 - 2x_4 &= 0 \\ 3x_1 - 5x_2 - 2x_3 - 3x_4 &= 1 \\ 2x_1 - 5x_2 - 2x_3 - 5x_4 &= -1 \\ -x_1 + 4x_2 + 4x_3 + 11x_4 &= 2 \end{aligned}$

(b) $\begin{aligned} x_1 - 2x_2 - x_3 - 2x_4 &= 1 \\ 3x_1 - 5x_2 - 2x_3 - 3x_4 &= -2 \\ 2x_1 - 5x_2 - 2x_3 - 5x_4 &= 0 \\ -x_1 + 4x_2 + 4x_3 + 11x_4 &= -3 \end{aligned}$

In Exercises 35–38, use the given inverse matrices to find
(a) $(AB)^{-1}$, (b) $(A^T)^{-1}$, (c) A^{-2}, and (d) $(2A)^{-1}$.

35. $A^{-1} = \begin{bmatrix} 2 & 5 \\ -7 & 6 \end{bmatrix}$, $B^{-1} = \begin{bmatrix} 7 & -3 \\ 2 & 0 \end{bmatrix}$

36. $A^{-1} = \begin{bmatrix} -\frac{2}{7} & \frac{1}{7} \\ \frac{3}{7} & \frac{2}{7} \end{bmatrix}$, $B^{-1} = \begin{bmatrix} \frac{5}{11} & \frac{2}{11} \\ \frac{3}{11} & -\frac{1}{11} \end{bmatrix}$

37. $A^{-1} = \begin{bmatrix} 1 & -\frac{1}{2} & \frac{3}{4} \\ \frac{3}{2} & \frac{1}{2} & -2 \\ \frac{1}{4} & 1 & \frac{1}{2} \end{bmatrix}$, $B^{-1} = \begin{bmatrix} 2 & 4 & \frac{5}{2} \\ -\frac{3}{4} & 2 & \frac{1}{4} \\ \frac{1}{4} & \frac{1}{2} & 2 \end{bmatrix}$

38. $A^{-1} = \begin{bmatrix} 1 & -4 & 2 \\ 0 & 1 & 3 \\ 4 & 2 & 1 \end{bmatrix}$, $B^{-1} = \begin{bmatrix} 6 & 5 & -3 \\ -2 & 4 & -1 \\ 1 & 3 & 4 \end{bmatrix}$

39. Find x such that the matrix
$$A = \begin{bmatrix} 3 & x \\ -2 & -3 \end{bmatrix}$$
is equal to its own inverse.

40. Find x such that the matrix
$$A = \begin{bmatrix} 4 & x \\ -2 & -3 \end{bmatrix}$$
is singular.

41. Find A given that
$$(2A)^{-1} = \begin{bmatrix} 1 & 2 \\ 3 & 4 \end{bmatrix}.$$

42. Show that the following matrix is invertible and find its inverse.
$$A = \begin{bmatrix} \sin\theta & \cos\theta \\ -\cos\theta & \sin\theta \end{bmatrix}$$

43. Prove that if A is an invertible matrix and k is a positive integer, then
$$(A^k)^{-1} = \underbrace{A^{-1}A^{-1}\cdots A^{-1}}_{k\ factors}.$$

44. Prove that if A is an invertible matrix, then $(A^T)^{-1} = (A^{-1})^T$.

45. Prove that the inverse of a symmetric nonsingular matrix is symmetric.

46. Prove that if C is an invertible matrix such that $CA = CB$, then $A = B$.

47. Prove that if $A^2 = A$, then $I - 2A = (I - 2A)^{-1}$.

48. Prove that if A, B, and C are square matrices and $ABC = I$, then B is invertible and $B^{-1} = CA$.

49. Prove that if A is invertible and $AB = O$, then $B = O$.

50. Prove that if $A^2 = A$, then either $A = I$ or A is singular.

51. Is the sum of two invertible matrices invertible? Explain why or why not. Illustrate your conclusion with appropriate examples.

52. Under what conditions will the diagonal matrix
$$A = \begin{bmatrix} a_{11} & 0 & 0 & \cdots & 0 \\ 0 & a_{22} & 0 & \cdots & 0 \\ \vdots & \vdots & \vdots & & \vdots \\ 0 & 0 & 0 & \cdots & a_{nn} \end{bmatrix}$$
be invertible? If A is invertible, find its inverse.

53. Use the result of Exercise 52 to find the inverse of the given matrix.

(a) $A = \begin{bmatrix} -1 & 0 & 0 \\ 0 & 3 & 0 \\ 0 & 0 & 2 \end{bmatrix}$ (b) $A = \begin{bmatrix} \frac{1}{2} & 0 & 0 \\ 0 & \frac{1}{3} & 0 \\ 0 & 0 & \frac{1}{4} \end{bmatrix}$

54. Let $A = \begin{bmatrix} 1 & 2 \\ -2 & 1 \end{bmatrix}$.

(a) Show that $A^2 - 2A + 5I = 0$, where I is the identity matrix of order 2.
(b) Show that $A^{-1} = \frac{1}{5}(2I - A)$.
(c) Show in general that for any square matrix satisfying $A^2 - 2A + 5I = 0$, the inverse of A is given by $A^{-1} = \frac{1}{5}(2I - A)$.

55. Let $\mathbf{u}$ be an $n \times 1$ column matrix satisfying $\mathbf{u}^T\mathbf{u} = 1$. The $n \times n$ matrix $H = I_n - 2\mathbf{u}\mathbf{u}^T$ is called a **Householder matrix**. Prove that H is symmetric and nonsingular.

2.4 ELEMENTARY MATRICES

In Section 1.2, we introduced the following three elementary row operations for matrices.
1. Interchange two rows.
2. Multiply a row by a nonzero constant.
3. Add a multiple of a row to another row.
In this section, we will see how matrix multiplication can be used to perform these operations.

Definition of an Elementary Matrix	An $n \times n$ matrix is called an **elementary matrix** if it can be obtained from I_n by a single elementary row operation.

REMARK: The identity matrix I_n is elementary by this definition because it can be obtained from itself by multiplying any one of its rows by 1.

EXAMPLE 1   *Elementary Matrices and Nonelementary Matrices*

Which of the following matrices are elementary? For those that are, describe the corresponding elementary row operation.

(a) $\begin{bmatrix} 1 & 0 & 0 \\ 0 & 3 & 0 \\ 0 & 0 & 1 \end{bmatrix}$ (b) $\begin{bmatrix} 1 & 0 & 0 \\ 0 & 1 & 0 \end{bmatrix}$ (c) $\begin{bmatrix} 1 & 0 & 0 \\ 0 & 1 & 0 \\ 0 & 0 & 0 \end{bmatrix}$

(d) $\begin{bmatrix} 1 & 0 & 0 \\ 0 & 0 & 1 \\ 0 & 1 & 0 \end{bmatrix}$ (e) $\begin{bmatrix} 1 & 0 \\ 2 & 1 \end{bmatrix}$ (f) $\begin{bmatrix} 1 & 0 & 0 \\ 0 & 2 & 0 \\ 0 & 0 & -1 \end{bmatrix}$

Solution   (a) This matrix *is* elementary. It can be obtained by multiplying the second row of I_3 by 3.
(b) This matrix is *not* elementary because it is not square.
(c) This matrix is *not* elementary because it was obtained by multiplying the third row of I_3 by 0 (row multiplication must be by a *nonzero* constant).
(d) This matrix is elementary. It can be obtained by interchanging the second and third rows of I_3.
(e) This matrix *is* elementary. It can be obtained by multiplying the first row of I_2 by 2 and adding the result to the second row.
(f) This matrix is *not* elementary because two elementary row operations are required to obtain it from I_3.

Elementary matrices are useful because they enable us to use matrix multiplication to perform elementary row operations, as demonstrated in Example 2.

EXAMPLE 2   *Elementary Matrices and Elementary Row Operations*

(a) In the following matrix product, E is the elementary matrix in which the first two rows of I_3 have been interchanged.

$$\overset{E}{\begin{bmatrix} 0 & 1 & 0 \\ 1 & 0 & 0 \\ 0 & 0 & 1 \end{bmatrix}} \overset{A}{\begin{bmatrix} 0 & 2 & 1 \\ 1 & -3 & 6 \\ 3 & 2 & -1 \end{bmatrix}} = \begin{bmatrix} 1 & -3 & 6 \\ 0 & 2 & 1 \\ 3 & 2 & -1 \end{bmatrix}$$

Note that we interchanged the first two rows of A by multiplying *on the left* by E.

(b) In the following matrix product, E is the elementary matrix in which the second row of I_3 has been multiplied by $\frac{1}{2}$.

$$\overset{E}{\begin{bmatrix} 1 & 0 & 0 \\ 0 & \frac{1}{2} & 0 \\ 0 & 0 & 1 \end{bmatrix}} \overset{A}{\begin{bmatrix} 1 & 0 & -4 & 1 \\ 0 & 2 & 6 & -4 \\ 0 & 1 & 3 & 1 \end{bmatrix}} = \begin{bmatrix} 1 & 0 & -4 & 1 \\ 0 & 1 & 3 & -2 \\ 0 & 1 & 3 & 1 \end{bmatrix}$$

Here the size of A is 3×4. However, A could be *any* $3 \times n$ matrix and multiplication on the left by E would still result in multiplying the second row of A by $\frac{1}{2}$.

(c) In the following product, E is the elementary matrix in which 2 times the first row of I_3 has been added to the second row.

$$\overset{E}{\begin{bmatrix} 1 & 0 & 0 \\ 2 & 1 & 0 \\ 0 & 0 & 1 \end{bmatrix}} \overset{A}{\begin{bmatrix} 1 & 0 & -1 \\ -2 & -2 & 3 \\ 0 & 4 & 5 \end{bmatrix}} = \begin{bmatrix} 1 & 0 & -1 \\ 0 & -2 & 1 \\ 0 & 4 & 5 \end{bmatrix}$$

Note that in the product EA, 2 times the first row of A has been added to the second row.

In each of the three products in Example 2, we were able to perform elementary row operations by multiplying *on the left* by an elementary matrix. We generalize this property of elementary matrices in the following theorem, which we state without proof.

Theorem 2.12 Representing Elementary Row Operations	Let E be the elementary matrix obtained by performing an elementary row operation on I_m. If that same elementary row operation is performed on an $m \times n$ matrix A, then the resulting matrix is given by the product EA.

REMARK: Be sure to remember that in Theorem 2.12, A is multiplied *on the left* by the elementary matrix E. Right multiplication by elementary matrices, which involves column operations, will not be considered in this text.

Most applications of elementary row operations require a sequence of operations. For instance, Gaussian elimination usually requires several elementary row operations to row reduce a matrix A. For elementary matrices, this sequence translates into multiplication (on the left) by several elementary matrices. The order of multiplication is important; the elementary matrix immediately to the left of A corresponds to the row operation performed first. The process is demonstrated in Example 3.

EXAMPLE 3   *Using Elementary Matrices*

Find a sequence of elementary matrices that can be used to write the following matrix in row-echelon form.

$$A = \begin{bmatrix} 0 & 1 & 3 & 5 \\ 1 & -3 & 0 & 2 \\ 2 & -6 & 2 & 0 \end{bmatrix}$$

Solution

Matrix	*Elementary Row Operation*	*Elementary Matrix*
$\begin{bmatrix} 1 & -3 & 0 & 2 \\ 0 & 1 & 3 & 5 \\ 2 & -6 & 2 & 0 \end{bmatrix}$ ← ←	**The first two rows are interchanged.**	$E_1 = \begin{bmatrix} 0 & 1 & 0 \\ 1 & 0 & 0 \\ 0 & 0 & 1 \end{bmatrix}$
$\begin{bmatrix} 1 & -3 & 0 & 2 \\ 0 & 1 & 3 & 5 \\ 0 & 0 & 2 & -4 \end{bmatrix}$ ←	**Adding -2 times the first row to the third row produces a new third row.**	$E_2 = \begin{bmatrix} 1 & 0 & 0 \\ 0 & 1 & 0 \\ -2 & 0 & 1 \end{bmatrix}$
$\begin{bmatrix} 1 & -3 & 0 & 2 \\ 0 & 1 & 3 & 5 \\ 0 & 0 & 1 & -2 \end{bmatrix}$ ←	**Multiplying the third row by $\frac{1}{2}$ produces a new third row.**	$E_3 = \begin{bmatrix} 1 & 0 & 0 \\ 0 & 1 & 0 \\ 0 & 0 & \frac{1}{2} \end{bmatrix}$

The three elementary matrices E_1, E_2, and E_3 can be used to perform the same elimination, as follows.

$$E_3 E_2 E_1 A = \begin{bmatrix} 1 & 0 & 0 \\ 0 & 1 & 0 \\ 0 & 0 & \frac{1}{2} \end{bmatrix} \begin{bmatrix} 1 & 0 & 0 \\ 0 & 1 & 0 \\ -2 & 0 & 1 \end{bmatrix} \begin{bmatrix} 0 & 1 & 0 \\ 1 & 0 & 0 \\ 0 & 0 & 1 \end{bmatrix} \begin{bmatrix} 0 & 1 & 3 & 5 \\ 1 & -3 & 0 & 2 \\ 2 & -6 & 2 & 0 \end{bmatrix}$$

$$= \begin{bmatrix} 1 & 0 & 0 \\ 0 & 1 & 0 \\ 0 & 0 & \frac{1}{2} \end{bmatrix} \begin{bmatrix} 1 & 0 & 0 \\ 0 & 1 & 0 \\ -2 & 0 & 1 \end{bmatrix} \begin{bmatrix} 1 & -3 & 0 & 2 \\ 0 & 1 & 3 & 5 \\ 2 & -6 & 2 & 0 \end{bmatrix}$$

$$= \begin{bmatrix} 1 & 0 & 0 \\ 0 & 1 & 0 \\ 0 & 0 & \frac{1}{2} \end{bmatrix} \begin{bmatrix} 1 & -3 & 0 & 2 \\ 0 & 1 & 3 & 5 \\ 0 & 0 & 2 & -4 \end{bmatrix}$$

$$= \begin{bmatrix} 1 & -3 & 0 & 2 \\ 0 & 1 & 3 & 5 \\ 0 & 0 & 1 & -2 \end{bmatrix}$$

REMARK: We should mention that the procedure demonstrated in Example 3 is primarily of theoretical interest. In other words, we are not suggesting this procedure as a practical method for performing Gaussian elimination.

The two matrices

$$A = \begin{bmatrix} 0 & 1 & 3 & 5 \\ 1 & -3 & 0 & 2 \\ 2 & -6 & 2 & 0 \end{bmatrix} \quad \text{and} \quad B = \begin{bmatrix} 1 & -3 & 0 & 2 \\ 0 & 1 & 3 & 5 \\ 0 & 0 & 1 & -2 \end{bmatrix}$$

are row-equivalent because you can obtain B by performing a sequence of row operations on A.

$$B = E_3 E_2 E_1 A$$

The definition of row-equivalent matrices can be restated using elementary matrices as follows.

Definition of Row Equivalence

Let A and B be $m \times n$ matrices. Matrix B is **row equivalent** to A if there exists a finite number of elementary matrices $E_1, E_2, \ldots, E_k$ such that

$$B = E_k E_{k-1} \cdots E_2 E_1 A .$$

We know from Section 2.3 that not all square matrices are invertible. Every elementary matrix, however, is invertible. Moreover, the inverse of an elementary matrix is itself an elementary matrix.

Theorem 2.13
Elementary Matrices Are Invertible

If E is an elementary matrix, then E^{-1} exists and is an elementary matrix.

To find the inverse of an elementary matrix E, we simply reverse the elementary row operation used to obtain E. For instance, the inverse of each of the three elementary matrices shown in Example 3 is as follows.

Elementary Matrix

$$E_1 = \begin{bmatrix} 0 & 1 & 0 \\ 1 & 0 & 0 \\ 0 & 0 & 1 \end{bmatrix} \quad \longleftarrow \begin{matrix} \text{Interchange} \\ \text{the first and} \\ \text{second rows.} \end{matrix}$$

$$E_2 = \begin{bmatrix} 1 & 0 & 0 \\ 0 & 1 & 0 \\ -2 & 0 & 1 \end{bmatrix} \quad \begin{matrix} \text{Add } -2 \text{ times} \\ \text{the first row to} \\ \longleftarrow \text{the third row.} \end{matrix}$$

$$E_3 = \begin{bmatrix} 1 & 0 & 0 \\ 0 & 1 & 0 \\ 0 & 0 & \frac{1}{2} \end{bmatrix} \quad \begin{matrix} \text{Multiply} \\ \text{the third row} \\ \longleftarrow \text{by } \frac{1}{2}. \end{matrix}$$

Inverse Matrix

$$E_1^{-1} = \begin{bmatrix} 0 & 1 & 0 \\ 1 & 0 & 0 \\ 0 & 0 & 1 \end{bmatrix} \quad \longleftarrow \begin{matrix} \text{Interchange} \\ \text{the first and} \\ \text{second rows.} \end{matrix}$$

$$E_2^{-1} = \begin{bmatrix} 1 & 0 & 0 \\ 0 & 1 & 0 \\ 2 & 0 & 1 \end{bmatrix} \quad \begin{matrix} \text{Add 2 times} \\ \text{the first row to} \\ \longleftarrow \text{the third row.} \end{matrix}$$

$$E_3^{-1} = \begin{bmatrix} 1 & 0 & 0 \\ 0 & 1 & 0 \\ 0 & 0 & 2 \end{bmatrix} \quad \begin{matrix} \text{Multiply} \\ \text{the third row} \\ \longleftarrow \text{by 2.} \end{matrix}$$

The following theorem tells us that every invertible matrix can be written as the product of elementary matrices.

Theorem 2.14 A Property of Invertible Matrices	A square matrix A is invertible if and only if it can be written as the product of elementary matrices.

Proof   To prove the theorem in one direction, we assume that A is the product of elementary matrices. Then, because every elementary matrix is invertible and the product of invertible matrices is invertible, it follows that A is invertible.

To prove the theorem in the other direction, we assume that A is invertible. From Theorem 2.11 we know that the system of linear equations represented by $A\mathbf{x} = O$ has only the trivial solution. But this implies that the augmented matrix $[A \; \vdots \; O]$ can be rewritten in the form $[I \; \vdots \; O]$ (using elementary row operations corresponding to $E_1, E_2, \ldots,$ and E_k). Therefore we have

$$E_k \cdots E_3 E_2 E_1 A = I$$

and it follows that

$$A = E_1^{-1} E_2^{-1} E_3^{-1} \cdots E_k^{-1}.$$

Thus A can be written as the product of elementary matrices, and the proof is complete.

The second part of this proof is illustrated in Example 4.

EXAMPLE 4   *Writing a Matrix as the Product of Elementary Matrices*

Find a sequence of elementary matrices whose product is

$$A = \begin{bmatrix} -1 & -2 \\ 3 & 8 \end{bmatrix}.$$

Solution   We begin by finding a sequence of elementary row operations that can be used to rewrite A in reduced row-echelon form.

Matrix	*Elementary Row Operation*	*Elementary Matrix*
$\begin{bmatrix} 1 & 2 \\ 3 & 8 \end{bmatrix} \longleftarrow$	**Multiplying the first row by -1 produces a new first row.**	$E_1 = \begin{bmatrix} -1 & 0 \\ 0 & 1 \end{bmatrix}$
$\begin{bmatrix} 1 & 2 \\ 0 & 2 \end{bmatrix} \longleftarrow$	**Adding -3 times the first row to the second row produces a new second row.**	$E_2 = \begin{bmatrix} 1 & 0 \\ -3 & 1 \end{bmatrix}$
$\begin{bmatrix} 1 & 2 \\ 0 & 1 \end{bmatrix} \longleftarrow$	**Multiplying the second row by $\frac{1}{2}$ produces a new second row.**	$E_3 = \begin{bmatrix} 1 & 0 \\ 0 & \frac{1}{2} \end{bmatrix}$

$$\begin{bmatrix} 1 & 0 \\ 0 & 1 \end{bmatrix} \longleftarrow \quad \begin{array}{l} \textbf{Adding } -2 \textbf{ times the second} \\ \textbf{row to the first row} \\ \textbf{produces a new first row.} \end{array} \qquad E_4 = \begin{bmatrix} 1 & -2 \\ 0 & 1 \end{bmatrix}$$

Now from the matrix product

$$E_4 E_3 E_2 E_1 A = I$$

we solve for A to obtain

$$A = E_1^{-1} E_2^{-1} E_3^{-1} E_4^{-1}.$$

This implies that

$$A = \overset{E_1^{-1}}{\begin{bmatrix} -1 & 0 \\ 0 & 1 \end{bmatrix}} \overset{E_2^{-1}}{\begin{bmatrix} 1 & 0 \\ 3 & 1 \end{bmatrix}} \overset{E_3^{-1}}{\begin{bmatrix} 1 & 0 \\ 0 & 2 \end{bmatrix}} \overset{E_4^{-1}}{\begin{bmatrix} 1 & 2 \\ 0 & 1 \end{bmatrix}}$$

$$= \begin{bmatrix} -1 & -2 \\ 3 & 8 \end{bmatrix}.$$

In Section 2.3 we described a process for finding the inverse of a nonsingular matrix A. There, we used Gauss-Jordan elimination to reduce the augmented matrix $[A \; \vdots \; I]$ to $[I \; \vdots \; A^{-1}]$. We can now use Theorem 2.14 to justify this procedure. Specifically, the proof of Theorem 2.14 allows us to write the product

$$I = E_k \cdots E_3 E_2 E_1 A .$$

Multiplying both sides of this equation (on the right) by A^{-1}, we can write

$$A^{-1} = E_k \cdots E_3 E_2 E_1 I.$$

In other words, a sequence of elementary matrices that reduces A to the identity also can be used to reduce the identity I to A^{-1}. Applying the corresponding sequence of elementary row operations to the matrices A and I simultaneously, we have

$$E_k \cdots E_3 E_2 E_1 [A \; \vdots \; I] = [I \; \vdots \; A^{-1}].$$

Of course, if A is singular, then no such sequence can be found.

Our next theorem ties together some important relationships between $n \times n$ matrices and systems of linear equations. We have proved the essential parts of this theorem already (see Theorems 2.11 and 2.14); we leave it up to you to fill in the other parts of the proof.

Theorem 2.15 Equivalent Conditions	If A is an $n \times n$ matrix, then the following statements are equivalent. 1. A is invertible. 2. $\mathbf{Ax} = \mathbf{b}$ has a unique solution for every $n \times 1$ column matrix $\mathbf{b}$. 3. $\mathbf{Ax} = O$ has only the trivial solution. 4. A is row-equivalent to I_n. 5. A can be written as the product of elementary matrices.

The *LU*–Factorization

Solving systems of linear equations is the most important application of linear algebra. At the heart of the most efficient and modern algorithms for solving linear systems $A\mathbf{x} = \mathbf{b}$ is the so-called *LU*–factorization, in which the square matrix A is expressed as a product, $A = LU$. Here L is a lower triangular matrix, and U is an upper triangular matrix.

By writing $A\mathbf{x} = LU\mathbf{x}$ and letting $U\mathbf{x} = \mathbf{y}$, you can solve for $\mathbf{x}$ in two stages. First solve $L\mathbf{y} = \mathbf{b}$ for $\mathbf{y}$; then solve $U\mathbf{x} = \mathbf{y}$ for $\mathbf{x}$. Each system is easy to solve because the coefficient matrices are triangular. In particular, neither system requires any row operations!

Definition of **LU–Factorization**	If the $n \times n$ matrix S can be written as the product of a lower triangular matrix L and an upper triangular matrix U, then we say that $A = LU$ is an **LU–factorization** of A.

EXAMPLE 5   *Finding the LU-Factorization of a Matrix*

(a) $\begin{bmatrix} 1 & 2 \\ 1 & 0 \end{bmatrix} = \begin{bmatrix} 1 & 0 \\ 1 & 1 \end{bmatrix} \begin{bmatrix} 1 & 2 \\ 0 & -2 \end{bmatrix}$

is an *LU*–factorization of the matrix $A = \begin{bmatrix} 1 & 2 \\ 1 & 0 \end{bmatrix}$ as the product of the lower triangular matrix $L = \begin{bmatrix} 1 & 0 \\ 1 & 1 \end{bmatrix}$ and the upper triangular matrix $U = \begin{bmatrix} 1 & 2 \\ 0 & -2 \end{bmatrix}$.

(b) $A = \begin{bmatrix} 1 & -3 & 0 \\ 0 & 1 & 3 \\ 2 & -10 & 2 \end{bmatrix} = \begin{bmatrix} 1 & 0 & 0 \\ 0 & 1 & 0 \\ 2 & -4 & 1 \end{bmatrix} \begin{bmatrix} 1 & -3 & 0 \\ 0 & 1 & 3 \\ 0 & 0 & 14 \end{bmatrix} = LU$

is an *LU*–factorization of the matrix A.

If a square matrix A can be row-reduced to an upper triangular matrix U *without any row interchanges,* then it is easy to find an *LU*–factorization of the matrix A. All you need to do is keep track of the individual row operations, as indicated in the following example.

EXAMPLE 6   *Finding the LU-Factorization of a Matrix*

Find the *LU*–factorization of the matrix $A = \begin{bmatrix} 1 & -3 & 0 \\ 0 & 1 & 3 \\ 2 & -10 & 2 \end{bmatrix}$.

Solution   Begin by row-reducing A to upper triangular form while keeping track of the elementary matrices used for each row operation.

$$\begin{matrix} \textit{Matrix} & & \textit{Elementary Matrix} \end{matrix}$$

$$\begin{bmatrix} 1 & -3 & 0 \\ 0 & 1 & 3 \\ 0 & -4 & 2 \end{bmatrix} \qquad E_1 = \begin{bmatrix} 1 & 0 & 0 \\ 0 & 1 & 0 \\ -2 & 0 & 1 \end{bmatrix}$$

Matrix   *Elementary Matrix*

$$\begin{bmatrix} 1 & -3 & 0 \\ 0 & 1 & 3 \\ 0 & 0 & 14 \end{bmatrix} \qquad E_2 = \begin{bmatrix} 1 & 0 & 0 \\ 0 & 1 & 0 \\ 0 & 4 & 1 \end{bmatrix}$$

The matrix U on the left is upper triangular, and it follows that $E_2 E_1 A = U$, or $A = E_1^{-1} E_2^{-1} U$. Since the product of the lower triangular matrices

$$E_1^{-1} E_2^{-1} = \begin{bmatrix} 1 & 0 & 0 \\ 0 & 1 & 0 \\ 2 & 0 & 1 \end{bmatrix} \begin{bmatrix} 1 & 0 & 0 \\ 0 & 1 & 0 \\ 0 & -4 & 1 \end{bmatrix} = \begin{bmatrix} 1 & 0 & 0 \\ 0 & 1 & 0 \\ 2 & -4 & 1 \end{bmatrix}$$

is again a lower triangular matrix L, the factorization $A = LU$ is complete. Note that this is the same LU–factorization as shown in Example 5(b) above.

In general, if A can be row-reduced to an upper triangular matrix U *without row interchanges,* then A has an LU–factorization.

$$E_k \cdots E_2 E_1 A = U$$
$$A = E_1^{-1} E_2^{-1} \cdots E_k^{-1} U$$
$$A = LU$$

Here, L is the product of the inverses of the elementary matrices used in the row reduction.

Note that the multipliers in Example 6 were -2 and 4, which are the negatives of the corresponding entries in L. This is true in general. If U can be obtained from A using only the row operation of adding a multiple of one row to another row, then the matrix L is lower triangular with 1's along the diagonal. Furthermore, the negative of each multiplier is in the same position used to introduce the corresponding zero in U.

Once you have obtained an LU–factorization of a matrix A, then you can solve the system of n linear equations in n unknowns $A\mathbf{x} = \mathbf{b}$ very efficiently in two steps.

1. Write $\mathbf{y} = U\mathbf{x}$ and solve $L\mathbf{y} = \mathbf{b}$ for $\mathbf{y}$.
2. Solve $U\mathbf{x} = \mathbf{y}$ for $\mathbf{x}$.

The column matrix $\mathbf{x}$ is the solution to the original system since

$$A\mathbf{x} = LU\mathbf{x} = L\mathbf{y} = \mathbf{b}.$$

The second step in this algorithm is just back-substitution because the matrix U is upper triangular. The first step is similar, except that it starts at the top of the matrix, since L is lower triangular. For this reason, the first step is often called **forward substitution.**

EXAMPLE 7   *Solving a Linear System with LU-Factorization*

Solve the linear system

$$\begin{aligned} x_1 - 3x_2 \quad\quad\;\; &= -5 \\ x_2 + 3x_3 &= -1 \\ 2x_1 - 10x_2 + 2x_3 &= -20 \end{aligned}$$

Solution   We obtained the *LU*–factorization of the coefficient matrix A in Example 6.

$$A = \begin{bmatrix} 1 & -3 & 0 \\ 0 & 1 & 3 \\ 2 & -10 & 2 \end{bmatrix} = \begin{bmatrix} 1 & 0 & 0 \\ 0 & 1 & 0 \\ 2 & -4 & 1 \end{bmatrix} \begin{bmatrix} 1 & -3 & 0 \\ 0 & 1 & 3 \\ 0 & 0 & 14 \end{bmatrix}$$

First, let $\mathbf{y} = U\mathbf{x}$ and solve the system $L\mathbf{y} = \mathbf{b}$.

$$\begin{bmatrix} 1 & 0 & 0 \\ 0 & 1 & 0 \\ 2 & -4 & 1 \end{bmatrix} \begin{bmatrix} y_1 \\ y_2 \\ y_3 \end{bmatrix} = \begin{bmatrix} -5 \\ -1 \\ -20 \end{bmatrix}$$

Note how easy this system is to solve using forward substitution. Starting with the first equation, $y_1 = -5$. The second equation then gives $y_2 = -1$. Finally, from the third equation,

$$2y_1 - 4y_2 + y_3 = -20$$
$$y_3 = -20 - 2y_1 + 4y_2$$
$$y_3 = -20 - 2(-5) + 4(-1)$$
$$y_3 = -14$$

Thus, the solution to $L\mathbf{y} = \mathbf{b}$ is

$$\mathbf{y} = \begin{bmatrix} -5 \\ -1 \\ -14 \end{bmatrix}.$$

Now solve the system $U\mathbf{x} = \mathbf{y}$ for $\mathbf{x}$ using back-substitution.

$$\begin{bmatrix} 1 & -3 & 0 \\ 0 & 1 & 3 \\ 0 & 0 & 14 \end{bmatrix} \begin{bmatrix} x_1 \\ x_2 \\ x_3 \end{bmatrix} = \begin{bmatrix} -5 \\ -1 \\ -14 \end{bmatrix}$$

From the bottom equation, $x_3 = -1$. Then, the second equation gives $x_2 + 3x_3 = x_2 + 3(-1) = -1$, or $x_2 = 2$. Finally, the first equation is $x_1 - 3x_2 = x_1 - 3(2) = -5$, or $x_1 = 1$. Thus, the solution to the original system of equations is

$$\mathbf{x} = \begin{bmatrix} 1 \\ 2 \\ -1 \end{bmatrix}.$$

SECTION 2.4 ☐ EXERCISES

In Exercises 1–10, determine whether the matrix is elementary. If it is, state the elementary row operation that was used to produce it.

1. $\begin{bmatrix} 1 & 0 \\ 0 & 2 \end{bmatrix}$ **2.** $\begin{bmatrix} 1 & 0 & 0 \\ 0 & 0 & 1 \end{bmatrix}$

3. $\begin{bmatrix} 1 & 0 \\ 2 & 1 \end{bmatrix}$ **4.** $\begin{bmatrix} 0 & 1 \\ 1 & 0 \end{bmatrix}$

5. $\begin{bmatrix} 2 & 0 & 0 \\ 0 & 0 & 1 \\ 0 & 1 & 0 \end{bmatrix}$ **6.** $\begin{bmatrix} 1 & 0 & 0 \\ 0 & 1 & 0 \\ 2 & 0 & 1 \end{bmatrix}$

7. $\begin{bmatrix} 1 & 0 & 0 \\ 0 & 1 & 0 \\ 0 & 0 & 0 \end{bmatrix}$

8. $\begin{bmatrix} 0 & 1 & 0 \\ 1 & 0 & 0 \\ 0 & 0 & 1 \end{bmatrix}$

9. $\begin{bmatrix} 1 & 0 & 0 & 0 \\ 0 & 1 & 0 & 0 \\ 0 & -5 & 1 & 0 \\ 0 & 0 & 0 & 1 \end{bmatrix}$

10. $\begin{bmatrix} 1 & 0 & 0 & 0 \\ 2 & 1 & 0 & 0 \\ 0 & 0 & 1 & 0 \\ 0 & 0 & -3 & 1 \end{bmatrix}$

In Exercises 11–14, let A, B, and C be given by

$$A = \begin{bmatrix} 1 & 2 & -3 \\ 0 & 1 & 2 \\ -1 & 2 & 0 \end{bmatrix}, \quad B = \begin{bmatrix} -1 & 2 & 0 \\ 0 & 1 & 2 \\ 1 & 2 & -3 \end{bmatrix},$$

$$C = \begin{bmatrix} 0 & 4 & -3 \\ 0 & 1 & 2 \\ -1 & 2 & 0 \end{bmatrix}.$$

11. Find an elementary matrix E such that $EA = B$.

12. Find an elementary matrix E such that $EA = C$.

13. Find an elementary matrix E such that $EB = A$.

14. Find an elementary matrix E such that $EC = A$.

In Exercises 15–24, find the inverse of the given elementary matrix.

15. $\begin{bmatrix} 0 & 1 \\ 1 & 0 \end{bmatrix}$

16. $\begin{bmatrix} 5 & 0 \\ 0 & 1 \end{bmatrix}$

17. $\begin{bmatrix} 1 & 0 \\ 4 & 1 \end{bmatrix}$

18. $\begin{bmatrix} 1 & -2 \\ 0 & 1 \end{bmatrix}$

19. $\begin{bmatrix} 0 & 0 & 1 \\ 0 & 1 & 0 \\ 1 & 0 & 0 \end{bmatrix}$

20. $\begin{bmatrix} 1 & 0 & 0 \\ 0 & 1 & 0 \\ 0 & -3 & 1 \end{bmatrix}$

21. $\begin{bmatrix} k & 0 & 0 \\ 0 & 1 & 0 \\ 0 & 0 & 1 \end{bmatrix}, \quad k \neq 0$

22. $\begin{bmatrix} 1 & 0 & 0 \\ 0 & 0 & 1 \\ 0 & 1 & 0 \end{bmatrix}$

23. $\begin{bmatrix} 1 & 0 & 0 & 0 \\ 0 & 1 & k & 0 \\ 0 & 0 & 1 & 0 \\ 0 & 0 & 0 & 1 \end{bmatrix}$

24. $\begin{bmatrix} 1 & 0 & 0 & 0 \\ 0 & 1 & 0 & 0 \\ 0 & 0 & 1/k & 0 \\ 0 & 0 & 0 & 1 \end{bmatrix}, \quad k \neq 0$

In Exercises 25–32, factor the matrix A into a product of elementary matrices.

25. $A = \begin{bmatrix} 1 & 2 \\ 1 & 0 \end{bmatrix}$

26. $A = \begin{bmatrix} 0 & 1 \\ 1 & 0 \end{bmatrix}$

27. $A = \begin{bmatrix} 4 & -1 \\ 3 & -1 \end{bmatrix}$

28. $A = \begin{bmatrix} 1 & 1 \\ 2 & 1 \end{bmatrix}$

29. $A = \begin{bmatrix} 1 & -2 & 0 \\ -1 & 3 & 0 \\ 0 & 0 & 1 \end{bmatrix}$

30. $A = \begin{bmatrix} 1 & 2 & 3 \\ 2 & 5 & 6 \\ 1 & 3 & 4 \end{bmatrix}$

31. $A = \begin{bmatrix} 2 & 0 & -8 \\ 2 & 2 & 2 \\ 0 & 2 & 7 \end{bmatrix}$

32. $A = \begin{bmatrix} -1 & 2 & 0 \\ 0 & 2 & 0 \\ 1 & 0 & 1 \end{bmatrix}$

33. E is the elementary matrix obtained by interchanging two rows in I_n. A is an $n \times n$ matrix.

    (a) How will EA compare with A?

    (b) Find E^2.

34. E is the elementary matrix obtained by multiplying a row in I_n by a nonzero constant c. A is an $n \times n$ matrix.

    (a) How will EA compare with A?

    (b) Find E^2.

35. Use elementary matrices to find the inverse of

$$A = \begin{bmatrix} 1 & a & 0 \\ 0 & 1 & 0 \\ 0 & 0 & 1 \end{bmatrix}\begin{bmatrix} 1 & 0 & 0 \\ b & 1 & 0 \\ 0 & 0 & 1 \end{bmatrix}\begin{bmatrix} 1 & 0 & 0 \\ 0 & 1 & 0 \\ 0 & 0 & c \end{bmatrix}, \quad c \neq 0.$$

36. Use elementary matrices to find the inverse of

$$A = \begin{bmatrix} 1 & 0 & 0 \\ 0 & 1 & 0 \\ a & b & c \end{bmatrix}, \quad c \neq 0.$$

37. Is the product of two elementary matrices always elementary? Explain why or why not and provide appropriate examples to illustrate your conclusion.

38. Is the sum of two elementary matrices always elementary? Explain why or why not and provide appropriate examples to illustrate your conclusion.

In Exercises 39–42, find a LU–factorization of the given matrix.

39. $\begin{bmatrix} 1 & 0 \\ -2 & 1 \end{bmatrix}$

40. $\begin{bmatrix} -2 & 1 \\ -6 & 4 \end{bmatrix}$

41. $\begin{bmatrix} 3 & 0 & 1 \\ 6 & 1 & 1 \\ -3 & 1 & 0 \end{bmatrix}$

42. $\begin{bmatrix} 2 & 0 & 0 \\ 0 & -3 & 1 \\ 10 & 12 & 3 \end{bmatrix}$

In Exercises 43 and 44, solve the linear system $A\mathbf{x} = \mathbf{b}$ by

    (a) finding the LU–factorization of the coefficient matrix A,

    (b) solving the lower triangular system $L\mathbf{y} = \mathbf{b}$, and

    (c) solving the upper triangular system $U\mathbf{x} = \mathbf{y}$.

43. $2x + y \quad\quad = \quad 1$
$\quad\quad\quad y - z = \quad 2$
$-2x + y + z = -2$

44. $2x_1 \quad\quad\quad\quad = \quad 4$
$-2x_1 + \; x_2 - x_3 \quad\quad = -4$
$\quad 6x_1 + 2x_2 + x_3 \quad\quad = \; 15$
$\quad\quad\quad\quad\quad - x_4 = -1$

45. Suppose you needed to solve many systems of linear equations $A\mathbf{x} = \mathbf{b}_i$, each having the same coefficient matrix A. Explain how you could use the LU–factorization technique to make the task easier, rather than solving each system individually using Gaussian elimination.

46. (a) Show that the matrix

$$A = \begin{bmatrix} 0 & 1 \\ 1 & 0 \end{bmatrix}$$

does not have an LU–factorization.

   (b) Find the LU–factorization of the matrix

$$A = \begin{bmatrix} a & b \\ c & d \end{bmatrix}$$

which has 1's along the main diagonal of L. Are there any restrictions on the matrix A?

In Exercises 47–52, determine whether the given matrix is idempotent. A square matrix A is **idempotent** if $A^2 = A$.

47. $\begin{bmatrix} 1 & 0 \\ 0 & 0 \end{bmatrix}$ **48.** $\begin{bmatrix} 0 & 1 \\ 1 & 0 \end{bmatrix}$

49. $\begin{bmatrix} 2 & 3 \\ -1 & -2 \end{bmatrix}$ **50.** $\begin{bmatrix} 2 & 3 \\ 1 & 2 \end{bmatrix}$

51. $\begin{bmatrix} 0 & 0 & 1 \\ 0 & 1 & 0 \\ 1 & 0 & 0 \end{bmatrix}$ **52.** $\begin{bmatrix} 0 & 1 & 0 \\ 1 & 0 & 0 \\ 0 & 0 & 1 \end{bmatrix}$

53. Determine a and b such that A is idempotent.

$$A = \begin{bmatrix} 1 & 0 \\ a & b \end{bmatrix}$$

54. Determine conditions on a, b, and c such that A is idempotent.

$$A = \begin{bmatrix} a & 0 \\ b & c \end{bmatrix}$$

55. Prove that if A is idempotent and invertible (of order n), then $A = I_n$.

56. Prove that if A is idempotent if and only if A^T is idempotent.

57. Prove that if A and B are idempotent and $AB = BA$, then AB is idempotent.

58. Prove that if A is row-equivalent to B, then B is row-equivalent to A.

59. Prove that if A is row-equivalent to B, and B is row-equivalent to C, then A is row-equivalent to C.

60. Let A be a nonsingular matrix. Prove that if B is row-equivalent to A, then B is also nonsingular.

2.5 APPLICATIONS OF MATRIX OPERATIONS

Stochastic Matrices

Many types of applications involve a finite set of *states* $\{S_1, S_2, \dots, S_n\}$ of a given population. For instance, residents of a city may live downtown or in the suburbs. Voters may vote Democrat, Republican, or for a third party. Soft drink consumers may buy Coca-Cola, Pepsi Cola, or another brand.

The probability that a member of a population will change from the jth state to the ith state is represented by a number p_{ij}, where

$$0 \leq p_{ij} \leq 1.$$

A probability of $p_{ij} = 0$ means that the member is certain not to change from the jth state to the ith state, whereas a probability of $p_{ij} = 1$ means that the member is certain to change from the jth state to the ith state.

The collection of all the probabilities is represented by an $n \times n$ matrix P as follows.

$$
P = \begin{array}{c} \overbrace{\begin{array}{cccc} S_1 & S_2 & \cdots & S_n \end{array}}^{From} \\ \begin{bmatrix} p_{11} & p_{12} & \cdots & p_{1n} \\ p_{21} & p_{22} & \cdots & p_{2n} \\ \vdots & \vdots & & \vdots \\ p_{n1} & p_{n2} & \cdots & p_{nn} \end{bmatrix} \begin{array}{l} S_1 \\ S_2 \\ \vdots \\ S_n \end{array} \end{array} \Bigg\} To
$$

P is called the **matrix of transition probabilities** because it gives the probabilities of each possible type of transition (or change) within the population.

At each transition, each member in a given state either must stay in that state or change to another state. For probabilities, this means that the sum of the entries in any column of P is 1. For instance, in the first column we have

$$p_{11} + p_{21} + \cdots + p_{n1} = 1.$$

In general, such a matrix is called **stochastic** (the term "stochastic" means "regarding conjecture"). That is, an $n \times n$ matrix P is called a **stochastic matrix** if each entry is a number between 0 and 1 and each column of P adds up to 1.

EXAMPLE 1   *Examples of Stochastic Matrices and Nonstochastic Matrices*

The matrices in parts (a) and (b) are stochastic, but the matrix in part (c) is not.

$$
\text{(a)} \begin{bmatrix} 1 & 0 & 0 \\ 0 & 1 & 0 \\ 0 & 0 & 1 \end{bmatrix} \qquad \text{(b)} \begin{bmatrix} \frac{1}{2} & \frac{1}{3} & \frac{1}{4} \\ \frac{1}{4} & 0 & \frac{3}{4} \\ \frac{1}{4} & \frac{2}{3} & 0 \end{bmatrix} \qquad \text{(c)} \begin{bmatrix} 0.1 & 0.2 & 0.3 \\ 0.2 & 0.3 & 0.4 \\ 0.3 & 0.4 & 0.5 \end{bmatrix}
$$

Example 2 describes the use of a stochastic matrix to measure consumer preference.

EXAMPLE 2   *A Consumer Preference Model*

Two competing companies offer cable television service to a city of 100,000 households. The change in cable subscriptions each year is given by the diagram in Figure 2.1. Company A now has 15,000 subscribers and Company B has 20,000 subscribers. How many subscribers will each company have one year from now?

Figure 2.1

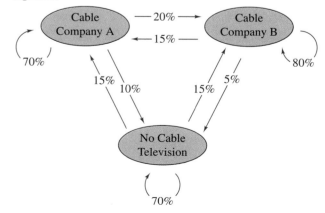

Solution   The matrix representing the given transition probabilities is

$$P = \begin{bmatrix} 0.70 & 0.15 & 0.15 \\ 0.20 & 0.80 & 0.15 \\ 0.10 & 0.05 & 0.70 \end{bmatrix} \begin{matrix} A \\ B \\ None \end{matrix}$$

From

$A \quad B \quad None$

To

and the **state matrix** representing the current population in each of the three states is

$$X = \begin{bmatrix} 15{,}000 \\ 20{,}000 \\ 65{,}000 \end{bmatrix} \begin{matrix} \text{A} \\ \text{B} \\ \text{None} \end{matrix}$$

To find the state matrix representing the population in each of the three states in one year, we multiply P times X to obtain

$$PX = \begin{bmatrix} 0.70 & 0.15 & 0.15 \\ 0.20 & 0.80 & 0.15 \\ 0.10 & 0.05 & 0.70 \end{bmatrix} \begin{bmatrix} 15{,}000 \\ 20{,}000 \\ 65{,}000 \end{bmatrix} = \begin{bmatrix} 23{,}250 \\ 28{,}750 \\ 48{,}000 \end{bmatrix}.$$

After one year Company A will have 23,250 subscribers and Company B will have 28,750 subscribers.

One of the appeals of the matrix solution given in Example 2 is that once the model has been created, it becomes easy to find the state matrices representing future years by repeatedly multiplying by the matrix P. This process is demonstrated in Example 3.

EXAMPLE 3   *A Consumer Preference Model*

Assuming that the matrix of transition probabilities given in Example 2 remains the same year after year, find the number of subscribers each cable television company will have after (a) two years, (b) five years, and (c) ten years.

Solution   (a) From Example 2 we know that the number of subscribers after one year is

$$PX = \begin{bmatrix} 23{,}250 \\ 28{,}750 \\ 48{,}000 \end{bmatrix}. \qquad \begin{matrix} \text{A} \\ \text{B} \\ \text{None} \end{matrix} \qquad \textbf{After one year}$$

Since the matrix of transition probabilities is the same from the first to the second year, the number of subscribers after two years must be $P(PX)$, which yields

$$P^2X = \begin{bmatrix} 27{,}788 \\ 34{,}850 \\ 37{,}363 \end{bmatrix}. \qquad \begin{matrix} \text{A} \\ \text{B} \\ \text{None} \end{matrix} \qquad \textbf{After two years}$$

(b) The number of subscribers after five years is

$$P^5X = \begin{bmatrix} 32{,}411 \\ 43{,}812 \\ 23{,}777 \end{bmatrix}. \quad \begin{matrix} \text{A} \\ \text{B} \\ \text{None} \end{matrix} \qquad \textbf{After five years}$$

(c) The number of subscribers after ten years is

$$P^{10}X = \begin{bmatrix} 33{,}287 \\ 47{,}147 \\ 19{,}566 \end{bmatrix}. \quad \begin{matrix} \text{A} \\ \text{B} \\ \text{None} \end{matrix} \qquad \textbf{After ten years}$$

In Example 3, notice that there is little difference between the number of subscribers after five years and after ten years. If the process shown in this example is continued, the number of subscribers eventually reaches a **steady state.** That is, as long as the matrix P doesn't change, the matrix product P^nX approaches a limit $\overline{X}$. In this particular example, the limit is given by the state matrix

$$\overline{X} = \begin{bmatrix} 33{,}333 \\ 47{,}619 \\ 19{,}048 \end{bmatrix}. \quad \begin{matrix} \text{A} \\ \text{B} \\ \text{None} \end{matrix} \qquad \textbf{Steady state}$$

You can check to see that $P\overline{X} = \overline{X}$.

Cryptography

A **cryptogram** is a message written according to a secret code (the Greek word "kryptos" means "hidden"). This section describes a method for using matrix multiplication to **encode** and **decode** messages.

We begin by assigning a number to each letter in the alphabet (with 0 assigned to a blank space) as follows.

0 = __	14 = N
1 = A	15 = O
2 = B	16 = P
3 = C	17 = Q
4 = D	18 = R
5 = E	19 = S
6 = F	20 = T
7 = G	21 = U
8 = H	22 = V
9 = I	23 = W
10 = J	24 = X
11 = K	25 = Y
12 = L	26 = Z
13 = M	

Then the message is converted to numbers and partitioned into **uncoded row matrices,** each having n entries, as demonstrated in Example 4.

EXAMPLE 4   *Forming Uncoded Row Matrices*

Write the uncoded row matrices of order 1×3 for the message MEET ME MONDAY.

Solution   Partitioning the message (including blank spaces, but ignoring other punctuation) into groups of three produces the following uncoded row matrices.

$$\underset{\substack{M \quad E \quad E}}{[13 \quad 5 \quad 5]} \underset{\substack{T \quad \_ \quad M}}{[20 \quad 0 \quad 13]} \underset{\substack{E \quad \_ \quad M}}{[5 \quad 0 \quad 13]} \underset{\substack{O \quad N \quad D}}{[15 \quad 14 \quad 4]} \underset{\substack{A \quad Y \quad \_}}{[1 \quad 25 \quad 0]}$$

Note that a blank space is used to fill out the last uncoded row matrix.

To **encode** a message we choose an $n \times n$ invertible matrix A and multiply the uncoded row matrices (on the right) by A to obtain **coded row matrices.** This process is demonstrated in Example 5.

EXAMPLE 5   *Encoding a Message*

Use the matrix

$$A = \begin{bmatrix} 1 & -2 & 2 \\ -1 & 1 & 3 \\ 1 & -1 & -4 \end{bmatrix}$$

to encode the message MEET ME MONDAY.

Solution   The coded row matrices are obtained by multiplying each of the uncoded row matrices found in Example 4 by the matrix A as follows.

| *Uncoded*
Row Matrix | *Encoding*
Matrix A | *Coded Row*
Matrix |

$$[13 \quad 5 \quad 5] \begin{bmatrix} 1 & -2 & 2 \\ -1 & 1 & 3 \\ 1 & -1 & -4 \end{bmatrix} = [13 \quad -26 \quad 21]$$

$$[20 \quad 0 \quad 13] \begin{bmatrix} 1 & -2 & 2 \\ -1 & 1 & 3 \\ 1 & -1 & -4 \end{bmatrix} = [33 \quad -53 \quad -12]$$

$$[5 \quad 0 \quad 13] \begin{bmatrix} 1 & -2 & 2 \\ -1 & 1 & 3 \\ 1 & -1 & -4 \end{bmatrix} = [18 \quad -23 \quad -42]$$

$$\begin{array}{ccc} \textit{Uncoded} & \textit{Encoding} & \textit{Coded Row} \\ \textit{Row Matrix} & \textit{Matrix A} & \textit{Matrix} \end{array}$$

$$\begin{bmatrix} 15 & 14 & 4 \end{bmatrix} \begin{bmatrix} 1 & -2 & 2 \\ -1 & 1 & 3 \\ 1 & -1 & -4 \end{bmatrix} = \begin{bmatrix} 5 & -20 & 56 \end{bmatrix}$$

$$\begin{bmatrix} 1 & 25 & 0 \end{bmatrix} \begin{bmatrix} 1 & -2 & 2 \\ -1 & 1 & 3 \\ 1 & -1 & -4 \end{bmatrix} = \begin{bmatrix} -24 & 23 & 77 \end{bmatrix}$$

Thus the sequence of coded row matrices is

$$\begin{bmatrix} 13 & -26 & 21 \end{bmatrix} \begin{bmatrix} 33 & -53 & -12 \end{bmatrix} \begin{bmatrix} 18 & -23 & -42 \end{bmatrix} \begin{bmatrix} 5 & -20 & 56 \end{bmatrix} \begin{bmatrix} -24 & 23 & 77 \end{bmatrix}.$$

Finally, removing the matrix notation produces the following cryptogram

$$13 \quad -26 \quad 21 \quad 33 \quad -53 \quad -12 \quad 18 \quad -23 \quad -42 \quad 5 \quad -20 \quad 56 \quad -24 \quad 23 \quad 77.$$

For those who do not know the matrix A, decoding the cryptogram found in Example 5 is difficult. But for an authorized receiver who knows the matrix A, decoding is simple. The receiver need only multiply the coded row matrices by A^{-1} to retrieve the uncoded row matrices. In other words, if

$$X = \begin{bmatrix} x_1 & x_2 & \cdots & x_n \end{bmatrix}$$

is an uncoded $1 \times n$ matrix, then $Y = XA$ is the corresponding encoded matrix. The receiver of the encoded matrix can decode Y by multiplying on the right by A^{-1} to obtain

$$YA^{-1} = (XA)A^{-1} = X.$$

This procedure is demonstrated in Example 6.

EXAMPLE 6   ***Decoding a Message***

Use the inverse of the matrix

$$A = \begin{bmatrix} 1 & -2 & 2 \\ -1 & 1 & 3 \\ 1 & -1 & -4 \end{bmatrix}$$

to decode the cryptogram

$$13 \quad -26 \quad 21 \quad 33 \quad -53 \quad -12 \quad 18 \quad -23 \quad -42 \quad 5 \quad -20 \quad 56 \quad -24 \quad 23 \quad 77.$$

Solution   We begin by using Gauss-Jordan elimination to find A^{-1}.

$$\begin{array}{cc} [A \,\vdots\, I] & [I \,\vdots\, A^{-1}] \end{array}$$

$$\begin{bmatrix} 1 & -2 & 2 & \vdots & 1 & 0 & 0 \\ -1 & 1 & 3 & \vdots & 0 & 1 & 0 \\ 1 & -1 & -4 & \vdots & 0 & 0 & 1 \end{bmatrix} \longrightarrow \begin{bmatrix} 1 & 0 & 0 & \vdots & -1 & -10 & -8 \\ 0 & 1 & 0 & \vdots & -1 & -6 & -5 \\ 0 & 0 & 1 & \vdots & 0 & -1 & -1 \end{bmatrix}$$

Now, to decode the message, we partition the message into groups of three to form the coded row matrices

$$[13 \ -26 \ \ \ 21][33 \ -53 \ -12][18 \ -23 \ -42][5 \ -20 \ \ \ 56][-24 \ \ \ 23 \ \ \ 77].$$

Then we multiply each coded row matrix by A^{-1} (on the right) to obtain the decoded row matrices.

Coded Row Matrix	Decoding Matrix A^{-1}	Decoded Row Matrix

$$[13 \ -26 \ \ \ 21]\begin{bmatrix} -1 & -10 & -8 \\ -1 & -6 & -5 \\ 0 & -1 & -1 \end{bmatrix} = [13 \ \ \ 5 \ \ \ 5]$$

$$[33 \ -53 \ -12]\begin{bmatrix} -1 & -10 & -8 \\ -1 & -6 & -5 \\ 0 & -1 & -1 \end{bmatrix} = [20 \ \ \ 0 \ \ \ 13]$$

$$[18 \ -23 \ -42]\begin{bmatrix} -1 & -10 & -8 \\ -1 & -6 & -5 \\ 0 & -1 & -1 \end{bmatrix} = [5 \ \ \ 0 \ \ \ 13]$$

$$[5 \ -20 \ \ \ 56]\begin{bmatrix} -1 & -10 & -8 \\ -1 & -6 & -5 \\ 0 & -1 & -1 \end{bmatrix} = [15 \ \ \ 14 \ \ \ 4]$$

$$[-24 \ \ \ 23 \ \ \ 77]\begin{bmatrix} -1 & -10 & -8 \\ -1 & -6 & -5 \\ 0 & -1 & -1 \end{bmatrix} = [1 \ \ \ 25 \ \ \ 0]$$

Thus the sequence of decoded row matrices is

$$[13 \ \ \ 5 \ \ \ 5][20 \ \ \ 0 \ \ \ 13][5 \ \ \ 0 \ \ \ 13][15 \ \ \ 14 \ \ \ 4][1 \ \ \ 25 \ \ \ 0]$$

and the message is

13	5	5	20	0	13	5	0	13	15	14	4	1	25	0.
M	E	E	T	_	M	E	_	M	O	N	D	A	Y	_

Leontief Input-Output Models

Matrix algebra has proved effective in analyzing problems concerning the input and output of an economic system. The model we discuss here, developed by the American economist Wassily W. Leontief, was first published in 1936. In 1973 Leontief was awarded a Nobel prize for his work in economics.

Suppose that an economic system has n different industries $\{I_1, I_2, \ldots, I_n\}$ each of which has **input** needs (raw materials, utilities) and an **output** (finished products). The **input coefficient** d_{ij} measures the amount of input the jth industry needs from the ith industry to produce one unit: The collection of input coefficients is given by the following $n \times n$ matrix. Units are measured in "dollar amounts."

$$D = \overbrace{\begin{bmatrix} \overset{I_1}{d_{11}} & \overset{I_2}{d_{12}} & \cdots & \overset{I_n}{d_{1n}} \\ d_{21} & d_{22} & \cdots & d_{2n} \\ \vdots & \vdots & & \vdots \\ d_{n1} & d_{n2} & \cdots & d_{nn} \end{bmatrix}}^{User} \left.\begin{matrix} I_1 \\ I_2 \\ \vdots \\ I_n \end{matrix}\right\} Supplier$$

This matrix is called the **input-output matrix.**

To understand how to use this matrix, imagine that the entries of D are given in dollars. For instance, if $d_{12} = 0.41$, then \$0.41 worth of Industry 1's product must be used to produce one dollar's worth of Industry 2's product. The total amount spent by the jth industry to produce one dollar's worth of output is given by the sum of the entries in the jth column. Thus, for this model to work, the values of d_{ij} must be such that $0 \le d_{ij} < 1$ and the sum of the entries of any column must be less than 1.

EXAMPLE 7   *Forming an Input-Output Matrix*

A system is composed of three industries with the following inputs.
1. To produce one dollar's worth of output, Industry A requires \$0.10 of its own product, \$0.15 of Industry B's product, and \$0.23 of Industry C's product.
2. To produce one dollar's worth of output, Industry B requires none of its own product, \$0.43 of Industry A's product, and \$0.03 of Industry C's product.
3. To produce one dollar's worth of output, Industry C requires \$0.02 of its own product, none of Industry A's product, and \$0.37 of Industry B's product.

The input-output matrix for this system is

$$D = \overbrace{\begin{bmatrix} \overset{A}{0.10} & \overset{B}{0.43} & \overset{C}{0.00} \\ 0.15 & 0.00 & 0.37 \\ 0.23 & 0.03 & 0.02 \end{bmatrix}}^{User} \left.\begin{matrix} A \\ B \\ C \end{matrix}\right\} Supplier$$

To develop the Leontief input-output model further, we denote the total output (in units produced) of the ith industry by x_i. If the economic system is **closed** (meaning that it sells its products only to industries within the system), then the total output of the ith industry is given by the linear equation

$$x_i = d_{i1}x_1 + d_{i2}x_2 + \cdots + d_{ir}x_n.$$

Thus, to satisfy the demand for its product, the ith industry must produce $d_{i1}x_1$ units for the first industry, $d_{i2}x_2$ units for the second industry, and so on.

On the other hand, if the industries within the system sell products to nonproducing groups (such as governments or charitable organizations) outside the system, then the system is called **open** and the total output of the ith industry is given by

$$x_i = d_{i1}x_1 + d_{i2}x_2 + \cdots + d_{in}x_n + e_i$$

where e_i represents the external demand for the ith industry's product. The collection of total outputs for an open system is therefore represented by the following system of n linear equations.

$$
\begin{aligned}
x_1 &= d_{11}x_1 + d_{12}x_2 + \cdots + d_{1n}x_n + e_1 \\
x_2 &= d_{21}x_1 + d_{22}x_2 + \cdots + d_{2n}x_n + e_2 \\
&\;\;\vdots \\
x_n &= d_{n1}x_1 + d_{n2}x_2 + \cdots + d_{nn}x_n + e_n
\end{aligned}
$$

The matrix form of this system is

$$X = DX + E$$

where X is called the **output matrix** and E is called the **external demand matrix.**

EXAMPLE 8   ***Solving for the Output Matrix of an Open Economic System***

Use the input-output matrix D given in Example 7 to solve for the output matrix X in the equation $X = DX + E$, where the external demand is given by

$$
E = \begin{bmatrix} 20{,}000 \\ 30{,}000 \\ 25{,}000 \end{bmatrix}.
$$

Solution   Letting I be the identity matrix, we can write the equation $X = DX + E$ as $IX = DX + E$, which means that

$$(I - D)X = E.$$

Using the matrix D found in Example 7 produces

$$
I - D = \begin{bmatrix} 0.90 & -0.43 & 0.00 \\ -0.15 & 1.00 & -0.37 \\ -0.23 & -0.03 & 0.98 \end{bmatrix}.
$$

Finally, applying Gauss-Jordan elimination to the system of linear equations represented by $(I - D)X = E$ produces

$$
\begin{bmatrix} 0.90 & -0.43 & 0.00 & 20{,}000 \\ -0.15 & 1.00 & -0.37 & 30{,}000 \\ -0.23 & -0.03 & 0.98 & 25{,}000 \end{bmatrix}
\longrightarrow
\begin{bmatrix} 1 & 0 & 0 & 46{,}616 \\ 0 & 1 & 0 & 51{,}058 \\ 0 & 0 & 1 & 38{,}014 \end{bmatrix}.
$$

Therefore the output matrix is

$$
X = \begin{bmatrix} 46{,}616 \\ 51{,}058 \\ 58{,}014 \end{bmatrix} \begin{matrix} \text{A} \\ \text{B} \\ \text{C} \end{matrix}
$$

and we conclude that the total output for the three industries is as follows.

Output for Industry A: 46,616 units
Output for Industry B: 51,058 units
Output for Industry C: 38,014 units

The economic system described in Examples 7 and 8 is, of course, a simple one. In the real world, an economic system would have many industries or industrial groups. For instance, an economic analysis of the major producing groups in the United States would include the following list (taken from the *Statistical Abstract of the United States*).

1. Farm products (grain, livestock, poultry, bulk milk)
2. Processed foods and feeds (beverages, dairy products)
3. Textile products and apparel (yarns, threads, clothing)
4. Hides, skins, and leather (shoes, upholstery)
5. Fuels and power (coal, gasoline, electricity)
6. Chemicals and allied products (drugs, plastic resins)
7. Rubber and plastic products (tires, plastic containers)
8. Lumber and wood products (plywood, pencils)
9. Pulp, paper, and allied products (cardboard, newsprint)
10. Metals and metal products (plumbing fixtures, cans)
11. Machinery and equipment (tractors, drills, computers)
12. Furniture and household durables (carpets, appliances)
13. Nonmetallic mineral products (glass, concrete, bricks)
14. Transportation equipment (automobiles, trucks, planes)
15. Miscellaneous products (toys, cameras, linear algebra texts)

A matrix of order 15×15 would be required to represent even these broad industrial groupings using the Leontief input-output model. A more detailed analysis could easily require an input-output matrix of an order greater than 100×100. Clearly this type of analysis could take place only with the aid of a computer.

Least Squares Regression Analysis

In this section we look at a procedure that is used in statistics to develop mathematical models. We begin with a visual example.

Figure 2.2

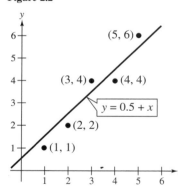

EXAMPLE 9   *A Visual Straight-Line Approximation*

Visually determine the straight line that best fits the points (1, 1), (2, 2), (3, 4), (4, 4), and (5, 6).

Solution   Plot the points as shown in Figure 2.2. It appears that a good choice would be the line whose slope is 1 and whose y-intercept is 0.5. The equation of this line is $y = 0.5 + x$.

An examination of the line shown in Figure 2.2 reveals that we can improve the fit by rotating the line counterclockwise slightly, as shown in Figure 2.3 (See p. 97.). It seems clear that this new line, the equation of which is $y = 1.2x$, fits the given points better than the original line.

Figure 2.3

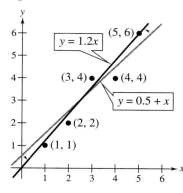

One way of measuring how well a function $y = f(x)$ fits a set of points

$$(x_1, y_1), (x_2, y_2), \ldots, (x_n, y_n)$$

is to compute the differences between the values given by the function $f(x_i)$ and the actual values y_i, as shown in Figure 2.4. By squaring these differences and summing the results, we obtain a measure of error that is called the **sum of squares error.** The sums of squares error for our two linear models are given in Table 2.1.

Figure 2.4

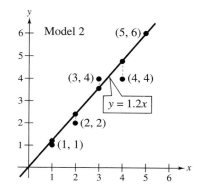

TABLE 2.1

Model #1: $f(x) = 0.5 + x$				Model #2: $f(x) = 1.2x$			
x_i	y_i	$f(x_i)$	$[y_i - f(x_i)]^2$	x_i	y_i	$f(x_i)$	$[y_i - f(x_i)]^2$
1	1	1.5	$(-0.5)^2$	1	1	1.2	$(-0.2)^2$
2	2	2.5	$(-0.5)^2$	2	2	2.4	$(-0.4)^2$
3	4	3.5	$(+0.5)^2$	3	4	3.6	$(+0.4)^2$
4	4	4.5	$(-0.5)^2$	4	4	4.8	$(-0.8)^2$
5	6	5.5	$(+0.5)^2$	5	6	6.0	$(+0.0)^2$
Total			1.25	Total			1.00

The sums of squares error confirm that the second model fits the given points better than the first.

Of all possible linear models for a given set of points, the model that has the best fit is defined to be the one that minimizes the sum of squares error. We call this model the **least squares regression line,** and the procedure for finding it is called the **method of least squares.**

Definition of Least Squares Regression Line

For a set of points $(x_1, y_1), (x_2, y_2), \ldots, (x_n, y_n)$,   the **least squares regression line** is given by the linear function

$$f(x) = a_0 + a_1 x$$

that minimizes the sum of squares error

$$[y_1 - f(x_1)]^2 + [y_2 - f(x_2)]^2 + \cdots + [y_n - f(x_n)]^2.$$

To find the least squares regression line for a set of points, we begin by forming the system of linear equations

$$\begin{aligned} y_1 &= f(x_1) + [y_1 - f(x_1)] \\ y_2 &= f(x_2) + [y_2 - f(x_2)] \\ &\vdots \\ y_n &= f(x_n) + [y_n - f(x_n)] \end{aligned}$$

where the right-hand term, $[y_i - f(x_i)]$, of each equation is thought of as the error in the approximation of y_i by $f(x_i)$. We then write this error as

$$e_i = y_i - f(x_i)$$

so that the system of equations takes the form

$$\begin{aligned} y_1 &= (a_0 + a_1 x_1) + e_1 \\ y_2 &= (a_0 + a_1 x_2) + e_2 \\ &\vdots \\ y_n &= (a_0 + a_1 x_n) + e_n. \end{aligned}$$

Now, if we define Y, X, A, and E as

$$Y = \begin{bmatrix} y_1 \\ y_2 \\ \vdots \\ y_n \end{bmatrix}, \qquad X = \begin{bmatrix} 1 & x_1 \\ 1 & x_2 \\ \vdots & \vdots \\ 1 & x_n \end{bmatrix}, \qquad A = \begin{bmatrix} a_0 \\ a_1 \end{bmatrix}, \qquad E = \begin{bmatrix} e_1 \\ e_2 \\ \vdots \\ e_n \end{bmatrix}$$

the n linear equations may be replaced by the matrix equation

$$Y = XA + E.$$

Note that the matrix X has two columns, a column of 1's (corresponding to a_0) and a column containing the x_i's. This matrix equation can be used to determine the coefficients of the least squares regression line as follows.

Matrix Form for Linear Regression

For the regression model $Y = XA + E$, the coefficients of the least squares regression line are given by the matrix equation

$$A = (X^T X)^{-1} X^T Y$$

and the sum of squares error is $E^T E$.

REMARK: A proof of this result can be found in any elementary statistics text. (See also Section 5.4.)

Example 10 demonstrates the use of this procedure to find the least squares regression line for the set of points given in Example 9.

EXAMPLE 10   ***Finding the Least Squares Regression Line***

Find the least squares regression line for the points (1, 1), (2, 2), (3, 4), (4, 4), and (5, 6). Then find the sum of squares error for this regression line.

Solution   Using the five given points, we find the matrices X and Y to be

$$X = \begin{bmatrix} 1 & 1 \\ 1 & 2 \\ 1 & 3 \\ 1 & 4 \\ 1 & 5 \end{bmatrix} \quad \text{and} \quad Y = \begin{bmatrix} 1 \\ 2 \\ 4 \\ 4 \\ 6 \end{bmatrix}.$$

This means that

$$X^T X = \begin{bmatrix} 1 & 1 & 1 & 1 & 1 \\ 1 & 2 & 3 & 4 & 5 \end{bmatrix} \begin{bmatrix} 1 & 1 \\ 1 & 2 \\ 1 & 3 \\ 1 & 4 \\ 1 & 5 \end{bmatrix} = \begin{bmatrix} 5 & 15 \\ 15 & 55 \end{bmatrix}$$

and

$$X^T Y = \begin{bmatrix} 1 & 1 & 1 & 1 & 1 \\ 1 & 2 & 3 & 4 & 5 \end{bmatrix} \begin{bmatrix} 1 \\ 2 \\ 4 \\ 4 \\ 6 \end{bmatrix} = \begin{bmatrix} 17 \\ 63 \end{bmatrix}.$$

Now, using $(X^T X)^{-1}$ to find the coefficient matrix A, we have

$$A = (X^T X)^{-1} X^T Y = \tfrac{1}{50} \begin{bmatrix} 55 & -15 \\ -15 & 5 \end{bmatrix} \begin{bmatrix} 17 \\ 63 \end{bmatrix}$$

$$= \begin{bmatrix} -0.2 \\ 1.2 \end{bmatrix}.$$

Thus the least squares regression line is

$$y = -0.2 + 1.2x.$$

See Figure 2.5. The sum of squares error for this line can be shown to be 0.8, which means that this line fits the data better than either of the two experimental linear models determined earlier.

Figure 2.5

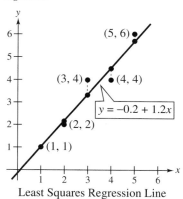

Least Squares Regression Line

SECTION 2.5 ☐ EXERCISES

Stochastic Matrices

In Exercises 1–6, determine whether the given matrix is stochastic.

1. $\begin{bmatrix} \frac{2}{5} & -\frac{2}{5} \\ \frac{3}{5} & \frac{7}{5} \end{bmatrix}$

2. $\begin{bmatrix} \frac{\sqrt{2}}{2} & \frac{\sqrt{2}}{2} \\ -\frac{\sqrt{2}}{2} & \frac{\sqrt{2}}{2} \end{bmatrix}$

3. $\begin{bmatrix} 0 & 1 & 0 \\ 0 & 0 & 1 \\ 1 & 0 & 0 \end{bmatrix}$

4. $\begin{bmatrix} 0.3 & 0.1 & 0.8 \\ 0.5 & 0.2 & 0.1 \\ 0.2 & 0.7 & 0.1 \end{bmatrix}$

5. $\begin{bmatrix} \frac{1}{3} & \frac{1}{6} & \frac{1}{4} \\ \frac{1}{3} & \frac{2}{3} & \frac{1}{4} \\ \frac{1}{3} & \frac{1}{6} & \frac{1}{2} \end{bmatrix}$

6. $\begin{bmatrix} 1 & 0 & 0 & 0 \\ 0 & 1 & 0 & 0 \\ 0 & 0 & 1 & 0 \\ 0 & 0 & 0 & 1 \end{bmatrix}$

C 7. The market research department at a manufacturing plant determines that 20% of the people who purchase their product during any given month will not purchase it the next month. On the other hand, 30% of the people who do not purchase the product during any given month will purchase it the next month. In a population of 1000 people, 100 people purchased the product this month. How many will purchase the product next month? In two months?

C 8. A medical researcher is studying the spread of a virus in a population of 1000 laboratory mice. During any given week there is an 80% probability that an infected mouse will overcome the virus, and during the same week there is a 10% probability that a noninfected mouse will become infected. One hundred mice are currently infected with the virus. How many will be infected next week? In two weeks?

C 9. A population of 10,000 is grouped as follows: 5000 nonsmokers, 2500 smokers of one pack or less per day, and 2500 smokers of more than one pack per day. During any given month there is a 5% probability that a nonsmoker will begin smoking a pack or less per day, and a 2% probability that a nonsmoker will begin smoking more than a pack per day. For smokers who smoke a pack or less per day, there is a 10% probability of quitting and 10% probability of increasing to more than a pack per day. For smokers who smoke more than a pack per day, there is a 5% probability of quitting and a 10% probability of dropping to a pack or less per day. How many people will be in each of the three groups in one month? In two months?

C 10. A population of 100,000 consumers is grouped as follows: 20,000 users of Brand A, 30,000 users of Brand B, and 50,000 who use neither brand. During any given month a Brand A user has a 20% probability of switching to Brand B and 5% probability of not using either brand. A Brand B user has a 15% probability of switching to Brand A and a 10% probability of not using either brand. A nonuser has a 10% probability of purchasing Brand A and a 15% probability of purchasing Brand B. How many people will be in each group in one month? In two months? In three months?

C 11. A college dormitory has 200 students. Those who watch an hour or more of television on any given day always watch for less than an hour the next day. One-fourth of those who watch television for less than an hour one day will watch an hour or more the next day. Half of the students watched television for an hour or more today. How many will watch television for an hour or more tomorrow? In two days? In thirty days?

C 12. A matrix of transition probabilities is given by

$$P = \begin{bmatrix} 0.6 & 0.1 & 0.1 \\ 0.2 & 0.7 & 0.1 \\ 0.2 & 0.2 & 0.8 \end{bmatrix}.$$

Find P^2X and P^3X for the state matrix

$$X = \begin{bmatrix} 100 \\ 100 \\ 800 \end{bmatrix}.$$

Then find the steady state matrix for P.

13. Prove that the product of two 2×2 stochastic matrices is stochastic.

14. Let P be a 2×2 stochastic matrix. Prove that there exists a 2×1 state matrix X with nonnegative entries such that $PX = X$.

Cryptography

In Exercises 15–18, find the uncoded row matrices of indicated order for the given messages. Then encode the message using the matrix A.

Message
15. SELL CONSOLIDATED

Row Matrix Order   *Encoding Matrix*

1×3 $A = \begin{bmatrix} 1 & -1 & 0 \\ 1 & 0 & -1 \\ -6 & 2 & 3 \end{bmatrix}$

16. PLEASE SEND MONEY

$$1 \times 3 \qquad A = \begin{bmatrix} 4 & 2 & 1 \\ -3 & -3 & -1 \\ 3 & 2 & 1 \end{bmatrix}$$

17. COME HOME SOON

$$1 \times 2 \qquad A = \begin{bmatrix} 1 & 2 \\ 3 & 5 \end{bmatrix}$$

18. HELP IS COMING

$$1 \times 4 \qquad A = \begin{bmatrix} -2 & 3 & -1 & -1 \\ -1 & 1 & 1 & 1 \\ -1 & -1 & 1 & 2 \\ 3 & 1 & -2 & -4 \end{bmatrix}$$

In Exercises 19–22, find A^{-1} to decode the given cryptogram.

19. $A = \begin{bmatrix} 1 & 2 \\ 3 & 5 \end{bmatrix}$,

11, 21, 64, 112, 25, 50, 29, 53, 23, 46, 40, 75, 55, 92

20. $A = \begin{bmatrix} 2 & 3 \\ 3 & 4 \end{bmatrix}$,

85, 120, 6, 8, 10, 15, 84, 117, 42, 56, 90, 125, 60, 80, 30, 45, 19, 26

21. $A = \begin{bmatrix} 4 & 2 & 1 \\ -3 & -3 & -1 \\ 3 & 2 & 1 \end{bmatrix}$,

33, 9, 9, 55, 28, 14, 95, 50, 25, 99, 53, 29, −22, −32, −9

22. $A = \begin{bmatrix} 1 & -1 & 0 \\ 1 & 0 & -1 \\ -6 & 2 & 3 \end{bmatrix}$,

9, −1, −9, 38, −19, −19, 28, −9, −19, −80, 25, 41, −64, 21, 31, −7, −4, 7

23. The following cryptogram was encoded with a 2×2 matrix.

8, 21, −15, −10, −13, −13, 5, 10, 5, 25, 5, 19, −1, 6, 20, 40, −18, −18, 1, 16

The last word of the message is __RON. What is the message?

24. The following cryptogram was encoded with a 2×2 matrix.

5, 2, 25, 11, −2, −7, −15, −15, 32, 14, −8, −13, 38, 19, −19, −19, 37, 16

The last word of the message is __SUE. What is the message?

Leontief Input-Output Models

25. A system composed of two industries, coal and steel, has the following inputs.

(a) To produce one dollar's worth of output, the coal industry requires $0.10 of its own product and $0.80 of steel.

(b) To produce one dollar's worth of output, the steel industry requires $0.10 of its own product and $0.20 of coal.

Find D, the input-output matrix for this system. Then solve for the output matrix X in the equation $X = DX + E$, where the external demand is given by

$$E = \begin{bmatrix} 10{,}000 \\ 20{,}000 \end{bmatrix}.$$

26. An industrial system has two industries with the following inputs.

(a) To produce one dollar's worth of output, Industry A requires $0.30 of its own product and $0.40 of Industry B's product.

(b) To produce one dollar's worth of output, Industry B requires $0.20 of its own product and $0.40 of Industry A's product.

Find D, the input-output matrix for this system. Then solve for the output matrix X in the equation $X = DX + E$, where the external demand is given by

$$E = \begin{bmatrix} 50{,}000 \\ 30{,}000 \end{bmatrix}.$$

C **27.** A small community includes a farmer, baker, and grocer with the following input-output matrix D and external demand matrix E.

$$D = \begin{bmatrix} 0.40 & 0.50 & 0.50 \\ 0.30 & 0.00 & 0.30 \\ 0.20 & 0.20 & 0.00 \end{bmatrix} \begin{matrix} \text{Farmer} \\ \text{Baker} \\ \text{Grocer} \end{matrix} \quad \text{and} \quad E = \begin{bmatrix} 1000 \\ 1000 \\ 1000 \end{bmatrix}$$

Farmer Baker Grocer

Solve for the output matrix X in the equation $X = DX + E$.

C **28.** An industrial system has three industries with the following input-output matrix D and external demand matrix E.

$$D = \begin{bmatrix} 0.2 & 0.4 & 0.4 \\ 0.4 & 0.2 & 0.2 \\ 0.0 & 0.2 & 0.2 \end{bmatrix} \quad \text{and} \quad E = \begin{bmatrix} 5000 \\ 2000 \\ 8000 \end{bmatrix}$$

Solve for the output matrix X in the equation $X = DX + E$.

Least Squares Regression Analysis

C In Exercises 29–32, (a) sketch the line that appears to be the best fit to the given points, (b) use the method of least squares to find the least squares regression line, and (c) calculate the sum of the squares error.

29.

30.

31.

32.

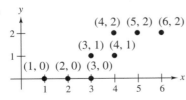

C In Exercises 33–42, find the least squares regression line for the given points.

33. $(-2, 0), (-1, 1), (0, 1), (1, 2)$

34. $(-4, -1), (-2, 0), (2, 4), (4, 5)$

35. $(-3, 0), (1, 4), (2, 6)$

36. $(-5, 1), (1, 3), (2, 3), (2, 5)$

37. $(-3, 4), (-1, 2), (1, 1), (3, 0)$

38. $(-5, 10), (-1, 8), (3, 6), (7, 4), (5, 5)$

39. $(0, 0), (1, 1), (2, 4)$

40. $(1, 0), (3, 3), (5, 6)$

41. $(0, 6), (4, 3), (5, 0), (8, -4), (10, -5)$

42. $(5, 2), (0, 0), (2, 1), (7, 4), (10, 6), (12, 6)$

C **43.** A store manager wants to know the demand for a certain product as a function of the price. The daily sales for three different prices of the product are given in the following table

Price (x)	$1.00	$1.25	$1.50
Demand (y)	450	375	330

(a) Find the least squares regression line for these data.

(b) Estimate the demand when the price is $1.40.

C **44.** A hardware retailer wants to know the demand for a certain tool as a function of the price. The monthly sales for four different prices of the tool are listed in the following table.

Price (x)	$25	$30	$35	$40
Demand (y)	82	75	67	55

(a) Find the least squares regression line for these data.

(b) Estimate the demand when the price is $32.95.

CHAPTER 2 ☐ REVIEW EXERCISES

In Exercises 1–6, perform the indicated matrix operations.

1. $\begin{bmatrix} 2 & 1 & 0 \\ 0 & 5 & -4 \end{bmatrix} - 3\begin{bmatrix} 5 & 3 & -6 \\ 0 & -2 & 5 \end{bmatrix}$

2. $-2\begin{bmatrix} 1 & 2 \\ 5 & -4 \\ 6 & 0 \end{bmatrix} + 8\begin{bmatrix} 7 & 1 \\ 1 & 2 \\ 1 & 4 \end{bmatrix}$

3. $\begin{bmatrix} 1 & 2 \\ 5 & -4 \\ 6 & 0 \end{bmatrix}\begin{bmatrix} 6 & -2 & 8 \\ 4 & 0 & 0 \end{bmatrix}$

4. $\begin{bmatrix} 1 & 5 \\ 2 & -4 \end{bmatrix}\begin{bmatrix} 6 & -2 & 8 \\ 4 & 0 & 0 \end{bmatrix}$

5. $\begin{bmatrix} 1 & 3 & 2 \\ 0 & 2 & -4 \\ 0 & 0 & 3 \end{bmatrix}\begin{bmatrix} 4 & -3 & 2 \\ 0 & 3 & -1 \\ 0 & 0 & 2 \end{bmatrix}$

6. $\begin{bmatrix} 2 & 1 \\ 6 & 0 \end{bmatrix}\begin{bmatrix} 4 & 2 \\ -3 & 1 \end{bmatrix} + \begin{bmatrix} -2 & 4 \\ 0 & 4 \end{bmatrix}$

In Exercises 7 and 8, write out the system of linear equations represented by the given matrix equation.

7. $\begin{bmatrix} 5 & 4 \\ -1 & 1 \end{bmatrix}\begin{bmatrix} x \\ y \end{bmatrix} = \begin{bmatrix} 2 \\ -22 \end{bmatrix}$

8. $\begin{bmatrix} 0 & 1 & -2 \\ -1 & 3 & 1 \\ 2 & -2 & 4 \end{bmatrix}\begin{bmatrix} x_1 \\ x_2 \\ x_3 \end{bmatrix} = \begin{bmatrix} -1 \\ 0 \\ 2 \end{bmatrix}$

In Exercises 9 and 10, write the given system of linear equations in matrix form.

9. $2x_1 + 3x_2 + x_3 = 10$
$2x_1 - 3x_2 - 3x_3 = 22$
$4x_1 - 2x_2 + 3x_3 = -2$

10. $-3x_1 - x_2 + x_3 = 0$
$2x_1 + 4x_2 - 5x_3 = -3$
$x_1 - 2x_2 + 3x_3 = 1$

In Exercises 11 and 12, find A^T, A^TA, and AA^T for the given matrix.

11. $\begin{bmatrix} 1 & 2 & -3 \\ 0 & 1 & 2 \end{bmatrix}$

12. $\begin{bmatrix} 1 \\ 3 \\ -1 \end{bmatrix}$

In Exercises 13–16, find the inverse of the given matrix (if it exists).

13. $\begin{bmatrix} 3 & -1 \\ 2 & -1 \end{bmatrix}$

14. $\begin{bmatrix} 4 & -1 \\ -8 & 2 \end{bmatrix}$

15. $\begin{bmatrix} 2 & 3 & 1 \\ 2 & -3 & -3 \\ 4 & 0 & 3 \end{bmatrix}$

16. $\begin{bmatrix} 1 & 1 & 1 & 1 \\ 0 & 1 & 1 & 1 \\ 0 & 0 & 1 & 1 \\ 0 & 0 & 0 & 1 \end{bmatrix}$

In Exercises 17 and 18, write the given system of linear equations in the form $A\mathbf{x} = \mathbf{b}$. Then find A^{-1} and use it to solve for $\mathbf{x}$.

17. $5x_1 + 4x_2 = 2$
$-x_1 + x_2 = -22$

18. $-x_1 + x_2 + 2x_3 = 1$
$2x_1 + 3x_2 + x_3 = -2$
$5x_1 + 4x_2 + 2x_3 = 4$

19. Find A, given that

$$(3A)^{-1} = \begin{bmatrix} 4 & -1 \\ 2 & 3 \end{bmatrix}.$$

20. Find x such that the matrix A is nonsingular.

$$A = \begin{bmatrix} 3 & 1 \\ x & -1 \end{bmatrix}$$

In Exercises 21 and 22, find the inverse of the given elementary matrix.

21. $\begin{bmatrix} 1 & 0 & 4 \\ 0 & 1 & 0 \\ 0 & 0 & 1 \end{bmatrix}$

22. $\begin{bmatrix} 1 & 0 & 0 \\ 0 & 6 & 0 \\ 0 & 0 & 1 \end{bmatrix}$

In Exercises 23–26, factor A into a product of elementary matrices.

23. $A = \begin{bmatrix} 2 & 3 \\ 0 & 1 \end{bmatrix}$

24. $A = \begin{bmatrix} -3 & 13 \\ 1 & -4 \end{bmatrix}$

25. $A = \begin{bmatrix} 1 & 0 & 1 \\ 0 & 1 & -2 \\ 0 & 0 & 4 \end{bmatrix}$

26. $A = \begin{bmatrix} 3 & 0 & 6 \\ 0 & 2 & 0 \\ 1 & 0 & 3 \end{bmatrix}$

27. Find two 2×2 matrices A such that $A^2 = I$.

28. Find two 2×2 matrices A such that $A^2 = O$.

29. Find three 2×2 matrices A such that $A^2 = A$.

30. Find 2×2 matrices A and B such that $AB = O$ but $BA \neq O$.

In Exercises 31 and 32, let the matrices X, Y, Z, and W be given by

$$X = \begin{bmatrix} 1 \\ 2 \\ 0 \\ 1 \end{bmatrix}, \quad Y = \begin{bmatrix} -1 \\ 0 \\ 3 \\ 2 \end{bmatrix}, \quad Z = \begin{bmatrix} 3 \\ 4 \\ -1 \\ 2 \end{bmatrix}, \quad W = \begin{bmatrix} 3 \\ 2 \\ -4 \\ -1 \end{bmatrix}.$$

31. (a) Find scalars a, b, and c such that $W = aX + bY + cZ$.
(b) Show that there do not exist scalars a and b such that $Z = aX + bY$.

32. Show that if $aX + bY + cZ = O$, then $a = b = c = 0$.

33. Let A, B, and $A + B$ be nonsingular matrices. Prove that $A^{-1} + B^{-1}$ is nonsingular by showing that

$$(A^{-1} + B^{-1})^{-1} = A(A + B)^{-1}B.$$

34. Let A, B, and C be $n \times n$ matrices and C be nonsingular. If $AC = CB$, does it follow that $A = B$? If so, prove it. If not, find an example for which the equation is false.

In Exercises 35 and 36, find the *LU*–factorization of the given matrix.

35. $\begin{bmatrix} 2 & 5 \\ 6 & 14 \end{bmatrix}$ **36.** $\begin{bmatrix} 1 & 1 & 1 \\ 1 & 2 & 2 \\ 1 & 2 & 3 \end{bmatrix}$

In Exercises 37 and 38, use the *LU*–factorization of the coefficient matrix to solve the linear system.

37. $\begin{aligned} x \quad\quad + z &= 3 \\ 2x + y + 2z &= 7 \\ 3x + 2y + 6z &= 8 \end{aligned}$ **38.** $\begin{aligned} 2x_1 + x_2 + x_3 - x_4 &= 7 \\ 3x_2 + x_3 - x_4 &= -3 \\ -2x_3 \quad\quad &= 2 \\ 2x_1 + x_2 + x_3 - 2x_4 &= 8 \end{aligned}$

Stochastic Matrices

In Exercises 39 and 40, determine whether the given matrix is stochastic.

39. $\begin{bmatrix} 1 & 0 & 0 \\ 0 & 0.5 & 0.1 \\ 0 & 0.1 & 0.5 \end{bmatrix}$ **40.** $\begin{bmatrix} 0.3 & 0.4 & 0.1 \\ 0.2 & 0.4 & 0.5 \\ 0.5 & 0.2 & 0.4 \end{bmatrix}$

In Exercises 41 and 42, use the given matrix of transition probabilities P and state matrix X to find the state matrices PX, P^2X, and P^3X.

41. $P = \begin{bmatrix} \frac{1}{2} & \frac{1}{4} \\ \frac{1}{2} & \frac{3}{4} \end{bmatrix}$, $X = \begin{bmatrix} 128 \\ 64 \end{bmatrix}$

C 42. $P = \begin{bmatrix} 0.6 & 0.2 & 0.0 \\ 0.2 & 0.7 & 0.1 \\ 0.2 & 0.1 & 0.9 \end{bmatrix}$, $X = \begin{bmatrix} 1000 \\ 1000 \\ 1000 \end{bmatrix}$

C 43. A country is divided into three regions. Each year, 10% of the residents of Region 1 move to Region 2 and 5% move to Region 3; 15% of the residents of Region 2 move to Region 1 and 5% to Region 3; and 10% of the residents of Region 3 move to Region 1 and 10% move to Region 2. This year each region has a population of 100,000. Find the population of each region (a) in one year and (b) in three years.

C 44. Find the steady state matrix for the populations described in Exercise 43.

Cryptography

In Exercises 45 and 46, find the uncoded row matrices of indicated order for the given messages. Then encode the message using the matrix A.

Message

45. ONE IF BY LAND

Row Matrix Order	Encoding Matrix
1×2	$A = \begin{bmatrix} 5 & 2 \\ 2 & 1 \end{bmatrix}$

46. BEAM ME UP SCOTTY

1×3	$A = \begin{bmatrix} 2 & 1 & 4 \\ 3 & 1 & 3 \\ -2 & -1 & -3 \end{bmatrix}$

In Exercises 47 and 48, find A^{-1} to decode the given cryptogram.

47. $A = \begin{bmatrix} 3 & -2 \\ -4 & 3 \end{bmatrix}$,

-45, 34, 36, -24, -43, 37, -23, 22, -37, 29, 57, -38, -39, 31

48. $A = \begin{bmatrix} 2 & -1 & -1 \\ -5 & 2 & 2 \\ 5 & -1 & -2 \end{bmatrix}$,

58, -3, -25, -48, 28, 19, -40, 13, 13, -98, 39, 39, 118, -25, -48, 28, -14, -14

Leontief Input-Output Models

49. An industrial system has two industries with the following inputs.

    (a) To produce one dollar's worth of output, Industry A requires $0.20 of its own product and $0.30 of Industry B's product.

    (b) To produce one dollar's worth of output, Industry B requires $0.10 of its own product and $0.50 of Industry A's product.

Find D, the input-output matrix for this system. Then solve for the output matrix X in the equation $X = DX + E$, where the external demand is given by

$$E = \begin{bmatrix} 40,000 \\ 80,000 \end{bmatrix}.$$

C 50. An industrial system has three industries with the following input-output matrix D and external demand matrix E.

$$D = \begin{bmatrix} 0.1 & 0.3 & 0.2 \\ 0.0 & 0.2 & 0.3 \\ 0.4 & 0.1 & 0.1 \end{bmatrix} \quad \text{and} \quad E = \begin{bmatrix} 3000 \\ 3500 \\ 8500 \end{bmatrix}$$

Solve for the output matrix X in the equation $X = DX + E$.

Least Squares Regression Analysis

C In Exercises 51–54, find the least squares regression line for the given points.

51. $(1, 5), (2, 4), (3, 2)$

52. $(2, 1), (3, 3), (4, 2), (5, 4), (6, 4)$

53. $(-2, 4), (-1, 2), (0, 1), (1, -2), (2, -3)$

54. $(1, 1), (1, 3), (1, 2), (1, 4), (2, 5)$

C **55.** A farmer used four test plots to determine the relationship between wheat yield in kilograms per square kilometer and the amount of fertilizer in hundreds of kilograms per square kilometer. The results are given in the following table.

Fertilizer (x)	1.0	1.5	2.0	2.5
Yield (y)	32	41	48	53

(a) Find the least squares regression line for these data.

(b) Estimate the yield for a fertilizer application of 160 kilograms per square kilometer.

C **56.** The Consumer Price Index (CPI) for all items for five years is given in the following table.

Year (x)	1980	1981	1982	1983	1984
CPI (y)	247.0	272.3	288.6	297.4	310.7

(a) Find the least squares regression line for these data. (Let $x = 0$ represent 1980.)

(b) Estimate the CPI for the years 1990 and 1994.

CHAPTER 2   PROJECTS

1   Exploring Matrix Multiplication

The first two test scores for Anna, Bruce, Chris, and David are given by the following matrix M.

	Test 1	Test 2
Anna	84	96
Bruce	56	72
Chris	78	83
David	82	91

1. Which test was more difficult? Which was easier?

2. How would you rank the performance of the four students?

3. Describe the meaning of the matrix products $M\begin{bmatrix} 1 \\ 0 \end{bmatrix}$ and $M\begin{bmatrix} 0 \\ 1 \end{bmatrix}$.

4. Describe the meaning of the matrix products $[1 \quad 0 \quad 0 \quad 0]M$ and $[0 \quad 0 \quad 1 \quad 0]M$.

5. Describe the meaning of the matrix products $M\begin{bmatrix} 1 \\ 1 \end{bmatrix}$ and $\frac{1}{2}M\begin{bmatrix} 1 \\ 1 \end{bmatrix}$.

6. Describe the meaning of the matrix products $[1 \quad 1 \quad 1 \quad 1]M$ and $\frac{1}{4}[1 \quad 1 \quad 1 \quad 1]M$.

7. Describe the meaning of the matrix product $\begin{bmatrix} 1 & 1 & 1 & 1 \end{bmatrix} M \begin{bmatrix} 1 \\ 1 \end{bmatrix}$.

8. Use matrix multiplication to express the combined overall average score on both tests.

9. As instructor, you would like to raise the scores on test 1 for all the students. How could you use matrix multiplication to scale the scores by a factor of 1.1?

2 Nilpotent Matrices

Let A be a nonzero square $n \times n$ matrix. Is it possible that a positive integer k exists such that $A^k = 0$? For example, find A^3 for the matrix

$$A = \begin{bmatrix} 0 & 1 & 2 \\ 0 & 0 & 1 \\ 0 & 0 & 0 \end{bmatrix}.$$

We say that a square matrix A is **nilpotent of index k** if $A \neq 0$, $A^2 \neq 0$, ..., $A^{k-1} \neq 0$, but $A^k = 0$. In this project you will explore the world of nilpotent matrices. You may wish to use matrix software or the matrix capabilities of a graphing calculator to help you answer the following questions.

1. What is the index of the nilpotent matrix A above?
2. Determine which of the following matrices are nilpotent and find their index.

(a) $\begin{bmatrix} 0 & 1 \\ 0 & 0 \end{bmatrix}$ (b) $\begin{bmatrix} 0 & 1 \\ 1 & 0 \end{bmatrix}$ (c) $\begin{bmatrix} 0 & 0 \\ 1 & 0 \end{bmatrix}$

(d) $\begin{bmatrix} 1 & 0 \\ 1 & 0 \end{bmatrix}$ (e) $\begin{bmatrix} 0 & 0 & 1 \\ 0 & 0 & 0 \\ 0 & 0 & 0 \end{bmatrix}$ (f) $\begin{bmatrix} 0 & 0 & 0 \\ 1 & 0 & 0 \\ 1 & 1 & 0 \end{bmatrix}$

3. Find 3×3 nilpotent matrices of index 2 and 3.
4. Find 4×4 nilpotent matrices of index 2, 3, and 4.
5. Find a nilpotent matrix of index 5.
6. Are nilpotent matrices invertible? Prove your answer.
7. If A is nilpotent, what can you say about A^T? Prove your answer.
8. If A is nilpotent, show that $I - A$ is invertible.

CHAPTER 2 ☐ MATLAB EXERCISES

1. Enter the matrices

$$A = \begin{bmatrix} 0 & -4 & 5 \\ 3 & 1 & -2 \\ 2 & 1 & 4 \end{bmatrix} \quad \text{and} \quad B = \begin{bmatrix} -5 & 6 & 7 \\ 0 & -1 & 2 \\ 4 & 0 & -3 \end{bmatrix}.$$

Use MATLAB to find

(a) $A + B$ (b) $B - 3A$ (c) AB (d) BA.

2. Enter the three matrices

$$A = \begin{bmatrix} 1 & \frac{1}{2} & \frac{1}{3} & \frac{1}{4} \\ \frac{1}{2} & \frac{1}{3} & \frac{1}{4} & \frac{1}{5} \\ \frac{1}{3} & \frac{1}{4} & \frac{1}{5} & \frac{1}{6} \\ \frac{1}{4} & \frac{1}{5} & \frac{1}{6} & \frac{1}{7} \end{bmatrix} \quad B = \begin{bmatrix} 1.0000 & 0.5000 & 0.3333 & 0.2500 \\ 0.5000 & 0.3333 & 0.2500 & 0.2000 \\ 0.3333 & 0.2500 & 0.2000 & 0.1667 \\ 0.2500 & 0.2000 & 0.1667 & 0.1429 \end{bmatrix}$$

$$C = \begin{bmatrix} 16 & -120 & 240 & -140 \\ -120 & 1200 & -2700 & 1680 \\ 240 & -2700 & 6480 & -4200 \\ -140 & 1680 & -4200 & 2800 \end{bmatrix}.$$

(a) Calculate $A - B$. Use the **format long** command to verify the result. Return to the standard short format with **format short.**

(b) Calculate AC and BC. Define what is meant by the inverse of a square matrix. What is the inverse of the matrix A? Of the matrix C?

3. Write the following system of linear equations in the form $AX = B$ and use the MATLAB command **A \ B** to solve the system.

$$\begin{aligned} 3x + 3y + 4z &= 2 \\ x + y + 4z &= -2 \\ 2x + 5y + 4z &= 3 \end{aligned}$$

Check your answer using **rref.**

4. Enter the matrices

$$A = \begin{bmatrix} 2 & -1 & 3 & 4 \\ 0 & 2 & -1 & -5 \\ 7 & -5 & 0 & 6 \\ -4 & 0 & 7 & 12 \end{bmatrix} \quad \text{and} \quad B = \textbf{pascal(4)}.$$

(a) Use the MATLAB command **trace** to find the traces of A, B, and $A + B$. What do you observe?

(b) What is the relationship between the trace of AB and the trace of $BA?$

5. Use the MATLAB command **diag** to form the 5×5 diagonal matrix D with diagonal entries 0, $-1, -2, -3$, and -4. Find the product $D^4 = DDDD$. If D is an $n \times n$ diagonal matrix, describe how to find the product D^k for any positive integer k.

6. Enter the three matrices

$$A = \begin{bmatrix} 1 & 2 & 3 & 4 \\ 2 & 3 & 4 & 5 \\ 3 & 4 & 5 & 6 \\ 4 & 5 & 6 & 7 \end{bmatrix} \quad B = \begin{bmatrix} 4 & -6 & 3 & 5 \\ 0 & -3 & -6 & 8 \\ 3 & 5 & 0 & 7 \\ -1 & 0 & -7 & 9 \end{bmatrix} \quad C = \begin{bmatrix} 16 & -1 & 4 & -1 \\ -3 & 12 & -7 & 8 \\ 4 & -5 & 0 & 0 \\ -14 & 3 & 2 & 8 \end{bmatrix}$$

(a) Calculate $AB - AC$ and $A(B - C)$. What do you observe?

(b) Calculate $3(AC)$, $A(3C)$, and $(3A)C$. What do you observe?

7. Let

$$A = \begin{bmatrix} 1 & \frac{1}{3} \\ 0 & \frac{1}{4} \end{bmatrix}.$$

Compute A^2, A^3, and A^8. Describe the matrix A^n for large n.

8. Enter the matrices

$$A11 = \begin{bmatrix} 1 & 0 \\ 0 & -1 \end{bmatrix} \qquad A12 = \textbf{zeros}(\textbf{2, 2}) \qquad A22 = \begin{bmatrix} 0 & 1 \\ 1 & 0 \end{bmatrix}.$$

(a) Form the 4×4 matrix A using the following MATLAB construction:

A = [A11 A12; A12 A22]

(b) Find the smallest value of n such that $A^n = A$.

9. Use the MATLAB command **inv** to find the inverse of the following matrix A. Then adjoin the identity matrix $I = \textbf{eye}(\textbf{3})$ to A to form the 3×6 matrix $B = \begin{bmatrix} A & I \end{bmatrix}$. Row-reduce B to compute the inverse of A again. What do you observe?

$$A = \begin{bmatrix} 1 & 2 & -1 \\ 3 & 7 & -10 \\ 7 & 16 & -21 \end{bmatrix}$$

10. Let A and B be the following 3×3 matrices.

$$A = \begin{bmatrix} 2 & 4 & \frac{5}{2} \\ -\frac{3}{4} & 2 & \frac{1}{4} \\ \frac{1}{4} & \frac{1}{2} & 2 \end{bmatrix} \qquad B = \begin{bmatrix} 1 & -\frac{1}{2} & \frac{3}{4} \\ \frac{3}{2} & \frac{1}{2} & -2 \\ \frac{1}{4} & 1 & \frac{1}{2} \end{bmatrix}$$

(a) Calculate $A^{-1}B^{-1}$, $(AB)^{-1}$, and $(BA)^{-1}$. What do you observe?

(b) Find $(A^{-1})^T$ and $(A^T)^{-1}$. What do you observe? Remember: The MATLAB command for the transpose of a matrix A is A'.

11. In this project you will use MATLAB to find the least squares regression line for the set of data $(1, 1)$, $(2, 2)$, $(3, 4)$, $(4, 4)$, and $(5, 6)$ from Example 10, Section 2.5.

(a) Form the following matrices.

$$X = \begin{bmatrix} 1 & 1 \\ 1 & 2 \\ 1 & 3 \\ 1 & 4 \\ 1 & 5 \end{bmatrix} \qquad Y = \begin{bmatrix} 1 \\ 2 \\ 4 \\ 4 \\ 6 \end{bmatrix}$$

(b) Let $A = (X^T X)^{-1} X^T Y$.

(c) Compare your answer with the MATLAB least squares command **polyfit**. (Hint: Let $X1 = X(:, 2)$ and type **polyfit(X1,Y,1)**.)

(d) Plot the data using the MATLAB commands

t = (0: 0.1: 6) ;
plot(X1,Y,'+')

(e) Plot the least squares line for these data by using the MATLAB commands

t = (0: 0.1: 6) ;
p=polyfit(X1,Y,1);
f=polyval(p,t);
plot(t,f,'*')

(f) You can combine the previous plots as follows

plot(X1,Y,'+',t,f,'*')

12. Repeat Exercise 11 for the data $(0, 6)$, $(4, 3)$, $(5, 0)$, $(8, -4)$, $(10, -5)$. Plot the data and the least squares line on the interval $[0, 10]$. That is, use **t = (0: 0.1: 10) ;**.

3 DETERMINANTS

Augustin-Louis
Cauchy

1 7 8 9 – 1 8 5 7

Augustin-Louis Cauchy was the eldest of six children of a French parliamentary lawyer. He was born in Paris six weeks after the fall of the Bastille. To escape the danger of the guillotine, Cauchy's father moved the family from Paris to their country home which bordered that of one of France's leading mathematicians, Pierre-Simon de Laplace. Laplace was the first to recognize young Cauchy's gift for mathematics and encouraged him to develop his talent.

In 1800 the Cauchy family moved back to Paris, where Cauchy began his formal schooling. He won several prizes, and his mathematical prowess began attracting attention. In 1810 Cauchy graduated as a civil engineer and was given a military commission that he reluctantly held for three years. Political turmoil then led Cauchy through a series of teaching positions that culminated with his appointment as professor of mathematical astronomy at the Sorbonne. By the age of 27 he was recognized as one of the greatest mathematicians of his day.

Cauchy was a prolific writer, publishing nearly 800 papers. His contributions to the study of mathematics were revolutionary, and he is often credited with bringing rigor to modern mathematics. For example, Cauchy was the first to rigorously define limits, continuity, and the convergence of an infinite series. In addition to founding complex number theory, he contributed to the theory of determinants and differential equations. It is interesting to note that Cauchy's work on determinants preceded Cayley's development of matrices.

3.1 THE DETERMINANT OF A MATRIX

Every *square* matrix can be associated with a real number called its **determinant.** Determinants have many uses, several of which will be encountered in this chapter. The first two sections of this chapter concentrate on procedures for evaluating the determinant of a matrix.

Historically, the use of determinants arose from the recognition of special patterns that occur in the solution of systems of linear equations. For instance, the general solution to the system

$$a_{11}x_1 + a_{12}x_2 = b_1$$
$$a_{21}x_1 + a_{22}x_2 = b_2$$

can be shown to be

$$x_1 = \frac{b_1 a_{22} - b_2 a_{12}}{a_{11}a_{22} - a_{21}a_{12}} \quad \text{and} \quad x_2 = \frac{b_2 a_{11} - b_1 a_{21}}{a_{11}a_{22} - a_{21}a_{12}}$$

provided that $a_{11}a_{22} - a_{21}a_{12} \neq 0$. Note that both fractions have the same denominator, $a_{11}a_{22} - a_{21}a_{12}$. This quantity is called the **determinant** of the coefficient matrix A.

Definition of the Determinant of a 2 × 2 Matrix

The **determinant** of the matrix

$$A = \begin{bmatrix} a_{11} & a_{12} \\ a_{21} & a_{22} \end{bmatrix}$$

is given by

$$\det(A) = |A| = a_{11}a_{22} - a_{21}a_{12}.$$

REMARK: In this text, $\det(A)$ and $|A|$ are used interchangeably to represent the determinant of a matrix. Vertical bars are also used to denote the absolute value of a real number; the context will show which use is intended. Furthermore, it is common practice to delete the matrix brackets and write

$$\begin{vmatrix} a_{11} & a_{12} \\ a_{21} & a_{22} \end{vmatrix} \quad \text{instead of} \quad \left| \begin{bmatrix} a_{11} & a_{12} \\ a_{21} & a_{22} \end{bmatrix} \right|.$$

A convenient method for remembering the formula for the determinant of a 2×2 matrix is shown in the following diagram.

$$|A| = \begin{vmatrix} a_{11} & a_{12} \\ a_{21} & a_{22} \end{vmatrix} = a_{11}a_{22} - a_{21}a_{12}$$

Note that the determinant is given by the difference of the products of the two diagonals of the matrix.

EXAMPLE 1   **The Determinant of a Matrix of Order 2**

Find the determinants of the following matrices.

(a) $A = \begin{bmatrix} 2 & -3 \\ 1 & 2 \end{bmatrix}$ (b) $B = \begin{bmatrix} 2 & 1 \\ 4 & 2 \end{bmatrix}$ (c) $C = \begin{bmatrix} 0 & 3 \\ 2 & 4 \end{bmatrix}$

Solution   (a) $|A| = \begin{vmatrix} 2 & -3 \\ 1 & 2 \end{vmatrix} = 2(2) - 1(-3) = 4 + 3 = 7$

(b) $|B| = \begin{vmatrix} 2 & 1 \\ 4 & 2 \end{vmatrix} = 2(2) - 4(1) = 4 - 4 = 0$

(c) $|C| = \begin{vmatrix} 0 & 3 \\ 2 & 4 \end{vmatrix} = 0(4) - 2(3) = 0 - 6 = -6$

REMARK: Note that the determinant of a matrix can be positive, zero, or negative.

The determinant of a matrix of order 1 is defined simply as the entry of the matrix. For instance, if $A = [-2]$, then $\det(A) = -2$. To define the determinant of a matrix of orders higher than 2, it is convenient to use the notions of **minors** and **cofactors**.

Definition of Minors and Cofactors of a Matrix

If A is a square matrix, then the **minor** M_{ij} of the element a_{ij} is the determinant of the matrix obtained by deleting the ith row and jth column of A. The **cofactor** C_{ij} is given by

$$C_{ij} = (-1)^{i+j}M_{ij}.$$

For example, if A is a 3×3 matrix, then the minors of a_{21} and a_{22} are as shown in the following diagram.

Minor of a_{21}

$$\begin{bmatrix} a_{11} & a_{12} & a_{13} \\ a_{21} & a_{22} & a_{23} \\ a_{31} & a_{32} & a_{33} \end{bmatrix}, \quad M_{21} = \begin{vmatrix} a_{12} & a_{13} \\ a_{32} & a_{33} \end{vmatrix}$$

Delete Row 2 and Column 1

Minor of a_{22}

$$\begin{bmatrix} a_{11} & a_{12} & a_{13} \\ a_{21} & a_{22} & a_{23} \\ a_{31} & a_{32} & a_{33} \end{bmatrix}, \quad M_{22} = \begin{vmatrix} a_{11} & a_{13} \\ a_{31} & a_{33} \end{vmatrix}$$

Delete Row 2 and Column 2

The minors and cofactors of a matrix differ at most in sign. To obtain the cofactors of a matrix, first find the minors and then apply the following checkerboard pattern of $+$'s and $-$'s.

Sign Pattern for Cofactors

$$\begin{bmatrix} + & - & + \\ - & + & - \\ + & - & + \end{bmatrix}$$

3×3 matrix

$$\begin{bmatrix} + & - & + & - \\ - & + & - & + \\ + & - & + & - \\ - & + & - & + \end{bmatrix}$$

4×4 matrix

$$\begin{bmatrix} + & - & + & - & + & \cdots \\ - & + & - & + & - & \cdots \\ + & - & + & - & + & \cdots \\ - & + & - & + & - & \cdots \\ + & - & + & - & + & \cdots \\ \vdots & \vdots & \vdots & \vdots & \vdots & \end{bmatrix}$$

$n \times n$ matrix

Note that *odd* positions (where $i + j$ is odd) have negative signs, and *even* positions (where $i + j$ is even) have positive signs.

EXAMPLE 2   *Finding the Minors and Cofactors of a Matrix*

Find all the minors and cofactors of

$$A = \begin{bmatrix} 0 & 2 & 1 \\ 3 & -1 & 2 \\ 4 & 0 & 1 \end{bmatrix}.$$

Solution   To find the minor M_{11}, we delete the first row and first column of A and evaluate the determinant of the resulting matrix.

$$\begin{bmatrix} 0 & 2 & 1 \\ 3 & -1 & 2 \\ 4 & 0 & 1 \end{bmatrix}, \quad M_{11} = \begin{vmatrix} -1 & 2 \\ 0 & 1 \end{vmatrix} = -1(1) - 0(2) = -1$$

Similarly, to find M_{12}, we delete the first row and second column.

$$\begin{bmatrix} 0 & 2 & 1 \\ 3 & -1 & 2 \\ 4 & 0 & 1 \end{bmatrix}, \quad M_{12} = \begin{vmatrix} 3 & 2 \\ 4 & 1 \end{vmatrix} = 3(1) - 4(2) = -5$$

Continuing this pattern, we obtain the following minors.

$$\begin{array}{lll} M_{11} = -1 & M_{12} = -5 & M_{13} = 4 \\ M_{21} = 2 & M_{22} = -4 & M_{23} = -8 \\ M_{31} = 5 & M_{32} = -3 & M_{33} = -6 \end{array}$$

Now, to find the cofactors, we combine our checkerboard pattern of signs with these minors to obtain

$$\begin{array}{lll} C_{11} = -1 & C_{12} = 5 & C_{13} = 4 \\ C_{21} = -2 & C_{22} = -4 & C_{23} = 8 \\ C_{31} = 5 & C_{32} = 3 & C_{33} = -6. \end{array}$$

Having defined the minors and cofactors of a matrix, we are ready for a general definition of the determinant of a matrix. The following definition is called **inductive** because it uses determinants of matrices of order $n - 1$ to define the determinant of a matrix of order n.

Definition of the Determinant of a Matrix

If A is a square matrix (of order 2 or greater), then the determinant of A is the sum of the entries in the first row of A multiplied by their cofactors. That is,

$$\det(A) = |A| = \sum_{j=1}^{n} a_{1j}C_{1j} = a_{11}C_{11} + a_{12}C_{12} + \cdots + a_{1n}C_{1n}.$$

R E M A R K : Try checking that for 2×2 matrices this definition yields $|A| = a_{11}a_{22} - a_{12}a_{21}$, as previously defined.

When this definition is used to evaluate a determinant, we say that we are **expanding by cofactors.** This procedure is demonstrated in Example 3.

EXAMPLE 3   *The Determinant of a Matrix of Order 3*

Find the determinant of

$$A = \begin{bmatrix} 0 & 2 & 1 \\ 3 & -1 & 2 \\ 4 & 0 & 1 \end{bmatrix}.$$

Solution   Note that this matrix is the same as that given in Example 2. There we found the cofactors of the entries in the first row to be

$$C_{11} = -1, \qquad C_{12} = 5, \qquad C_{13} = 4.$$

Therefore, by the definition of a determinant, we have the following.

$$|A| = a_{11}C_{11} + a_{12}C_{12} + a_{13}C_{13} \qquad \text{First row expansion}$$
$$= 0(-1) + 2(5) + 1(4)$$
$$= 14$$

Although we defined the determinant as an expansion by the cofactors in the first row, it can be shown that the determinant can be evaluated by *any* row or column. For instance, we could expand the 3×3 matrix in Example 3 by the second row to obtain

$$|A| = a_{21}C_{21} + a_{22}C_{22} + a_{23}C_{23} \qquad \text{Second row expansion}$$
$$= 3(-2) + (-1)(-4) + 2(8) = 14$$

or by the first column to obtain

$$|A| = a_{11}C_{11} + a_{21}C_{21} + a_{31}C_{31} \qquad \text{First column expansion}$$
$$= 0(-1) + 3(-2) + 4(5) = 14.$$

Try some other possibilities to see that the determinant of A can be evaluated by expanding by *any* row or column. This result is stated formally in the following theorem, called Laplace's Expansion of a Determinant, after the French mathematician Pierre-Simon de Laplace (1749–1827).

Theorem 3.1

Expansion by Cofactors

Let A be a square matrix of order n. Then the determinant of A is given by

$$\det(A) = |A| = \sum_{j=1}^{n} a_{ij}C_{ij} = a_{i1}C_{i1} + a_{i2}C_{i2} + \cdots + a_{in}C_{in} \qquad \text{ith row expansion}$$

or

$$\det(A) = |A| = \sum_{i=1}^{n} a_{ij}C_{ij} = a_{1j}C_{1j} + a_{2j}C_{2j} + \cdots + a_{nj}C_{nj}. \qquad \text{jth column expansion}$$

When expanding by cofactors we do not need to evaluate the cofactors of zero entries, because a zero entry times its cofactor is zero.

$$a_{ij}C_{ij} = (0)C_{ij} = 0$$

Thus the row (or column) containing the most zeros is usually the best choice for expansion by cofactors. This is demonstrated in the next example.

EXAMPLE 4   *The Determinant of a Matrix of Order 4*

Find the determinant of

$$A = \begin{bmatrix} 1 & -2 & 3 & 0 \\ -1 & 1 & 0 & 2 \\ 0 & 2 & 0 & 3 \\ 3 & 4 & 0 & -2 \end{bmatrix}.$$

Solution

Inspecting this matrix, we see that three of the entries in the third column are zeros. Thus we can eliminate some of the work in the expansion by using the third column.

$$|A| = 3(C_{13}) + 0(C_{23}) + 0(C_{33}) + 0(C_{43})$$

Because C_{23}, C_{33}, and C_{43} have zero coefficients, we need only find the cofactor C_{13}. To do this, we delete the first row and third column of A and evaluate the determinant of the resulting matrix.

$$C_{13} = (-1)^{1+3} \begin{vmatrix} -1 & 1 & 2 \\ 0 & 2 & 3 \\ 3 & 4 & -2 \end{vmatrix} = \begin{vmatrix} -1 & 1 & 2 \\ 0 & 2 & 3 \\ 3 & 4 & -2 \end{vmatrix}$$

Expanding by cofactors in the second row yields the following.

$$C_{13} = (0)(-1)^3 \begin{vmatrix} 1 & 2 \\ 4 & -2 \end{vmatrix} + (2)(-1)^4 \begin{vmatrix} -1 & 2 \\ 3 & -2 \end{vmatrix} + (3)(-1)^5 \begin{vmatrix} -1 & 1 \\ 3 & 4 \end{vmatrix}$$
$$= 0 + 2(1)(-4) + 3(-1)(-7)$$
$$= 13$$

Thus we obtain

$$|A| = 3(13) = 39.$$

There is an alternative method that is commonly used for evaluating the determinant of a 3×3 matrix A. To apply this method, copy the first and second columns of A to form fourth and fifth columns. The determinant of A is then obtained by adding (or subtracting) the products of the six diagonals, as shown in the following diagram.

We leave it to you to confirm that the determinant of A is given by the following.

$$|A| = a_{11}a_{22}a_{33} + a_{12}a_{23}a_{31} + a_{13}a_{21}a_{32} - a_{31}a_{22}a_{13} - a_{32}a_{23}a_{11} - a_{33}a_{21}a_{12}$$

EXAMPLE 5   *The Determinant of a Matrix of Order 3*

Find the determinant of

$$A = \begin{bmatrix} 0 & 2 & 1 \\ 3 & -1 & 2 \\ 4 & -4 & 1 \end{bmatrix}.$$

Solution We begin by recopying the first two columns and then computing the six diagonal products as follows.

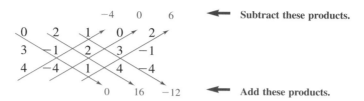

Now, by adding the lower three products and subtracting the upper three products, we find the determinant of A to be

$$|A| = 0 + 16 - 12 - (-4) - 0 - 6 = 2.$$

REMARK: The diagonal process illustrated in Example 5 is valid *only* for matrices of order 3. For matrices of higher orders, another method must be used.

Triangular Matrices

Evaluating determinants of matrices of order 4 or higher can be tedious. There is, however, an important exception: the determinant of a **triangular** matrix. A square matrix is called **upper triangular** if it has all zero entries below its main diagonal, and **lower triangular** if it has all zero entries above its main diagonal. A matrix that is both upper and lower triangular is called **diagonal.** That is, a diagonal matrix is one in which all entries above and below the main diagonal are zero.

Upper Triangular Matrix   *Lower Triangular Matrix*

$$\begin{bmatrix} a_{11} & a_{12} & a_{13} & \cdots & a_{1n} \\ 0 & a_{22} & a_{23} & \cdots & a_{2n} \\ 0 & 0 & a_{33} & \cdots & a_{3n} \\ \vdots & \vdots & \vdots & & \vdots \\ 0 & 0 & 0 & \cdots & a_{nn} \end{bmatrix} \qquad \begin{bmatrix} a_{11} & 0 & 0 & \cdots & 0 \\ a_{21} & a_{22} & 0 & \cdots & 0 \\ a_{31} & a_{32} & a_{33} & \cdots & 0 \\ \vdots & \vdots & \vdots & & \vdots \\ a_{n1} & a_{n2} & a_{n3} & \cdots & a_{nn} \end{bmatrix}$$

To find the determinant of a triangular matrix, we simply form the product of the entries on the main diagonal. It is easy to see that this procedure is valid for triangular matrices of order 2 or 3. For instance, the determinant of

$$A = \begin{bmatrix} 2 & 3 & -1 \\ 0 & -1 & 2 \\ 0 & 0 & 3 \end{bmatrix}$$

can be found by expanding by the third row to obtain

$$|A| = 0\begin{vmatrix} 3 & -1 \\ -1 & 2 \end{vmatrix} - 0\begin{vmatrix} 2 & -1 \\ 0 & 2 \end{vmatrix} + 3\begin{vmatrix} 2 & 3 \\ 0 & -1 \end{vmatrix} = 3(2)(-1),$$

which is the product of the entries on the main diagonal.

Theorem 3.2	If A is a triangular matrix of order n, then its determinant is the product of the entries on the main diagonal. That is,
Determinant of a Triangular Matrix	$$\det(A) = |A| = a_{11}a_{22}a_{33} \cdots a_{nn}.$$

Proof   We use *mathematical induction** to prove this theorem for the case in which A is an upper triangular matrix. The case in which A is lower triangular can be proven similarly. If A has order 1, then $A = [a_{11}]$ and the determinant is given by

$$|A| = a_{11}.$$

Assuming that the theorem is true for any upper triangular matrix of order $k - 1$, we now consider an upper triangular matrix A of order k. Expanding by the kth row, we obtain

$$|A| = 0C_{k1} + 0C_{k2} + \cdots + 0C_{k\,k-1} + a_{kk}C_{kk} = a_{kk}C_{kk}.$$

Now, we note that $C_{kk} = (-1)^{2k}M_{kk} = M_{kk}$, where M_{kk} is the determinant of the upper triangular matrix formed by deleting the kth row and column of A. Since this matrix is of order $k - 1$, we can apply our induction assumption to write the following.

$$\begin{aligned} |A| &= a_{kk}M_{kk} = a_{kk}(a_{11}a_{22}a_{33} \cdots a_{k-1\,k-1}) \\ &= a_{11}a_{22}a_{33} \cdots a_{kk} \end{aligned}$$

EXAMPLE 6   *The Determinant of a Triangular Matrix*

Find the determinants of the following matrices.

(a) $A = \begin{bmatrix} 2 & 0 & 0 & 0 \\ 4 & -2 & 0 & 0 \\ -5 & 6 & 1 & 0 \\ 1 & 5 & 3 & 3 \end{bmatrix}$ (b) $B = \begin{bmatrix} -1 & 0 & 0 & 0 & 0 \\ 0 & 3 & 0 & 0 & 0 \\ 0 & 0 & 2 & 0 & 0 \\ 0 & 0 & 0 & 4 & 0 \\ 0 & 0 & 0 & 0 & -2 \end{bmatrix}$

Solution   (a) The determinant of this triangular matrix is given by $|A| = (2)(-2)(1)(3) = -12$.

(b) This *diagonal* matrix is both upper and lower triangular. Therefore its determinant is given by $|B| = (-1)(3)(2)(4)(-2) = 48$.

---

*A discussion of mathematical induction can be found in the Appendix.

SECTION 3.1 ☐ EXERCISES

In Exercises 1–12, find the determinant of the given matrix.

1. $[1]$

2. $[-3]$

3. $\begin{bmatrix} 2 & 1 \\ 3 & 4 \end{bmatrix}$

4. $\begin{bmatrix} -3 & 1 \\ 5 & 2 \end{bmatrix}$

5. $\begin{bmatrix} 5 & 2 \\ -6 & 3 \end{bmatrix}$

6. $\begin{bmatrix} 2 & -2 \\ 4 & 3 \end{bmatrix}$

7. $\begin{bmatrix} -7 & 6 \\ \frac{1}{2} & 3 \end{bmatrix}$

8. $\begin{bmatrix} 4 & -3 \\ 0 & 0 \end{bmatrix}$

9. $\begin{bmatrix} 2 & 6 \\ 0 & 3 \end{bmatrix}$

10. $\begin{bmatrix} 2 & -3 \\ -6 & 9 \end{bmatrix}$

11. $\begin{bmatrix} \lambda - 3 & 2 \\ 4 & \lambda - 1 \end{bmatrix}$

12. $\begin{bmatrix} \lambda - 2 & 0 \\ 4 & \lambda - 4 \end{bmatrix}$

In Exercises 13–16, find (a) the minors and (b) the cofactors of the given matrix.

13. $\begin{bmatrix} 1 & 2 \\ 3 & 4 \end{bmatrix}$

14. $\begin{bmatrix} -1 & 0 \\ 2 & 1 \end{bmatrix}$

15. $\begin{bmatrix} -3 & 2 & 1 \\ 4 & 5 & 6 \\ 2 & -3 & 1 \end{bmatrix}$

16. $\begin{bmatrix} -3 & 4 & 2 \\ 6 & 3 & 1 \\ 4 & -7 & -8 \end{bmatrix}$

17. Find the determinant of the matrix in Exercise 15 using the method of expansion by cofactors. Use (a) the second row and (b) the second column.

18. Find the determinant of the matrix in Exercise 16 using the method of expansion by cofactors. Use (a) the third row and (b) the first column.

In Exercises 19–36, use expansion by cofactors to find the determinant of the given matrix.

19. $\begin{bmatrix} 1 & 4 & -2 \\ 3 & 2 & 0 \\ -1 & 4 & 3 \end{bmatrix}$

20. $\begin{bmatrix} 2 & -1 & 3 \\ 1 & 4 & 4 \\ 1 & 0 & 2 \end{bmatrix}$

21. $\begin{bmatrix} 2 & 4 & 6 \\ 0 & 3 & 1 \\ 0 & 0 & -5 \end{bmatrix}$

22. $\begin{bmatrix} -3 & 0 & 0 \\ 7 & 11 & 0 \\ 1 & 2 & 2 \end{bmatrix}$

23. $\begin{bmatrix} 6 & 3 & -7 \\ 0 & 0 & 0 \\ 4 & -6 & 3 \end{bmatrix}$

24. $\begin{bmatrix} 2 & 3 & 1 \\ 0 & 5 & -2 \\ 0 & 0 & -2 \end{bmatrix}$

25. $\begin{bmatrix} 0.1 & 0.2 & 0.3 \\ -0.3 & 0.2 & 0.2 \\ 0.5 & 0.4 & 0.4 \end{bmatrix}$

26. $\begin{bmatrix} -0.4 & 0.4 & 0.3 \\ 0.2 & 0.2 & 0.2 \\ 0.3 & 0.2 & 0.2 \end{bmatrix}$

27. $\begin{bmatrix} x & y & 1 \\ 2 & 3 & 1 \\ 0 & -1 & 1 \end{bmatrix}$

28. $\begin{bmatrix} x & y & 1 \\ -2 & -2 & 1 \\ 1 & 5 & 1 \end{bmatrix}$

29. $\begin{bmatrix} 3 & 6 & -5 & 4 \\ -2 & 0 & 6 & 0 \\ 1 & 1 & 2 & 2 \\ 0 & 3 & -1 & -1 \end{bmatrix}$

30. $\begin{bmatrix} 2 & 6 & 6 & 2 \\ 2 & 7 & 3 & 6 \\ 1 & 5 & 0 & 1 \\ 3 & 7 & 0 & 7 \end{bmatrix}$

31. $\begin{bmatrix} 5 & 3 & 0 & 6 \\ 4 & 6 & 4 & 12 \\ 0 & 2 & -3 & 4 \\ 0 & 1 & -2 & 2 \end{bmatrix}$

32. $\begin{bmatrix} 1 & 4 & 3 & 2 \\ -5 & 6 & 2 & 1 \\ 0 & 0 & 0 & 0 \\ 3 & -2 & 1 & 5 \end{bmatrix}$

33. $\begin{bmatrix} 3 & 0 & 7 & 0 \\ 2 & 6 & 11 & 12 \\ 4 & 1 & -1 & 2 \\ 1 & 5 & 2 & 10 \end{bmatrix}$

34. $\begin{bmatrix} 3 & 2 & 4 & -1 & 5 \\ -2 & 0 & 1 & 3 & 2 \\ 1 & 0 & 0 & 4 & 0 \\ 6 & 0 & 2 & -1 & 0 \\ 3 & 0 & 5 & 1 & 0 \end{bmatrix}$

35. $\begin{bmatrix} 5 & 2 & 0 & 0 & -2 \\ 0 & 1 & 4 & 3 & 2 \\ 0 & 0 & 2 & 6 & 3 \\ 0 & 0 & 3 & 4 & 1 \\ 0 & 0 & 0 & 0 & 2 \end{bmatrix}$

36. $\begin{bmatrix} 4 & 3 & -2 & 1 & 2 \\ 0 & 0 & 0 & 0 & 0 \\ 1 & 2 & -7 & 13 & 12 \\ 6 & -2 & 5 & 6 & 7 \\ 1 & 4 & 2 & 0 & 9 \end{bmatrix}$

In Exercises 37–42, find the determinant of the given triangular matrix.

37. $\begin{bmatrix} -2 & 0 & 0 \\ 4 & 6 & 0 \\ -3 & 7 & 2 \end{bmatrix}$ **38.** $\begin{bmatrix} 5 & 0 & 0 \\ 0 & 6 & 0 \\ 0 & 0 & -3 \end{bmatrix}$

39. $\begin{bmatrix} 5 & 8 & -4 & 2 \\ 0 & 0 & 6 & 0 \\ 0 & 0 & 2 & 2 \\ 0 & 0 & 0 & -1 \end{bmatrix}$ **40.** $\begin{bmatrix} 4 & 0 & 0 & 0 \\ -1 & \frac{1}{2} & 0 & 0 \\ 3 & 5 & 3 & 0 \\ -8 & 7 & 0 & -2 \end{bmatrix}$

41. $\begin{bmatrix} -1 & 4 & 2 & 1 & -3 \\ 0 & 3 & -4 & 5 & 2 \\ 0 & 0 & 2 & 7 & 0 \\ 0 & 0 & 0 & 5 & -1 \\ 0 & 0 & 0 & 0 & 1 \end{bmatrix}$

42. $\begin{bmatrix} 7 & 0 & 0 & 0 & 0 \\ -8 & \frac{1}{4} & 0 & 0 & 0 \\ 4 & 5 & 2 & 0 & 0 \\ 3 & -3 & 5 & -1 & 0 \\ 1 & 13 & 4 & 1 & -2 \end{bmatrix}$

In Exercises 43 and 44, find the values of λ for which the given determinant is zero.

43. $\begin{vmatrix} \lambda - 1 & -4 \\ -2 & \lambda + 1 \end{vmatrix}$ **44.** $\begin{vmatrix} \lambda + 1 & 0 & 0 \\ 4 & \lambda & 3 \\ 2 & 8 & \lambda + 5 \end{vmatrix}$

45. The determinant of a 2 × 2 matrix involves 2 products. The determinant of a 3 × 3 matrix involves 6 triple products. Show that the determinant of a 4 × 4 matrix involves 24 quadruple products. (In general, the determinant of an $n \times n$ matrix involves $n!$ n-fold products.)

46. Show that the system of linear equations

$$ax + by = e$$
$$cx + dy = f$$

has a unique solution if and only if the determinant of the coefficient matrix is nonzero.

47. Verify the following equation.

$$\begin{vmatrix} 1 & 1 & 1 \\ a & b & c \\ a^2 & b^2 & c^2 \end{vmatrix} = (a - b)(b - c)(c - a)$$

48. Verify the following equation.

$$\begin{vmatrix} 1 & 1 & 1 \\ a & b & c \\ a^3 & b^3 & c^3 \end{vmatrix} = (a - b)(b - c)(c - a)(a + b + c)$$

49. Verify the following equation.

$$\begin{vmatrix} x & 0 & c \\ -1 & x & b \\ 0 & -1 & a \end{vmatrix} = ax^2 + bx + c$$

50. Use the equation given in Exercise 49 as a model to find a determinant that is equal to $ax^3 + bx^2 + cx + d$.

51. Explain why it is easy to calculate the determinant of a matrix that has an entire row of zeros.

3.2 EVALUATION OF A DETERMINANT USING ELEMENTARY OPERATIONS

Which of the following two determinants is easier to evaluate?

$$|A| = \begin{vmatrix} 1 & -2 & 3 & 1 \\ 4 & -6 & 3 & 2 \\ -2 & 4 & -9 & -3 \\ 3 & -6 & 9 & 2 \end{vmatrix} \quad \text{or} \quad |B| = \begin{vmatrix} 1 & -2 & 3 & 1 \\ 0 & 2 & -9 & -2 \\ 0 & 0 & -3 & -1 \\ 0 & 0 & 0 & -1 \end{vmatrix}$$

Given what you now know about the determinant of a triangular matrix, it is clear that the second determinant is *much* easier to evaluate. Its determinant is simply the product of the entries on the main diagonal. That is,

$$|B| = (1)(2)(-3)(-1) = 6.$$

On the other hand, using expansion by cofactors (the only technique discussed so far) to evaluate the first determinant is messy. For instance, if we expand by cofactors across the first row, we have the following.

$$|A| = 1\begin{vmatrix} -6 & 3 & 2 \\ 4 & -9 & -3 \\ -6 & 9 & 2 \end{vmatrix} + 2\begin{vmatrix} 4 & 3 & 2 \\ -2 & -9 & -3 \\ 3 & 9 & 2 \end{vmatrix} + 3\begin{vmatrix} 4 & -6 & 2 \\ -2 & 4 & -3 \\ 3 & -6 & 2 \end{vmatrix} - 1\begin{vmatrix} 4 & -6 & 3 \\ -2 & 4 & -9 \\ 3 & -6 & 9 \end{vmatrix}$$

Evaluating the determinants of these four 3×3 matrices produces

$$|A| = (1)(-60) + (2)(39) + (3)(-10) - (1)(-18) = 6.$$

It is not coincidental that these two determinants have the same value. In fact, we obtained the matrix B by performing elementary row operations on matrix A. (Try verifying this.) In this section, we consider the effect of elementary row (and column) operations on the value of a determinant. Here is an example.

EXAMPLE 1   *The Effect of Elementary Row Operations on a Determinant*

(a) The matrix B was obtained from A by interchanging the rows of A.

$$|A| = \begin{vmatrix} 2 & -3 \\ 1 & 4 \end{vmatrix} = 11 \quad \text{and} \quad |B| = \begin{vmatrix} 1 & 4 \\ 2 & -3 \end{vmatrix} = -11$$

(b) The matrix B was obtained from A by adding -2 times the first row of A to the second row of A.

$$|A| = \begin{vmatrix} 1 & -3 \\ 2 & -4 \end{vmatrix} = 2 \quad \text{and} \quad |B| = \begin{vmatrix} 1 & -3 \\ 0 & 2 \end{vmatrix} = 2$$

(c) The matrix B was obtained from A by multiplying the first row of A by $\frac{1}{2}$.

$$|A| = \begin{vmatrix} 2 & -8 \\ -2 & 9 \end{vmatrix} = 2 \quad \text{and} \quad |B| = \begin{vmatrix} 1 & -4 \\ -2 & 9 \end{vmatrix} = 1$$

In Example 1, we see that interchanging two rows of the matrix changed the sign of its determinant. Adding a multiple of one row to another did not change the determinant. Finally, multiplying a row by a nonzero constant multiplied the determinant by that same constant. The following theorem generalizes these observations. The proof of part 1 is found in Appendix A, and the proofs of the other two parts are left as exercises. (See Exercises 39 and 40.)

Theorem 3.3

Elementary Row Operations and Determinants

Let A and B be square matrices.

1. If B is obtained from A by interchanging two rows of A, then

$$\det(B) = -\det(A).$$

2. If B is obtained from A by adding a multiple of a row of A to another row of A, then

$$\det(B) = \det(A).$$

3. If B is obtained from A by multiplying a row of A by a nonzero constant c, then

$$\det(B) = c \det(A).$$

REMARK: Note that the third property allows us to take a common factor out of a row. For instance,

$$\begin{vmatrix} 2 & 4 \\ 1 & 3 \end{vmatrix} = 2 \begin{vmatrix} 1 & 2 \\ 1 & 3 \end{vmatrix}. \qquad \textbf{Factor 2 out of first row}$$

Theorem 3.3 provides a practical way to evaluate determinants. (This method works particularly well with computers.) To find the determinant of a matrix A, we use elementary row operations to obtain a triangular matrix B that is row equivalent to A. For each step in the elimination process, we use Theorem 3.3 to determine the effect of the elementary row operation on the determinant. Finally, we find the determinant of B by forming the product of the entries on its main diagonal. This process is demonstrated in the next example.

EXAMPLE 2   *Evaluating a Determinant Using Elementary Row Operations*

Find the determinant of

$$A = \begin{bmatrix} 2 & -3 & 10 \\ 1 & 2 & -2 \\ 0 & 1 & -3 \end{bmatrix}.$$

Solution   Using elementary row operations, we rewrite A in triangular form as follows.

$$\begin{vmatrix} 2 & -3 & 10 \\ 1 & 2 & -2 \\ 0 & 1 & -3 \end{vmatrix} = - \begin{vmatrix} 1 & 2 & -2 \\ 2 & -3 & 10 \\ 0 & 1 & -3 \end{vmatrix} \qquad \longleftarrow \quad \textbf{Interchange the first two rows.}$$

$$= - \begin{vmatrix} 1 & 2 & -2 \\ 0 & -7 & 14 \\ 0 & 1 & -3 \end{vmatrix} \qquad \longleftarrow \quad \begin{array}{l} \textbf{Adding } -2 \textbf{ times the first row to the} \\ \textbf{second row produces a new second row.} \end{array}$$

$$= 7 \begin{vmatrix} 1 & 2 & -2 \\ 0 & 1 & -2 \\ 0 & 1 & -3 \end{vmatrix} \qquad \longleftarrow \quad \textbf{Factor } -7 \textbf{ out of the second row.}$$

$$= 7 \begin{vmatrix} 1 & 2 & -2 \\ 0 & 1 & -2 \\ 0 & 0 & -1 \end{vmatrix}$$

Adding -1 times the second row to the third row produces a new third row.

Now, because the final matrix is triangular, we conclude that the determinant is

$$|A| = 7(1)(1)(-1) = -7.$$

Determinants and Elementary Column Operations

Although Theorem 3.3 was stated in terms of elementary *row* operations, the theorem remains valid if the word "row" is replaced by the word "column." Operations performed on the columns of a matrix (rather than the rows) are called **elementary column operations,** and two matrices are called **column equivalent** if one can be obtained from the other by elementary column operations. The column version of Theorem 3.3 is illustrated as follows.

$$\begin{vmatrix} 2 & 1 & -3 \\ 4 & 0 & 1 \\ 0 & 0 & 2 \end{vmatrix} = - \begin{vmatrix} 1 & 2 & -3 \\ 0 & 4 & 1 \\ 0 & 0 & 2 \end{vmatrix} \qquad \begin{vmatrix} 2 & 3 & -5 \\ 4 & 1 & 0 \\ -2 & 4 & -3 \end{vmatrix} = 2 \begin{vmatrix} 1 & 3 & -5 \\ 2 & 1 & 0 \\ -1 & 4 & -3 \end{vmatrix}$$

Interchange the first two columns

Factor 2 out of the first column.

In evaluating a determinant by hand, it is occasionally convenient to use elementary column operations, as shown in Example 3.

EXAMPLE 3   *Evaluating a Determinant Using Elementary Column Operations*

Find the determinant of

$$A = \begin{bmatrix} -1 & 2 & 2 \\ 3 & -6 & 4 \\ 5 & -10 & -3 \end{bmatrix}.$$

Solution   Because the first two columns of A are multiples of each other, we can obtain a column of zeros by adding 2 times the first column to the second column as follows.

$$\begin{vmatrix} -1 & 2 & 2 \\ 3 & -6 & 4 \\ 5 & -10 & -3 \end{vmatrix} = \begin{vmatrix} -1 & 0 & 2 \\ 3 & 0 & 4 \\ 5 & 0 & -3 \end{vmatrix}$$

At this point we need not continue to rewrite the matrix in triangular form. Since there is an entire column of zeros, we simply conclude that the determinant is zero. The validity of this conclusion follows from Theorem 3.1. Specifically, by expanding by cofactors along the second column, we have

$$|A| = (0)C_{12} + (0)C_{22} + (0)C_{32} = 0.$$

Example 3 shows that if one column of a matrix is a scalar multiple of another column, we can immediately conclude that the determinant of the matrix is zero. This is one of three conditions, listed next, that yield a determinant of zero.

Theorem 3.4	If A is a square matrix and any of the following conditions is true, then $\det(A) = 0$.
Conditions That Yield a Zero Determinant	1. An entire row (or an entire column) consists of zeros. 2. Two rows (or columns) are equal. 3. One row (or column) is a multiple of another row (or column).

Proof   Each part of this theorem is easily verified by using elementary row operations and expansion by cofactors. For example, if an entire row or column is zero, then each cofactor in the expansion is multiplied by zero. And if condition 2 or 3 is true, then we can use elementary row or column operations to create a row or column with all zeros.

Recognizing the conditions listed in Theorem 3.4 can make evaluating a determinant much easier. For instance

$$\begin{vmatrix} 0 & 0 & 0 \\ 2 & 4 & -5 \\ 3 & -5 & 2 \end{vmatrix} = 0, \qquad \begin{vmatrix} 1 & -2 & 4 \\ 0 & 1 & 2 \\ 1 & -2 & 4 \end{vmatrix} = 0, \qquad \begin{vmatrix} 1 & 2 & -3 \\ 2 & -1 & -6 \\ -2 & 0 & 6 \end{vmatrix} = 0.$$

The first row has all zeros.   *The first and third rows are the same.*   *The third column is a multiple of the first column.*

Do not conclude that Theorem 3.4 gives the *only* conditions that produce a determinant of zero. The theorem is often used indirectly. That is, you can begin with a matrix that does not satisfy any of the conditions of Theorem 3.4 and, through elementary row or column operations, obtain a matrix that does satisfy one of the conditions. Then you may conclude that the original matrix has a determinant of zero. This process is demonstrated in Example 4.

EXAMPLE 4   *A Matrix with a Zero Determinant*

Find the determinant of

$$A = \begin{bmatrix} 1 & 4 & 1 \\ 2 & -1 & 0 \\ 0 & 18 & 4 \end{bmatrix}.$$

Solution   Adding -2 times the first row to the second row produces

$$|A| = \begin{vmatrix} 1 & 4 & 1 \\ 2 & -1 & 0 \\ 0 & 18 & 4 \end{vmatrix} = \begin{vmatrix} 1 & 4 & 1 \\ 0 & -9 & -2 \\ 0 & 18 & 4 \end{vmatrix}.$$

Now, because the second and third rows are multiples of each other, we conclude that the determinant is zero.

In Example 4 we could have obtained a matrix with a row of all zeros by performing an additional elementary row operation (adding 2 times the second row to the third row). This is true in general. That is, a square matrix has a determinant of zero if and only if it is row (or column) equivalent to a matrix that has at least one row (or column) consisting entirely of zeros. We will prove this result in the next section.

We have now surveyed two general methods for evaluating determinants. Of these, the method using elementary row operations to reduce the matrix to triangular form is usually faster than cofactor expansion along a row or column. If the size of the matrix is large, then the number of arithmetic operations for cofactor expansion can become extremely big. For this reason most computer and calculator algorithms use the method involving elementary row operations. The following table gives the number of additions (plus subtractions) and multiplications (plus divisions) needed for each of these two methods for matrices of order 3, 5, and 10.

	Cofactor Expansion		Row Reduction	
Order n	Additions	Multiplications	Additions	Multiplications
3	5	9	5	10
5	119	205	30	45
10	3,628,799	6,235,300	285	339

In fact, the number of operations for the cofactor expansion of an $n \times n$ matrix grows like $n!$ $(n! = 1 \cdot 2 \cdot 3 \cdots (n - 1) \cdot n)$. Since $30! \approx 2.65 \times 10^{32}$, even a relatively small 30×30 matrix would require over 10^{32} operations. If a computer could do one trillion operations per second, it would still take over one trillion years to compute the determinant of this matrix using cofactor expansion! Yet, row reduction would take only a few seconds!

When evaluating a determinant *by hand*, you can sometimes save steps by using elementary row (or column) operations to create a row (or column) having zeros in all but one position and then using cofactor expansion to reduce the order of the matrix by one. This approach is illustrated in the next two examples.

EXAMPLE 5   *Evaluating a Determinant*

Find the determinant of

$$A = \begin{bmatrix} -3 & 5 & 2 \\ 2 & -4 & -1 \\ -3 & 0 & 6 \end{bmatrix}.$$

Solution   Notice that the matrix A already has one zero in the third row. We can create another zero in the third row by adding 2 times the first column to the third column as follows.

$$|A| = \begin{vmatrix} -3 & 5 & 2 \\ 2 & -4 & -1 \\ -3 & 0 & 6 \end{vmatrix} = \begin{vmatrix} -3 & 5 & -4 \\ 2 & -4 & 3 \\ -3 & 0 & 0 \end{vmatrix}$$

Expanding by cofactors along the third row produces

$$|A| = -3(-1)^4 \begin{vmatrix} 5 & -4 \\ -4 & 3 \end{vmatrix}$$

$$= -3(-1) = 3.$$

EXAMPLE 6   *Evaluating a Determinant*

Evaluate the determinant of

$$A = \begin{bmatrix} 2 & 0 & 1 & 3 & -2 \\ -2 & 1 & 3 & 2 & -1 \\ 1 & 0 & -1 & 2 & 3 \\ 3 & -1 & 2 & 4 & -3 \\ 1 & 1 & 3 & 2 & 0 \end{bmatrix}.$$

Solution   Because the second column of this matrix already has two zeros, we choose it for cofactor expansion. Two additional zeros can be created in the second column by adding the second row to the fourth row, and then adding -1 times the second row to the fifth row.

$$|A| = \begin{vmatrix} 2 & 0 & 1 & 3 & -2 \\ -2 & 1 & 3 & 2 & -1 \\ 1 & 0 & -1 & 2 & 3 \\ 3 & -1 & 2 & 4 & -3 \\ 1 & 1 & 3 & 2 & 0 \end{vmatrix} = \begin{vmatrix} 2 & 0 & 1 & 3 & -2 \\ -2 & 1 & 3 & 2 & -1 \\ 1 & 0 & -1 & 2 & 3 \\ 1 & 0 & 5 & 6 & -4 \\ 3 & 0 & 0 & 0 & 1 \end{vmatrix}$$

$$= (1)(-1)^4 \begin{vmatrix} 2 & 1 & 3 & -2 \\ 1 & -1 & 2 & 3 \\ 1 & 5 & 6 & -4 \\ 3 & 0 & 0 & 1 \end{vmatrix}$$

(Note that we have now reduced the problem of finding the determinant of a 5 × 5 matrix to finding the determinant of a 4 × 4 matrix.) Because we already have two zeros in the fourth row, it is chosen for the next cofactor expansion. Adding -3 times the fourth column to the first column produces the following.

$$|A| = \begin{vmatrix} 2 & 1 & 3 & -2 \\ 1 & -1 & 2 & 3 \\ 1 & 5 & 6 & -4 \\ 3 & 0 & 0 & 1 \end{vmatrix} = \begin{vmatrix} 8 & 1 & 3 & -2 \\ -8 & -1 & 2 & 3 \\ 13 & 5 & 6 & -4 \\ 0 & 0 & 0 & 1 \end{vmatrix}$$

$$= (1)(-1)^8 \begin{vmatrix} 8 & 1 & 3 \\ -8 & -1 & 2 \\ 13 & 5 & 6 \end{vmatrix}$$

Finally, adding the second row to the first row and then expanding by cofactors along the first row gives

$$|A| = \begin{vmatrix} 8 & 1 & 3 \\ -8 & -1 & 2 \\ 13 & 5 & 6 \end{vmatrix} = \begin{vmatrix} 0 & 0 & 5 \\ -8 & -1 & 2 \\ 13 & 5 & 6 \end{vmatrix}$$

$$= 5(-1)^4 \begin{vmatrix} -8 & -1 \\ 13 & 5 \end{vmatrix}$$

$$= 5(-40 + 13) = -135.$$

SECTION 3.2 ❑ EXERCISES

In Exercises 1–14, which property of determinants is illustrated by the given equation?

1. $\begin{vmatrix} 2 & -6 \\ 1 & -3 \end{vmatrix} = 0$

2. $\begin{vmatrix} -4 & 5 \\ 12 & -15 \end{vmatrix} = 0$

3. $\begin{vmatrix} 1 & 4 & 2 \\ 0 & 0 & 0 \\ 5 & 6 & -7 \end{vmatrix} = 0$

4. $\begin{vmatrix} -4 & 3 & 2 \\ 8 & 0 & 0 \\ -4 & 3 & 2 \end{vmatrix} = 0$

5. $\begin{vmatrix} 1 & 3 & 4 \\ -7 & 2 & -5 \\ 6 & 1 & 2 \end{vmatrix} = -\begin{vmatrix} 1 & 4 & 3 \\ -7 & -5 & 2 \\ 6 & 2 & 1 \end{vmatrix}$

6. $\begin{vmatrix} 1 & 3 & 4 \\ -2 & 2 & 0 \\ 1 & 6 & 2 \end{vmatrix} = -\begin{vmatrix} 1 & 6 & 2 \\ -2 & 2 & 0 \\ 1 & 3 & 4 \end{vmatrix}$

7. $\begin{vmatrix} 5 & 10 \\ 2 & -7 \end{vmatrix} = 5\begin{vmatrix} 1 & 2 \\ 2 & -7 \end{vmatrix}$

8. $\begin{vmatrix} 1 & 8 & -3 \\ 3 & -12 & 6 \\ 7 & 4 & 9 \end{vmatrix} = 12\begin{vmatrix} 1 & 2 & -1 \\ 3 & -3 & 2 \\ 7 & 1 & 3 \end{vmatrix}$

9. $\begin{vmatrix} 5 & 0 & 10 \\ 25 & -30 & 40 \\ -15 & 5 & 20 \end{vmatrix} = 5^3\begin{vmatrix} 1 & 0 & 2 \\ 5 & -6 & 8 \\ -3 & 1 & 4 \end{vmatrix}$

10. $\begin{vmatrix} 6 & 0 & 0 & 0 \\ 0 & 6 & 0 & 0 \\ 0 & 0 & 6 & 0 \\ 0 & 0 & 0 & 6 \end{vmatrix} = 6^4\begin{vmatrix} 1 & 0 & 0 & 0 \\ 0 & 1 & 0 & 0 \\ 0 & 0 & 1 & 0 \\ 0 & 0 & 0 & 1 \end{vmatrix}$

11. $\begin{vmatrix} 2 & -3 \\ 8 & 7 \end{vmatrix} = \begin{vmatrix} 2 & -3 \\ 0 & 19 \end{vmatrix}$

12. $\begin{vmatrix} 1 & -3 & 2 \\ 5 & 2 & -1 \\ -1 & 0 & 6 \end{vmatrix} = \begin{vmatrix} 1 & -3 & 2 \\ 0 & 17 & -11 \\ -1 & 0 & 6 \end{vmatrix}$

13. $\begin{vmatrix} 3 & 2 & 4 \\ -2 & 1 & 5 \\ 5 & -7 & -20 \end{vmatrix} = \begin{vmatrix} 3 & 2 & -6 \\ -2 & 1 & 0 \\ 5 & -7 & 15 \end{vmatrix}$

14. $\begin{vmatrix} 5 & 4 & 2 \\ 4 & -3 & 4 \\ 7 & 6 & 3 \end{vmatrix} = -\begin{vmatrix} 5 & 4 & 2 \\ -4 & 3 & -4 \\ 7 & 6 & 3 \end{vmatrix}$

In Exercises 15–28, use elementary row or column operations to evaluate the determinant.

15. $\begin{vmatrix} 1 & 7 & -3 \\ 1 & 3 & 1 \\ 4 & 8 & 1 \end{vmatrix}$

16. $\begin{vmatrix} 1 & 1 & 1 \\ 2 & -1 & -2 \\ 1 & -2 & -1 \end{vmatrix}$

17. $\begin{vmatrix} 2 & -1 & -1 \\ 1 & 3 & 2 \\ 1 & 1 & 3 \end{vmatrix}$

18. $\begin{vmatrix} 3 & -1 & -3 \\ -1 & -4 & -2 \\ 3 & -1 & -1 \end{vmatrix}$

19. $\begin{vmatrix} 4 & 3 & -2 \\ 5 & 4 & 1 \\ -2 & 3 & 4 \end{vmatrix}$ **20.** $\begin{vmatrix} 3 & 8 & -7 \\ 0 & -5 & 4 \\ 6 & 1 & 6 \end{vmatrix}$

21. $\begin{vmatrix} 5 & -8 & 0 \\ 9 & 7 & 4 \\ -8 & 7 & 1 \end{vmatrix}$ **22.** $\begin{vmatrix} 4 & -8 & 5 \\ 8 & -5 & 3 \\ 8 & 5 & 2 \end{vmatrix}$

23. $\begin{vmatrix} 4 & -7 & 9 & 1 \\ 6 & 2 & 7 & 0 \\ 3 & 6 & -3 & 3 \\ 0 & 7 & 4 & -1 \end{vmatrix}$ **24.** $\begin{vmatrix} 9 & -4 & 2 & 5 \\ 2 & 7 & 6 & -5 \\ 4 & 1 & -2 & 0 \\ 7 & 3 & 4 & 10 \end{vmatrix}$

25. $\begin{vmatrix} 1 & -2 & 7 & 9 \\ 3 & -4 & 5 & 5 \\ 3 & 6 & 1 & -1 \\ 4 & 5 & 3 & 2 \end{vmatrix}$ **26.** $\begin{vmatrix} 0 & -3 & 8 & 2 \\ 8 & 1 & -1 & 6 \\ -4 & 6 & 0 & 9 \\ -7 & 0 & 0 & 14 \end{vmatrix}$

27. $\begin{vmatrix} 1 & -1 & 8 & 4 & 2 \\ 2 & 6 & 0 & -4 & 3 \\ 2 & 0 & 2 & 6 & 2 \\ 0 & 2 & 8 & 0 & 0 \\ 0 & 1 & 1 & 2 & 2 \end{vmatrix}$

28. $\begin{vmatrix} 3 & -2 & 4 & 3 & 1 \\ -1 & 0 & 2 & 1 & 0 \\ 5 & -1 & 0 & 3 & 2 \\ 4 & 7 & -8 & 0 & 0 \\ 1 & 2 & 3 & 0 & 2 \end{vmatrix}$

In Exercises 29–34, find the determinant of the given elementary matrix. (Assume $k \neq 0$.)

29. $\begin{bmatrix} 1 & 0 & 0 \\ 0 & k & 0 \\ 0 & 0 & 1 \end{bmatrix}$ **30.** $\begin{bmatrix} 1 & 0 & 0 \\ 0 & 1 & 0 \\ 0 & 0 & k \end{bmatrix}$

31. $\begin{bmatrix} 0 & 1 & 0 \\ 1 & 0 & 0 \\ 0 & 0 & 1 \end{bmatrix}$ **32.** $\begin{bmatrix} 0 & 0 & 1 \\ 0 & 1 & 0 \\ 1 & 0 & 0 \end{bmatrix}$

33. $\begin{bmatrix} 1 & 0 & 0 \\ k & 1 & 0 \\ 0 & 0 & 1 \end{bmatrix}$ **34.** $\begin{bmatrix} 1 & 0 & 0 \\ 0 & 1 & 0 \\ 0 & k & 1 \end{bmatrix}$

35. Prove the following property.

$$\begin{vmatrix} a_{11} & a_{12} & a_{13} \\ a_{21} & a_{22} & a_{23} \\ a_{31} & a_{32} & a_{33} \end{vmatrix} + \begin{vmatrix} b_{11} & a_{12} & a_{13} \\ b_{21} & a_{22} & a_{23} \\ b_{31} & a_{32} & a_{33} \end{vmatrix} = \begin{vmatrix} (a_{11} + b_{11}) & a_{12} & a_{13} \\ (a_{21} + b_{21}) & a_{22} & a_{23} \\ (a_{31} + b_{31}) & a_{32} & a_{33} \end{vmatrix}$$

36. Prove the following property.

$$\begin{vmatrix} 1+a & 1 & 1 \\ 1 & 1+b & 1 \\ 1 & 1 & 1+c \end{vmatrix} = abc\left(1 + \frac{1}{a} + \frac{1}{b} + \frac{1}{c}\right),$$

$$a \neq 0, \quad b \neq 0, \quad c \neq 0$$

In Exercises 37 and 38, evaluate the given determinant.

37. $\begin{vmatrix} \cos\theta & \sin\theta \\ -\sin\theta & \cos\theta \end{vmatrix}$ **38.** $\begin{vmatrix} \sec\theta & \tan\theta \\ \tan\theta & \sec\theta \end{vmatrix}$

39. Prove part 2 of Theorem 3.3.

40. Prove part 3 of Theorem 3.3.

41. Suppose a computer operator charges $0.001 (one tenth of a cent) for each addition and subtraction, and $0.003 for each multiplication and division. Contrast the costs of calculating the determinant of a 10×10 matrix by cofactor expansion and by row reduction. Which method would you prefer to use for calculating determinants?

3.3 PROPERTIES OF DETERMINANTS

In this section we discuss several important properties of determinants. We begin by considering the determinant of the product of two matrices.

EXAMPLE 1   ***The Determinant of a Matrix Product***

Find $|A|$, $|B|$, and $|AB|$ for the following matrices.

$$A = \begin{bmatrix} 1 & -2 & 2 \\ 0 & 3 & 2 \\ 1 & 0 & 1 \end{bmatrix} \quad \text{and} \quad B = \begin{bmatrix} 2 & 0 & 1 \\ 0 & -1 & -2 \\ 3 & 1 & -2 \end{bmatrix}$$

Solution   Using the techniques described in the previous section, we can show that $|A|$ and $|B|$ have the following values.

$$|A| = \begin{vmatrix} 1 & -2 & 2 \\ 0 & 3 & 2 \\ 1 & 0 & 1 \end{vmatrix} = -7 \quad \text{and} \quad |B| = \begin{vmatrix} 2 & 0 & 1 \\ 0 & -1 & -2 \\ 3 & 1 & -2 \end{vmatrix} = 11$$

The matrix product AB is given by

$$AB = \begin{bmatrix} 1 & -2 & 2 \\ 0 & 3 & 2 \\ 1 & 0 & 1 \end{bmatrix} \begin{bmatrix} 2 & 0 & 1 \\ 0 & -1 & -2 \\ 3 & 1 & -2 \end{bmatrix} = \begin{bmatrix} 8 & 4 & 1 \\ 6 & -1 & -10 \\ 5 & 1 & -1 \end{bmatrix}.$$

Therefore the determinant of AB is

$$|AB| = \begin{vmatrix} 8 & 4 & 1 \\ 6 & -1 & -10 \\ 5 & 1 & -1 \end{vmatrix} = -77.$$

In Example 1, note that the determinant of the matrix product is given by the product of the determinants. That is,

$$|AB| = |A||B|$$
$$-77 = (-7)(11).$$

This is true in general, as indicated in the following theorem. A proof of Theorem 3.5 is given in Appendix A.

Theorem 3.5

Determinant of a Matrix Product

If A and B are square matrices of order n, then

$$\det (AB) = \det(A) \det(B).$$

REMARK: Theorem 3.5 can be extended to include the product of any finite number of matrices. That is,

$$|A_1 A_2 A_3 \cdots A_k| = |A_1||A_2||A_3| \cdots |A_k|.$$

The relationship between $|A|$ and $|cA|$ is given in the next theorem.

Theorem 3.6

Determinant of a Scalar Multiple of a Matrix

If A is an $n \times n$ matrix and c is a scalar, then the determinant of cA is given by

$$\det (cA) = c^n \det(A).$$

Proof   This formula can be proven by repeated applications of part 3 of Theorem 3.3. That is, we factor the scalar c out of each of the n rows of $|cA|$ to obtain

$$|cA| = c^n|A|.$$

EXAMPLE 2   ***The Determinant of a Scalar Multiple of a Matrix***

Find the determinant of the following matrix.

$$A = \begin{bmatrix} 10 & -20 & 40 \\ 30 & 0 & 50 \\ -20 & -30 & 10 \end{bmatrix}$$

Solution   Because

$$A = 10\begin{bmatrix} 1 & -2 & 4 \\ 3 & 0 & 5 \\ -2 & -3 & 1 \end{bmatrix} \quad \text{and} \quad \begin{vmatrix} 1 & -2 & 4 \\ 3 & 0 & 5 \\ -2 & -3 & 1 \end{vmatrix} = 5,$$

we can apply Theorem 3.6 to conclude that

$$|A| = 10^3\begin{vmatrix} 1 & -2 & 4 \\ 3 & 0 & 5 \\ -2 & -3 & 1 \end{vmatrix} = 1000(5) = 5000.$$

Theorems 3.5 and 3.6 provide formulas for evaluating the determinant of the product of two matrices and a scalar multiple of a matrix. These theorems do not, however, list a formula for the determinant of the *sum* of two matrices. It is important to note that the sum of the determinants of two matrices usually does not equal the determinant of their sum. That is, in general,

$$|A| + |B| \neq |A + B|.$$

For instance, if

$$A = \begin{bmatrix} 6 & 2 \\ 2 & 1 \end{bmatrix} \quad \text{and} \quad B = \begin{bmatrix} 3 & 7 \\ 0 & -1 \end{bmatrix},$$

then $|A| = 2$ and $|B| = -3$, but $|A + B| = -18$.

Determinants and the Inverse of a Matrix

We saw in Chapter 2 that some square matrices are not invertible. However, it can be difficult to tell simply by inspection whether a matrix possesses an inverse. For instance, can you tell which of the following two matrices is invertible?

$$A = \begin{bmatrix} 0 & 2 & -1 \\ 3 & -2 & 1 \\ 3 & 2 & -1 \end{bmatrix} \quad \text{or} \quad B = \begin{bmatrix} 0 & 2 & -1 \\ 3 & -2 & 1 \\ 3 & 2 & 1 \end{bmatrix}$$

The next theorem shows that determinants are useful for classifying square matrices as invertible or noninvertible.

Theorem 3.7 Determinant of an Invertible Matrix	A square matrix A is invertible (nonsingular) if and only if $\det(A) \neq 0.$

Proof   To prove the theorem in one direction, we assume that A is invertible. Then $AA^{-1} = I$, and by Theorem 3.5 we may write

$$|A||A^{-1}| = |I|.$$

Now, because $|I| = 1$, we know that neither determinant on the left is zero. Specifically, then $|A| \neq 0$.

To prove the theorem in the other direction, we assume that the determinant of A is nonzero. Then, using Gauss-Jordan elimination, we find a matrix B, in reduced row-echelon form, that is row equivalent to A. Because B is in reduced row-echelon form, it must be the identity matrix I or it must have at least one row that consists entirely of zeros. But if B has a row of all zeros, then by Theorem 3.4 we know that $|B| = 0$, which would imply that $|A| = 0$. Because we assumed $|A|$ is nonzero, we can conclude that $B = I$. Therefore A is row equivalent to the identity matrix, and by Theorem 2.15 we know that A is invertible.

EXAMPLE 3   *Classifying Square Matrices as Singular or Nonsingular*

Which of the following matrices possesses an inverse?

$$\text{(a)} \begin{bmatrix} 0 & 2 & -1 \\ 3 & -2 & 1 \\ 3 & 2 & -1 \end{bmatrix} \quad \text{(b)} \begin{bmatrix} 0 & 2 & -1 \\ 3 & -2 & 1 \\ 3 & 2 & 1 \end{bmatrix}$$

Solution   (a) Because

$$\begin{vmatrix} 0 & 2 & -1 \\ 3 & -2 & 1 \\ 3 & 2 & -1 \end{vmatrix} = 0,$$

we conclude that this matrix has no inverse (it is singular).

(b) Because

$$\begin{vmatrix} 0 & 2 & -1 \\ 3 & -2 & 1 \\ 3 & 2 & 1 \end{vmatrix} = -12 \neq 0,$$

we conclude that this matrix has an inverse (it is nonsingular).

The following theorem gives a convenient way to find the determinant of the inverse of a matrix.

Theorem 3.8	If A is invertible, then
Determinant of an Inverse Matrix	$$\det(A^{-1}) = \frac{1}{\det(A)}.$$

Proof Because A is invertible, $AA^{-1} = I$, and we can apply Theorem 3.5 to conclude that $|A||A^{-1}| = |I| = 1$. Moreover, because A is invertible, we also know that $|A| \neq 0$, and we can divide by $|A|$ to obtain

$$|A^{-1}| = \frac{1}{|A|}.$$

EXAMPLE 4 *Determinant of the Inverse of a Matrix*

Find $|A^{-1}|$ for the matrix

$$A = \begin{bmatrix} 1 & 0 & 3 \\ 0 & -1 & 2 \\ 2 & 1 & 0 \end{bmatrix}.$$

Solution One way to solve this problem is to find A^{-1} and then evaluate its determinant. It is simpler, however, to apply Theorem 3.8 as follows. We find the determinant of A,

$$|A| = \begin{vmatrix} 1 & 0 & 3 \\ 0 & -1 & 2 \\ 2 & 1 & 0 \end{vmatrix} = 4,$$

and then use the formula $|A^{-1}| = 1/|A|$ to conclude that $|A^{-1}| = \frac{1}{4}$.

REMARK: In Example 4, the inverse of A is

$$A^{-1} = \begin{bmatrix} -\frac{1}{2} & \frac{3}{4} & \frac{3}{4} \\ 1 & -\frac{3}{2} & -\frac{1}{2} \\ \frac{1}{2} & -\frac{1}{4} & -\frac{1}{4} \end{bmatrix}.$$

Try evaluating the determinant of this matrix directly. Then compare your answer with that obtained in Example 4.

Note that Theorem 3.7 (a matrix is invertible if and only if its determinant is nonzero) provides another equivalent condition that can be added to the list given in Theorem 2.15. All six conditions are summarized as follows.

Equivalent Conditions

If A is an $n \times n$ matrix, then the following statements are equivalent.
1. A is invertible.
2. $A\mathbf{x} = \mathbf{b}$ has a unique solution for every $n \times 1$ matrix $\mathbf{b}$.
3. $A\mathbf{x} = O$ has only the trivial solution.
4. A is row equivalent to I_n.
5. A can be written as the product of elementary matrices.
6. $\det(A) \neq 0$

REMARK: In Section 3.2 we mentioned that a square matrix A has a determinant of zero if and only if A is row equivalent to a matrix that has at least one row consisting entirely of zeros. The validity of this statement follows from the equivalence of properties 4 and 6.

EXAMPLE 5   *Systems of Linear Equations*

Which of the following systems has a unique solution?

(a)
$$\begin{aligned} 2x_2 - x_3 &= -1 \\ 3x_1 - 2x_2 + x_3 &= 4 \\ 3x_1 + 2x_2 - x_3 &= -4 \end{aligned}$$

(b)
$$\begin{aligned} 2x_2 - x_3 &= -1 \\ 3x_1 - 2x_2 + x_3 &= 4 \\ 3x_1 + 2x_2 + x_3 &= -4 \end{aligned}$$

Solution

From Example 3 we know that the coefficient matrices for these two systems have the following determinants.

(a) $\begin{vmatrix} 0 & 2 & -1 \\ 3 & -2 & 1 \\ 3 & 2 & -1 \end{vmatrix} = 0$

(b) $\begin{vmatrix} 0 & 2 & -1 \\ 3 & -2 & 1 \\ 3 & 2 & 1 \end{vmatrix} = -12$

Therefore, using the preceding list of equivalent conditions, we conclude that only the second system has a unique solution.

Determinants and the Transpose of a Matrix

The following theorem tells us that the determinant of the transpose of a square matrix is equal to the determinant of the matrix. This theorem can be proven using mathematical induction and Theorem 3.1, which states that a determinant can be evaluated using cofactor expansion along a row *or* a column. The details of the proof are left to you. (See Exercise 40.)

Theorem 3.9

Determinant of a Transpose

If A is a square matrix, then

$$\det(A) = \det(A^T).$$

EXAMPLE 6   *The Determinant of a Transpose*

Show that $|A| = |A^T|$ for the following matrix.

$$A = \begin{bmatrix} 3 & 1 & -2 \\ 2 & 0 & 0 \\ -4 & -1 & 5 \end{bmatrix}$$

Solution   To find the determinant of A, we expand by cofactors along the second *row* to obtain

$$|A| = 2(-1)^3 \begin{vmatrix} 1 & -2 \\ -1 & 5 \end{vmatrix} = -2(3) = -6.$$

To find the determinant of

$$A^T = \begin{vmatrix} 3 & 2 & -4 \\ 1 & 0 & -1 \\ -2 & 0 & 5 \end{vmatrix},$$

we expand by cofactors down the second *column* to obtain

$$|A^T| = 2(-1)^3 \begin{vmatrix} 1 & -1 \\ -2 & 5 \end{vmatrix} = -2(3) = -6.$$

Thus $|A| = |A^T|$.

Introduction to Eigenvalues

We close this section with a look ahead to one of the most important topics of linear algebra—**eigenvalues.** One application of eigenvalues involves the study of population growth. For example, suppose that, of a population of rabbits raised in a laboratory, half of the rabbits survive their first year, and of those, half survive their second year. Their maximum life span is three years. Furthermore, during the first year the rabbits produce no offspring, whereas the average number of offspring is 6 during the second year and 8 during the third year. If there are 24 rabbits in each age class now, what will the distribution be in one year? In twenty years?

As you will find in Chapter 7, the solution to this application depends on the concept of **eigenvalues.** You will see later that eigenvalues are used in a wide variety of real-life applications of linear algebra. Besides population growth, eigenvalues are used in solving systems of differential equations, quadratic forms, and in all areas of engineering and science.

The central question of the **eigenvalue problem** can be stated as follows. If A is an $n \times n$ matrix, do there exist $n \times 1$ nonzero matrices **x** such that A**x** is a scalar multiple **x?** The scalar is usually denoted by λ (the Greek letter lambda) and is called an **eigenvalue** of A, and the nonzero column matrix **x** an **eigenvector** of A corresponding to λ. Thus the fundamental equation for the eigenvalue problem is

$$A\mathbf{x} = \lambda\mathbf{x}.$$

EXAMPLE 7   *Verifying Eigenvalues and Eigenvectors*

Let $A = \begin{bmatrix} 1 & 4 \\ 2 & 3 \end{bmatrix}$, $\quad \mathbf{x}_1 = \begin{bmatrix} 1 \\ 1 \end{bmatrix}$, $\quad$ and $\quad \mathbf{x}_2 = \begin{bmatrix} 2 \\ -1 \end{bmatrix}$.

Verify that $\lambda_1 = 5$ is an eigenvalue of A corresponding to $\mathbf{x}_1$, and that $\lambda_2 = -1$ is an eigenvalue of A corresponding to $\mathbf{x}_2$.

Solution   To verify that $\lambda_1 = 5$ is an eigenvalue of A corresponding to $\mathbf{x}_1$, we can multiply the matrices A and $\mathbf{x}_1$ as follows.

$$A\mathbf{x}_1 = \begin{bmatrix} 1 & 4 \\ 2 & 3 \end{bmatrix}\begin{bmatrix} 1 \\ 1 \end{bmatrix} = \begin{bmatrix} 5 \\ 5 \end{bmatrix} = 5\begin{bmatrix} 1 \\ 1 \end{bmatrix} = \lambda_1 \mathbf{x}_1$$

Similarly,

$$A\mathbf{x}_2 = \begin{bmatrix} 1 & 4 \\ 2 & 3 \end{bmatrix}\begin{bmatrix} 2 \\ -1 \end{bmatrix} = \begin{bmatrix} -2 \\ 1 \end{bmatrix} = -1\begin{bmatrix} 2 \\ -1 \end{bmatrix} = \lambda_2 \mathbf{x}_2.$$

From this example, we see that it is easy to verify if a given scalar λ and $n \times 1$ matrix $\mathbf{x}$ satisfy the equation $A\mathbf{x} = \lambda\mathbf{x}$. Notice also that if $\mathbf{x}$ is an eigenvector corresponding to λ, then so is any nonzero multiple of $\mathbf{x}$. For instance, the column matrices

$$\begin{bmatrix} 2 \\ 2 \end{bmatrix} \quad \text{and} \quad \begin{bmatrix} -7 \\ -7 \end{bmatrix}$$

are also eigenvectors of A corresponding to $\lambda_1 = 5$.

Given an $n \times n$ matrix A, how do we find the eigenvalues and corresponding eigenvectors? The key is to write the equation $A\mathbf{x} = \lambda\mathbf{x}$ in the equivalent form

$$(\lambda I - A)\mathbf{x} = 0,$$

where I is the $n \times n$ identity matrix. This homogeneous system of equations has nonzero solutions if and only if the coefficient matrix $(\lambda I - A)$ is singular; that is, if and only if the determinant of $(\lambda I - A)$ is zero. The equation $\det(\lambda I - A) = 0$ is called the **characteristic equation** of A, and is a polynomial equation of degree n in the variable λ. Once we find the eigenvalues of A, we can use Gaussian elimination to find the corresponding eigenvectors, as shown in the next example.

EXAMPLE 8   *Finding Eigenvalues and Eigenvectors*

Find the eigenvalues and corresponding eigenvectors of the matrix $A = \begin{bmatrix} 1 & 4 \\ 2 & 3 \end{bmatrix}$.

Solution   The characteristic equation of A is

$$|\lambda I - A| = \left| \begin{bmatrix} \lambda & 0 \\ 0 & \lambda \end{bmatrix} - \begin{bmatrix} 1 & 4 \\ 2 & 3 \end{bmatrix} \right|$$

$$= \begin{vmatrix} \lambda - 1 & -4 \\ -2 & \lambda - 3 \end{vmatrix}$$

$$= \lambda^2 - 4\lambda + 3 - 8$$

$$= \lambda^2 - 4\lambda - 5$$

$$= (\lambda - 5)(\lambda + 1) = 0$$

This gives two eigenvalues, $\lambda_1 = 5$ and $\lambda_2 = -1$.

To find the corresponding eigenvectors we solve the homogeneous linear system $(\lambda I - A)\mathbf{x} = 0$. For $\lambda_1 = 5$, the coefficient matrix is

$$5I - A = \begin{bmatrix} 5 - 1 & -4 \\ -2 & 5 - 3 \end{bmatrix} = \begin{bmatrix} 4 & -4 \\ -2 & 2 \end{bmatrix},$$

which row-reduces to

$$\begin{bmatrix} 1 & -1 \\ 0 & 0 \end{bmatrix}.$$

The solutions of the homogeneous system having this coefficient matrix are all of the form

$$\begin{bmatrix} t \\ t \end{bmatrix},$$

where t is a real number. Thus, the eigenvectors corresponding to $\lambda_1 = 5$ are the nonzero scalar multiples of

$$\begin{bmatrix} 1 \\ 1 \end{bmatrix}.$$

Similarly, for $\lambda_2 = -1$, the corresponding coefficient matrix is

$$-1I - A = \begin{bmatrix} -1 - 1 & -4 \\ -2 & -1 - 3 \end{bmatrix} = \begin{bmatrix} -2 & -4 \\ -2 & -4 \end{bmatrix},$$

which row-reduces to

$$\begin{bmatrix} 1 & 2 \\ 0 & 0 \end{bmatrix}.$$

The solutions of the homogeneous system having this coefficient matrix are all of the form

$$\begin{bmatrix} 2t \\ -t \end{bmatrix},$$

where t is a real number. Thus, the eigenvectors corresponding to the eigenvalue $\lambda_2 = -1$ are the nonzero multiples of

$$\begin{bmatrix} 2 \\ -1 \end{bmatrix}.$$

Eigenvalues and eigenvectors have ample applications in mathematics, engineering, biology, and other sciences. You will see one such application to stochastic processes at the end of this chapter. In Chapter 7 you will study eigenvalues and their applications in more detail and learn how to solve the rabbit population problem presented earlier.

SECTION 3.3 ☐ EXERCISES

In Exercises 1–6, find (a) $|A|$, (b) $|B|$, (c) AB, and (d) $|AB|$. Then verify that $|A||B| = |AB|$.

1. $A = \begin{bmatrix} -1 & 0 \\ 0 & 3 \end{bmatrix}$, $B = \begin{bmatrix} 2 & 0 \\ 0 & -1 \end{bmatrix}$

2. $A = \begin{bmatrix} 0 & 2 \\ 2 & 0 \end{bmatrix}$, $B = \begin{bmatrix} -1 & 2 \\ 3 & 0 \end{bmatrix}$

3. $A = \begin{bmatrix} -2 & 1 \\ 4 & -2 \end{bmatrix}$, $B = \begin{bmatrix} 1 & 1 \\ 0 & -1 \end{bmatrix}$

4. $A = \begin{bmatrix} 1 & 2 \\ 2 & 4 \end{bmatrix}$, $B = \begin{bmatrix} -1 & 2 \\ 3 & 0 \end{bmatrix}$

5. $A = \begin{bmatrix} -1 & 2 & 1 \\ 1 & 0 & 1 \\ 0 & 1 & 0 \end{bmatrix}$, $B = \begin{bmatrix} -1 & 0 & 0 \\ 0 & 2 & 0 \\ 0 & 0 & 3 \end{bmatrix}$

6. $A = \begin{bmatrix} 2 & 0 & 1 \\ 1 & -1 & 2 \\ 3 & 1 & 0 \end{bmatrix}$, $B = \begin{bmatrix} 2 & -1 & 4 \\ 0 & 1 & 3 \\ 3 & -2 & 1 \end{bmatrix}$

In Exercises 7–10, use the fact that $|cA| = c^n|A|$ to evaluate the determinant of the given $n \times n$ matrix.

7. $A = \begin{bmatrix} 4 & 2 \\ 6 & -8 \end{bmatrix}$

8. $A = \begin{bmatrix} 5 & 15 \\ 10 & -20 \end{bmatrix}$

9. $A = \begin{bmatrix} -3 & 6 & 9 \\ 6 & 9 & 12 \\ 9 & 12 & 15 \end{bmatrix}$

10. $A = \begin{bmatrix} 4 & 16 & 0 \\ 12 & -8 & 8 \\ 16 & 20 & -4 \end{bmatrix}$

In Exercises 11 and 12, find (a) $|A|$, (b) $|B|$, (c) $|A + B|$. Then verify that $|A| + |B| \neq |A + B|$.

11. $A = \begin{bmatrix} -1 & 1 \\ 2 & 0 \end{bmatrix}$, $B = \begin{bmatrix} 1 & -1 \\ -2 & 0 \end{bmatrix}$

12. $A = \begin{bmatrix} 1 & -2 \\ 1 & 0 \end{bmatrix}$, $B = \begin{bmatrix} 3 & -2 \\ 0 & 0 \end{bmatrix}$

In Exercises 13–16, find (a) $|A^T|$, (b) $|A^2|$, (c) $|AA^T|$, (d) $|2A|$, and (e) $|A^{-1}|$.

13. $A = \begin{bmatrix} 6 & -11 \\ 4 & -5 \end{bmatrix}$

14. $A = \begin{bmatrix} -4 & 10 \\ 5 & 6 \end{bmatrix}$

15. $A = \begin{bmatrix} 2 & 0 & 5 \\ 4 & -1 & 6 \\ 3 & 2 & 1 \end{bmatrix}$

16. $A = \begin{bmatrix} 1 & 5 & 4 \\ 0 & -6 & 2 \\ 0 & 0 & -3 \end{bmatrix}$

17. Let A and B be square matrices of order 4 such that $|A| = -5$ and $|B| = 3$. Find (a) $|AB|$, (b) $|A^3|$, (c) $|3B|$, (d) $|(AB)^T|$, and (e) $|A^{-1}|$.

18. Let A and B be square matrices of order 3 such that $|A| = 10$ and $|B| = 12$. Find (a) $|AB|$, (b) $|A^4|$, (c) $|2B|$, (d) $|(AB)^T|$, and (e) $|A^{-1}|$.

In Exercises 19–26, use a determinant to decide whether the given matrix is singular or nonsingular.

19. $\begin{bmatrix} 5 & 4 \\ 10 & 8 \end{bmatrix}$

20. $\begin{bmatrix} 3 & -6 \\ 4 & 2 \end{bmatrix}$

21. $\begin{bmatrix} 14 & 7 \\ 2 & 3 \end{bmatrix}$

22. $\begin{bmatrix} 1 & 0 & 4 \\ 0 & 6 & 3 \\ 2 & -1 & 4 \end{bmatrix}$

23. $\begin{bmatrix} \frac{1}{2} & \frac{3}{2} & 2 \\ \frac{2}{3} & -\frac{1}{3} & 0 \\ 1 & 1 & 1 \end{bmatrix}$

24. $\begin{bmatrix} 2 & -1 & 6 \\ 1 & -3 & 4 \\ 4 & -2 & 12 \end{bmatrix}$

25. $\begin{bmatrix} 1 & 0 & -8 & 2 \\ 0 & 8 & -1 & 10 \\ 0 & 0 & 0 & 1 \\ 0 & 0 & 0 & 2 \end{bmatrix}$

26. $\begin{bmatrix} 0.8 & 0.2 & -0.6 & 0.1 \\ -1.2 & 0.6 & 0.6 & 0 \\ 0.7 & -0.3 & 0.1 & 0 \\ 0.2 & -0.3 & 0.6 & 0 \end{bmatrix}$

In Exercises 27–30, use the determinant of the coefficient matrix to determine whether the given system of linear equations has a unique solution.

27. $\begin{aligned} x_1 - x_2 + x_3 &= 4 \\ 2x_1 - x_2 + x_3 &= 6 \\ 3x_1 - 2x_2 + 2x_3 &= 0 \end{aligned}$ **28.** $\begin{aligned} x_1 + x_2 - x_3 &= 4 \\ 2x_1 - x_2 + x_3 &= 6 \\ 3x_1 - 2x_2 + 2x_3 &= 0 \end{aligned}$

C 29. $\begin{aligned} 2x_1 + x_2 + 5x_3 + x_4 &= 5 \\ x_1 + x_2 - 3x_3 - 4x_4 &= -1 \\ 2x_1 + 2x_2 + 2x_3 - 3x_4 &= 2 \\ x_1 + 5x_2 - 6x_3 \qquad &= 3 \end{aligned}$

C 30. $\begin{aligned} x_1 - x_2 - x_3 - x_4 &= 0 \\ x_1 + x_2 - x_3 - x_4 &= 0 \\ x_1 + x_2 + x_3 - x_4 &= 0 \\ x_1 + x_2 + x_3 + x_4 &= 6 \end{aligned}$

In Exercises 31 and 32, find the value(s) of k such that A is singular.

31. $A = \begin{bmatrix} k-1 & 3 \\ 2 & k-2 \end{bmatrix}$ **32.** $A = \begin{bmatrix} 1 & 0 & 3 \\ 2 & -1 & 0 \\ 4 & 2 & k \end{bmatrix}$

33. Let A and B be $n \times n$ matrices such that $AB = I$. Prove that $|A| \neq 0$ and $|B| \neq 0$.

34. Let A and B be $n \times n$ matrices such that AB is singular. Prove that either A or B is singular.

35. Find two 2×2 matrices such that $|A| + |B| = |A + B|$.

36. Verify the following equation.

$$\begin{vmatrix} a+b & a & a \\ a & a+b & a \\ a & a & a+b \end{vmatrix} = b^2(3a + b)$$

37. Let A be an $n \times n$ matrix each of whose rows adds up to zero. Find $|A|$.

38. Illustrate the result of Exercise 37 with the matrix

$$A = \begin{bmatrix} 2 & -1 & -1 \\ -3 & 1 & 2 \\ 0 & -2 & 2 \end{bmatrix}.$$

39. Let A be an invertible matrix such that all the entries of A and A^{-1} are integers. Prove that $|A| = \pm 1$.

40. Prove Theorem 3.9. That is, prove that if A is a square matrix, then $|A| = |A^T|$.

41. Let A and P be $n \times n$ matrices, with P invertible. Does $P^{-1}AP = A$? Illustrate your conclusion with appropriate examples. What can you say about the two determinants $|P^{-1}AP|$ and $|A|$?

42. Let A be an $n \times n$ nonzero matrix satisfying $A^{10} = 0$. Explain why A must be singular. What properties of determinants are you using in your argument?

43. A square matrix is called **skew-symmetric** if $A^T = -A$. Prove that if A is an $n \times n$ skew-symmetric matrix, then $|A| = (-1)^n |A|$.

44. Let A be a skew-symmetric matrix of odd order. Use the result of Exercise 43 to prove that $|A| = 0$.

In Exercises 45–50, determine whether the given matrix is orthogonal. An invertible square matrix A is called **orthogonal** if $A^{-1} = A^T$.

45. $\begin{bmatrix} 0 & 1 \\ 1 & 0 \end{bmatrix}$ **46.** $\begin{bmatrix} 1 & -1 \\ -1 & -1 \end{bmatrix}$

47. $\begin{bmatrix} 0 & 0 \\ 1 & 0 \end{bmatrix}$ **48.** $\begin{bmatrix} 1/\sqrt{2} & -1/\sqrt{2} \\ -1/\sqrt{2} & -1/\sqrt{2} \end{bmatrix}$

49. $\begin{bmatrix} 1 & 0 & 0 \\ 0 & 0 & 1 \\ 0 & 1 & 0 \end{bmatrix}$ **50.** $\begin{bmatrix} 1/\sqrt{2} & 0 & -1/\sqrt{2} \\ 0 & 1 & 0 \\ 1/\sqrt{2} & 0 & 1/\sqrt{2} \end{bmatrix}$

51. Prove that if A is an orthogonal matrix, then $|A| = \pm 1$.

52. If A is an idempotent matrix ($A^2 = A$), prove that the determinant of A is either 0 or 1.

53. Let S be an $n \times n$ singular matrix. Prove that for any $n \times n$ matrix B, the matrix SB is also singular.

54. Let A_{11}, A_{12}, and A_{22} be $n \times n$ matrices. Find the determinant of the partitioned matrix

$$\begin{bmatrix} A_{11} & A_{12} \\ 0 & A_{22} \end{bmatrix}$$

in terms of the determinants of A_{11}, A_{12}, and A_{22}.

In Exercises 55–58, verify that λ_i is an eigenvalue of A and that $\mathbf{x}_i$ is a corresponding eigenvector.

55. $A = \begin{bmatrix} 1 & 2 \\ 0 & -3 \end{bmatrix};$ $\lambda_1 = 1,$ $\mathbf{x}_1 = \begin{bmatrix} 1 \\ 0 \end{bmatrix};$

$\lambda_2 = -3,$ $\mathbf{x}_2 = \begin{bmatrix} -1 \\ 2 \end{bmatrix}$

56. $A = \begin{bmatrix} 4 & 3 \\ 1 & 2 \end{bmatrix};$ $\lambda_1 = 5,$ $\mathbf{x}_1 = \begin{bmatrix} 3 \\ 1 \end{bmatrix};$

$\lambda_2 = 1,$ $\mathbf{x}_2 = \begin{bmatrix} -1 \\ 1 \end{bmatrix}$

57. $A = \begin{bmatrix} 1 & 1 & 1 \\ 0 & 1 & 0 \\ 1 & 1 & 1 \end{bmatrix}$; $\lambda_1 = 2$, $\mathbf{x}_1 = \begin{bmatrix} 1 \\ 0 \\ 1 \end{bmatrix}$;

$\lambda_2 = 0$, $\mathbf{x}_2 = \begin{bmatrix} -1 \\ 0 \\ 1 \end{bmatrix}$; $\lambda_3 = 1$, $\mathbf{x}_3 = \begin{bmatrix} -1 \\ 1 \\ -1 \end{bmatrix}$

58. $A = \begin{bmatrix} 1 & -2 & 1 \\ 0 & 1 & 4 \\ 0 & 0 & 2 \end{bmatrix}$; $\lambda_1 = 1$, $\mathbf{x}_1 = \begin{bmatrix} 1 \\ 0 \\ 0 \end{bmatrix}$;

$\lambda_2 = 2$, $\mathbf{x}_2 = \begin{bmatrix} -7 \\ 4 \\ 1 \end{bmatrix}$

In Exercises 59–62, find (a) the characteristic equation, (b) the eigenvalues, and (c) the corresponding eigenvectors of the matrix.

59. $\begin{bmatrix} 4 & -5 \\ 2 & -3 \end{bmatrix}$ **60.** $\begin{bmatrix} 2 & 2 \\ 2 & 2 \end{bmatrix}$

61. $\begin{bmatrix} 1 & -1 & -1 \\ 1 & 3 & 1 \\ -3 & 1 & -1 \end{bmatrix}$ **62.** $\begin{bmatrix} 2 & 0 & 1 \\ 0 & 3 & 4 \\ 0 & 0 & 1 \end{bmatrix}$

3.4 APPLICATIONS OF DETERMINANTS

The Adjoint of a Matrix

In this subsection, we develop an explicit formula for the inverse of a nonsingular matrix. In the next subsection, we use this formula to derive a theorem known as Cramer's Rule.

Recall from Section 3.1 that the cofactor C_{ij} of a matrix A is defined to be $(-1)^{i+j}$ times the determinant of the matrix obtained by deleting the ith row and jth column of A. If A is a square matrix, then the **matrix of cofactors** of A has the form

$$\begin{bmatrix} C_{11} & C_{12} & \cdots & C_{1n} \\ C_{21} & C_{22} & \cdots & C_{2n} \\ \vdots & \vdots & & \vdots \\ C_{n1} & C_{n2} & \cdots & C_{nn} \end{bmatrix}.$$

The transpose of this matrix is called the **adjoint** of A and is denoted by adj(A). That is,

$$\text{adj}(A) = \begin{bmatrix} C_{11} & C_{21} & \cdots & C_{n1} \\ C_{12} & C_{22} & \cdots & C_{n2} \\ \vdots & \vdots & & \vdots \\ C_{1n} & C_{2n} & \cdots & C_{nn} \end{bmatrix}.$$

EXAMPLE 1   *Finding the Adjoint of a Square Matrix*

Find the adjoint of

$$A = \begin{bmatrix} -1 & 3 & 2 \\ 0 & -2 & 1 \\ 1 & 0 & -2 \end{bmatrix}.$$

Solution   The cofactor C_{11} is given by

$$\begin{bmatrix} -1 & 3 & 2 \\ 0 & -2 & 1 \\ 1 & 0 & -2 \end{bmatrix} \quad \longrightarrow \quad C_{11} = (-1)^2 \begin{vmatrix} -2 & 1 \\ 0 & -2 \end{vmatrix} = 4.$$

Continuing this process produces the following matrix of cofactors of A.

$$\begin{bmatrix} \begin{vmatrix} -2 & 1 \\ 0 & -2 \end{vmatrix} & -\begin{vmatrix} 0 & 1 \\ 1 & -2 \end{vmatrix} & \begin{vmatrix} 0 & -2 \\ 1 & 0 \end{vmatrix} \\ -\begin{vmatrix} 3 & 2 \\ 0 & -2 \end{vmatrix} & \begin{vmatrix} -1 & 2 \\ 1 & -2 \end{vmatrix} & -\begin{vmatrix} -1 & 3 \\ 1 & 0 \end{vmatrix} \\ \begin{vmatrix} 3 & 2 \\ -2 & 1 \end{vmatrix} & -\begin{vmatrix} -1 & 2 \\ 0 & 1 \end{vmatrix} & \begin{vmatrix} -1 & 3 \\ 0 & -2 \end{vmatrix} \end{bmatrix} = \begin{bmatrix} 4 & 1 & 2 \\ 6 & 0 & 3 \\ 7 & 1 & 2 \end{bmatrix}$$

The transpose of this matrix is the adjoint of A. That is,

$$\text{adj}(A) = \begin{bmatrix} 4 & 6 & 7 \\ 1 & 0 & 1 \\ 2 & 3 & 2 \end{bmatrix}.$$

The adjoint of a matrix A can be used to find the inverse of A, as indicated in the following theorem.

Theorem 3.10	If A is an $n \times n$ invertible matrix, then
The Inverse of a Matrix Given by Its Adjoint	$$A^{-1} = \frac{1}{\det(A)} \text{adj}(A).$$

Proof   We begin by looking at the product of A with its adjoint.

$$A \, \text{adj}(A) = \begin{bmatrix} a_{11} & a_{12} & \cdots & a_{1n} \\ a_{21} & a_{22} & \cdots & a_{2n} \\ \vdots & \vdots & & \vdots \\ a_{i1} & a_{i2} & \cdots & a_{in} \\ \vdots & \vdots & & \vdots \\ a_{n1} & a_{n2} & \cdots & a_{nn} \end{bmatrix} \begin{bmatrix} C_{11} & C_{21} & \cdots & C_{j1} & \cdots & C_{n1} \\ C_{12} & C_{22} & \cdots & C_{j2} & \cdots & C_{n2} \\ \vdots & \vdots & & \vdots & & \vdots \\ C_{1n} & C_{2n} & \cdots & C_{jn} & \cdots & C_{nn} \end{bmatrix}$$

The entry in the ith row and jth column of this product is given by

$$a_{i1}C_{j1} + a_{i2}C_{j2} + \cdots + a_{in}C_{jn}.$$

If $i = j$, then this sum is simply the cofactor expansion of A along its ith row, which means that the sum is the determinant of A. On the other hand, if $i \neq j$, then the sum is zero. To see this, consider the following matrix B in which the jth row of A has been replaced with the ith row of A.

$$B = \begin{bmatrix} a_{11} & a_{12} & \cdots & a_{1n} \\ a_{21} & a_{22} & \cdots & a_{2n} \\ \vdots & \vdots & & \vdots \\ a_{i1} & a_{i2} & \cdots & a_{in} \\ \vdots & \vdots & & \vdots \\ a_{i1} & a_{i2} & \cdots & a_{in} \\ \vdots & \vdots & & \vdots \\ a_{n1} & a_{n2} & \cdots & a_{nn} \end{bmatrix} \begin{array}{l} \\ \\ \\ \longleftarrow \ \textit{i}\text{th row} \\ \\ \longleftarrow \ \textit{j}\text{th row} \\ \\ \\ \end{array}$$

Cofactor expansion along the jth row of B produces

$$|B| = a_{i1}C_{j1} + a_{i2}C_{j2} + \cdots + a_{in}C_{jn},$$

and because B has two identical rows we know from Theorem 3.4 that $|B| = 0$. Thus the product $A \ \text{adj}(A)$ has the form

$$A \ \text{adj}(A) = \begin{bmatrix} |A| & 0 & \cdots & 0 \\ 0 & |A| & \cdots & 0 \\ \vdots & \vdots & & \vdots \\ 0 & 0 & \cdots & |A| \end{bmatrix} = |A|I.$$

Finally, we have

$$A\left[\frac{1}{|A|} \text{adj}(A) \right] = I,$$

which implies that

$$A^{-1} = \frac{1}{|A|} \text{adj}(A).$$

If A is a 2×2 matrix

$$A = \begin{bmatrix} a & b \\ c & d \end{bmatrix},$$

then the adjoint of A is simply

$$\text{adj}(A) = \begin{bmatrix} d & -b \\ -c & a \end{bmatrix}.$$

Moreover, if A is invertible, then from Theorem 3.10 we have

$$A^{-1} = \frac{1}{|A|} \operatorname{adj}(A) = \frac{1}{ad - bc} \begin{bmatrix} d & -b \\ -c & a \end{bmatrix},$$

which agrees with the result given in Section 2.3.

EXAMPLE 2   *Using the Adjoint of a Matrix to Find Its Inverse*

Use the adjoint of

$$A = \begin{bmatrix} -1 & 3 & 2 \\ 0 & -2 & 1 \\ 1 & 0 & -2 \end{bmatrix}$$

to find A^{-1}.

Solution   The determinant of this matrix is $|A| = 3$. using the adjoint of A (found in Example 1), we find the inverse of A to be

$$A^{-1} = \frac{1}{|A|} \operatorname{adj}(A) = \frac{1}{3} \begin{bmatrix} 4 & 6 & 7 \\ 1 & 0 & 1 \\ 2 & 3 & 2 \end{bmatrix} = \begin{bmatrix} \frac{4}{3} & 2 & \frac{7}{3} \\ \frac{1}{3} & 0 & \frac{1}{3} \\ \frac{2}{3} & 1 & \frac{2}{3} \end{bmatrix}.$$

We can check to see that this matrix is the inverse of A by multiplying to obtain

$$AA^{-1} = \begin{bmatrix} -1 & 3 & 2 \\ 0 & -2 & 1 \\ 1 & 0 & -2 \end{bmatrix} \begin{bmatrix} \frac{4}{3} & 2 & \frac{7}{3} \\ \frac{1}{3} & 0 & \frac{1}{3} \\ \frac{2}{3} & 1 & \frac{2}{3} \end{bmatrix} = \begin{bmatrix} 1 & 0 & 0 \\ 0 & 1 & 0 \\ 0 & 0 & 1 \end{bmatrix}.$$

REMARK: Theorem 3.10 is not particularly efficient for calculating inverses. The Gauss-Jordan elimination method discussed in Section 2.3 is much better. This theorem is theoretically useful, however, because it provides a concise formula for the inverse of a matrix.

Cramer's Rule

Cramer's Rule, named after Gabriel Cramer (1704–1752), is a formula that uses determinants to solve a system of n linear equations in n variables. This rule can be applied only to systems of linear equations that have unique solutions.

To see how Cramer's Rule arises, let's look at the solution of a general system involving two linear equations in two unknowns.

$$a_{11}x_1 + a_{12}x_2 = b_1$$
$$a_{21}x_1 + a_{22}x_2 = b_2$$

Multiplying the first equation by $-a_{21}$ and the second by a_{11}, and adding the results produces

$$-a_{21}a_{11}x_1 - a_{21}a_{12}x_2 = -a_{21}b_1$$

$$\frac{a_{11}a_{21}x_1 + a_{11}a_{22}x_2 = a_{11}b_2}{(a_{11}a_{22} - a_{21}a_{12})x_2 = a_{11}b_2 - a_{21}b_1}.$$

Solving for x_2 (provided $a_{11}a_{22} - a_{21}a_{12} \neq 0$) produces

$$x_2 = \frac{a_{11}b_2 - a_{21}b_1}{a_{11}a_{22} - a_{21}a_{12}}.$$

In a similar way, we can solve for x_1 to obtain

$$x_1 = \frac{a_{22}b_1 - a_{12}b_2}{a_{11}a_{22} - a_{21}a_{12}}.$$

Finally, recognizing that the numerator and denominator for both x_1 and x_2 can be represented as determinants, we have

$$x_1 = \frac{\begin{vmatrix} b_1 & a_{12} \\ b_2 & a_{22} \end{vmatrix}}{\begin{vmatrix} a_{11} & a_{12} \\ a_{21} & a_{22} \end{vmatrix}}, \qquad x_2 = \frac{\begin{vmatrix} a_{11} & b_1 \\ a_{21} & b_2 \end{vmatrix}}{\begin{vmatrix} a_{11} & a_{12} \\ a_{21} & a_{22} \end{vmatrix}}, \qquad a_{11}a_{22} - a_{21}a_{12} \neq 0.$$

The denominator for both x_1 and x_2 is simply the determinant of the coefficient matrix A. The determinant forming the numerator for x_1 can be obtained from A by replacing its first column by the column representing the constants of the system. The determinant forming the numerator for x_2 can be obtained in a similar way. We denote these two determinants by $|A_1|$ and $|A_2|$ as follows.

$$|A_1| = \begin{vmatrix} b_1 & a_{12} \\ b_2 & a_{22} \end{vmatrix} \qquad \text{and} \qquad |A_2| = \begin{vmatrix} a_{11} & b_1 \\ a_{21} & b_2 \end{vmatrix}$$

Thus we have

$$x_1 = \frac{|A_1|}{|A|} \qquad \text{and} \qquad x_2 = \frac{|A_2|}{|A|}.$$

This determinant form of the solution is called **Cramer's Rule.**

EXAMPLE 3   *Using Cramer's Rule*

Use Cramer's Rule to solve the following system of linear equations.

$$4x_1 - 2x_2 = 10$$
$$3x_1 - 5x_2 = 11$$

Solution   First we find the determinant of the coefficient matrix.

$$|A| = \begin{vmatrix} 4 & -2 \\ 3 & -5 \end{vmatrix} = -14$$

Since $|A| \neq 0$, we know that the system has a unique solution, and applying Cramer's Rule produces

$$x_1 = \frac{|A_1|}{|A|} = \frac{\begin{vmatrix} 10 & -2 \\ 11 & -5 \end{vmatrix}}{-14} = \frac{-28}{-14} = 2$$

$$x_2 = \frac{|A_2|}{|A|} = \frac{\begin{vmatrix} 4 & 10 \\ 3 & 11 \end{vmatrix}}{-14} = \frac{14}{-14} = -1.$$

Thus the solution is $x_1 = 2$ and $x_2 = -1$.

Cramer's Rule generalizes easily to systems of n linear equations in n variables. The value of each variable is given as the quotient of two determinants. The denominator is the determinant of the coefficient matrix, and the numerator is the determinant of the matrix formed by replacing the column corresponding to the variable being solved for with the column representing the constants. For example, the solution for x_3 in the system

$$\begin{array}{l} a_{11}x_1 + a_{12}x_2 + a_{13}x_3 = b_1 \\ a_{21}x_1 + a_{22}x_2 + a_{23}x_3 = b_2 \\ a_{31}x_1 + a_{32}x_2 + a_{33}x_3 = b_3 \end{array}$$

is given by

$$x_3 = \frac{|A_3|}{|A|} = \frac{\begin{vmatrix} a_{11} & a_{12} & b_1 \\ a_{21} & a_{22} & b_2 \\ a_{31} & a_{32} & b_3 \end{vmatrix}}{\begin{vmatrix} a_{11} & a_{12} & a_{13} \\ a_{21} & a_{22} & a_{23} \\ a_{31} & a_{32} & a_{33} \end{vmatrix}}.$$

Theorem 3.11

Cramer's Rule

If a system of n linear equations in n variables has a coefficient matrix with a nonzero determinant $|A|$, then the solution to the system is given by

$$x_1 = \frac{\det(A_1)}{\det(A)}, \quad x_2 = \frac{\det(A_2)}{\det(A)}, \quad \ldots, \quad x_n = \frac{\det(A_n)}{\det(A)},$$

where the ith column of A_i is the column of constants in the system of equations.

Proof   Let the system be represented by $AX = B$. Since $|A|$ is nonzero, we can write

$$X = A^{-1}B = \frac{1}{|A|} \, \mathrm{adj}(A)B = \begin{bmatrix} x_1 \\ x_2 \\ \vdots \\ x_n \end{bmatrix}.$$

If the entries of B are $b_1, b_2, \ldots, b_n$, then x_i is given by

$$x_i = \frac{1}{|A|}(b_1 C_{1i} + b_2 C_{2i} + \cdots + b_n C_{ni}).$$

But the sum (in parentheses) is precisely the cofactor expansion of A_i, which means that $x_i = |A_i|/|A|$, and the proof is complete.

EXAMPLE 4   *Using Cramer's Rule*

Use Cramer's Rule to solve the following system of linear equations for x.

$$\begin{array}{rrrcr} -x & + 2y & - 3z & = & 1 \\ 2x & & + z & = & 0 \\ 3x & - 4y & + 4z & = & 2 \end{array}$$

Solution   The determinant of the coefficient matrix is

$$|A| = \begin{vmatrix} -1 & 2 & -3 \\ 2 & 0 & 1 \\ 3 & -4 & 4 \end{vmatrix} = 10.$$

Since $|A| \neq 0$, we know that the solution is unique, and Cramer's Rule may be applied to solve for x as follows.

$$x = \frac{\begin{vmatrix} 1 & 2 & -3 \\ 0 & 0 & 1 \\ 2 & -4 & 4 \end{vmatrix}}{10} = \frac{(-1)^5 \begin{vmatrix} 1 & 2 \\ 2 & -4 \end{vmatrix}}{10} = \frac{(-1)(-8)}{10} = \frac{4}{5}$$

REMARK: Try applying Cramer's Rule in Example 4 to solve for y and z. You will see that the solution is $y = -\frac{3}{2}$ and $z = -\frac{8}{5}$.

Area, Volume, and Equations of Lines and Planes

Determinants have many applications in analytic geometry. Several are presented here. The first application is finding the area of a triangle in the xy-plane.

Area of a Triangle in the xy-Plane

The area of the triangle whose vertices are (x_1, y_1), (x_2, y_2), and (x_3, y_3) is given by

$$\text{Area} = \pm \frac{1}{2} \det \begin{bmatrix} x_1 & y_1 & 1 \\ x_2 & y_2 & 1 \\ x_3 & y_3 & 1 \end{bmatrix},$$

when the sign ($\pm$) is chosen to give a positive area.

Proof   We prove the case for $y_i > 0$. Assume that $x_1 \leq x_3 \leq x_2$ and that (x_3, y_3) lies above the line segment connecting (x_1, y_1) and (x_2, y_2), as shown in Figure 3.1. Consider the three trapezoids whose vertices are as follows.

Trapezoid #1: $(x_1, 0), (x_1, y_1), (x_3, y_3), (x_3, 0)$
Trapezoid #2: $(x_3, 0), (x_3, y_3), (x_2, y_2), (x_2, 0)$
Trapezoid #3: $(x_1, 0), (x_1, y_1), (x_2, y_2), (x_2, 0)$

Figure 3.1

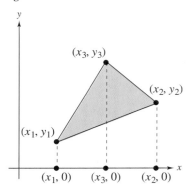

The area of the given triangle is equal to the sum of the areas of the first two trapezoids less the area of the third. Therefore

$$\text{Area} = \tfrac{1}{2}(y_1 + y_3)(x_3 - x_1) + \tfrac{1}{2}(y_3 + y_2)(x_2 - x_3) - \tfrac{1}{2}(y_1 + y_2)(x_2 - x_1)$$
$$= \tfrac{1}{2}(x_1 y_2 + x_2 y_3 + x_3 y_1 - x_1 y_3 - x_2 y_1 - x_3 y_2)$$
$$= \tfrac{1}{2}\begin{vmatrix} x_1 & y_1 & 1 \\ x_2 & y_2 & 1 \\ x_3 & y_3 & 1 \end{vmatrix}.$$

If the vertices do not occur in the order $x_1 \leq x_3 \leq x_2$ or if the vertex (x_3, y_3) is not above the line segment connecting the other two vertices, then the formula may give the negative of the area.

EXAMPLE 5   *Finding the Area of a Triangle*

Find the area of the triangle whose vertices are $(1, 0)$, $(2, 2)$, and $(4, 3)$, as shown in Figure 3.2.

Solution   It is unnecessary to know the relative position of the three vertices. We simply evaluate the determinant

$$\tfrac{1}{2}\begin{vmatrix} 1 & 0 & 1 \\ 2 & 2 & 1 \\ 4 & 3 & 1 \end{vmatrix} = -\tfrac{3}{2}$$

and conclude that the area of the triangle is $\tfrac{3}{2}$.

Figure 3.2

Figure 3.3

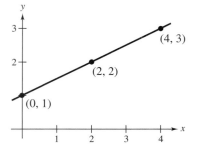

Suppose the three points in Example 5 had been on the same line. What would have happened had we applied our area formula to three such points? The answer is that the determinant would have been zero. Consider, for instance, the collinear points $(0, 1)$, $(2, 2)$, and $(4, 3)$, shown in Figure 3.3.

The determinant giving the area of the "triangle" having these three points as vertices is

$$\frac{1}{2} \begin{vmatrix} 0 & 1 & 1 \\ 2 & 2 & 1 \\ 4 & 3 & 1 \end{vmatrix} = 0.$$

We generalize this result as follows.

Text for Collinear Points in the xy-plane

Three points (x_1, y_1), (x_2, y_2), and (x_3, y_3) are collinear if and only if

$$\det \begin{bmatrix} x_1 & y_1 & 1 \\ x_2 & y_2 & 1 \\ x_3 & y_3 & 1 \end{bmatrix} = 0.$$

The following determinant form for the equation of the line passing through two points in the xy-plane is a corollary to the test for collinear points.

Two-Point Form of the Equation of a Line

The equation of the line passing through the distinct points (x_1, y_1) and (x_2, y_2) is given by

$$\det \begin{bmatrix} x & y & 1 \\ x_1 & y_1 & 1 \\ x_2 & y_2 & 1 \end{bmatrix} = 0.$$

EXAMPLE 6   *Finding the Equation of the Line Passing Through Two Points*

Find the equation of the line passing through the points $(2, 4)$ and $(-1, 3)$.

Solution   Applying the determinant formula for the equation of the line passing through these two points produces

$$\begin{vmatrix} x & y & 1 \\ 2 & 4 & 1 \\ -1 & 3 & 1 \end{vmatrix} = 0.$$

To evaluate this determinant, we expand by cofactors along the top row to obtain

$$x \begin{vmatrix} 4 & 1 \\ 3 & 1 \end{vmatrix} - y \begin{vmatrix} 2 & 1 \\ -1 & 1 \end{vmatrix} + 1 \begin{vmatrix} 2 & 4 \\ -1 & 3 \end{vmatrix} = x - 3y + 10 = 0.$$

Therefore the equation of the line is

$$x - 3y = -10.$$

The formula for the area of a triangle in the plane has a straightforward generalization to three-dimensional space, which is presented without proof as follows.

Volume of a Tetrahedron

The volume of the tetrahedron whose vertices are (x_1, y_1, z_1), (x_2, y_2, z_2), (x_3, y_3, z_3), and (x_4, y_4, z_4) is given by

$$\text{Volume} = \pm\tfrac{1}{6}\det\begin{bmatrix} x_1 & y_1 & z_1 & 1 \\ x_2 & y_2 & z_2 & 1 \\ x_3 & y_3 & z_3 & 1 \\ x_4 & y_4 & z_4 & 1 \end{bmatrix},$$

where the sign $(\pm)$ is chosen to give a positive volume.

EXAMPLE 7   ***Finding the Volume of a Tetrahedron***

Find the volume of the tetrahedron whose vertices are $(0, 4, 1)$, $(4, 0, 0)$, $(3, 5, 2)$, and $(2, 2, 5)$, as shown in Figure 3.4.

Figure 3.4

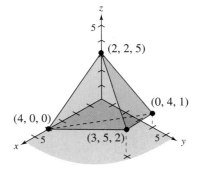

Solution   Using the determinant formula for volume produces

$$\tfrac{1}{6}\begin{vmatrix} 0 & 4 & 1 & 1 \\ 4 & 0 & 0 & 1 \\ 3 & 5 & 2 & 1 \\ 2 & 2 & 5 & 1 \end{vmatrix} = \tfrac{1}{6}(-72) = -12.$$

Therefore the volume of the tetrahedron is 12.

If four points in three-dimensional space happen to lie in the same plane, then the determinant in the formula for volume turns out to be zero. Thus we have the following test.

Test for Coplanar Points in Space

Four points (x_1, y_1, z_1), (x_2, y_2, z_2), (x_3, y_3, z_3), and (x_4, y_4, z_4) are coplanar if and only if

$$\det \begin{bmatrix} x_1 & y_1 & z_1 & 1 \\ x_2 & y_2 & z_2 & 1 \\ x_3 & y_3 & z_3 & 1 \\ x_4 & y_4 & z_4 & 1 \end{bmatrix} = 0.$$

This test now provides the following determinant form for the equation of a plane passing through three points in space.

Three-Point Form of the Equation of a Plane

The equation of the plane passing through the distinct points (x_1, y_1, z_1), (x_2, y_2, z_2), and (x_3, y_3, z_3) is given by

$$\det \begin{bmatrix} x & y & z & 1 \\ x_1 & y_1 & z_1 & 1 \\ x_2 & y_2 & z_2 & 1 \\ x_3 & y_3 & z_3 & 1 \end{bmatrix} = 0.$$

EXAMPLE 8   *Finding the Equation of the Plane Passing Through Three Points*

Find the equation of the plane passing through the points $(0, 1, 0)$, $(-1, 3, 2)$, and $(-2, 0, 1)$.

Solution   Using the determinant form of the equation of the plane passing through three points produces

$$\begin{vmatrix} x & y & z & 1 \\ 0 & 1 & 0 & 1 \\ -1 & 3 & 2 & 1 \\ -2 & 0 & 1 & 1 \end{vmatrix} = 0.$$

To evaluate this determinant, we subtract the fourth column from the second column to obtain

$$\begin{vmatrix} x & y-1 & z & 1 \\ 0 & 0 & 0 & 1 \\ -1 & 2 & 2 & 1 \\ -2 & -1 & 1 & 1 \end{vmatrix} = 0.$$

Now, expanding by cofactors along the second row yields

$$4x - 3y + 5z = -3.$$

SECTION 3.4 ☐ EXERCISES

The Adjoint of a Matrix

In Exercises 1–8, find the adjoint of the matrix A. Then use the adjoint to find the inverse of A, if possible.

1. $A = \begin{bmatrix} 1 & 2 \\ 3 & 4 \end{bmatrix}$

2. $A = \begin{bmatrix} -1 & 0 \\ 0 & 4 \end{bmatrix}$

3. $A = \begin{bmatrix} 1 & 0 & 0 \\ 0 & 2 & 6 \\ 0 & -4 & -12 \end{bmatrix}$

4. $A = \begin{bmatrix} 1 & 2 & 3 \\ 0 & 1 & -1 \\ 2 & 2 & 2 \end{bmatrix}$

5. $A = \begin{bmatrix} -3 & -5 & -7 \\ 2 & 4 & 3 \\ 0 & 1 & -1 \end{bmatrix}$

6. $A = \begin{bmatrix} 0 & 1 & 1 \\ 1 & 2 & 3 \\ -1 & -1 & -2 \end{bmatrix}$

7. $A = \begin{bmatrix} -1 & 2 & 0 & 1 \\ 3 & -1 & 4 & 1 \\ 0 & 0 & 1 & 2 \\ -1 & 1 & 1 & 2 \end{bmatrix}$

8. $A = \begin{bmatrix} 1 & 1 & 1 & 0 \\ 1 & 1 & 0 & 1 \\ 1 & 0 & 1 & 1 \\ 0 & 1 & 1 & 1 \end{bmatrix}$

9. Prove that if $|A| = 1$ and all entries of A are integers, then all entries of $|A^{-1}|$ must also be integers.

10. Prove that if an $n \times n$ matrix A is not invertible, then $A[\text{adj}(A)]$ is the zero matrix.

In Exercises 11 and 12, prove the given formula for a nonsingular $n \times n$ matrix A. Assume $n \geq 3$.

11. $|\text{adj}(A)| = |A|^{n-1}$

12. $\text{adj}(\text{adj}(A)) = |A|^{n-2}A$

13. Illustrate the formula given in Exercise 11 for the matrix
$$A = \begin{bmatrix} 1 & 0 \\ 1 & -2 \end{bmatrix}.$$

14. Illustrate the formula given in Exercise 12 for the matrix
$$A = \begin{bmatrix} -1 & 3 \\ 1 & 2 \end{bmatrix}.$$

15. Prove that if A is an $n \times n$ invertible matrix, then $\text{adj}(A^{-1}) = [\text{adj}(A)]^{-1}$.

16. Illustrate the formula given in Exercise 15 for the matrix
$$A = \begin{bmatrix} 1 & 3 \\ 1 & 2 \end{bmatrix}.$$

Cramer's Rule

In Exercises 17–32, use Cramer's Rule to solve the given system of linear equations, if possible.

17. $\begin{aligned} x_1 + 2x_2 &= 5 \\ -x_1 + x_2 &= 1 \end{aligned}$

18. $\begin{aligned} 2x_1 - x_2 &= -10 \\ 3x_1 + 2x_2 &= -1 \end{aligned}$

19. $\begin{aligned} 3x_1 + 4x_2 &= -2 \\ 5x_1 + 3x_2 &= 4 \end{aligned}$

20. $\begin{aligned} 18x_1 + 12x_2 &= 13 \\ 30x_1 + 24x_2 &= 23 \end{aligned}$

21. $\begin{aligned} 20x_1 + 8x_2 &= 11 \\ 12x_1 - 24x_2 &= 21 \end{aligned}$

22. $\begin{aligned} 13x_1 - 6x_2 &= 17 \\ 26x_1 - 12x_2 &= 8 \end{aligned}$

23. $\begin{aligned} -0.4x_1 + 0.8x_2 &= 1.6 \\ 2x_1 - 4x_2 &= 5.0 \end{aligned}$

24. $\begin{aligned} -0.4x_1 + 0.8x_2 &= 1.6 \\ 0.2x_1 + 0.3x_2 &= 0.6 \end{aligned}$

25. $\begin{aligned} 3x_1 + 6x_2 &= 5 \\ 6x_1 + 12x_2 &= 10 \end{aligned}$

26. $\begin{aligned} 3x_1 + 2x_2 &= 1 \\ 2x_1 + 10x_2 &= 6 \end{aligned}$

27. $\begin{aligned} 4x_1 - x_2 - x_3 &= 1 \\ 2x_1 + 2x_2 + 3x_3 &= 10 \\ 5x_1 - 2x_2 - 2x_3 &= -1 \end{aligned}$

28. $\begin{aligned} 4x_1 - 2x_2 + 3x_3 &= -2 \\ 2x_1 + 2x_2 + 5x_3 &= 16 \\ 8x_1 - 5x_2 - 2x_3 &= 4 \end{aligned}$

29. $\begin{aligned} 3x_1 + 4x_2 + 4x_3 &= 11 \\ 4x_1 - 4x_2 + 6x_3 &= 11 \\ 6x_1 - 6x_2 &= 3 \end{aligned}$

30. $\begin{aligned} 14x_1 - 21x_2 - 7x_3 &= -21 \\ -4x_1 + 2x_2 - 2x_3 &= 2 \\ 56x_1 - 21x_2 + 7x_3 &= 7 \end{aligned}$

31. $\begin{aligned} 3x_1 + 3x_2 + 5x_3 &= 1 \\ 3x_1 + 5x_2 + 9x_3 &= 2 \\ 5x_1 + 9x_2 + 17x_3 &= 4 \end{aligned}$

32. $\begin{aligned} 2x_1 + 3x_2 + 5x_3 &= 4 \\ 3x_1 + 5x_2 + 9x_3 &= 7 \\ 5x_1 + 9x_2 + 17x_3 &= 13 \end{aligned}$

C In Exercises 33–36, use Cramer's Rule to solve for x_1.

33. $\begin{aligned} 7x_1 - 3x_2 \quad\;\; + 2x_4 &= 41 \\ -2x_1 + x_2 \quad\;\; - x_4 &= -13 \\ 4x_1 \quad\;\; + x_3 - 2x_4 &= 12 \\ -x_1 + x_2 \quad\;\; - x_4 &= -8 \end{aligned}$

34. $\begin{aligned} 2x_1 + 5x_2 \quad\;\; + x_4 &= 11 \\ x_1 + 4x_2 + 2x_3 - 2x_4 &= -7 \\ 2x_1 - 2x_2 + 5x_3 + x_4 &= 3 \\ x_1 \quad\;\; - 3x_4 &= 1 \end{aligned}$

35. $\begin{aligned} 5x_1 - 3x_2 + x_3 &= 2 \\ 2x_1 + 2x_2 - 3x_3 &= 4 \\ x_1 - 7x_2 + 8x_3 &= -6 \end{aligned}$

36. $\begin{aligned} 3x_1 + 2x_2 + 5x_3 &= 4 \\ 4x_1 - 3x_2 - 4x_3 &= 1 \\ -8x_1 + 2x_2 + 3x_3 &= 0 \end{aligned}$

37. Use Cramer's Rule to solve the following system of linear equations for x and y.

$$kx + (1 - k)y = 1$$
$$(1 - k)x + \quad ky = 3$$

For what value(s) of k will the system be inconsistent?

38. Verify the following system of linear equations in cos A, cos B, and cos C for the triangle shown in Figure 3.5.

$$c \cos B + b \cos C = a$$
$$c \cos A \qquad + a \cos C = b$$
$$b \cos A + a \cos B \qquad = c$$

Then use Cramer's Rule to solve for cos C, and use the result to verify the Law of Cosines,

$$c^2 = a^2 + b^2 - 2ab \cos C.$$

Figure 3.5

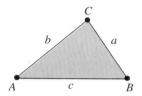

Area, Volume, and Equations of Lines and Planes

In Exercises 39–42, find the area of the triangle having the given vertices.

39. $(0, 0), (2, 0), (0, 3)$
40. $(1, 1), (2, 4), (4, 2)$
41. $(-1, 2), (2, 2), (-2, 4)$
42. $(1, 1), (-1, 1), (0, -2)$

In Exercises 43–46, determine whether the given points are collinear.

43. $(1, 2), (3, 4), (5, 6)$
44. $(-1, 0), (1, 1), (3, 3)$
45. $(-2, 5), (0, -1), (3, -9)$
46. $(-1, -3), (-4, 7), (2, -13)$

In Exercises 47–50, find an equation of the line passing through the given points.

47. $(0, 0), (3, 4)$
48. $(-4, 7), (2, 4)$
49. $(-2, 3), (-2, -4)$
50. $(1, 4), (3, 4)$

In Exercises 51–54, find the volume of the tetrahedron having the given vertices.

51. $(1, 0, 0), (0, 1, 0), (0, 0, 1), (1, 1, 1)$
52. $(1, 1, 1), (0, 0, 0), (2, 1, -1), (-1, 1, 2)$
53. $(3, -1, 1), (4, -4, 4), (1, 1, 1), (0, 0, 1)$
54. $(0, 0, 0), (0, 2, 0), (3, 0, 0), (1, 1, 4)$

In Exercises 55–58, determine whether the given points are coplanar.

55. $(-4, 1, 0), (0, 1, 2), (4, 3, -1), (0, 0, 1)$
56. $(1, 2, 3), (-1, 0, 1), (0, -2, -5), (2, 6, 11)$
57. $(0, 0, -1), (0, -1, 0), (1, 1, 0), (2, 1, 2)$
58. $(1, 2, 7), (-3, 6, 6), (4, 4, 2), (3, 3, 4)$

In Exercises 59–62, find an equation of the plane passing through the given points.

59. $(1, -2, 1), (-1, -1, 7), (2, -1, 3)$
60. $(0, -1, 0), (1, 1, 0), (2, 1, 2)$
61. $(0, 0, 0), (1, -1, 0), (0, 1, -1)$
62. $(1, 2, 7), (4, 4, 2), (3, 3, 4)$

CHAPTER 3 ☐ REVIEW EXERCISES

In Exercises 1–18, find the determinant of the given matrix.

1. $\begin{bmatrix} 4 & -1 \\ 2 & 2 \end{bmatrix}$

2. $\begin{bmatrix} 0 & -3 \\ 1 & 2 \end{bmatrix}$

3. $\begin{bmatrix} -3 & 1 \\ 6 & -2 \end{bmatrix}$

4. $\begin{bmatrix} -2 & 0 \\ 0 & 3 \end{bmatrix}$

5. $\begin{bmatrix} 1 & 4 & -2 \\ 0 & -3 & 1 \\ 1 & 1 & -1 \end{bmatrix}$

6. $\begin{bmatrix} 5 & 0 & 2 \\ 0 & -1 & 3 \\ 0 & 0 & 1 \end{bmatrix}$

7. $\begin{bmatrix} -2 & 0 & 0 \\ 0 & -3 & 0 \\ 0 & 0 & -1 \end{bmatrix}$

8. $\begin{bmatrix} -15 & 0 & 4 \\ 3 & 0 & -5 \\ 12 & 0 & 6 \end{bmatrix}$

9. $\begin{bmatrix} -3 & 6 & 9 \\ 9 & 12 & -3 \\ 0 & 15 & -6 \end{bmatrix}$

10. $\begin{bmatrix} -15 & 0 & 3 \\ 3 & 9 & -6 \\ 12 & -3 & 6 \end{bmatrix}$

C 11. $\begin{bmatrix} 2 & 0 & -1 & 4 \\ -1 & 2 & 0 & 3 \\ 3 & 0 & 1 & 2 \\ -2 & 0 & 3 & 1 \end{bmatrix}$

C 12. $\begin{bmatrix} 2 & 0 & 0 & 0 \\ -3 & 1 & 0 & 0 \\ 4 & -1 & 3 & 0 \\ 5 & 2 & 1 & -1 \end{bmatrix}$

C 13. $\begin{bmatrix} -4 & 1 & 2 & 3 \\ 1 & -2 & 1 & 2 \\ 2 & -1 & 3 & 4 \\ 1 & 2 & 2 & -1 \end{bmatrix}$ **C 14.** $\begin{bmatrix} 3 & -1 & 2 & 1 \\ -2 & 0 & 1 & -3 \\ -1 & 2 & -3 & 4 \\ -2 & 1 & -2 & 1 \end{bmatrix}$

C 15. $\begin{bmatrix} -1 & 1 & -1 & 0 & 0 \\ 0 & 1 & -1 & 0 & 1 \\ 1 & 0 & 1 & -1 & 0 \\ 0 & -1 & 0 & 1 & -1 \\ 0 & 1 & 1 & -1 & 1 \end{bmatrix}$

C 16. $\begin{bmatrix} 1 & 2 & -1 & 3 & 4 \\ 2 & 3 & -1 & 2 & -2 \\ 1 & 2 & 0 & 1 & -1 \\ 1 & 0 & 2 & -1 & 0 \\ 0 & -1 & 1 & 0 & 2 \end{bmatrix}$

17. $\begin{bmatrix} -1 & 0 & 0 & 0 & 0 \\ 0 & -1 & 0 & 0 & 0 \\ 0 & 0 & -1 & 0 & 0 \\ 0 & 0 & 0 & -1 & 0 \\ 0 & 0 & 0 & 0 & -1 \end{bmatrix}$

18. $\begin{bmatrix} 0 & 0 & 0 & 0 & 2 \\ 0 & 0 & 0 & 2 & 0 \\ 0 & 0 & 2 & 0 & 0 \\ 0 & 2 & 0 & 0 & 0 \\ 2 & 0 & 0 & 0 & 0 \end{bmatrix}$

In Exercises 19 and 20, find (a) $|A|$, (b) $|B|$, (c) AB, and (d) $|AB|$. Then verify that $|A||B| = |AB|$.

19. $A = \begin{bmatrix} -1 & 2 \\ 0 & 1 \end{bmatrix}$, $B = \begin{bmatrix} 3 & 4 \\ 2 & 1 \end{bmatrix}$

20. $A = \begin{bmatrix} 1 & 2 & 3 \\ 4 & 5 & 6 \\ 7 & 8 & 0 \end{bmatrix}$, $B = \begin{bmatrix} 1 & 2 & 1 \\ 0 & -1 & 1 \\ 0 & 2 & 3 \end{bmatrix}$

In Exercises 21 and 22, find (a) $|A^T|$, (b) $|A^3|$, (c) $|A^TA|$, and (d) $|5A|$.

21. $A = \begin{bmatrix} -2 & 6 \\ 1 & 3 \end{bmatrix}$ **22.** $A = \begin{bmatrix} 3 & 0 & 1 \\ -1 & 0 & 0 \\ 2 & 1 & 2 \end{bmatrix}$

In Exercises 23 and 24, find (a) $|A|$ (b) $|A^{-1}|$.

23. $A = \begin{bmatrix} 1 & 0 & -4 \\ 0 & 3 & 2 \\ -2 & 7 & 6 \end{bmatrix}$ **24.** $A = \begin{bmatrix} 2 & -1 & 4 \\ 5 & 0 & 3 \\ 1 & -2 & 0 \end{bmatrix}$

In Exercises 25–30, use the determinant of the coefficient matrix to determine whether the given system of linear equations has a unique solution.

25. $5x + 4y = 2$
$-x + y = -22$

26. $2x - 5y = 2$
$3x - 7y = 1$

27. $-x + y + 2z = 1$
$2x + 3y + z = -2$
$5x + 4y + 2z = 4$

28. $2x + 3y + z = 10$
$2x - 3y - 3z = 22$
$8x + 6y = -2$

29. $x_1 + 2x_2 + 6x_3 = 1$
$2x_1 + 5x_2 + 15x_3 = 4$
$3x_1 + x_2 + 3x_3 = -6$

C 30. $x_1 + 5x_2 + 3x_3 = 14$
$4x_1 + 2x_2 + 5x_3 = 3$
$3x_3 + 8x_4 + 6x_5 = 16$
$2x_1 + 4x_2 - 2x_5 = 0$
$2x_1 - x_3 = 0$

31. If A is a 3×3 matrix such that $|A| = 2$, then what is the value of $|4A|$?

32. If A is a 4×4 matrix such that $|A| = -1$, then what is the value of $|2A|$?

33. Prove the following property.

$$\begin{vmatrix} a_{11} & a_{12} & a_{13} \\ a_{21} & a_{22} & a_{23} \\ a_{31} + c_{31} & a_{32} + c_{32} & a_{33} + c_{33} \end{vmatrix} =$$

$$\begin{vmatrix} a_{11} & a_{12} & a_{13} \\ a_{21} & a_{22} & a_{23} \\ a_{31} & a_{32} & a_{33} \end{vmatrix} + \begin{vmatrix} a_{11} & a_{12} & a_{13} \\ a_{21} & a_{22} & a_{23} \\ c_{31} & c_{32} & c_{33} \end{vmatrix}$$

34. Illustrate the property given in Exercise 33 for the following.

$$A = \begin{bmatrix} 1 & 0 & 2 \\ 1 & -1 & 2 \\ 2 & 1 & -1 \end{bmatrix}, \quad c_{31} = 3, \quad c_{32} = 0, \quad c_{33} = 1$$

35. Find the determinant of the following $n \times n$ matrix.

$$\begin{bmatrix} 1-n & 1 & 1 & \cdots & 1 \\ 1 & 1-n & 1 & \cdots & 1 \\ \vdots & \vdots & \vdots & & \vdots \\ 1 & 1 & 1 & \cdots & 1-n \end{bmatrix}$$

36. Show that

$$\begin{vmatrix} a & 1 & 1 & 1 \\ 1 & a & 1 & 1 \\ 1 & 1 & a & 1 \\ 1 & 1 & 1 & a \end{vmatrix} = (a + 3)(a - 1)^3.$$

In Exercises 37 and 38, find the eigenvalues and corresponding eigenvectors of the matrix.

37. $\begin{bmatrix} -3 & 10 \\ 5 & 2 \end{bmatrix}$

38. $\begin{bmatrix} 1 & 0 & 0 \\ -2 & 3 & 0 \\ 0 & 0 & 4 \end{bmatrix}$

(Calculus) In Exercises 39–42, find the Jacobian of the given functions. If x, y, and z are continuous functions of u, v, and w with continuous first partial derivatives, the **Jacobians** $J(u, v)$ and $J(u, v, w)$ are given by

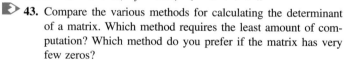

39. $x = \frac{1}{2}(v - u)$, $y = \frac{1}{2}(v + u)$

40. $x = au + bv$, $y = cu + dv$

41. $x = \frac{1}{2}(u + v)$, $y = \frac{1}{2}(u - v)$, $z = 2uvw$

42. $x = u - v + w$, $y = 2uv$, $z = u + v + w$

43. Compare the various methods for calculating the determinant of a matrix. Which method requires the least amount of computation? Which method do you prefer if the matrix has very few zeros?

44. Prove that if $|A| = |B| \neq 0$, then there exists a matrix C such that $|C| = 1$, and
$A = CB$.

The Adjoint of a Matrix

In Exercises 45 and 46, find the adjoint of the given matrix.

45. $\begin{bmatrix} 1 & 0 & 0 \\ 2 & 1 & 0 \\ 2 & -1 & 1 \end{bmatrix}$

46. $\begin{bmatrix} 1 & 2 \\ -2 & 0 \end{bmatrix}$

Cramer's Rule

In Exercises 47–50, use the determinant of the coefficient matrix to determine whether the given system of linear equations has a unique solution. If it does, use Cramer's Rule to find the solution.

47. $0.2x - 0.1y = 0.07$
$0.4x - 0.5y = -0.01$

48. $2x + y = 0.3$
$3x - y = -1.3$

49. $2x_1 + 3x_2 + 3x_3 = 3$
$6x_1 + 6x_2 + 12x_3 = 13$
$12x_1 + 9x_2 - x_3 = 2$

50. $4x_1 + 4x_2 + 4x_3 = 5$
$4x_1 - 2x_2 - 8x_3 = 1$
$8x_1 + 2x_2 - 4x_3 = 6$

Area, Volume, and Equations of Lines and Planes

In Exercises 51 and 52, use a determinant to find the area of the triangle with the given vertices.

51. $(1, 0), (5, 0), (5, 8)$

52. $(-4, 0), (4, 0), (0, 6)$

In Exercises 53 and 54, use a determinant to find an equation of the line passing through the given points.

53. $(-4, 0), (4, 4)$

54. $(2, 5), (6, -1)$

In Exercises 55 and 56, find an equation of the plane passing through the given points.

55. $(0, 0, 0), (1, 0, 3), (0, 3, 4)$

56. $(0, 0, 0), (2, -1, 1), (-3, 2, 5)$

CHAPTER 3   PROJECTS

1   Eigenvalues and Stochastic Matrices

In Section 2.5, you studied a consumer preference model for competing cable television companies. The matrix representing the transition probabilities was
$$P = \begin{bmatrix} 0.70 & 0.15 & 0.15 \\ 0.20 & 0.80 & 0.15 \\ 0.10 & 0.05 & 0.70 \end{bmatrix}.$$
Given the initial state matrix X, you observed that the number of subscribers after one year is given by the product PX.

$$X = \begin{bmatrix} 15{,}000 \\ 20{,}000 \\ 65{,}000 \end{bmatrix} \longrightarrow PX = \begin{bmatrix} 0.70 & 0.15 & 0.15 \\ 0.20 & 0.80 & 0.15 \\ 0.10 & 0.05 & 0.70 \end{bmatrix} \begin{bmatrix} 15{,}000 \\ 20{,}000 \\ 65{,}000 \end{bmatrix} = \begin{bmatrix} 23{,}250 \\ 28{,}750 \\ 48{,}000 \end{bmatrix}$$

After ten years, the number of subscribers had nearly reached a **steady state.**

$$X = \begin{bmatrix} 15{,}000 \\ 20{,}000 \\ 65{,}000 \end{bmatrix} \longrightarrow P^{10}X = \begin{bmatrix} 33{,}287 \\ 47{,}147 \\ 19{,}566 \end{bmatrix}$$

That is, for large values of n, the product P^nX approaches a limit $\overline{X}$, $P\overline{X} = \overline{X}$.

From your knowledge of eigenvalues, this means that 1 is an eigenvalue of P with corresponding eigenvector $\overline{X}$.

1. Use a computer or calculator to show that the eigenvalues and eigenvectors of P are

Eigenvalue	*Eigenvector*
$\lambda_1 = 1$	$\mathbf{x}_1 = \begin{bmatrix} 7 \\ 10 \\ 4 \end{bmatrix}$
$\lambda_2 = 0.65$	$\mathbf{x}_2 = \begin{bmatrix} 0 \\ -1 \\ 1 \end{bmatrix}$
$\lambda_3 = 0.55$	$\mathbf{x}_3 = \begin{bmatrix} -2 \\ 1 \\ 1 \end{bmatrix}$

2. Let S be the matrix whose columns are the eigenvectors of P. Show that $S^{-1}PS$ is a diagonal matrix D. What are the entries along the diagonal of D?
3. Show that $P^n = (SDS^{-1})^n = SD^nS^{-1}$. Use this result to calculate $P^{10}X$ and verify the result from Section 2.5.

2   The Cayley-Hamilton Theorem

The **characteristic polynomial** of a square matrix A is given by the determinant $|\lambda I - A|$. If the order of A is n, then the characteristic polynomial $p(\lambda)$ is an nth-degree polynomial in the variable λ.

$$p(\lambda) = \det(\lambda I - A) = \lambda^n + c_{n-1}\lambda^{n-1} + \cdots + c_2\lambda^2 + c_1\lambda + c_0$$

The Cayley-Hamilton theorem asserts that every square matrix satisfies its characteristic polynomial. That is, for the $n \times n$ matrix A,

$$p(A) = A^n + c_{n-1}A^{n-1} + \cdots + c_2A^2 + c_1A + c_0I = 0.$$

Note that this is a matrix equation. The zero on the right is the $n \times n$ zero matrix, and the coefficient c_0 has been multiplied by the $n \times n$ identity matrix I.

1. Verify the Cayley-Hamilton theorem for the matrix
$$\begin{bmatrix} 2 & -2 \\ -2 & -1 \end{bmatrix}.$$

2. Verify the Cayley-Hamilton theorem for the matrix
$$\begin{bmatrix} 6 & 0 & 4 \\ -2 & 1 & 3 \\ 2 & 0 & 4 \end{bmatrix}.$$

3. Prove the Cayley-Hamilton theorem for the case of an arbitrary 2×2 matrix A,
$$A = \begin{bmatrix} a & b \\ c & d \end{bmatrix}.$$

4. If A is nonsingular and $p(A) = A^n + c_{n-1}A^{n-1} + \cdots + c_1A + c_0I = 0$, show that
$$A^{-1} = \frac{1}{c_0}(-A^{n-1} - c_{n-1}A^{n-2} - \cdots - c_2A - c_1I).$$
Use this result to find the inverse of the matrix
$$A = \begin{bmatrix} 1 & 2 \\ 3 & 5 \end{bmatrix}.$$

5. The Cayley-Hamilton theorem can be used to calculate powers A^n of the square matrix A. For example, the characteristic polynomial of the matrix
$$A = \begin{bmatrix} 3 & -1 \\ 2 & -1 \end{bmatrix}$$
is $p(\lambda) = \lambda^2 - 2\lambda - 1$.
The Cayley-Hamilton theorem implies that
$$A^2 - 2A - I = 0 \quad \text{or} \quad A^2 = 2A + I.$$
Thus, A^2 is given in terms of lower powers of A.
$$A^2 = 2A + I = 2\begin{bmatrix} 3 & -1 \\ 2 & -1 \end{bmatrix} + \begin{bmatrix} 1 & 0 \\ 0 & 1 \end{bmatrix} = \begin{bmatrix} 7 & -2 \\ 4 & -1 \end{bmatrix}$$

Similarly, multiplying both sides of the equation $A^2 = 2A + I$ by A gives A^3 in terms of lower powers of A, $A^3 = 2A^2 + A$.
(a) Use this method to find A^3 and A^4.
(b) Find A^5 for the matrix
$$\begin{bmatrix} 0 & 0 & 1 \\ 2 & 2 & -1 \\ 1 & 0 & 2 \end{bmatrix}.$$

CHAPTER 3 □ MATLAB EXERCISES

1. Use MATLAB to calculate the determinants of the following matrices.

(a) $\begin{bmatrix} 2 & -3 \\ -6 & 9 \end{bmatrix}$ (b) $\begin{bmatrix} -5 & 6 & 7 \\ 0 & -1 & 2 \\ 4 & 0 & -3 \end{bmatrix}$

(c) **pascal(4)**   (d) **hilb(8)**

2. Let

$$A = \begin{bmatrix} 1 & 4 \\ 2 & -1 \end{bmatrix}.$$

Use the MATLAB determinant command **det** to compute **det(2 $*$ eye(2) $-$ A)**. Find an integer value of t such that $\det(tI - A) = 0$.

3. Choose arbitrary 4×4 matrices A and B. Compute $\det(A) \det(B)$, and $\det(AB)$. What do you observe? Do the same for $\det(A) + \det(B)$ and $\det(A + B)$.

4. Choose an arbitrary real number t. Form the matrix

$$A = \begin{bmatrix} \cos(t) & \sin(t) \\ -\sin(t) & \cos(t) \end{bmatrix}$$

and calculate its determinant. Does the value of the determinant depend on t?

5. Consider the matrices

$$A = \begin{bmatrix} 2 & 0 & 1 \\ 1 & -1 & 2 \\ 3 & 1 & 1 \end{bmatrix} \quad \text{and} \quad B = \begin{bmatrix} 2 & -1 & 4 \\ 0 & -1 & 3 \\ 3 & -2 & 1 \end{bmatrix}.$$

   (a) Verify that $\det(A) \det(B) = \det(AB)$.
   (b) Verify that $\det(A^T) = \det(A)$.
   (c) Verify that $\det(A^{-1}) = 1/\det(A)$.

6. In this exercise, we will use Cramer's rule to solve the linear system $A\mathbf{x} = \mathbf{b}$ from Example 3, Section 3.4. Let

$$A = \begin{bmatrix} 4 & -2 \\ 3 & -5 \end{bmatrix} \quad \text{and} \quad \mathbf{b} = \begin{bmatrix} 10 \\ 11 \end{bmatrix}$$

be the coefficient matrix and the right-hand side, respectively. To form the matrix A_1, we need to replace the first column of A with **b**. To do this, type

A1 = A
A1($:$,[1]) = B

The solution x_1 is obtained by typing

det(A1)/det(A)

You can calculate x_2 in a similar manner.

A2 = A
A2($:$,[2]) = B
det(A2)/det(A)

7. Use the Cramer's Rule algorithm from Exercise 6 to solve the following linear system. Compare your answer with that obtained using **rref.**

$$\begin{aligned} 3x + 3y + 4z &= 2 \\ x + y + 4z &= -2 \\ 2x + 5y + 4z &= 3 \end{aligned}$$

CUMULATIVE TEST FOR CHAPTERS 1–3

Take this test as you would take a test in class. After you are done, check your work against the answers at the back of the book.

   1. Solve the following system of linear equations.

$$\begin{aligned} x_1 - 2x_2 &= 3 \\ -x_1 + 6x_2 &= -1 \end{aligned}$$

2. Solve the following system of linear equations.
$$\begin{array}{rcrcrcr} 4x_1 & + & x_2 & - & 3x_3 & = & 11 \\ 2x_1 & - & 3x_2 & + & 2x_3 & = & 9 \\ x_1 & + & x_2 & + & x_3 & = & -3 \end{array}$$

3. Find the solution set of the system of linear equations represented by the following augmented matrix.
$$\begin{bmatrix} 0 & 1 & -1 & 0 & 2 \\ 1 & 0 & 2 & -1 & 0 \\ 1 & 2 & 0 & -1 & 4 \end{bmatrix}$$

4. Solve the homogeneous linear system corresponding to the following coefficient matrix.
$$\begin{bmatrix} 1 & 2 & 1 & -2 \\ 0 & 0 & 2 & -4 \\ -2 & -4 & 1 & -2 \end{bmatrix}$$

5. Find conditions on k such that the following system is consistent.
$$\begin{array}{rcr} x + 2y - z & = & 3 \\ -x - y + z & = & 2 \\ -x + y + z & = & k \end{array}$$

6. Find $A + B$ and $2A - 3B$ if
$$A = \begin{bmatrix} 1 & 2 & -1 \\ 3 & 0 & 2 \end{bmatrix} \quad \text{and} \quad B = \begin{bmatrix} 0 & -1 & 2 \\ 4 & 3 & -5 \end{bmatrix}.$$

7. Find AB and BA (if they are defined) given
$$A = \begin{bmatrix} 1 & 2 \\ 0 & 1 \\ -1 & 0 \end{bmatrix} \quad \text{and} \quad B = \begin{bmatrix} -1 & 0 \\ 1 & 1 \end{bmatrix}.$$

8. A manufacturer produces three different models of a given product that are shipped to two different warehouses. The number of units of model i that are shipped to warehouse j is represented by a_{ij} in the matrix
$$A = \begin{bmatrix} 200 & 300 \\ 600 & 350 \\ 250 & 400 \end{bmatrix}.$$
The price in dollars per unit is represented by the matrix
$$B = \begin{bmatrix} 12.50 & 9.00 & 21.50 \end{bmatrix}.$$
Find the product BA and state what each entry of the product represents.

9. Solve for x and y in the matrix equation $2A - B = I$ if
$$A = \begin{bmatrix} -1 & 1 \\ 2 & 3 \end{bmatrix} \quad \text{and} \quad B = \begin{bmatrix} x & 2 \\ y & 5 \end{bmatrix}.$$

10. Find $A^T A$ for the matrix
$$A = \begin{bmatrix} 1 & 2 & 3 \\ 4 & 5 & 6 \end{bmatrix}.$$

11. Find the inverse(s) (if they exist) of the given matrices.
$$\begin{bmatrix} -2 & 3 \\ 4 & 6 \end{bmatrix} \quad \begin{bmatrix} -2 & 3 \\ 3 & 6 \end{bmatrix}$$

12. Find the inverse of the matrix

$$\begin{bmatrix} 1 & 1 & 0 \\ -3 & 6 & 5 \\ 0 & 1 & 0 \end{bmatrix}.$$

13. Factor the matrix

$$A = \begin{bmatrix} 2 & -4 \\ 1 & 0 \end{bmatrix}$$

into a product of elementary matrices.

14. Find the determinant of the matrix

$$\begin{bmatrix} 0 & 1 & 3 \\ 1 & -1 & 2 \\ 5 & 8 & -4 \end{bmatrix}.$$

15. Find the following determinants if

$$A = \begin{bmatrix} 1 & -3 \\ 4 & 2 \end{bmatrix} \quad \text{and} \quad B = \begin{bmatrix} -2 & 1 \\ 0 & 5 \end{bmatrix}.$$

(a) $|A|$ (b) $|B|$ (c) $|AB|$ (d) $|A^{-1}|$

16. If $|A| = 7$ and A is order 4, then find the following determinants.

(a) $|3A|$ (b) $|A^T|$ (c) $|A^{-1}|$ (d) $|A^3|$

17. Use linear equations to find the parabola $y = ax^2 + bx + c$ that passes through the points $(-1, 2)$, $(0, 1)$ and $(2, 6)$. Sketch the points and the parabola.

18. Let x_1, x_2, x_3, and b be the following column matrices.

$$x_1 = \begin{bmatrix} 1 \\ 0 \\ 1 \end{bmatrix} \quad x_2 = \begin{bmatrix} 1 \\ 1 \\ 0 \end{bmatrix} \quad x_3 = \begin{bmatrix} 0 \\ 1 \\ 1 \end{bmatrix} \quad b = \begin{bmatrix} 1 \\ 2 \\ 3 \end{bmatrix}$$

Find constants a, b, and c such that $ax_1 + bx_2 + cx_3 = \mathbf{b}.$

19. Let A, B, and C be three nonzero $n \times n$ matrices such that $AC = BC$. Does it follow that $A = B$? Prove your answer.

20. For any matrix B, prove that the matrix $B^T B$ is symmetric.

21. Prove that if the matrix A has an inverse, then the inverse is unique.

22. (a) Define row equivalence of matrices.

(b) Prove that if A is row-equivalent to B and B is row-equivalent to C, then A is row-equivalent to C.

23. A matrix A is **skew-symmetric** if $A^T = -A$. Prove that the determinant of an odd order skew-symmetric matrix is zero.

24. A matrix A is **idempotent** if $A^2 = A$.

(a) Give three examples of idempotent 2×2 matrices.

(b) Find the determinant of an idempotent matrix.

25. Let A and B be nonsingular matrices of the same order.

(a) Is the sum $A + B$ nonsingular? Prove your answer.

(b) Is the product AB nonsingular? Prove your answer.

26. Describe all possible 2×2 reduced row-echelon matrices.

4 VECTOR SPACES

William Rowan
Hamilton
1 8 0 5 – 1 8 6 5

illiam Rowan Hamilton is generally recognized as Ireland's leading mathematician. The record of his early education is astonishing. By age five he could read and translate Latin, Greek, and Hebrew. By age ten he was fluent in French and Italian and was beginning to study Oriental languages. At seventeen, he had a grasp of calculus and astronomy.

Hamilton's formal education began when he entered Trinity College in Dublin at age eighteen. He so impressed his teachers there that after four years in undergraduate school he was elected to the position of professor of astronomy. In his first year on the faculty, he published an impressive work on optics entitled *A Theory of Systems of Rays,* 1828. This paper firmly established Hamilton's reputation, and it has become one of the classics in Western science. In it Hamilton included some of his own methods for working with systems of linear equations. He also introduced the notion of the characteristic equation of a matrix.

During the last twenty years of his life, Hamilton devoted most of his mathematical creativity to developing the theory of a special type of number he called a *quaternion.* This work paved the way for the development of the modern notion of a vector, and we still use Hamilton's **i, j, k** notation for the standard unit vectors in 3-space.

4.1 VECTORS IN R^n

You are probably already familiar with two- and three-dimensional vectors as they are used in physics and engineering. There, a vector is characterized by two quantities (length and direction) and is represented by a directed line segment. In this chapter you will see that these are only two special types of vectors. They are, however, important here because they have nice geometrical representations that help us understand the more general definition of a vector.

We begin with a short review of vectors in the plane, which is the way vectors were developed historically.

Vectors in the Plane

A **vector*** in the plane is represented geometrically by a **directed line segment** whose **initial point** is the origin and whose **terminal point** is the point (x_1, x_2), as shown in

---

*The term *vector* derives from the Latin word *vectus,* meaning "to carry." The idea is that if you were to carry something from the origin to the point (x_1, x_2), the trip could be pictured by the directed line segment from $(0, 0)$ to (x_1, x_2).

Figure 4.1

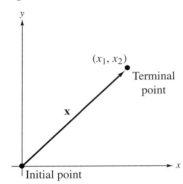

Figure 4.1. We represent this vector by the same **ordered pair** used to represent its terminal point. That is,

$$\mathbf{x} = (x_1, x_2).$$

The coordinates x_1 and x_2 are called the **components** of the vector $\mathbf{x}$. Two vectors in the plane $\mathbf{u} = (u_1, u_2)$ and $\mathbf{v} = (v_1, v_2)$ are **equal** if and only if $u_1 = v_1$ and $u_2 = v_2$.

REMARK: We use lowercase letters set in bold type (such as $\mathbf{u}$, $\mathbf{v}$, $\mathbf{w}$, and $\mathbf{x}$) to represent vectors.

EXAMPLE 1   *Vectors in the Plane*

Use directed line segments to represent the following vectors in the plane.
(a) $\mathbf{u} = (2, 3)$ (b) $\mathbf{v} = (-1, 2)$

Solution   To represent these vectors, we draw a directed line segment from the origin to the indicated terminal point, as shown in Figure 4.2.

Figure 4.2

(a)

(b)

Figure 4.3

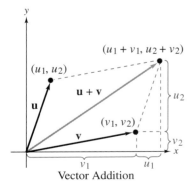

Vector Addition

The first basic vector operation is **vector addition.** To add two vectors in the plane, we add their corresponding components. That is, the **sum** of $\mathbf{u}$ and $\mathbf{v}$ is the vector given by

$$\mathbf{u} + \mathbf{v} = (u_1, u_2) + (v_1, v_2)$$
$$= (u_1 + v_1, u_2 + v_2).$$

Geometrically, we can represent the sum of two vectors in the plane as the diagonal of a parallelogram having $\mathbf{u}$ and $\mathbf{v}$ as its adjacent sides, as shown in Figure 4.3.

EXAMPLE 2   *Adding Two Vectors in the Plane*

Find the sum of the following vectors.
(a) $\mathbf{u} = (1, 4)$, $\mathbf{v} = (2, -2)$
(b) $\mathbf{u} = (3, -2)$, $\mathbf{v} = (-3, 2)$
(c) $\mathbf{u} = (2, 1)$, $\mathbf{v} = (0, 0)$

Solution   (a) $\mathbf{u} + \mathbf{v} = (1, 4) + (2, -2) = (3, 2)$
(b) $\mathbf{u} + \mathbf{v} = (3, -2) + (-3, 2) = (0, 0)$
(c) $\mathbf{u} + \mathbf{v} = (2, 1) + (0, 0) = (2, 1)$

Figure 4.4

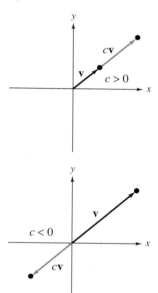

REMARK: In Example 2, the vector $(0, 0)$ is called the **zero vector** and is denoted by **0.**

The second basic vector operation is called **scalar multiplication.** To multiply a vector **v** by a scalar c, we multiply each of the components of **v** by c. That is,

$$c\mathbf{v} = c(v_1, v_2) = (cv_1, cv_2).$$

Recall from Chapter 2 that we use the word *scalar* to mean a real number. Historically, this usage arose from the fact that multiplying a vector by a real number changes the "scale" of the vector. For instance, if a vector **v** is multiplied by 2, the resulting vector $2\mathbf{v}$ is a vector having the same direction as **v** and twice the length. In general, for a scalar c, the vector $c\mathbf{v}$ will be c times as long as **v**. Moreover, if c is positive, then $c\mathbf{v}$ has the same direction as **v,** and if c is negative, then $c\mathbf{v}$ and **v** have opposite directions. This is shown in Figure 4.4.
The product of a vector **v** with the scalar -1 is denoted by

$$-\mathbf{v} = (-1)\mathbf{v}.$$

We call $-\mathbf{v}$ the **negative** of **v.** The **difference** of **u** and **v** is defined to be

$$\mathbf{u} - \mathbf{v} = \mathbf{u} + (-\mathbf{v}),$$

and we say that **v** is **subtracted** from **u.**

EXAMPLE 3   *Operations with Vectors in the Plane*

Given $\mathbf{v} = (-2, 5)$ and $\mathbf{u} = (3, 4)$, find the following vectors.
(a) $\frac{1}{2}\mathbf{v}$ (b) $\mathbf{u} - \mathbf{v}$ (c) $\mathbf{v} + 2\mathbf{u}$

Solution   (a) Since $\mathbf{v} = (-2, 5)$, we have

$$\tfrac{1}{2}\mathbf{v} = \left(\tfrac{1}{2}(-2), \tfrac{1}{2}(5)\right) = \left(-1, \tfrac{5}{2}\right).$$

(b) By the definition of vector subtraction, we have

$$\mathbf{u} - \mathbf{v} = (3 - (-2), 4 - 5) = (5, -1).$$

(c) Since $2\mathbf{u} = (6, 8)$, it follows that

$$\begin{aligned}
\mathbf{v} + 2\mathbf{u} &= (-2, 5) + (6, 8) \\
&= (-2 + 6, 5 + 8) \\
&= (4, 13).
\end{aligned}$$

Vector addition and scalar multiplication share many properties with matrix addition and scalar multiplication. The ten properties listed in the following theorem play a fundamental role in linear algebra. In fact, we will see in the next section that it is precisely these ten properties that we choose to abstract from vectors in the plane to define the general notion of a vector space.

Theorem 4.1

Properties of Vector Addition and Scalar Multiplication

Let $\mathbf{u}$, $\mathbf{v}$, and $\mathbf{w}$ be vectors in the plane, and let c and d be scalars.

1. $\mathbf{u} + \mathbf{v}$ is a vector in the plane.		**Closure under addition**
2. $\mathbf{u} + \mathbf{v} = \mathbf{v} + \mathbf{u}$		**Commutative property of addition**
3. $(\mathbf{u} + \mathbf{v}) + \mathbf{w} = \mathbf{u} + (\mathbf{v} + \mathbf{w})$		**Associative property of addition**
4. $\mathbf{u} + \mathbf{0} = \mathbf{u}$		
5. $\mathbf{u} + (-\mathbf{u}) = \mathbf{0}$		
6. $c\mathbf{u}$ is a vector in the plane.		**Closure under scalar multiplication**
7. $c(\mathbf{u} + \mathbf{v}) = c\mathbf{u} + c\mathbf{v}$		**Distributive property**
8. $(c + d)\mathbf{u} = c\mathbf{u} + d\mathbf{u}$		**Distributive property**
9. $c(d\mathbf{u}) = (cd)\mathbf{u}$		
10. $1(\mathbf{u}) = \mathbf{u}$		

Proof   The proof of each property is a straightforward application of the definition of vector addition and scalar multiplication combined with the corresponding properties of addition and multiplication of real numbers. For instance, to prove the associative property of vector addition, we can write

$$\begin{aligned}
(\mathbf{u} + \mathbf{v}) + \mathbf{w} &= [(u_1, u_2) + (v_1, v_2)] + (w_1, w_2) \\
&= (u_1 + v_1, u_2 + v_2) + (w_1, w_2) \\
&= ((u_1 + v_1) + w_1, (u_2 + v_2) + w_2) \\
&= (u_1 + (v_1 + w_1), u_2 + (v_2 + w_2)) \\
&= (u_1, u_2) + (v_1 + w_1, v_2 + w_2) \\
&= (u_1, u_2) + [(v_1, v_2) + (w_1, w_2)] \\
&= \mathbf{u} + (\mathbf{v} + \mathbf{w}).
\end{aligned}$$

Similarly, to prove the right distributive property of scalar multiplication over addition, we can write

$$\begin{aligned}
(c + d)\mathbf{u} &= (c + d)(u_1, u_2) \\
&= ((c + d)u_1, (c + d)u_2) \\
&= (cu_1 + du_1, cu_2 + du_2) \\
&= (cu_1, cu_2) + (du_1, du_2) \\
&= c(u_1, u_2) + d(u_1, u_2) = c\mathbf{u} + d\mathbf{u}.
\end{aligned}$$

The proofs of the other eight properties are left to you. (See Exercise 39.)

REMARK: Note that the associative property of vector addition allows us to write such expressions as $\mathbf{u} + \mathbf{v} + \mathbf{w}$ without ambiguity because we obtain the same vector sum whichever addition is performed first.

Vectors in R^n

Using vectors in the plane as our model, we now extend our discussion of vectors to n-space. The notation we use moves from the ordered pair (x_1, x_2) to an **ordered n-tuple.** For instance, an ordered triple has the form (x_1, x_2, x_3), an ordered quadruple has the form (x_1, x_2, x_3, x_4), and a general ordered n-tuple has the form $(x_1, x_2, x_3, \ldots, x_n)$. We call the set of all n-tuples **n-space** and denote it by R^n.

$R^1 = $ 1-space $= $ set of all real numbers
$R^2 = $ 2-space $= $ set of all order pairs of real numbers
$R^3 = $ 3-space $= $ set of all ordered triples of real numbers
$R^4 = $ 4-space $= $ set of all ordered quadruples of real numbers

$$\vdots$$

$R^n = $ n-space $= $ set of all ordered n-tuples of real numbers

Our practice of using an ordered pair to represent either a point or a vector in R^2 continues in R^n. That is, an n-tuple $(x_1, x_2, x_3, \ldots, x_n)$ can be viewed as a **point** in R^n with the x_i's as its coordinates or as a **vector**

$$\mathbf{x} = (x_1, x_2, x_3, \ldots, x_n) \qquad \text{Vector in } R^n$$

with the x_i's as its components. As usual, two vectors in R^n are **equal** if and only if corresponding components are equal. [In the case of $n = 2$ or $n = 3$, we occasionally use the familiar (x, y) or (x, y, z) notation.]

The sum of two vectors in R^n and the scalar multiple of a vector in R^n are defined as follows. We call these operations the **standard operations in R^n.**

Definition of Vector Addition and Scalar Multiplication in R^n	Let $\mathbf{u} = (u_1, u_2, u_3, \ldots, u_n)$ and $\mathbf{v} = (v_1, v_2, v_3, \ldots, v_n)$ be vectors in R^n and let c be a real number. Then the **sum** of $\mathbf{u}$ and $\mathbf{v}$ is defined to be the vector $$\mathbf{u} + \mathbf{v} = (u_1 + v_1, u_2 + v_2, u_3 + v_3, \ldots, u_n + v_n),$$ and the **scalar multiple** of $\mathbf{u}$ by c is defined to be the vector $$c\mathbf{u} = (cu_1, cu_2, cu_3, \ldots, cu_n).$$

As with 2-space, we define the **negative** of a vector in R^n to be

$$-\mathbf{u} = (-u_1, -u_2, -u_3, \ldots, -u_n)$$

and the **difference** two vectors in R^n to be

$$\mathbf{u} - \mathbf{v} = (u_1 - v_1, u_2 - v_2, u_3 - v_3, \ldots, u_n - v_n).$$

The **zero vector** in R^n is given by $\mathbf{0} = (0, 0, \ldots, 0)$.

EXAMPLE 4   *Vector Operations in R^3*

Given $\mathbf{u} = (0, -4, 3)$ and $\mathbf{v} = (1, 3, -2)$ in R^3, find the following vectors.
(a) $\mathbf{u} + \mathbf{v}$ (b) $3\mathbf{u}$ (c) $\mathbf{v} - 3\mathbf{u}$

Solution   (a) To add two vectors, add their corresponding components as follows.

$$\mathbf{u} + \mathbf{v} = (0, -4, 3) + (1, 3, -2) = (1, -1, 1)$$

(b) To multiply a vector by a scalar, multiply each component by the scalar as follows.

$$3\mathbf{u} = 3(0, -4, 3) = (0, -12, 9)$$

(c) Using the result of part (b), we have

$$\mathbf{v} - 3\mathbf{u} = (1, 3, -2) - (0, -12, 9) = (1, 15, -11).$$

The following properties of vector addition and scalar multiplication, for vectors in R^n, are the same as those listed in Theorem 4.1 for vectors in a plane. Their proofs, based on the definitions of vector addition and scalar multiplication in R^n, are left as an exercise. (See Exercise 40.)

Theorem 4.2

Properties of Vector Addition and Scalar Multiplication

Let $\mathbf{u}$, $\mathbf{v}$, and $\mathbf{w}$ be vectors in R^n, and let c and d be scalars.
1. $\mathbf{u} + \mathbf{v}$ is a vector in R^n.   2. $\mathbf{u} + \mathbf{v} = \mathbf{v} + \mathbf{u}$
3. $(\mathbf{u} + \mathbf{v}) + \mathbf{w} = \mathbf{u} + (\mathbf{v} + \mathbf{w})$ 4. $\mathbf{u} + \mathbf{0} = \mathbf{u}$
5. $\mathbf{u} + (-\mathbf{u}) = \mathbf{0}$ 6. $c\mathbf{u}$ is a vector in R^n.
7. $c(\mathbf{u} + \mathbf{v}) = c\mathbf{u} + c\mathbf{v}$ 8. $(c + d)\mathbf{u} = c\mathbf{u} + d\mathbf{u}$
9. $c(d\mathbf{u}) = (cd)\mathbf{u}$ 10. $1(\mathbf{u}) = \mathbf{u}$

Using the ten properties given in Theorem 4.2, we can perform algebraic manipulations with vectors in R^n in much the same way as we do with real numbers, as demonstrated in the next example.

EXAMPLE 5   *Vector Operations in R^4*

Let $\mathbf{u} = (2, -1, 5, 0)$, $\mathbf{v} = (4, 3, 1, -1)$, and $\mathbf{w} = (-6, 2, 0, 3)$ be vectors in R^4. Solve for $\mathbf{x}$ in each of the following.
(a) $\mathbf{x} = 2\mathbf{u} - (\mathbf{v} + 3\mathbf{w})$ (b) $3(\mathbf{x} + \mathbf{w}) = 2\mathbf{u} - \mathbf{v} + \mathbf{x}$

Solution   (a) Using the properties listed in Theorem 4.2, we have

$$\begin{aligned}
\mathbf{x} &= 2\mathbf{u} - (\mathbf{v} + 3\mathbf{w}) \\
&= 2\mathbf{u} - \mathbf{v} - 3\mathbf{w} \\
&= (4, -2, 10, 0) - (4, 3, 1, -1) - (-18, 6, 0, 9) \\
&= (4 - 4 + 18, -2 - 3 - 6, 10 - 1 - 0, 0 + 1 - 9) \\
&= (18, -11, 9, -8).
\end{aligned}$$

(b) We begin by solving for **x** as follows.

$$3(\mathbf{x} + \mathbf{w}) = 2\mathbf{u} - \mathbf{v} + \mathbf{x}$$
$$3\mathbf{x} + 3\mathbf{w} = 2\mathbf{u} - \mathbf{v} + \mathbf{x}$$
$$3\mathbf{x} - \mathbf{x} = 2\mathbf{u} - \mathbf{v} - 3\mathbf{w}$$
$$2\mathbf{x} = 2\mathbf{u} - \mathbf{v} - 3\mathbf{w}$$
$$\mathbf{x} = \tfrac{1}{2}(2\mathbf{u} - \mathbf{v} - 3\mathbf{w})$$

Then the result of part (a) produces

$$\mathbf{x} = \tfrac{1}{2}(18, -11, 9, -8)$$
$$= \left(9, -\tfrac{11}{2}, \tfrac{9}{2}, -4\right).$$

We call the zero vector **0** in R^n the **additive identity** in R^n. Similarly, we call the vector $-\mathbf{v}$ the **additive inverse** of **v**. The following theorem summarizes several important properties of the additive identity and additive inverse in R^n.

Theorem 4.3 Properties of Additive Identity and Additive Inverses	Let **v** be a vector in R^n, and let c be a scalar. Then the following properties are true. 1. The additive identity is unique. That is, if $\mathbf{v} + \mathbf{u} = \mathbf{v}$, then $\mathbf{u} = \mathbf{0}$. 2. The additive inverse of **v** is unique. That is, if $\mathbf{v} + \mathbf{u} = \mathbf{0}$, then $\mathbf{u} = -\mathbf{v}$. 3. $0\mathbf{v} = \mathbf{0}$ 4. $c\mathbf{0} = \mathbf{0}$ 5. If $c\mathbf{v} = \mathbf{0}$, then $c = 0$ or $\mathbf{v} = \mathbf{0}$. 6. $-(-\mathbf{v}) = \mathbf{v}$

Proof   To prove the first property, we assume that $\mathbf{v} + \mathbf{u} = \mathbf{v}$. Then the following steps are justified by Theorem 4.2.

$\mathbf{v} + \mathbf{u} = \mathbf{v}$	Given
$(\mathbf{v} + \mathbf{u}) + (-\mathbf{v}) = \mathbf{v} + (-\mathbf{v})$	Add $-\mathbf{v}$ to both sides.
$(\mathbf{v} + \mathbf{u}) + (-\mathbf{v}) = \mathbf{0}$	Additive inverse
$\mathbf{v} + [\mathbf{u} + (-\mathbf{v})] = \mathbf{0}$	Associative property
$\mathbf{v} + [(-\mathbf{v}) + \mathbf{u}] = \mathbf{0}$	Commutative property
$[\mathbf{v} + (-\mathbf{v})] + \mathbf{u} = \mathbf{0}$	Associative property
$\mathbf{0} + \mathbf{u} = \mathbf{0}$	Additive inverse
$\mathbf{u} + \mathbf{0} = \mathbf{0}$	Commutative property
$\mathbf{u} = \mathbf{0}$	Additive identity

As you gain experience in reading and writing proofs involving vector algebra, you will not need to list this many steps. For now, however, it's a good idea. We suggest that you try writing proofs for the other five properties. (See Exercise 41.) As you do, use Theorem 4.2 to justify each step of your proof.

REMARK: In properties 3 and 5 of Theorem 4.3, note that two different zeros are used, the scalar 0 and the vector **0**.

The next example illustrates an important type of problem in linear algebra—writing one vector $\mathbf{x}$ as the sum of scalar multiples of other vectors $\mathbf{v}_1, \mathbf{v}_2, \ldots,$ and $\mathbf{v}_n$. That is,

$$\mathbf{x} = c_1\mathbf{v}_1 + c_2\mathbf{v}_2 + \cdots + c_n\mathbf{v}_n.$$

We call the vector $\mathbf{x}$ a **linear combination** of the vectors $\mathbf{v}_1, \mathbf{v}_2, \ldots,$ and $\mathbf{v}_n$.

EXAMPLE 6   *Writing a Vector as a Linear Combination of Other Vectors*

Given $\mathbf{x} = (-1, -2, -2)$, $\mathbf{u} = (0, 1, 4)$, $\mathbf{v} = (-1, 1, 2)$, and $\mathbf{w} = (3, 1, 2)$ in R^3, find scalars a, b, and c such that

$$\mathbf{x} = a\mathbf{u} + b\mathbf{v} + c\mathbf{w}.$$

Solution   By writing

$$\overbrace{(-1, -2, -2)}^{\mathbf{x}} = a\overbrace{(0, 1, 4)}^{\mathbf{u}} + b\overbrace{(-1, 1, 2)}^{\mathbf{v}} + c\overbrace{(3, 1, 2)}^{\mathbf{w}}$$
$$= (-b + 3c, a + b + c, 4a + 2b + 2c),$$

we can equate corresponding components so that they form the following system of three linear equations in a, b, and c.

$$\begin{array}{ll} -b + 3c = -1 & \text{Equation from first component} \\ a + b + c = -2 & \text{Equation from second component} \\ 4a + 2b + 2c = -2 & \text{Equation from third component} \end{array}$$

Using the techniques of Chapter 1, we solve for a, b, and c and get $a = 1$, $b = -2$, and $c = -1$. Thus we have found that

$$\mathbf{x} = \mathbf{u} - 2\mathbf{v} - \mathbf{w}.$$

Try using vector addition and scalar multiplication to check this result.

DISCOVERY

Is the vector $(1, 1)$ a linear combination of the vectors $(1, 2)$ and $(-2, -4)$? Graph these vectors in the plane and explain your answer geometrically. Similarly, determine if the vector $(1, 1)$ is a linear combination of the vectors $(1, 2)$ and $(2, 1)$. What is the geometric significance of these two questions? Is every vector in R^2 a linear combination of the vectors $(1, 2)$ and $(2, 1)$? Give a geometric explanation for your answer.

We will often find it useful to represent a vector $\mathbf{u} = (u_1, u_2, \ldots, u_n)$ in R^n as either a $1 \times n$ row matrix (row vector),

$$\mathbf{u} = \begin{bmatrix} u_1 & u_2 & \cdots & u_n \end{bmatrix},$$

or an $n \times 1$ column matrix (column vector),

$$\mathbf{u} = \begin{bmatrix} u_1 \\ u_2 \\ \vdots \\ u_n \end{bmatrix}.$$

This approach is valid because the matrix operations of addition and scalar multiplication give the same results as the corresponding vector operations. That is, the matrix sums

$$\mathbf{u} + \mathbf{v} = \begin{bmatrix} u_1 & u_2 & \cdots & u_n \end{bmatrix} + \begin{bmatrix} v_1 & v_2 & \cdots & v_n \end{bmatrix}$$
$$= \begin{bmatrix} u_1 + v_1 & u_2 + v_2 & \cdots & u_n + v_n \end{bmatrix}$$

and

$$\mathbf{u} + \mathbf{v} = \begin{bmatrix} u_1 \\ u_2 \\ \vdots \\ u_n \end{bmatrix} + \begin{bmatrix} v_1 \\ v_2 \\ \vdots \\ v_n \end{bmatrix} = \begin{bmatrix} u_1 + v_1 \\ u_2 + v_2 \\ \vdots \\ u_n + v_n \end{bmatrix}$$

yield the same results as the vector operation of addition,

$$\mathbf{u} + \mathbf{v} = (u_1, u_2, \ldots, u_n) + (v_1, v_2, \ldots, v_n) = (u_1 + v_1, u_2 + v_2, \ldots, u_n + v_n).$$

The same argument applies to scalar multiplication. The only difference in the three notations for vectors is how the components are displayed; the underlying operations are the same.

SECTION 4.1   ☐   EXERCISES

In Exercises 1–6, find the vector $\mathbf{v}$ and illustrate the indicated vector operations geometrically, where $\mathbf{u} = (2, -1)$ and $\mathbf{w} = (1, 2)$.

1. $\mathbf{v} = \frac{3}{2}\mathbf{u}$ **2.** $\mathbf{v} = \mathbf{u} + \mathbf{w}$ **3.** $\mathbf{v} = \mathbf{u} + 2\mathbf{w}$

4. $\mathbf{v} = -\mathbf{u} + \mathbf{w}$ **5.** $\mathbf{v} = \frac{1}{2}(3\mathbf{u} + \mathbf{w})$ **6.** $\mathbf{v} = \mathbf{u} - 2\mathbf{w}$

7. Given the vector $\mathbf{v} = (2, 3)$, sketch (a) $2\mathbf{v}$, (b) $-3\mathbf{v}$, and (c) $\frac{1}{2}\mathbf{v}$.

8. Given the vector $\mathbf{v} = (-1, 2)$, sketch (a) $4\mathbf{v}$, (b) $-\frac{1}{2}\mathbf{v}$, and (c) $0\mathbf{v}$.

In Exercises 9–14, let $\mathbf{u} = (1, 2, 3)$, $\mathbf{v} = (2, 2, -1)$, and $\mathbf{w} = (4, 0, -4)$.

9. Find $\mathbf{u} - \mathbf{v}$ and $\mathbf{v} - \mathbf{u}$.   **10.** Find $\mathbf{u} - \mathbf{v} + 2\mathbf{w}$.

11. Find $2\mathbf{u} + 4\mathbf{v} - \mathbf{w}$.   **12.** Find $5\mathbf{u} - 3\mathbf{v} - \frac{1}{2}\mathbf{w}$.

13. Find $\mathbf{z}$, where $2\mathbf{z} - 3\mathbf{u} = \mathbf{w}$.

14. Find $\mathbf{z}$, where $2\mathbf{u} + \mathbf{v} - \mathbf{w} + 3\mathbf{z} = \mathbf{0}$.

15. Given the vector $\mathbf{v} = (1, 2, 2)$, sketch (a) $2\mathbf{v}$, (b) $-\mathbf{v}$, and (c) $\frac{1}{2}\mathbf{v}$.

16. Given the vector $\mathbf{v} = (2, 0, 1)$, sketch (a) $-\mathbf{v}$, (b) $2\mathbf{v}$, and (c) $\frac{1}{2}\mathbf{v}$.

17. Which of the following vectors are scalar multiples of $\mathbf{z} = (3, 2, -5)$?

(a) $\mathbf{u} = (-6, -4, 10)$ (b) $\mathbf{v} = \left(2, \frac{4}{3}, -\frac{10}{3}\right)$

(c) $\mathbf{w} = (6, 4, 10)$

18. Which of the following vectors are scalar multiples of $\mathbf{z} = \left(\frac{1}{2}, -\frac{2}{3}, \frac{3}{4}\right)$?

(a) $\mathbf{u} = (6, -4, 9)$ (b) $\mathbf{v} = \left(-1, \frac{4}{3}, -\frac{3}{2}\right)$

(c) $\mathbf{w} = (12, 0, 9)$

In Exercises 19–22, find (a) $\mathbf{u} - \mathbf{v}$ and (b) $2(\mathbf{u} + 3\mathbf{v})$.

19. $\mathbf{u} = (4, 0, -3, 5)$, $\mathbf{v} = (0, 2, 5, 4)$

20. $\mathbf{u} = (0, 4, 3, 4, 4)$, $\mathbf{v} = (6, 8, -3, 3, -5)$

21. $\mathbf{u} = (-7, 0, 0, 0, 9)$, $\mathbf{v} = (2, -3, -2, 3, 3)$

22. $\mathbf{u} = (6, -5, 4, 3)$, $\mathbf{v} = \left(-2, \frac{5}{3}, -\frac{4}{3}, -1\right)$

In Exercises 23 and 24, solve for $\mathbf{w}$ given that $\mathbf{u} = (1, -1, 0, 1)$ and $\mathbf{v} = (0, 2, 3, -1)$.

23. $2\mathbf{w} = \mathbf{u} - 3\mathbf{v}$ **24.** $\mathbf{w} + \mathbf{u} = -\mathbf{v}$

In Exercises 25–28, if possible write $\mathbf{v}$ as a linear combination of $\mathbf{u}$ and $\mathbf{w}$, where $\mathbf{u} = (1, 2)$ and $\mathbf{w} = (1, -1)$.

25. $\mathbf{v} = (2, 1)$ **26.** $\mathbf{v} = (0, 3)$

27. $\mathbf{v} = (3, 0)$ **28.** $\mathbf{v} = (1, -1)$

In Exercises 29 and 30, find $\mathbf{w}$ such that $2\mathbf{u} + \mathbf{v} - 3\mathbf{w} = \mathbf{0}$.

29. $\mathbf{u} = (0, 2, 7, 5)$, $\mathbf{v} = (-3, 1, 4, -8)$

30. $\mathbf{u} = (0, 0, -8, 1)$, $\mathbf{v} = (1, -8, 0, 7)$

In Exercises 31–34, if possible write $\mathbf{v}$ as a linear combination of $\mathbf{u}_1$, $\mathbf{u}_2$, and $\mathbf{u}_3$.

31. $\mathbf{u}_1 = (2, 3, 5)$, $\mathbf{u}_2 = (1, 2, 4)$, $\mathbf{u}_3 = (-2, 2, 3)$,
$\mathbf{v} = (10, 1, 4)$

32. $\mathbf{u}_1 = (1, 3, 5)$, $\mathbf{u}_2 = (2, -1, 3)$, $\mathbf{u}_3 = (-3, 2, -4)$,
$\mathbf{v} = (-1, 7, 2)$

33. $\mathbf{u}_1 = (1, 1, 2, 2)$, $\mathbf{u}_2 = (2, 3, 5, 6)$, $\mathbf{u}_3 = (-3, 1, -4, 2)$,
$\mathbf{v} = (0, 5, 3, 0)$

34. $\mathbf{u}_1 = (1, 3, 2, 1)$, $\mathbf{u}_2 = (2, -2, -5, 4)$, $\mathbf{u}_3 = (2, -1, 3, 6)$,
$\mathbf{v} = (2, 5, -4, 0)$

In Exercises 35 and 36, the zero vector $\mathbf{0} = (0, 0, 0)$ can be written as a linear combination of the vectors $\mathbf{v}_1$, $\mathbf{v}_2$, and $\mathbf{v}_3$ as $\mathbf{0} = 0\mathbf{v}_1 + 0\mathbf{v}_2 + 0\mathbf{v}_3$. We call this the *trivial* solution. Can you find a *nontrivial* way of writing $\mathbf{0}$ as a linear combination of the three given vectors?

35. $\mathbf{v}_1 = (1, 0, 1)$, $\mathbf{v}_2 = (-1, 1, 2)$, $\mathbf{v}_3 = (0, 1, 4)$

36. $\mathbf{v}_1 = (1, 0, 1)$, $\mathbf{v}_2 = (-1, 1, 2)$, $\mathbf{v}_3 = (0, 1, 3)$

37. Illustrate properties 1–10 of Theorem 4.2 for
$\mathbf{u} = (2, -1, 3, 6)$, $\mathbf{v} = (1, 4, 0, 1)$, $\mathbf{w} = (3, 0, 2, 0)$, $c = 5$, and $d = -2$.

38. Illustrate properties 1–10 of Theorem 4.2 for $\mathbf{u} = (2, -1, 3)$, $\mathbf{v} = (3, 4, 0)$, $\mathbf{w} = (7, 8, -4)$, $c = 2$, and $d = -1$.

39. Complete the proof of Theorem 4.1.

40. Prove Theorem 4.2.

41. Complete the proof of Theorem 4.3.

42. For each of the following matrices, can you write the third column of the matrix as a linear combination of the first two columns?

(a) $\begin{bmatrix} 1 & 2 & 3 \\ 7 & 8 & 9 \\ 4 & 5 & 6 \end{bmatrix}$ (b) $\begin{bmatrix} 1 & 2 & 3 \\ 7 & 8 & 9 \\ 4 & 5 & 7 \end{bmatrix}$

43. Let $A\mathbf{x} = \mathbf{b}$ be a system of m linear equations in n unknowns. Designate the columns of A as $\mathbf{a}_1, \mathbf{a}_2, \ldots, \mathbf{a}_n$. If $\mathbf{b}$ is a linear combination of these n column vectors, explain why this implies that the linear system is consistent. Illustrate your answer with appropriate examples. What can you conclude about the linear system if $\mathbf{b}$ is not a linear combination of the columns of A?

44. How could you describe vector subtraction geometrically? What is the relationship between vector subtraction and the basic vector operations of addition and scalar multiplication?

4.2 VECTOR SPACES

In Theorem 4.2 we listed ten special properties of vector addition and scalar multiplication in R^n. Suitable definitions of addition and scalar multiplication reveal that many other mathematical quantities (such as matrices, polynomials, and functions) also share these ten properties. We call *any* set that satisfies these properties (or **axioms**) a **vector space**, and the objects in the set are called **vectors.**

It is important to realize that the following definition of a vector space is precisely that—a *definition*. We do not need to prove anything, since we are simply listing the axioms required of vector spaces. We call this type of definition an **abstraction** because we are abstracting a collection of properties from a particular setting R^n to form the axioms for a more general setting.

Definition of Vector Space

Let V be a set on which two operations (**vector addition** and **scalar multiplication**) are defined. If the following axioms are satisfied for every $\mathbf{u}$, $\mathbf{v}$, and $\mathbf{w}$ in V and every scalar (real number) c and d, then V is called a **vector space.**

Addition:

1. $\mathbf{u} + \mathbf{v}$ is in V.   Closure under addition
2. $\mathbf{u} + \mathbf{v} = \mathbf{v} + \mathbf{u}$ Commutative property
3. $\mathbf{u} + (\mathbf{v} + \mathbf{w}) = (\mathbf{u} + \mathbf{v}) + \mathbf{w}$ Associative property
4. V has a **zero vector 0** such that for   Additive identity
   every $\mathbf{u}$ in V, $\mathbf{u} + \mathbf{0} = \mathbf{u}$.
5. For every $\mathbf{u}$ in V, there is a vector   Additive inverse
   in V denoted by $-\mathbf{u}$ such that
   $\mathbf{u} + (-\mathbf{u}) = \mathbf{0}$.

Scalar Multiplication:

6. $c\mathbf{u}$ is in V.   Closure under scalar multiplication
7. $c(\mathbf{u} + \mathbf{v}) = c\mathbf{u} + c\mathbf{v}$ Distributive property
8. $(c + d)\mathbf{u} = c\mathbf{u} + d\mathbf{u}$ Distributive property
9. $c(d\mathbf{u}) = (cd)\mathbf{u}$ Associative property
10. $1(\mathbf{u}) = \mathbf{u}$ Scalar identity

It is important to realize that a vector space consists of four entities: a set of vectors, a set of scalars, and two operations. When you refer to a vector space V, be sure that all four entities are clearly stated or understood. Unless stated otherwise, we assume that the set of scalars is the set of real numbers. (In Chapter 8, we will discuss complex vector spaces, in which the set of scalars is the set of complex numbers.)

The first two examples of vector spaces are not surprising. They are, in fact, the models we used to form the ten vector space axioms.

EXAMPLE 1   ***R^2 with the Standard Operations Is a Vector Space***

The set of all ordered pairs of real numbers R^2 with the standard operations is a vector space. To verify this, look back at Theorem 4.1. Vectors in this space have the form

$$\mathbf{v} = (v_1, v_2).$$

EXAMPLE 2   ***R^n with the Standard Operations Is a Vector Space***

The set of all ordered n-tuples of real numbers R^n with the standard operations is a vector space. This is verified by Theorem 4.2. Vectors in this space are of the form

$$\mathbf{v} = (v_1, v_2, v_3, \ldots, v_n).$$

REMARK: From Example 2 we can conclude that R^1, the set of real numbers (with the usual operations of addition and multiplication), is a vector space.

The next three examples describe vector spaces in which the basic set V does not consist of ordered n-tuples. In each example we will describe the set V and define the two vector operations. Then, to show that the set is a vector space, we must verify all ten axioms.

EXAMPLE 3   ***The Vector Space of All 2×3 Matrices***

Show that the set of all 2×3 matrices with the operations of matrix addition and scalar multiplication is a vector space.

Solution   If A and B are 2×3 matrices and c is a scalar, then $A + B$ and cA are also 2×3 matrices. Therefore the set is closed under matrix addition and scalar multiplication. Moreover, the other eight vector space axioms follow directly from Theorems 2.1 and 2.2 (see Section 2.2). Therefore we can conclude that the set is a vector space. Vectors in this space have the form

$$A = \begin{bmatrix} a_{11} & a_{12} & a_{13} \\ a_{21} & a_{22} & a_{23} \end{bmatrix}.$$

REMARK: In the same way that we are able to show that the set of all 2×3 matrices is a vector space, we can show that the set of all $m \times n$ matrices, denoted by $M_{m,n}$, is a vector space.

EXAMPLE 4   *The Vector Space of All Polynomials of Degree 2 or Less*

Let P_2 be the set of all polynomials of the form

$$p(x) = a_2 x^2 + a_1 x + a_0,$$

where a_0, a_1, and a_2 are real numbers. The *sum* of two polynomials $p(x) = a_2 x^2 + a_1 x + a_0$ and $q(x) = b_2 x^2 + b_1 x + b_0$ is defined in the usual way by

$$p(x) + q(x) = (a_2 + b_2)x^2 + (a_1 + b_1)x + (a_0 + b_0),$$

and the *scalar multiple* of $p(x)$ by the scalar c is defined by

$$cp(x) = ca_2 x^2 + ca_1 x + ca_0.$$

Show that P_2 is a vector space.

Solution   Verification of each of the ten vector space axioms is a straightforward application of the properties of real numbers. For instance, because the set of real numbers is closed under addition, it follows that $a_2 + b_2$, $a_1 + b_1$, and $a_0 + b_0$ are real numbers, and

$$p(x) + q(x) = (a_2 + b_2)x^2 + (a_1 + b_1)x + (a_0 + b_0)$$

is in the set P_2 because it is a polynomial of degree two or less. Thus P_2 is closed under addition. Similarly, we can use the fact that the set of real numbers is closed under multiplication to show that P_2 is closed under scalar multiplication. To verify the commutative axiom of addition, we write

$$\begin{aligned}
p(x) + q(x) &= (a_2 x^2 + a_1 x + a_0) + (b_2 x^2 + b_1 x + b_0) \\
&= (a_2 + b_2)x^2 + (a_1 + b_1)x + (a_0 + b_0) \\
&= (b_2 + a_2)x^2 + (b_1 + a_1)x + (b_0 + a_0) \\
&= (b_2 x^2 + b_1 x + b_0) + (a_2 x^2 + a_1 x + a_0) \\
&= q(x) + p(x).
\end{aligned}$$

Can you see where we used the commutative property of addition of real numbers? The zero vector in this space is the zero polynomial given by $\mathbf{0}(x) = 0$, for all x. Try verifying the other vector space axioms. You then may conclude that P_2 is a vector space.

REMARK: Even though the zero polynomial $\mathbf{0}(x) = 0$ has no degree, we often describe P_2 as the set of all polynomials of degree 2 *or less.*

We define P_n to be the set of all polynomials of degree n or less (together with the zero polynomial). The procedure used to verify that P_2 is a vector space can be extended to show that P_n, with the usual operations of polynomial addition and scalar multiplication, is a vector space.

EXAMPLE 5   *The Vector Space of Continuous Functions (Calculus)*

Let $C(-\infty, \infty)$ be the set of all real-valued continuous functions defined on the entire real line. This set consists of all polynomial functions and all other functions that are continuous on the entire real line. For instance, $f(x) = \sin x$ and $g(x) = e^x$ are members of the set. Addition is defined by

$$(\mathbf{f} + \mathbf{g})(x) = \mathbf{f}(x) + \mathbf{g}(x),$$

as shown in Figure 4.5. Scalar multiplication is defined by

$$(c\mathbf{f})(x) = c[\mathbf{f}(x)].$$

Show that $C(-\infty, \infty)$ is a vector space.

Figure 4.5

Solution   To verify that the set $C(-\infty, \infty)$ is closed under addition and scalar multiplication, we use a result from calculus—that the sum of two continuous functions is continuous and the product of a scalar and a continuous function is continuous. To verify that the set $C(-\infty, \infty)$ has an additive identity, we consider the function $\mathbf{f}_0$ that has a value of zero for all x. That is,

$$\mathbf{f}_0(x) = 0, \quad x \text{ is any real number.}$$

This function is continuous on the entire real line (its graph is simply the line $y = 0$). Hence it is in the set $C(-\infty, \infty)$. Moreover, if $\mathbf{f}$ is any other function that is continuous on the entire real line, then

$$(\mathbf{f} + \mathbf{f}_0)(x) = \mathbf{f}(x) + \mathbf{f}_0(x) = \mathbf{f}(x) + 0 = \mathbf{f}(x).$$

Hence $\mathbf{f}_0$ is the additive identity in $C(-\infty, \infty)$. We leave verification of the other axioms to you.

For convenience, we provide a summary of some important vector spaces that will be referred to frequently in the remainder of this text. In each case the operations are the standard ones.

Summary of Important Vector Spaces

$R = $ set of all real numbers
$R^2 = $ set of all ordered pairs
$R^3 = $ set of all ordered triples
$R^n = $ set of all n-tuples
$C(-\infty, \infty) = $ set of all continuous functions defined on the real line
$C[a, b] = $ set of all continuous functions defined on a closed interval $[a, b]$
$P = $ set of all polynomials
$P_n = $ set of all polynomials of degree $\leq n$
$M_{m,n} = $ set of all $m \times n$ matrices
$M_{n,n} = $ set of all $n \times n$ *square* matrices

We have seen how versatile the concept of a vector space is. For instance, a vector can be a real number, an n-tuple, a matrix, a polynomial, a continuous function, and so on. But what is the purpose? Why have we bothered to define this abstraction? There are several reasons, but the most important is that this abstraction turns out to be mathematically efficient in the sense that we can now derive general results that apply to all vector spaces. Once a theorem has been proven for an abstract vector space, we need not give separate proofs for *n*-tuples, matrices, and polynomials. We can simply point out that the theorem is true for any vector space, regardless of the particular form the vectors happen to take. This process is illustrated in Theorem 4.4.

Theorem 4.4

Properties of Scalar Multiplication

Let $\mathbf{v}$ be any element of a vector space V, and let c be any scalar. Then the following properties are true.
1. $0\mathbf{v} = \mathbf{0}$
2. $c\mathbf{0} = \mathbf{0}$
3. If $c\mathbf{v} = \mathbf{0}$, then $c = 0$ or $\mathbf{v} = \mathbf{0}$.
4. $(-1)\mathbf{v} = -\mathbf{v}$

Proof   To prove these properties, we are restricted to using the ten vector space axioms. For instance, to prove the second property, we note from axiom 4 that $\mathbf{0} = \mathbf{0} + \mathbf{0}$. This allows us to write the following steps.

$$
\begin{aligned}
c\mathbf{0} &= c(\mathbf{0} + \mathbf{0}) && \text{Additive identity} \\
c\mathbf{0} &= c\mathbf{0} + c\mathbf{0} && \text{Left distributive property} \\
c\mathbf{0} + (-c\mathbf{0}) &= (c\mathbf{0} + c\mathbf{0}) + (-c\mathbf{0}) && \text{Add } -c\mathbf{0} \text{ to both sides.} \\
c\mathbf{0} + (-c\mathbf{0}) &= c\mathbf{0} + [c\mathbf{0} + (-c\mathbf{0})] && \text{Associative property} \\
\mathbf{0} &= c\mathbf{0} + \mathbf{0} && \text{Additive inverse} \\
\mathbf{0} &= c\mathbf{0} && \text{Additive identity}
\end{aligned}
$$

To prove the third property, let us suppose that $c\mathbf{v} = \mathbf{0}$. To show that this implies either $c = 0$ or $\mathbf{v} = \mathbf{0}$, we assume that $c \neq 0$. (If $c = 0$, we have nothing more to prove.) Now, since $c \neq 0$, we use the reciprocal $1/c$ to show that $\mathbf{v} = \mathbf{0}$ as follows.

$$
\mathbf{v} = 1\mathbf{v} = \left(\frac{1}{c}\right)(c)\mathbf{v} = \frac{1}{c}(c\mathbf{v}) = \frac{1}{c}(\mathbf{0}) = \mathbf{0}
$$

Note that the last step uses property 2 (the one we just proved). We leave the proofs of the first and fourth properties to you. (See Exercises 34 and 35.)

The remaining examples in this section describe some sets (with operations) that *do not* form vector spaces. To show that a set is not a vector space, we need only find one thing wrong. For example, if we can find two members of V that do not commute ($\mathbf{u} + \mathbf{v} \neq \mathbf{v} + \mathbf{u}$), then regardless of how many other members of V do commute and how many of the other ten axioms are satisfied, we may still conclude that V is not a vector space.

EXAMPLE 6   ***The Set of Integers Is Not a Vector Space***

The set of all integers (with the standard operations) does not form a vector space because it is not closed under scalar multiplication. For example,

$$
\tfrac{1}{2}(1) = \tfrac{1}{2}.
$$

Scalar   *Integer*   *Noninteger*

REMARK: In Example 6, notice that a single failure of one of the ten vector space axioms suffices to show that a set is not a vector space.

In Example 4 we showed that the set of all polynomials of degree 2 or less forms a vector space. We will now see that the set of all polynomials whose degree is exactly 2 does not form a vector space.

EXAMPLE 7   **The Set of Second-Degree Polynomials Is Not a Vector Space**

The set of all second-degree polynomials is not a vector space because it is not closed under addition. To see this, consider the second-degree polynomials

$$p(x) = x^2 \quad \text{and} \quad q(x) = -x^2 + x + 1,$$

whose sum is the *first*-degree polynomial

$$p(x) + q(x) = x + 1.$$

The sets in Examples 6 and 7 are not vector spaces because they fail one or both closure axioms. In the next example we look at a set that passes both tests for closure but still fails to be a vector space.

EXAMPLE 8   **A Set That Is Not a Vector Space**

Let $V = R^2$, the set of all ordered pairs of real numbers, with the standard operation of addition and the following *nonstandard* definition of scalar multiplication:

$$c(x_1, x_2) = (cx_1, 0).$$

Show that V is not a vector space.

Solution   In this example, the operation of scalar multiplication is not the standard one. For instance, the product of the scalar 2 times the ordered pair $(3, 4)$ does not equal $(6, 8)$. Instead, the second component of the product is 0,

$$2(3, 4) = (2 \cdot 3, 0) = (6, 0).$$

This example is interesting because it actually satisfies the first nine axioms of the definition of vector space (try showing this). Only when we get to the tenth axiom do we get into trouble. In attempting to verify that axiom, we see that this nonstandard definition of scalar multiplication gives us

$$1(1, 1) = (1, 0) \neq (1, 1).$$

Hence, the tenth axiom is not verified, and the set (together with the two given operations) is not a vector space.

Do not be confused by the notation used for scalar multiplication in Example 8. In writing

$$c(x_1, x_2) = (cx_1, 0),$$

we are *defining* the scalar multiple of (x_1, x_2) by c to be $(cx_1, 0)$. As it turns out, this nonstandard definition fails to satisfy the tenth vector space axiom.

SECTION 4.2 ☐ EXERCISES

In Exercises 1–6, describe the zero vector (the additive identity) of the given vector space.

1. R^4 **2.** $C(-\infty, \infty)$ **3.** $M_{2,3}$

4. $M_{1,4}$ **5.** P_3 **6.** $M_{2,2}$

In Exercises 7–12, describe the additive inverse of a vector in the given vector space.

7. R^4 **8.** $C(-\infty, \infty)$ **9.** $M_{2,3}$

10. $M_{1,4}$ **11.** P_3 **12.** $M_{2,2}$

In Exercises 13–24, determine whether the given set, together with the indicated operations, is a vector space. If it is not, identify at least one of the ten vector space axioms that fails.

13. $M_{4,6}$ with the standard operations

14. $M_{1,1}$ with the standard operations

15. The set of all fifth-degree polynomials with the standard operations

16. P, the set of all polynomials, with the standard operations

17. The set $\{(x, x): x \text{ is a real number}\}$ with the standard operations

18. The set $\{(x, y): x \geq 0, y \text{ is a real number}\}$ with the standard operations in R^2

19. The set of all 2×2 matrices of the form

$$\begin{bmatrix} a & b \\ c & 0 \end{bmatrix}$$

with the standard operations

20. The set of all 2×2 matrices of the form

$$\begin{bmatrix} a & b \\ c & 1 \end{bmatrix}$$

with the standard operations

21. The set of all 2×2 singular matrices with the standard operations

22. The set of all 2×2 nonsingular matrices with the standard operations

23. The set of all 2×2 diagonal matrices with the standard operations

24. $C[0, 1]$, the set of all continuous functions defined on the interval $[0, 1]$, with the standard operations

25. Rather than use the standard definitions of addition and scalar multiplication in R^2, suppose that we define these two operations as follows.

(a) $(x_1, y_1) + (x_2, y_2) = (x_1 + x_2, y_1 + y_2)$
$c(x, y) = (cx, y)$

(b) $(x_1, y_1) + (x_2, y_2) = (x_1, 0)$
$c(x, y) = (cx, cy)$

(c) $(x_1, y_1) + (x_2, y_2) = (x_1 + x_2, y_1 + y_2)$
$c(x, y) = (\sqrt{cx}, \sqrt{cy})$

With these new definitions, is R^2 a vector space? Justify your answer.

26. Rather than use the standard definitions of addition and scalar multiplication in R^3, suppose that we define these two operations as follows.

(a) $(x_1, y_1, z_1) + (x_2, y_2, z_2) = (x_1 + x_2, y_1 + y_2, z_1 + z_2)$
$c(x, y, z) = (cx, cy, 0)$

(b) $(x_1, y_1, z_1) + (x_2, y_2, z_2) = (0, 0, 0)$
$c(x, y, z) = (cx, cy, cz)$

(c) $(x_1, y_1, z_1) + (x_2, y_2, z_2)$
$= (x_1 + x_2 + 1, y_1 + y_2 + 1, z_1 + z_2 + 1)$
$c(x, y, z) = (cx, cy, cz)$

(d) $(x_1, y_1, z_1) + (x_2, y_2, z_2)$
$= (x_1 + x_2 + 1, y_1 + y_2 + 1, z_1 + z_2 + 1)$
$c(x, y, z) = (cx + c - 1, cy + c - 1, cz + c - 1)$

With these new definitions, is R^3 a vector space? Justify your answer.

27. Prove in full detail that $M_{2,2}$, with the standard operations, is a vector space.

28. Prove in full detail that the set $\{(x, 2x): x \text{ is a real number}\}$, with the standard operations in R^2, is a vector space.

29. Determine whether the set R^2, with the operations

$(x_1, y_1) + (x_2, y_2) = (x_1 x_2, y_1 y_2)$

and

$c(x_1, y_1) = (cx_1, cy_1)$,

is a vector space. If it is, verify each vector space axiom; if not, state all vector space axioms that fail.

30. Let V be the set of all positive real numbers. Determine whether V is a vector space with the following operations.

$x + y = xy$ **Addition**

$cx = x^c$ **Scalar Multiplication**

If it is, verify each vector space axiom: if not, state all vector space axioms that fail.

31. Prove that in a given vector space V, the zero vector is unique.

32. Prove that in a given vector space V, the additive inverse of a vector is unique.

33. Prove the cancellation property for vector addition. That is, if **u**, **v**, and **w** are vectors in a vector space V such that $\mathbf{u} + \mathbf{w} = \mathbf{v} + \mathbf{w}$, then $\mathbf{u} = \mathbf{v}$.

34. Prove property 1 of Theorem 4.4.

35. Prove property 4 of Theorem 4.4.

4.3 SUBSPACES OF VECTOR SPACES

In most important applications in linear algebra, vector spaces occur as **subspaces** of larger spaces. For instance, we will see that the solution set of a homogeneous system of linear equations in n variables is a subspace of R^n. (See Theorem 4.16.)

We say that a subset of a vector space is a subspace if it is itself a vector space (with the *same* operations), as stated in the following definition.

Definition of Subspace of a Vector Space	A nonempty subset W of a vector space V is called a **subspace** of V if W is itself a vector space under the operations of addition and scalar multiplication defined in V.

EXAMPLE 1   *A Subspace of R^3*

Show that the set

$$W = \{(x_1, 0, x_3): x_1 \text{ and } x_3 \text{ are real numbers}\}$$

is a subspace of R^3 with the standard operations.

Figure 4.6

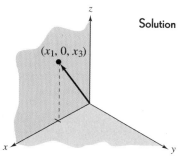

Solution   The set W is nonempty since it contains the zero vector $(0, 0, 0)$.

Graphically, the set W can be interpreted as simply the xz-plane, as shown in Figure 4.6. The set W is closed under addition because the sum of any two vectors in the xz-plane must also lie in the xz-plane. That is, if $(x_1, 0, x_3)$ and $(y_1, 0, y_3)$ are in W, then their sum $(x_1 + y_1, 0, x_3 + y_3)$ is also in W (since the second component is zero). Similarly, to see that W is closed under scalar multiplication, let $(x_1, 0, x_3)$ be in W and let c be a scalar. Then $c(x_1, 0, x_3) = (cx_1, 0, cx_3)$ has zero as its second component and must therefore be in W. The other eight vector space axioms can be verified as well, and we leave this to you. In fact, these axioms are automatically true, since they were true in the larger vector space R^3.

To establish that a set W is a vector space we must verify all ten vector space properties. However, if W is a subset of a larger vector space V (and the operations defined on W are the *same* as those defined on V), then most of the ten properties are *inherited* from the larger space and need no verification. The following theorem tells us that it is sufficient to test for closure in order to establish that a nonempty subset of a vector space is a subspace.

Theorem 4.5 Test for a Subspace	If W is a nonempty subset of a vector space V, then W is a subspace of V if and only if the following closure conditions hold. 1. If **u** and **v** are in W, then $\mathbf{u} + \mathbf{v}$ is in W. 2. If **u** is in W and c is any scalar, then $c\mathbf{u}$ is in W.

Proof   The proof of the theorem in one direction is straightforward. That is, if W is a subspace of V, then W is a vector space and must be closed under addition and scalar multiplication.

To prove the theorem in the other direction, we assume that W is closed under addition and scalar multiplication. Note that if $\mathbf{u}$, $\mathbf{v}$, and $\mathbf{w}$ are in W, then they are also in V. Consequently, vector space axioms 2, 3, 7, 8, 9, and 10 are satisfied automatically. Furthermore, because W is closed under addition and scalar multiplication, it follows that for any $\mathbf{v}$ in W and scalar $c = 0$,

$$c\mathbf{v} = \mathbf{0}$$

and

$$(-1)\mathbf{v} = -\mathbf{v}.$$

Both lie in W, thus satisfying the remaining axioms 4 and 5.

REMARK: Note that if W is a subspace of a vector space V, then both W and V must have the same zero vector $\mathbf{0}$. (See Exercise 26.)

Since a subspace of a vector space is itself a vector space, it must contain the zero vector. In fact, the simplest subspace of a vector space is the one consisting only of the zero vector,

$$W = \{\mathbf{0}\}.$$

We call this subspace the **zero subspace.** Another obvious subspace of V is V itself. Every vector space possesses these two trivial subspaces, and subspaces other than these two are called **proper** (or nontrivial) subspaces.

EXAMPLE 2   *A Subspace of $M_{2,2}$*

Let W be the set of all 2×2 symmetric matrices. Show that W is a subspace of the vector space $M_{2,2}$, with the standard operations of matrix addition and scalar multiplication.

Solution   Recall that a matrix is called symmetric if it is equal to its own transpose. Since $M_{2,2}$ is a vector space, we need only show that W (a subset of $M_{2,2}$) satisfies the conditions of Theorem 4.5. We begin by observing that W is *nonempty*. W is closed under addition because $A_1 = A_1^T$ and $A_2 = A_2^T$ implies that

$$(A_1 + A_2)^T = A_1^T + A_2^T = A_1 + A_2.$$

Hence, if A_1 and A_2 are symmetric matrices of order 2, then so is $A_1 + A_2$. Similarly, W is closed under scalar multiplication because $A = A^T$ implies that

$$(cA)^T = cA^T = cA.$$

Hence, if A is a symmetric matrix of order 2, then so is cA.

We can generalize the result of Example 2. That is, for any positive integer n, the set of symmetric matrices of order n is a subspace of the vector space $M_{n,n}$ with the standard operations. The next example describes a subset of $M_{n,n}$ that is *not* a subspace.

EXAMPLE 3   *The Set of Singular Matrices Is Not a Subspace $M_{n,n}$*

Let W be the set of singular matrices of order 2. Show that W is not a subspace of $M_{2,2}$ with the standard operations.

Solution   By Theorem 4.5 we can show that a subset W is not a subspace by showing either that W is empty, that W is not closed under addition, or that W is not closed under scalar multiplication. For this particular set, W is nonempty and closed under scalar multiplication, but it is not closed under addition. To see this, let A and B be given by

$$A = \begin{bmatrix} 1 & 0 \\ 0 & 0 \end{bmatrix} \quad \text{and} \quad B = \begin{bmatrix} 0 & 0 \\ 0 & 1 \end{bmatrix}.$$

Then A and B are both singular (noninvertible), but their sum

$$A + B = \begin{bmatrix} 1 & 0 \\ 0 & 1 \end{bmatrix}$$

is nonsingular (invertible). Therefore W is not closed under addition, and by Theorem 4.5 we can conclude that it is not a subspace of $M_{2,2}$.

EXAMPLE 4   *The Set of First-Quadrant Vectors Is Not a Subspace of R^2*

Show that $W = \{(x_1, x_2): x_1 \geq 0 \text{ and } x_2 \geq 0\}$, with the standard operations, is not a subspace of R^2.

Solution   This set is nonempty and closed under addition. It is not, however, closed under scalar multiplication. To see this, we note that $(1, 1)$ is in W, but the scalar multiple

$$(-1)(1, 1) = (-1, -1)$$

is not in W. Therefore W is not a subspace of R^2.

We often encounter sequences of subspaces that are nested in each other. For instance, consider the vector spaces $P_0, P_1, P_2, P_3, \ldots$, and P_n, where P_k is the set of all polynomials of degree less than or equal to k, with the standard operations. It is easy to show that if $j \leq k$, then P_j is a subspace of P_k. Thus we can write

$$P_0 \subset P_1 \subset P_2 \subset P_3 \subset \cdots \subset P_n.$$

Another nesting of subspaces is describe in Example 5.

EXAMPLE 5   *Subspaces of Functions (Calculus)*

Let W_5 be the *vector space* of all functions defined on $[0, 1]$, and let W_1, W_2, W_3, and W_4 be defined as follows.

W_1 = set of all polynomial functions defined on the interval $[0, 1]$
W_2 = set of all functions that are differentiable on $[0, 1]$
W_3 = set of all functions that are continuous on $[0, 1]$
W_4 = set of all functions that are integrable on $[0, 1]$

Show that $W_1 \subset W_2 \subset W_3 \subset W_4 \subset W_5$ and that W_i is a subspace of W_j for $i \leq j$.

Solution   From calculus we know that every polynomial function is differentiable on $[0, 1]$. Therefore $W_1 \subset W_2$. Moreover, $W_2 \subset W_3$ because every differentiable function is continuous, $W_3 \subset W_4$ because every continuous function is integrable, and $W_4 \subset W_5$ because every integrable function is, of course, a function. Therefore we have $W_1 \subset W_2 \subset W_3 \subset W_4 \subset W_5$, as shown in Figure 4.7. We leave the verification that W_i is a subspace of W_j for $i \leq j$ to you.

Figure 4.7

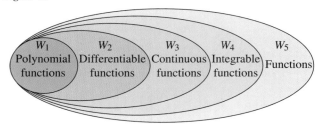

Note in Example 5 that if U, V, and W are vector spaces such that W is a subspace of V and V is a subspace of U, then W is also a subspace of U. This special case of the following theorem tells us that the intersection of two subspaces is a subspace, as shown in Figure 4.8.

Figure 4.8

The intersection of
two subspaces is
a subspace.

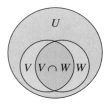

Theorem 4.6

The Intersection of Two Subspaces Is a Subspace

If V and W are both subspaces of a vector space U, then the intersection of V and W (denoted by $V \cap W$) is also a subspace of U.

Proof   Since V and W are both subspaces of U, we know that both contain the zero vector. Thus $V \cap W$ is nonempty. To show that $V \cap W$ is closed under addition, we let $\mathbf{v}_1$ and $\mathbf{v}_2$ be any two vectors in $V \cap W$. Then since V and W are both subspaces of U, we know that both are closed under addition. Therefore, since $\mathbf{v}_1$ and $\mathbf{v}_2$ are both in V, their sum $\mathbf{v}_1 + \mathbf{v}_2$ must be in V. Similarly, $\mathbf{v}_1 + \mathbf{v}_2$ is in W since $\mathbf{v}_1$ and $\mathbf{v}_2$ are both in W. But this implies that $\mathbf{v}_1 + \mathbf{v}_2$ is in $V \cap W$, and it follows that $V \cap W$ is closed under addition. We leave it to you to show (by a similar argument) that $V \cap W$ is closed under scalar multiplication. (See Exercise 30.)

REMARK: Theorem 4.6 states that the *intersection* of two subspaces is a subspace. In Exercise 22 you are asked to show that the *union* of two subspaces is not (in general) a subspace.

Subspace of R^n

R^n is a convenient source for examples of vector spaces, and we devote the remainder of this section to looking at subspaces of R^n.

EXAMPLE 6   *Determining Subspaces of R^2*

Which of these two subsets is a subspace of R^2?
(a) The set of points on the line given by $x + 2y = 0$
(b) The set of points on the line given by $x + 2y = 1$

Solution   (a) Solving for x, we see that a point in R^2 is on the line $x + 2y = 0$ if and only if it has the form

$$(-2t, t), \quad t \text{ is any real number.}$$

To show that this set is closed under addition, we let $\mathbf{v}_1 = (-2t_1, t_1)$ and $\mathbf{v}_2 = (-2t_2, t_2)$ be any two points on the line. Then we have

$$\begin{aligned}
\mathbf{v}_1 + \mathbf{v}_2 &= (-2t_1, t_1) + (-2t_2, t_2) \\
&= (-2(t_1 + t_2), t_1 + t_2) \\
&= (-2t_3, t_3),
\end{aligned}$$

where $t_3 = t_1 + t_2$. Therefore $\mathbf{v}_1 + \mathbf{v}_2$ lies on the line, and the set is closed under addition. In a similar way we can show that the set is closed under scalar multiplication. Thus this set *is* a subspace of R^2.

(b) This subset of R^2 is not a subspace of R^2. An easy way to see this is to note that the zero vector $(0, 0)$ is not on the line. Since every subspace must contain the zero vector, this subset is not a subspace.

Of the two lines in Example 6, the one that is a subspace of R^2 is the one that passes through the origin. It can be shown that this is characteristic of subspaces of R^2. That is, if W is a subset of R^2, then it is a subspace if and only if one of the following is true.
1. W consists of the *single point* $(0, 0)$.
2. W consists of all points on a *line* that passes through the origin.
3. W consists of all of R^2.
The three possibilities are shown graphically in Figure 4.9.

Figure 4.9

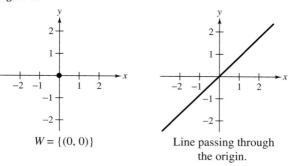

$W = \{(0, 0)\}$ Line passing through $W = R^2$
                                 the origin.

As an example of a subset of R^2 that is not a subspace, consider the points on the unit circle $x^2 + y^2 = 1$. The points $(1, 0)$ and $(0, 1)$ are in the subset, but their sum $(1, 1)$ is not. (See Figure 4.10.) Hence this subset is not closed under addition.

R E M A R K : Another way we can tell that the subset shown in Figure 4.10 is not a subspace of R^2 is by noting that it does not contain the zero vector (the origin).

EXAMPLE 7   *Determining Subspaces of R^3*

Which of the following subsets is a subspace of R^3?
(a) $W = \{(x_1, x_2, 1): x_1 \text{ and } x_2 \text{ are real numbers}\}$
(b) $W = \{(x_1, x_1 + x_3, x_3): x_1 \text{ and } x_3 \text{ are real numbers}\}$

Solution

(a) Since $\mathbf{0} = (0, 0, 0)$ is not in W, we know that W is *not* a subspace of R^3.
(b) This set is nonempty, since it contains the zero vector $(0, 0, 0)$.

Let $\mathbf{v} = (v_1, v_1 + v_3, v_3)$ and $\mathbf{u} = (u_1, u_1 + u_3, u_3)$ be two vectors in W, and let c be any real number. We show that W is closed under addition as follows.

$$
\begin{aligned}
\mathbf{v} + \mathbf{u} &= (v_1 + u_1, v_1 + v_3 + u_1 + u_3, v_3 + u_3) \\
&= (v_1 + u_1, (v_1 + u_1) + (v_3 + u_3), v_3 + u_3) \\
&= (x_1, x_1 + x_3, x_3)
\end{aligned}
$$

where $x_1 = v_1 + u_1$ and $x_3 = v_3 + u_3$. Hence $\mathbf{v} + \mathbf{u}$ is in W (because it is of the proper form.) Similarly, W is closed under scalar multiplication because

$$
\begin{aligned}
c\mathbf{v} &= (cv_1, c(v_1 + v_3), cv_3) \\
&= (cv_1, cv_1 + cv_3, cv_3) \\
&= (x_1, x_1 + x_3, x_3),
\end{aligned}
$$

where $x_1 = cv_1$ and $x_3 = cv_3$. Hence $c\mathbf{v}$ is in W. Finally, since W is closed under addition and scalar multiplication, we conclude that it *is* a subspace of R^3.

Figure 4.10

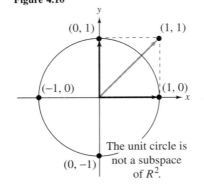

The unit circle is not a subspace of R^2.

In Example 7, note that the graph of each subset is a plane in R^3. However, the only one that is a *subspace* is the one represented by a plane that passes through the origin. (See Figure 4.11.)

In general we can show that a subset W of R^3 is a subspace of R^3 (with the standard operations) if and only if it has one of the following forms.
1. W consists of the *single point* $(0, 0, 0)$.
2. W consists of all points on a *line* that passes through the origin.
3. W consists of all points on a *plane* that passes through the origin.
4. W consists of all of R^3.

Figure 4.11

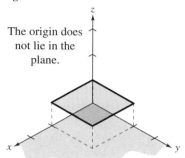

The origin does not lie in the plane.

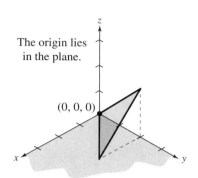

The origin lies in the plane.

$(0, 0, 0)$

SECTION 4.3 ☐ EXERCISES

In Exercises 1–6, verify that W is a subspace of V. In each case assume that V has the standard operations.

1. $W = \{(x_1, x_2, x_3, 0): x_1, x_2,$ and x_3 are real numbers$\}$
   $V = R^4$

2. $W = \{(x, y, 2x - 3y): x$ and y are real numbers$\}$
   $V = R^3$

3. W is the set of all 2×2 matrices of the form
$$\begin{bmatrix} 0 & a \\ b & 0 \end{bmatrix}.$$
   $V = M_{2,2}$

4. W is the set of all 3×2 matrices of the form
$$\begin{bmatrix} a & b \\ a + b & 0 \\ 0 & c \end{bmatrix}.$$
   $V = M_{3,2}$

5. (Calculus) W is the set of all functions that are continuous on $[0, 1]$. V is the set of all functions that are integrable on $[0, 1]$.

6. (Calculus) W is the set of all functions that are differentiable on $[0, 1]$. V is the set of all functions that are continuous on $[0, 1]$.

In Exercises 7–12, W is not a subspace of the given vector space. Verify this by giving a specific example that violates the test for a vector subspace (Theorem 4.5).

7. W is the set of all vectors in R^3 whose third component is -1.

8. W is the set of all vectors in R^2 whose components are rational numbers.

9. W is the set of all nonnegative functions in $C(-\infty, \infty)$.

10. W is the set of all vectors in R^3 whose components are nonnegative.

11. W is the set of all matrices in $M_{n,n}$ with zero determinants.

12. W is the set of all matrices in $M_{n,n}$ such that $A^2 = A$.

13. Which of the following subsets of $C(-\infty, \infty)$ are subspaces of $C(-\infty, \infty)$?

   (a) The set of all nonnegative functions: $f(x) \geq 0$
   (b) The set of all even functions: $f(-x) = f(x)$
   (c) The set of all odd functions: $f(-x) = -f(x)$
   (d) The set of all constant functions: $f(x) = c$
   (e) The set of all functions such that $f(0) = 0$
   (f) The set of all functions such that $f(0) = 1$

14. Which of the following subsets of $M_{n,n}$ are subspaces of $M_{n,n}$ with the standard operations?

   (a) The set of all $n \times n$ upper triangular matrices
   (b) The set of all $n \times n$ matrices with integer entries
   (c) The set of all $n \times n$ matrices A that commute with a given $n \times n$ matrix B
   (d) The set of all $n \times n$ singular matrices
   (e) The set of all $n \times n$ invertible matrices
   (f) The set of all $n \times n$ matrices whose entries add up to zero

In Exercises 15–20, determine whether the set W is a subspace R^3 with the standard operations. Justify your answer.

15. $W = \{(x_1, 0, x_3): x_1$ and x_3 are real numbers$\}$

16. $W = \{(x_1, x_2, 4): x_1$ and x_2 are real numbers$\}$

17. $W = \{(a, b, a + 2b): a$ and b are real numbers$\}$

18. $W = \{(s, s - t, t): s$ and t are real numbers$\}$

19. $W = \{(x_1, x_2, x_1 x_2): x_1$ and x_2 are real numbers$\}$

20. $W = \{(x_1, 1/x_1, x_3): x_1$ and x_3 are real numbers, $x_1 \neq 0\}$

21. Prove that a nonempty set W is a subspace of a vector space V if and only if $ax + by$ is an element of W where a and b are any scalars and x and y are in W.

22. Give an example showing that the union of two subspaces of a vector space V is not necessarily a subspace of V.

23. Let $\mathbf{x}$, $\mathbf{y}$, and $\mathbf{z}$ be vectors in a vector space V. Show that the set of all linear combinations of $\mathbf{x}$, $\mathbf{y}$, and $\mathbf{z}$

$$W = \{a\mathbf{x} + b\mathbf{y} + c\mathbf{z} : a, b, \text{ and } c \text{ are scalars}\}$$

is a subspace of V. This subspace is called the **span** of $\{\mathbf{x}, \mathbf{y}, \mathbf{z}\}$.

24. Let A be a fixed 2×3 matrix. Prove that the set

$$W = \left\{ \mathbf{x} \in R^3 : A\mathbf{x} = \begin{bmatrix} 1 \\ 2 \end{bmatrix} \right\}$$

is not a subspace of R^3.

25. Let A be a fixed $m \times n$ matrix. Prove that the set

$$W = \{\mathbf{x} \in R^n : A\mathbf{x} = \mathbf{0}\}$$

is a subspace of R^n.

26. Let W be a subspace of the vector space V. Prove that the zero vector in V is also the zero vector in W.

27. Let A be a fixed 2×2 matrix. Prove that the set $W = \{X : XA = AX\}$ is a subspace of $M_{2,2}$.

28. (Calculus) Determine whether the set

$$S = \left\{ f \in C[0, 1] : \int_0^1 f(x)\,dx = 0 \right\}$$

is a subspace of $C[0, 1]$. Prove your answer.

29. Let V and W be two subspaces of a vector space U. Prove that the set

$$V + W = \{\mathbf{u} : \mathbf{u} = \mathbf{v} + \mathbf{w} \text{ where } \mathbf{v} \in V \text{ and } \mathbf{w} \in W\}$$

is a subspace of U. Describe $V + W$ if V and W are the following subspaces of $U = R^2$:

$V = \{(x, 0) : x \text{ is a real number}\}$ and $W = \{(0, y) : y \text{ is a real number}\}$

30. Complete the proof of Theorem 4.6 by showing that the intersection of two subspaces of a vector space is closed under scalar multiplication.

4.4 SPANNING SETS AND LINEAR INDEPENDENCE

In this section we begin to develop procedures for representing each vector in a vector space as a **linear combination** of a select number of vectors in the space.

Definition of Linear Combination of Vectors

A vector $\mathbf{v}$ in a vector space V is called a **linear combination** of the vectors $\mathbf{u}_1, \mathbf{u}_2, \ldots, \mathbf{u}_k$ in V if $\mathbf{v}$ can be written in the form

$$\mathbf{v} = c_1\mathbf{u}_1 + c_2\mathbf{u}_2 + \cdots + c_k\mathbf{u}_k,$$

where $c_1, c_2, \ldots, c_k$ are scalars.

Often, one or more of the vectors in a given set can be written as linear combinations of other vectors in the set. The following examples illustrate this possibility.

EXAMPLE 1   ***Examples of Linear Combinations***

(a) For the following set of vectors in R^3,

$$S = \{\underset{\mathbf{v}_1}{(1, 3, 1)}, \underset{\mathbf{v}_2}{(0, 1, 2)}, \underset{\mathbf{v}_3}{(1, 0, -5)}\},$$

$\mathbf{v}_1$ is a linear combination of $\mathbf{v}_2$ and $\mathbf{v}_3$ because

$$\begin{aligned} \mathbf{v}_1 = 3\mathbf{v}_2 + \mathbf{v}_3 &= 3(0, 1, 2) + (1, 0, -5) \\ &= (1, 3, 1). \end{aligned}$$

(b) For the following set of vectors in $M_{2,2}$,

$$S = \left\{ \overset{\mathbf{v}_1}{\begin{bmatrix} 0 & 8 \\ 2 & 1 \end{bmatrix}}, \overset{\mathbf{v}_2}{\begin{bmatrix} 0 & 2 \\ 1 & 0 \end{bmatrix}}, \overset{\mathbf{v}_3}{\begin{bmatrix} -1 & 3 \\ 1 & 2 \end{bmatrix}}, \overset{\mathbf{v}_4}{\begin{bmatrix} -2 & 0 \\ 1 & 3 \end{bmatrix}} \right\},$$

$\mathbf{v}_1$ is a linear combination of $\mathbf{v}_2$, $\mathbf{v}_3$, and $\mathbf{v}_4$ because

$$\mathbf{v}_1 = \mathbf{v}_2 + 2\mathbf{v}_3 - \mathbf{v}_4$$

$$= \begin{bmatrix} 0 & 2 \\ 1 & 0 \end{bmatrix} + 2\begin{bmatrix} -1 & 3 \\ 1 & 2 \end{bmatrix} - \begin{bmatrix} -2 & 0 \\ 1 & 3 \end{bmatrix}$$

$$= \begin{bmatrix} 0 & 8 \\ 2 & 1 \end{bmatrix}.$$

In Example 1 it was easy to verify that one of the vectors in the set S is a linear combination of the other vectors because we were given the appropriate coefficients to form the linear combination. In the next example we demonstrate a procedure for finding the coefficients.

EXAMPLE 2   *Finding a Linear Combination*

Write the vector $\mathbf{w} = (1, 1, 1)$ as a linear combination of vectors in the following set.

$$S = \{ \overset{\mathbf{v}_1}{(1, 2, 3)}, \overset{\mathbf{v}_2}{(0, 1, 2)}, \overset{\mathbf{v}_3}{(-1, 0, 1)} \}$$

Solution   We need to find scalars c_1, c_2, and c_3 such that

$$(1, 1, 1) = c_1(1, 2, 3) + c_2(0, 1, 2) + c_3(-1, 0, 1)$$
$$= (c_1 - c_3, 2c_1 + c_2, 3c_1 + 2c_2 + c_3).$$

By equating corresponding components, we arrive at the following system of linear equations.

$$\begin{aligned} c_1 \quad\quad - c_3 &= 1 \\ 2c_1 + c_2 \quad\quad &= 1 \\ 3c_1 + 2c_2 + c_3 &= 1 \end{aligned}$$

Using Gauss-Jordan elimination, we find that this system has an infinite number of solutions, each of the form

$$c_1 = 1 + t, \quad\quad c_2 = -1 - 2t, \quad\quad c_3 = t.$$

For instance, to obtain one solution, we could let $t = 1$. Then $c_2 = -3$ and $c_1 = 2$, and we have

$$\mathbf{w} = 2\mathbf{v}_1 - 3\mathbf{v}_2 + \mathbf{v}_3.$$

Other choices for t would yield other ways to write $\mathbf{w}$ as a linear combination of $\mathbf{v}_1$, $\mathbf{v}_2$, and $\mathbf{v}_3$.

EXAMPLE 3   *Finding a Linear Combination*

If possible, write the vector $\mathbf{w} = (1, -2, 2)$ as a linear combination of vectors in the set S given in Example 2.

Solution   Following the procedure given in Example 2, we obtain the system

$$\begin{array}{rcl}
c_1 \quad\quad - c_3 &=& 1 \\
2c_1 + c_2 \quad\quad &=& -2 \\
3c_1 + 2c_2 + c_3 &=& 2.
\end{array}$$

The augmented matrix of this system reduces to

$$\begin{bmatrix} 1 & 0 & -1 & 1 \\ 0 & 1 & 2 & -4 \\ 0 & 0 & 0 & 7 \end{bmatrix}.$$

From the third row we conclude that the system of equations is inconsistent, and therefore there is no solution. Consequently, $\mathbf{w}$ *cannot* be written as a linear combination of $\mathbf{v}_1$, $\mathbf{v}_2$, and $\mathbf{v}_3$.

Spanning Sets

If every vector in a given vector space can be written as a linear combination of vectors in a given set S, then we say that S is a **spanning set** of the vector space.

Definition of Spanning Set of a Vector Space	Let $S = \{\mathbf{v}_1, \mathbf{v}_2, \ldots, \mathbf{v}_k\}$ be a subset of a vector space V. The set S is called a **spanning set** of V if every vector in V can be written as a linear combination of vectors in S. In such cases we say that S **spans** V.

EXAMPLE 4   *Examples of Spanning Sets*

(a) The set $S = \{(1, 0, 0), (0, 1, 0), (0, 0, 1)\}$ spans R^3, since any vector $\mathbf{u} = (u_1, u_2, u_3)$ in R^3 can be written as

$$\begin{aligned} \mathbf{u} &= u_1(1, 0, 0) + u_2(0, 1, 0) + u_3(0, 0, 1) \\ &= (u_1, u_2, u_3). \end{aligned}$$

(b) The set $S = \{1, x, x^2\}$ spans P_2, since any polynomial $p(x) = a + bx + cx^2$ in P_2 can be written as

$$p(x) = a(1) + b(x) + c(x^2) = a + bx + cx^2.$$

The spanning sets given in Example 4 are called the **standard spanning sets** of R^3 and P_2, respectively. (We will say more about standard spanning sets in the next section.) In the next example we look at a nonstandard spanning set of R^3.

EXAMPLE 5   *A Spanning Set for R^3*

Show that the set $S = \{(1, 2, 3), (0, 1, 2), (-2, 0, 1)\}$ spans R^3.

Solution   Let $\mathbf{u} = (u_1, u_2, u_3)$ be *any* vector in R^3. We seek scalars c_1, c_2, and c_3 such that

$$(u_1, u_2, u_3) = c_1(1, 2, 3) + c_2(0, 1, 2) + c_3(-2, 0, 1)$$
$$= (c_1 - 2c_3, 2c_1 + c_2, 3c_1 + 2c_2 + c_3) .$$

This vector equation produces the system

$$
\begin{aligned}
c_1 \quad\quad\ - 2c_3 &= u_1 \\
2c_1 + c_2 \quad\quad\ &= u_2 \\
3c_1 + 2c_2 + c_3 &= u_3.
\end{aligned}
$$

The coefficient matrix for this system has a nonzero determinant, and it follows from the list of equivalent conditions given in Section 3.3 that the system has a unique solution. Therefore any vector in R^3 can be written as a linear combination of the vectors in S, and we conclude that the set S spans R^3.

EXAMPLE 6   *A Set That Does Not Span R^3*

From Example 3 we know that the set

$$S = \{(1, 2, 3), (0, 1, 2), (-1, 0, 1)\}$$

does not span R^3 because $\mathbf{w} = (1, -2, 2)$ is in R^3 and cannot be expressed as a linear combination of the vectors in S.

Comparing the sets of vectors in Examples 5 and 6, we note that the sets are the same except for a seemingly insignificant difference in the third vector.

$$S_1 = \{(1, 2, 3), (0, 1, 2), (-2, 0, 1)\} \qquad \text{Example 5}$$
$$S_2 = \{(1, 2, 3), (0, 1, 2), (-1, 0, 1)\} \qquad \text{Example 6}$$

The difference, however, is significant, for the set S_1 spans R^3, whereas the set S_2 does not. The reason for this difference may be seen in Figure 4.12. The vectors in S_2 lie in a common plane; the vectors in S_1 do not.

Figure 4.12

$S_1 = \{(1, 2, 3), (0, 1, 2), (-2, 0, 1)\}$
The vectors in S_1 do not lie
in a common plane.

$S_2 = \{(1, 2, 3), (0, 1, 2), (-1, 0, 1)\}$
The vectors in S_2 lie in a
common plane.

Although the set S_2 does not span all of R^3, it does span a subspace of R^3, namely the plane in which the three vectors in S_2 lie. We call this subspace the **span of S_2,** as indicated in the following definition.

Definition of the Span of a Set	If $S = \{v_1, v_2, \ldots, v_k\}$ is a set of vectors in a vector space V, then the **span of S** is the set of all linear combinations of vectors in S, $$\text{span}(S) = \{c_1 v_1 + c_2 v_2 + \cdots + c_k v_k : c_1, c_2, \ldots, c_k \text{ are real numbers}\}.$$ The span of S is denoted by $\text{span}(S)$ or $\text{span}\{v_1, v_2, \ldots, v_k\}$. If $\text{span}(S) = V$, we say that V is **spanned** by $\{v_1, v_2, \ldots, v_k\}$, or that S **spans** V.

The following theorem tells us that the span of any finite nonempty subset of a vector space V is a subspace of V.

Theorem 4.7 Span(S) Is a Subspace of V	If $S = \{v_1, v_2, \ldots, v_k\}$ is a set of vectors in a vector space V, then $\text{span}(S)$ is a subspace of V. Moreover, $\text{span}(S)$ is the smallest subspace of V that contains S, in the sense that every other subspace of V that contains S must contain $\text{span}(S)$.

Proof   To show that $\text{span}(S)$, the set of all linear combinations of $v_1, v_2, \ldots, v_k$, is a subspace of V, we show that it is closed under addition and scalar multiplication. Consider any two vectors u and v in $\text{span}(S)$,

$$u = c_1 v_1 + c_2 v_2 + \cdots + c_k v_k$$
$$v = d_1 v_1 + d_2 v_2 + \cdots + d_k v_k,$$

where $c_1, c_2, \ldots, c_k$ and $d_1, d_2, \ldots, d_k$ are scalars. Then

$$u + v = (c_1 + d_1) v_1 + (c_2 + d_2) v_2 + \cdots + (c_k + d_k) v_k$$

and

$$cu = (cc_1) v_1 + (cc_2) v_2 + \cdots + (cc_k) v_k,$$

which means that $u + v$ and cu are also in $\text{span}(S)$ because they can be written as linear combinations of vectors in S. Therefore $\text{span}(S)$ is a subspace of V. We leave as an exercise the proof that $\text{span}(S)$ is the smallest subspace of V that contains S. (See Exercise 40.)

Linear Dependence and Linear Independence

For a given set of vectors $S = \{v_1, v_2, \ldots, v_k\}$ in a vector space V, the vector equation

$$c_1 v_1 + c_2 v_2 + \cdots + c_k v_k = 0$$

always has the **trivial solution** $c_1 = 0, c_2 = 0, \ldots, c_k = 0$. Often, however, there are also **nontrivial** solutions. For instance, in Example 1(a) we saw that in the set

$$S = \{\overset{\mathbf{v}_1}{(1, 3, 1)}, \overset{\mathbf{v}_2}{(0, 1, 2)}, \overset{\mathbf{v}_3}{(1, 0, -5)}\},$$

the vector $\mathbf{v}_1$ can be written as a linear combination of the other two as follows.

$$\mathbf{v}_1 = 3\mathbf{v}_2 + \mathbf{v}_3$$

Hence the vector equation

$$c_1\mathbf{v}_1 + c_2\mathbf{v}_2 + c_3\mathbf{v}_3 = \mathbf{0}$$

has a nontrivial solution in which the coefficients are *not all zero:*

$$c_1 = 1, \qquad c_2 = -3, \qquad c_3 = -1.$$

We describe this characteristic by saying that the set S is **linearly dependent.** Had the *only* solution been the trivial one ($c_1 = c_2 = c_3 = 0$), then the set S would have been **linearly independent.** This notion is essential to the study of linear algebra, and is stated formally in the following definition.

Definition of Linear Dependence and Linear Independence	A set of vectors $S = \{\mathbf{v}_1, \mathbf{v}_2, \ldots, \mathbf{v}_k\}$ in a vector space V is called **linearly independent** if the vector equation $$c_1\mathbf{v}_1 + c_2\mathbf{v}_2 + \cdots + c_k\mathbf{v}_k = \mathbf{0}$$ has only the trivial solution, $c_1 = 0, c_2 = 0, \ldots, c_k = 0$. If there are also nontrivial solutions, then S is called **linearly dependent.**

EXAMPLE 7   ***Examples of Linearly Dependent Sets***

(a) The set $S = \{(1, 2), (2, 4)\}$ in R^2 is linearly dependent because

$$-2(1, 2) + (2, 4) = (0, 0).$$

(b) The set $S = \{(1, 0), (0, 1), (-2, 5)\}$ in R^2 is linearly dependent because

$$2(1, 0) - 5(0, 1) + (-2, 5) = (0, 0).$$

(c) The set $S = \{(0, 0), (1, 2)\}$ in R^2 is linearly dependent because

$$1(0, 0) + 0(1, 2) = (0, 0).$$

The next example demonstrates a procedure for testing whether a set of vectors is linearly independent or dependent.

EXAMPLE 8   *Testing for Linear Independence*

Determine whether the following set of vectors in R^3 is linearly independent or linearly dependent.

$$S = \{\overset{v_1}{(1, 2, 3)}, \overset{v_2}{(0, 1, 2)}, \overset{v_3}{(-2, 0, 1)}\},$$

Solution   To test for linear independence or linear dependence, we form the vector equation

$$c_1 v_1 + c_2 v_2 + c_3 v_3 = \mathbf{0}.$$

If the only solution to this equation is $c_1 = c_2 = c_3 = 0$, then the set S is linearly independent. Otherwise S is linearly dependent. Expanding this equation, we have

$$c_1(1, 2, 3) + c_2(0, 1, 2) + c_3(-2, 0, 1) = (0, 0, 0)$$
$$(c_1 - 2c_3, 2c_1 + c_2, 3c_1 + 2c_2 + c_3) = (0, 0, 0),$$

which yields the following homogeneous system of linear equations in c_1, c_2, and c_3.

$$\begin{aligned} c_1 \quad\quad - 2c_3 &= 0 \\ 2c_1 + c_2 \quad\quad &= 0 \\ 3c_1 + 2c_2 + c_3 &= 0 \end{aligned}$$

The augmented matrix of this system reduces by Gauss-Jordan elimination as follows.

$$\begin{bmatrix} 1 & 0 & -2 & 0 \\ 2 & 1 & 0 & 0 \\ 3 & 2 & 1 & 0 \end{bmatrix} \longrightarrow \begin{bmatrix} 1 & 0 & 0 & 0 \\ 0 & 1 & 0 & 0 \\ 0 & 0 & 1 & 0 \end{bmatrix}$$

This implies that the only solution is the trivial solution

$$c_1 = c_2 = c_3 = 0.$$

Therefore S is linearly independent.

We summarize the steps shown in Example 8 as follows.

Testing for Linear Independence and Linear Dependence

Let $S = \{v_1, v_2, \ldots, v_k\}$ be a set of vectors in a vector space V. To determine whether S is linearly independent or linearly dependent, perform the following steps.
1. From the vector equation $c_1 v_1 + c_2 v_2 + \cdots + c_k v_k = \mathbf{0}$, write a homogeneous system of linear equations in the variables $c_1, c_2, \ldots,$ and c_k.
2. Use Gaussian elimination to solve the system for $c_1, c_2, \ldots,$ and c_k.
3. If the system has only the trivial solution, $c_1 = 0, c_2 = 0, \ldots, c_k = 0$, then the set S is linearly independent. If the system also has nontrivial solutions, then S is linearly dependent.

EXAMPLE 9   ***Testing for Linear Independence***

Determine whether the following set of vectors in P_2 is linearly independent or linearly dependent.

$$S = \{\overset{\mathbf{v}_1}{1 + x - 2x^2}, \overset{\mathbf{v}_2}{2 + 5x - x^2}, \overset{\mathbf{v}_3}{x + x^2}\}$$

Solution   Expanding the equation $c_1\mathbf{v}_1 + c_2\mathbf{v}_2 + c_3\mathbf{v}_3 = \mathbf{0}$ produces

$$c_1(1 + x - 2x^2) + c_2(2 + 5x - x^2) + c_3(x + x^2) = 0 + 0x + 0x^2$$
$$(c_1 + 2c_2) + (c_1 + 5c_2 + c_3)x + (-2c_1 - c_2 + c_3)x^2 = 0 + 0x + 0x^2.$$

By equating corresponding coefficients of equal powers of x, we arrive at the following homogeneous system of linear equations in c_1, c_2, and c_3.

$$\begin{aligned}
c_1 + 2c_2 \quad\quad &= 0 \\
c_1 + 5c_2 + c_3 &= 0 \\
-2c_1 - c_2 + c_3 &= 0
\end{aligned}$$

The augmented matrix of this system reduces by Gaussian elimination as follows.

$$\begin{bmatrix} 1 & 2 & 0 & 0 \\ 1 & 5 & 1 & 0 \\ -2 & -1 & 1 & 0 \end{bmatrix} \longrightarrow \begin{bmatrix} 1 & 2 & 0 & 0 \\ 0 & 1 & \frac{1}{3} & 0 \\ 0 & 0 & 0 & 0 \end{bmatrix}$$

This implies that the system has an infinite number of solutions. Therefore the system must have nontrivial solutions, and we conclude that the set S is linearly dependent.

For instance, one nontrivial solution is $c_1 = 2$, $c_2 = -1$, and $c_3 = 3$, which yields the nontrivial linear combination

$$(2)(1 + x - 2x^2) + (-1)(2 + 5x - x^2) + (3)(x + x^2) = 0.$$

EXAMPLE 10   ***Testing for Linear Independence***

Determine whether the following set of vectors in $M_{4,1}$ is linearly independent or linearly dependent

$$S = \left\{ \overset{\mathbf{v}_1}{\begin{bmatrix} 1 \\ 0 \\ -1 \\ 0 \end{bmatrix}}, \overset{\mathbf{v}_2}{\begin{bmatrix} 1 \\ 1 \\ 0 \\ 2 \end{bmatrix}}, \overset{\mathbf{v}_3}{\begin{bmatrix} 0 \\ 3 \\ 1 \\ -2 \end{bmatrix}}, \overset{\mathbf{v}_4}{\begin{bmatrix} 0 \\ 1 \\ -1 \\ 2 \end{bmatrix}} \right\}$$

Solution   From the equation $c_1\mathbf{v}_1 + c_2\mathbf{v}_2 + c_3\mathbf{v}_3 + c_4\mathbf{v}_4 = \mathbf{0}$ we obtain

$$c_1\begin{bmatrix} 1 \\ 0 \\ -1 \\ 0 \end{bmatrix} + c_2\begin{bmatrix} 1 \\ 1 \\ 0 \\ 2 \end{bmatrix} + c_3\begin{bmatrix} 0 \\ 3 \\ 1 \\ -2 \end{bmatrix} + c_4\begin{bmatrix} 0 \\ 1 \\ -1 \\ 2 \end{bmatrix} = \begin{bmatrix} 0 \\ 0 \\ 0 \\ 0 \end{bmatrix}.$$

This equation produces the following system of linear equations.

$$\begin{array}{rcrcrcrcl} c_1 &+& c_2 & & & & &=& 0 \\ & & c_2 &+& 3c_3 &+& c_4 &=& 0 \\ -c_1 & & &+& c_3 &-& c_4 &=& 0 \\ & & 2c_2 &-& 2c_3 &+& 2c_4 &=& 0 \end{array}$$

Using Gaussian elimination or a computer, we can row reduce the augmented matrix of this system as follows.

$$\begin{bmatrix} 1 & 1 & 0 & 0 & 0 \\ 0 & 1 & 3 & 1 & 0 \\ -1 & 0 & 1 & -1 & 0 \\ 0 & 2 & -2 & 2 & 0 \end{bmatrix} \longrightarrow \begin{bmatrix} 1 & 1 & 0 & 0 & 0 \\ 0 & 1 & 3 & 1 & 0 \\ 0 & 0 & 1 & 1 & 0 \\ 0 & 0 & 0 & 1 & 0 \end{bmatrix}$$

Thus the system has only the trivial solution, and we conclude that the set S is linearly independent.

If a set of vectors is linearly dependent, then by definition the equation

$$c_1\mathbf{v}_1 + c_2\mathbf{v}_2 + \cdots + c_k\mathbf{v}_k = \mathbf{0}$$

has a nontrivial solution (a solution for which not all the c_i's are zero). For instance, if $c_1 \neq 0$, then we can solve this equation for $\mathbf{v}_1$ and write $\mathbf{v}_1$ as a linear combination of the other vectors $\mathbf{v}_2, \mathbf{v}_3, \ldots$, and $\mathbf{v}_k$. In other words, the vector $\mathbf{v}_1$ *depends* on the other vectors in the set. This property is characteristic of a linearly dependent set.

Theorem 4.8

A Property of Linearly Dependent Sets

A set $S = \{\mathbf{v}_1, \mathbf{v}_2, \ldots, \mathbf{v}_k\}$, $k \geq 2$, is linearly dependent if and only if at least one of the vectors $\mathbf{v}_j$ can be written as a linear combination of the other vectors in S.

Proof   To prove the theorem in one direction, we assume that S is a linearly dependent set. Then there exist scalars $c_1, c_2, c_3, \ldots, c_k$ (not all zero) such that

$$c_1\mathbf{v}_1 + c_2\mathbf{v}_2 + c_3\mathbf{v}_3 + \cdots + c_k\mathbf{v}_k = \mathbf{0}.$$

Because one of the coefficients must be nonzero, no generality is lost by assuming that $c_1 \neq 0$. Then solving for $\mathbf{v}_1$ as a linear combination of the other vectors produces

$$c_1\mathbf{v}_1 = -c_2\mathbf{v}_2 - c_3\mathbf{v}_3 - \cdots - c_k\mathbf{v}_k$$
$$\mathbf{v}_1 = -\frac{c_2}{c_1}\mathbf{v}_2 - \frac{c_3}{c_1}\mathbf{v}_3 - \cdots - \frac{c_k}{c_1}\mathbf{v}_k.$$

Conversely, suppose the vector $\mathbf{v}_1$ in S is a linear combination of the other vectors. That is,

$$\mathbf{v}_1 = c_2\mathbf{v}_2 + c_3\mathbf{v}_3 + \cdots + c_k\mathbf{v}_k.$$

Then the equation $-\mathbf{v}_1 + c_2\mathbf{v}_2 + c_3\mathbf{v}_3 + \cdots + c_k\mathbf{v}_k = \mathbf{0}$ has at least one coefficient, -1, that is nonzero, and we conclude that S is linearly dependent.

EXAMPLE 11   *Writing a Vector as a Linear Combination of Other Vectors*

In Example 9 we determined that the set

$$S = \{\overset{\mathbf{v}_1}{1 + x - 2x^2}, \overset{\mathbf{v}_2}{2 + 5x - x^2}, \overset{\mathbf{v}_3}{x + x^2}\}$$

is linearly dependent. Show that one of the vectors in this set can be written as a linear combination of the other two.

Solution   In Example 9 we found that the equation $c_1\mathbf{v}_1 + c_2\mathbf{v}_2 + c_3\mathbf{v}_3 = \mathbf{0}$ produces the system

$$\begin{aligned} c_1 + 2c_2 \quad\quad &= 0 \\ c_1 + 5c_2 + c_3 &= 0 \\ -2c_1 - c_2 + c_3 &= 0. \end{aligned}$$

This system has an infinite number of solutions given by $c_3 = 3t$, $c_2 = -t$, and $c_1 = 2t$. By letting $t = 1$, we obtain the equation $2\mathbf{v}_1 - \mathbf{v}_2 + 3\mathbf{v}_3 = \mathbf{0}$. Therefore we can write $\mathbf{v}_2$ as a linear combination of $\mathbf{v}_1$ and $\mathbf{v}_3$ as follows.

$$\mathbf{v}_2 = 2\mathbf{v}_1 + 3\mathbf{v}_3$$

A check yields

$$\begin{aligned} 2 + 5x - x^2 &= 2(1 + x - 2x^2) + 3(x + x^2) \\ &= 2 + 2x - 4x^2 + 3x + 3x^2 \\ &= 2 + 5x - x^2. \end{aligned}$$

Theorem 4.8 has a practical corollary that provides a simple test for determining whether *two* vectors are linearly dependent. In Exercise 59 you are asked to prove this corollary.

Corollary to Theorem 4.8   Two vectors $\mathbf{u}$ and $\mathbf{v}$ in a vector space V are linearly dependent if and only if one is a scalar multiple of the other.

EXAMPLE 12   *Testing for Linear Dependence for Two Vectors*

(a) The set

$$S = \{\overset{\mathbf{v}_1}{(1, 2, 0)}, \overset{\mathbf{v}_2}{(-2, 2, 1)}\}$$

is linearly independent because $\mathbf{v}_1$ and $\mathbf{v}_2$ are not scalar multiples of each other, as shown in Figure 4.13(a).

(b) The set

$$S = \{(\overset{\mathbf{v}_1}{4, -4, -2}), (\overset{\mathbf{v}_2}{-2, 2, 1})\}$$

is linearly dependent because $\mathbf{v}_1 = -2\mathbf{v}_2$, as shown in Figure 4.13(b).

Figure 4.13

(a)

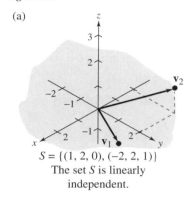

$S = \{(1, 2, 0), (-2, 2, 1)\}$
The set S is linearly
independent.

(b)

$S = \{(4, -4, -2), (-2, 2, 1)\}$
The set S is linearly
dependent since $\mathbf{v}_1 = -2\mathbf{v}_2$.

SECTION 4.4 ☐ EXERCISES

In Exercises 1–4, determine which vectors **u, v,** and **w** can be written as linear combinations of the vectors in S.

1. $S = \{(2, -1, 3), (5, 0, 4)\}$

 (a) $\mathbf{u} = (0, -5, 7)$
 (b) $\mathbf{v} = \left(16, -\frac{1}{2}, \frac{27}{2}\right)$
 (c) $\mathbf{w} = (3, 6, -2)$

2. $S = \{(1, 2, -2), (2, -1, 1)\}$

 (a) $\mathbf{u} = (1, 17, -17)$
 (b) $\mathbf{v} = \left(3, -\frac{2}{3}, \frac{2}{3}\right)$
 (c) $\mathbf{w} = (8, -4, 3)$

3. $S = \{(2, 0, 7), (2, 4, 5)(2, -12, 13)\}$

 (a) $\mathbf{u} = (4, -20, 24)$
 (b) $\mathbf{v} = (-1, 0, 0)$
 (c) $\mathbf{w} = (6, 24, 9)$

4. $S = \{(6, -7, 8, 6), (4, 6, -4, 1)\}$

 (a) $\mathbf{u} = (0, 2, -1, 0)$
 (b) $\mathbf{v} = (32, -112, 108, 53)$
 (c) $\mathbf{w} = \left(25, \frac{27}{2}, -4, 13\right)$

In Exercises 5–10, determine whether the given set S spans R^2. If the set does not span R^2, give a geometrical description of the subspace that it does span.

5. $S = \{(2, 1), (-1, 2)\}$ **6.** $S = \{(5, 0), (5, -4)\}$

7. $S = \{(-3, 5)\}$
8. $S = \{(1, 3), (-2, -6), (4, 12)\}$
9. $S = \{(-1, 2), (2, -4)\}$
10. $S = \{(-1, 4), (4, -1), (1, 1)\}$

In Exercises 11–16, determine whether the given set S spans R^3. If the set does not span R^3, give a geometrical description of the subspace that it does span.

11. $S = \{(4, 7, 3), (-1, 2, 6), (2, -3, 5)\}$
12. $S = \{(6, 7, 6), (3, 2, -4), (1, -3, 2)\}$
13. $S = \{(-2, 5, 0), (4, 6, 3)\}$
14. $S = \{(1, 0, 1), (1, 1, 0), (0, 1, 1)\}$
15. $S = \{(1, -2, 0), (0, 0, 1), (-1, 2, 0)\}$
16. $S = \{(1, 0, 3), (2, 0, -1), (4, 0, 5), (2, 0, 6)\}$

In Exercises 17–28, determine whether the set S is linearly independent or dependent.

17. $S = \{(-2, 2), (3, 5)\}$ **18.** $S = \{(-2, 4), (1, -2)\}$
19. $S = \{(0, 0), (1, -1)\}$ **20.** $S = \{(1, 0), (1, 1), (2, -1)\}$
21. $S = \{(1, -4, 1), (6, 3, 2)\}$
22. $S = \{(6, 2, 1), (-1, 3, 2)\}$
23. $S = \{(1, 1, 1), (2, 2, 2), (3, 3, 3)\}$
24. $S = \left\{\left(\frac{3}{4}, \frac{5}{2}, \frac{3}{2}\right), (3, 4, \frac{7}{2}), \left(-\frac{3}{2}, 6, 2\right)\right\}$
25. $S = \{(-4, -3, 4), (1, -2, 3), (6, 0, 0)\}$

26. $S = \{(1, 0, 0), (0, 4, 0), (0, 0, -6)(1, 5, -3)\}$

27. $S = \{(4, -3, 6, 2), (1, 8, 3, 1), (3, -2, -1, 0)\}$

28. $S = \{(0, 0, 0, 1), (0, 0, 1, 1), (0, 1, 1, 1), (1, 1, 1, 1)\}$

In Exercises 29–32, show that the given set is linearly dependent by finding a nontrivial linear combination (of vectors in the set) whose sum is the zero vector. Then express one of the vectors in the set as a linear combination of the other vectors in the set.

29. $S = \{(3, 4), (-1, 1), (2, 0)\}$

30. $S = \{(2, 4), (-1, -2), (0, 6)\}$

31. $S = \{(1, 1, 1), (1, 1, 0), (0, 1, 1), (0, 0, 1)\}$

32. $S = \{(1, 2, 3, 4), (1, 0, 1, 2), (1, 4, 5, 6)\}$

33. For which values of t are the following sets linearly independent?

    (a) $S = \{(t, 1, 1), (1, t, 1), (1, 1, t)\}$

    (b) $S = \{(t, 1, 1), (1, 0, 1), (1, 1, 3t)\}$

34. For which values of t are the following sets linearly independent?

    (a) $S = \{(t, 0, 0), (0, 1, 0), (0, 0, 1)\}$

    (b) $S = \{(t, t, t), (t, 1, 0), (t, 0, 1)\}$

35. Given the matrices

$$A = \begin{bmatrix} 2 & -3 \\ 4 & 1 \end{bmatrix} \quad \text{and} \quad B = \begin{bmatrix} 0 & 5 \\ 1 & -2 \end{bmatrix}$$

in $M_{2,2}$, determine which of the following are linear combinations of A and B.

    (a) $\begin{bmatrix} 6 & -19 \\ 10 & 7 \end{bmatrix}$ (b) $\begin{bmatrix} 6 & 2 \\ 9 & 11 \end{bmatrix}$ (c) $\begin{bmatrix} -2 & 28 \\ 1 & -11 \end{bmatrix}$

    (d) $\begin{bmatrix} 0 & 0 \\ 0 & 0 \end{bmatrix}$

36. Determine whether the following matrices from $M_{2,2}$ form a linearly independent set.

$$A = \begin{bmatrix} 1 & -1 \\ 4 & 5 \end{bmatrix}, \quad B = \begin{bmatrix} 4 & 3 \\ -2 & 3 \end{bmatrix}, \quad C = \begin{bmatrix} 1 & -8 \\ 22 & 23 \end{bmatrix}$$

37. Determine which of the sets in P_2 are linearly independent.

    (a) $S = \{2 - x, 2x - x^2, 6 - 5x + x^2\}$

    (b) $S = \{x^2 - 1, 2x + 5\}$

    (c) $S = \{x^2 + 3x + 1, 2x^2 + x - 1, 4x\}$

38. Determine whether the set $S = \{x^2 - 2x, x^3 + 8, x^3 - x^2, x^2 - 4\}$ spans P_3.

39. By inspection, determine why each of the following sets is linearly dependent.

    (a) $S = \{(1, -2), (2, 3), (-2, 4)\}$

    (b) $S = \{(1, -6, 2), (2, -12, 4)\}$

    (c) $S = \{(0, 0), (1, 0)\}$

40. Complete the proof of Theorem 4.7.

In Exercises 41 and 42, determine whether the sets S_1 and S_2 span the same subspace of R^3.

41. $S_1 = \{(1, 2, -1), (0, 1, 1), (2, 5, -1)\}$

    $S_2 = \{(-2, -6, 0), (1, 1, -2)\}$

42. $S_1 = \{(0, 0, 1), (0, 1, 1), (2, 1, 1)\}$

    $S_2 = \{(1, 1, 1), (1, 1, 2), (2, 1, 1)\}$

In Exercises 43 and 44, determine whether the set in $C(-\infty, \infty)$ is linearly independent.

43. $S = \{3, \sin^2 x, \cos^2 x\}$

44. $S = \{\cos x, \sin x, \cos^2 x, 1\}$

In Exercises 45 and 46, prove that the set of vectors is linearly independent and spans R^3.

45. $B = \{(1, 1, 1), (1, 1, 0), (1, 0, 0)\}$

46. $B = \{(1, 2, 3), (3, 2, 1), (0, 0, 1)\}$

47. Prove that a nonempty subset of a finite set of linearly independent vectors is linearly independent.

48. Prove that if S_1 is a nonempty subset of the finite set S_2 and S_1 is linearly dependent, then so is S_2.

49. Prove that any set of vectors containing the zero vector is linearly dependent.

50. Given that $\{u_1, u_2, \ldots, u_n\}$ is a linearly independent set of vectors and that the set $\{u_1, u_2, \ldots, u_n, v\}$ is linearly dependent, prove that v is a linear combination of the u_i's.

51. Let $\{v_1, v_2, \ldots, v_k\}$ be a linearly independent set of vectors in a vector space V. Delete the vector v_k from this set and prove that the set $\{v_1, v_2, \ldots, v_{k-1}\}$ cannot span V.

52. If V is spanned by $\{v_1, v_2, \ldots, v_k\}$ and one of these vectors can be written as a linear combination of the other $k - 1$ vectors, prove that the span of these $k - 1$ vectors is also V.

▷ **53.** The set $\{(1, 2, 3), (1, 0, -2), (-1, 0, 2)\}$ is linearly dependent, but $(1, 2, 3)$ cannot be written as a linear combination of $(1, 0, -2)$ and $(-1, 0, 2)$. Why does this statement not contradict Theorem 4.8?

▷ **54.** Under what conditions will a set consisting of a single vector be linearly independent?

55. Let $S = \{u, v\}$ be a linearly independent set. Prove that the set $\{u + v, u - v\}$ is linearly independent.

56. Let u, v, and w be any three vectors from a vector space V. Determine whether the set of vectors $\{v - u, w - v, u - w\}$ is linearly independent or dependent.

57. Let $f_1(x) = 3x$ and $f_2(x) = |x|$. Graph both functions on the interval $-2 \leq x \leq 2$. Show that these functions are linearly dependent in the vector space $C[0, 1]$, but linearly independent in $C[-1, 1]$.

58. Let A be a nonsingular matrix of order 3. Prove that if $\{\mathbf{v}_1, \mathbf{v}_2, \mathbf{v}_3\}$ is a linearly independent set in $M_{3,1}$, then the set $\{A\mathbf{v}_1, A\mathbf{v}_2, A\mathbf{v}_3\}$ is also linearly independent. Show by means of an example that this property is not true if A is singular.

59. Prove the corollary to Theorem 4.8: Two vectors $\mathbf{u}$ and $\mathbf{v}$ are linearly independent if and only if one is a scalar multiple of the other.

4.5 BASIS AND DIMENSION

In this section we continue our study of spanning sets. In particular, we look at spanning sets (in a vector space) that are both linearly independent *and* span the entire space. Such a set forms a **basis** of the vector space. (The plural of *basis* is *bases.*)

Definition of Basis

A set of vectors $S = \{\mathbf{v}_1, \mathbf{v}_2, \ldots, \mathbf{v}_n\}$ in a vector space V is called a **basis** for V if the following conditions are true.
1. S spans V.
2. S is linearly independent.

REMARK: This definition tells us that a basis has two features. A basis S must have *enough vectors* to span V, but *not so many vectors* that one of them could be written as a linear combination of the other vectors in S.

This definition does not imply that every vector space has a basis consisting of a finite number of vectors. In this text, however, our discussion of bases is restricted to those consisting of a finite number of vectors. Moreover, if a vector space V has a basis consisting of a finite number of vectors, then V is **finite dimensional.** Otherwise V is called **infinite dimensional.** (The vector space P of *all* polynomials is infinite dimensional, as is the vector space $C(-\infty, \infty)$ of all continuous functions defined on the real line.) We will also say that the vector space $V = \{\mathbf{0}\}$, consisting of the zero vector alone, is finite dimensional.

EXAMPLE 1   *The Standard Basis for R^3*

Show that the following set is a basis for R^3.

$$S = \{(1, 0, 0), (0, 1, 0), (0, 0, 1)\}$$

Solution   Example 4(a) in Section 4.4 shows that S spans R^3. Furthermore, S is linearly independent because the vector equation

$$c_1(1, 0, 0) + c_2(0, 1, 0) + c_3(0, 0, 1) = (0, 0, 0)$$

has only the trivial solution $c_1 = c_2 = c_3 = 0$. (Try verifying this.) Therefore S is a basis for R^3.

The basis $S = \{(1, 0, 0), (0, 1, 0), (0, 0, 1)\}$ is called the **standard basis** for R^3. This result can be generalized to n-space. That is, the vectors

$$\mathbf{e}_1 = (1, 0, \ldots, 0)$$
$$\mathbf{e}_2 = (0, 1, \ldots, 0)$$
$$\vdots$$
$$\mathbf{e}_n = (0, 0, \ldots, 1)$$

form a basis for R^n called the **standard basis** for R^n.

The next two examples describe nonstandard bases for R^2 and R^3.

EXAMPLE 2   *A Nonstandard Basis for R^2*

Show that the set

$$\overset{\mathbf{v}_1}{}\quad\overset{\mathbf{v}_2}{}$$
$$S = \{(1, 1), (1, -1)\}$$

is a basis for R^2.

Solution   According to the definition of a basis for a vector space, we must show that S spans R^2 and that S is linearly independent.

To verify that S spans R^2, we let $\mathbf{x} = (x_1, x_2)$ represent an arbitrary vector in R^2. To show that $\mathbf{x}$ can be written as a linear combination of $\mathbf{v}_1$ and $\mathbf{v}_2$, we consider the equation

$$c_1\mathbf{v}_1 + c_2\mathbf{v}_2 = \mathbf{x}$$
$$c_1(1, 1) + c_2(1, -1) = (x_1, x_2)$$
$$(c_1 + c_2, c_1 - c_2) = (x_1, x_2).$$

Equating corresponding components, we have the following system of linear equations.

$$c_1 + c_2 = x_1$$
$$c_1 - c_2 = x_2$$

Since the coefficient matrix of this system has a nonzero determinant, we know the system has a unique solution. Therefore we conclude that S spans R^2.

To show that S is linearly independent, we consider the following linear combination.

$$c_1\mathbf{v}_1 + c_2\mathbf{v}_2 = \mathbf{0}$$
$$c_1(1, 1) + c_2(1, -1) = (0, 0)$$
$$(c_1 + c_2, c_1 - c_2) = (0, 0)$$

Equating corresponding components, we have the following homogeneous system.

$$c_1 + c_2 = 0$$
$$c_1 - c_2 = 0$$

Since the coefficient matrix of this system has a nonzero determinant, we know that the system has only the trivial solution $c_1 = c_2 = 0$. Therefore S is linearly independent.

Thus S is a linearly independent spanning set for R^2, and we conclude that it is a basis for R^2.

EXAMPLE 3   *A Nonstandard Basis for R^3*

From Examples 5 and 8 in the previous section we know that

$$S = \{(1, 2, 3), (0, 1, 2), (-2, 0, 1)\}$$

spans R^3 and is linearly independent. Therefore S is a basis for R^3.

EXAMPLE 4   *A Basis of Polynomials*

Show that the vector space P_3 has the following basis.

$$S = \{1, x, x^2, x^3\}$$

Solution   It is clear that S spans P_3 because the span of S consists of all polynomials of the form

$$a_0 + a_1 x + a_2 x^2 + a_3 x^3, \quad a_0, a_1, a_2, \text{ and } a_3 \text{ are real,}$$

which is precisely the form for all polynomials in P_3.

To verify the linear independence of S, recall that the zero vector $\mathbf{0}$ in P_3 is the polynomial $\mathbf{0}(x) = 0$ for all x. Thus the test for linear independence yields the equation

$$a_0 + a_1 x + a_2 x^2 + a_3 x^3 = \mathbf{0}(x) = 0, \quad \text{for all } x.$$

This third-degree polynomial is said to be identically equal to zero. From algebra we know that for a polynomial to be identically equal to zero, all of its coefficients must be zero; that is, $a_0 = a_1 = a_2 = a_3 = 0$. Hence S is linearly independent and is therefore a basis for P_3.

REMARK: The basis $S = \{1, x, x^2, x^3\}$ is called the **standard basis** for P_3. Similarly, the **standard basis** for P_n is

$$S = \{1, x, x^2, \ldots, x^n\}.$$

EXAMPLE 5   *A Basis for $M_{2,2}$*

It can be verified that the set

$$S = \left\{ \begin{bmatrix} 1 & 0 \\ 0 & 0 \end{bmatrix}, \begin{bmatrix} 0 & 1 \\ 0 & 0 \end{bmatrix}, \begin{bmatrix} 0 & 0 \\ 1 & 0 \end{bmatrix}, \begin{bmatrix} 0 & 0 \\ 0 & 1 \end{bmatrix} \right\}$$

is a basis for $M_{2,2}$. We call this set the **standard basis** for $M_{2,2}$. In a similar manner, the standard basis for the vector space $M_{m,n}$ consists of the mn distinct $m \times n$ matrices having a single 1 and all the other entries equal to zero.

One important use of a basis for a vector space is that it gives us a means of representing *every* vector in the space. The following is a beautiful theorem which tells us that for a given basis, this representation is unique.

Theorem 4.9	If $S = \{\mathbf{v}_1, \mathbf{v}_2, \ldots, \mathbf{v}_n\}$ is a basis for a vector space V, then every vector in V can be written in one and only one way as a linear combination of vectors in S.
Uniqueness of Basis Representation	

Proof   The existence portion of the proof is straightforward. That is, because S spans V, we know that an arbitrary vector $\mathbf{u}$ in V can be expressed as $\mathbf{u} = c_1\mathbf{v}_1 + c_2\mathbf{v}_2 + \cdots + c_n\mathbf{v}_n$.

To prove uniqueness (that a given vector can be represented in only one way), we suppose that $\mathbf{u}$ has another representation $\mathbf{u} = b_1\mathbf{v}_1 + b_2\mathbf{v}_2 + \cdots + b_n\mathbf{v}_n$. Subtracting the second representation from the first produces

$$\mathbf{u} - \mathbf{u} = (c_1 - b_1)\mathbf{v}_1 + (c_2 - b_2)\mathbf{v}_2 + \cdots + (c_n - b_n)\mathbf{v}_n = \mathbf{0}$$

However, since S is linearly independent, the only solution to this equation is the trivial solution

$$c_1 - b_1 = 0, \qquad c_2 - b_2 = 0, \qquad \ldots, \qquad c_n - b_n = 0,$$

which means that $c_i = b_i$ for all $i = 1, 2, \ldots, n$. Hence $\mathbf{u}$ has only one representation for the given basis S.

EXAMPLE 6   *Uniqueness of Basis Representation*

Let $\mathbf{u} = (u_1, u_2, u_3)$ be any vector in R^3. Show that the equation $\mathbf{u} = c_1\mathbf{v}_1 + c_2\mathbf{v}_2 + c_3\mathbf{v}_3$ has a unique solution for the basis $S = \{\mathbf{v}_1, \mathbf{v}_2, \mathbf{v}_3\} = \{(1, 2, 3), (0, 1, 2), (-2, 0, 1)\}$.

Solution   From the equation

$$
\begin{aligned}
(u_1, u_2, u_3) &= c_1(1, 2, 3) + c_2(0, 1, 2) + c_3(-2, 0, 1) \\
&= (c_1 - 2c_3, 2c_1 + c_2, 3c_1 + 2c_2 + c_3),
\end{aligned}
$$

the following system of linear equations is obtained.

$$
\begin{array}{rcl}
c_1 \qquad\quad - 2c_3 &=& u_1 \\
2c_1 + c_2 \qquad\quad &=& u_2 \\
3c_1 + 2c_2 + c_3 &=& u_3
\end{array}
\quad\Longrightarrow\quad
\underbrace{\begin{bmatrix} 1 & 0 & -2 \\ 2 & 1 & 0 \\ 3 & 2 & 1 \end{bmatrix}}_{A}
\underbrace{\begin{bmatrix} c_1 \\ c_2 \\ c_3 \end{bmatrix}}_{\mathbf{c}}
=
\underbrace{\begin{bmatrix} u_1 \\ u_2 \\ u_3 \end{bmatrix}}_{\mathbf{u}}
$$

Since the matrix A is invertible, we know that this system has a unique solution given by $\mathbf{c} = A^{-1}\mathbf{u}$. Solving for A^{-1} gives

$$A^{-1} = \begin{bmatrix} -1 & 4 & -2 \\ 2 & -7 & 4 \\ -1 & 2 & -1 \end{bmatrix},$$

which implies that

$$
\begin{aligned}
c_1 &= -u_1 + 4u_2 - 2u_3 \\
c_2 &= 2u_1 - 7u_2 + 4u_3 \\
c_3 &= -u_1 + 2u_2 - u_3.
\end{aligned}
$$

For instance, the vector $\mathbf{u} = (1, 0, 0)$ can be represented uniquely as a linear combination of $\mathbf{v}_1$, $\mathbf{v}_2$, and $\mathbf{v}_3$ as follows.

$$(1, 0, 0) = -\mathbf{v}_1 + 2\mathbf{v}_2 - \mathbf{v}_3$$

We now present two major results concerning bases.

Theorem 4.10	If $S = \{\mathbf{v}_1, \mathbf{v}_2, \ldots, \mathbf{v}_n\}$ is a basis for a vector space V, then every set containing more than n vectors in V is linearly dependent.
Bases and Linear Dependence	

Proof   Let $S_1 = \{\mathbf{u}_1, \mathbf{u}_2, \ldots, \mathbf{u}_m\}$ be any set of m vectors in V, where $m > n$. To show that S_1 is linearly *dependent,* we need to find scalars $k_1, k_2, \ldots, k_m$ (not all zero) such that

$$k_1\mathbf{u}_1 + k_2\mathbf{u}_2 + \cdots + k_m\mathbf{u}_m = \mathbf{0} \qquad \text{Equation 1}$$

Since S is a basis for V, it follows that each $\mathbf{u}_i$ is a linear combination of vectors in S, and we write

$$\begin{aligned}
\mathbf{u}_1 &= c_{11}\mathbf{v}_1 + c_{21}\mathbf{v}_2 + \cdots + c_{n1}\mathbf{v}_n \\
\mathbf{u}_2 &= c_{12}\mathbf{v}_1 + c_{22}\mathbf{v}_2 + \cdots + c_{n2}\mathbf{v}_n \\
&\;\;\vdots \qquad\quad \vdots \qquad\quad \vdots \qquad\qquad \vdots \\
\mathbf{u}_m &= c_{1m}\mathbf{v}_1 + c_{2m}\mathbf{v}_2 + \cdots + c_{nm}\mathbf{v}_n.
\end{aligned}$$

Substituting each of these representation of $\mathbf{u}_i$ into Equation 1 and regrouping terms produces

$$d_1\mathbf{v}_1 + d_2\mathbf{v}_2 + \cdots + d_n\mathbf{v}_n = \mathbf{0},$$

where $d_i = c_{i1}k_1 + c_{i2}k_2 + \cdots + c_{im}k_m$. However, since the $\mathbf{v}_i$'s form a linearly independent set, we conclude that each $d_i = 0$. Thus the following system of equations is obtained.

$$\begin{aligned}
c_{11}k_1 + c_{12}k_2 + \cdots + c_{1m}k_m &= 0 \\
c_{21}k_1 + c_{22}k_2 + \cdots + c_{2m}k_m &= 0 \\
\vdots \qquad\quad \vdots \qquad\qquad \vdots \qquad\;\; \vdots \\
c_{n1}k_1 + c_{n2}k_2 + \cdots + c_{nm}k_m &= 0
\end{aligned}$$

But this homogeneous system has fewer equations than variables $k_1, k_2, \ldots, k_m$, and from Theorem 1.1 we know that it must have *nontrivial* solutions. Consequently, S_1 is linearly dependent.

EXAMPLE 7   ***Linearly Dependent Sets in R^3 and P_3***

(a) Since R^3 has a basis consisting of three vectors, the set

$$S = \{(1, 2, -1), (1, 1, 0), (2, 3, 0), (5, 9, -1)\}$$

must be linearly dependent.

(b) Since P_3 has a basis consisting of four vectors, the set

$$S = \{(1, 1 + x, 1 - x, 1 + x + x^2, 1 - x + x^2\}$$

must be linearly dependent.

Since R^n has the standard basis consisting of n vectors, it follows from Theorem 4.10 that every set of vectors in R^n containing more than n vectors must be linearly dependent. Another significant consequence of Theorem 4.10 is given in the following theorem.

Theorem 4.11

Number of Vectors in a Basis

If a vector space V has one basis with n vectors, then every basis for V has n vectors.

Proof   Let

$$S_1 = \{\mathbf{v}_1, \mathbf{v}_2, \dots, \mathbf{v}_n\}$$

be the given basis for V, and let

$$S_2 = \{\mathbf{u}_1, \mathbf{u}_2, \dots, \mathbf{u}_m\}$$

be any other basis for V. Since S_1 is a basis and S_2 is linearly independent, Theorem 4.10 implies that $m \leq n$. Similarly, $n \leq m$ because S_1 is linearly independent and S_2 is a basis. Consequently, $n = m$.

EXAMPLE 8   *Spanning Sets and Bases*

Use Theorem 4.11 to explain why each of the following statements is true.
(a) The set $S_1 = \{(3, 2, 1), (7, -1, 4)\}$ is not a basis for R^3.
(b) The set

$$S_2 = \{x + 2, x^2, x^3 - 1, 3x + 1, x^2 - 2x + 3\}$$

is not a basis for P_3.

Solution   (a) The standard basis for R^3 has three vectors, and S_1 has only two. Hence, by Theorem 4.11, S_1 cannot be a basis for R^3.
(b) The standard basis for P_3, $S = \{1, x, x^2, x^3\}$, has four elements. Therefore, by Theorem 4.11, the given set S_2 has too many elements to be a basis for P_3.

The Dimension of a Vector Space

Our discussion of spanning sets, linear independence, and bases has brought us to an important place in the study of vector spaces. Theorem 4.11 tells us that if a vector space V has a basis consisting of n vectors, then every other basis for the space also has n vectors. We call the number n the **dimension** of V.

Definition of Dimension of a Vector Space	If a vector space V has a basis consisting of n vectors, then the number n is called the **dimension** of V, denoted by $\dim(V) = n$. If V consists of the zero vector alone, the dimension of V is defined as zero.

This definition allows us to observe the following about the dimensions of some familiar vector spaces. In each case we determined the dimension by simply counting the number of vectors in the standard basis.

1. The dimension of R^n with the standard operations is n.
2. The dimension of P_n with the standard operations is $n + 1$.
3. The dimension of $M_{m,n}$ with the standard operations is mn.

If W is a subspace of an n-dimensional vector space, then it can be shown that W is finite dimensional and that the dimension of W is less than or equal to n. (See Exercise 59.) In the next three examples, we look at a technique for determining the dimension of a subspace. Basically, we determine the dimension by finding a set of linearly independent vectors that spans the subspace. This set is a basis for the subspace, and the dimension of the subspace is the number of vectors in the basis.

EXAMPLE 9   *Finding the Dimension of a Subspace*

Determine the dimensions of the following subspaces of R^3.
(a) $W = \{(d, c - d, c): c \text{ and } d \text{ are real numbers}\}$
(b) $W = \{(2b, b, 0): b \text{ is a real number}\}$

Solution   The goal in each example is to find a set of linearly independent vectors that spans the subspace.
(a) By writing the representative vector $(d, c - d, c)$ as

$$(d, c - d, c) = (0, c, c) + (d, -d, 0)$$
$$= c(0, 1, 1) + d(1, -1, 0),$$

we see that W is spanned by the set

$$S = \{(0, 1, 1), (1, -1, 0)\}.$$

Using the techniques described in the previous section, we can show that this set is linearly independent. Therefore it is a basis for W, and we conclude that W is a two-dimensional subspace of R^3.
(b) By writing the representative vector $(2b, b, 0)$ as

$$(2b, b, 0) = b(2, 1, 0),$$

we see that W is spanned by the set $S = \{(2, 1, 0)\}$. Therefore W is a one-dimensional subspace of R^3.

REMARK: In Example 9(a), the subspace W is a two-dimensional plane in R^3 determined by the vectors $(0, 1, 1)$ and $(1, -1, 0)$. In Example 9(b) the subspace is a one-dimensional line.

EXAMPLE 10 *Finding the Dimension of a Subspace*

Find the dimension of the subspace W of R^4 spanned by

$$S = \{\overset{v_1}{(-1, 2, 5, 0)}, \overset{v_2}{(3, 0, 1, -2)}, \overset{v_3}{(-5, 4, 9, 2)}\} \ .$$

Solution Although W is spanned by the set S, S is not a basis for W because S is a linearly dependent set. Specifically, v_3 can be written as a linear combination of v_1 and v_2 as follows.

$$v_3 = 2v_1 - v_2$$

This means that W is spanned by the set $S_1 = \{v_1, v_2\}$. Moreover, S_1 is linearly independent, as neither vector is a scalar multiple of the other, and we conclude that the dimension of W is 2.

EXAMPLE 11 *Finding the Dimension of a Subspace*

Let W be the subspace of all symmetric matrices in $M_{2,2}$. What is the dimension of W?

Solution Every 2×2 symmetric matrix has the following form.

$$A = \begin{bmatrix} a & b \\ b & c \end{bmatrix} = \begin{bmatrix} a & 0 \\ 0 & 0 \end{bmatrix} + \begin{bmatrix} 0 & b \\ b & 0 \end{bmatrix} + \begin{bmatrix} 0 & 0 \\ 0 & c \end{bmatrix}$$

$$= a\begin{bmatrix} 1 & 0 \\ 0 & 0 \end{bmatrix} + b\begin{bmatrix} 0 & 1 \\ 1 & 0 \end{bmatrix} + c\begin{bmatrix} 0 & 0 \\ 0 & 1 \end{bmatrix}$$

Therefore the set

$$S = \left\{ \begin{bmatrix} 1 & 0 \\ 0 & 0 \end{bmatrix}, \begin{bmatrix} 0 & 1 \\ 1 & 0 \end{bmatrix}, \begin{bmatrix} 0 & 0 \\ 0 & 1 \end{bmatrix} \right\}$$

spans W. Moreover, S can be shown to be linearly independent, and we conclude that the dimension of W is 3.

Usually, to conclude that a set $S = \{v_1, v_2, \ldots, v_n\}$ is a basis for a vector space V, we must show that S satisfies two conditions: S spans V and is linearly independent. However, if V is known to have a dimension of n, then the following theorem tells us that both conditions need not be checked. Either one will suffice. The proof is left as an exercise. (See Exercise 60.)

Theorem 4.12

Basis Tests in an n-Dimensional Space

Let V be a vector space of dimension n.
1. If $S = \{v_1, v_2, \ldots, v_n\}$ is a linearly independent set of vectors in V, then S is a basis for V.
2. If $S = \{v_1, v_2, \ldots, v_n\}$ spans V, then S is a basis for V.

EXAMPLE 12   *Testing for a Basis in an n-Dimensional Space*

Show that the following set of vectors is a basis for $M_{5,1}$.

$$S = \left\{ \overset{\mathbf{v}_1}{\begin{bmatrix} 1 \\ 2 \\ -1 \\ 3 \\ 4 \end{bmatrix}}, \overset{\mathbf{v}_2}{\begin{bmatrix} 0 \\ 1 \\ 3 \\ -2 \\ 3 \end{bmatrix}}, \overset{\mathbf{v}_3}{\begin{bmatrix} 0 \\ 0 \\ 2 \\ -1 \\ 5 \end{bmatrix}}, \overset{\mathbf{v}_4}{\begin{bmatrix} 0 \\ 0 \\ 0 \\ 2 \\ -3 \end{bmatrix}}, \overset{\mathbf{v}_5}{\begin{bmatrix} 0 \\ 0 \\ 0 \\ 0 \\ -2 \end{bmatrix}} \right\}$$

Solution   Since S has five vectors and the dimension of $M_{5,1}$ is five, we can apply Theorem 4.12, verifying that S is a basis by showing either that S is linearly independent or that S spans $M_{5,1}$. To show the first of these, we form the vector equation

$$c_1\mathbf{v}_1 + c_2\mathbf{v}_2 + c_3\mathbf{v}_3 + c_4\mathbf{v}_4 + c_5\mathbf{v}_5 = \mathbf{0},$$

which yields the following homogeneous system of linear equations.

$$
\begin{aligned}
c_1 & & & & & = 0 \\
2c_1 &+ c_2 & & & & = 0 \\
-c_1 &+ 3c_2 &+ 2c_3 & & & = 0 \\
3c_1 &- 2c_2 &- c_3 &+ 2c_4 & & = 0 \\
4c_1 &+ 3c_2 &+ 5c_3 &- 3c_4 &- 2c_5 & = 0
\end{aligned}
$$

Since this system has only the trivial solution, S must be linearly independent. Therefore, by Theorem 4.12, S is a basis for $M_{5,1}$.

SECTION 4.5 □ EXERCISES

In Exercises 1–4, write the standard basis for the given vector space.

1. R^6 **2.** $M_{4,1}$ **3.** $M_{2,4}$ **4.** P_4

In Exercises 5–8, explain why S is not a basis for R^2.

5. $S = \{(1, 2), (1, 0), (0, 1)\}$
6. $S = \{(-4, 5), (0, 0)\}$
7. $S = \{(6, -5), (12, -10)\}$
8. $S = \{(-3, 2)\}$

In Exercises 9–12, explain why S is not a basis for R^3.

9. $S = \{(1, 3, 0), (4, 1, 2), (-2, 5, -2)\}$
10. $S = \{(7, 0, 3), (8, -4, 1)\}$
11. $S = \{(0, 0, 0), (1, 0, 0), (0, 1, 0)\}$
12. $S = \{(6, 4, 1), (3, -5, 1), (8, 13, 6), (0, 6, 9)\}$

In Exercises 13 and 14, explain why S is not a basis for P_2.

13. $S = \{1, 2x, x^2 - 4, 5x\}$
14. $S = \{1 - x, 1 - x^2, 3x^2 - 2x - 1\}$

In Exercises 15 and 16, explain why S is not a basis for $M_{2,2}$.

15. $S = \left\{ \begin{bmatrix} 1 & 0 \\ 0 & 1 \end{bmatrix}, \begin{bmatrix} 0 & 1 \\ 1 & 0 \end{bmatrix} \right\}$

16. $S = \left\{ \begin{bmatrix} 1 & 0 \\ 0 & 0 \end{bmatrix}, \begin{bmatrix} 0 & 1 \\ 1 & 0 \end{bmatrix}, \begin{bmatrix} 1 & 0 \\ 0 & 1 \end{bmatrix}, \begin{bmatrix} 8 & -4 \\ -4 & 3 \end{bmatrix} \right\}$

In Exercises 17–20, determine whether the set $\{\mathbf{v}_1, \mathbf{v}_2\}$ is a basis for R^2.

17.

18.

19.

20.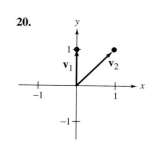

In Exercises 21–26, determine whether S is a basis for the indicated vector space.

21. $S = \{(3, -2), (4, 5)\}$ for R^2

22. $S = \{(1, 5, 3), (0, 1, 2), (0, 0, 6)\}$ for R^3

23. $S = \{(0, 3, -2), (4, 0, 3), (-8, 15, -16)\}$ for R^3

24. $S = \{(0, 0, 0), (1, 5, 6), (6, 2, 1)\}$ for R^3

25. $S = \{(-1, 2, 0, 0), (2, 0, -1, 0), (3, 0, 0, 4), (0, 0, 5, 0)\}$ for R^4

26. $S = \{(1, 0, 0, 1), (0, 2, 0, 2), (1, 0, 1, 0), (0, 2, 2, 0)\}$ for R^4

In Exercises 27 and 28, determine whether S is a basis for $M_{2,2}$.

27. $S = \left\{ \begin{bmatrix} 2 & 0 \\ 0 & 3 \end{bmatrix}, \begin{bmatrix} 1 & 4 \\ 0 & 1 \end{bmatrix}, \begin{bmatrix} 0 & 1 \\ 3 & 2 \end{bmatrix}, \begin{bmatrix} 0 & 1 \\ 2 & 0 \end{bmatrix} \right\}$

28. $S = \left\{ \begin{bmatrix} 1 & 2 \\ -5 & 4 \end{bmatrix}, \begin{bmatrix} 2 & -7 \\ 6 & 2 \end{bmatrix}, \begin{bmatrix} 4 & -9 \\ 11 & 12 \end{bmatrix}, \begin{bmatrix} 12 & -16 \\ 17 & 42 \end{bmatrix} \right\}$

In Exercises 29 and 30, determine whether S is a basis for P_3.

29. $S = \{t^3 - 2t^2 + 1, t^2 - 4, t^3 + 2t, 5t\}$

30. $S = \{4t - t^2, 5 + t^3, 3t + 5, 2t^3 - 3t^2\}$

In Exercises 31–34, determine whether S is a basis for R^3. If it is, write $\mathbf{u} = (8, 3, 8)$ as a linear combination of the vectors in S.

31. $S = \{(4, 3, 2), (0, 3, 2), (0, 0, 2)\}$

32. $S = \{(0, 0, 0), (1, 3, 4), (6, 1, -2)\}$

33. $S = \{(\frac{2}{3}, \frac{5}{2}, 1), (1, \frac{3}{2}, 0), (2, 12, 6)\}$

34. $S = \{(1, 4, 7), (3, 0, 1), (2, 1, 2)\}$

In Exercises 35–38, determine the dimension of the given vector space.

35. R^6 **36.** R **37.** P_7 **38.** $M_{2,3}$

39. Find a basis for $D_{3,3}$ (the vector space of all 3×3 diagonal matrices). What is the dimension of this vector space?

40. Find a basis for the vector space of all 3×3 symmetric matrices. What is the dimension of this vector space?

41. Find all subsets of the following set that form a basis for R^2.
$S = \{(1, 0), (0, 1), (1, 1)\}$

42. Find all subsets of the following set that form a basis for R^3.
$S = \{(1, 3, -2), (-4, 1, 1), (-2, 7, -3), (2, 1, 1)\}$

43. Find a basis for R^2 that includes the vector $(1, 1)$.

44. Find a basis for R^3 that includes the set $S = \{(1, 0, 2), (0, 1, 1)\}$

In Exercises 45 and 46, (a) give a geometric description, (b) find a basis, and (c) determine the dimension of the subspace W of R^2.

45. $W = \{(2t, t)\}: t$ is a real number$\}$

46. $W = \{(0, t): t$ is a real number$\}$

In Exercises 47 and 48, (a) give a geometric description, (b) find a basis, and (c) determine the dimension of the subspace W of R^3.

47. $W = \{(2t, t, -t): t$ is a real number$\}$

48. $W = \{(2s - t, s, t): s$ and t are real numbers$\}$

In Exercises 49–52, find (a) a basis and (b) the dimension of the subspace W of R^4.

49. $W = \{(2s - t, s, t, s): s$ and t are real numbers$\}$

50. $W = \{(5t, -3t, t, t): t$ is a real number$\}$

51. $W = \{(0, 6t, t, -t): t$ is a real number$\}$

52. $W = \{(s + 4t, t, s, 2s - t): s$ and t are real numbers$\}$

In Exercises 53–56, determine whether the given statement is true or false. Give a reason for your answer.

53. If $\dim(V) = n$, then there exists a set of $n - 1$ vectors in V that will span V.

54. If $\dim(V) = n$, then there exists a set of $n + 1$ vectors in V that will span V.

55. If $\dim(V) = n$, then any set of $n + 1$ vectors in V must be dependent.

56. If $\dim(V) = n$, then any set of $n - 1$ vectors in V must be independent.

57. Prove that if $S = \{\mathbf{v}_1, \mathbf{v}_2, \ldots, \mathbf{v}_n\}$ is a basis for a vector space V and c is a nonzero scalar, then the set $S_1 = \{c\mathbf{v}_1, c\mathbf{v}_2, \ldots, c\mathbf{v}_n\}$ is also a basis for V.

58. Prove that the vector space P of all polynomials is infinite dimensional. [Hint: Assume it has dimension n and then show that n polynominals cannot span P.]

59. Prove that if W is a subspace of a finite dimensional vector space V, then the dimension of W is less than or equal to the dimension of V.

60. Prove Theorem 4.12.

61. (a) Let S_1 = span$((1, 0, 0), (1, 1, 0))$ and S_2 = span$((0, 0, 1),$ $(0, 1, 0))$ be subspaces of R^3. Find a basis and the dimension of each of the subspaces $S_1, S_2, S_1 \cap S_2$, and $S_1 + S_2$.

(b) Let S_1 and S_2 be two two-dimensional subspaces of R^3. Is it possible that $S_1 \cap S_2 = \{(0, 0, 0)\}$? (See Exercise 29 in Section 4.3 for the definition of $S_1 + S_2$.)

62. Let S be a spanning set for the finite dimensional vector space V. Prove that there exists a subset S' of S which forms a basis for V.

63. Let S be a linearly independent set of vectors from the finite dimensional vector space V. Prove that there exists a basis for V containing S.

64. Let V be a vector space of dimension n. Prove that any set of less than n vectors cannot span V.

4.6 RANK OF A MATRIX AND SYSTEMS OF LINEAR EQUATIONS

In this section we investigate the vector space spanned by the **row vectors** (or **column vectors**) of a matrix. Then we show how these spaces relate to solutions of systems of linear equations.

We begin with some terminology. For an $m \times n$ matrix A, the n-tuples corresponding to the rows of A are called the **row vectors** of A.

$$A = \begin{bmatrix} a_{11} & a_{12} & \cdots & a_{1n} \\ a_{21} & a_{22} & \cdots & a_{2n} \\ \vdots & \vdots & & \vdots \\ a_{m1} & a_{m2} & \cdots & a_{mn} \end{bmatrix}$$

Row vectors of A

$(a_{11}, a_{12}, \cdots, a_{1n})$
$(a_{21}, a_{22}, \cdots, a_{2n})$
$\vdots$
$(a_{m1}, a_{m2}, \cdots, a_{mn})$

Similarly, the columns of A are called the **column vectors** of A. We will find it useful to preserve the column notation for these column vectors.

$$A = \begin{bmatrix} a_{11} & a_{12} & \cdots & a_{1n} \\ a_{21} & a_{22} & \cdots & a_{2n} \\ \vdots & \vdots & & \vdots \\ a_{m1} & a_{m2} & \cdots & a_{mn} \end{bmatrix}$$

Column vectors of A

$$\begin{bmatrix} a_{11} \\ a_{21} \\ \vdots \\ a_{m1} \end{bmatrix} \begin{bmatrix} a_{12} \\ a_{22} \\ \vdots \\ a_{m2} \end{bmatrix} \cdots \begin{bmatrix} a_{1n} \\ a_{2n} \\ \vdots \\ a_{mn} \end{bmatrix}$$

EXAMPLE 1   *Row Vectors and Column Vectors*

For the matrix

$$A = \begin{bmatrix} 0 & 1 & -1 \\ -2 & 3 & 4 \end{bmatrix}$$

the row vectors are $(0, 1, -1)$ and $(-2, 3, 4)$ and the column vectors are

$$\begin{bmatrix} 0 \\ -2 \end{bmatrix}, \quad \begin{bmatrix} 1 \\ 3 \end{bmatrix} \quad \text{and} \quad \begin{bmatrix} -1 \\ 4 \end{bmatrix}$$

In Example 1, note that for an $m \times n$ matrix A, the row vectors are vectors in R^n and the column vectors are vectors in R^m. This leads us to the following definitions of the **row space** and **column space** of a matrix.

Definition of Row and Column Space of a Matrix

Let A be an $m \times n$ matrix.
1. The **row space** of A is the subspace of R^n spanned by the row vectors of A.
2. The **column space** of A is the subspace of R^m spanned by the column vectors of A.

As it turns out, the row and column spaces of A share many properties. However, because of our familiarity with elementary row operations, we will begin by looking at the row space of a matrix. Recall that two matrices are row equivalent if one can be obtained from the other by elementary row operations. The following theorem tells us that row-equivalent matrices have the same row space.

Theorem 4.13

Row-Equivalent Matrices Have the Same Row Space

If an $m \times n$ matrix A is row-equivalent to an $m \times n$ matrix B, then the row space of A is equal to the row space of B.

Proof   Since the rows of B can be obtained from the rows of A by elementary row operations (scalar multiplication and addition), if follows that the row vectors of B can be written as linear combinations of the row vectors of A. Hence the row vectors of B lie in the row space of A, and the subspace spanned by the row vectors of B is contained in the row space of A. But it is also true that the rows of A can be obtained from the rows of B by elementary row operations. Thus we can conclude that the two row spaces are subspaces of each other and are therefore equal.

REMARK: Note that this theorem says that the row space of a matrix is not changed by elementary row operations. Elementary row operations can, however, change the *column* space.

If the matrix B is in row-echelon form, then its nonzero row vectors form a linearly independent set. (Try verifying this.) Consequently, they form a basis for the row space of B, and by Theorem 4.13 they also form a basis for the row space of A. This important result is stated in the next theorem.

Theorem 4.14

Basis for the Row Space of a Matrix

If a matrix A is row-equivalent to a matrix B in row-echelon form, then the nonzero row vectors of B form a basis for the row space of A.

EXAMPLE 2   *Finding a Basis for a Row Space*

Find a basis for the row space of

$$A = \begin{bmatrix} 1 & 3 & 1 & 3 \\ 0 & 1 & 1 & 0 \\ -3 & 0 & 6 & -1 \\ 3 & 4 & -2 & 1 \\ 2 & 0 & -4 & -2 \end{bmatrix}$$

Solution   Using elementary *row* operations, we rewrite A in row-echelon form as follows.

$$B = \begin{bmatrix} 1 & 3 & 1 & 3 \\ 0 & 1 & 1 & 0 \\ 0 & 0 & 0 & 1 \\ 0 & 0 & 0 & 0 \\ 0 & 0 & 0 & 0 \end{bmatrix} \begin{matrix} \mathbf{w}_1 \\ \mathbf{w}_2 \\ \mathbf{w}_3 \\ \\ \end{matrix}$$

By Theorem 4.14, we conclude that the nonzero row vectors of B, $\mathbf{w}_1 = (1, 3, 1, 3)$, $\mathbf{w}_2 = (0, 1, 1, 0)$, and $\mathbf{w}_3 = (0, 0, 0, 1)$, form a basis for the row space of A.

The technique used in Example 2 to find the row space of a matrix can be used to solve the following type of problem. Suppose we are asked to find a basis for the subspace spanned by the set $S = \{\mathbf{v}_1, \mathbf{v}_2, \ldots, \mathbf{v}_k\}$ in R^n. By using the vectors in S to form the rows of a matrix A, we could use elementary row operations to rewrite A in row-echelon form. The nonzero rows of this matrix will then form a basis for the subspace spanned by S. This is demonstrated in Example 3.

EXAMPLE 3   ***Finding a Basis for a Subspace***

Find a basis for the subspace of R^3 spanned by

$$S = \{\overset{\mathbf{v}_1}{(-1, 2, 5)}, \overset{\mathbf{v}_2}{(3, 0, 3)}, \overset{\mathbf{v}_3}{(5, 1, 8)}\}.$$

Solution   We begin by using $\mathbf{v}_1$, $\mathbf{v}_2$, and $\mathbf{v}_3$ to form the rows of a matrix A. Then we write A in row-echelon form as follows.

$$A = \begin{bmatrix} -1 & 2 & 5 \\ 3 & 0 & 3 \\ 5 & 1 & 8 \end{bmatrix} \begin{matrix} \mathbf{v}_1 \\ \mathbf{v}_2 \\ \mathbf{v}_3 \end{matrix} \quad \longrightarrow \quad B = \begin{bmatrix} 1 & -2 & -5 \\ 0 & 1 & 3 \\ 0 & 0 & 0 \end{bmatrix} \begin{matrix} \mathbf{w}_1 \\ \mathbf{w}_2 \\ \end{matrix}$$

Therefore, the nonzero row vectors of B, $\mathbf{w}_1 = (1, -2, -5)$ and $\mathbf{w}_2 = (0, 1, 3)$, form a basis for the row space of A. That is, they form a basis for the subspace spanned by $S = \{\mathbf{v}_1, \mathbf{v}_2, \mathbf{v}_3\}$.

To find a basis for the column space of a matrix A, we have two options. On the one hand, we could use the fact that the column space of A is equal to the row space of A^T and apply the technique of Example 2 to the matrix A^T. On the other hand, observe that although row operations can change the column space of a matrix, they do not change the dependency relationships between columns. You are asked to prove this fact in Exercise 50.

For example, consider the row equivalent matrices A and B from Example 2.

$$A = \begin{bmatrix} 1 & 3 & 1 & 3 \\ 0 & 1 & 1 & 0 \\ -3 & 0 & 6 & -1 \\ 3 & 4 & -2 & 1 \\ 2 & 0 & -4 & -2 \end{bmatrix} \qquad B = \begin{bmatrix} 1 & 3 & 1 & 3 \\ 0 & 1 & 1 & 0 \\ 0 & 0 & 0 & 1 \\ 0 & 0 & 0 & 0 \\ 0 & 0 & 0 & 0 \end{bmatrix}$$

$\qquad\qquad \mathbf{a}_1 \quad \mathbf{a}_2 \quad \mathbf{a}_3 \quad \mathbf{a}_4 \qquad\qquad\quad \mathbf{b}_1 \quad \mathbf{b}_2 \quad \mathbf{b}_3 \quad \mathbf{b}_4$

Notice that columns 1, 2, and 3 of matrix B satisfy the equation $\mathbf{b}_3 = -2\mathbf{b}_1 + \mathbf{b}_2$, and so do the corresponding columns of matrix A; that is, $\mathbf{a}_3 = -2\mathbf{a}_1 + \mathbf{a}_2$. Similarly, the column vectors $\mathbf{b}_1$, $\mathbf{b}_2$, and $\mathbf{b}_4$ of matrix B are linearly independent, and so are the corresponding columns of matrix A.

In the following example, we show how to find a basis for the column space of a matrix using both of these methods.

EXAMPLE 4   *Finding a Basis for the Column Space of a Matrix*

Find a basis for the column space of the matrix A given in Example 2.

$$A = \begin{bmatrix} 1 & 3 & 1 & 3 \\ 0 & 1 & 1 & 0 \\ -3 & 0 & 6 & -1 \\ 3 & 4 & -2 & 1 \\ 2 & 0 & -4 & -2 \end{bmatrix}$$

Solution 1   We begin by taking the transpose of A and then use elementary row operations to write A^T in row-echelon form.

$$A^T = \begin{bmatrix} 1 & 0 & -3 & 3 & 2 \\ 3 & 1 & 0 & 4 & 0 \\ 1 & 1 & 6 & -2 & -4 \\ 3 & 0 & -1 & 1 & -2 \end{bmatrix} \longrightarrow \begin{bmatrix} 1 & 0 & -3 & 3 & 2 \\ 0 & 1 & 9 & -5 & -6 \\ 0 & 0 & 1 & -1 & -1 \\ 0 & 0 & 0 & 0 & 0 \end{bmatrix} \begin{matrix} \mathbf{w}_1 \\ \mathbf{w}_2 \\ \mathbf{w}_3 \\ \ \end{matrix}$$

Thus $\mathbf{w}_1 = (1, 0, -3, 3, 2)$, $\mathbf{w}_2 = (0, 1, 9, -5, -6)$, and $\mathbf{w}_3 = (0, 0, 1, -1, -1)$ form a basis for the row space of A^T. This is equivalent to saying that the column vectors

$$\begin{bmatrix} 1 \\ 0 \\ -3 \\ 3 \\ 2 \end{bmatrix}, \quad \begin{bmatrix} 0 \\ 1 \\ 9 \\ -5 \\ -6 \end{bmatrix}, \quad \text{and} \quad \begin{bmatrix} 0 \\ 0 \\ 1 \\ -1 \\ -1 \end{bmatrix}$$

form a basis for the column space of A.

Solution 2   In Example 2, we used row operations on the original matrix A to obtain its row-echelon form B. It is easy to see that in the matrix B, the first, second, and fourth column vectors are linearly independent (these columns have the leading ones). Hence, the corresponding columns of the matrix A are linearly independent, and a basis for the column space consists of the vectors

$$\begin{bmatrix} 1 \\ 0 \\ -3 \\ 3 \\ 2 \end{bmatrix}, \quad \begin{bmatrix} 3 \\ 1 \\ 0 \\ 4 \\ 0 \end{bmatrix}, \quad \text{and} \quad \begin{bmatrix} 3 \\ 0 \\ -1 \\ 1 \\ -2 \end{bmatrix}$$

Notice that this is a different basis for the column space from that obtained in the first solution. We leave it to you to verify that these bases span the same subspace of R^5.

REMARK: Notice that in the second solution, the row-echelon form B indicates which columns of A form the basis of the column space. You do not use the column vectors of B to form the basis.

Notice in Examples 2 and 4 that both the row space and the column space of A have a dimension of three (as there are *three* vectors in both bases). The following theorem tells us that the row space and column space of a matrix always have the same dimension.

Theorem 4.15

Row and Column Spaces Have Equal Dimensions

If A is an $m \times n$ matrix, then the row space and column space of A have the same dimension.

Proof   Let $\mathbf{v}_1, \mathbf{v}_2, \ldots,$ and $\mathbf{v}_m$ be the row vectors and $\mathbf{u}_1, \mathbf{u}_2, \ldots,$ and $\mathbf{u}_n$ be the column vectors of the matrix

$$A = \begin{bmatrix} a_{11} & a_{12} & \cdots & a_{1n} \\ a_{21} & a_{22} & \cdots & a_{2n} \\ \vdots & \vdots & & \vdots \\ a_{m1} & a_{m2} & \cdots & a_{mn} \end{bmatrix}.$$

Suppose the row space of A has dimension r and basis $S = \{\mathbf{b}_1, \mathbf{b}_2, \ldots, \mathbf{b}_r\}$, where $\mathbf{b}_i = (b_{i1}, b_{i2}, \ldots, b_{in})$. Using this basis, we can write the row vectors of A as

$$\begin{aligned} \mathbf{v}_1 &= c_{11}\mathbf{b}_1 + c_{12}\mathbf{b}_2 + \cdots + c_{1r}\mathbf{b}_r \\ \mathbf{v}_2 &= c_{21}\mathbf{b}_1 + c_{22}\mathbf{b}_2 + \cdots + c_{2r}\mathbf{b}_r \\ &\vdots \\ \mathbf{v}_m &= c_{m1}\mathbf{b}_1 + c_{m2}\mathbf{b}_2 + \cdots + c_{mr}\mathbf{b}_r. \end{aligned}$$

Now, if we let $\mathbf{c}_i = [c_{1i} \ c_{2i} \ \cdots \ c_{mi}]^T$, this system of vector equations can be rewritten as follows.

$$\mathbf{u}_1 = [a_{11} \ a_{21} \ \cdots \ a_{m1}]^T = b_{11}\mathbf{c}_1 + b_{21}\mathbf{c}_2 + \cdots + b_{r1}\mathbf{c}_r$$
$$\mathbf{u}_2 = [a_{12} \ a_{22} \ \cdots \ a_{m2}]^T = b_{12}\mathbf{c}_1 + b_{22}\mathbf{c}_2 + \cdots + b_{r2}\mathbf{c}_r$$
$$\vdots$$
$$\mathbf{u}_n = [a_{1n} \ a_{2n} \ \cdots \ a_{mn}]^T = b_{1n}\mathbf{c}_1 + b_{2n}\mathbf{c}_2 + \cdots + b_{rn}\mathbf{c}_r$$

Since each column vector of A is a linear combination of r vectors, we know that the dimension of the column space of A is less than or equal to r (the dimension of the row space of A). That is,

$$\dim(\text{column space of } A) \leq \dim(\text{row space of } A).$$

Repeating this procedure for A^T, we can conclude that the dimension of the column space of A^T is less than or equal to the dimension of the row space of A^T. But this implies that the dimension of the row space of A is less than or equal to the dimension of the column space of A. That is,

$$\dim(\text{row space of } A) \leq \dim(\text{column space of } A).$$

Therefore the two dimensions must be equal.

The dimension of the row (or column) space of a matrix has the following special name.

Definition of the Rank of a Matrix

The dimension of the row (or column) space of a matrix A is called the **rank** of A and is denoted by rank(A).

REMARK: Some texts distinguish between the *row rank* and *column rank* of a matrix. But because these ranks are equal (Theorem 4.15), we do not distinguish between them.

EXAMPLE 5   ***Finding the Rank of a Matrix***

Find the rank of the matrix

$$A = \begin{bmatrix} 1 & -2 & 0 & 1 \\ 2 & 1 & 5 & -3 \\ 0 & 1 & 3 & 5 \end{bmatrix}.$$

Solution   We convert to row-echelon form as follows.

$$A = \begin{bmatrix} 1 & -2 & 0 & 1 \\ 2 & 1 & 5 & -3 \\ 0 & 1 & 3 & 5 \end{bmatrix} \longrightarrow B = \begin{bmatrix} 1 & -2 & 0 & 1 \\ 0 & 1 & 1 & -1 \\ 0 & 0 & 1 & 3 \end{bmatrix}$$

Since B has three nonzero rows, the rank of A is 3.

The Nullspace of a Matrix

The notions of row and column spaces and rank have some important applications to systems of linear equations. Consider first the homogeneous linear system $A\mathbf{x} = \mathbf{0}$, where A is an $m \times n$ matrix, $\mathbf{x} = [x_1 \ x_2 \ \ldots \ x_n]^T$ is the column vector of unknowns, and $\mathbf{0} = [0 \ 0 \ \ldots \ 0]^T$ is the zero vector in R^m.

$$\begin{bmatrix} a_{11} & a_{12} & \cdots & a_{1n} \\ a_{21} & a_{22} & \cdots & a_{2n} \\ \vdots & \vdots & & \vdots \\ a_{m1} & a_{m2} & \cdots & a_{mn} \end{bmatrix} \begin{bmatrix} x_1 \\ x_2 \\ \vdots \\ x_n \end{bmatrix} = \begin{bmatrix} 0 \\ 0 \\ \vdots \\ 0 \end{bmatrix}$$

The following theorem tells us that the set of all solutions of this homogeneous system is a subspace of R^n.

Theorem 4.16

Solutions of a Homogeneous System

If A is an $m \times n$ matrix, then the set of all solutions of the homogeneous system of linear equations

$$A\mathbf{x} = \mathbf{0}$$

is a subspace of R^n. This subspace is called the **nullspace** of A and is denoted by $N(A)$. Thus,

$$N(A) = \{\mathbf{x} \in R^n : A\mathbf{x} = \mathbf{0}\}.$$

The dimension of the nullspace of A is called the **nullity** of A.

Proof   Since A is an $m \times n$ matrix, we know that $\mathbf{x}$ has size $n \times 1$. Thus the set of all solutions of the system is a *subset* of R^n. This set is clearly nonempty, since $A\mathbf{0} = \mathbf{0}$. We verify that it is a subspace by showing that it is closed under the operations of addition and scalar multiplication. Let $\mathbf{x}_1$ and $\mathbf{x}_2$ be two solution vectors of the system $A\mathbf{x} = \mathbf{0}$, and let c be a scalar. Since $A\mathbf{x}_1 = \mathbf{0}$ and $A\mathbf{x}_2 = \mathbf{0}$, we know that

$$A(\mathbf{x}_1 + \mathbf{x}_2) = A\mathbf{x}_1 + A\mathbf{x}_2 = \mathbf{0} + \mathbf{0} = \mathbf{0} \qquad \text{Addition}$$

and

$$A(c\mathbf{x}_1) = c(A\mathbf{x}_1) = c(\mathbf{0}) = \mathbf{0}. \qquad \text{Scalar multiplication}$$

Thus both $(\mathbf{x}_1 + \mathbf{x}_2)$ and $c\mathbf{x}_1$ are solutions of $A\mathbf{x} = \mathbf{0}$, and we conclude that the set of all solutions forms a subspace of R^n.

REMARK: The nullspace of A is also called the **solution space** of the system $A\mathbf{x} = \mathbf{0}$.

EXAMPLE 6   *Finding the Solution Space of a Homogeneous System*

Find the nullspace of the following matrix.

$$A = \begin{bmatrix} 1 & 2 & -2 & 1 \\ 3 & 6 & -5 & 4 \\ 1 & 2 & 0 & 3 \end{bmatrix}.$$

Solution   The nullspace of A is the solution space of the homogeneous system $A\mathbf{x} = \mathbf{0}$.

To solve this system, we need to write the augmented matrix $[A \vdots \mathbf{0}]$ in reduced row-echelon form. However, because the system of equations is homogeneous, the right-hand column of the augmented matrix consists entirely of zeros and will not change as we do row operations. Hence, it is sufficient to find the reduced row-echelon form of A.

$$A = \begin{bmatrix} 1 & 2 & -2 & 1 \\ 3 & 6 & -5 & 4 \\ 1 & 2 & 0 & 3 \end{bmatrix} \longrightarrow \begin{bmatrix} 1 & 2 & 0 & 3 \\ 0 & 0 & 1 & 1 \\ 0 & 0 & 0 & 0 \end{bmatrix}$$

The system of equations corresponding to the reduced row-echelon form is

$$x_1 + 2x_2 \quad\quad + 3x_4 = 0$$
$$x_3 + \ x_4 = 0.$$

Choosing x_2 and x_4 as free variables, we can represent the solutions in the following parametric form.

$$x_1 = -2s - 3t, \quad x_2 = s, \quad x_3 = -t, \quad x_4 = t$$

This means that the solution space of $A\mathbf{x} = \mathbf{0}$ consists of all solution vectors $\mathbf{x}$ of the form

$$\mathbf{x} = \begin{bmatrix} x_1 \\ x_2 \\ x_3 \\ x_4 \end{bmatrix} = \begin{bmatrix} -2s - 3t \\ s \\ -t \\ t \end{bmatrix} = s\begin{bmatrix} -2 \\ 1 \\ 0 \\ 0 \end{bmatrix} + t\begin{bmatrix} -3 \\ 0 \\ -1 \\ 1 \end{bmatrix}.$$

Thus, a basis for the nullspace of A consists of the vectors

$$\begin{bmatrix} -2 \\ 1 \\ 0 \\ 0 \end{bmatrix} \quad \text{and} \quad \begin{bmatrix} -3 \\ 0 \\ -1 \\ 1 \end{bmatrix}.$$

In other words, these two vectors are solutions to $A\mathbf{x} = \mathbf{0}$, and all solutions to this homogeneous system are linear combinations of these two vectors.

In Example 6, the matrix A has four columns. Furthermore, the rank of the matrix is 2, and the dimension of the nullspace is 2. Therefore, we see that

number of columns = rank + nullity.

One way to see this is to look at the reduced row-echelon form of A.

$$\begin{bmatrix} 1 & 2 & 0 & 3 \\ 0 & 0 & 1 & 1 \\ 0 & 0 & 0 & 0 \end{bmatrix}$$

The columns with the leading ones (columns 1 and 3) determine the rank of the matrix. The other columns (2 and 4) determine the nullity of the matrix because they correspond to the free variables. This relationship is generalized in the following theorem, the proof for which is given in Appendix A.

Theorem 4.17	If A is an $m \times n$ matrix of rank r, then the dimension of the solution space of $A\mathbf{x} = \mathbf{0}$ is $n - r$. That is,
Dimension of the Solution Space	$$n = \text{rank}(A) + \text{nullity}(A).$$

The following example illustrates this theorem and explores more closely the column space of a matrix.

EXAMPLE 7   *Rank and Nullity of a Matrix*

Let the column vectors of the matrix A be denoted by $\mathbf{a}_1$, $\mathbf{a}_2$, $\mathbf{a}_3$, $\mathbf{a}_4$, and $\mathbf{a}_5$.

$$A = \begin{bmatrix} 1 & 0 & -2 & 1 & 0 \\ 0 & -1 & -3 & 1 & 3 \\ -2 & -1 & 1 & -1 & 3 \\ 0 & 3 & 9 & 0 & -12 \end{bmatrix}$$
$$\quad\;\; \mathbf{a}_1 \;\; \mathbf{a}_2 \;\; \mathbf{a}_3 \;\; \mathbf{a}_4 \;\; \mathbf{a}_5$$

(a) Find the rank and nullity of A.
(b) Find a subset of the column vectors of A that forms a basis for the column space of A.
(c) If possible, write the third column of A as a linear combination of the first two columns.

Solution   Let B be the reduced row-echelon form of A.

$$A = \begin{bmatrix} 1 & 0 & -2 & 1 & 0 \\ 0 & -1 & -3 & 1 & 3 \\ -2 & -1 & 1 & -1 & 3 \\ 0 & 3 & 9 & 0 & -12 \end{bmatrix} \longrightarrow B = \begin{bmatrix} 1 & 0 & -2 & 0 & 1 \\ 0 & 1 & 3 & 0 & -4 \\ 0 & 0 & 0 & 1 & -1 \\ 0 & 0 & 0 & 0 & 0 \end{bmatrix}$$
$$\quad\;\; \mathbf{a}_1 \;\; \mathbf{a}_2 \;\; \mathbf{a}_3 \;\; \mathbf{a}_4 \;\; \mathbf{a}_5 \qquad\qquad\qquad \mathbf{b}_1 \;\; \mathbf{b}_2 \;\; \mathbf{b}_3 \;\; \mathbf{b}_4 \;\; \mathbf{b}_5$$

(a) Since B has 3 nonzero rows, the rank of A is 3. Furthermore, the number of columns of A is $n = 5$ which implies that the nullity of A is $n - \text{rank} = 5 - 3 = 2$.

(b) Since the first, second, and fourth column vectors of B are linearly independent, the corresponding column vectors of A,

$$\mathbf{a}_1 = \begin{bmatrix} 1 \\ 0 \\ -2 \\ 0 \end{bmatrix}, \qquad \mathbf{a}_2 = \begin{bmatrix} 0 \\ -1 \\ -1 \\ 3 \end{bmatrix}, \qquad \text{and} \qquad \mathbf{a}_4 = \begin{bmatrix} 1 \\ 1 \\ -1 \\ 0 \end{bmatrix},$$

form a basis for the column space of A.

(c) The third column of B is a linear combination of the first two columns: $\mathbf{b}_3 = -2\mathbf{b}_1 + 3\mathbf{b}_2$. Therefore, the same dependency relationship holds for the corresponding columns of matrix A.

$$\mathbf{a}_3 = \begin{bmatrix} -2 \\ -3 \\ 1 \\ 9 \end{bmatrix} = -2\begin{bmatrix} 1 \\ 0 \\ -2 \\ 0 \end{bmatrix} + 3\begin{bmatrix} 0 \\ -1 \\ -1 \\ 3 \end{bmatrix} = -2\mathbf{a}_1 + 3\mathbf{a}_2$$

Solutions of Systems of Linear Equations

We now know that the set of all solution vectors of the *homogeneous* linear system $A\mathbf{x} = \mathbf{0}$ is a subspace. Is this true also of the set of all solution vectors of the *nonhomogeneous* system $A\mathbf{x} = \mathbf{b}$, where $\mathbf{b} \neq \mathbf{0}$? The answer is "no," because the zero vector is never a solution to a nonhomogeneous system. There is a relationship, however, between the set of solutions of the two systems $A\mathbf{x} = \mathbf{0}$ and $A\mathbf{x} = \mathbf{b}$. Specifically, if $\mathbf{x}_p$ is a *particular* solution of the nonhomogeneous system $A\mathbf{x} = \mathbf{b}$, then *every* solution of this system can be written in the form

$$\mathbf{x} = \mathbf{x}_p + \mathbf{x}_h,$$

$$\underset{\substack{\text{Solution} \\ \text{of } A\mathbf{x}\,=\,\mathbf{b}}}{\uparrow} \quad \underset{\substack{\text{Solution} \\ \text{of } A\mathbf{x}\,=\,\mathbf{0}}}{\uparrow}$$

where $\mathbf{x}_h$ is a solution to the corresponding homogeneous system $A\mathbf{x} = \mathbf{0}$. The following theorem states this important result.

Theorem 4.18 Solutions of a Nonhomogeneous Linear System	If $\mathbf{x}_p$ is a particular solution of the nonhomogeneous system $A\mathbf{x} = \mathbf{b}$, then every solution of this system can be written in the form $\mathbf{x} = \mathbf{x}_p + \mathbf{x}_h$, where $\mathbf{x}_h$ is a solution to the corresponding homogeneous system $A\mathbf{x} = \mathbf{0}$.

Proof   Let $\mathbf{x}$ be any solution of $A\mathbf{x} = \mathbf{b}$. Then $(\mathbf{x} - \mathbf{x}_p)$ is a solution of the homogeneous system $A\mathbf{x} = \mathbf{0}$, since

$$A(\mathbf{x} - \mathbf{x}_p) = A\mathbf{x} - A\mathbf{x}_p = \mathbf{b} - \mathbf{b} = \mathbf{0}.$$

Letting $\mathbf{x}_h = \mathbf{x} - \mathbf{x}_p$, we have $\mathbf{x} = \mathbf{x}_p + \mathbf{x}_h$.

EXAMPLE 8   *Finding the Solution Set of a Nonhomogeneous System*

Find the set of all solution vectors of the following system of linear equations.

$$\begin{array}{rrrrr} x_1 & & -\ 2x_3 & +\ x_4 & =\ 5 \\ 3x_1 & +\ x_2 & -\ 5x_3 & & =\ 8 \\ x_1 & +\ 2x_2 & & -\ 5x_4 & =\ -9 \end{array}$$

Solution   The augmented matrix for the system $A\mathbf{x} = \mathbf{b}$ reduces as follows.

$$\begin{bmatrix} 1 & 0 & -2 & 1 & 5 \\ 3 & 1 & -5 & 0 & 8 \\ 1 & 2 & 0 & -5 & -9 \end{bmatrix} \longrightarrow \begin{bmatrix} 1 & 0 & -2 & 1 & 5 \\ 0 & 1 & 1 & -3 & -7 \\ 0 & 0 & 0 & 0 & 0 \end{bmatrix}$$

The system of linear equations corresponding to the reduced row-echelon matrix is

$$x_1 \quad - 2x_3 + \quad x_4 = \quad 5$$
$$x_2 + \quad x_3 - 3x_4 = -7.$$

Letting $x_3 = s$ and $x_4 = t$, we can write a representative solution vector of $A\mathbf{x} = \mathbf{b}$ as follows.

$$\mathbf{x} = \begin{bmatrix} x_1 \\ x_2 \\ x_3 \\ x_4 \end{bmatrix} = \begin{bmatrix} 2s - t + 5 \\ -s + 3t - 7 \\ s + 0t + 0 \\ 0s + t + 0 \end{bmatrix} = s \begin{bmatrix} 2 \\ -1 \\ 1 \\ 0 \end{bmatrix} + t \begin{bmatrix} -1 \\ 3 \\ 0 \\ 1 \end{bmatrix} + \begin{bmatrix} 5 \\ -7 \\ 0 \\ 0 \end{bmatrix}$$
$$= s\mathbf{u}_1 + t\mathbf{u}_2 + \mathbf{x}_p$$

We see that $\mathbf{x}_p$ is a *particular* solution vector of $A\mathbf{x} = \mathbf{b}$, and $\mathbf{x}_h = s\mathbf{u}_1 + t\mathbf{u}_2$ represents an arbitrary vector in the solution space of $A\mathbf{x} = \mathbf{0}$.

The final theorem in this section describes how the column space of a matrix can be used to determine whether a system of linear equations is consistent.

Theorem 4.19

Solutions of a System of Linear Equations

The system of linear equations $A\mathbf{x} = \mathbf{b}$ is consistent if and only if $\mathbf{b}$ is in the column space of A.

Proof   Let

$$A = \begin{bmatrix} a_{11} & a_{12} & \cdots & a_{1n} \\ a_{21} & a_{22} & \cdots & a_{2n} \\ \vdots & \vdots & & \vdots \\ a_{m1} & a_{m2} & \cdots & a_{mn} \end{bmatrix}, \quad \mathbf{x} = \begin{bmatrix} x_1 \\ x_2 \\ \vdots \\ x_n \end{bmatrix} \quad \text{and} \quad \mathbf{b} = \begin{bmatrix} b_1 \\ b_2 \\ \vdots \\ b_m \end{bmatrix}$$

be the coefficient matrix, the column matrix of unknowns, and the right-hand side, respectively, of the system $A\mathbf{x} = \mathbf{b}$. Then

$$A\mathbf{x} = \begin{bmatrix} a_{11} & a_{12} & \cdots & a_{1n} \\ a_{21} & a_{22} & \cdots & a_{2n} \\ \vdots & \vdots & & \vdots \\ a_{m1} & a_{m2} & \cdots & a_{mn} \end{bmatrix} \begin{bmatrix} x_1 \\ x_2 \\ \vdots \\ x_n \end{bmatrix}$$

$$= \begin{bmatrix} a_{11}x_1 + a_{12}x_2 + \cdots + a_{1n}x_n \\ a_{21}x_1 + a_{22}x_2 + \cdots + a_{2n}x_n \\ \vdots & \vdots & & \vdots \\ a_{m1}x_1 + a_{m2}x_2 + \cdots + a_{mn}x_n \end{bmatrix}$$

$$= x_1 \begin{bmatrix} a_{11} \\ a_{21} \\ \vdots \\ a_{m1} \end{bmatrix} + x_2 \begin{bmatrix} a_{12} \\ a_{22} \\ \vdots \\ a_{m2} \end{bmatrix} + \cdots + x_n \begin{bmatrix} a_{1n} \\ a_{2n} \\ \vdots \\ a_{mn} \end{bmatrix}.$$

Hence, $A\mathbf{x} = \mathbf{b}$ if and only if $\mathbf{b}$ is a linear combination of the columns of A. That is, the system is consistent if and only if $\mathbf{b}$ is in the subspace of R^m spanned by the columns of A.

EXAMPLE 9   ***Consistency of a System of Linear Equations***

Consider the system of linear equations

$$\begin{array}{rcl} x_1 + x_2 - x_3 &=& -1 \\ x_1 \quad\quad + x_3 &=& 3 \\ 3x_1 + 2x_2 - x_3 &=& 1 \end{array}$$

The rank of the coefficient matrix is equal to the rank of the augmented matrix.

$$A = \begin{bmatrix} 1 & 1 & -1 \\ 1 & 0 & 1 \\ 3 & 2 & -1 \end{bmatrix} \longrightarrow \begin{bmatrix} 1 & 0 & 1 \\ 0 & 1 & -2 \\ 0 & 0 & 0 \end{bmatrix}$$

$$[A : \mathbf{b}] = \begin{bmatrix} 1 & 1 & -1 & -1 \\ 1 & 0 & 1 & 3 \\ 3 & 2 & -1 & 1 \end{bmatrix} \longrightarrow \begin{bmatrix} 1 & 0 & 1 & 3 \\ 0 & 1 & -2 & -4 \\ 0 & 0 & 0 & 0 \end{bmatrix}$$

Hence, $\mathbf{b}$ is in the column space of A, and the system of linear equations is consistent.

Systems of Linear Equations with Square Coefficient Matrices

The final result in this section summarizes several major results involving systems of linear equations, matrices, determinants, and vector spaces.

Summary of Equivalent Conditions for Square Matrices

If A is an $n \times n$ matrix, then the following conditions are equivalent.
1. A is invertible.
2. $A\mathbf{x} = \mathbf{b}$ has a unique solution for any $n \times 1$ matrix $\mathbf{b}$.
3. $A\mathbf{x} = \mathbf{0}$ has only the trivial solution.
4. A is row equivalent to I_n.
5. $|A| \neq 0$.
6. Rank(A) $= n$.
7. The n row vectors of A are linearly independent.
8. The n column vectors of A are linearly independent.

SECTION 4.6 ☐ EXERCISES*

In Exercises 1–8, find (a) the rank of the matrix, (b) a basis for the row space, and (c) a basis for the column space.

1. $\begin{bmatrix} 1 & 0 \\ 0 & 2 \end{bmatrix}$

2. $\begin{bmatrix} 1 & 2 & 3 \end{bmatrix}$

3. $\begin{bmatrix} 2 & 4 \\ 1 & 6 \end{bmatrix}$

4. $\begin{bmatrix} 1 & -3 & 2 \\ 4 & 2 & 1 \end{bmatrix}$

5. $\begin{bmatrix} 4 & 20 & 31 \\ 6 & -5 & -6 \\ 2 & -11 & -16 \end{bmatrix}$

6. $\begin{bmatrix} 2 & -3 & 1 \\ 5 & 10 & 6 \\ 8 & -7 & 5 \end{bmatrix}$

7. $\begin{bmatrix} -2 & -4 & 4 & 5 \\ 3 & 6 & -6 & -4 \\ -2 & -4 & 4 & 9 \end{bmatrix}$

8. $\begin{bmatrix} 2 & 4 & -3 & -6 \\ 7 & 14 & -6 & -3 \\ -2 & -4 & 1 & -2 \\ 2 & 4 & -2 & -2 \end{bmatrix}$

In Exercises 9–12, find a basis for the subspace of R^4 spanned by S.

9. $S = \{(2, 9, -2, 53), (-3, 2, 3, -2), (8, -3, -8, 17),$
   $(0, -3, 0, 15)\}$

10. $S = \{(6, -3, 6, 34), (3, -2, 3, 19), (8, 3, -9, 6),$
   $(-2, 0, 6, -5)\}$

11. $S = \{(-3, 2, 5, 28), (-6, 1, -8, -1), (14, -10, 12, -10),$
   $(0, 5, 12, 50)\}$

12. $S = \{(2, 5, -3, -2), (-2, -3, 2, -5), (1, 3, -2, 2),$
   $(-1, -5, 3, 5)\}$

In Exercises 13–18, find a basis and the dimension of the solution space of $A\mathbf{x} = \mathbf{0}$.

13. $A = \begin{bmatrix} 2 & -1 \\ 1 & 3 \end{bmatrix}$

14. $A = \begin{bmatrix} 2 & -1 \\ -6 & 3 \end{bmatrix}$

15. $A = \begin{bmatrix} 1 & 2 & 3 \end{bmatrix}$

16. $A = \begin{bmatrix} 1 & 2 & 3 \\ 0 & 1 & 0 \end{bmatrix}$

17. $A = \begin{bmatrix} 1 & 2 & -3 \\ 2 & -1 & 4 \\ 4 & 3 & -2 \end{bmatrix}$

18. $A = \begin{bmatrix} 1 & 2 & -3 \\ 2 & 6 & -11 \\ 1 & -2 & 7 \end{bmatrix}$

In Exercises 19–24, find (a) a basis and (b) the dimension of the solution space of the given homogeneous system of linear equations.

19. $\begin{aligned} -x + y + z &= 0 \\ 3x - y &= 0 \\ 2x - 4y - 5z &= 0 \end{aligned}$

20. $\begin{aligned} 4x - y + 2z &= 0 \\ 2x + 3y - z &= 0 \\ 3x + y + z &= 0 \end{aligned}$

*The answers involving bases given in the back of the text are not unique.

21. $\begin{aligned} x - 2y + 3z &= 0 \\ -3x + 6y - 9z &= 0 \end{aligned}$

22. $\begin{aligned} 3x_1 + 3x_2 + 15x_3 + 11x_4 &= 0 \\ x_1 - 3x_2 + x_3 + x_4 &= 0 \\ 2x_1 + 3x_2 + 11x_3 + 8x_4 &= 0 \end{aligned}$

C 23. $\begin{aligned} 9x_1 - 4x_2 - 2x_3 - 20x_4 &= 0 \\ 12x_1 - 6x_2 - 4x_3 - 29x_4 &= 0 \\ 3x_1 - 2x_2 - 7x_4 &= 0 \\ 3x_1 - 2x_2 - x_3 - 8x_4 &= 0 \end{aligned}$

C 24. $\begin{aligned} x_1 + 3x_2 + 2x_3 + 22x_4 + 13x_5 &= 0 \\ x_1 + x_3 - 2x_4 + x_5 &= 0 \\ 3x_1 + 6x_2 + 5x_3 + 42x_4 + 27x_5 &= 0 \end{aligned}$

In Exercises 25–30, (a) determine whether the nonhomogeneous system $A\mathbf{x} = \mathbf{b}$ is consistent and (b) if the system is consistent, write the solution in the form $\mathbf{x} = \mathbf{x}_h + \mathbf{x}_p$, where $\mathbf{x}_h$ is a solution of $A\mathbf{x} = \mathbf{0}$ and $\mathbf{x}_p$ is a particular solution of $A\mathbf{x} = \mathbf{b}$.

25. $\begin{aligned} x + 3y + 10z &= 18 \\ -2x + 7y + 32z &= 29 \\ -x + 3y + 14z &= 12 \\ x + y + 2z &= 8 \end{aligned}$

26. $\begin{aligned} 3x - 8y + 4z &= 19 \\ -6y + 2z + 4w &= 5 \\ 5x + 22z + w &= 29 \\ x - 2y + 2z &= 8 \end{aligned}$

27. $\begin{aligned} 3w - 2x + 16y - 2z &= -7 \\ -w + 5x - 14y + 18z &= 29 \\ 3w - x + 14y + 2z &= 1 \end{aligned}$

28. $\begin{aligned} 2x - 4y + 5z &= 8 \\ -7x + 14y + 4z &= -28 \\ 3x - 6y + z &= 12 \end{aligned}$

C 29. $\begin{aligned} x_1 + 2x_2 + x_3 + x_4 + 5x_5 &= 0 \\ -5x_1 - 10x_2 + 3x_3 + 3x_4 + 55x_5 &= -8 \\ x_1 + 2x_2 + 2x_3 - 3x_4 - 5x_5 &= 14 \\ -x_1 - 2x_2 + x_3 + x_4 + 15x_5 &= -2 \end{aligned}$

C 30. $\begin{aligned} 5x_1 - 4x_2 + 12x_3 - 33x_4 + 14x_5 &= -4 \\ -2x_1 + x_2 - 6x_3 + 12x_4 - 8x_5 &= 1 \\ 2x_1 - x_2 + 6x_3 - 12x_4 + 8x_5 &= -1 \end{aligned}$

In Exercises 31–34, determine whether $\mathbf{b}$ is in the column space of A. If it is, write $\mathbf{b}$ as a linear combination of the column vectors of A.

31. $A = \begin{bmatrix} -1 & 2 \\ 4 & 0 \end{bmatrix}$, $\mathbf{b} = \begin{bmatrix} 3 \\ 4 \end{bmatrix}$

32. $A = \begin{bmatrix} -1 & 2 \\ 2 & -4 \end{bmatrix}$, $\mathbf{b} = \begin{bmatrix} 2 \\ 4 \end{bmatrix}$

33. $A = \begin{bmatrix} 1 & 3 & 0 \\ -1 & 1 & 0 \\ 2 & 0 & 1 \end{bmatrix}$, $\mathbf{b} = \begin{bmatrix} 1 \\ 2 \\ -3 \end{bmatrix}$

34. $A = \begin{bmatrix} 1 & 3 & 2 \\ -1 & 1 & 2 \\ 0 & 1 & 1 \end{bmatrix}$, $\mathbf{b} = \begin{bmatrix} 1 \\ 1 \\ 0 \end{bmatrix}$

35. Explain why the row vectors of a 4×3 matrix form a linearly dependent set. (Assume all matrix entries are distinct.)

36. Explain why the column vectors of a 3×4 matrix form a linearly dependent set. (Assume all matrix entries are distinct.)

37. Prove that if A is not square, then either the row vectors of A or the column vectors of A form a linearly dependent set.

38. Give an example showing that the rank of the product of two matrices can be less than the rank of either matrix.

39. Give examples of matrices A and B of the same size such that

(a) rank$(A + B)$ < rank(A) and rank$(A + B)$ < rank(B)
(b) rank$(A + B)$ = rank(A) and rank$(A + B)$ = rank(B)
(c) rank$(A + B)$ > rank(A) and rank$(A + B)$ > rank(B).

40. Prove that the nonzero row vectors of a matrix in row-echelon form are linearly independent.

41. Let A be an $m \times n$ matrix (where $m < n$) whose rank is r.

(a) What is the largest value r can be?
(b) How many vectors are in a basis of the row space of A?
(c) How many vectors are in a basis of the column space of A?
(d) Which vector space R^k has the row space as a subspace?
(e) Which vector space R^k has the column space as a subspace?

42. Show that the three points (x_1, y_1), (x_2, y_2), and (x_3, y_3) in a plane are collinear if and only if the matrix

$$\begin{bmatrix} x_1 & y_1 & 1 \\ x_2 & y_2 & 1 \\ x_3 & y_3 & 1 \end{bmatrix}$$

has rank less than 3.

43. Given the matrices A and B, show that the row vectors of AB are in the row space of B and the column vectors of AB are in the column space of A.

44. Find the rank of the matrix

$$\begin{bmatrix} 1 & 2 & 3 & \cdots & n \\ n+1 & n+2 & n+3 & \cdots & 2n \\ 2n+1 & 2n+2 & 2n+3 & \cdots & 3n \\ \vdots & \vdots & \vdots & & \vdots \\ n^2-n+1 & n^2-n+2 & n^2-n+3 & \cdots & n^2 \end{bmatrix}$$

for $n = 2$, 3, and 4. Can you find a pattern in these ranks?

45. Prove the following properties of the system of linear equations in n variables $A\mathbf{x} = \mathbf{b}$.

(a) If rank(A) = rank$([A:\mathbf{b}])$ = n, then the system has a unique solution.
(b) If rank(A) = rank$([A:\mathbf{b}])$ < n, then the system has an infinite number of solutions.
(c) If rank(A) < rank$([A \vdots \mathbf{b}])$, then the system is inconsistent.

46. Given the following row-equivalent matrices A and B:

$$A = \begin{pmatrix} 1 & 2 & 1 & 0 & 0 \\ 2 & 5 & 1 & 1 & 0 \\ 3 & 7 & 2 & 2 & -2 \\ 4 & 9 & 3 & -1 & 4 \end{pmatrix}$$

$$B = \begin{pmatrix} 1 & 0 & 3 & 0 & -4 \\ 0 & 1 & -1 & 0 & 2 \\ 0 & 0 & 0 & 1 & -2 \\ 0 & 0 & 0 & 0 & 0 \end{pmatrix},$$

answer the following questions about the matrix A.

(a) Find the rank and nullity of A.
(b) Find a basis for the nullspace of A.
(c) Find a basis for the row space of A.
(d) Find a basis for the column space of A.
(e) Determine whether or not the rows of A are linearly independent.
(f) Let the columns of A be denoted $\mathbf{a}_1$, $\mathbf{a}_2$, $\mathbf{a}_3$, $\mathbf{a}_4$, and $\mathbf{a}_5$. Which of the following sets are linearly independent?

(i) $\{\mathbf{a}_1, \mathbf{a}_2, \mathbf{a}_4\}$　(ii) $\{\mathbf{a}_1, \mathbf{a}_2, \mathbf{a}_3\}$　(iii) $\{\mathbf{a}_1, \mathbf{a}_3, \mathbf{a}_5\}$

47. Let A be an $m \times n$ matrix.

(a) Prove that the system of linear equations $A\mathbf{x} = \mathbf{b}$ is consistent for all column vectors $\mathbf{b}$ if and only if the rank of A is m.
(b) Prove that the homogeneous system of linear equations $A\mathbf{x} = \mathbf{0}$ has only the trivial solution if and only if the columns of A are linearly independent.

48. Let A and B be square matrices of order n satisfying $A\mathbf{x} = B\mathbf{x}$ for all $\mathbf{x} \in R^n$.

(a) Find the nullspace and nullity of $A - B$.
(b) Show that A and B must be identical.

49. Let A be an $m \times n$ matrix. Prove that $N(A) \subset N(A^TA)$.

50. Prove that row operations do not change the dependency relationships between columns of an $m \times n$ matrix.

4.7 COORDINATES AND CHANGE OF BASIS

In Section 4.5, we saw that if B is a basis for a vector space V, then every vector $\mathbf{x}$ in V can be expressed in one and only one way as a linear combination of vectors in B. The coefficients in the linear combination are the **coordinates of x relative to B.** In the context of coordinates, the order of the vectors in this basis is important, and we will emphasize this sometimes by saying that the basis B is an *ordered* basis.

Coordinate Representation Relative to a Basis

Let $B = \{\mathbf{v}_1, \mathbf{v}_2, \ldots, \mathbf{v}_n\}$ be an ordered basis for a vector space V and let $\mathbf{x}$ be a vector in V such that

$$\mathbf{x} = c_1\mathbf{v}_1 + c_2\mathbf{v}_2 + \cdots + c_n\mathbf{v}_n.$$

The scalars $c_1, c_2, \ldots, c_n$ are called the **coordinates of x relative to the basis B.** The **coordinate matrix** (or **coordinate vector**) **of x relative to B** is the column matrix in R^n whose components are the coordinates of $\mathbf{x}$.

$$[\mathbf{x}]_B = \begin{bmatrix} c_1 \\ c_2 \\ \vdots \\ c_n \end{bmatrix}$$

Coordinate Representation in R^n

In R^n, the notation for coordinate matrices conforms to the usual component notation, except that we use column notation for the coordinate matrix. In other words, writing a vector in R^n as $\mathbf{x} = (x_1, x_2, \ldots, x_n)$ means that the x_i's are the coordinates of $\mathbf{x}$ *relative to the standard basis S in R^n.* Thus we have

$$[\mathbf{x}]_S = \begin{bmatrix} x_1 \\ x_2 \\ \vdots \\ x_n \end{bmatrix}.$$

EXAMPLE 1   *Coordinates and Components in R^n*

Find the coordinate matrix of $\mathbf{x} = (-2, 1, 3)$ in R^3 relative to the standard basis $S = \{(1, 0, 0), (0, 1, 0), (0, 0, 1)\}$.

Solution   Since $\mathbf{x}$ can be written as

$$\begin{aligned} \mathbf{x} &= (-2, 1, 3) \\ &= -2(1, 0, 0) + 1(0, 1, 0) + 3(0, 0, 1), \end{aligned}$$

we see that the coordinate matrix of $\mathbf{x}$ relative to the standard basis is simply

$$[\mathbf{x}]_S = \begin{bmatrix} -2 \\ 1 \\ 3 \end{bmatrix}.$$

Thus, the components of $\mathbf{x}$ are the same as its coordinates relative to the standard basis.

EXAMPLE 2   ***Finding a Coordinate Matrix Relative to a Standard Basis***

The coordinate matrix of $\mathbf{x}$ in R^2 relative to the (nonstandard) ordered basis $B = \{\mathbf{v}_1, \mathbf{v}_2\}$ $= \{(1, 0), (1, 2)\}$ is

$$[\mathbf{x}]_B = \begin{bmatrix} 3 \\ 2 \end{bmatrix}.$$

Find the coordinates of $\mathbf{x}$ relative to the standard basis $B' = \{\mathbf{e}_1, \mathbf{e}_2\} = \{(1, 0), (0, 1)\}$.

Solution   Since $[\mathbf{x}]_B = \begin{bmatrix} 3 \\ 2 \end{bmatrix}$, we can write

$$\mathbf{x} = 3\mathbf{v}_1 + 2\mathbf{v}_2 = 3(1, 0) + 2(1, 2) = (5, 4).$$

Moreover, since $(5, 4) = 5(1, 0) + 4(0, 1)$, it follows that the coordinates of $\mathbf{x}$ relative to B' are given by

$$[\mathbf{x}]_{B'} = \begin{bmatrix} 5 \\ 4 \end{bmatrix}.$$

Figure 4.14 compares these two coordinate representations.

Figure 4.14

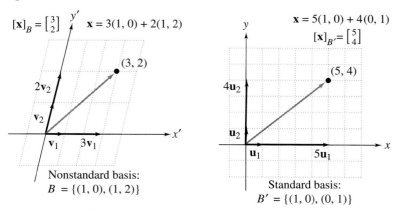

Nonstandard basis:
$B = \{(1, 0), (1, 2)\}$

Standard basis:
$B' = \{(1, 0), (0, 1)\}$

Example 2 shows that the procedure for finding the coordinate matrix relative to a *standard* basis is reasonably straightforward. The problem becomes a bit tougher, however, when we must find the coordinate matrix relative to a *nonstandard* basis. Here is an example.

EXAMPLE 3   *Finding a Coordinate Matrix Relative to a Nonstandard Basis*

Find the coordinate matrix of $\mathbf{x} = (1, 2, -1)$ in R^3 relative to the (nonstandard) basis

$$B' = \{\mathbf{u}_1, \mathbf{u}_2, \mathbf{u}_3\} = \{(1, 0, 1), (0, -1, 2), (2, 3, -5)\}.$$

Solution   We begin by writing $\mathbf{x}$ as a linear combination of $\mathbf{u}_1, \mathbf{u}_2,$ and $\mathbf{u}_3$.

$$\mathbf{x} = c_1\mathbf{u}_1 + c_2\mathbf{u}_2 + c_3\mathbf{u}_3$$
$$(1, 2, -1) = c_1(1, 0, 1) + c_2(0, -1, 2) + c_3(2, 3, -5)$$

Equating corresponding components produces the following system of linear equations.

$$
\begin{array}{rcl}
c_1 \quad\quad\; + 2c_3 &=& 1 \\
-c_2 + 3c_3 &=& 2 \\
c_1 + 2c_2 - 5c_3 &=& -1
\end{array}
\quad\longrightarrow\quad
\begin{bmatrix} 1 & 0 & 2 \\ 0 & -1 & 3 \\ 1 & 2 & -5 \end{bmatrix}
\begin{bmatrix} c_1 \\ c_2 \\ c_3 \end{bmatrix}
=
\begin{bmatrix} 1 \\ 2 \\ -1 \end{bmatrix}
$$

The solution of this system is $c_1 = 5$, $c_2 = -8$, and $c_3 = -2$. Thus $\mathbf{x} = 5(1, 0, 1) + (-8)$ $(0, -1, 2) + (-2)(2, 3, -5)$, and the coordinate matrix of $\mathbf{x}$ relative to B' is

$$[\mathbf{x}]_{B'} = \begin{bmatrix} 5 \\ -8 \\ -2 \end{bmatrix}.$$

REMARK: Note that the solution in Example 3 is written as

$$[\mathbf{x}]_{B'} = \begin{bmatrix} 5 \\ -8 \\ -2 \end{bmatrix}.$$

It would be incorrect to write the solution as

$$\mathbf{x} = \begin{bmatrix} 5 \\ -8 \\ -2 \end{bmatrix}.$$

Do you see why?

Change of Basis in R^n

The procedure demonstrated in Examples 2 and 3 is called a **change of basis.** That is, we were given the coordinates of a vector relative to one basis B and asked to find the coordinates relative to another basis B'.

For instance, if in Example 3 we let B be the standard basis, then the problem of finding the coordinate matrix of $\mathbf{x} = (1, 2, -1)$ relative to the basis B' becomes one of solving for $c_1, c_2,$ and c_3 in the matrix equation

$$\begin{bmatrix} 1 & 0 & 2 \\ 0 & -1 & 3 \\ 1 & 2 & -5 \end{bmatrix} \begin{bmatrix} c_1 \\ c_2 \\ c_3 \end{bmatrix} = \begin{bmatrix} 1 \\ 2 \\ -1 \end{bmatrix}.$$

$\quad\quad P \quad\quad\quad [\mathbf{x}]_{B'} \quad\quad [\mathbf{x}]_B$

We call P the **transition matrix from B' to B,** where $[\mathbf{x}]_{B'}$ is the coordinate matrix of $\mathbf{x}$ relative to B', and $[\mathbf{x}]_B$ is the coordinate matrix of $\mathbf{x}$ relative to B. Multiplication by the transition matrix P changes a coordinate matrix relative to B' into a coordinate matrix relative to B. That is,

$$P[\mathbf{x}]_{B'} = [\mathbf{x}]_B. \quad\quad \text{Change of basis from } B' \text{ to } B$$

To perform a change of basis from B to B', we use the matrix P^{-1} (the **transition matrix from B to B'**) and write

$$[\mathbf{x}]_{B'} = P^{-1}[\mathbf{x}]_B. \quad\quad \text{Change of basis from } B \text{ to } B'$$

This means that the change of basis problem in Example 3 can be represented by the matrix equation

$$\begin{bmatrix} c_1 \\ c_2 \\ c_3 \end{bmatrix} = \begin{bmatrix} -1 & 4 & 2 \\ 3 & -7 & -3 \\ 1 & -2 & -1 \end{bmatrix} \begin{bmatrix} 1 \\ 2 \\ -1 \end{bmatrix} = \begin{bmatrix} 5 \\ -8 \\ -2 \end{bmatrix}.$$

$\quad\quad\quad\quad P^{-1} \quad\quad\quad [\mathbf{x}]_B \quad [\mathbf{x}]_{B'}$

This discussion generalizes as follows. Suppose that

$$B = \{\mathbf{v}_1, \mathbf{v}_2, \dots, \mathbf{v}_n\} \quad\quad \text{and} \quad\quad B' = \{\mathbf{u}_1, \mathbf{u}_2, \dots, \mathbf{u}_n\}$$

are two ordered bases for R^n. If $\mathbf{x}$ is a vector in R^n and

$$[\mathbf{x}]_B = \begin{bmatrix} c_1 \\ c_2 \\ \cdot \\ \cdot \\ \cdot \\ c_n \end{bmatrix} \quad\quad \text{and} \quad\quad [\mathbf{x}]_{B'} = \begin{bmatrix} d_1 \\ d_2 \\ \cdot \\ \cdot \\ \cdot \\ d_n \end{bmatrix}$$

are the coordinate matrices of $\mathbf{x}$ relative to B and B', then the **transition matrix P from B' to B** is the matrix P such that

$$[\mathbf{x}]_B = P[\mathbf{x}]_{B'}.$$

The following theorem tells us that the transition matrix P is invertible and that its inverse is the **transition matrix from B to B'.** That is,

$$[\mathbf{x}]_{B'} = P^{-1}[\mathbf{x}]_B.$$

Coordinate matrix of $\mathbf{x}$ *relative to* B'	*Transition matrix from B to B'*	*Coordinate matrix of* $\mathbf{x}$ *relative to* B

Theorem 4.20

The Inverse of a Transition Matrix

If P is the transition matrix from a basis B' to a basis B in R^n, then P is invertible and the transition matrix from B to B' is given by P^{-1}.

There is a nice way to use Gauss-Jordan elimination to find the transition matrix P^{-1}. First we define two matrices B and B' whose columns correspond to the vectors in B and B'. That is,

$$B = \begin{bmatrix} v_{11} & v_{12} & \cdots & v_{1n} \\ v_{21} & v_{22} & \cdots & v_{2n} \\ \vdots & \vdots & & \vdots \\ v_{n1} & v_{n2} & \cdots & v_{nn} \end{bmatrix} \quad \text{and} \quad B' = \begin{bmatrix} u_{11} & u_{12} & \cdots & u_{1n} \\ u_{21} & u_{22} & \cdots & u_{2n} \\ \vdots & \vdots & & \vdots \\ u_{n1} & u_{n2} & \cdots & u_{nn} \end{bmatrix}.$$

$$\quad\;\; \mathbf{v}_1 \quad\; \mathbf{v}_2 \qquad\;\; \mathbf{v}_n \qquad\qquad\qquad \mathbf{u}_1 \quad\; \mathbf{u}_2 \qquad\;\; \mathbf{u}_n$$

Then, by reducing the $n \times 2n$ matrix $[B' \vdots B]$ so that the identity matrix I_n occurs in place of B', we obtain the matrix $[I_n \vdots P^{-1}]$. This procedure is stated formally in the following theorem. (For a proof of Theorems 4.20 and 4.21, see Appendix A.)

Theorem 4.21

Transition Matrix from B to B'

Let $B = \{\mathbf{v}_1, \mathbf{v}_2, \ldots, \mathbf{v}_n\}$ and $B' = \{\mathbf{u}_1, \mathbf{u}_2, \ldots, \mathbf{u}_n\}$ be two bases for R^n. Then the transition matrix P^{-1} from B to B' can be found by using Gauss-Jordan elimination on the $n \times 2n$ matrix $[B' \vdots B]$ as follows.

$$[B' \vdots B] \longrightarrow [I_n \vdots P^{-1}]$$

In the following example we apply this procedure to the change of basis problem given in Example 3.

EXAMPLE 4   *Finding a Transition Matrix*

Find the transition matrix from B to B' for the following bases in R^3.

$$B = \{(1, 0, 0), (0, 1, 0), (0, 0, 1)\}$$

and

$$B' = \{(1, 0, 1), (0, -1, 2), (2, 3, -5)\}$$

Solution   First we use the vectors in the two bases to form the matrices B and B'.

$$B = \begin{bmatrix} 1 & 0 & 0 \\ 0 & 1 & 0 \\ 0 & 0 & 1 \end{bmatrix} \quad \text{and} \quad B' = \begin{bmatrix} 1 & 0 & 2 \\ 0 & -1 & 3 \\ 1 & 2 & -5 \end{bmatrix}$$

Then we adjoin B to B' to form the matrix $[B' \vdots B]$ and use Gauss-Jordan elimination to rewrite $[B' \vdots B]$ as $[I_3 \vdots P^{-1}]$.

$$\begin{bmatrix} 1 & 0 & 2 & \vdots & 1 & 0 & 0 \\ 0 & -1 & 3 & \vdots & 0 & 1 & 0 \\ 1 & 2 & -5 & \vdots & 0 & 0 & 1 \end{bmatrix} \longrightarrow \begin{bmatrix} 1 & 0 & 0 & \vdots & -1 & 4 & 2 \\ 0 & 1 & 0 & \vdots & 3 & -7 & -3 \\ 0 & 0 & 1 & \vdots & 1 & -2 & -1 \end{bmatrix}$$

From this we conclude that the transition matrix from B to B' is

$$P^{-1} = \begin{bmatrix} -1 & 4 & 2 \\ 3 & -7 & -3 \\ 1 & -2 & -1 \end{bmatrix}.$$

Try multiplying P^{-1} by the coordinate matrix of $\mathbf{x} = (1, 2, -1)$ to see that the result is the same as the one obtained in Example 3.

Note that when B is the standard basis, as in Example 4, the process of changing $[B' \vdots B]$ to $[I_n \vdots P^{-1}]$ becomes

$$[B' \vdots I_n] \longrightarrow [I_n \vdots P^{-1}].$$

But this is the same process used to find inverse matrices in Section 2.3. In other words, if B is the standard basis in R^n, then the transition matrix from B to B' is given by

$$P^{-1} = (B')^{-1}. \qquad \textbf{Standard basis to nonstandard basis}$$

The process is even simpler if B' is the standard basis, because the matrix $[B' \vdots B]$ is already in the form $[I_n \vdots B] = [I_n \vdots P^{-1}]$. In this case, the transition matrix is simply

$$P^{-1} = B. \qquad \textbf{Nonstandard basis to standard basis}$$

For instance, the transition matrix in Example 2 from $B = \{(1, 0), (1, 2)\}$ to $B' = \{(1, 0), (0, 1)\}$ is

$$P^{-1} = B = \begin{bmatrix} 1 & 1 \\ 0 & 2 \end{bmatrix}.$$

EXAMPLE 5   *Finding a Transition Matrix*

Find the transition matrix from B to B' for the following bases for R^2.

$$B = \{(-3, 2), (4, -2)\}$$

and

$$B' = \{(-1, 2), (2, -2)\}$$

Solution   We begin by forming the matrix

$$[B' \vdots B] = \begin{bmatrix} -1 & 2 & \vdots & -3 & 4 \\ 2 & -2 & \vdots & 2 & -2 \end{bmatrix}$$

and use Gauss-Jordan elimination to obtain the transition matrix P^{-1} form B to B':

$$[I_2 \vdots P^{-1}] = \begin{bmatrix} 1 & 0 & \vdots & -1 & 2 \\ 0 & 1 & \vdots & -2 & 3 \end{bmatrix}.$$

Thus we have

$$P^{-1} = \begin{bmatrix} -1 & 2 \\ -2 & 3 \end{bmatrix}.$$

In Example 5, if we had found the transition matrix from B' to B (rather than from B to B'), we would have obtained

$$[B \vdots B'] = \begin{bmatrix} -3 & 4 & \vdots & -1 & 2 \\ 2 & -2 & \vdots & 2 & -2 \end{bmatrix},$$

which reduces to

$$[I_2 \vdots P] = \begin{bmatrix} 1 & 0 & \vdots & 3 & -2 \\ 0 & 1 & \vdots & 2 & -1 \end{bmatrix}.$$

Therefore the transition matrix from B' to B is

$$P = \begin{bmatrix} 3 & -2 \\ 2 & -1 \end{bmatrix}.$$

We can verify that this is the inverse of the transition matrix found in Example 5 by multiplication:

$$PP^{-1} = \begin{bmatrix} 3 & -2 \\ 2 & -1 \end{bmatrix} \begin{bmatrix} -1 & 2 \\ -2 & 3 \end{bmatrix} = \begin{bmatrix} 1 & 0 \\ 0 & 1 \end{bmatrix} = I_2.$$

Coordinate Representation in General n-Dimensional Spaces

One benefit of coordinate representation is that it enables us to represent vectors in an arbitrary n-dimensional space using the same notation we use in R^n. For instance, in Example 6, note that the coordinate matrix of a vector in P_3 is a vector in R^4.

EXAMPLE 6   *Coordinate Representation in P_3*

Find the coordinate matrix of $\mathbf{p} = 3x^3 - 2x^2 + 4$ relative to the standard basis in P_3,

$$S = \{1, x, x^2, x^3\}.$$

Solution   First we write $\mathbf{p}$ as a linear combination of the basis vectors (in the given order).

$$\mathbf{p} = 4(1) + 0(x) + (-2)(x^2) + 3(x^3)$$

This tells us that the coordinate matrix of $\mathbf{p}$ relative to S is

$$[\mathbf{p}]_S = \begin{bmatrix} 4 \\ 0 \\ -2 \\ 3 \end{bmatrix}.$$

In the previous section we saw that it is sometimes convenient to represent $n \times 1$ matrices as n-tuples. The next example adds some justification to this practice.

EXAMPLE 7   *Coordinate Representation in $M_{3,1}$*

Find the coordinate matrix of

$$X = \begin{bmatrix} -1 \\ 4 \\ 3 \end{bmatrix}$$

relative to the standard basis in $M_{3,1}$,

$$S = \left\{ \begin{bmatrix} 1 \\ 0 \\ 0 \end{bmatrix}, \begin{bmatrix} 0 \\ 1 \\ 0 \end{bmatrix}, \begin{bmatrix} 0 \\ 0 \\ 1 \end{bmatrix} \right\}.$$

Solution   Since X can be written as

$$X = \begin{bmatrix} -1 \\ 4 \\ 3 \end{bmatrix}$$

$$= (-1) \begin{bmatrix} 1 \\ 0 \\ 0 \end{bmatrix} + 4 \begin{bmatrix} 0 \\ 1 \\ 0 \end{bmatrix} + 3 \begin{bmatrix} 0 \\ 0 \\ 1 \end{bmatrix},$$

the coordinate matrix of X relative to S is $[X]_S = \begin{bmatrix} -1 \\ 4 \\ 3 \end{bmatrix}$.

REMARK: Section 6.2 has more about the use of R^n to represent an arbitrary n-dimensional vector space.

Theorems 4.20 and 4.21 can be generalized to cover arbitrary n-dimensional spaces. This text, however, does not do that.

SECTION 4.7 ☐ EXERCISES

In Exercises 1–6, you are given the coordinate matrix of **x** relative to a (nonstandard) basis B. Find the coordinate vector of **x** relative to the standard basis in R^n.

1. $B = \{(2, -1), (0, 1)\}$, $[\mathbf{x}]_B = [4, 1]^T$
2. $B = \{(-1, 4), (4, -1)\}$, $[\mathbf{x}]_B = [-2, 3]^T$

3. $B = \{(1, 0, 1), (1, 1, 0), (0, 1, 1)\}$, $[\mathbf{x}]_B = [2, 3, 1]^T$
4. $B = \{(\frac{3}{4}, \frac{5}{2}, \frac{3}{2}), (3, 4, \frac{7}{2}), (-\frac{3}{2}, 6, 2)\}$, $[\mathbf{x}]_B = [2, 0, 4]^T$
5. $B = \{(0, 0, 0, 1), (0, 0, 1, 1), (0, 1, 1, 1), (1, 1, 1, 1)\}$,
    $[\mathbf{x}]_B = [1, -2, 3, -1]^T$
6. $B = \{(4, 0, 7, 3), (0, 5, -1, -1), (-3, 4, 2, 1), (0, 1, 5, 0)\}$,
    $[\mathbf{x}]_B = [-2, 3, 4, 1]^T$

In Exercises 7–12, find the coordinate matrix for $\mathbf{x}$ in R^n relative to the basis B.

7. $B = \{(4, 0), (0, 3)\}, \quad \mathbf{x} = (12, 6)$
8. $B = \{(-6, 7), (4, -3)\}, \quad \mathbf{x} = (-26, 32)$
9. $B = \{(8, 11, 0), (7, 0, 10), (1, 4, 6)\}, \quad \mathbf{x} = (3, 19, 2)$
10. $B = \{(\frac{3}{2}, 4, 1), (\frac{3}{4}, \frac{5}{2}, 0), (1, \frac{1}{2}, 2)\}, \quad \mathbf{x} = (3, -\frac{1}{2}, 8)$
11. $B = \{(4, 3, 3), (-11, 0, 11), (0, 9, 2)\}, \quad \mathbf{x} = (11, 18, -7)$
12. $B = \{(9, -3, 15, 4), (3, 0, 0, 1), (0, -5, 6, 8), (3, -4, 2, -3)\}$
    $\mathbf{x} = (0, -20, 7, 15)$

In Exercises 13–22, find the transition matrix from B to B'.

13. $B = \{(1, 0), (0, 1)\}, \quad B' = \{(2, 4), (1, 3)\}$
14. $B = \{(1, 0), (0, 1)\}, \quad B' = \{(1, 1), (5, 6)\}$
15. $B = \{(2, 4), (-1, 3)\}, \quad B' = \{(1, 0), (0, 1)\}$
16. $B = \{(1, 1), (1, 0)\}, \quad B' = \{(1, 0), (0, 1)\}$
17. $B = \{(1, 0, 0), (0, 1, 0), (0, 0, 1)\},$
    $B' = \{(1, 0, 0), (0, 2, 8), (6, 0, 12)\}$
18. $B = \{(1, 0, 0), (0, 1, 0), (0, 0, 1)\},$
    $B' = \{(1, 3, -1), (2, 7, -4), (2, 9, -7)\}$
19. $B = \{(1, 3, 3), (1, 5, 6), (1, 4, 5)\},$
    $B' = \{(1, 0, 0), (0, 1, 0), (0, 0, 1)\}$
20. $B = \{(2, -1, 4), (0, 2, 1), (-3, 2, 1)\},$
    $B' = \{(1, 0, 0), (0, 1, 0), (0, 0, 1)\}$
C 21. $B = \{(1, 0, 0, 0), (0, 1, 0, 0), (0, 0, 1, 0), (0, 0, 0, 1)\},$
    $B' = \{(1, 3, 2, -1), (-2, -5, -5, 4), (-1, -2, -2, 4),$
    $(-2, -3, -5, 11)\}$
C 22. $B = \{(1, 1, 1, 1), (0, 1, 1, 1), (0, 0, 1, 1), (0, 0, 0, 1)\},$
    $B' = \{(1, 0, 0, 0), (0, 1, 0, 0), (0, 0, 1, 0), (0, 0, 0, 1)\}$

In Exercises 23–26, (a) find the transition matrix from B to B', (b) use Theorem 4.21 to find the transition matrix from B' to B, (c) verify that the two transition matrices are inverses of each other, and (d) find $[\mathbf{x}]_B$ given $[\mathbf{x}]_{B'}$.

23. $B = \{(1, 3), (-2, -2)\}, \quad B' = \{(-12, 0), (-4, 4)\},$
    $[\mathbf{x}]_{B'} = \begin{bmatrix} -1 \\ 3 \end{bmatrix}$

24. $B = \{(2, -2), (6, 3)\}, \quad B' = \{(1, 1), (32, 31)\},$
    $[\mathbf{x}]_{B'} = \begin{bmatrix} 2 \\ -1 \end{bmatrix}$

25. $B = \{(1, 0, 2), (0, 1, 3), (1, 1, 1)\},$
    $B' = \{(2, 1, 1), (1, 0, 0), (0, 2, 1)\},$
    $[\mathbf{x}]_{B'} = \begin{bmatrix} 1 \\ 2 \\ -1 \end{bmatrix}$

26. $B = \{(1, 1, 1), (1, -1, 1), (0, 0, 1)\},$
    $B' = \{(2, 2, 0), (0, 1, 1), (1, 0, 1)\},$
    $[\mathbf{x}]_{B'} = \begin{bmatrix} 2 \\ 3 \\ 1 \end{bmatrix}$

In Exercises 27 and 28, find the coordinate matrix of $\mathbf{p}$ relative to the standard basis in P_2.

27. $\mathbf{p} = x^2 + 11x + 4$　　　28. $\mathbf{p} = 3x^2 + 114x + 13$

In Exercises 29 and 30, find the coordinate of X relative to the standard basis in $M_{3,1}$.

29. $X = \begin{bmatrix} 0 \\ 3 \\ 2 \end{bmatrix}$　　　30. $X = \begin{bmatrix} 2 \\ -1 \\ 4 \end{bmatrix}$

31. Let P be the transition matrix from B'' to B', and let Q be the transition matrix from B' to B. What is the transition matrix from B'' to B?

32. Let P be the transition matrix from B'' to B', and let Q be the transition matrix from B' to B. What is the transition matrix from B to B''?

▷ 33. Let B and B' be two bases for the vector space R^n. Discuss the nature of the transition matrix from B to B' if one of the bases is the standard basis.

▷ 34. Is it possible for a transition matrix to equal the identity matrix? Illustrate your answer with appropriate examples.

4.8 APPLICATIONS OF VECTOR SPACES

Linear Differential Equations (Calculus)

A **linear differential equation of order n** is of the form

$$y^{(n)} + g_{n-1}(x)y^{(n-1)} + \cdots + g_1(x)y' + g_0(x)y = f(x),$$

where $g_0, g_1, \ldots, g_n$, and f are functions of x with a common domain. If $f(x) = 0$, the equation is **homogeneous**. Otherwise it is **nonhomogeneous**. A function y is called a **solution** of the linear differential equation if the equation is satisfied when y and its first n derivatives are substituted into the equation.

EXAMPLE 1   *A Second-Order Linear Differential Equation*

Show that both $y_1 = e^x$ and $y_2 = e^{-x}$ are solutions of the second-order linear differential equation $y'' - y = 0$.

Solution   For the function $y_1 = e^x$, we have $y_1' = e^x$ and $y_1'' = e^x$. Therefore

$$y_1'' - y_1 = e^x - e^x = 0,$$

and $y_1 = e^x$ is a solution of the given linear differential equation. Similarly, for $y_2 = e^{-x}$, we have $y_2' = -e^{-x}$ and $y_2'' = e^{-x}$. This implies that

$$y_2'' - y_2 = e^{-x} - e^{-x} = 0.$$

Therefore $y_2 = e^{-x}$ is also a solution of the given linear differential equation.

There are two important observations that we can make about Example 1. The first is that in the vector space $C''(-\infty, \infty)$ of all twice differentiable functions defined on the entire real line, the two solutions $y_1 = e^x$ and $y_2 = e^{-x}$ are *linearly independent*. This means that the only solution of

$$C_1 y_1 + C_2 y_2 = 0$$

that is valid for all x is $C_1 = C_2 = 0$. The second observation is that every *linear combination* of y_1 and y_2 is also a solution of the given linear differential equation. To see this, let $y = C_1 y_1 + C_2 y_2$. Then

$$y = C_1 e^x + C_2 e^{-x}$$
$$y' = C_1 e^x - C_2 e^{-x}$$
$$y'' = C_1 e^x + C_2 e^{-x}.$$

Substituting into the differential equation $y'' - y = 0$ produces

$$y'' - y = (C_1 e^x + C_2 e^{-x}) - (C_1 e^x + C_2 e^{-x}) = 0.$$

Thus $y = C_1 e^x + C_2 e^{-x}$ is a solution.

These two observations are generalized in the following theorem, which we state without proof.

Solutions of a Linear Homogeneous Differential Equation

Every nth-order linear homogeneous differential equation

$$y^{(n)} + g_{n-1}(x)y^{(n-1)} + \cdots + g_1(x)y' + g_0(x)y = 0.$$

has n linearly independent solutions. Moreover, if $\{y_1, y_2, \ldots, y_n\}$ is a set of linearly independent solutions, then every solution is of the form

$$y = C_1 y_1 + C_2 y_2 + \cdots + C_n y_n,$$

where $C_1, C_2, \ldots,$ and C_n are real numbers.

REMARK: We call $y = C_1y_1 + C_2y_2 + \cdots + C_ny_n$ the **general solution** of the given differential equation.

In light of the preceding theorem, you can see the importance of being able to determine whether a set of solutions is linearly independent. Before describing a way of testing for linear independence, we give a preliminary definition.

Definition of the Wronskian of a Set of Functions	Let $\{y_1, y_2, \ldots, y_n\}$ be a set of functions each of which possesses $n - 1$ derivatives on an interval I. The determinant

$$W(y_1, y_2, \ldots, y_n) = \begin{vmatrix} y_1 & y_2 & \cdots & y_n \\ y_1' & y_2' & \cdots & y_n' \\ \vdots & \vdots & & \vdots \\ y_1^{(n-1)} & y_2^{(n-1)} & \cdots & y_n^{(n-1)} \end{vmatrix}$$

is called the **Wronskian** of the given set of functions.

REMARK: The Wronskian of a set of functions is named after the Polish mathematician Josef Maria Wronski (1778–1853).

EXAMPLE 2   *Finding the Wronskian of a Set of Functions*

(a) The Wronskian of the set $\{1 - x, 1 + x, 2 - x\}$ is

$$W = \begin{vmatrix} 1 - x & 1 + x & 2 - x \\ -1 & 1 & -1 \\ 0 & 0 & 0 \end{vmatrix}$$

$$= 0.$$

(b) The Wronskian of the set $\{x, x^2, x^3\}$ is

$$W = \begin{vmatrix} x & x^2 & x^3 \\ 1 & 2x & 3x^2 \\ 0 & 2 & 6x \end{vmatrix}$$

$$= 2x^3.$$

The Wronskian in part (a) of Example 2 is said to be **identically equal to zero,** because it is zero for any value of x. The Wronskian in part (b) is not identically equal to zero because values of x exist for which this Wronskian is nonzero.

The following theorem shows how the Wronskian of a set of functions can be used to test for linear independence.

Wronskian Test for Linear Independence	Let $\{y_1, y_2, \ldots, y_n\}$ be a set of n solutions of an nth-order linear homogeneous differential equation. This set is linearly independent if and only if the Wronskian is not identically equal to zero.

REMARK: This test does *not* apply to an arbitrary set of functions. Each of the functions $y_1, y_2, \ldots,$ and y_n must be a solution of the same linear homogeneous differential equation of order n.

EXAMPLE 3   *Testing a Set of Solutions for Linear Independence*

Determine whether $\{1, \cos x, \sin x\}$ is a set of linearly independent solutions of the linear homogeneous differential equation

$$y''' + y' = 0.$$

Solution   We begin by observing that each of the given functions is a solution of $y''' + y' = 0$. (Try checking this.) Next, testing for linear independence produces the Wronskian of the three functions as follows.

$$W = \begin{vmatrix} 1 & \cos x & \sin x \\ 0 & -\sin x & \cos x \\ 0 & -\cos x & -\sin x \end{vmatrix} = \sin^2 x + \cos^2 x = 1$$

Since W is not identically equal to zero, we conclude that the set $\{1, \cos x, \sin x\}$ is linearly independent. Moreover, because this set consists of three linearly independent solutions of a third-order linear homogeneous differential equation, we conclude that the general solution is

$$y = C_1 + C_2 \cos x + C_3 \sin x.$$

EXAMPLE 4   *Testing a Set of Solutions for Linear Independence*

Determine whether $\{e^x, xe^x, (x+1)e^x\}$ is a set of linearly independent solutions of the linear homogeneous differential equation

$$y''' - 3y'' + 3y' - y = 0.$$

Solution   As in Example 3, we begin by verifying that each of the given functions is actually a solution of $y''' - 3y'' + 3y' - y = 0$. (We leave this verification to you.) Testing for linear independence produces the Wronskian of the three functions as follows.

$$W = \begin{vmatrix} e^x & xe^x & (x+1)e^x \\ e^x & (x+1)e^x & (x+2)e^x \\ e^x & (x+2)e^x & (x+3)e^x \end{vmatrix} = 0$$

Thus the set $\{e^x, xe^x, (x+1)e^x\}$ is linearly dependent.

In Example 4, we used the Wronskian to determine that the set $\{e^x, xe^x, (x+1)e^x\}$ is linearly dependent. Another way to determine the linear dependence of this set is to observe that the third function is a linear combination of the first two. That is, $(x+1)e^x = e^x + xe^x$. Try showing that the different set

$$\{e^x, xe^x, x^2 e^x\}$$

forms a linearly independent set of solutions of the differential equation $y''' - 3y'' + 3y' - y = 0$.

Conic Sections and Rotation

Every conic section in the xy-plane has an equation of the form

$$ax^2 + bxy + cy^2 + dx + ey + f = 0.$$

Identifying the graph of this equation is fairly simple so long as b, the coefficient of the xy-term, is zero. In such cases the conic axes are parallel to the coordinate axes, and the indentification is accomplished by writing the equation in standard (completed square) form. The standard forms of the equations of the four basic conics are given in the following summary. For circles, ellipses, and hyperbolas, the point (h, k) is the center. For parabolas, the point (h, k) is the vertex.

Standard Forms of Equations of Conics

Circle (r = radius):

$$(x - h)^2 + (y - k)^2 = r^2$$

Ellipse (2α = major axis length, 2β = minor axis length):

Hyperbola (2α = transverse axis length, 2β = conjugate axis length):

Standard Forms of Equations of Conics (Continued)

Parabola (p = directed distance from vertex to focus):

$$(x - h)^2 = 4p(y - k)$$

$$(y - k)^2 = 4p(x - h)$$

EXAMPLE 5   **Identifying Conic Sections**

(a) The standard form of $x^2 - 2x + 4y - 3 = 0$ is

$$(x - 1)^2 = 4(-1)(y - 1).$$

Thus the graph of this equation is a parabola with the vertex at $(h, k) = (1, 1)$. The axis of the parabola is vertical. Since $p = -1$, the focus is the point $(1, 0)$. Finally, since the focus lies below the vertex, the parabola opens downward, as shown in Figure 4.15(a).

(b) The standard form of $x^2 + 4y^2 + 6x - 8y + 9 = 0$ is

$$\frac{(x + 3)^2}{2^2} + \frac{(y - 1)^2}{1^2} = 1.$$

Thus the graph of this equation is an ellipse with its center at $(h, k) = (-3, 1)$. The major axis is horizontal, and its length is $2\alpha = 4$. The length of the minor axis is $2\beta = 2$. The vertices of this ellipse occur at $(-5, 1)$ and $(-1, 1)$, and the endpoints of the minor axis occur at $(-3, 2)$ and $(-3, 0)$, as shown in Figure 4.15(b).

Figure 4.15

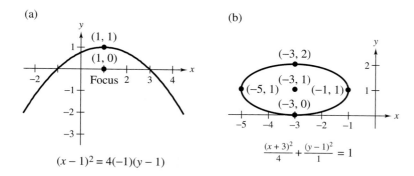

(a) $(x - 1)^2 = 4(-1)(y - 1)$

(b) $\dfrac{(x + 3)^2}{4} + \dfrac{(y - 1)^2}{1} = 1$

Figure 4.16

The equations of the conics in Example 5 have no xy-term. Consequently, the axes of the corresponding conics are parallel to the coordinate axes. For second-degree polynomial equations that have an xy-term, the axes of the corresponding conics are not parallel to the coordinate axes. In such cases it is helpful to *rotate* the standard axes to form a new x'-axis and y'-axis. The required rotation angle θ (measured counter-clockwise) is given by $\cot 2\theta = (a - c)/b$. With this rotation, the standard basis in the plane

$$B = \{(1, 0), (0, 1)\}$$

is rotated to form the new basis

$$B' = \{(\cos \theta, \sin \theta), (-\sin \theta, \cos \theta)\}$$

as shown in Figure 4.16.

To find the coordinates of a point (x, y) relative to this new basis, we can use a transition matrix, as demonstrated in Example 6.

EXAMPLE 6   **A Transition Matrix for Rotation in the Plane**

Find the coordinates of a point (x, y) in R^2 relative to the basis

$$B' = \{(\cos \theta, \sin \theta), (-\sin \theta, \cos \theta)\}.$$

Solution   By Theorem 4.21 we have

$$[B' \vdots B] = \begin{bmatrix} \cos \theta & -\sin \theta & \vdots & 1 & 0 \\ \sin \theta & \cos \theta & \vdots & 0 & 1 \end{bmatrix},$$

which reduces to the form

$$[I \vdots P^{-1}] = \begin{bmatrix} 1 & 0 & \vdots & \cos \theta & \sin \theta \\ 0 & 1 & \vdots & -\sin \theta & \cos \theta \end{bmatrix}.$$

By letting $[x', y']^T$ be the coordinates of (x, y) relative to B', we can use the transition matrix P^{-1} as follows.

$$\begin{bmatrix} \cos \theta & \sin \theta \\ -\sin \theta & \cos \theta \end{bmatrix} \begin{bmatrix} x \\ y \end{bmatrix} = \begin{bmatrix} x' \\ y' \end{bmatrix}$$

Thus the x' and y' coordinates are given by

$$\begin{aligned} x' &= x \cos \theta + y \sin \theta \\ y' &= -x \sin \theta + y \cos \theta. \end{aligned}$$

The last two equations in Example 6 give the $x'y'$-coordinates in terms of the xy-coordinates. To perform a rotation of axes for a second-degree polynomial equation, it is helpful to express the xy-coordinates in terms of the $x'y'$-coordinates. To do this, we solve the last two equations in Example 6 for x and y to obtain

$$x = x' \cos \theta - y' \sin \theta \quad \text{and} \quad y = x' \sin \theta + y' \cos \theta.$$

Substituting these expressions for x and y into the given second-degree equation produces a second-degree polynomial equation in x' and y' that has no $x'y'$-term.

Rotation of Axes

The second-degree equation $ax^2 + bxy + cy^2 + dx + ey + f = 0$ can be written in the form

$$a'(x')^2 + c'(y')^2 + d'x' + e'y' + f' = 0$$

by rotating the coordinate axes counterclockwise through the angle θ, where θ is defined by $\cot 2\theta = (a - c)/b$. The coefficients of the new equation are obtained from the substitutions

$$x = x' \cos \theta - y' \sin \theta$$
$$y = x' \sin \theta + y' \cos \theta.$$

REMARK: When we solve for $\sin \theta$ and $\cos \theta$, the trigonometric identity $\cot 2\theta = (\cot^2 \theta - 1)/(2 \cot \theta)$ is often useful.

Example 7 demonstrates how to identify the graph of a second-degree polynomial by rotating the coordinate axes.

EXAMPLE 7   *Rotation of a Conic Section*

Perform a rotation of axes to eliminate the xy-term in

$$5x^2 - 6xy + 5y^2 + 14\sqrt{2}x - 2\sqrt{2}y + 18 = 0,$$

and sketch the graph of the resulting equation in the $x'y'$-plane.

Solution   The angle of rotation is given by

$$\cot 2\theta = \frac{a - c}{b} = 0.$$

This implies that $\theta = \pi/4$. Thus

$$\sin \theta = \frac{1}{\sqrt{2}} \quad \text{and} \quad \cos \theta = \frac{1}{\sqrt{2}}.$$

By substituting

$$x = x' \cos \theta - y' \sin \theta = \frac{1}{\sqrt{2}}(x' - y')$$

and

$$y = x' \sin \theta + y' \cos \theta = \frac{1}{\sqrt{2}}(x' + y')$$

into the original equation and simplifying, we obtain

$$(x')^2 + 4(y')^2 + 6x' - 8y' + 9 = 0.$$

Finally, by completing the square, we find the standard form of this equation to be

$$\frac{(x' + 3)^2}{2^2} + \frac{(y' - 1)^2}{1^2} = 1,$$

which is the equation of an ellipse, as shown in Figure 4.17.

Figure 4.17

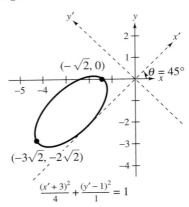

$$\frac{(x' + 3)^2}{4} + \frac{(y' - 1)^2}{1} = 1$$

In Example 7 the new (rotated) basis for R^2 is

$$B' = \left\{ \left(\frac{1}{\sqrt{2}}, \frac{1}{\sqrt{2}} \right), \left(-\frac{1}{\sqrt{2}}, \frac{1}{\sqrt{2}} \right) \right\},$$

and the coordinates of the vertices of the ellipse relative to B' are $[-5, 1]^T$ and $[-1, 1]^T$. To find the coordinates of the vertices relative to the standard basis $B = \{(1, 0), (0, 1)\}$, we use the equations

$$x = \frac{1}{\sqrt{2}}(x' - y') \quad \text{and} \quad y = \frac{1}{\sqrt{2}}(x' + y')$$

to obtain

$$(-3\sqrt{2}, -2\sqrt{2}) \quad \text{and} \quad (-\sqrt{2}, 0),$$

as shown in Figure 4.17.

SECTION 4.8 ☐ EXERCISES

Linear Differential Equations (Calculus)

In Exercises 1–4, determine which functions are solutions of the given linear differential equation.

1. $y'' + y = 0$

(a) e^x (b) $\sin x$ (c) $\cos x$ (d) $\sin x - \cos x$

2. $y''' + 3y'' + 3y' + y = 0$

(a) x (b) e^x (c) e^{-x} (d) xe^{-x}

3. $y'' + 4y' + 4y = 0$

(a) e^{-2x} (b) xe^{-2x} (c) x^2e^{-2x} (d) $(x + 2)e^{-2x}$

4. $y'''' - 2y''' + y'' = 0$

(a) 1 (b) x (c) x^2 (d) e^x

In Exercises 5–8, find the Wronskian for the given set of functions.

5. $\{e^x, e^{-x}\}$ **6.** $\{x, \sin x, \cos x\}$

7. $\{e^{-x}, xe^{-x}, (x + 3)e^{-x}\}$ **8.** $\{1, e^x, e^{2x}\}$

In Exercises 9–16, test the given set of solutions for linear independence.

Differential Equation	Solutions
9. $y'' + y = 0$	$\{\sin x, \cos x\}$
10. $y'' + 4y' + 4y = 0$	$\{e^{-2x}, xe^{-2x}\}$
11. $y''' + 4y'' + 4y' = 0$	$\{e^{-2x}, xe^{-2x}, (2x + 1)e^{-2x}\}$
12. $y'' + y' = 0$	$\{1, \sin x, \cos x\}$
13. $y'' + y' = 0$	$\{2, -1 + 2\sin x, 1 + \sin x\}$
14. $y''' + 3y'' + 3y' + y = 0$	$\{e^{-x}, xe^{-x}, x^2e^{-x}\}$
15. $y''' + 3y'' + 3y' + y = 0$	$\{e^{-x}, xe^{-x}, e^{-x} + xe^{-x}\}$
16. $y'''' - 2y''' + y'' = 0$	$\{1, x, e^x, xe^x\}$

17. Find the general solution of the differential equation given in Exercise 9.

18. Find the general solution of the differential equation given in Exercise 10.

19. Find the general solution of the differential equation given in Exercise 12.

20. Find the general solution of the differential equation given in Exercise 16.

21. Prove that $y = C_1 \cos ax + C_2 \sin ax$ is the general solution of $y'' + a^2 y = 0$, $a \neq 0$.

22. Prove that the set $\{e^{ax}, e^{bx}\}$ is linearly independent if and only if $a \neq b$.

23. Prove that the set $\{e^a x, xe^{ax}\}$ is linearly independent.

24. Prove that the set $\{e^{ax} \cos bx, e^{ax} \sin bx\}$, where $b \neq 0$, is linearly independent.

25. Is the sum of two solutions of a nonhomogeneous linear differential equation also a solution? Explain your answer.

26. Is the scalar multiple of a solution of a nonhomogeneous linear differential equation also a solution? Explain your answer.

Conic Sections and Rotation

In Exercises 27–36, identify and sketch the graph of the given equation.

27. $y^2 + x = 0$ **28.** $5x^2 + 3y^2 - 15 = 0$

29. $\dfrac{x^2}{9} - \dfrac{y^2}{16} - 1 = 0$ **30.** $x^2 - 2x + 8y + 17 = 0$

31. $9x^2 + 25y^2 - 36x - 50y + 61 = 0$

32. $9x^2 - y^2 + 54x + 10y + 55 = 0$

33. $x^2 + 4y^2 + 4x + 32y + 64 = 0$

34. $2x^2 - y^2 + 4x + 10y - 22 = 0$

35. $x^2 + 4x + 6y - 2 = 0$ **36.** $y^2 + 8x + 6y + 25 = 0$

In Exercises 37–44, perform a rotation of axes to eliminate the xy-term, and sketch the graph of the conic.

37. $xy + 1 = 0$ **38.** $4x^2 + 2xy + 4y^2 - 15 = 0$

39. $5x^2 - 2xy + 5y^2 - 24 = 0$

40. $x^2 + 2xy + y^2 - 8x + 8y = 0$

41. $13x^2 + 6\sqrt{3}\, xy + 7y^2 - 16 = 0$

42. $3x^2 - 2\sqrt{3}\, xy + y^2 + 2x + 2\sqrt{3}\, y = 0$

43. $x^2 + 2\sqrt{3}\, xy + 3y^2 - 2\sqrt{3}\, x + 2y + 16 = 0$

44. $7x^2 - 2\sqrt{3}\, xy + 5y^2 = 16$

In Exercises 45 and 46, perform a rotation of axes to eliminate the xy-term and sketch the graph of the "degenerate" conic.

45. $x^2 - 2xy + y^2 = 0$ **46.** $5x^2 - 2xy + 5y^2 = 0$

47. Prove that a rotation of $\theta = \pi/4$ will eliminate the xy-term from the equation
$$ax^2 + bxy + ay^2 + dx + ey + f = 0.$$

48. Prove that a rotation of θ, where $\cot 2\theta = (a - c)/b$, will eliminate the xy-term from the equation
$$ax^2 + bxy + cy^2 + dx + ey + f = 0.$$

49. For the equation $ax^2 + bxy + cy^2 = 0$, define the matrix A to be
$$A = \begin{bmatrix} a & b/2 \\ b/2 & c \end{bmatrix}.$$
Prove that if $|A| \neq 0$, then the graph of $ax^2 + bxy + cy^2 = 0$ is two intersecting lines.

50. In Exercise 49, let $|A| = 0$ and describe the graph of $ax^2 + bxy + cy^2 = 0$.

CHAPTER 4 ☐ REVIEW EXERCISES

In Exercises 1–4, find (a) $\mathbf{u} + \mathbf{v}$, (b) $2\mathbf{v}$, (c) $\mathbf{u} - \mathbf{v}$, and (d) $3\mathbf{u} - 2\mathbf{v}$.

1. $\mathbf{u} = (-1, 2, 3)$, $\mathbf{v} = (1, 0, 2)$

2. $\mathbf{u} = (-1, 2, 1)$, $\mathbf{v} = (0, 1, 1)$

3. $\mathbf{u} = (3, -1, 2, 3)$, $\mathbf{v} = (0, 2, 2, 1)$

4. $\mathbf{u} = (0, 1, -1, 2)$, $\mathbf{v} = (1, 0, 0, 2)$

In Exercises 5 and 6, solve for $\mathbf{x}$ given that $\mathbf{u} = (1, -1, 2)$, $\mathbf{v} = (0, 2, 3)$, and $\mathbf{w} = (0, 1, 1)$.

5. $2\mathbf{x} - \mathbf{u} + 3\mathbf{v} + \mathbf{w} = \mathbf{0}$ **6.** $3\mathbf{x} + 2\mathbf{u} - \mathbf{v} + 2\mathbf{w} = \mathbf{0}$

In Exercises 7 and 8, write $\mathbf{v}$ as a linear combination of $\mathbf{u}_1$, $\mathbf{u}_2$, and $\mathbf{u}_3$, if possible.

7. $\mathbf{v} = (1, 2, 3, 5)$, $\mathbf{u}_1 = (1, 2, 3, 4)$, $\mathbf{u}_2 = (-1, -2, -3, 4)$, $\mathbf{u}_3 = (0, 0, 1, 1)$

8. $\mathbf{v} = (4, 4, 5)$, $\mathbf{u}_1 = (1, 2, 3)$, $\mathbf{u}_2 = (-2, 0, 1)$, $\mathbf{u}_3 = (1, 0, 0)$

In Exercises 9 and 10, describe the zero vector and the additive inverse of a vector in the given vector space.

9. $M_{3,4}$ **10.** P_8

In Exercises 11–16, determine whether W is a subspace of the given vector space.

11. $W = \{(x, y): x = 2y\}$, $V = R^2$

12. $W = \{(x, y): x - y = 1\}$, $V = R^2$

13. $W = \{(x, 2x, 3x): x \text{ is a real number}\}$, $V = R^3$

14. $W = \{(x, y, z): x \geq 0\}$, $V = R^3$

15. $W = \{f: f(0) = -1\}$, $V = C[-1, 1]$

16. $W = \{f: f(-1) = 0\}$, $V = C[-1, 1]$

17. Which of the following subsets of R^3 is a subspace of R^3?

  (a) $W = \{(x_1, x_2, x_3): x_1{}^2 + x_2{}^2 + x_3{}^2 = 0\}$

  (b) $W = \{(x_1, x_2, x_3): x_1{}^2 + x_2{}^2 + x_3{}^2 = 1\}$

18. Which of the following subsets of R^3 is a subspace of R^3?

  (a) $W = \{(x_1, x_2, x_3): x_1 + x_2 + x_3 = 0\}$

  (b) $W = \{(x_1, x_2, x_3): x_1 + x_2 + x_3 = 1\}$

In Exercises 19–24, determine whether S (a) spans R^3, (b) is linearly independent, and (c) is a basis for R^3.

19. $S = \{(1, -2, 7), (-5, 6, 4), (3, 6, -9), (5, 1, 2)\}$

20. $S = \{(4, -5, 6), (1, 3, 9)\}$

21. $S = \{(1, -5, 4), (11, 6, -1), (2, 3, 5)\}$

22. $S = \{(4, 0, 1), (0, -3, 2), (5, 10, 0)\}$

23. $S = \{(-\frac{1}{2}, \frac{3}{4}, -1), (5, 2, 3), (-4, 6, -8)\}$

24. $S = \{(1, 0, 0), (0, 1, 0), (0, 0, 1), (-1, 2, -3)\}$

25. Determine whether $S = \{1 - t, 2t + 3t^2, t^2 - 2t^3, 2 + t^3\}$ is a basis for P_3.

26. Determine whether the following set is a basis for $M_{2,2}$.

$$S = \left\{ \begin{bmatrix} 1 & 0 \\ 2 & 3 \end{bmatrix}, \begin{bmatrix} -2 & 1 \\ -1 & 0 \end{bmatrix}, \begin{bmatrix} 3 & 4 \\ 2 & 3 \end{bmatrix}, \begin{bmatrix} -3 & -3 \\ 1 & 3 \end{bmatrix} \right\}$$

In Exercises 27 and 28, find (a) a basis and (b) the dimension of the solution space of the homogeneous system of equations.

27. $2x_1 + 4x_2 + 3x_3 - 6x_4 = 0$

  $x_1 + 2x_2 + 2x_3 - 5x_4 = 0$

  $3x_1 + 6x_2 + 5x_3 - 11x_4 = 0$

28. $3x_1 + 8x_2 + 2x_3 + 3x_4 = 0$

  $4x_1 + 6x_2 + 2x_3 - x_4 = 0$

  $3x_1 + 4x_2 + x_3 - 3x_4 = 0$

In Exercises 29–32, find a basis for the solution space of $Ax = 0$. Then verify that rank(A) + nullity(A) = n.

29. $A = \begin{bmatrix} 5 & -8 \\ -10 & 16 \end{bmatrix}$ **30.** $A = \begin{bmatrix} 1 & 4 \\ 3 & 2 \end{bmatrix}$

31. $A = \begin{bmatrix} 2 & -3 & -6 & -4 \\ 1 & 5 & -3 & 11 \\ 2 & 7 & -6 & 16 \end{bmatrix}$ **32.** $A = \begin{bmatrix} 1 & 3 & 2 \\ 4 & -1 & -18 \\ -1 & 3 & 10 \\ 1 & 2 & 0 \end{bmatrix}$

In Exercises 33–36, find (a) the rank and (b) a basis for the row space of the given matrix.

33. $\begin{bmatrix} 1 & 2 \\ -4 & 3 \\ 6 & 1 \end{bmatrix}$ **34.** $\begin{bmatrix} 2 & -1 & 4 \\ 1 & 5 & 6 \\ 1 & 16 & 14 \end{bmatrix}$

35. $\begin{bmatrix} 7 & 0 & 2 \\ 4 & 1 & 6 \\ -1 & 16 & 14 \end{bmatrix}$ **36.** $\begin{bmatrix} 1 & -4 & 0 & 4 \end{bmatrix}$

In Exercises 37–40, find the coordinate matrix of x relative to the standard basis.

37. $B = \{(1, 1), (-1, 1)\}, \quad [x]_B = [3, 5]^T$

38. $B = \{(2, 0), (3, 3)\}, \quad [x]_B = [1, 1]^T$

39. $B = \{(1, 0, 0), (1, 1, 0), (0, 1, 1)\}, \quad [x]_B = [2, 0, -1]^T$

40. $B = \{(\frac{1}{2}, \frac{1}{2}), (1, 0)\}, \quad [x]_B = [\frac{1}{2}, \frac{1}{2}]^T$

In Exercises 41–44, find the coordinate matrix of x relative to the given (nonstandard) basis for R^n.

41. $B' = \{(5, 0), (0, -8)\}, \quad x = (2, 2)$

42. $B' = \{(1, 2, 3), (1, 2, 0), (0, -6, 2)\}, \quad x = (3, -3, 0)$

43. $B' = \{(9, -3, 15, 4), (-3, 0, 0, -1), (0, -5, 6, 8), (-3, 4, -2, 3)\}, \quad x = (21, -5, 43, 14)$

44. $B' = \{(1, 0, 0), (0, 1, 0), (1, 1, 1)\}, \quad x = (4, -2, 9)$

In Exercises 45 and 46, find the coordinate matrix of x relative to the basis B'.

45. $B = \{(1, 1), (-1, 1)\}, \quad B' = \{(0, 1), (1, 2)\}, \quad [x]_B = [3, -3]^T$

46. $B = \{(1, 0, 0), (1, 1, 0), (1, 1, 1)\}, \quad B' = \{(0, 0, 1), (0, 1, 1), (1, 1, 1)\}, \quad [x]_B = [-1, 2, -3]^T$

In Exercises 47–50, find the transition matrix from B to B'.

47. $B = \{(1, -1), (3, 1)\}, \quad B' = \{(1, 0), (0, 1)\}$

48. $B = \{(1, 0, 0), (0, 1, 0), (0, 0, 1)\}, \quad B' = \{(0, 0, 1), (0, 1, 0), (1, 0, 0)\}$

49. $B = \{(1, -1), (3, 1)\}, \quad B' = \{(1, 2), (-1, 0)\}$

50. $B = \{(1, 1, 1), (1, 1, 0), (1, 0, 0)\}, \quad B' = \{(1, 2, 3), (0, 1, 0), (1, 0, 1)\}$

51. Let W be the subspace of P_3 of all polynomials such that $p(0) = 0$, and let U be the subspace of all polynomials such that $p(1) = 0$. Find a basis for W, a basis for U, and a basis for their intersection $W \cap U$.

52. (Calculus) Let $V = C'(-\infty, \infty)$, the vector space of all continuously differentiable functions on the real line.

  (a) Prove that $W = \{f: f' = 3f\}$ is a subspace of V.

  (b) Prove that $U = \{f: f' = f + 1\}$ is not a subspace of V.

53. Let $B = \{p_1(x), p_2(x), \ldots, p_n(x), p_{n+1}(x)\}$ be a basis for P_n. Must B contain a polynomial of each degree 0, 1, 2, $\ldots$, n? Explain your reasoning.

54. Let A and B be $n \times n$ matrices with $A \neq O$ and $B \neq O$. Prove that if A is symmetric and B is skew-symmetric ($B^T = -B$), then $\{A, B\}$ is a linearly independent set.

55. Let $V = P_5$ and consider the set W of all polynomials of the form $(x^3 + x)p(x)$, where $p(x)$ is in P_2. Is W a subspace of V? Prove your answer.

56. Let $\mathbf{v}_1$, $\mathbf{v}_2$, and $\mathbf{v}_3$ be three linearly independent vectors in a vector space V. Is the set $\{\mathbf{v}_1 - \mathbf{v}_2, \mathbf{v}_2 - \mathbf{v}_3, \mathbf{v}_3 - \mathbf{v}_1\}$ linearly dependent or linearly independent?

57. Let A be an $n \times n$ square matrix. Prove that the row vectors of A are linearly dependent if and only if the column vectors of A are linearly dependent.

58. Let A be an $n \times n$ square matrix, and let λ be a scalar. Prove that the set
$$S = \{\mathbf{x}: A\mathbf{x} = \lambda\mathbf{x}\}$$
is a subspace of R^n. Determine the dimension of S if $\lambda = 3$ and
$$A = \begin{bmatrix} 3 & 1 & 0 \\ 0 & 3 & 0 \\ 0 & 0 & 1 \end{bmatrix}.$$

59. Let $f(x) = x$ and $g(x) = |x|$.

    (a) Show that $\mathbf{f}$ and $\mathbf{g}$ are linearly independent in $C[-1, 1]$.

    (b) Show that $\mathbf{f}$ and $\mathbf{g}$ are linearly dependent in $C[0, 1]$.

60. Given a set of functions, describe how their domain can influence whether or not the set is linearly independent or dependent.

Linear Differential Equations (Calculus)

In Exercises 61 and 62, determine which functions are solutions of the given linear differential equation.

61. $y'' - y' - 6y = 0$
    (a) e^{3x} (b) e^{2x} (c) e^{-3x} (d) e^{-2x}

62. $y'''' - y = 0$
    (a) e^x (b) e^{-x} (c) $\cos x$ (d) $\sin x$

In Exercises 63 and 64, find the Wronskian for the given set of functions.

63. $\{1, x, e^x\}$ **64.** $\{1, x, 2 + x\}$

In Exercises 65–68, test the given set of solutions for linear independence.

Differential Equation	Solutions
65. $y'' + 6y' + 9y = 0$	$\{e^{-3x}, xe^{-3x}\}$
66. $y'' + 6y' + 9y = 0$	$\{e^{-3x}, 3e^{-3x}\}$
67. $y''' - 6y'' + 11y' - 6y = 0$	$\{e^x, e^{2x}, e^x - e^{2x}\}$
68. $y'' + 4y = 0$	$\{\sin 2x, \cos 2x\}$

Conic Sections and Rotation

In Exercises 69–72, identify and sketch the graph of the given equation.

69. $x^2 + y^2 - 4x + 2y - 4 = 0$

70. $x^2 - y^2 + 2x - 3 = 0$

71. $2x^2 - 20x - y + 46 = 0$

72. $4x^2 + y^2 + 32x + 4y + 63 = 0$

In Exercises 73 and 74, perform a rotation of axes to eliminate the xy-term, and sketch the graph of the conic.

73. $xy = 3$ **74.** $9x^2 + 4xy + 9y^2 - 20 = 0$

CHAPTER 4   PROJECTS

1   Solutions to Linear Systems

Write a short paragraph to answer each of the following questions about solutions to systems of linear equations. You should not perform any calculations, but instead base your explanations on the appropriate properties from the text.

    1. One solution to the homogeneous linear system
$$\begin{aligned} x + 2y + z + 3w &= 0 \\ x - y \quad\quad + w &= 0 \\ y - z + 2w &= 0 \end{aligned}$$

is $x = -2$, $y = -1$, $z = 1$, and $w = 1$. Explain why $x = 4$, $y = 2$, $z = -2$, and $w = -2$ must also be a solution. Do not perform any row operations!

2. The vectors $\mathbf{x}_1$ and $\mathbf{x}_2$ are solutions to the homogeneous linear system $A\mathbf{x} = \mathbf{0}$. Explain why the vector $2\mathbf{x}_1 - 3\mathbf{x}_2$ must also be a solution.

3. Consider the two system represented by the following augmented matrices.

$$\begin{bmatrix} 1 & 1 & -5 & 3 \\ 1 & 0 & -2 & 1 \\ 2 & -1 & -1 & 0 \end{bmatrix} \qquad \begin{bmatrix} 1 & 1 & -5 & -9 \\ 1 & 0 & -2 & -3 \\ 2 & -1 & -1 & 0 \end{bmatrix}$$

If the first system is known to be consistent, explain why the second system is also consistent. Do not perform any row operations!

4. The vectors $\mathbf{x}_1$ and $\mathbf{x}_2$ are solutions to the linear system $A\mathbf{x} = \mathbf{b}$. Is the vector $2\mathbf{x}_1 - 3\mathbf{x}_2$ also a solution? Why or why not?

5. The linear systems $A\mathbf{x} = \mathbf{b}_1$ and $A\mathbf{x} = \mathbf{b}_2$ are consistent. Is the system $A\mathbf{x} = \mathbf{b}_1 + \mathbf{b}_2$ necessarily consistent? Why or why not?

6. Consider the linear system $A\mathbf{x} = \mathbf{b}$. If the rank of A equals the rank of the augmented matrix for the system, explain why the system must be consistent. Contrast this to the case in which the rank of A is less than the rank of the augmented matrix.

2 Direct Sum

Let U and W be subspaces of the vector space V. You learned in Section 4.3 that the intersection $U \cap W$ is also a subspace of V, whereas the union $U \cup W$ is, in general, not a subspace. In this project you will explore the **sum** and **direct sum** of subspaces, focusing especially on their geometrical interpretation in R^n.

1. Define the sum of the subspaces U and W as follows.

   $U + W = \{\mathbf{u} + \mathbf{w} : \mathbf{u} \in U, \mathbf{w} \in W\}$

   Prove that $U + W$ is a subspace of V.

2. Consider the following subspaces of $V = R^3$.

   $U = \{(x, y, x - y) : x, y \in R\}$
   $W = \{(x, 0, x) : x \in R\}$
   $Z = \{(x, x, x) : x \in R\}$

   Find $U + W$, $U + Z$, and $W + Z$.

3. If U and W are subspaces of V such that $V = U + W$ and $U \cap W = \emptyset$, prove that every vector in V has a *unique* representation of the form $\mathbf{u} + \mathbf{w}$, where $\mathbf{u}$ is in U and $\mathbf{w}$ is in W. In this case, we say that V is the **direct sum** of U and W, and write

   $V = U \oplus W$.   Direct sum

   Which of the sums in part (2) of this project are direct sums?

4. Let $V = U \oplus W$ and suppose that $\{\mathbf{u}_1, \mathbf{u}_2, \ldots, \mathbf{u}_k\}$ is a basis for the subspace U and $\{\mathbf{w}_1, \mathbf{w}_2, \ldots, \mathbf{w}_m\}$ is a basis for the subspace W. Prove that the set

   $\{\mathbf{u}_1, \ldots, \mathbf{u}_k, \mathbf{w}_1, \ldots, \mathbf{w}_m\}$

   is a basis for V.

5. Consider the following subspaces of $V = R^3$.

   $U = \{(x, 0, y) : x, y \in R\}$
   $W = \{(0, x, y) : x, y \in R\}$

Show that $R^3 = U + W$. Is R^3 the *direct* sum of U and W? What are the dimensions of U, W, $U \cap W$, and $U + W$? In general, formulate a conjecture that relates the dimensions of U, W, $U \cap W$, and $U + W$.

6. Can you find two 2-dimensional subspaces of R^3 whose intersection is just the zero vector? Why or why not?

CHAPTER 4 ☐ MATLAB EXERCISES

1. Let $\mathbf{u}_1 = (1, 1, 2, 2)$, $\mathbf{u}_2 = (2, 3, 5, 6)$, and $\mathbf{u}_3 = (2, -1, 3, 6)$. Use MATLAB to write (if possible) the vector $\mathbf{v}$ as a linear combination of the vectors $\mathbf{u}_1$, $\mathbf{u}_2$, and $\mathbf{u}_3$.

    (a) $\mathbf{v} = (0, 5, 3, 0)$

    (b) $\mathbf{v} = (-1, 6, 1, -4)$

2. Use MATLAB to determine whether the given set of vectors spans $\mathbf{R}^4$.

    (a) $\{(1, -2, 3, 4), (2, 4, 5, 0), (-2, 0, 0, 4), (3, 2, 1, -4)\}$

    (b) $\{(0, 1, -1, 1), (2, -2, 3, 1), (7, 0, 1, 0), (5, 2, -2, -1)\}$

3. Use MATLAB to determine whether the set is linearly independent or dependent.

    (a) $\{(0, 1, -3, 4), (-1, 0, 0, 2), (0, 5, 3, 0), (-1, 7, -3, -6)\}$

    (b) $\{(0, 0, 1, 2, 3), (0, 0, 2, 3, 1), (1, 2, 3, 4, 5), (2, 1, 0, 0, 0), (-1, -3, -5, 0, 0)\}$

4. Use MATLAB to determine whether the set of vectors forms a basis of $\mathbf{R}^4$.

    (a) $\{(1, -2, 3, 4), (2, 4, 5, 0), (-2, 0, 0, 4), (3, 2, 1, -4)\}$

    (b) $\{(0, 1, -1, 1), (2, -2, 3, 1), (7, 0, 1, 0), (5, 2, -2, -1)\}$

    (c) $\{(0, 1, -3, 4), (-1, 0, 0, 2), (0, 5, 3, 0), (-1, 7, -3, -6)\}$

    (d) $\{(0, 0, 1, 2), (0, 2, 3, 1), (1, 3, 4, 5), (2, 1, 0, 0), (-3, -5, 0, 0)\}$

5. Suppose you want to find a basis for $\mathbf{R}^4$ that contains the vectors $\mathbf{v}_1 = (1, 1, 0, 0)$ and $\mathbf{v}_2 = (1, 0, 1, 0)$. One way to do this is to consider the set of vectors consisting of $\mathbf{v}_1$ and $\mathbf{v}_2$, together with the standard basis vectors, $\mathbf{e}_1 = (1, 0, 0, 0)$, $\mathbf{e}_2 = (0, 1, 0, 0)$, $\mathbf{e}_3 = (0, 0, 1, 0)$, and $\mathbf{e}_4 = (0, 0, 0, 1)$. Let A be the matrix whose columns consist of the vectors $\mathbf{v}_1$, $\mathbf{v}_2$, $\mathbf{e}_1$, $\mathbf{e}_2$, $\mathbf{e}_3$, and $\mathbf{e}_4$, and apply **rref** to A to obtain

$$A = \begin{bmatrix} 1 & 1 & 1 & 0 & 0 & 0 \\ 1 & 0 & 0 & 1 & 0 & 0 \\ 0 & 1 & 0 & 0 & 1 & 0 \\ 0 & 0 & 0 & 0 & 0 & 1 \end{bmatrix} \longrightarrow \begin{bmatrix} 1 & 0 & 0 & 1 & 0 & 0 \\ 0 & 1 & 0 & 0 & 1 & 0 \\ 0 & 0 & 1 & -1 & -1 & 0 \\ 0 & 0 & 0 & 0 & 0 & 1 \end{bmatrix}.$$

Since the leading ones of the reduced matrix on the right are in columns 1, 2, 3, and 6, a basis for $\mathbf{R}^4$ consists of the corresponding column vectors of A: $\{\mathbf{v}_1, \mathbf{v}_2, \mathbf{e}_1, \mathbf{e}_4\}$.

A convenient way to construct the matrix A is to define the matrix B whose columns are the given vectors $\mathbf{v}_1$ and $\mathbf{v}_2$. Then A is simply the matrix obtained by adjoining the 4×4 identity matrix to B: $A = [B \quad \text{eye}(4)]$.

Use this algorithm to find a basis for $\mathbf{R}^5$ that contains the given vectors.

    (a) $\mathbf{v}_1 = (2, 1, 0, 0, 0)$, $\mathbf{v}_2 = (-1, 0, 1, 0, 0)$

    (b) $\mathbf{v}_1 = (1, 0, 2, 0, 0)$, $\mathbf{v}_2 = (1, 1, 2, 0, 0)$, $\mathbf{v}_3 = (1, 1, 1, 0, 1)$

6. Use MATLAB to find a subset of the given set of vectors that forms a basis for the span of the vectors.

(a) $\{(1, 2, -1, 0), (-3, -6, 3, 0), (1, 0, 0, 1), (-2, -2, 1, -1)\}$

(b) $\{(0, 0, 1, 1, 0), (1, 1, 0, 0, 1), (1, 1, 1, 1, 1), (1, 1, 2, 2, 1), (0, 0, 3, 3, 1), (0, 0, 0, 0, 1)\}$

7. Let

$$A = \begin{bmatrix} -1 & 2 & 0 & 0 & 3 \\ 0 & 2 & 3 & -1 & 2 \\ -1 & 4 & 3 & -1 & 5 \\ 2 & -4 & 0 & 0 & -6 \\ 0 & 0 & 0 & 1 & 1 \end{bmatrix}.$$

(a) Find a basis for the row space of A.

(b) Find a basis for the column space of A.

(c) Use the MATLAB command **rank** to find the rank of A.

8. Find a basis for the nullspace of the given matrix A. Then verify that the sum of the rank and nullity of A equals the number of columns.

(a) $A = \begin{bmatrix} 1 & 2 & 3 & 4 \\ 5 & 6 & 7 & 8 \\ 9 & 10 & 11 & 12 \\ 13 & 14 & 15 & 16 \end{bmatrix}$

(b) $A = \text{hilb}(5)$

(c) $A = \text{pascal}(5)$

(d) $A = \text{magic}(6)$

9. Let $\{(1, 0, 1), (0, -1, 2), (2, 3, -5)\}$ be a (nonstandard) basis for $\mathbf{R}^3$. You can find the coordinate matrix of $\mathbf{x} = (1, 2, -1)$ relative to this basis by writing $\mathbf{x}$ as a linear combination of the basis vectors. That is, the coordinate matrix is the solution vector to the linear system $B\mathbf{c} = \mathbf{x}$, where the basis vectors form the columns of B. Use MATLAB to solve this system and compare your answer to Section 4.7, Example 3.

10. Let $B = \{(1, 0, 0), (0, 1, 0), (0, 0, 1)\}$ and $B1 = \{(1, 0, 1), (0, -1, 2), (2, 3, -5)\}$ be the two bases of R^3 given in Section 4.7, Example 4. We can use MATLAB to find the transition matrix from B to $B1$ by first forming the two matrices

$$B = \begin{bmatrix} 1 & 0 & 0 \\ 0 & 1 & 0 \\ 0 & 0 & 1 \end{bmatrix} \quad \text{and} \quad B1 = \begin{bmatrix} 1 & 0 & 2 \\ 0 & -1 & 3 \\ 1 & 2 & -5 \end{bmatrix}.$$

Adjoin B and $B1$ by using the MATLAB command $\mathbf{C = [B1 \quad B]}$. Let A be the reduced row-echelon form of C, $\mathbf{A = rref(C)}$. Finally, $PINV = P^{-1}$ is obtained by deleting the first three columns of this reduced matrix using the MATLAB command $\mathbf{PINV = A(:,4:6)}$. You obtain P simply by inverting $PINV$.

Find the transition matrix from B to $B1$.

(a) $B = \{(-3, 2), (4, -2)\}$, $B1 = \{(-1, 2), (2, -2)\}$.

(b) $B = \{(1, 1, 1, 1), (0, 1, 1, 1), (0, 0, 1, 1), (0, 0, 0, 1)\}$,

   $B1 = \{(1, 0, 1, 0), (1, 0, -1, 0), (0, 1, 0, 1), (0, 1, 0, -1)\}$

5 INNER PRODUCT SPACES

Jean-Baptiste Joseph Fourier

1 7 6 8 – 1 8 3 0

Jean-Baptiste Joseph Fourier was born in Auxerre, France. Orphaned at the age of eight, he entered a local military college run by Benedictines. After the revolution he returned to the military academy at Auxerre as a professor of mathematics. Fourier soon gained a reputation as a gifted teacher and mathematician.

When Napoleon created the École Normale in 1794, he appointed Fourier to the chair of mathematics. Fourier's innovative approach to education brought rapid success, and before long the college (now called the Polytechnique) was graduating talented scientists, engineers, and mathematicians.

In 1798 Fourier accompanied Napoleon as the French invaded Egypt. He remained in Egypt, founding schools and teaching, until 1801, when he returned to France to accept a governmental position at Grenoble. There, in addition to doing his administrative work, Fourier conducted research in mathematical physics and wrote one of his most famous papers, *The Mathematical Theory of Heat,* 1811, which was awarded the Grand Prize by the Academy of Sciences of Paris.

In 1822 Fourier published a classic text, which has the same title as his earlier paper on heat. This work contains many important results dealing with differential equations, eigenvalues, and representation of functions by trigonometric series (later called Fourier series). His work with Fourier series forced mathematicians to reconsider the then accepted, but narrow, definition of a function.

In 1824 Fourier was appointed secretary of the Academy of Sciences, a position he held until his death in 1830.

5.1 LENGTH AND DOT PRODUCT IN R^n

Section 4.1 mentioned that vectors in the plane can be characterized as directed line segments having a certain *length* and *direction*. In this section we use R^2 as a model to define these and other geometric properties (such as distance and angle) for vectors in R^n. Then in the next section these ideas are extended to general vector spaces.

We begin by reviewing the definition of the length of a vector in R^2. If $\mathbf{v} = (v_1, v_2)$ is a vector in the plane, then the **length** of $\mathbf{v}$, denoted by $\|\mathbf{v}\|$, is defined to be

$$\|\mathbf{v}\| = \sqrt{v_1{}^2 + v_2{}^2}.$$

This definition corresponds to the usual notion of length in Euclidean geometry. That is, the vector $\mathbf{v}$ is thought of as the hypotenuse of a right triangle whose sides have lengths of $|v_1|$ and $|v_2|$, as shown in Figure 5.1. Applying the Pythagorean Theorem produces

$$\|\mathbf{v}\|^2 = |v_1|^2 + |v_2|^2 = v_1{}^2 + v_2{}^2.$$

Using R^2 as a model, we define the length of a vector in R^n as follows.

Figure 5.1

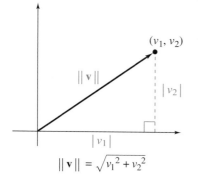

$$\|\mathbf{v}\| = \sqrt{v_1{}^2 + v_2{}^2}$$

Definition of Length of a Vector in R^n	The **length** of a vector $\mathbf{v} = (v_1, v_2, \ldots, v_n)$ in R^n is given by $$\|\mathbf{v}\| = \sqrt{v_1^2 + v_2^2 + \cdots + v_n^2}.$$

REMARK: The length of a vector is also called its **norm**. If $\|\mathbf{v}\| = 1$, then the vector $\mathbf{v}$ is called a **unit vector**.

This definition shows that the length of a vector cannot be negative. That is, $\|\mathbf{v}\| \geq 0$. Moreover, $\|\mathbf{v}\| = 0$ if and only if $\mathbf{v}$ is the zero vector $\mathbf{0}$.

EXAMPLE 1   *The Length of a Vector in R^n*

(a) In R^5, the length of $\mathbf{v} = (0, -2, 1, 4, -2)$ is given by
$$\|\mathbf{v}\| = \sqrt{0^2 + (-2)^2 + 1^2 + 4^2 + (-2)^2} = \sqrt{25} = 5.$$

(b) In R^3, the length of $\mathbf{v} = (2/\sqrt{17}, -2/\sqrt{17}, 3/\sqrt{17})$ is given by
$$\|\mathbf{v}\| = \sqrt{\left(\frac{2}{\sqrt{17}}\right)^2 + \left(-\frac{2}{\sqrt{17}}\right)^2 + \left(\frac{3}{\sqrt{17}}\right)^2} = \sqrt{\frac{17}{17}} = 1.$$

Because its length is 1, $\mathbf{v}$ is a unit vector, as shown in Figure 5.2.

Figure 5.2

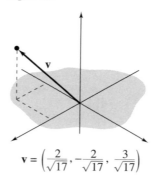

$$\mathbf{v} = \left(\frac{2}{\sqrt{17}}, -\frac{2}{\sqrt{17}}, \frac{3}{\sqrt{17}}\right)$$

Each vector in the standard basis for R^n has length 1 and is called a **standard unit vector** in R^n. In physics and engineering it is common to denote the standard unit vectors in R^2 and R^3 as follows.

$$\{\mathbf{i}, \mathbf{j}\} = \{(1, 0), (0, 1)\} \quad \text{and} \quad \{\mathbf{i}, \mathbf{j}, \mathbf{k}\} = \{(1, 0, 0), (0, 1, 0), (0, 0, 1)\}$$

Two nonzero vectors $\mathbf{u}$ and $\mathbf{v}$ in R^n are **parallel** if one is a scalar multiple of the other— that is, $\mathbf{u} = c\mathbf{v}$. Moreover, if $c > 0$, then $\mathbf{u}$ and $\mathbf{v}$ have the **same direction,** and if $c < 0$, $\mathbf{u}$ and $\mathbf{v}$ have **opposite directions.** The following theorem gives a formula for finding the length of a scalar multiple of a vector.

Theorem 5.1

Length of a Scalar Multiple

Let $\mathbf{v}$ be a vector in R^n and c a scalar. Then

$$\|c\mathbf{v}\| = |c|\,\|\mathbf{v}\|,$$

where $|c|$ is the absolute value of c.

Proof   Because $c\mathbf{v} = (cv_1, cv_2, \ldots, cv_n)$, it follows that

$$\|c\mathbf{v}\| = \|(cv_1, cv_2, \ldots, cv_n)\|$$
$$= \sqrt{(cv_1)^2 + (cv_2)^2 + \cdots + (cv_n)^2}$$
$$= \sqrt{c^2(v_1^2 + v_2^2 + \cdots + v_n^2)}$$
$$= |c|\sqrt{v_1^2 + v_2^2 + \cdots + v_n^2} = |c|\,\|\mathbf{v}\|.$$

One important use of Theorem 5.1 is in finding a unit vector having the same direction as a given vector. The following theorem provides a procedure for doing this.

Theorem 5.2

Unit Vector in the Direction of v

If $\mathbf{v}$ is a nonzero vector in R^n, then the vector

$$\mathbf{u} = \frac{\mathbf{v}}{\|\mathbf{v}\|}$$

has length 1 and has the same direction as $\mathbf{v}$. We call $\mathbf{u}$ the **unit vector in the direction of v.**

Proof   Since $\mathbf{v}$ is nonzero, we know that $\|\mathbf{v}\| \neq 0$. Thus $1/\|\mathbf{v}\|$ is positive, and we can write $\mathbf{u}$ as a positive scalar multiple of $\mathbf{v}$.

$$\mathbf{u} = \left(\frac{1}{\|\mathbf{v}\|}\right)\mathbf{v}$$

Therefore it follows that $\mathbf{u}$ has the same direction as $\mathbf{v}$. Finally, $\mathbf{u}$ has length 1 because

$$\|\mathbf{u}\| = \left\|\frac{\mathbf{v}}{\|\mathbf{v}\|}\right\| = \frac{1}{\|\mathbf{v}\|}\|\mathbf{v}\| = 1.$$

The process of finding the unit vector in the direction of $\mathbf{v}$ is called **normalizing** the vector $\mathbf{v}$, as demonstrated in the next example.

EXAMPLE 2   *Finding a Unit Vector*

Find the unit vector in the direction of $\mathbf{v} = (3, -1, 2)$, and verify that this vector has length 1.

Solution   The unit vector in the direction of $\mathbf{v}$ is

$$\frac{\mathbf{v}}{\|\mathbf{v}\|} = \frac{(3, -1, 2)}{\sqrt{3^2 + (-1)^2 + 2^2}} = \frac{1}{\sqrt{14}}(3, -1, 2) = \left(\frac{3}{\sqrt{14}}, \frac{-1}{\sqrt{14}}, \frac{2}{\sqrt{14}}\right),$$

which is a unit vector, since

$$\sqrt{\left(\frac{3}{\sqrt{14}}\right)^2 + \left(\frac{-1}{\sqrt{14}}\right)^2 + \left(\frac{2}{\sqrt{14}}\right)^2} = \sqrt{\frac{14}{14}} = 1.$$

Distance Between Two Vectors in R^n

To define the **distance between two vectors** in R^n, we look once again at our model R^2. The Distance Formula from analytic geometry tells us that the distance d between two points in the plane, (u_1, u_2) and (v_1, v_2), is given by

$$d = \sqrt{(u_1 - v_1)^2 + (u_2 - v_2)^2}.$$

In vector terminology, this distance can be viewed as the length of $\mathbf{u} - \mathbf{v}$, where $\mathbf{u} = (u_1, u_2)$ and $\mathbf{v} = (v_1, v_2)$, as shown in Figure 5.3. That is,

$$\|\mathbf{u} - \mathbf{v}\| = \sqrt{(u_1 - v_1)^2 + (u_2 - v_2)^2},$$

which leads us to the following definition.

Figure 5.3

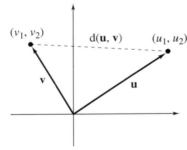

$$d(\mathbf{u}, \mathbf{v}) = \|\mathbf{u} - \mathbf{v}\| = \sqrt{(u_1 - v_1)^2 + (u_2 - v_2)^2}$$

Definition of Distance Between Two Vectors	The **distance between two vectors u and v** in R^n is $$d(\mathbf{u}, \mathbf{v}) = \|\mathbf{u} - \mathbf{v}\|.$$

The following properties of distance are easily verified.

1. $d(\mathbf{u}, \mathbf{v}) \geq 0$
2. $d(\mathbf{u}, \mathbf{v}) = 0$ if and only if $\mathbf{u} = \mathbf{v}$.
3. $d(\mathbf{u}, \mathbf{v}) = d(\mathbf{v}, \mathbf{u})$

EXAMPLE 3   *Finding the Distance Between Two Vectors*

The distance between $\mathbf{u} = (0, 2, 2)$ and $\mathbf{v} = (2, 0, 1)$ is

$$d(\mathbf{u}, \mathbf{v}) = \|\mathbf{u} - \mathbf{v}\| = \|(0 - 2, 2 - 0, 2 - 1)\|$$
$$= \sqrt{(-2)^2 + 2^2 + 1^2} = 3.$$

Dot Product and the Angle Between Two Vectors

Figure 5.4

Angle Between Two Vectors

To find the angle θ $(0 \le \theta \le \pi)$ between two nonzero vectors $\mathbf{u} = (u_1, u_2)$ and $\mathbf{v} = (v_1, v_2)$ in R^2, we can apply the Law of Cosines to the triangle shown in Figure 5.4 to obtain

$$\|\mathbf{v} - \mathbf{u}\|^2 = \|\mathbf{u}\|^2 + \|\mathbf{v}\|^2 - 2\|\mathbf{u}\|\,\|\mathbf{v}\| \cos \theta.$$

By expanding and solving for $\cos \theta$, we obtain

$$\cos \theta = \frac{u_1 v_1 + u_2 v_2}{\|\mathbf{u}\|\,\|\mathbf{v}\|}.$$

The numerator of the quotient on the right is defined to be the **dot product** of $\mathbf{u}$ and $\mathbf{v}$ and is denoted by

$$\mathbf{u} \cdot \mathbf{v} = u_1 v_1 + u_2 v_2.$$

This definition is generalized to R^n as follows.

Definition of Dot Product in R^n

The **dot product** of $\mathbf{u} = (u_1, u_2, \ldots, u_n)$ and $\mathbf{v} = (v_1, v_2, \ldots, v_n)$ is the *scalar* quantity

$$\mathbf{u} \cdot \mathbf{v} = u_1 v_1 + u_2 v_2 + \cdots + u_n v_n.$$

REMARK: Be sure you see that the dot product of two vectors is defined to be a scalar, not another vector.

EXAMPLE 4   *Finding the Dot Product of Two Vectors*

The dot product of $\mathbf{u} = (1, 2, 0, -3)$ and $\mathbf{v} = (3, -2, 4, 2)$ is

$$\mathbf{u} \cdot \mathbf{v} = (1)(3) + (2)(-2) + (0)(4) + (-3)(2) = -7.$$

Theorem 5.3

Properties of the Dot Product

If $\mathbf{u}$, $\mathbf{v}$, and $\mathbf{w}$ are vectors in R^n and c is a scalar, then the following properties are true.

1. $\mathbf{u} \cdot \mathbf{v} = \mathbf{v} \cdot \mathbf{u}$
2. $\mathbf{u} \cdot (\mathbf{v} + \mathbf{w}) = \mathbf{u} \cdot \mathbf{v} + \mathbf{u} \cdot \mathbf{w}$
3. $c(\mathbf{u} \cdot \mathbf{v}) = (c\mathbf{u}) \cdot \mathbf{v} = \mathbf{u} \cdot (c\mathbf{v})$
4. $\mathbf{v} \cdot \mathbf{v} = \|\mathbf{v}\|^2$
5. $\mathbf{v} \cdot \mathbf{v} \ge 0$, and $\mathbf{v} \cdot \mathbf{v} = 0$ if and only if $\mathbf{v} = \mathbf{0}$.

Proof   The proofs of the properties follow easily from the definition of dot product. For example, to prove the first property, we can write

$$\mathbf{u} \cdot \mathbf{v} = u_1v_1 + u_2v_2 + \cdots + u_nv_n$$
$$= v_1u_1 + v_2u_2 + \cdots + v_nu_n = \mathbf{v} \cdot \mathbf{u}.$$

In Section 4.1 R^n was defined to be the *set* of all ordered n-tuples of real numbers. When R^n is combined with the standard operations of vector addition, scalar multiplication, vector length, and the dot product, the resulting vector space is called **Euclidean n-space.** In the remainder of this text, unless we state otherwise we will assume R^n to have the standard Euclidean operations.

EXAMPLE 5   *Finding Dot Products*

Given $\mathbf{u} = (2, -2)$, $\mathbf{v} = (5, 8)$, and $\mathbf{w} = (-4, 3)$, find the following.

(a) $\mathbf{u} \cdot \mathbf{v}$ (b) $(\mathbf{u} \cdot \mathbf{v})\mathbf{w}$ (c) $\mathbf{u} \cdot (2\mathbf{v})$ (d) $\|\mathbf{w}\|^2$ (e) $\mathbf{u} \cdot (\mathbf{v} - 2\mathbf{w})$

Solution   (a) By definition, we have

$$\mathbf{u} \cdot \mathbf{v} = 2(5) + (-2)(8) = -6.$$

(b) Using the result in part (a), we have

$$(\mathbf{u} \cdot \mathbf{v})\mathbf{w} = -6\mathbf{w} = -6(-4, 3) = (24, -18).$$

(c) By property 3 of Theorem 5.3, we have

$$\mathbf{u} \cdot (2\mathbf{v}) = 2(\mathbf{u} \cdot \mathbf{v}) = 2(-6) = -12.$$

(d) By property 4 of Theorem 5.3, we have

$$\|\mathbf{w}\|^2 = \mathbf{w} \cdot \mathbf{w} = (-4)(-4) + (3)(3) = 25.$$

(e) Since $2\mathbf{w} = (-8, 6)$, we have

$$\mathbf{v} - 2\mathbf{w} = (5 - (-8), 8 - 6) = (13, 2).$$

Consequently,

$$\mathbf{u} \cdot (\mathbf{v} - 2\mathbf{w}) = 2(13) + (-2)(2) = 26 - 4 = 22.$$

EXAMPLE 6   *Using Properties of the Dot Product*

Given two vectors $\mathbf{u}$ and $\mathbf{v}$ in R^n such that $\mathbf{u} \cdot \mathbf{u} = 39$, $\mathbf{u} \cdot \mathbf{v} = -3$, and $\mathbf{v} \cdot \mathbf{v} = 79$, evaluate $(\mathbf{u} + 2\mathbf{v}) \cdot (3\mathbf{u} + \mathbf{v})$.

Solution   Using Theorem 5.3, we can rewrite the given dot product as

$$(\mathbf{u} + 2\mathbf{v}) \cdot (3\mathbf{u} + \mathbf{v}) = \mathbf{u} \cdot (3\mathbf{u} + \mathbf{v}) + (2\mathbf{v}) \cdot (3\mathbf{u} + \mathbf{v})$$
$$= \mathbf{u} \cdot (3\mathbf{u}) + \mathbf{u} \cdot \mathbf{v} + (2\mathbf{v}) \cdot (3\mathbf{u}) + (2\mathbf{v}) \cdot \mathbf{v}$$
$$= 3(\mathbf{u} \cdot \mathbf{u}) + \mathbf{u} \cdot \mathbf{v} + 6(\mathbf{v} \cdot \mathbf{u}) + 2(\mathbf{v} \cdot \mathbf{v})$$

$$= 3(\mathbf{u} \cdot \mathbf{u}) + 7(\mathbf{u} \cdot \mathbf{v}) + 2(\mathbf{v} \cdot \mathbf{v})$$
$$= 3(39) + 7(-3) + 2(79) = 254.$$

DISCOVERY

How does the dot product of two vectors compare to the product of their lengths? For instance, let $\mathbf{u} = (1, 1)$ and $\mathbf{v} = (-4, -3)$. Calculate $\mathbf{u} \cdot \mathbf{v}$ and $\|\mathbf{u}\| \|\mathbf{v}\|$. Repeat this experiment with other choices for $\mathbf{u}$ and $\mathbf{v}$. Formulate a conjecture about the relationship between $\mathbf{u} \cdot \mathbf{v}$ and $\|\mathbf{u}\| \|\mathbf{v}\|$.

To define the angle θ between two vectors $\mathbf{u}$ and $\mathbf{v}$ in R^n, we would like to use the R^2 formula

$$\cos \theta = \frac{\mathbf{u} \cdot \mathbf{v}}{\|\mathbf{u}\| \|\mathbf{v}\|}.$$

In order for such a definition to make sense, however, we must know that the value of the right-hand side of this formula cannot exceed 1 in absolute value. This fact comes from a famous theorem named after the French mathematician Augustin Louis Cauchy (1789–1857) and the German mathematician Hermann Schwarz (1843–1921).

Theorem 5.4

The Cauchy-Schwarz Inequality

If $\mathbf{u}$ and $\mathbf{v}$ are vectors in R^n, then

$$|\mathbf{u} \cdot \mathbf{v}| \leq \|\mathbf{u}\| \|\mathbf{v}\|,$$

where $|\mathbf{u} \cdot \mathbf{v}|$ denotes the *absolute value* of $\mathbf{u} \cdot \mathbf{v}$.

Proof   *Case 1.* If $\mathbf{u} = \mathbf{0}$, then it follows that $|\mathbf{u} \cdot \mathbf{v}| = |\mathbf{0} \cdot \mathbf{v}| = 0$ and $\|\mathbf{u}\| \|\mathbf{v}\| = 0\|\mathbf{v}\| = 0$. Hence the theorem is true if $\mathbf{u} = \mathbf{0}$.
Case 2. If $\mathbf{u} \neq \mathbf{0}$, we let t be any real number and consider the vector $t\mathbf{u} + \mathbf{v}$. Since $(t\mathbf{u} + \mathbf{v}) \cdot (t\mathbf{u} + \mathbf{v}) \geq 0$, it follows that

$$(t\mathbf{u} + \mathbf{v}) \cdot (t\mathbf{u} + \mathbf{v}) = t^2(\mathbf{u} \cdot \mathbf{u}) + 2t(\mathbf{u} \cdot \mathbf{v}) + \mathbf{v} \cdot \mathbf{v} \geq 0.$$

Now, letting $a = \mathbf{u} \cdot \mathbf{u}$, $b = 2(\mathbf{u} \cdot \mathbf{v})$, and $c = \mathbf{v} \cdot \mathbf{v}$, we obtain the quadratic inequality $at^2 + bt + c \geq 0$. Since this quadratic is never negative, it has either no real roots or a single repeated real root. But by the quadratic formula, this implies that the discriminant, $b^2 - 4ac$, is less than or equal to zero. Thus

$$b^2 - 4ac \leq 0$$
$$b^2 \leq 4ac$$
$$4(\mathbf{u} \cdot \mathbf{v})^2 \leq 4(\mathbf{u} \cdot \mathbf{u})(\mathbf{v} \cdot \mathbf{v})$$
$$(\mathbf{u} \cdot \mathbf{v})^2 \leq (\mathbf{u} \cdot \mathbf{u})(\mathbf{v} \cdot \mathbf{v}).$$

Taking the square root of both sides produces

$$|\mathbf{u} \cdot \mathbf{v}| \leq \sqrt{\mathbf{u} \cdot \mathbf{u}} \sqrt{\mathbf{v} \cdot \mathbf{v}} = \|\mathbf{u}\| \|\mathbf{v}\|.$$

EXAMPLE 7   *An Example of the Cauchy-Schwarz Inequality*

Verify the Cauchy-Schwarz Inequality for $\mathbf{u} = (1, -1, 3)$ and $\mathbf{v} = (2, 0, -1)$.

Solution   Since $\mathbf{u} \cdot \mathbf{v} = -1$, $\mathbf{u} \cdot \mathbf{u} = 11$, and $\mathbf{v} \cdot \mathbf{v} = 5$, we have

$$|\mathbf{u} \cdot \mathbf{v}| = |-1| = 1$$

and

$$\|\mathbf{u}\| \|\mathbf{v}\| = \sqrt{\mathbf{u} \cdot \mathbf{u}} \sqrt{\mathbf{v} \cdot \mathbf{v}} = \sqrt{11} \sqrt{5} = \sqrt{55}.$$

Thus the inequality holds, and we have $|\mathbf{u} \cdot \mathbf{v}| \leq \|\mathbf{u}\| \|\mathbf{v}\|$.

The Cauchy-Schwarz Inequality now allows us to define the angle between two nonzero vectors in R^n.

Definition of the Angle Between Two Vectors in R^n

The **angle** θ between two nonzero vectors in R^n is given by

$$\cos \theta = \frac{\mathbf{u} \cdot \mathbf{v}}{\|\mathbf{u}\| \|\mathbf{v}\|}, \quad 0 \leq \theta \leq \pi.$$

REMARK: We do not define the angle between the zero vector and another vector.

EXAMPLE 8   *Finding the Angle Between Two Vectors*

The angle between $\mathbf{u} = (-4, 0, 2, -2)$ and $\mathbf{v} = (2, 0, -1, 1)$ is given by

$$\cos \theta = \frac{\mathbf{u} \cdot \mathbf{v}}{\|\mathbf{u}\| \|\mathbf{v}\|} = \frac{-12}{\sqrt{24} \sqrt{6}} = -\frac{12}{\sqrt{144}} = -1.$$

Consequently, $\theta = \pi$. It makes sense that $\mathbf{u}$ and $\mathbf{v}$ should have opposite directions, because $\mathbf{u} = -2\mathbf{v}$.

Note that because $\|\mathbf{u}\|$ and $\|\mathbf{v}\|$ are always positive, $\mathbf{u} \cdot \mathbf{v}$ and $\cos \theta$ will always have the same sign. Moreover, since the cosine is positive in the first quadrant and negative in the second quadrant, the sign of the dot product of two vectors can be used to determine whether the angle between them is acute or obtuse, as shown in Figure 5.5.

Figure 5.5

Figure 5.5 shows that two nonzero vectors meet at a right angle if and only if their dot product is zero. We say that two such vectors are **orthogonal** (or perpendicular), as stated in the following definition.

Definition of Orthogonal Vectors	Two vectors **u** and **v** in R^n are **orthogonal** if $$\mathbf{u} \cdot \mathbf{v} = 0.$$

REMARK: Even though the angle between the zero vector and another vector is not defined, it is convenient to extend the definition of orthogonality to include the zero vector. In other words, we say that the vector **0** is orthogonal to every vector.

EXAMPLE 9   *Orthogonal Vectors in R^n*

(a) The vectors $\mathbf{u} = (1, 0, 0)$ and $\mathbf{v} = (0, 1, 0)$ are orthogonal, since

$$\mathbf{u} \cdot \mathbf{v} = (1)(0) + (0)(1) + (0)(0) = 0.$$

(b) The vectors $\mathbf{u} = (3, 2, -1, 4)$ and $\mathbf{v} = (1, -1, 1, 0)$ are orthogonal, since

$$\mathbf{u} \cdot \mathbf{v} = (3)(1) + (2)(-1) + (-1)(1) + (4)(0) = 0.$$

EXAMPLE 10   *Finding Orthogonal Vectors*

Determine all vectors in R^2 that are orthogonal to $\mathbf{u} = (4, 2)$.

Figure 5.6

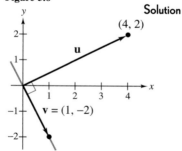

Solution   Let $\mathbf{v} = (v_1, v_2)$ be orthogonal to **u**. Then

$$\mathbf{u} \cdot \mathbf{v} = (4, 2) \cdot (v_1, v_2)$$
$$= 4v_1 + 2v_2 = 0,$$

which implies that $2v_2 = -4v_1$ and $v_2 = -2v_1$. Therefore every vector that is orthogonal to $(4, 2)$ is of the form

$$\mathbf{v} = (t, -2t) = t(1, -2),$$

where t is a real number. (See Figure 5.6.)

We can use the Cauchy-Schwarz Inequality to prove another well-known inequality called the **Triangle Inequality**. The name Triangle Inequality is derived from the interpretation of the theorem in R^2, illustrated for the vectors **u** and **v** in Figure 5.7. If we consider $\|\mathbf{u}\|$ and $\|\mathbf{v}\|$ to be the lengths of two sides of a triangle, we see that the length of the third side is $\|\mathbf{u} + \mathbf{v}\|$. Moreover, since the length of any side of a triangle cannot be greater than the sum of the lengths of the other two sides, we have

$$\|\mathbf{u} + \mathbf{v}\| \leq \|\mathbf{u}\| + \|\mathbf{v}\|.$$

Figure 5.7

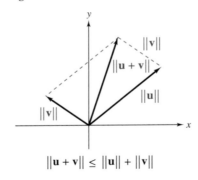

$$\|\mathbf{u} + \mathbf{v}\| \le \|\mathbf{u}\| + \|\mathbf{v}\|$$

This result is generalized to R^n in the following theorem.

Theorem 5.5

The Triangle Inequality

If $\mathbf{u}$ and $\mathbf{v}$ are vectors in R^n, then

$$\|\mathbf{u} + \mathbf{v}\| \le \|\mathbf{u}\| + \|\mathbf{v}\|.$$

Proof   Using the properties of the dot product, we have

$$
\begin{aligned}
\|\mathbf{u} + \mathbf{v}\|^2 &= (\mathbf{u} + \mathbf{v}) \cdot (\mathbf{u} + \mathbf{v}) \\
&= \mathbf{u} \cdot (\mathbf{u} + \mathbf{v}) + \mathbf{v} \cdot (\mathbf{u} + \mathbf{v}) \\
&= \mathbf{u} \cdot \mathbf{u} + 2(\mathbf{u} \cdot \mathbf{v}) + \mathbf{v} \cdot \mathbf{v} \\
&= \|\mathbf{u}\|^2 + 2(\mathbf{u} \cdot \mathbf{v}) + \|\mathbf{v}\|^2 \\
&\le \|\mathbf{u}\|^2 + 2|\mathbf{u} \cdot \mathbf{v}| + \|\mathbf{v}\|^2.
\end{aligned}
$$

Now, by the Cauchy-Schwarz Inequality $|\mathbf{u} \cdot \mathbf{v}| \le \|\mathbf{u}\| \, \|\mathbf{v}\|$, and we can write

$$
\begin{aligned}
\|\mathbf{u} + \mathbf{v}\|^2 &\le \|\mathbf{u}\|^2 + 2|\mathbf{u} \cdot \mathbf{v}| + \|\mathbf{v}\|^2 \\
&\le \|\mathbf{u}\|^2 + 2\|\mathbf{u}\| \, \|\mathbf{v}\| + \|\mathbf{v}\|^2 \\
&= (\|\mathbf{u}\| + \|\mathbf{v}\|)^2.
\end{aligned}
$$

Since both $\|\mathbf{u} + \mathbf{v}\|$ and $(\|\mathbf{u}\| + \|\mathbf{v}\|)$ are nonnegative, taking the square root of both sides yields

$$\|\mathbf{u} + \mathbf{v}\| \le \|\mathbf{u}\| + \|\mathbf{v}\|.$$

REMARK: Equality occurs in the Triangle Inequality if and only if the vectors $\mathbf{u}$ and $\mathbf{v}$ have the same direction. (See Exercise 76.)

From the proof of the Triangle Inequality we have

$$\|\mathbf{u} + \mathbf{v}\|^2 = \|\mathbf{u}\|^2 + 2(\mathbf{u} \cdot \mathbf{v}) + \|\mathbf{v}\|^2.$$

If **u** and **v** are orthogonal, then $\mathbf{u} \cdot \mathbf{v} = 0$, and we have the following extension of the **Pythagorean Theorem** to R^n.

Theorem 5.6	If **u** and **v** are vectors in R^n, then **u** and **v** are orthogonal if and only if
The Pythagorean Theorem	$$\|\mathbf{u} + \mathbf{v}\|^2 = \|\mathbf{u}\|^2 + \|\mathbf{v}\|^2.$$

Figure 5.8

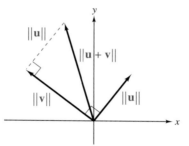

This result is illustrated graphically in Figure 5.8.

The Dot Product and Matrix Multiplication

We have often found it useful to represent a vector $\mathbf{u} = (u_1, u_2, \ldots, u_n)$ in R^n as an $n \times 1$ column matrix. In this notation, the dot product of two vectors

$$\mathbf{u} = \begin{bmatrix} u_1 \\ u_2 \\ \vdots \\ u_n \end{bmatrix} \quad \text{and} \quad \mathbf{v} = \begin{bmatrix} v_1 \\ v_2 \\ \vdots \\ v_n \end{bmatrix}$$

can be represented as the matrix product of the transpose of **u** times **v**.

$$\mathbf{u} \cdot \mathbf{v} = \mathbf{u}^T \mathbf{v} = [u_1 \ u_2 \ \cdots \ u_n] \begin{bmatrix} v_1 \\ v_2 \\ \vdots \\ v_n \end{bmatrix} = [u_1 v_1 + u_2 v_2 + \cdots + u_n v_n]$$

For example, the dot product of the vectors

$$\mathbf{u} = \begin{bmatrix} 1 \\ 2 \\ -1 \end{bmatrix} \quad \text{and} \quad \mathbf{v} = \begin{bmatrix} 3 \\ -2 \\ 4 \end{bmatrix}$$

is given by

$$\mathbf{u} \cdot \mathbf{v} = \mathbf{u}^T \mathbf{v}$$

$$= [1 \quad 2 \quad -1] \begin{bmatrix} 3 \\ -2 \\ 4 \end{bmatrix}$$

$$= [(1)(3) + (2)(-2) + (-1)(4)] = -5$$

In this light, many of the properties of the dot product are direct consequences of the corresponding properties of matrix multiplication.

SECTION 5.1 □ EXERCISES

In Exercises 1–8, find the length of the given vector.

1. $\mathbf{v} = (4, 3)$ **2.** $\mathbf{v} = (0, 1)$ **3.** $\mathbf{v} = (1, 0, 0)$

4. $\mathbf{v} = (1, 2, 2)$ **5.** $\mathbf{v} = (0, 0, 0)$ **6.** $\mathbf{v} = (1, 0, 3)$

7. $\mathbf{v} = (4, 0, -3, 5)$ **8.** $\mathbf{v} = (0, 4, 3, 4, -4)$

In Exercises 9–12, find (a) $\|\mathbf{u}\|$, (b) $\|\mathbf{v}\|$, and (c) $\|\mathbf{u} + \mathbf{v}\|$.

9. $\mathbf{u} = (0, 4, 3)$, $\mathbf{v} = (1, -2, 1)$

10. $\mathbf{u} = (1, \frac{1}{2})$, $\mathbf{v} = (2, -\frac{1}{2})$

11. $\mathbf{u} = (0, 1, -1, 2)$, $\mathbf{v} = (1, 1, 3, 0)$

12. $\mathbf{u} = (1, 0, 0, 0)$, $\mathbf{v} = (0, 1, 0, 0)$

In Exercises 13–16, find a unit vector (a) in the direction of $\mathbf{u}$ and (b) in the direction opposite that of $\mathbf{u}$.

13. $\mathbf{u} = (-5, 12)$ **14.** $\mathbf{u} = (1, -1)$

15. $\mathbf{u} = (3, 2, -5)$ **16.** $\mathbf{u} = (1, 0, 2, 2)$

17. For what values of c is $\|c(1, 2, 3)\| = 1$?

18. For what values of c is $\|c(2, 2, -1)\| = 3$?

In Exercises 19–22, find the vector $\mathbf{v}$ with the given length that has the same direction as the vector $\mathbf{u}$.

19. $\|\mathbf{v}\| = 4$, $\mathbf{u} = (1, 1)$ **20.** $\|\mathbf{v}\| = 4$, $\mathbf{u} = (-1, 1)$

21. $\|\mathbf{v}\| = 2$, $\mathbf{u} = (\sqrt{3}, 3, 0)$

22. $\|\mathbf{v}\| = 3$, $\mathbf{u} = (0, 2, 1, -1)$

23. Given the vector $\mathbf{v} = (8, 8, 6)$, find $\mathbf{u}$ such that

   (a) $\mathbf{u}$ has the same direction as $\mathbf{v}$ and one-half its length.

   (b) $\mathbf{u}$ has the direction opposite that of $\mathbf{v}$ and one-fourth its length.

24. Given the vector $\mathbf{v} = (-1, 3, 0, 4)$, find $\mathbf{u}$ such that

   (a) $\mathbf{u}$ has the same direction as $\mathbf{v}$ and one-half its length.

   (b) $\mathbf{u}$ has the direction opposite that of $\mathbf{v}$ and one-fourth its length.

In Exercises 25–28, find the distance between $\mathbf{u}$ and $\mathbf{v}$.

25. $\mathbf{u} = (1, -1)$, $\mathbf{v} = (-1, 1)$

26. $\mathbf{u} = (3, 4)$, $\mathbf{v} = (7, 1)$

27. $\mathbf{u} = (1, 1, 2)$, $\mathbf{v} = (-1, 3, 0)$

28. $\mathbf{u} = (0, 1, 2, 3)$, $\mathbf{v} = (1, 0, 4, -1)$

In Exercises 29–34, find (a) $\mathbf{u} \cdot \mathbf{v}$, (b) $\mathbf{u} \cdot \mathbf{u}$, (c) $\|\mathbf{u}\|^2$, (d) $(\mathbf{u} \cdot \mathbf{v})\mathbf{v}$, and (e) $\mathbf{u} \cdot (2\mathbf{v})$.

29. $\mathbf{u} = (3, 4)$, $\mathbf{v} = (2, -3)$

30. $\mathbf{u} = (5, 12)$, $\mathbf{v} = (-3, 2)$

31. $\mathbf{u} = (2, -1, 1)$, $\mathbf{v} = (1, 0, -1)$

32. $\mathbf{u} = (-1, 1, -2)$, $\mathbf{v} = (1, -3, -2)$

33. $\mathbf{u} = (4, 0, -3, 5)$, $\mathbf{v} = (0, 2, 5, 4)$

34. $\mathbf{u} = (0, 4, 3, 4, 4)$, $\mathbf{v} = (6, 8, -3, 3, -5)$

35. Find $(\mathbf{u} + \mathbf{v}) \cdot (2\mathbf{u} - \mathbf{v})$, given that $\mathbf{u} \cdot \mathbf{u} = 4$, $\mathbf{u} \cdot \mathbf{v} = -5$, and $\mathbf{v} \cdot \mathbf{v} = 10$.

36. Find $(3\mathbf{u} - \mathbf{v}) \cdot (\mathbf{u} - 3\mathbf{v})$, given that $\mathbf{u} \cdot \mathbf{u} = 8$, $\mathbf{u} \cdot \mathbf{v} = 7$, and $\mathbf{v} \cdot \mathbf{v} = 6$.

In Exercises 37 and 38, verify the Cauchy-Schwarz Inequality for the given vectors.

37. $\mathbf{u} = (3, 4)$, $\mathbf{v} = (2, -3)$

38. $\mathbf{u} = (1, 1, -2)$, $\mathbf{v} = (1, -3, -2)$

In Exercises 39–46, find the angle θ between the given vectors.

39. $\mathbf{u} = (1, 1)$, $\mathbf{v} = (2, -2)$

40. $\mathbf{u} = (3, 1)$, $\mathbf{v} = (2, -1)$

41. $\mathbf{u} = (3, 1)$, $\mathbf{v} = (-2, 4)$

42. $\mathbf{u} = \left(\cos\dfrac{\pi}{6}, \sin\dfrac{\pi}{6}\right)$, $\mathbf{v} = \left(\cos\dfrac{3\pi}{4}, \sin\dfrac{3\pi}{4}\right)$

43. $\mathbf{u} = (1, 1, 1)$, $\mathbf{v} = (2, 1, -1)$

44. $\mathbf{u} = (2, 3, 1)$, $\mathbf{v} = (-3, 2, 0)$

45. $\mathbf{u} = (0, 1, 0, 1)$, $\mathbf{v} = (3, 3, 3, 3)$

46. $\mathbf{u} = (1, 3, -1, 2, 0)$, $\mathbf{v} = (-1, 4, 5, -3, 2)$

In Exercises 47–52, determine all vectors $\mathbf{v}$ that are orthogonal to the given vector $\mathbf{u}$.

47. $\mathbf{u} = (0, 5)$ **48.** $\mathbf{u} = (2, 7)$ **49.** $\mathbf{u} = (-3, 2)$

50. $\mathbf{u} = (0, 0)$ **51.** $\mathbf{u} = (4, -1, 0)$

52. $\mathbf{u} = (0, 1, 0, 0, 0)$

In Exercises 53–60, determine whether $\mathbf{u}$ and $\mathbf{v}$ are orthogonal, parallel, or neither.

53. $\mathbf{u} = (4, 0)$, $\mathbf{v} = (1, 1)$

54. $\mathbf{u} = (2, 18)$, $\mathbf{v} = \left(\frac{3}{2}, -\frac{1}{6}\right)$

55. $\mathbf{u} = (4, 3)$, $\mathbf{v} = \left(\frac{1}{2}, -\frac{2}{3}\right)$

56. $\mathbf{u} = \left(-\frac{1}{3}, \frac{2}{3}\right)$, $\mathbf{v} = (2, -4)$

57. $\mathbf{u} = (0, 1, 6)$, $\mathbf{v} = (1, -2, -1)$

58. $\mathbf{u} = (-2, 3, -1)$, $\mathbf{v} = (2, 1, -1)$

59. $\mathbf{u} = (\cos\theta, \sin\theta, -1)$, $\quad \mathbf{v} = (\sin\theta, -\cos\theta, 0)$

60. $\mathbf{u} = \left(4, \frac{3}{2}, -1, \frac{1}{2}\right)$, $\quad \mathbf{v} = \left(-2, -\frac{3}{4}, \frac{1}{2}, -\frac{1}{4}\right)$

In Exercises 61 and 62, write a short paragraph explaining why the given expression is meaningless. Assume that $\mathbf{u}$ and $\mathbf{v}$ are vectors in R^n, and c is a scalar.

61. (a) $\|\mathbf{u} \cdot \mathbf{v}\|$ (b) $\mathbf{u} + (\mathbf{u} \cdot \mathbf{v})$

62. (a) $(\mathbf{u} \cdot \mathbf{v}) \cdot \mathbf{u}$ (b) $c \cdot (\mathbf{u} \cdot \mathbf{v})$

In Exercises 63 and 64, verify the Triangle Inequality for the given vectors.

63. $\mathbf{u} = (4, 0)$, $\quad \mathbf{v} = (1, 1)$

64. $\mathbf{u} = (1, 1, 1)$, $\quad \mathbf{v} = (0, 1, -2)$

In Exercises 65 and 66, verify the Pythagorean Theorem for the given vectors.

65. $\mathbf{u} = (1, -1)$, $\quad \mathbf{v} = (1, 1)$

66. $\mathbf{u} = (3, 4, -2)$, $\quad \mathbf{v} = (4, -3, 0)$

67. What is known about θ, the angle between $\mathbf{u}$ and $\mathbf{v}$, if
(a) $\mathbf{u} \cdot \mathbf{v} = 0$ (b) $\mathbf{u} \cdot \mathbf{v} > 0$ (c) $\mathbf{u} \cdot \mathbf{v} < 0$?

68. Let $\mathbf{v} = (v_1, v_2)$ be a vector in R^2. Show that $(v_2, -v_1)$ is orthogonal to $\mathbf{v}$, and use this fact to find two unit vectors orthogonal to $(12, 5)$.

69. Find the angle between the diagonal of a cube and one of its edges.

70. Find the angle between the diagonal of a cube and the diagonal of one of its sides.

71. Prove that if $\mathbf{u}$, $\mathbf{v}$, and $\mathbf{w}$ are vectors in R^n, then
$(\mathbf{u} + \mathbf{v}) \cdot \mathbf{w} = \mathbf{u} \cdot \mathbf{w} + \mathbf{v} \cdot \mathbf{w}$.

72. Prove that if $\mathbf{u}$ is orthogonal to $\mathbf{v}$ and $\mathbf{w}$, then $\mathbf{u}$ is orthogonal to $c\mathbf{v} + d\mathbf{w}$ for any scalars c and d.

73. Prove that if $\mathbf{u}$ and $\mathbf{v}$ are vectors in R^n, then
$\mathbf{u} \cdot \mathbf{v} = \frac{1}{4}\|\mathbf{u} + \mathbf{v}\|^2 - \frac{1}{4}\|\mathbf{u} - \mathbf{v}\|^2$.

74. Prove that if $\mathbf{u}$ and $\mathbf{v}$ are vectors in R^n, then
$\|\mathbf{u} + \mathbf{v}\|^2 + \|\mathbf{u} - \mathbf{v}\|^2 = 2\|\mathbf{u}\|^2 + 2\|\mathbf{v}\|^2$.

75. Prove that the vectors $\mathbf{u} = (\cos\theta)\mathbf{i} - (\sin\theta)\mathbf{j}$ and $\mathbf{v} = (\sin\theta)\mathbf{i} + (\cos\theta)\mathbf{j}$ are orthogonal unit vectors for any value of θ. Graph $\mathbf{u}$ and $\mathbf{v}$ for $\theta = \pi/3$.

76. Prove that $\|\mathbf{u} + \mathbf{v}\| = \|\mathbf{u}\| + \|\mathbf{v}\|$ if and only if $\mathbf{u}$ and $\mathbf{v}$ have the same direction.

77. The vector $\mathbf{u} = (3240, 1450, 2235)$ gives the number of bushels of corn, oats, and wheat raised by a farmer in a certain year. The vector $\mathbf{v} = (2.22, 1.85, 3.25)$ gives the price in dollars per bushel of each of the crops. Find the dot product $\mathbf{u} \cdot \mathbf{v}$, and explain what information it gives.

78. Let $\mathbf{x}$ be a solution to the $m \times n$ homogeneous linear system of equations $A\mathbf{x} = \mathbf{0}$. Explain why $\mathbf{x}$ is orthogonal to the row vectors of A.

79. Use the matrix multiplication interpretation of the dot product, $\mathbf{u} \cdot \mathbf{v} = \mathbf{u}^T\mathbf{v}$, to prove the first three properties of Theorem 5.3.

5.2 INNER PRODUCT SPACES

In Section 5.1 we extended the concepts of length, distance, and angle from R^2 to R^n. This section extends the concepts one step further—to general vector spaces. We accomplish this by using the notion of an **inner product** of two vectors.

We already have one example of an inner product: the *dot product* in R^n. The dot product, called the **Euclidean inner product,** is only one of several inner products that can be defined on R^n. To distinguish between the standard inner product and other possible inner products, we use the following notation.

$$\mathbf{u} \cdot \mathbf{v} = \text{dot product (Euclidean inner product for } R^n)$$
$$\langle \mathbf{u}, \mathbf{v} \rangle = \text{general inner product for vector space } V$$

To define a general inner product, we proceed in much the same way as we did to define a general vector space. That is, we list a set of axioms that must be satisfied in order for a function to qualify as an inner product. The axioms parallel the four properties of the dot product given in Theorem 5.3.

Definition of Inner Product

Let $\mathbf{u}$, $\mathbf{v}$, and $\mathbf{w}$ be vectors in a vector space V, and let c be any scalar. An **inner product** on V is a function that associates a real number $\langle \mathbf{u}, \mathbf{v} \rangle$ with each pair of vectors $\mathbf{u}$ and $\mathbf{v}$ and satisfies the following axioms.

1. $\langle \mathbf{u}, \mathbf{v} \rangle = \langle \mathbf{v}, \mathbf{u} \rangle$
2. $\langle \mathbf{u}, \mathbf{v} + \mathbf{w} \rangle = \langle \mathbf{u}, \mathbf{v} \rangle + \langle \mathbf{u}, \mathbf{w} \rangle$
3. $c\langle \mathbf{u}, \mathbf{v} \rangle = \langle c\mathbf{u}, \mathbf{v} \rangle$
4. $\langle \mathbf{v}, \mathbf{v} \rangle \geq 0$, and $\langle \mathbf{v}, \mathbf{v} \rangle = 0$ if and only if $\mathbf{v} = \mathbf{0}$.

REMARK: A vector space V with an inner product is called an **inner product space.** When we refer to an inner product space, we assume that the set of scalars is the set of real numbers. (In Chapter 8, we will discuss *complex* inner product spaces.)

EXAMPLE 1   ***The Euclidean Inner Product for R^n***

Show that the dot product in R^n satisfies the four axioms of an inner product.

Solution   In R^n the dot product of two vectors $\mathbf{u} = (u_1, u_2, \ldots, u_n)$ and $\mathbf{v} = (v_1, v_2, \ldots, v_n)$ is given by

$$\mathbf{u} \cdot \mathbf{v} = u_1 v_1 + u_2 v_2 + \cdots + u_n v_n.$$

By Theorem 5.3 we know that this dot product satisfies the required four axioms, and thus it is an inner product on R^n.

The Euclidean inner product is not the only inner product that can be defined on R^n. A different inner product is illustrated in Example 2. Note that to show that a function is an inner product you must show that the four inner product axioms are satisfied.

EXAMPLE 2   ***A Different Inner Product for R^2***

Show that the following function defines an inner product on R^2.

$$\langle \mathbf{u}, \mathbf{v} \rangle = u_1 v_1 + 2u_2 v_2,$$

where $\mathbf{u} = (u_1, u_2)$ and $\mathbf{v} = (v_1, v_2)$.

Solution   1. Since the product of real numbers is commutative, we have

$$\langle \mathbf{u}, \mathbf{v} \rangle = u_1 v_1 + 2u_2 v_2 = v_1 u_1 + 2v_2 u_2 = \langle \mathbf{v}, \mathbf{u} \rangle.$$

2. Let $\mathbf{w} = (w_1, w_2)$. Then

$$\begin{aligned}
\langle \mathbf{u}, \mathbf{v} + \mathbf{w} \rangle &= u_1(v_1 + w_1) + 2u_2(v_2 + w_2) \\
&= u_1 v_1 + u_1 w_1 + 2u_2 v_2 + 2u_2 w_2 \\
&= (u_1 v_1 + 2u_2 v_2) + (u_1 w_1 + 2u_2 w_2) \\
&= \langle \mathbf{u}, \mathbf{v} \rangle + \langle \mathbf{u}, \mathbf{w} \rangle.
\end{aligned}$$

3. If c is any scalar, then

$$c\langle \mathbf{u}, \mathbf{v} \rangle = c(u_1v_1 + 2u_2v_2) = (cu_1)v_1 + 2(cu_2)v_2 = \langle c\mathbf{u}, \mathbf{v} \rangle.$$

4. Since the square of a real number is nonnegative, we have

$$\langle \mathbf{v}, \mathbf{v} \rangle = v_1^2 + 2v_2^2 \geq 0.$$

Moreover, this expression is equal to zero if and only if $\mathbf{v} = \mathbf{0}$ (that is, if and only if $v_1 = v_2 = 0$).

Example 2 can be generalized to show that

$$\langle \mathbf{u}, \mathbf{v} \rangle = c_1u_1v_1 + c_2u_2v_2 + \cdots + c_nu_nv_n, \quad c_i > 0$$

is an inner product on R^n. The positive constants $c_1, \ldots, c_n$ are called **weights.** If any c_i is negative or 0, then this function does not define an inner product.

EXAMPLE 3   *A Function That Is Not an Inner Product*

Show that the following function is not an inner product on R^3.

$$\langle \mathbf{u}, \mathbf{v} \rangle = u_1v_1 - 2u_2v_2 + u_3v_3,$$

where $\mathbf{u} = (u_1, u_2, u_3)$ and $\mathbf{v} = (v_1, v_2, v_3)$.

Solution   We observe that axiom 4 is not satisfied. For example, let $\mathbf{v} = (1, 2, 1)$. Then $\langle \mathbf{v}, \mathbf{v} \rangle = (1)(1) - 2(2)(2) + (1)(1) = -6$, which is less than zero.

EXAMPLE 4   *An Inner Product on $M_{2,2}$*

Let

$$A = \begin{bmatrix} a_{11} & a_{12} \\ a_{21} & a_{22} \end{bmatrix} \quad \text{and} \quad B = \begin{bmatrix} b_{11} & b_{12} \\ b_{21} & b_{22} \end{bmatrix}$$

be matrices in the vector space $M_{2,2}$. The function given by

$$\langle A, B \rangle = a_{11}b_{11} + a_{21}b_{21} + a_{12}b_{12} + a_{22}b_{22}$$

is an inner product on $M_{2,2}$. The verification of the four inner product axioms is left to you.

From calculus we obtain the inner product described in the next example. The verification of the inner product properties depends on the properties of the definite integral.

EXAMPLE 5   *An Inner Product Defined by a Definite Integral (Calculus)*

Let $\mathbf{f}$ and $\mathbf{g}$ be real-valued continuous functions in the vector space $C[a, b]$. Show that

$$\langle \mathbf{f}, \mathbf{g} \rangle = \int_a^b f(x)g(x)\, dx$$

defines an inner product on $C[a, b]$.

Solution   We use familiar properties from calculus to verify the four parts of the definition.

1. $\langle \mathbf{f}, \mathbf{g} \rangle = \int_a^b f(x)g(x) \, dx = \int_a^b g(x)f(x) \, dx = \langle \mathbf{g}, \mathbf{f} \rangle$

2. $\langle \mathbf{f}, \mathbf{g} + \mathbf{h} \rangle = \int_a^b f(x)[g(x) + h(x)] \, dx$

$$= \int_a^b [f(x)g(x) + f(x)h(x)] \, dx$$

$$= \int_a^b f(x)g(x) \, dx + \int_a^b f(x)h(x) \, dx$$

$$= \langle \mathbf{f}, \mathbf{g} \rangle + \langle \mathbf{f}, \mathbf{h} \rangle$$

3. $c\langle \mathbf{f}, \mathbf{g} \rangle = c \int_a^b f(x)g(x) \, dx = \int_a^b cf(x)g(x) \, dx = \langle c\mathbf{f}, \mathbf{g} \rangle$

4. Since $[f(x)]^2 \geq 0$ for all x, we know from calculus that

$$\langle \mathbf{f}, \mathbf{f} \rangle = \int_a^b [f(x)]^2 dx \geq 0$$

with

$$\langle \mathbf{f}, \mathbf{f} \rangle = \int_a^b [f(x)]^2 dx = 0$$

if and only if $\mathbf{f}$ is the zero function in $C[a, b]$.

The following theorem lists some easily verified properties of inner products.

Theorem 5.7

Properties of Inner Products

Let $\mathbf{u}$, $\mathbf{v}$, and $\mathbf{w}$ be vectors in an inner product space V, and let c be any real number.
1. $\langle \mathbf{0}, \mathbf{v} \rangle = \langle \mathbf{v}, \mathbf{0} \rangle = 0$
2. $\langle \mathbf{u} + \mathbf{v}, \mathbf{w} \rangle = \langle \mathbf{u}, \mathbf{w} \rangle + \langle \mathbf{v}, \mathbf{w} \rangle$
3. $\langle \mathbf{u}, c\mathbf{v} \rangle = c\langle \mathbf{u}, \mathbf{v} \rangle$

Proof   We prove the first property and leave the proofs of the other two properties as exercises. (See Exercises 57 and 58.) From the definition of an inner product we know that $\langle \mathbf{0}, \mathbf{v} \rangle = \langle \mathbf{v}, \mathbf{0} \rangle$, so we need only show one of these to be zero. Using the fact that $0(\mathbf{v}) = \mathbf{0}$, we have

$$\langle \mathbf{0}, \mathbf{v} \rangle = \langle 0(\mathbf{v}), \mathbf{v} \rangle = 0\langle \mathbf{v}, \mathbf{v} \rangle = 0.$$

The definitions of norm (or length), distance, and angle for general inner product spaces closely parallel those given for Euclidean n-space. Note that the definition of the angle θ between $\mathbf{u}$ and $\mathbf{v}$ presumes that

$$-1 \le \frac{\langle \mathbf{u}, \mathbf{v} \rangle}{\|\mathbf{u}\| \|\mathbf{v}\|} \le 1$$

for a general inner product, which follows from the Cauchy-Schwarz Inequality given later in Theorem 5.8.

Definition of Norm, Distance, and Angle	Let $\mathbf{u}$ and $\mathbf{v}$ be vectors in an inner product space V. 1. The **norm** (or **length**) of $\mathbf{u}$ is $\|\mathbf{u}\| = \sqrt{\langle \mathbf{u}, \mathbf{u} \rangle}$. 2. The **distance** between $\mathbf{u}$ and $\mathbf{v}$ is $d(\mathbf{u}, \mathbf{v}) = \|\mathbf{u} - \mathbf{v}\|$. 3. The **angle** between two nonzero vectors $\mathbf{u}$ and $\mathbf{v}$ is given by $$\cos \theta = \frac{\langle \mathbf{u}, \mathbf{v} \rangle}{\|\mathbf{u}\| \|\mathbf{v}\|}, \quad 0 \le \theta \le \pi.$$ 4. $\mathbf{u}$ and $\mathbf{v}$ are **orthogonal** if $\langle \mathbf{u}, \mathbf{v} \rangle = 0$.

REMARK: If $\|\mathbf{v}\| = 1$, then $\mathbf{v}$ is called a **unit vector.** Moreover, if $\mathbf{v}$ is any nonzero vector in an inner product space V, then the vector $\mathbf{u} = \mathbf{v}/\|\mathbf{v}\|$ is a unit vector and is called the **unit vector in the direction of v.**

EXAMPLE 6   *Finding Inner Products*

For polynomials $\mathbf{p} = a_0 + a_1 x + \cdots + a_n x^n$ and $\mathbf{q} = b_0 + b_1 x + \cdots + b_n x^n$ in the vector space P_n, the function given by

$$\langle \mathbf{p}, \mathbf{q} \rangle = a_0 b_0 + a_1 b_1 + \cdots + a_n b_n$$

is an inner product. Let $p(x) = 1 - 2x^2$, $q(x) = 4 - 2x + x^2$, and $r(x) = x + 2x^2$ be polynomials in P_2, and determine the following.

(a) $\langle \mathbf{p}, \mathbf{q} \rangle$ (b) $\langle \mathbf{q}, \mathbf{r} \rangle$ (c) $\|\mathbf{q}\|$ (d) $d(\mathbf{p}, \mathbf{q})$

Solution   (a) The inner product of $\mathbf{p}$ and $\mathbf{q}$ is given by

$$\langle \mathbf{p}, \mathbf{q} \rangle = a_0 b_0 + a_1 b_1 + a_2 b_2$$
$$= (1)(4) + (0)(-2) + (-2)(1) = 2.$$

(b) The inner product of $\mathbf{q}$ and $\mathbf{r}$ is given by

$$\langle \mathbf{q}, \mathbf{r} \rangle = (4)(0) + (-2)(1) + (1)(2) = 0.$$

(c) The norm of $\mathbf{q}$ is given by

$$\|\mathbf{q}\| = \sqrt{\langle \mathbf{q}, \mathbf{q} \rangle} = \sqrt{4^2 + (-2)^2 + 1^2} = \sqrt{21}.$$

(d) The distance between $\mathbf{p}$ and $\mathbf{q}$ is given by

$$d(\mathbf{p}, \mathbf{q}) = \|\mathbf{p} - \mathbf{q}\| = \|(1 - 2x^2) - (4 - 2x + x^2)\|$$
$$= \|-3 + 2x - 3x^2\|$$
$$= \sqrt{(-3)^2 + 2^2 + (-3)^2} = \sqrt{22}.$$

Notice that the vectors $\mathbf{q}$ and $\mathbf{r}$ are orthogonal.

Orthogonality depends on the particular inner product used. That is, two vectors may be orthogonal with respect to one inner product but not another. Try reworking Example 6 using the inner product $\langle \mathbf{p}, \mathbf{q} \rangle = a_0 b_0 + a_1 b_1 + 2a_2 b_2$. With this inner product the only orthogonal pair is $\mathbf{p}$ and $\mathbf{q}$.

EXAMPLE 7   *Using the Inner Product on $C[0, 1]$ (Calculus)*

Use the inner product defined in Example 5 and the functions $f(x) = x$ and $g(x) = x^2$ in $C[0, 1]$ to find the following.

(a) $\|\mathbf{f}\|$ (b) $d(\mathbf{f}, \mathbf{g})$

Solution   (a) Since $f(x) = x$, we have

$$\|\mathbf{f}\|^2 = \langle \mathbf{f}, \mathbf{f} \rangle = \int_0^1 (x)(x)\, dx = \int_0^1 x^2\, dx$$

$$= \left[\frac{x^3}{3} \right]_0^1 = \frac{1}{3}.$$

Therefore $\|\mathbf{f}\| = 1/\sqrt{3}$.

(b) To find $d(\mathbf{f}, \mathbf{g})$, we write

$$[d(\mathbf{f}, \mathbf{g})]^2 = \langle \mathbf{f} - \mathbf{g}, \mathbf{f} - \mathbf{g} \rangle = \int_0^1 [f(x) - g(x)]^2\, dx = \int_0^1 [x - x^2]^2\, dx$$

$$= \int_0^1 [x^2 - 2x^3 + x^4]\, dx$$

$$= \left[\frac{x^3}{3} - \frac{x^4}{2} + \frac{x^5}{5} \right]_0^1 = \frac{1}{30}.$$

Therefore $d(\mathbf{f}, \mathbf{g}) = \dfrac{1}{\sqrt{30}}.$

TECHNOLOGY
NOTE

Many calculators and computers have built-in routines for approximating definite integrals. For example, on the TI-85, you can use the fnInt command from the CALC menu to verify Example 7(b) as follows.

$$\sqrt{(\text{fnInt}((x - x^2)^2, x, 0, 1))}$$

The result should be approximately $0.182574 \approx \dfrac{1}{\sqrt{30}}$.

In Example 7, we found that the distance between the functions $f(x) = x$ and $g(x) = x^2$ in $C[0, 1]$ is $1/\sqrt{30} \approx 0.183$. In practice, the *actual* distance between a pair of vectors is not so useful as the *relative* distance between several pairs. For instance, the distance between $g(x) = x^2$ and $h(x) = x^2 + 1$ in $C[0, 1]$ is 1. From Figure 5.9, this seems reasonable. That is, whatever norm is defined on $C[0, 1]$, it seems reasonable that we would want to say that **f** and **g** are closer than **g** and **h**.

Figure 5.9

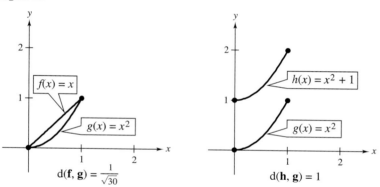

$$d(\mathbf{f}, \mathbf{g}) = \frac{1}{\sqrt{30}} \qquad d(\mathbf{h}, \mathbf{g}) = 1$$

The properties of length and distance that were listed for R^n in the previous section also hold for general inner product spaces. For instance, if **u** and **v** are vectors in an inner product space, then the following properties are true.

Properties of Norm	*Properties of Distance*
1. $\|\mathbf{u}\| \geq 0$	1. $d(\mathbf{u}, \mathbf{v}) \geq 0$
2. $\|\mathbf{u}\| = 0$ if and only if $\mathbf{u} = \mathbf{0}$.	2. $d(\mathbf{u}, \mathbf{v}) = 0$ if and only if $\mathbf{u} = \mathbf{v}$.
3. $\|c\mathbf{u}\| = |c| \, \|\mathbf{u}\|$	3. $d(\mathbf{u}, \mathbf{v}) = d(\mathbf{v}, \mathbf{u})$

The next theorem lists the general inner product space versions of the Cauchy-Schwarz Inequality, the Triangle Inequality, and the general Pythagorean Theorem.

Theorem 5.8   Let $\mathbf{u}$ and $\mathbf{v}$ be vectors in an inner product space V.
1. Cauchy-Schwarz Inequality: $|\langle \mathbf{u}, \mathbf{v} \rangle| \leq \|\mathbf{u}\| \, \|\mathbf{v}\|$
2. Triangle Inequality: $\|\mathbf{u} + \mathbf{v}\| \leq \|\mathbf{u}\| + \|\mathbf{v}\|$
3. Pythagorean Theorem: $\mathbf{u}$ and $\mathbf{v}$ are orthogonal if and only if
$$\|\mathbf{u} + \mathbf{v}\|^2 = \|\mathbf{u}\|^2 + \|\mathbf{v}\|^2.$$

The proofs of these three results parallel those given for Theorems 5.4, 5.5, and 5.6. We simply substitute $\langle \mathbf{u}, \mathbf{v} \rangle$ for the Euclidean inner product $\mathbf{u} \cdot \mathbf{v}$.

EXAMPLE 8   ***An Example of the Cauchy-Schwarz Inequality (Calculus)***

Let $f(x) = 1$ and $g(x) = x$ be functions in the vector space $C[0, 1]$, with the inner product defined in Example 5. Verify that
$$|\langle \mathbf{f}, \mathbf{g} \rangle| \leq \|\mathbf{f}\| \, \|\mathbf{g}\|.$$

Solution   For the left side of this inequality we have
$$\langle \mathbf{f}, \mathbf{g} \rangle = \int_0^1 f(x)g(x)\, dx = \int_0^1 x\, dx = \frac{x^2}{2}\Big]_0^1 = \frac{1}{2}.$$

For the right side of the inequality we have
$$\|\mathbf{f}\|^2 = \int_0^1 f(x)f(x)\, dx = \int_0^1 dx = x\Big]_0^1 = 1$$

and
$$\|\mathbf{g}\|^2 = \int_0^1 g(x)g(x)\, dx = \int_0^1 x^2\, dx = \frac{x^3}{3}\Big]_0^1 = \frac{1}{3}.$$

Therefore
$$\|\mathbf{f}\| \, \|\mathbf{g}\| = \sqrt{(1)\left(\frac{1}{3}\right)} = \frac{1}{\sqrt{3}} \approx 0.577,$$

and it follows that $|\langle \mathbf{f}, \mathbf{g} \rangle| \leq \|\mathbf{f}\| \, \|\mathbf{g}\|$.

Orthogonal Projections in Inner Product Spaces

Let $\mathbf{u}$ and $\mathbf{v}$ be vectors in the plane. If $\mathbf{v}$ is nonzero, then we can orthogonally project $\mathbf{u}$ onto $\mathbf{v}$, as shown in Figure 5.10. This projection is denoted by $\text{proj}_\mathbf{v}\mathbf{u}$. Since $\text{proj}_\mathbf{v}\mathbf{u}$ is a scalar multiple of $\mathbf{v}$, we can write
$$\text{proj}_\mathbf{v}\mathbf{u} = a\mathbf{v}.$$

If $a > 0$, as shown in Figure 5.10(a), then $\cos \theta > 0$ and the length of $\text{proj}_\mathbf{v}\mathbf{u}$ is

$$\|a\mathbf{v}\| = \|\mathbf{u}\| \cos \theta = \frac{\|\mathbf{u}\| \|\mathbf{v}\| \cos \theta}{\|\mathbf{v}\|} = \frac{\mathbf{u} \cdot \mathbf{v}}{\|\mathbf{v}\|},$$

which implies that $a = (\mathbf{u} \cdot \mathbf{v})/\|\mathbf{v}\|^2 = (\mathbf{u} \cdot \mathbf{v})/(\mathbf{v} \cdot \mathbf{v})$. Therefore

$$\text{proj}_\mathbf{v}\mathbf{u} = \frac{\mathbf{u} \cdot \mathbf{v}}{\mathbf{v} \cdot \mathbf{v}} \mathbf{v}.$$

If $a < 0$, as shown in Figure 5.10(b), then it can be shown that the orthogonal projection of $\mathbf{u}$ onto $\mathbf{v}$ is given by the same formula.

Figure 5.10

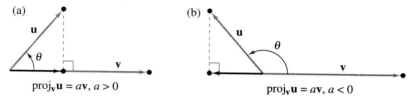

(a) $\text{proj}_\mathbf{v}\mathbf{u} = a\mathbf{v},\ a > 0$

(b) $\text{proj}_\mathbf{v}\mathbf{u} = a\mathbf{v},\ a < 0$

EXAMPLE 9   *Finding the Orthogonal Projection of **u** onto **v***

In R^2, the orthogonal projection of $\mathbf{u} = (4, 2)$ onto $\mathbf{v} = (3, 4)$ is given by

$$\text{proj}_\mathbf{v}\mathbf{u} = \frac{\mathbf{u} \cdot \mathbf{v}}{\mathbf{v} \cdot \mathbf{v}} \mathbf{v} = \frac{(4, 2) \cdot (3, 4)}{(3, 4) \cdot (3, 4)} (3, 4)$$

$$= \frac{20}{25}(3, 4)$$

$$= \left(\frac{12}{5}, \frac{16}{5}\right),$$

as shown in Figure 5.11.

Figure 5.11

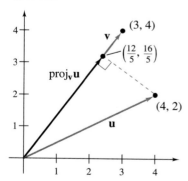

The notion of orthogonal projection extends naturally to a general inner product space in the following way.

Definition of Orthogonal Projection

Let $\mathbf{u}$ and $\mathbf{v}$ be vectors in an inner product space V, such that $\mathbf{v} \neq \mathbf{0}$. Then the **orthogonal projection** of $\mathbf{u}$ onto $\mathbf{v}$ is given by

$$\text{proj}_\mathbf{v}\mathbf{u} = \frac{\langle \mathbf{u}, \mathbf{v} \rangle}{\langle \mathbf{v}, \mathbf{v} \rangle} \mathbf{v}.$$

REMARK: If $\mathbf{v}$ is a unit vector, then $\langle \mathbf{v}, \mathbf{v} \rangle = \|\mathbf{v}\|^2 = 1$, and the formula for the orthogonal projection of $\mathbf{u}$ onto $\mathbf{v}$ takes the following simpler form.

$$\text{proj}_\mathbf{v}\mathbf{u} = \langle \mathbf{u}, \mathbf{v} \rangle \mathbf{v}$$

EXAMPLE 10   *Finding an Orthogonal Projection in R^3*

Use the Euclidean inner product in R^3 to find the orthogonal projection of $\mathbf{u} = (6, 2, 4)$ onto $\mathbf{v} = (1, 2, 0)$.

Solution   Since $\mathbf{u} \cdot \mathbf{v} = 10$ and $\|\mathbf{v}\|^2 = \mathbf{v} \cdot \mathbf{v} = 5$, the orthogonal projection of $\mathbf{u}$ onto $\mathbf{v}$ is

$$\begin{aligned}
\text{proj}_\mathbf{v}\mathbf{u} &= \frac{\mathbf{u} \cdot \mathbf{v}}{\mathbf{v} \cdot \mathbf{v}} \mathbf{v} \\
&= \frac{10}{5}(1, 2, 0) \\
&= 2(1, 2, 0) \\
&= (2, 4, 0).
\end{aligned}$$

REMARK: Notice in Example 10 that $\mathbf{u} - \text{proj}_\mathbf{v}\mathbf{u} = (6, 2, 4) - (2, 4, 0) = (4, -2, 4)$ is orthogonal to $\mathbf{v} = (1, 2, 0)$. This is true in general: If $\mathbf{u}$ and $\mathbf{v}$ are nonzero vectors in an inner product space, then $\mathbf{u} - \text{proj}_\mathbf{v}\mathbf{u}$ is orthogonal to $\mathbf{v}$. (See Exercise 56.)

An important property of orthogonal projections that will be used in approximation problems (Section 5.4) is given in the following theorem. It states that, of all possible scalar multiples of a vector $\mathbf{v}$, the orthogonal projection of $\mathbf{u}$ onto $\mathbf{v}$ is the one that is closest to $\mathbf{u}$, as shown in Figure 5.12. For instance, in Example 10, this theorem implies that, of all the scalar multiples of the vector $\mathbf{v} = (1, 2, 0)$, the vector $\text{proj}_\mathbf{v}\mathbf{u} = (2, 4, 0)$ is closest to $\mathbf{u} = (6, 2, 4)$. You are asked to prove this explicitly in Exercise 61.

Figure 5.12

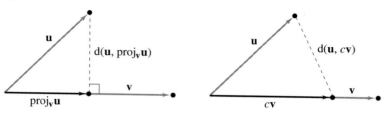

Theorem 5.9

Orthogonal Projection and Distance

Let **u** and **v** be two vectors in an inner product space V, such that $\mathbf{v} \neq \mathbf{0}$. Then

$$d(\mathbf{u}, \text{proj}_\mathbf{v}\mathbf{u}) < d(\mathbf{u}, c\mathbf{v}), \quad c \neq \frac{\langle \mathbf{u}, \mathbf{v} \rangle}{\langle \mathbf{v}, \mathbf{v} \rangle}.$$

Proof Let $b = \langle \mathbf{u}, \mathbf{v} \rangle / \langle \mathbf{v}, \mathbf{v} \rangle$. Then we can write

$$\|\mathbf{u} - c\mathbf{v}\|^2 = \|(\mathbf{u} - b\mathbf{v}) + (b - c)\mathbf{v}\|^2,$$

where $(\mathbf{u} - b\mathbf{v})$ and $(b - c)\mathbf{v}$ are orthogonal. You can verify this by using the inner product axioms to show that

$$\langle (\mathbf{u} - b\mathbf{v}), (b - c)\mathbf{v} \rangle = 0.$$

Now, by the Pythagorean Theorem we can write

$$\|(\mathbf{u} - b\mathbf{v}) + (b - c)\mathbf{v}\|^2 = \|\mathbf{u} - b\mathbf{v}\|^2 + \|(b - c)\mathbf{v}\|^2,$$

which implies that

$$\|\mathbf{u} - c\mathbf{v}\|^2 = \|\mathbf{u} - b\mathbf{v}\|^2 + (b - c)^2\|\mathbf{v}\|^2.$$

Since $b \neq c$ and $\mathbf{v} \neq \mathbf{0}$, we know that $(b - c)^2\|\mathbf{v}\|^2 > 0$. Therefore

$$\|\mathbf{u} - b\mathbf{v}\|^2 < \|\mathbf{u} - c\mathbf{v}\|^2,$$

and it follows that

$$d(\mathbf{u}, b\mathbf{v}) < d(\mathbf{u}, c\mathbf{v}).$$

The next example discusses a well-known type of orthogonal projection in the inner product space $C[a, b]$.

EXAMPLE 11   ***Finding an Orthogonal Projection in $C[a, b]$ (Calculus)***

Let $f(x) = 1$ and $g(x) = x$ be functions in $C[0, 1]$. Use the inner product given in Example 5 to find the orthogonal projection of **f** onto **g**.

Solution   From Example 8 we know that

$$\langle \mathbf{f}, \mathbf{g} \rangle = \tfrac{1}{2} \quad \text{and} \quad \|\mathbf{g}\|^2 = \langle \mathbf{g}, \mathbf{g} \rangle = \tfrac{1}{3}.$$

Therefore the orthogonal projection of $\mathbf{f}$ onto $\mathbf{g}$ is

$$\text{proj}_{\mathbf{g}}\mathbf{f} = \frac{\langle \mathbf{f}, \mathbf{g} \rangle}{\langle \mathbf{g}, \mathbf{g} \rangle} \mathbf{g} = \frac{1/2}{1/3} x$$

$$= \frac{3}{2} x$$

SECTION 5.2 ☐ EXERCISES

In Exercises 1–10, find (a) $\langle \mathbf{u}, \mathbf{v} \rangle$, (b) $\|\mathbf{u}\|$, and (c) $d(\mathbf{u}, \mathbf{v})$ for the given inner product defined in R^n.

1. $\mathbf{u} = (3, 4), \quad \mathbf{v} = (5, -12), \quad \langle \mathbf{u}, \mathbf{v} \rangle = \mathbf{u} \cdot \mathbf{v}$
2. $\mathbf{u} = (1, 1), \quad \mathbf{v} = (7, 9), \quad \langle \mathbf{u}, \mathbf{v} \rangle = \mathbf{u} \cdot \mathbf{v}$
3. $\mathbf{u} = (-4, 3), \quad \mathbf{v} = (0, 5), \quad \langle \mathbf{u}, \mathbf{v} \rangle = 3u_1v_1 + u_2v_2$
4. $\mathbf{u} = (0, -6), \quad \mathbf{v} = (-1, 1), \quad \langle \mathbf{u}, \mathbf{v} \rangle = u_1v_1 + 2u_2v_2$
5. $\mathbf{u} = (0, 9, 4), \quad \mathbf{v} = (9, -2, -4), \quad \langle \mathbf{u}, \mathbf{v} \rangle = \mathbf{u} \cdot \mathbf{v}$
6. $\mathbf{u} = (1, -5, 9), \quad \mathbf{v} = (-8, 5, 5), \quad \langle \mathbf{u}, \mathbf{v} \rangle = \mathbf{u} \cdot \mathbf{v}$
7. $\mathbf{u} = (8, 0, -8), \quad \mathbf{v} = (8, 3, 16),$
   $\langle \mathbf{u}, \mathbf{v} \rangle = 2u_1v_1 + 3u_2v_2 + u_3v_3$
8. $\mathbf{u} = (1, 1, 1), \quad \mathbf{v} = (2, 5, 2),$
   $\langle \mathbf{u}, \mathbf{v} \rangle = u_1v_1 + 2u_2v_2 + u_3v_3$
9. $\mathbf{u} = (8, -3, -1), \quad \mathbf{v} = (-5, 4, 9),$
   $\langle \mathbf{u}, \mathbf{v} \rangle = u_1v_1 + 2u_2v_2 + u_3v_3$
10. $\mathbf{u} = (2, 0, 1, -1), \quad \mathbf{v} = (2, 2, 0, 1), \quad \langle \mathbf{u}, \mathbf{v} \rangle = \mathbf{u} \cdot \mathbf{v}$

(Calculus) In Exercises 11–14, use the given functions $\mathbf{f}$ and $\mathbf{g}$ in $C[-1, 1]$ to find (a) $\langle \mathbf{f}, \mathbf{g} \rangle$, (b) $\|\mathbf{f}\|$, and (c) $d(\mathbf{f}, \mathbf{g})$ for the inner product given by

$$\langle \mathbf{f}, \mathbf{g} \rangle = \int_{-1}^{1} f(x)g(x)\, dx.$$

11. $f(x) = x^2, \quad g(x) = x^2 + 1$
12. $f(x) = -x, \quad g(x) = x^2 - x + 2$
13. $f(x) = x, \quad g(x) = e^x$ 14. $f(x) = 1, \quad g(x) = 3x^2 - 1$

In Exercises 15 and 16, use the inner product

$\langle A, B \rangle = 2a_{11}b_{11} + a_{12}b_{12} + a_{21}b_{21} + 2a_{22}b_{22}$

to find (a) $\langle A, B \rangle$, (b) $\|A\|$, and (c) $d(A, B)$ for the given matrices in $M_{2,2}$.

15. $A = \begin{bmatrix} -1 & 3 \\ 4 & -2 \end{bmatrix}, \quad B = \begin{bmatrix} 0 & -2 \\ 1 & 1 \end{bmatrix}$

16. $A = \begin{bmatrix} 1 & 0 \\ 0 & 1 \end{bmatrix}, \quad B = \begin{bmatrix} 0 & 1 \\ 1 & 0 \end{bmatrix}$

In Exercises 17 and 18, use the inner product

$\langle \mathbf{p}, \mathbf{q} \rangle = a_0b_0 + a_1b_1 + a_2b_2$

to find (a) $\langle \mathbf{p}, \mathbf{q} \rangle$, (b) $\|\mathbf{p}\|$, and (c) $d(\mathbf{p}, \mathbf{q})$ for the given polynomials in P_2.

17. $p(x) = 1 - x + 3x^2, \quad q(x) = x - x^2$
18. $p(x) = 1 + x^2, \quad q(x) = 1 - x^2$

In Exercises 19–22, prove that the indicated function is an inner product.

19. $\langle \mathbf{u}, \mathbf{v} \rangle$ given in Exercise 3   20. $\langle \mathbf{u}, \mathbf{v} \rangle$ given in Exercise 7
21. $\langle A, B \rangle$ given in Exercises 15 and 16
22. $\langle \mathbf{p}, \mathbf{q} \rangle$ given in Exercises 17 and 18

In Exercises 23–26, state why $\langle \mathbf{u}, \mathbf{v} \rangle$ is not an inner product for $\mathbf{u} = (u_1, u_2)$ and $\mathbf{v} = (v_1, v_2)$ in R^2.

23. $\langle \mathbf{u}, \mathbf{v} \rangle = u_1v_1$ 24. $\langle \mathbf{u}, \mathbf{v} \rangle = u_1v_1 - u_2v_2$
25. $\langle \mathbf{u}, \mathbf{v} \rangle = u_1^2v_1^2 + u_2^2v_2^2$
26. $\langle \mathbf{u}, \mathbf{v} \rangle = 3u_1v_2 - u_2v_1$

In Exercises 27–32, find the angle between the given vectors.

27. $\mathbf{u} = (3, 4), \quad \mathbf{v} = (5, -12), \quad \langle \mathbf{u}, \mathbf{v} \rangle = \mathbf{u} \cdot \mathbf{v}$

28. $u = (-4, 3)$, $v = (0, 5)$, $\langle u, v \rangle = 3u_1v_1 + u_2v_2$

29. $u = (1, 1, 1)$, $v = (2, -2, 2)$,
$\langle u, v \rangle = u_1v_1 + 2u_2v_2 + u_3v_3$

30. $p(x) = 1 - x + x^2$, $q(x) = 1 + x + x^2$,
$\langle p, q \rangle = a_0b_0 + a_1b_1 + a_2b_2$

31. (Calculus) $f(x) = x$, $g(x) = x^2$,
$$\langle f, g \rangle = \int_{-1}^{1} f(x)g(x)\, dx$$

32. (Calculus) $f(x) = 1$, $g(x) = x^2$,
$$\langle f, g \rangle = \int_{-1}^{1} f(x)g(x)\, dx$$

In Exercises 33–38, verify (a) the Cauchy-Schwarz Inequality and (b) the Triangle Inequality.

33. $u = (5, 12)$, $v = (3, 4)$, $\langle u, v \rangle = u \cdot v$

34. $u = (1, 0, 4)$, $v = (-5, 4, 1)$, $\langle u, v \rangle = u \cdot v$

35. $p(x) = 2x$, $q(x) = 3x^2 + 1$, $\langle p, q \rangle = a_0b_0 + a_1b_1 + a_2b_2$

36. $A = \begin{bmatrix} 0 & 3 \\ 2 & 1 \end{bmatrix}$, $B = \begin{bmatrix} -3 & 1 \\ 4 & 3 \end{bmatrix}$,
$\langle A, B \rangle = a_{11}b_{11} + a_{12}b_{12} + a_{21}b_{21} + a_{22}b_{22}$

37. (Calculus) $f(x) = \sin x$, $g(x) = \cos x$,
$$\langle f, g \rangle = \int_{-\pi}^{\pi} f(x)g(x)\, dx$$

38. (Calculus) $f(x) = 1$, $g(x) = \cos \pi x$,
$$\langle f, g \rangle = \int_{0}^{2} f(x)g(x)\, dx$$

(Calculus) In Exercises 39–42, show that f and g are orthogonal in the inner product space $C[a, b]$ with the inner product given by
$$\langle f, g \rangle = \int_{a}^{b} f(x)g(x)\, dx.$$

39. $C[-\pi, \pi]$, $f(x) = \cos x$, $g(x) = \sin x$

40. $C[-1, 1]$, $f(x) = x$, $g(x) = \frac{1}{2}(3x^2 - 1)$

41. $C[-1, 1]$, $f(x) = x$, $g(x) = \frac{1}{2}(5x^3 - 3x)$

42. $C[0, \pi]$, $f(x) = 1$, $g(x) = \cos(2nx)$, $n = 1, 2, 3, \ldots$

In Exercises 43 and 44, (a) find $proj_v u$, (b) find $proj_u v$, and (c) sketch a graph of both results.

43. $u = (1, 2)$, $v = (2, 1)$ **44.** $u = (-1, 3)$, $v = (4, 4)$

In Exercises 45 and 46, find (a) $proj_v u$ and (b) $proj_u v$.

45. $u = (1, 3, -2)$, $v = (0, -1, 1)$

46. $u = (0, 1, 3, -6)$, $v = (-1, 1, 2, 2)$

(Calculus) In Exercises 47–52, find the orthogonal projection of f onto g. Use the inner product in $C[a, b]$ given by
$$\langle f, g \rangle = \int_{a}^{b} f(x)g(x)\, dx.$$

47. $C[-1, 1]$, $f(x) = x$, $g(x) = 1$

48. $C[-1, 1]$, $f(x) = x^3 - x$, $g(x) = 2x - 1$

49. $C[0, 1]$, $f(x) = x$, $g(x) = e^x$

50. $C[-\pi, \pi]$, $f(x) = \sin x$, $g(x) = \cos x$

51. $C[-\pi, \pi]$, $f(x) = 1$, $g(x) = \sin 3x$

52. $C[-\pi, \pi]$, $f(x) = \sin 2x$, $g(x) = \sin 3x$

53. Let $u = (4, 2)$ and $v = (2, -2)$ be vectors in R^2 with the inner product $\langle u, v \rangle = u_1v_1 + 2u_2v_2$.
(a) Show that u and v are orthogonal.
(b) Sketch the vectors u and v. Are they orthogonal in the Euclidean sense?

54. Prove that $\|u + v\|^2 + \|u - v\|^2 = 2\|u\|^2 + 2\|v\|^2$ for any vectors u and v in an inner product space V.

55. Prove that the following function is an inner product for R^n.
$\langle u, v \rangle = c_1u_1v_1 + c_2u_2v_2 + \cdots + c_nu_nv_n$, $c_i > 0$

56. Let u and v be nonzero vectors in an inner product space V. Prove that $u - proj_v u$ is orthogonal to v.

57. Prove property 2 of Theorem 5.7. That is, prove that if u, v, and w are vectors in an inner product space, then $\langle u + v, w \rangle = \langle u, w \rangle + \langle v, w \rangle$.

58. Prove property 3 of Theorem 5.7. That is, prove that if u and v are vectors in an inner product space and c is a scalar, then $\langle u, cv \rangle = c\langle u, v \rangle$.

59. Let W be a subspace of the inner product space V.
(a) Prove that the following set $W^\perp$ is a subspace of V.
$W^\perp = \{v \in V: \langle v, w \rangle = 0 \text{ for all } w \in W\}$
(b) Find $W^\perp$ if $W = \text{span}(1, 2, 3)$ in $V = R^3$.

60. Let $\langle u, v \rangle$ be the Euclidean inner product on R^n. Prove that for any $n \times n$ matrix A, (a) $\langle A^Tu, v \rangle = \langle u, Av \rangle$ and (b) $\langle A^TAu, u \rangle = \|Au\|^2$.

61. Let $u = (6, 2, 4)$ and $v = (1, 2, 0)$ be the two vectors in Example 10. Without using Theorem 5.9, show that among all the scalar multiples cv of the vector v, the projection of u onto v is the vector closest to u.

5.3 ORTHONORMAL BASES: GRAM-SCHMIDT PROCESS

We saw in Section 4.7 that a vector space can have many different bases. While studying that section you should have noticed that certain bases are more convenient than others. For example, R^3 has the convenient standard basis

$$B = \{(1, 0, 0), (0, 1, 0), (0, 0, 1)\}.$$

This set is the *standard* basis for R^3 because it has special characteristics that are particularly useful. One important characteristic is that the three vectors in the basis are *mutually orthogonal.* That is,

$$(1, 0, 0) \cdot (0, 1, 0) = 0$$
$$(1, 0, 0) \cdot (0, 0, 1) = 0$$
$$(0, 1, 0) \cdot (0, 0, 1) = 0.$$

A second important characteristic is that each vector in the basis is a *unit vector.*

This section identifies some advantages of bases consisting of mutually orthogonal unit vectors and develops a procedure, known as the **Gram-Schmidt orthonormalization process,** for constructing such bases.

Definition of Orthogonal and Orthonormal Sets	A set S of vectors in an inner product space V is called **orthogonal** if every pair of vectors in S is orthogonal. If, in addition, each vector in the set is a unit vector, then S is called **orthonormal.**

Figure 5.13

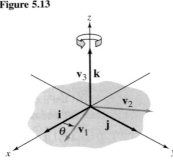

For $S = \{\mathbf{v}_1, \mathbf{v}_2, \ldots, \mathbf{v}_n\}$, this definition has the following form

Orthogonal
1. $\langle \mathbf{v}_i, \mathbf{v}_j \rangle = 0, \ i \neq j$

Orthonormal
1. $\langle \mathbf{v}_i, \mathbf{v}_j \rangle = 0, \ i \neq j$
2. $\|\mathbf{v}_i\| = 1, \ i = 1, 2, \ldots, n$

If S is a *basis,* then it is called an **orthogonal basis** or an **orthonormal basis,** respectively.

The standard basis in R^n is orthonormal, but it is not the only orthonormal basis for R^n. For instance, a nonstandard orthonormal basis for R^3 can be formed by rotating the standard basis about the z-axis to form

$$B = \{(\cos \theta, \sin \theta, 0), (-\sin \theta, \cos \theta, 0), (0, 0, 1)\},$$

as shown in Figure 5.13. Try verifying that the dot product of any two distinct vectors in B is zero, and that each vector in B is a unit vector. Example 1 describes another nonstandard orthonormal basis for R^3.

EXAMPLE 1   *A Nonstandard Orthonormal Basis in R^3*

Show that the following set is an orthonormal basis for R^3.

$$S = \left\{ \overset{v_1}{\left(\frac{1}{\sqrt{2}}, \frac{1}{\sqrt{2}}, 0 \right)}, \overset{v_2}{\left(-\frac{\sqrt{2}}{6}, \frac{\sqrt{2}}{6}, \frac{2\sqrt{2}}{3} \right)}, \overset{v_3}{\left(\frac{2}{3}, -\frac{2}{3}, \frac{1}{3} \right)} \right\}$$

Solution: First we show that the three vectors are mutually orthogonal.

$$\mathbf{v}_1 \cdot \mathbf{v}_2 = -\frac{1}{6} + \frac{1}{6} + 0 = 0$$

$$\mathbf{v}_1 \cdot \mathbf{v}_3 = \frac{2}{3\sqrt{2}} - \frac{2}{3\sqrt{2}} + 0 = 0$$

Figure 5.14

$$\mathbf{v}_2 \cdot \mathbf{v}_3 = -\frac{\sqrt{2}}{9} - \frac{\sqrt{2}}{9} + \frac{2\sqrt{2}}{9} = 0$$

Furthermore, each vector is of length 1, because

$$\|\mathbf{v}_1\| = \sqrt{\mathbf{v}_1 \cdot \mathbf{v}_1} = \sqrt{\tfrac{1}{2} + \tfrac{1}{2} + 0} = 1$$

$$\|\mathbf{v}_2\| = \sqrt{\mathbf{v}_2 \cdot \mathbf{v}_2} = \sqrt{\tfrac{2}{36} + \tfrac{2}{36} + \tfrac{8}{9}} = 1$$

$$\|\mathbf{v}_3\| = \sqrt{\mathbf{v}_3 \cdot \mathbf{v}_3} = \sqrt{\tfrac{4}{9} + \tfrac{4}{9} + \tfrac{1}{9}} = 1.$$

Therefore S is an orthonormal set. Since the three vectors do not lie in the same plane (see Figure 5.14), we know that they span R^3. Hence by Theorem 4.12 they form a (nonstandard) orthonormal basis for R^3.

EXAMPLE 2 *An Orthonormal Basis for P_3*

In P_3, with the inner product

$$\langle \mathbf{p}, \mathbf{q} \rangle = a_0 b_0 + a_1 b_1 + a_2 b_2 + a_3 b_3,$$

the standard basis $B = \{1, x, x^2, x^3\}$ is orthonormal. The verification of this is left as an exercise. (See Exercise 11.)

The orthogonal set in the following example is used to construct Fourier approximations of continuous functions. (See Section 5.5.)

EXAMPLE 3 *An Orthogonal Set in $C[0, 2\pi]$ (Calculus)*

In $C[0, 2\pi]$, with the inner product

$$\langle \mathbf{f}, \mathbf{g} \rangle = \int_0^{2\pi} f(x)g(x) \, dx,$$

show that the set

$$S = \{1, \sin x, \cos x, \sin 2x, \cos 2x, \ldots, \sin nx, \cos nx\}$$

is orthogonal.

Solution: To show that this set is orthogonal, we need to verify the following inner products, where m and n are positive integers.

$$\langle 1, \sin nx \rangle = \int_0^{2\pi} \sin nx \, dx = 0$$

$$\langle 1, \cos nx \rangle = \int_0^{2\pi} \cos nx \, dx = 0$$

$$\langle \sin mx, \cos nx \rangle = \int_0^{2\pi} \sin mx \cos nx \, dx = 0$$

$$\langle \sin mx, \sin nx \rangle = \int_0^{2\pi} \sin mx \sin nx \, dx = 0, \quad m \neq n$$

$$\langle \cos mx, \cos nx \rangle = \int_0^{2\pi} \cos mx \cos nx \, dx = 0, \quad m \neq n$$

We verify one of these and leave the others to you. If $m \neq n$, then we use the formula for rewriting a product of trigonometric functions as a sum to obtain

$$\int_0^{2\pi} \sin mx \cos nx \, dx = \frac{1}{2} \int_0^{2\pi} [\sin (m + n)x + \sin (m - n)x] \, dx$$

$$= -\frac{1}{2} \left[\frac{\cos(m + n)x}{m + n} + \frac{\cos(m - n)x}{m - n} \right]_0^{2\pi} = 0.$$

If $m = n$, then $\displaystyle\int_0^{2\pi} \sin mx \cos mx \, dx = \frac{1}{2m} \Big[\sin^2 mx \Big]_0^{2\pi} = 0.$

Note that in Example 3 we showed only that the set S is orthogonal. This particular set is not orthonormal. An orthonormal set may be formed, however, by normalizing each vector in S. That is, since

$$\| 1 \|^2 = \int_0^{2\pi} dx = 2\pi$$

$$\| \sin nx \|^2 = \int_0^{2\pi} \sin^2 nx \, dx = \pi$$

$$\| \cos nx \|^2 = \int_0^{2\pi} \cos^2 nx \, dx = \pi,$$

it follows that the set

$$\left\{ \frac{1}{\sqrt{2\pi}}, \frac{1}{\sqrt{\pi}} \sin x, \frac{1}{\sqrt{\pi}} \cos x, \ldots, \frac{1}{\sqrt{\pi}} \sin nx, \frac{1}{\sqrt{\pi}} \cos nx \right\}$$

is orthonormal.

Each set in Examples 1, 2, and 3 is linearly independent. Linear independence is a characteristic of any orthogonal set of nonzero vectors, as stated in the following theorem.

Theorem 5.10

Orthogonal Sets Are Linearly Independent

If $S = \{\mathbf{v}_1, \mathbf{v}_2, \ldots, \mathbf{v}_n\}$ is an orthogonal set of *nonzero* vectors in an inner product space V, then S is linearly independent.

Proof: We need to show that the vector equation

$$c_1\mathbf{v}_1 + c_2\mathbf{v}_2 + \cdots + c_n\mathbf{v}_n = \mathbf{0}$$

implies that $c_1 = c_2 = \cdots = c_n = 0$. To do this, we form the inner product of the left side of the equation with each vector in S. That is, for each i,

$$\langle (c_1\mathbf{v}_1 + c_2\mathbf{v}_2 + \cdots + c_i\mathbf{v}_i + \cdots + c_n\mathbf{v}_n), \mathbf{v}_i \rangle = \langle \mathbf{0}, \mathbf{v}_i \rangle$$

$$c_1\langle \mathbf{v}_1, \mathbf{v}_i \rangle + c_2\langle \mathbf{v}_2, \mathbf{v}_i \rangle + \cdots + c_i\langle \mathbf{v}_i, \mathbf{v}_i \rangle + \cdots + c_n\langle \mathbf{v}_n, \mathbf{v}_i \rangle = 0.$$

Now, since S is orthogonal, $\langle \mathbf{v}_i, \mathbf{v}_j \rangle = 0$ for $j \neq i$, and thus the equation reduces to

$$c_i\langle \mathbf{v}_i \cdot \mathbf{v}_i \rangle = 0.$$

But because each vector in S is nonzero, we know that

$$\langle \mathbf{v}_i, \mathbf{v}_i \rangle = \|\mathbf{v}_i\|^2 \neq 0.$$

Hence every c_i must be zero and the set must be linearly independent.

As a consequence of Theorems 4.12 and 5.10, we have the following result.

Corollary to Theorem 5.10

If V is an inner product space of dimension n, then any orthogonal set of n nonzero vectors is a basis of V.

EXAMPLE 4   *Using Orthogonality to Test for a Basis*

Show that the following set is a basis for R^4.

$$\overset{\mathbf{v}_1}{} \quad \overset{\mathbf{v}_2}{} \quad \overset{\mathbf{v}_3}{} \quad \overset{\mathbf{v}_4}{}$$

$$S = \{(2, 3, 2, -2), (1, 0, 0, 1), (-1, 0, 2, 1), (-1, 2, -1, 1)\}$$

Solution: We begin by noting that the set S has four nonzero vectors. Thus, by the corollary to Theorem 5.10, we can show that it is a basis for R^4 by showing that it is an orthogonal set.

A test for orthogonality shows that

$$\mathbf{v}_1 \cdot \mathbf{v}_2 = 2 + 0 + 0 - 2 = 0$$
$$\mathbf{v}_1 \cdot \mathbf{v}_3 = -2 + 0 + 4 - 2 = 0$$
$$\mathbf{v}_1 \cdot \mathbf{v}_4 = -2 + 6 - 2 - 2 = 0$$
$$\mathbf{v}_2 \cdot \mathbf{v}_3 = -1 + 0 + 0 + 1 = 0$$
$$\mathbf{v}_2 \cdot \mathbf{v}_4 = -1 + 0 + 0 + 1 = 0$$
$$\mathbf{v}_3 \cdot \mathbf{v}_4 = 1 + 0 - 2 + 1 = 0$$

Thus S is orthogonal, and by the corollary to Theorem 5.10 it is a basis for R^4.

Figure 5.15

$$\mathbf{w} = \mathbf{w}_1 + \mathbf{w}_2 = c_1\mathbf{i} + c_2\mathbf{j}$$

Section 4.7 discussed a technique for finding a coordinate representation relative to a nonstandard basis. If the basis is *orthonormal*, this procedure can be streamlined.

Before presenting this result, we look at an example in R^2. Figure 5.15 shows that $\mathbf{i} = (1, 0)$ and $\mathbf{j} = (0, 1)$ form an orthonormal basis for R^2. Any vector $\mathbf{w}$ in R^2 can be represented as $\mathbf{w} = \mathbf{w}_1 + \mathbf{w}_2$, where $\mathbf{w}_1 = \text{proj}_{\mathbf{i}}\mathbf{w}$ and $\mathbf{w}_2 = \text{proj}_{\mathbf{j}}\mathbf{w}$. Since $\mathbf{i}$ and $\mathbf{j}$ are unit vectors, it follows that $\mathbf{w}_1 = (\mathbf{w} \cdot \mathbf{i})\mathbf{i}$ and $\mathbf{w}_2 = (\mathbf{w} \cdot \mathbf{j})\mathbf{j}$. Consequently,

$$\mathbf{w} = \mathbf{w}_1 + \mathbf{w}_2 = (\mathbf{w} \cdot \mathbf{i})\mathbf{i} + (\mathbf{w} \cdot \mathbf{j})\mathbf{j} = c_1\mathbf{i} + c_2\mathbf{j},$$

which shows us that the coefficients c_1 and c_2 are simply the dot products of $\mathbf{w}$ with the respective basis vectors. This result is generalized in the next theorem.

Theorem 5.11

Coordinates Relative to an Orthonormal Basis

If $B = \{\mathbf{v}_1, \mathbf{v}_2, \ldots, \mathbf{v}_n\}$ is an orthonormal basis for an inner product space V, then the coordinate representation of a vector $\mathbf{w}$ with respect to B is

$$\mathbf{w} = \langle\mathbf{w}, \mathbf{v}_1\rangle\mathbf{v}_1 + \langle\mathbf{w}, \mathbf{v}_2\rangle\mathbf{v}_2 + \cdots + \langle\mathbf{w}, \mathbf{v}_n\rangle\mathbf{v}_n.$$

Proof: Since B is a basis for V, there must exist unique scalars $c_1, c_2, \ldots, c_n$ such that

$$\mathbf{w} = c_1\mathbf{v}_1 + c_2\mathbf{v}_2 + \cdots + c_n\mathbf{v}_n.$$

Taking the inner product (with $\mathbf{v}_i$) of both sides of this equation, we have

$$\langle\mathbf{w}, \mathbf{v}_i\rangle = \langle(c_1\mathbf{v}_1 + c_2\mathbf{v}_2 + \cdots + c_n\mathbf{v}_n), \mathbf{v}_i\rangle$$

$$= c_1\langle\mathbf{v}_1, \mathbf{v}_i\rangle + c_2\langle\mathbf{v}_2, \mathbf{v}_i\rangle + \cdots + c_n\langle\mathbf{v}_n, \mathbf{v}_i\rangle,$$

and by the orthogonality of B this equation reduces to

$$\langle\mathbf{w}, \mathbf{v}_i\rangle = c_i\langle\mathbf{v}_i, \mathbf{v}_i\rangle.$$

As B is orthonormal, we have $\langle\mathbf{v}_i, \mathbf{v}_i\rangle = \|\mathbf{v}_i\|^2 = 1$, and it follows that $\langle\mathbf{w}, \mathbf{v}_i\rangle = c_i$.

In Theorem 5.11 the coordinates of $\mathbf{w}$ relative to the *orthonormal* basis B are called the **Fourier coefficients** of $\mathbf{w}$ relative to B, after the French mathematician Jean-Baptiste Joseph Fourier (1768-1830). The corresponding coordinate matrix of $\mathbf{w}$ relative to B is

$$[\mathbf{w}]_B = [c_1 \ c_2 \ \cdots \ c_n]^T$$

$$= [\langle \mathbf{w}, \mathbf{v}_1 \rangle \ \langle \mathbf{w}, \mathbf{v}_2 \rangle \ \cdots \ \langle \mathbf{w}, \mathbf{v}_n \rangle]^T.$$

EXAMPLE 5   ***Representing Vectors Relative to an Orthonormal Basis***

Find the coordinates of $\mathbf{w} = (5, -5, 2)$ relative to the following orthonormal basis for R^3.

$$B = \left\{ \overset{\mathbf{v}_1}{\left(\tfrac{3}{5}, \tfrac{4}{5}, 0 \right)}, \overset{\mathbf{v}_2}{\left(-\tfrac{4}{5}, \tfrac{3}{5}, 0 \right)}, \overset{\mathbf{v}_3}{(0, 0, 1)} \right\}$$

Solution: Since B is orthonormal, we can use Theorem 5.11 to find the required coordinates.

$$\mathbf{w} \cdot \mathbf{v}_1 = (5, -5, 2) \cdot \left(\tfrac{3}{5}, \tfrac{4}{5}, 0 \right) = -1$$

$$\mathbf{w} \cdot \mathbf{v}_2 = (5, -5, 2) \cdot \left(-\tfrac{4}{5}, \tfrac{3}{5}, 0 \right) = -7$$

$$\mathbf{w} \cdot \mathbf{v}_3 = (5, -5, 2) \cdot (0, 0, 1) = 2$$

Thus the coordinate matrix relative to B is $[\mathbf{w}]_B = \begin{bmatrix} -1 \\ -7 \\ 2 \end{bmatrix}$.

Gram-Schmidt Orthonormalization Process

Having seen one of the advantages of orthonormal bases (the straightforwardness of coordinate representation), we now look at a procedure for finding such a basis. This procedure is called the **Gram-Schmidt orthonormalization process,** after the Danish mathematician Jorgen Pederson Gram (1850–1916) and the German mathematician Erhardt Schmidt (1876–1959). It has three steps.

1. Begin with a basis for the inner product space. It need not be orthogonal nor consist of unit vectors.
2. Convert the given basis to an orthogonal basis.
3. Normalize each vector in the orthogonal basis to form an orthonormal basis.

REMARK: The Gram-Schmidt orthonormalization process leads to a matrix factorization similar to the LU–factorization you studied in Chapter 2. You are asked to investigate this QR–**factorization** in Project 1 at the end of this chapter.

Theorem 5.12

Gram-Schmidt Orthonormalization Process

1. Let $B = \{\mathbf{v}_1, \mathbf{v}_2, \ldots, \mathbf{v}_n\}$ be a basis for an inner product space V.
2. Let $B' = \{\mathbf{w}_1, \mathbf{w}_2, \ldots, \mathbf{w}_n\}$ where $\mathbf{w}_i$ is given by

$$\mathbf{w}_1 = \mathbf{v}_1$$

$$\mathbf{w}_2 = \mathbf{v}_2 - \frac{\langle \mathbf{v}_2, \mathbf{w}_1 \rangle}{\langle \mathbf{w}_1, \mathbf{w}_1 \rangle} \mathbf{w}_1$$

Theorem 5.12

Gram-Schmidt Orthonormalization Process

(Continued)

$$w_3 = v_3 - \frac{\langle v_3, w_1 \rangle}{\langle w_1, w_1 \rangle} w_1 - \frac{\langle v_3, w_2 \rangle}{\langle w_2, w_2 \rangle} w_2$$

$$\vdots$$

$$w_n = v_n - \frac{\langle v_n, w_1 \rangle}{\langle w_1, w_1 \rangle} w_1 - \frac{\langle v_n, w_2 \rangle}{\langle w_2, w_2 \rangle} w_2 - \cdots - \frac{\langle v_n, w_{n-1} \rangle}{\langle w_{n-1}, w_{n-1} \rangle} w_{n-1}.$$

Then B' is an *orthogonal* basis for V.

3. Let $u_i = w_i / \|w_i\|$. Then the set $B'' = \{u_1, u_2, \ldots, u_n\}$ is an *orthonormal* basis for V. Moreover, $\text{span}\{v_1, v_2, \ldots, v_k\} = \text{span}\{u_1, u_2, \ldots, u_k\}$ for $k = 1, 2, \ldots n$.

Figure 5.16

$\{v_1, v_2\}$ is a basis for R^2.

Rather than give a general proof of this theorem, it seems more instructive to discuss a special case for which we can use a geometric model. Let $\{v_1, v_2\}$ be a basis for R^2, as shown in Figure 5.16. To determine an orthogonal basis for R^2, we first choose one of the original vectors, say v_1. Now we want to find a second vector that is orthogonal to v_1. Figure 5.17 shows that $v_2 - \text{proj}_{v_1} v_2$ has this property. Thus, by letting

$$w_1 = v_1 \quad \text{and} \quad w_2 = v_2 - \text{proj}_{v_1} v_2 = v_2 - \frac{v_2 \cdot w_1}{w_1 \cdot w_1} w_1,$$

we can conclude that the set $\{w_1, w_2\}$ is orthogonal. By the corollary to Theorem 5.10, it is therefore a basis for R^2. Finally, by normalizing w_1 and w_2, we obtain the following orthonormal basis for R^2.

$$\{u_1, u_2\} = \left\{ \frac{w_1}{\|w_1\|}, \frac{w_2}{\|w_2\|} \right\}$$

Figure 5.17

$w_2 = v_2 - \text{proj}_{v_1} v_2$
is orthogonal to $w_1 = v_1$

EXAMPLE 6   ***Applying the Gram-Schmidt Orthonormalization Process***

Apply the Gram-Schmidt orthonormalization process to the following basis of R^2.

$$B = \{\overset{v_1}{(1, 1)}, \overset{v_2}{(0, 1)}\}$$

Solution   The Gram-Schmidt orthonormalization process produces

$$\mathbf{w}_1 = \mathbf{v}_1 = (1, 1)$$

$$\mathbf{w}_2 = \mathbf{v}_2 - \frac{\mathbf{v}_2 \cdot \mathbf{w}_1}{\mathbf{w}_1 \cdot \mathbf{w}_1} \mathbf{w}_1$$

$$= (0, 1) - \tfrac{1}{2}(1, 1) = \left(-\tfrac{1}{2}, \tfrac{1}{2}\right).$$

The set $B' = \{\mathbf{w}_1, \mathbf{w}_2\}$ is an orthogonal basis for R^2. By normalizing each vector in B', we obtain

$$\mathbf{u}_1 = \frac{\mathbf{w}_1}{\|\mathbf{w}_1\|} = \frac{1}{\sqrt{2}}(1, 1) = \frac{\sqrt{2}}{2}(1, 1) = \left(\frac{\sqrt{2}}{2}, \frac{\sqrt{2}}{2}\right)$$

$$\mathbf{u}_2 = \frac{\mathbf{w}_2}{\|\mathbf{w}_2\|} = \frac{1}{1/\sqrt{2}}\left(-\frac{1}{2}, \frac{1}{2}\right) = \frac{\sqrt{2}}{2}(-1, 1) = \left(-\frac{\sqrt{2}}{2}, \frac{\sqrt{2}}{2}\right).$$

Thus $B'' = \{\mathbf{u}_1, \mathbf{u}_2\}$ is an orthonormal basis for R^2. See Figure 5.18.

Figure 5.18

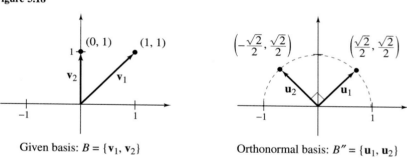

Given basis: $B = \{\mathbf{v}_1, \mathbf{v}_2\}$ Orthonormal basis: $B'' = \{\mathbf{u}_1, \mathbf{u}_2\}$

REMARK: An orthonormal set derived by the Gram-Schmidt orthonormalization process depends on the order of the vectors in the basis. For instance, try reworking Example 6 with the original basis ordered as $\{\mathbf{v}_2, \mathbf{v}_1\}$ rather than $\{\mathbf{v}_1, \mathbf{v}_2\}$.

EXAMPLE 7   ***Applying the Gram-Schmidt Orthonormalization Process***

Apply the Gram-Schmidt orthonormalization process to the following basis of R^3.

$$\overset{\mathbf{v}_1}{\phantom{B = \{}} \quad \overset{\mathbf{v}_2}{} \quad \overset{\mathbf{v}_3}{}$$
$$B = \{(1, 1, 0), (1, 2, 0), (0, 1, 2)\}$$

Solution   Applying the Gram-Schmidt orthonormalization process produces

$$\mathbf{w}_1 = \mathbf{v}_1 = (1, 1, 0)$$

$$\mathbf{w}_2 = \mathbf{v}_2 - \frac{\mathbf{v}_2 \cdot \mathbf{w}_1}{\mathbf{w}_1 \cdot \mathbf{w}_1} \mathbf{w}_1$$

$$= (1, 2, 0) - \frac{3}{2}(1, 1, 0) = \left(-\frac{1}{2}, \frac{1}{2}, 0\right)$$

$$\mathbf{w}_3 = \mathbf{v}_3 - \frac{\mathbf{v}_3 \cdot \mathbf{w}_1}{\mathbf{w}_1 \cdot \mathbf{w}_1} \mathbf{w}_1 - \frac{\mathbf{v}_3 \cdot \mathbf{w}_2}{\mathbf{w}_2 \cdot \mathbf{w}_2} \mathbf{w}_2$$

$$= (0, 1, 2) - \frac{1}{2}(1, 1, 0) - \frac{1/2}{1/2}\left(-\frac{1}{2}, \frac{1}{2}, 0\right)$$

$$= (0, 0, 2).$$

The set $B' = \{\mathbf{w}_1, \mathbf{w}_2, \mathbf{w}_3\}$ is an orthogonal basis for R^3. Normalizing each vector in B' produces

$$\mathbf{u}_1 = \frac{\mathbf{w}_1}{\|\mathbf{w}_1\|} = \frac{1}{\sqrt{2}}(1, 1, 0) = \left(\frac{\sqrt{2}}{2}, \frac{\sqrt{2}}{2}, 0\right)$$

$$\mathbf{u}_2 = \frac{\mathbf{w}_2}{\|\mathbf{w}_2\|} = \frac{1}{1/\sqrt{2}}\left(-\frac{1}{2}, \frac{1}{2}, 0\right) = \left(-\frac{\sqrt{2}}{2}, \frac{\sqrt{2}}{2}, 0\right)$$

$$\mathbf{u}_3 = \frac{\mathbf{w}_3}{\|\mathbf{w}_3\|} = \frac{1}{2}(0, 0, 2) = (0, 0, 1).$$

Thus $B'' = \{\mathbf{u}_1, \mathbf{u}_2, \mathbf{u}_3\}$ is an orthonormal basis for R^3.

Examples 6 and 7 applied the Gram-Schmidt orthonormalization process to bases for R^2 and R^3. The process works equally well for a subspace of an inner product space. The procedure is demonstrated in the next example.

EXAMPLE 8   *Applying the Gram-Schmidt Orthonormalization Process*

The vectors $\mathbf{v}_1 = (0, 1, 0)$ and $\mathbf{v}_2 = (1, 1, 1)$ span a plane in R^3. Find an orthonormal basis for this subspace.

Solution   Applying the Gram-Schmidt orthonormalization process produces

$$\mathbf{w}_1 = \mathbf{v}_1 = (0, 1, 0)$$

$$\mathbf{w}_2 = \mathbf{v}_2 - \frac{\mathbf{v}_2 \cdot \mathbf{w}_1}{\mathbf{w}_1 \cdot \mathbf{w}_1} \mathbf{w}_1$$

$$= (1, 1, 1) - \frac{1}{1}(0, 1, 0)$$

$$= (1, 0, 1).$$

Normalizing $\mathbf{w}_1$ and $\mathbf{w}_2$ produces the orthonormal set

$$\mathbf{u}_1 = \frac{\mathbf{w}_1}{\|\mathbf{w}_1\|} = (0, 1, 0)$$

$$\mathbf{u}_2 = \frac{\mathbf{w}_2}{\|\mathbf{w}_2\|} = \frac{1}{\sqrt{2}}(1, 0, 1) = \left(\frac{\sqrt{2}}{2}, 0, \frac{\sqrt{2}}{2}\right).$$

See Figure 5.19.

EXAMPLE 9   *Applying the Gram-Schmidt Orthonormalization Process (Calculus)*

Apply the Gram-Schmidt orthonormalization process to the basis $B = \{1, x, x^2\}$ in P_2, using the inner product

$$\langle \mathbf{p}, \mathbf{q} \rangle = \int_{-1}^{1} p(x)q(x)\, dx.$$

Solution   Let $B = \{1, x, x^2\} = \{\mathbf{v}_1, \mathbf{v}_2, \mathbf{v}_3\}$. Then we have

$$\mathbf{w}_1 = \mathbf{v}_1 = 1$$

$$\mathbf{w}_2 = \mathbf{v}_2 - \frac{\langle \mathbf{v}_2, \mathbf{w}_1 \rangle}{\langle \mathbf{w}_1, \mathbf{w}_1 \rangle} \mathbf{w}_1 = x - \frac{0}{2}(1) = x$$

$$\mathbf{w}_3 = \mathbf{v}_3 - \frac{\langle \mathbf{v}_3, \mathbf{w}_1 \rangle}{\langle \mathbf{w}_1, \mathbf{w}_1 \rangle} \mathbf{w}_1 - \frac{\langle \mathbf{v}_3, \mathbf{w}_2 \rangle}{\langle \mathbf{w}_2, \mathbf{w}_2 \rangle} \mathbf{w}_2$$

$$= x^2 - \frac{2/3}{2}(1) - \frac{0}{2/3}(x) = x^2 - \frac{1}{3}.$$

(In Exercises 33–36 you are asked to verify these calculations.) Now, by normalizing $B' = \{\mathbf{w}_1, \mathbf{w}_2, \mathbf{w}_3\}$, we have

$$\mathbf{u}_1 = \frac{\mathbf{w}_1}{\|\mathbf{w}_1\|} = \frac{1}{\sqrt{2}}(1) = \frac{1}{\sqrt{2}}$$

$$\mathbf{u}_2 = \frac{\mathbf{w}_2}{\|\mathbf{w}_2\|} = \frac{1}{\sqrt{2/3}}(x) = \frac{\sqrt{3}}{\sqrt{2}}x$$

$$\mathbf{u}_3 = \frac{\mathbf{w}_3}{\|\mathbf{w}_3\|} = \frac{1}{\sqrt{8/45}}\left(x^2 - \frac{1}{3}\right) = \frac{\sqrt{5}}{2\sqrt{2}}(3x^2 - 1).$$

Figure 5.19

REMARK: The polynomials $\mathbf{u}_1$, $\mathbf{u}_2$, and $\mathbf{u}_3$ in Example 9 are called the first three **normalized Legendre polynomials,** after the French mathematician Adrien Marie Legendre (1752–1833).

The computations in the Gram-Schmidt orthonormalization process are sometimes simpler when each vector $\mathbf{w}_i$ is normalized *before* it is used to determine the next vector. This **alternative form of the Gram-Schmidt orthonormalization process** has the following steps.

$$\mathbf{u}_1 = \frac{\mathbf{w}_1}{\|\mathbf{w}_1\|} = \frac{\mathbf{v}_1}{\|\mathbf{v}_1\|}$$

$$\mathbf{u}_2 = \frac{\mathbf{w}_2}{\|\mathbf{w}_2\|}, \text{ where } \mathbf{w}_2 = \mathbf{v}_2 - \langle \mathbf{v}_2, \mathbf{u}_1 \rangle \mathbf{u}_1$$

$$\mathbf{u}_3 = \frac{\mathbf{w}_3}{\|\mathbf{w}_3\|}, \text{ where } \mathbf{w}_3 = \mathbf{v}_3 - \langle \mathbf{v}_3, \mathbf{u}_1 \rangle \mathbf{u}_1 - \langle \mathbf{v}_3, \mathbf{u}_2 \rangle \mathbf{u}_2$$

$$\vdots$$

$$\mathbf{u}_n = \frac{\mathbf{w}_n}{\|\mathbf{w}_n\|}, \text{ where } \mathbf{w}_n = \mathbf{v}_n - \langle \mathbf{v}_n, \mathbf{u}_1 \rangle \mathbf{u}_1 - \cdots - \langle \mathbf{v}_n, \mathbf{u}_{n-1} \rangle \mathbf{u}_{n-1}$$

EXAMPLE 10   *Alternative Form of Gram-Schmidt Orthonormalization Process*

Find an orthonormal basis for the solution space of the following homogeneous system of linear equations.

$$x_1 + x_2 \qquad + 7x_4 = 0$$
$$2x_1 + x_2 + 2x_3 + 6x_4 = 0$$

Solution   The augmented matrix for this system reduces as follows.

$$\begin{bmatrix} 1 & 1 & 0 & 7 & 0 \\ 2 & 1 & 2 & 6 & 0 \end{bmatrix} \longrightarrow \begin{bmatrix} 1 & 0 & 2 & -1 & 0 \\ 0 & 1 & -2 & 8 & 0 \end{bmatrix}$$

If we let $x_3 = s$ and $x_4 = t$, each solution of the system has the form

$$\begin{bmatrix} x_1 \\ x_2 \\ x_3 \\ x_4 \end{bmatrix} = \begin{bmatrix} -2s + t \\ 2s - 8t \\ s \\ t \end{bmatrix} = s \begin{bmatrix} -2 \\ 2 \\ 1 \\ 0 \end{bmatrix} + t \begin{bmatrix} 1 \\ -8 \\ 0 \\ 1 \end{bmatrix}.$$

Therefore one basis for the solution space is

$$B = \{\mathbf{v}_1, \mathbf{v}_2\} = \{(-2, 2, 1, 0), (1, -8, 0, 1)\}.$$

To find an orthonormal basis $B' = \{\mathbf{u}_1, \mathbf{u}_2\}$, we use the alternative form of the Gram-Schmidt orthonormalization process as follows.

$$\mathbf{u}_1 = \frac{\mathbf{v}_1}{\|\mathbf{v}_1\|} = \tfrac{1}{3}(-2, 2, 1, 0) = \left(-\tfrac{2}{3}, \tfrac{2}{3}, \tfrac{1}{3}, 0\right)$$

$$\mathbf{w}_2 = \mathbf{v}_2 - \langle \mathbf{v}_2, \mathbf{u}_1 \rangle \mathbf{u}_1$$

$$= (1, -8, 0, 1) - \left[(1, -8, 0, 1) \cdot \left(-\tfrac{2}{3}, \tfrac{2}{3}, \tfrac{1}{3}, 0\right) \right]\left(-\tfrac{2}{3}, \tfrac{2}{3}, \tfrac{1}{3}, 0\right)$$

$$= (-3, -4, 2, 1)$$

$$\mathbf{u}_2 = \frac{\mathbf{w}_2}{\|\mathbf{w}_2\|} = \frac{1}{\sqrt{30}}(-3, -4, 2, 1) = \left(-\frac{3}{\sqrt{30}}, -\frac{4}{\sqrt{30}}, \frac{2}{\sqrt{30}}, \frac{1}{\sqrt{30}}\right)$$

SECTION 5.3 ☐ EXERCISES

In Exercises 1–10, determine whether the set of vectors in R^n is orthogonal, orthonormal, or neither.

1. $\{(-4, 6), (5, 0)\}$ **2.** $\{(11, 4), (8, -3)\}$

3. $\{(\frac{3}{5}, \frac{4}{5}), (-\frac{4}{5}, \frac{3}{5})\}$ **4.** $\{(1, 2), (-\frac{2}{5}, \frac{1}{5})\}$

5. $\{(4, -1, 1), (-1, 0, 4), (-4, -17, -1)\}$

6. $\left\{\left(\frac{\sqrt{2}}{2}, 0, \frac{\sqrt{2}}{2}\right), \left(-\frac{\sqrt{6}}{6}, \frac{\sqrt{6}}{3}, \frac{\sqrt{6}}{6}\right), \left(\frac{\sqrt{3}}{3}, \frac{\sqrt{3}}{3}, -\frac{\sqrt{3}}{3}\right)\right\}$

7. $\left\{\left(\frac{\sqrt{2}}{3}, 0, -\frac{\sqrt{2}}{6}\right), \left(0, \frac{2\sqrt{5}}{5}, -\frac{\sqrt{5}}{5}\right), \left(\frac{\sqrt{5}}{5}, 0, \frac{1}{2}\right)\right\}$

8. $\{(-6, 3, 2, 1), (2, 0, 6, 0)\}$

9. $\left\{\left(\frac{\sqrt{2}}{2}, 0, 0, \frac{\sqrt{2}}{2}\right), \left(0, \frac{\sqrt{2}}{2}, \frac{\sqrt{2}}{2}, 0\right), \left(-\frac{1}{2}, \frac{1}{2}, -\frac{1}{2}, \frac{1}{2}\right)\right\}$

10. $\left\{\left(\frac{\sqrt{10}}{10}, 0, 0, \frac{3\sqrt{10}}{10}\right), (0, 0, 1, 0), (0, 1, 0, 0),\right.$

$\left.\left(-\frac{3\sqrt{10}}{10}, 0, 0, \frac{\sqrt{10}}{10}\right)\right\}$

11. Complete Example 2 by verifying that $\{1, x, x^2, x^3\}$ is an orthonormal basis for P_3 with the inner product $\langle \mathbf{p}, \mathbf{q}\rangle = a_0 b_0 + a_1 b_1 + a_2 b_2 + a_3 b_3$.

12. Verify that $\{(\sin\theta, \cos\theta), (\cos\theta, -\sin\theta)\}$ is an orthonormal basis for R^2.

In Exercises 13–18, find the coordinates of $\mathbf{x}$ relative to the orthonormal basis B in R^n.

13. $B = \left\{\left(-\frac{2\sqrt{13}}{13}, \frac{3\sqrt{13}}{13}\right), \left(\frac{3\sqrt{13}}{13}, \frac{2\sqrt{13}}{13}\right)\right\}$, $\mathbf{x} = (1, 2)$

14. $B = \left\{\left(\frac{\sqrt{5}}{5}, \frac{2\sqrt{5}}{5}\right), \left(-\frac{2\sqrt{5}}{5}, \frac{\sqrt{5}}{5}\right)\right\}$, $\mathbf{x} = (-3, 4)$

15. $B = \left\{\left(\frac{\sqrt{10}}{10}, 0, \frac{3\sqrt{10}}{10}\right), (0, 1, 0), \left(-\frac{3\sqrt{10}}{10}, 0, \frac{\sqrt{10}}{10}\right)\right\}$,

$\mathbf{x} = (2, -2, 1)$

16. $B = \{(1, 0, 0), (0, 1, 0), (0, 0, 1)\}$, $\mathbf{x} = (3, -5, 11)$

17. $B = \{(\frac{3}{5}, \frac{4}{5}, 0), (-\frac{4}{5}, \frac{3}{5}, 0), (0, 0, 1)\}$, $\mathbf{x} = (5, 10, 15)$

18. $B = \{(\frac{5}{13}, 0, \frac{12}{13}, 0), (0, 1, 0, 0), (-\frac{12}{13}, 0, \frac{5}{13}, 0), (0, 0, 0, 1)\}$,

$\mathbf{x} = (2, -1, 4, 3)$

In Exercises 19–26, use the Gram-Schmidt orthonormalization process to transform the given basis of R^n into an orthonormal basis. Use the Euclidean inner product for R^n and use the vectors in the order in which they are given.

19. $B = \{(3, 4), (1, 0)\}$ **20.** $B = \{(0, 1), (2, 5)\}$

21. $B = \{(1, -1), (1, 1)\}$

22. $B = \{(1, 0, 0), (1, 1, 1), (1, 1, -1)\}$

23. $B = \{(4, -3, 0), (1, 2, 0), (0, 0, 4)\}$

24. $B = \{(0, 1, 2), (2, 0, 0), (1, 1, 1)\}$

25. $B = \{(0, 1, 1), (1, 1, 0), (1, 0, 1)\}$

26. $B = \{(3, 4, 0, 0), (-1, 1, 0, 0), (2, 1, 0, -1), (0, 1, 1, 0)\}$

In Exercises 27–32, use the Gram-Schmidt orthonormalization process to transform the given basis of a subspace of R^n into an orthonormal basis for the subspace. Use the Euclidean inner product for R^n and use the vectors in the order in which they are given.

27. $B = \{(-8, 3, 5)\}$ **28.** $B = \{(4, -7, 6)\}$

29. $B = \{(3, 4, 0), (1, 0, 0)\}$ **30.** $B = \{(1, 2, 0), (2, 0, -2)\}$

31. $B = \{(1, 2, -1, 0), (2, 2, 0, 1)\}$

32. $B = \{(7, 24, 0, 0), (0, 0, 1, 1), (0, 0, 1, -2)\}$

(Calculus) In Exercises 33–36, let $B = \{1, x, x^2\}$ be a basis for P_2 with the inner product

$$\langle \mathbf{p}, \mathbf{q}\rangle = \int_{-1}^{1} p(x)q(x)\, dx.$$

Complete Example 9 by verifying the indicated inner products.

33. $\langle x, 1\rangle = 0$ **34.** $\langle 1, 1\rangle = 2$

35. $\langle x^2, 1\rangle = \frac{2}{3}$ **36.** $\langle x^2, x\rangle = 0$

In Exercises 37–40, find an orthonormal basis for the solution space of the given homogeneous system of linear equations.

37. $2x_1 + x_2 - 6x_3 + 2x_4 = 0$

$x_1 + 2x_2 - 3x_3 + 4x_4 = 0$

$x_1 + x_2 - 3x_3 + 2x_4 = 0$

38. $x_1 + x_2 - 3x_3 - 2x_4 = 0$

$2x_1 - x_2 \qquad\quad - x_4 = 0$

$3x_1 + x_2 - 5x_3 - 4x_4 = 0$

39. $x_1 + x_2 - x_3 - x_4 = 0$

$2x_1 + x_2 - 2x_3 - 2x_4 = 0$

40. $x + 3y - 3z = 0$

In Exercises 41–46, let $p(x) = a_0 + a_1x + a_2x^2$ and $q(x) = b_0 + b_1x + b_2x^2$ be vectors in P_2 with

$$\langle p, q \rangle = a_0b_0 + a_1b_1 + a_2b_2.$$

Determine whether the given second-degree polynomials form an orthonormal set, and if not, use the Gram-Schmidt orthonormalization process to form an orthonormal set.

41. $\left\{ \dfrac{x^2 + 1}{\sqrt{2}}, \dfrac{x^2 + x - 1}{\sqrt{3}} \right\}$

42. $\{ \sqrt{2}(x^2 - 1), \sqrt{2}(x^2 + x + 2) \}$

43. $\{ x^2, x^2 + 2x, x^2 + 2x + 1 \}$

44. $\{ 1, x, x^2 \}$

45. $\{ x^2 - 1, x - 1 \}$

46. $\left\{ \dfrac{3x^2 + 4x}{5}, \dfrac{-4x^2 + 3x}{5}, 1 \right\}$

47. Use the inner product $\langle \mathbf{u}, \mathbf{v} \rangle = 2u_1v_1 + u_2v_2$ in R^2 and the Gram-Schmidt orthonormalization process to transform $\{(2, -1), (-2, 10)\}$ into an orthonormal basis.

48. Show that the result of Exercise 47 is not an orthonormal basis when the Euclidean inner product on R^2 is used.

49. Prove that if $\mathbf{w}$ is orthogonal to each vector in $S = \{\mathbf{v}_1, \mathbf{v}_2, \ldots, \mathbf{v}_n\}$, then $\mathbf{w}$ is orthogonal to every linear combination of vectors in S.

50. Let $\{\mathbf{u}_1, \mathbf{u}_2, \ldots, \mathbf{u}_n\}$ be an orthonormal basis for R^n. Prove that $\| \mathbf{v} \|^2 = |\mathbf{v} \cdot \mathbf{u}_1|^2 + |\mathbf{v} \cdot \mathbf{u}_2|^2 + \cdots + |\mathbf{v} \cdot \mathbf{u}_n|^2$ for any vector $\mathbf{v}$ in R^n. This equation is called **Parseval's equality.**

51. Let P be an $n \times n$ matrix. Prove that the following conditions are equivalent.

(a) $P^{-1} = P^T$. (We call such a matrix *orthogonal.*)

(b) The row vectors of P form an orthonormal basis for R^n.

(c) The column vectors form an orthonormal basis for R^n.

52. Use the given matrices to illustrate the result of Exercise 51.

(a) $P = \begin{bmatrix} -1 & 0 & 0 \\ 0 & 0 & 1 \\ 0 & -1 & 0 \end{bmatrix}$

(b) $P = \begin{bmatrix} 1/\sqrt{2} & 1/\sqrt{2} & 0 \\ 1/\sqrt{2} & -1/\sqrt{2} & 0 \\ 0 & 0 & 1 \end{bmatrix}$

53. Find an orthonormal basis for R^4 that includes the vectors

$$\mathbf{v}_1 = \left(\frac{1}{\sqrt{2}}, 0, \frac{1}{\sqrt{2}}, 0 \right) \quad \text{and} \quad \mathbf{v}_2 = \left(0, -\frac{1}{\sqrt{2}}, 0, \frac{1}{\sqrt{2}} \right).$$

54. Let **W** be a subspace of R^n. Prove that the following set is a subspace of R^n.

$$W^\perp = \{ \mathbf{v} : \mathbf{w} \cdot \mathbf{v} = 0 \text{ for every } \mathbf{w} \text{ in } W \}$$

Then prove that the intersection of W and $W^\perp$ is $\{\mathbf{0}\}$.

In Exercises 55–58, find bases for the following four **fundamental subspaces** of the given matrix A.

$N(A) = $ nullspace of A $N(A^T) = $ nullspace of A^T

$R(A) = $ column space of A $R(A^T) = $ column space of A^T

Then show that $N(A) = R(A^T)^\perp$ and $N(A^T) = R(A)^\perp$.

55. $\begin{bmatrix} 1 & 1 & -1 \\ 0 & 2 & 1 \\ 1 & 3 & 0 \end{bmatrix}$

56. $\begin{bmatrix} 0 & 1 & -1 \\ 0 & -2 & 2 \\ 0 & -1 & 1 \end{bmatrix}$

57. $\begin{bmatrix} 1 & 0 & 1 \\ 1 & 1 & 1 \end{bmatrix}$

58. $\begin{bmatrix} 0 & 0 & 1 & 2 & 0 \\ 1 & -2 & 0 & 2 & 0 \\ -1 & 2 & 1 & 0 & 0 \\ 0 & 0 & 1 & 2 & 1 \end{bmatrix}$

59. Let A be an $m \times n$ matrix.

(a) Explain why $R(A^T)$ is the same as the row space of A.

(b) Prove that $N(A) \subset R(A^T)^\perp$.

(c) Prove that $N(A) = R(A^T)^\perp$.

(d) Prove that $N(A^T) = R(A)^\perp$.

5.4. MATHEMATICAL MODELS AND LEAST SQUARES ANALYSIS

In this section, we look at *inconsistent* systems of linear equations, and show how to find the "best possible solution" of such systems. The necessity of "solving" inconsistent systems arises in the computation of the least squares regression line, as illustrated in Example 1.

EXAMPLE 1   *Least Squares Regression Line*

Figure 5.20

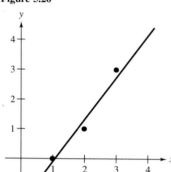

Let $(1, 0)$, $(2, 1)$, and $(3, 3)$ be three points in the plane, as shown in Figure 5.20. How could we find the line $y = c_0 + c_1 x$ that "best fits" these points? One way to proceed is to note that if the three points were collinear, then the following system of equations would be consistent.

$$c_0 + c_1 = 0$$
$$c_0 + 2c_1 = 1$$
$$c_0 + 3c_1 = 3$$

This system can be written in the matrix form $A\mathbf{x} = \mathbf{b}$, where

$$A = \begin{bmatrix} 1 & 1 \\ 1 & 2 \\ 1 & 3 \end{bmatrix}, \qquad \mathbf{b} = \begin{bmatrix} 0 \\ 1 \\ 3 \end{bmatrix}, \qquad \text{and} \qquad \mathbf{x} = \begin{bmatrix} c_0 \\ c_1 \end{bmatrix}.$$

However, because the points are not collinear, the system is inconsistent. Although it is impossible to find $\mathbf{x}$ such that $A\mathbf{x} = \mathbf{b}$, we can look for an $\mathbf{x}$ that *minimizes* the norm of the error $\|A\mathbf{x} - \mathbf{b}\|$. The solution

$$\mathbf{x} = \begin{bmatrix} c_0 \\ c_1 \end{bmatrix}$$

to this minimization problem is called the **least squares regression line** $y = c_0 + c_1 x$.

In Section 2.5, we briefly studied the least squares regression line and how to calculate it using matrices. Now, we combine the ideas of orthogonality and projection to develop this concept in more generality. To begin, consider the linear system $A\mathbf{x} = \mathbf{b}$, where A is an $m \times n$ matrix and $\mathbf{b}$ is a column vector in R^m. We already know how to use Gaussian elimination with back-substitution to solve for $\mathbf{x}$ if the system is consistent. However, if the system is inconsistent, it is still useful to find the "best possible" solution, that is, the value of $\mathbf{x}$ for which the difference between $A\mathbf{x}$ and $\mathbf{b}$ is small. One way to define "best possible" is to require that the norm of $A\mathbf{x} - \mathbf{b}$ be minimized. This definition is the heart of the **least squares problem.**

Least Squares Problem

Given an $m \times n$ matrix A and a vector $\mathbf{b}$ in R^m, the **least squares problem** is to find $\mathbf{x}$ in R^n such that $\|A\mathbf{x} - \mathbf{b}\|^2$ is minimized.

REMARK: The term **least squares** comes from the fact that minimizing $\|A\mathbf{x} - \mathbf{b}\|$ is equivalent to minimizing $\|A\mathbf{x} - \mathbf{b}\|^2$, which is a sum of squares.

Orthogonal Subspaces

In order to solve the least squares problem, we need first to develop the concept of orthogonal subspaces. Two subspaces of R^n are said to be **orthogonal** if the vectors in each subspace are orthogonal to the vectors in the other subspace.

Definition of Orthogonal Subspaces	The subspaces S_1 and S_2 of R^n are **orthogonal** if $\mathbf{v}_1 \cdot \mathbf{v}_2 = 0$ for all $\mathbf{v}_1$ in S_1 and all $\mathbf{v}_2$ in S_2.

EXAMPLE 2   *Orthogonal Subspaces*

The subspaces

$$S_1 = \text{span}\left(\begin{bmatrix} 1 \\ 0 \\ 1 \end{bmatrix}, \begin{bmatrix} 1 \\ 1 \\ 0 \end{bmatrix}\right) \qquad \text{and} \qquad S_2 = \text{span}\left(\begin{bmatrix} -1 \\ 1 \\ 1 \end{bmatrix}\right)$$

are orthogonal because the dot product of any vector in S_1 times any vector in S_2 is zero.

Notice in Example 2 that the zero vector is the only vector common to both S_1 and S_2. This is true in general. If S_1 and S_2 are orthogonal subspaces of R^n, then their intersection consists only of the zero vector. You are asked to prove this fact in Exercise 33.

Given a subspace S of R^n, the set of all vectors orthogonal to every vector in S is called the **orthogonal complement** of S, as given in the following definition.

Definition of Orthogonal Complement	If S is a subspace of R^n, then the **orthogonal complement of S** is the set $$S^{\perp} = \{\mathbf{u} \in R^n : \mathbf{v} \cdot \mathbf{u} = 0 \text{ for all vectors } \mathbf{v} \in S\}.$$

The orthogonal complement of the trivial subspace $\{\mathbf{0}\}$ is all of R^n, and conversely, the orthogonal complement of R^n is the trivial subspace $\{\mathbf{0}\}$. In Example 2, the subspace S_1 is the orthogonal complement of S_2, and the subspace S_2 is the orthogonal complement of S_1. In general, the orthogonal complement of a subspace is itself a subspace of R^n (see Exercise 34). We can find the orthogonal complement of a subspace of R^n by finding the nullspace of a matrix, as illustrated in the next example.

EXAMPLE 3   *Finding the Orthogonal Complement*

Find the orthogonal complement of the subspace S of R^4 spanned by the two column vectors $\mathbf{v}_1$ and $\mathbf{v}_2$ of the matrix A.

$$A = \begin{bmatrix} 1 & 0 \\ 2 & 0 \\ 1 & 0 \\ 0 & 1 \end{bmatrix}$$
$$\quad \mathbf{v}_1 \quad \mathbf{v}_2$$

Solution   A vector $\mathbf{u} \in R^4$ will be in the orthogonal complement of S if its dot product with the two columns of A, $\mathbf{v}_1$ and $\mathbf{v}_2$, is zero. If we take the transpose of A, then we see that the orthogonal complement of S consists of all the vectors $\mathbf{u}$ such that $A^T\mathbf{u} = \mathbf{0}$.

$$A^T\mathbf{u} = \mathbf{0}$$

$$\begin{bmatrix} 1 & 2 & 1 & 0 \\ 0 & 0 & 0 & 1 \end{bmatrix} \begin{bmatrix} x_1 \\ x_2 \\ x_3 \\ x_4 \end{bmatrix} = \begin{bmatrix} 0 \\ 0 \end{bmatrix}$$

That is, the orthogonal complement of S is the nullspace of the matrix A^T: $S^\perp = N(A^T)$. Using the techniques for solving homogeneous linear systems, we find that a basis for the orthogonal complement consists of the two vectors

$$\mathbf{u}_1 = \begin{bmatrix} -2 \\ 1 \\ 0 \\ 0 \end{bmatrix} \quad \text{and} \quad \mathbf{u}_2 = \begin{bmatrix} -1 \\ 0 \\ 1 \\ 0 \end{bmatrix}.$$

Notice in Example 3 that R^4 is split up into two subspaces, $S = \text{span}(\mathbf{v}_1, \mathbf{v}_2)$ and $S^\perp = \text{span}(\mathbf{u}_1, \mathbf{u}_2)$. In fact, the four vectors $\mathbf{v}_1, \mathbf{v}_2, \mathbf{u}_1, \mathbf{u}_2$ form a basis for R^4. Each vector in R^4 can be *uniquely* written as a sum of a vector from S and a vector from $S^\perp$. This concept is generalized in the following definition.

Definition of Direct Sum   Let S_1 and S_2 be two subspaces of R^n. If each vector $\mathbf{x} \in R^n$ can be uniquely written as a sum of a vector $\mathbf{s}_1$ from S_1 and a vector $\mathbf{s}_2$ from S_2, $\mathbf{x} = \mathbf{s}_1 + \mathbf{s}_2$, then R^n is the **direct sum** of S_1 and S_2, and we write $R^n = S_1 \oplus S_2$.

EXAMPLE 4   *Direct Sum*

(a) From Example 2, we see that R^3 is the direct sum of the subspaces

$$S_1 = \text{span}\left(\begin{bmatrix} 1 \\ 0 \\ 1 \end{bmatrix}, \begin{bmatrix} 1 \\ 1 \\ 0 \end{bmatrix}\right) \qquad \text{and} \qquad S_2 = \text{span}\left(\begin{bmatrix} -1 \\ 1 \\ 1 \end{bmatrix}\right).$$

(b) From Example 3 we see that $R^4 = S \oplus S^{\perp}$, where

$$S = \text{span}\left(\begin{bmatrix} 1 \\ 2 \\ 1 \\ 0 \end{bmatrix}, \begin{bmatrix} 0 \\ 0 \\ 0 \\ 1 \end{bmatrix}\right) \qquad \text{and} \qquad S^{\perp} = \text{span}\left(\begin{bmatrix} -2 \\ 1 \\ 0 \\ 0 \end{bmatrix}, \begin{bmatrix} -1 \\ 0 \\ 1 \\ 0 \end{bmatrix}\right).$$

The following theorem collects some important facts about orthogonal complements and direct sums. Its proof can be found in Appendix A.

Theorem 5.13

Properties of Orthogonal Subspaces

Let S be a subspace of R^n. Then the following properties are true.

1. $\dim(S) + \dim(S^{\perp}) = n$
2. $R^n = S \oplus S^{\perp}$
3. $(S^{\perp})^{\perp} = S$

We studied the projection of one vector onto another in Section 5.3. We now generalize this to projections of a vector $\mathbf{v}$ onto a subspace S. Since $R^n = S \oplus S^{\perp}$, every vector $\mathbf{v}$ in R^n can be uniquely written as a sum of a vector from S and a vector from $S^{\perp}$:

$$\mathbf{v} = \mathbf{v}_1 + \mathbf{v}_2, \qquad \mathbf{v}_1 \in S, \quad \mathbf{v}_2 \in S^{\perp}.$$

The vector $\mathbf{v}_1$ is called the **projection** of $\mathbf{v}$ onto the subspace S, and is denoted $\mathbf{v}_1 = \text{proj}_S\mathbf{v}$. Furthermore, $\mathbf{v}_2 = \mathbf{v} - \mathbf{v}_1 = \mathbf{v} - \text{proj}_S\mathbf{v}$, which implies that the vector $\mathbf{v} - \text{proj}_S\mathbf{v}$ is orthogonal to the subspace S.

Given a subspace S of R^n, we can use the Gram-Schmidt orthonormalization process to calculate an orthonormal basis for S. It is then an easy matter to compute the projection of a vector $\mathbf{v}$ onto S using the following theorem. You are asked to prove this theorem in Exercise 35.

Theorem 5.14

Projection onto a Subspace

If $\{\mathbf{u}_1, \mathbf{u}_2, \ldots, \mathbf{u}_t\}$ is an orthonormal basis for the subspace S of R^n, and $\mathbf{v} \in R^n$, then

$$\text{proj}_S\mathbf{v} = (\mathbf{v} \cdot \mathbf{u}_1)\,\mathbf{u}_1 + (\mathbf{v} \cdot \mathbf{u}_2)\,\mathbf{u}_2 + \cdots + (\mathbf{v} \cdot \mathbf{u}_t)\,\mathbf{u}_t.$$

EXAMPLE 5   *Projection onto a Subspace*

Find the projection of the vector $\mathbf{v} = \begin{bmatrix} 1 \\ 1 \\ 3 \end{bmatrix}$ onto the subspace S of R^3 spanned by the

vectors $\mathbf{w}_1 = \begin{bmatrix} 0 \\ 3 \\ 1 \end{bmatrix}$ and $\mathbf{w}_2 = \begin{bmatrix} 2 \\ 0 \\ 0 \end{bmatrix}$.

Solution   By normalizing $\mathbf{w}_1$ and $\mathbf{w}_2$, we obtain an orthonormal basis for S.

Figure 5.21

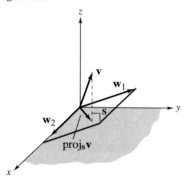

$$\{\mathbf{u}_1, \mathbf{u}_2\} = \left\{ \frac{1}{\sqrt{10}} \mathbf{w}_1, \frac{1}{2} \mathbf{w}_2 \right\} = \left\{ \begin{bmatrix} 0 \\ 3/\sqrt{10} \\ 1/\sqrt{10} \end{bmatrix}, \begin{bmatrix} 1 \\ 0 \\ 0 \end{bmatrix} \right\}$$

We now use Theorem 5.14 to find the projection of $\mathbf{v}$ onto S.

$$\text{proj}_S \mathbf{v} = (\mathbf{v} \cdot \mathbf{u}_1) \, \mathbf{u}_1 + (\mathbf{v} \cdot \mathbf{u}_2) \, \mathbf{u}_2$$

$$= \frac{6}{\sqrt{10}} \begin{bmatrix} 0 \\ 3/\sqrt{10} \\ 1/\sqrt{10} \end{bmatrix} + 1 \begin{bmatrix} 1 \\ 0 \\ 0 \end{bmatrix}$$

$$= \begin{bmatrix} 1 \\ \frac{9}{5} \\ \frac{3}{5} \end{bmatrix}$$

The projection of $\mathbf{v}$ onto the plane S is illustrated in Figure 5.21.

Theorem 5.9 said that among all the scalar multiples of a vector $\mathbf{u}$, the orthogonal projection of $\mathbf{v}$ onto $\mathbf{u}$ is the one that is closest to $\mathbf{v}$. Example 5 suggests that this property is also true for projections onto subspaces. That is, among all the vectors in the subspace S, the vector $\text{proj}_S \mathbf{v}$ is the closest vector to $\mathbf{v}$. These two results are illustrated in Figure 5.22.

Figure 5.22

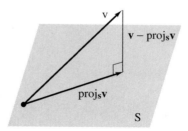

Theorem 5.15	Let S be a subspace of R^n and $\mathbf{v} \in R^n$. Then for all $\mathbf{u} \in S$, $\mathbf{u} \neq \text{proj}_s\mathbf{v}$,
Orthogonal Projection and Distance	$\|\mathbf{v} - \text{proj}_s\mathbf{v}\| < \|\mathbf{v} - \mathbf{u}\|.$

Proof   Let $\mathbf{u} \in S$, $\mathbf{u} \neq \text{proj}_s\mathbf{v}$. By adding and subtracting the same quantity $\text{proj}_s\mathbf{v}$ to the vector $\mathbf{v} - \mathbf{u}$, we obtain

$$\mathbf{v} - \mathbf{u} = (\mathbf{v} - \text{proj}_s\mathbf{v}) + (\text{proj}_s\mathbf{v} - \mathbf{u}).$$

Observe that $(\text{proj}_s\mathbf{v} - \mathbf{u})$ is in S and $(\mathbf{v} - \text{proj}_s\mathbf{v})$ is orthogonal to S. Hence $(\mathbf{v} - \text{proj}_s\mathbf{v})$ and $(\text{proj}_s\mathbf{v} - \mathbf{u})$ are orthogonal vectors, and we can use the Pythagorean Theorem (Theorem 5.6) to obtain

$$\|\mathbf{v} - \mathbf{u}\|^2 = \|\mathbf{v} - \text{proj}_s\mathbf{v}\|^2 + \|\text{proj}_s\mathbf{v} - \mathbf{u}\|^2.$$

Since $\mathbf{u} \neq \text{proj}_s\mathbf{v}$, the second term on the right is positive, and we have

$$\|\mathbf{v} - \text{proj}_s\mathbf{v}\| < \|\mathbf{v} - \mathbf{u}\|.$$

Fundamental Subspaces of a Matrix

We need to develop one more idea before solving the least squares problem. Recall that if A is an $m \times n$ matrix, the column space of A is a subspace of R^m consisting of all vectors of the form $A\mathbf{x}$, $\mathbf{x} \in R^n$. The four **fundamental subspaces** of the matrix A are defined as follows (see Exercises 55–59 in Section 5.3).

$$N(A) = \text{nullspace of } A \qquad N(A^T) = \text{nullspace of } A^T$$
$$R(A) = \text{column space of } A \qquad R(A^T) = \text{column space of } A^T$$

It turns out that these subspaces play a crucial role in the solution of the least squares problem.

EXAMPLE 6   *Fundamental Subspaces*

Find the four fundamental subspaces for the matrix

$$A = \begin{bmatrix} 1 & 2 & 0 \\ 0 & 0 & 1 \\ 0 & 0 & 0 \\ 0 & 0 & 0 \end{bmatrix}.$$

Solution   The column space of A is simply the span of the first and third columns, since the second column is a scalar multiple of the first.

$$R(A) = \text{span}\left(\begin{bmatrix} 1 \\ 0 \\ 0 \\ 0 \end{bmatrix}, \begin{bmatrix} 0 \\ 1 \\ 0 \\ 0 \end{bmatrix}\right)$$

The column space of A^T is equivalent to the row space of A, which is spanned by the first two rows.

$$R(A^T) = \text{span}\left(\begin{bmatrix} 1 \\ 2 \\ 0 \end{bmatrix}, \begin{bmatrix} 0 \\ 0 \\ 1 \end{bmatrix}\right)$$

The nullspace of A is the solution space of the homogeneous system $A\mathbf{x} = \mathbf{0}$.

$$N(A) = \text{span}\left(\begin{bmatrix} -2 \\ 1 \\ 0 \end{bmatrix}\right)$$

Finally, the nullspace of A^T is the solution space of the homogeneous system whose coefficient matrix is A^T.

$$N(A^T) = \text{span}\left(\begin{bmatrix} 0 \\ 0 \\ 1 \\ 0 \end{bmatrix}, \begin{bmatrix} 0 \\ 0 \\ 0 \\ 1 \end{bmatrix}\right)$$

Observe in Example 6 that $R(A)$ and $N(A^T)$ are orthogonal subspaces of R^4, and $R(A^T)$ and $N(A)$ are orthogonal subspaces of R^3. In fact, even more about these subspaces is true, as stated in the following theorem.

Theorem 5.16 Fundamental Subspaces of a Matrix	If A is an $m \times n$ matrix then 1. $R(A)$ and $N(A^T)$ are orthogonal subspaces of R^m. 2. $R(A^T)$ and $N(A)$ are orthogonal subspaces of R^n. 3. $R(A) \oplus N(A^T) = R^m$. 4. $R(A^T) \oplus N(A) = R^n$.

Proof   To prove part 1, let $\mathbf{v} \in R(A)$ and $\mathbf{u} \in (A^T)$. Because the column space of A is equal to the row space of A^T, we see that $A^T\mathbf{u} = \mathbf{0}$ implies that $\mathbf{u} \cdot \mathbf{v} = 0$. Part 2 follows from applying part 1 to A^T.

To prove part 3, we observe that $R(A)^\perp = N(A^T)$. Hence,

$$R^m = R(A) \oplus R(A)^\perp = R(A) \oplus N(A^T).$$

A similar argument applied to $R(A^T)$ proves part 4.

Least Squares

Figure 5.23

We have now developed all the tools needed to solve the least squares problem. Recall that we are attempting to find a vector $\mathbf{x}$ that minimizes $\|A\mathbf{x} - \mathbf{b}\|$, where A is an $m \times n$ matrix and $\mathbf{b}$ is a vector in R^m. Let S be the column space of A: $S = R(A)$. We can assume that $\mathbf{b}$ is not in S, for otherwise the system $A\mathbf{x} = \mathbf{b}$ would be consistent. Hence, we are looking for a vector $A\mathbf{x}$ in S that is as close as possible to $\mathbf{b}$, as indicated in Figure 5.23.

From Theorem 5.15 we know that the desired vector is the projection of $\mathbf{b}$ onto S. Letting $A\hat{\mathbf{x}} = \text{proj}_S\mathbf{b}$ be that projection, we see that $A\hat{\mathbf{x}} - \mathbf{b} = \text{proj}_S\mathbf{b} - \mathbf{b}$ is orthogonal to $S = R(A)$. But this implies that $A\hat{\mathbf{x}} - \mathbf{b}$ is in $R(A)^\perp$, which equals $N(A^T)$ by Theorem 5.16. This is the crucial observation: $A\hat{\mathbf{x}} - \mathbf{b}$ is in the nullspace of A^T. Thus, we have the following:

$$A^T(A\hat{\mathbf{x}} - \mathbf{b}) = \mathbf{0}$$

$$A^TA\hat{\mathbf{x}} - A^T\mathbf{b} = \mathbf{0}$$

$$A^T A\hat{\mathbf{x}} = A^T\mathbf{b}.$$

Therefore, the solution to the least squares problem comes down to solving the $n \times n$ linear system of equations

$$A^TA\mathbf{x} = A^T\mathbf{b}.$$

These equations are called the **normal equations** of the least squares problem $A\mathbf{x} = \mathbf{b}$.

EXAMPLE 7   *Solving the Normal Equations*

Find the solution to the least squares problem

$$A\mathbf{x} = \mathbf{b}$$

$$\begin{bmatrix} 1 & 1 \\ 1 & 2 \\ 1 & 3 \end{bmatrix} \begin{bmatrix} c_0 \\ c_1 \end{bmatrix} = \begin{bmatrix} 0 \\ 1 \\ 3 \end{bmatrix}$$

that was presented in Example 1.

Solution   We begin by calculating the following matrix products.

$$A^TA = \begin{bmatrix} 1 & 1 & 1 \\ 1 & 2 & 3 \end{bmatrix} \begin{bmatrix} 1 & 1 \\ 1 & 2 \\ 1 & 3 \end{bmatrix} = \begin{bmatrix} 3 & 6 \\ 6 & 14 \end{bmatrix}$$

Figure 5.24

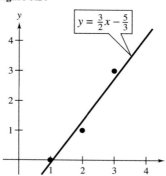

$y = \frac{3}{2}x - \frac{5}{3}$

$$A^T\mathbf{b} = \begin{bmatrix} 1 & 1 & 1 \\ 1 & 2 & 3 \end{bmatrix} \begin{bmatrix} 0 \\ 1 \\ 3 \end{bmatrix} = \begin{bmatrix} 4 \\ 11 \end{bmatrix}$$

The normal equations are

$$A^T A\mathbf{x} = A^T\mathbf{b}$$

$$\begin{bmatrix} 3 & 6 \\ 6 & 14 \end{bmatrix} \begin{bmatrix} c_0 \\ c_1 \end{bmatrix} = \begin{bmatrix} 4 \\ 11 \end{bmatrix}.$$

The solution of this system of equations is

$$\mathbf{x} = \begin{bmatrix} -\frac{5}{3} \\ \frac{3}{2} \end{bmatrix},$$

which implies that the least squares regression line for the data is $y = \frac{3}{2}x - \frac{5}{3}$, as indicated in Figure 5.24.

TECHNOLOGY NOTE

Many computers and calculators have built-in programs for finding the least squares regression line for a set of data points. If you have access to such a program, try verifying the result of Example 7.

REMARK: For an $m \times n$ matrix A, the normal equations form an $n \times n$ system of linear equations. This system is always consistent, but it may have an infinite number of solutions. It can be shown, however, that there is a unique solution if the rank of A is n.

The following example illustrates how to solve the projection problem from Example 5 using normal equations.

EXAMPLE 8   ***Orthogonal Projection onto a Subspace***

Find the orthogonal projection of the vector $\mathbf{b} = \begin{bmatrix} 1 \\ 1 \\ 3 \end{bmatrix}$ onto the column space S of the matrix

$$A = \begin{bmatrix} 0 & 2 \\ 3 & 0 \\ 1 & 0 \end{bmatrix}.$$

Solution   We will find the orthogonal projection of $\mathbf{b}$ onto S by first solving the least squares problem $A\mathbf{x} = \mathbf{b}$. As in Example 7, we calculate the following matrix products.

$$A^T A = \begin{bmatrix} 0 & 3 & 1 \\ 2 & 0 & 0 \end{bmatrix} \begin{bmatrix} 0 & 2 \\ 3 & 0 \\ 1 & 0 \end{bmatrix} = \begin{bmatrix} 10 & 0 \\ 0 & 4 \end{bmatrix}$$

$$A^T\mathbf{b} = \begin{bmatrix} 0 & 3 & 1 \\ 2 & 0 & 0 \end{bmatrix} \begin{bmatrix} 1 \\ 1 \\ 3 \end{bmatrix} = \begin{bmatrix} 6 \\ 2 \end{bmatrix}$$

The normal equations are

$$A^TA\mathbf{x} = A^T\mathbf{b}$$

$$\begin{bmatrix} 10 & 0 \\ 0 & 4 \end{bmatrix} \begin{bmatrix} x_1 \\ x_2 \end{bmatrix} = \begin{bmatrix} 6 \\ 2 \end{bmatrix}.$$

The solution to these equations is easily seen to be

$$\mathbf{x} = \begin{bmatrix} x_1 \\ x_2 \end{bmatrix} = \begin{bmatrix} \frac{3}{5} \\ \frac{1}{2} \end{bmatrix}.$$

Finally, the projection of $\mathbf{b}$ onto S is given by

$$A\mathbf{x} = \begin{bmatrix} 0 & 2 \\ 3 & 0 \\ 1 & 0 \end{bmatrix} \begin{bmatrix} \frac{3}{5} \\ \frac{1}{2} \end{bmatrix} = \begin{bmatrix} 1 \\ \frac{9}{5} \\ \frac{3}{5} \end{bmatrix},$$

which agrees with the solution obtained in Example 5.

Mathematical Modeling

Least squares problems play a fundamental role in mathematical modeling of real-life phenomena. In the next example, we show how to model the world population using a least squares quadratic polynomial.

EXAMPLE 9   *World Population*

The following table gives the world population in billions for five different years. (Source: World Population Data Sheet.)

Year	1970	1975	1980	1985	1990
Population (y)	3.7	4.1	4.5	4.8	5.3

Let $x = 0$ represent the year 1980. Find the least squares regression quadratic polynomial $y = c_0 + c_1x + c_2x^2$ for these data and use the model to estimate the population for the year 2010.

Solution   By substituting the data points $(-10, 3.7)$, $(-5, 4.1)$, $(0, 4.5)$, $(5, 4.8)$, and $(10, 5.3)$, into the quadratic polynomial $y = c_0 + c_1x + c_2x^2$, we obtain the following system of linear equations.

$$c_0 - 10c_1 + 100c_2 = 3.7$$

$$c_0 - 5c_1 + 25c_2 = 4.1$$

$$c_0 \qquad\qquad = 4.5$$

$$c_0 + 5c_1 + 25c_2 = 4.8$$

$$c_0 + 10c_1 + 100c_2 = 5.3$$

This produces the least squares problem

$$\mathbf{Ax = b}$$

$$\begin{bmatrix} 1 & -10 & 100 \\ 1 & -5 & 25 \\ 1 & 0 & 0 \\ 1 & 5 & 25 \\ 1 & 10 & 100 \end{bmatrix} \begin{bmatrix} c_0 \\ c_1 \\ c_2 \end{bmatrix} = \begin{bmatrix} 3.7 \\ 4.1 \\ 4.5 \\ 4.8 \\ 5.3 \end{bmatrix}$$

The normal equations are

$$A^T A\mathbf{x} = A^T\mathbf{b}$$

$$\begin{bmatrix} 5 & 0 & 250 \\ 0 & 250 & 0 \\ 250 & 0 & 21250 \end{bmatrix} \begin{bmatrix} c_0 \\ c_1 \\ c_2 \end{bmatrix} = \begin{bmatrix} 22.4 \\ 19.5 \\ 1122.5 \end{bmatrix}$$

and their solution is

$$\mathbf{x} = \begin{bmatrix} c_0 \\ c_1 \\ c_2 \end{bmatrix} \approx \begin{bmatrix} 4.4657143 \\ 0.078000 \\ 0.0002857 \end{bmatrix}.$$

Hence, the least squares quadratic polynomial for these data is

$$y = 4.4657143 + 0.078x + 0.0002857x^2.$$

Evaluating this polynomial at $x = 30$ gives the estimate of the world population for the year 2010:

$$y = 4.4657143 + 0.078(30) + 0.0002857(30)^2 \approx 7.1 \text{ billion.}$$

Least squares models can arise in many other contexts. Section 5.5 explores some applications of least squares to approximation of functions. In the final example of this section, we use a nonlinear model to find a relationship between the period of a planet and its mean distance from the Sun.

EXAMPLE 10   *Application to Astronomy*

The following table gives the mean distance x and the period y of the six planets that are closest to the Sun. The mean distance is given in terms of astronomical units (where the earth's mean distance is defined to be 1.0), and the period is given in years. Find a model for these data.

Planet	Mercury	Venus	Earth	Mars	Jupiter	Saturn
Period, y	0.241	0.615	1.0	1.881	11.861	29.457
Distance, x	0.387	0.723	1.0	1.523	5.203	9.541

If you plot the data as given, they do not seem to lie on a straight line. However, by taking the logarithm of each coordinate, you obtain points of the form ($\ln x$, $\ln y$), as shown in the following table.

Planet	Mercury	Venus	Earth	Mars	Jupiter	Saturn
$\ln y$	−1.423	−0.486	0.0	0.632	2.473	3.383
$\ln x$	−0.949	−0.324	0.0	0.421	1.649	2.256

Figure 5.25 shows a plot of the transformed points and suggests that the least squares regression line would be a good fit. Using the techniques of this section, we find that the line is

$$\ln y = 1.5 \ln x \quad \text{or} \quad y = x^{3/2}.$$

Figure 5.25

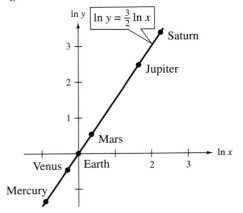

TECHNOLOGY NOTE

You can use a computer or calculator with a built-in power regression program to verify the result of Example 10. For example, on the TI-85 calculator, the power fit program from the STAT menu gives $y \approx 1.00042x^{1.49954}$.

SECTION 5.4 ☐ EXERCISES

In Exercises 1–4, determine whether the given sets are orthogonal.

1. $S_1 = \text{span}\left\{\begin{bmatrix} 2 \\ 1 \\ -1 \end{bmatrix}, \begin{bmatrix} 0 \\ 1 \\ 1 \end{bmatrix}\right\}$ $S_2 = \text{span}\left\{\begin{bmatrix} -1 \\ 2 \\ 0 \end{bmatrix}\right\}$

2. $S_1 = \text{span}\left\{\begin{bmatrix} -3 \\ 0 \\ 1 \end{bmatrix}\right\}$ $S_2 = \text{span}\left\{\begin{bmatrix} 2 \\ 1 \\ 6 \end{bmatrix}, \begin{bmatrix} 0 \\ 1 \\ 0 \end{bmatrix}\right\}$

3. $S_1 = \text{span}\left\{\begin{bmatrix} 1 \\ 1 \\ 1 \\ 1 \end{bmatrix}\right\}$ $S_2 = \text{span}\left\{\begin{bmatrix} -1 \\ 1 \\ -1 \\ 1 \end{bmatrix}, \begin{bmatrix} 0 \\ 2 \\ -2 \\ 0 \end{bmatrix}\right\}$

4. $S_1 = \text{span}\left\{\begin{bmatrix} 0 \\ 0 \\ 2 \\ 1 \end{bmatrix}, \begin{bmatrix} 0 \\ 0 \\ 1 \\ -2 \end{bmatrix}\right\}$ $S_2 = \text{span}\left\{\begin{bmatrix} 3 \\ 2 \\ 0 \\ 0 \end{bmatrix}, \begin{bmatrix} 0 \\ 1 \\ -2 \\ 2 \end{bmatrix}\right\}$

In Exercises 5–8, find the orthogonal complement $S^{\perp}$ of the given subspace S.

5. S is the subspace of R^3 consisting of the xz-plane.

6. S is the subspace of R^5 consisting of all vectors whose third and fourth components are zero.

7. $S = \text{span}\left\{\begin{bmatrix} 1 \\ 2 \\ 0 \\ 0 \end{bmatrix}, \begin{bmatrix} 0 \\ 1 \\ 0 \\ 1 \end{bmatrix}\right\}$ **8.** $S = \text{span}\left\{\begin{bmatrix} 0 \\ 1 \\ -1 \\ 1 \end{bmatrix}\right\}$

9. Find the orthogonal complement of the *solution* to Exercise 7.

10. Find the orthogonal complement of the *solution* to Exercise 8.

In Exercises 11–14, find the projection of the vector **v** onto the subspace S.

11. $S = \text{span}\left\{\begin{bmatrix} 0 \\ 0 \\ -1 \\ 1 \end{bmatrix}, \begin{bmatrix} 0 \\ 1 \\ 1 \\ 1 \end{bmatrix}\right\}$, $\mathbf{v} = \begin{bmatrix} 1 \\ 0 \\ 1 \\ 1 \end{bmatrix}$

12. $S = \text{span}\left\{\begin{bmatrix} -1 \\ 2 \\ 0 \\ 0 \end{bmatrix}, \begin{bmatrix} 0 \\ 0 \\ 1 \\ 0 \end{bmatrix}, \begin{bmatrix} 0 \\ 0 \\ 0 \\ 1 \end{bmatrix}\right\}$, $\mathbf{v} = \begin{bmatrix} 1 \\ 1 \\ 1 \\ 1 \end{bmatrix}$

13. $S = \text{span}\left\{\begin{bmatrix} 1 \\ 0 \\ 1 \end{bmatrix}, \begin{bmatrix} 0 \\ 1 \\ 1 \end{bmatrix}\right\}$, $\mathbf{v} = \begin{bmatrix} 2 \\ 3 \\ 4 \end{bmatrix}$

14. $S = \text{span}\left\{\begin{bmatrix} 1 \\ 1 \\ 1 \\ 1 \end{bmatrix}, \begin{bmatrix} 0 \\ 1 \\ -1 \\ 0 \end{bmatrix}, \begin{bmatrix} 0 \\ 1 \\ 1 \\ 0 \end{bmatrix}\right\}$, $\mathbf{v} = \begin{bmatrix} 1 \\ 2 \\ 3 \\ 4 \end{bmatrix}$

In Exercises 15 and 16, find the orthogonal projection of $\mathbf{b} = [2 \ -2 \ 1]^T$ onto the column space of the matrix A.

15. $A = \begin{bmatrix} 1 & 2 \\ 0 & 1 \\ 1 & 1 \end{bmatrix}$ **16.** $A = \begin{bmatrix} 0 & 2 \\ 1 & 1 \\ 1 & 3 \end{bmatrix}$

In Exercises 17–20, find bases for the four fundamental subspaces of the given matrix A.

17. $A = \begin{bmatrix} 1 & 2 & 3 \\ 0 & 1 & 0 \end{bmatrix}$ **18.** $A = \begin{bmatrix} 0 & -1 & 1 \\ 1 & 2 & 0 \\ 1 & 1 & 1 \end{bmatrix}$

19. $A = \begin{bmatrix} 1 & 0 & 0 & 1 \\ 0 & 1 & 1 & 1 \\ 1 & 1 & 1 & 2 \\ 1 & 2 & 2 & 3 \end{bmatrix}$

20. $A = \begin{bmatrix} 1 & 0 & -1 \\ 0 & -1 & 1 \\ 1 & 1 & 0 \\ 1 & 0 & 1 \end{bmatrix}$

In Exercises 21–24, find the least squares solution to the system $A\mathbf{x} = \mathbf{b}$.

21. $A = \begin{bmatrix} 2 & 1 \\ 1 & 2 \\ 1 & 1 \end{bmatrix}$ $\mathbf{b} = \begin{bmatrix} 2 \\ 0 \\ -3 \end{bmatrix}$

22. $A = \begin{bmatrix} 0 & 1 \\ 1 & 0 \\ 1 & 2 \end{bmatrix}$ $\mathbf{b} = \begin{bmatrix} -1 \\ -1 \\ 3 \end{bmatrix}$

23. $A = \begin{bmatrix} 1 & 0 & 1 \\ 1 & 1 & 1 \\ 0 & 1 & 1 \\ 1 & 1 & 0 \end{bmatrix}$ $\mathbf{b} = \begin{bmatrix} 4 \\ -1 \\ 0 \\ 1 \end{bmatrix}$

24. $A = \begin{bmatrix} 0 & 2 & 0 \\ 1 & 1 & 0 \\ -1 & 0 & 1 \\ 1 & 1 & 1 \\ 0 & 0 & 1 \end{bmatrix}$ $\mathbf{b} = \begin{bmatrix} 0 \\ 1 \\ 0 \\ 0 \\ 1 \end{bmatrix}$

In Exercises 25–28, find the least squares regression line for the given data points. Graph the points and the line on the same set of axes.

25. $(-1, 1), (1, 0), (3, -3)$

26. $(-2, -1), (-1, 0), (1, 0), (2, 2)$

27. $(-3, -3), (-2, -2), (0, 0), (1, 2)$

28. $(-2, 1), (-1, 2), (0, 1), (1, 2), (2, 1)$

In Exercises 29 and 30, find the least squares quadratic polynomial for the given data points.

29. $(-2, 0), (-1, 0), (0, 1), (1, 2), (2, 5)$

30. $(0, 0), (2, 2), (3, 6), (4, 12)$

C **31.** *Annual Sales* The following table shows the annual sales, in millions of dollars, for *Kmart Corporation* and *Wal-Mart Stores* for 1985 through 1992. Find an appropriate least squares model for each and use the model to predict sales for 1993. (*Source: Kmart Corporation and Wal-Mart Stores*)

Year	1985	1986	1987	1988
Kmart	22,420	23,812	25,627	27,301
Wal-Mart	8,452	11,909	15,959	20,649

Year	1989	1990	1991	1992
Kmart	29,533	32,070	34,580	37,725
Wal-Mart	25,811	32,602	43,887	55,550

C **32.** *Production and Consumption* The accompanying table gives the total domestic production x, and the domestic consumption y, of lumber in the United States from 1983 through 1990. The measurements are in millions of board feet. (*Source*: Current Industrial Reports.) Find an appropriate model for the relationship between production and consumption.

x	34.6	37.1	36.4	42.0
y	48.7	52.7	53.5	57.4

x	44.9	44.6	43.6	43.9
y	61.8	58.8	58.8	54.5

33. Prove that if S_1 and S_2 are orthogonal subspaces of R^n, then their intersection consists only of the zero vector.

34. Prove that the orthogonal complement of a subspace of R^n is itself a subspace of R^n.

35. Prove Theorem 5.14.

36. Prove that if S_1 and S_2 are subspaces of R^n and $R^n = S_1 \oplus S_2$, then $S_1 \cap S_2 = \{\mathbf{0}\}$.

37. Describe the normal equations for the least squares problem if the $m \times n$ matrix A has orthonormal columns.

5.5 APPLICATIONS OF INNER PRODUCT SPACES

The Cross Product of Two Vectors in Space

Many problems in linear algebra involve finding a vector that is orthogonal to each vector in a given set. Here we look at a vector product that yields a vector in R^3 that is orthogonal to two given vectors. This vector product is called the **cross product,** and it is most conveniently defined and calculated with vectors written in standard unit vector form as follows.

$$\mathbf{v} = (v_1, v_2, v_3) = v_1\mathbf{i} + v_2\mathbf{j} + v_3\mathbf{k}$$

Definition of Cross Product of Two Vectors	Let $\mathbf{u} = u_1\mathbf{i} + u_2\mathbf{j} + u_3\mathbf{k}$ and $\mathbf{v} = v_1\mathbf{i} + v_2\mathbf{j} + v_3\mathbf{k}$ be vectors in R^3. The **cross product** of $\mathbf{u}$ and $\mathbf{v}$ is the vector $$\mathbf{u} \times \mathbf{v} = (u_2v_3 - u_3v_2)\mathbf{i} - (u_1v_3 - u_3v_1)\mathbf{j} + (u_1v_2 - u_2v_1)\mathbf{k}.$$

REMARK: The cross product is defined only for vectors in R^3. We do not define the cross product of two vectors in R^2 or of vectors in R^n, $n > 3$.

A convenient way to remember the formula for the cross product $\mathbf{u} \times \mathbf{v}$ is to use the following determinant form.

$$\mathbf{u} \times \mathbf{v} = \begin{vmatrix} \mathbf{i} & \mathbf{j} & \mathbf{k} \\ u_1 & u_2 & u_3 \\ v_1 & v_2 & v_3 \end{vmatrix} \quad \longleftarrow \text{Components of u} \\ \longleftarrow \text{Components of v}$$

Technically this is not a determinant because the entries are not all real numbers. Nevertheless, it is useful because it provides an easy way to remember the cross product formula. Using cofactor expansion along the first row, we obtain

$$\mathbf{u} \times \mathbf{v} = (u_2v_3 - u_3v_2)\mathbf{i} - (u_1v_3 - u_3v_1)\mathbf{j} + (u_1v_2 - u_2v_1)\mathbf{k}$$

$$= \begin{vmatrix} u_2 & u_3 \\ v_2 & v_3 \end{vmatrix}\mathbf{i} - \begin{vmatrix} u_1 & u_3 \\ v_1 & v_3 \end{vmatrix}\mathbf{j} + \begin{vmatrix} u_1 & u_2 \\ v_1 & v_2 \end{vmatrix}\mathbf{k},$$

which yields the formula given in the definition. Be sure to note that the **j**-component is preceded by a minus sign.

EXAMPLE 1   *Finding the Cross Product of Two Vectors*

Given $\mathbf{u} = \mathbf{i} - 2\mathbf{j} + \mathbf{k}$ and $\mathbf{v} = 3\mathbf{i} + \mathbf{j} - 2\mathbf{k},$ find the following.

(a) $\mathbf{u} \times \mathbf{v}$ (b) $\mathbf{v} \times \mathbf{u}$ (c) $\mathbf{v} \times \mathbf{v}$

Solution   (a) $\mathbf{u} \times \mathbf{v} = \begin{vmatrix} \mathbf{i} & \mathbf{j} & \mathbf{k} \\ 1 & -2 & 1 \\ 3 & 1 & -2 \end{vmatrix} = \begin{vmatrix} -2 & 1 \\ 1 & -2 \end{vmatrix} \mathbf{i} - \begin{vmatrix} 1 & 1 \\ 3 & -2 \end{vmatrix} \mathbf{j} + \begin{vmatrix} 1 & -2 \\ 3 & 1 \end{vmatrix} \mathbf{k}$

$$= 3\mathbf{i} + 5\mathbf{j} + 7\mathbf{k}$$

(b) $\mathbf{v} \times \mathbf{u} = \begin{vmatrix} \mathbf{i} & \mathbf{j} & \mathbf{k} \\ 3 & 1 & -2 \\ 1 & -2 & 1 \end{vmatrix} = -3\mathbf{i} - 5\mathbf{j} - 7\mathbf{k}$

Note that this result is the negative of that in part (a).

(c) $\mathbf{v} \times \mathbf{v} = \begin{vmatrix} \mathbf{i} & \mathbf{j} & \mathbf{k} \\ 3 & 1 & -2 \\ 3 & 1 & -2 \end{vmatrix} = \begin{vmatrix} 1 & -2 \\ 1 & -2 \end{vmatrix} \mathbf{i} - \begin{vmatrix} 3 & -2 \\ 3 & -2 \end{vmatrix} \mathbf{j} + \begin{vmatrix} 3 & 1 \\ 3 & 1 \end{vmatrix} \mathbf{k}$

$$= 0\mathbf{i} + 0\mathbf{j} + 0\mathbf{k} = \mathbf{0}$$

The results obtained in Example 1 suggest some interesting *algebraic* properties of the cross product. For instance,

$$\mathbf{u} \times \mathbf{v} = -(\mathbf{v} \times \mathbf{u}) \quad \text{and} \quad \mathbf{v} \times \mathbf{v} = \mathbf{0}.$$

These properties, along with several others, are given in the following theorem.

Theorem 5.17

Algebraic Properties of the Cross Product

If $\mathbf{u}$, $\mathbf{v}$, and $\mathbf{w}$ are vectors in R^3 and c is a scalar, then the following properties are true.

1. $\mathbf{u} \times \mathbf{v} = -(\mathbf{v} \times \mathbf{u})$
2. $\mathbf{u} \times (\mathbf{v} + \mathbf{w}) = (\mathbf{u} \times \mathbf{v}) + (\mathbf{u} \times \mathbf{w})$
3. $c(\mathbf{u} \times \mathbf{v}) = c\mathbf{u} \times \mathbf{v} = \mathbf{u} \times c\mathbf{v}$
4. $\mathbf{u} \times \mathbf{0} = \mathbf{0} \times \mathbf{u} = \mathbf{0}$
5. $\mathbf{u} \times \mathbf{u} = \mathbf{0}$
6. $\mathbf{u} \cdot (\mathbf{v} \times \mathbf{w}) = (\mathbf{u} \times \mathbf{v}) \cdot \mathbf{w}$

Proof   We prove only the first property, leaving the proofs of the other properties as exercises. (See Exercises 17–21.) Let $\mathbf{u}$ and $\mathbf{v}$ be given by

$$\mathbf{u} = u_1\mathbf{i} + u_2\mathbf{j} + u_3\mathbf{k} \quad \text{and} \quad \mathbf{v} = v_1\mathbf{i} + v_2\mathbf{j} + v_3\mathbf{k}.$$

Then $\mathbf{u} \times \mathbf{v}$ is

$$\mathbf{u} \times \mathbf{v} = \begin{vmatrix} \mathbf{i} & \mathbf{j} & \mathbf{k} \\ u_1 & u_2 & u_3 \\ v_1 & v_2 & v_3 \end{vmatrix}$$

$$= (u_2v_3 - u_3v_2)\mathbf{i} - (u_1v_3 - u_3v_1)\mathbf{j} + (u_1v_2 - u_2v_1)\mathbf{k},$$

and $\mathbf{v} \times \mathbf{u}$ is

$$\mathbf{v} \times \mathbf{u} = \begin{vmatrix} \mathbf{i} & \mathbf{j} & \mathbf{k} \\ v_1 & v_2 & v_3 \\ u_1 & u_2 & u_3 \end{vmatrix}$$

$$= (v_2 u_3 - v_3 u_2)\mathbf{i} - (v_1 u_3 - v_3 u_1)\mathbf{j} + (v_1 u_2 - v_2 u_1)\mathbf{k}$$

$$= -(u_2 v_3 - u_3 v_2)\mathbf{i} + (u_1 v_3 - u_3 v_1)\mathbf{j} - (u_1 v_2 - u_2 v_1)\mathbf{k}$$

$$= -(\mathbf{u} \times \mathbf{v}).$$

Property 1 of Theorem 5.17 tells us that the vectors $\mathbf{u} \times \mathbf{v}$ and $\mathbf{v} \times \mathbf{u}$ have equal lengths but opposite directions. The geometric implication of this result will be discussed after we establish some *geometric* properties of the cross product of two vectors.

Theorem 5.18

Geometric Properties of the Cross Product

If $\mathbf{u}$ and $\mathbf{v}$ are nonzero vectors in R^3, then the following properties are true.
1. $\mathbf{u} \times \mathbf{v}$ is orthogonal to both $\mathbf{u}$ and $\mathbf{v}$.
2. The angle θ between $\mathbf{u}$ and $\mathbf{v}$ is given by
   $$\|\mathbf{u} \times \mathbf{v}\| = \|\mathbf{u}\|\,\|\mathbf{v}\| \sin \theta.$$
3. $\mathbf{u}$ and $\mathbf{v}$ are parallel if and only if $\mathbf{u} \times \mathbf{v} = \mathbf{0}$.
4. The parallelogram having $\mathbf{u}$ and $\mathbf{v}$ as adjacent sides has an area of $\|\mathbf{u} \times \mathbf{v}\|$.

Proof   We prove property 4, leaving the proofs of the other properties to you. (See Exercises 22–24.) To prove property 4, let $\mathbf{u}$ and $\mathbf{v}$ represent adjacent sides of a parallelogram, as shown in Figure 5.26. By property 2, the area of the parallelogram is given by

$$\text{Area} = \overbrace{\|\mathbf{u}\|}^{Base}\ \overbrace{\|\mathbf{v}\| \sin \theta}^{Height}$$

$$= \|\mathbf{u} \times \mathbf{v}\|.$$

Figure 5.26

Property 1 states that the vector $\mathbf{u} \times \mathbf{v}$ is orthogonal to both $\mathbf{u}$ and $\mathbf{v}$. This implies that $\mathbf{u} \times \mathbf{v}$ (and $\mathbf{v} \times \mathbf{u}$) is orthogonal to the plane determined by $\mathbf{u}$ and $\mathbf{v}$. One way to remember the orientation of the vectors **u**, **v**, and **u** × **v** is to compare them with the unit vectors **i**, **j**, and **k**, as shown in Figure 5.27. The three vectors **u**, **v**, and **u** × **v** form a *right-handed system*, whereas the three vectors **u**, **v**, and **v** × **u** form a *left-handed system*.

Figure 5.27

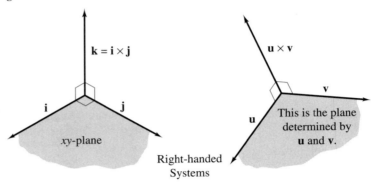

$\mathbf{k} = \mathbf{i} \times \mathbf{j}$

i

j

xy-plane

Right-handed
Systems

u × **v**

v

u

This is the plane
determined by
u and **v**.

EXAMPLE 2   *Finding a Vector Orthogonal to Two Given Vectors*

Find a unit vector that is orthogonal to both

$$\mathbf{u} = \mathbf{i} - 4\mathbf{j} + \mathbf{k} \quad \text{and} \quad \mathbf{v} = 2\mathbf{i} + 3\mathbf{j}.$$

Figure 5.28

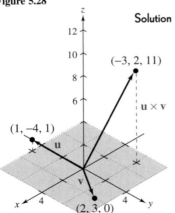

(−3, 2, 11)

u × **v**

(1, −4, 1)

u

v

(2, 3, 0)

Solution   From property 1 of Theorem 5.18 we know that the cross product

$$\mathbf{u} \times \mathbf{v} = \begin{vmatrix} \mathbf{i} & \mathbf{j} & \mathbf{k} \\ 1 & -4 & 1 \\ 2 & 3 & 0 \end{vmatrix} = -3\mathbf{i} + 2\mathbf{j} + 11\mathbf{k}$$

is orthogonal to both **u** and **v**, as shown in Figure 5.28. Then by dividing by the length of **u** × **v**,

$$\|\mathbf{u} \times \mathbf{v}\| = \sqrt{(-3)^2 + 2^2 + 11^2} = \sqrt{134},$$

we obtain the unit vector

$$\frac{\mathbf{u} \times \mathbf{v}}{\|\mathbf{u} \times \mathbf{v}\|} = -\frac{3}{\sqrt{134}}\mathbf{i} + \frac{2}{\sqrt{134}}\mathbf{j} + \frac{11}{\sqrt{134}}\mathbf{k},$$

which is orthogonal to both **u** and **v**.

EXAMPLE 3   *Finding the Area of a Parallelogram*

Find the area of the parallelogram that has

$$\mathbf{u} = -3\mathbf{i} + 4\mathbf{j} + \mathbf{k} \quad \text{and} \quad \mathbf{v} = -2\mathbf{j} + 6\mathbf{k}$$

as adjacent sides, as shown in Figure 5.29.

Figure 5.29

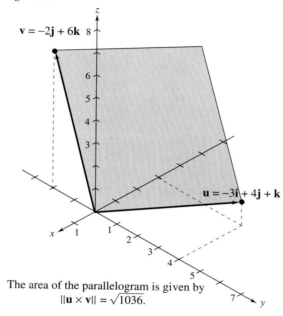

$\mathbf{v} = -2\mathbf{j} + 6\mathbf{k}$

$\mathbf{u} = -3\mathbf{i} + 4\mathbf{j} + \mathbf{k}$

The area of the parallelogram is given by
$\|\mathbf{u} \times \mathbf{v}\| = \sqrt{1036}.$

Solution   From property 4 of Theorem 5.18 we know that the area of this parallelogram is given by $\|\mathbf{u} \times \mathbf{v}\|$. Thus since

$$\mathbf{u} \times \mathbf{v} = \begin{vmatrix} \mathbf{i} & \mathbf{j} & \mathbf{k} \\ -3 & 4 & 1 \\ 0 & -2 & 6 \end{vmatrix} = 26\mathbf{i} + 18\mathbf{j} + 6\mathbf{k},$$

the area of the parallelogram is

$$\|\mathbf{u} \times \mathbf{v}\| = \sqrt{26^2 + 18^2 + 6^2} = \sqrt{1036} \approx 32.19.$$

Least Squares Approximations (Calculus)

Many problems in the physical sciences and engineering involve an approximation of a function **f** by another function **g**. If **f** is in $C[a, b]$ (the inner product space of all continuous functions on $[a, b]$, then usually **g** is chosen from a given subspace W of $C[a, b]$. For instance, to approximate the function

$$f(x) = e^x, \quad 0 \le x \le 1$$

we could choose one of the following forms of **g**.

Figure 5.30

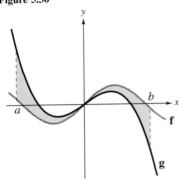

1. $g(x) = a_0 + a_1x, \quad 0 \le x \le 1$ Linear
2. $g(x) = a_0 + a_1x + a_2x^2, \quad 0 \le x \le 1$ Quadratic
3. $g(x) = a_0 + a_1 \cos x + a_2 \sin x, \quad 0 \le x \le 1$ Trigonometric

Before discussing ways of finding the function g, we must define how one function can "best" approximate another function. One natural way would be to require that the area bounded by the graphs of f and g on the interval $[a, b]$,

$$\text{Area} = \int_a^b |f(x) - g(x)| \, dx,$$

be a minimum with respect to other functions in the subspace W, as shown in Figure 5.30. But because integrands involving absolute value are often difficult to evaluate, it is more common to square the integrand to obtain

$$\int_a^b [f(x) - g(x)]^2 \, dx.$$

With this criterion, the function **g** is called the **least squares approximation** of **f** with respect to the inner product space W.

Definition of Least Squares Approximation

Let **f** be continuous on $[a, b]$, and let W be a subspace of $C[a, b]$. A function **g** in W is called a **least squares approximation** of **f** with respect to W if the value of

$$I = \int_a^b [f(x) - g(x)]^2 \, dx$$

is a minimum with respect to all other functions in W.

REMARK: If the subspace W in this definition is the entire space $C[a, b]$, then $g(x) = f(x)$, which implies that $I = 0$.

EXAMPLE 4   *Finding a Least Squares Approximation*

Find the least squares approximation $g(x) = a_0 + a_1x$ for

$$f(x) = e^x, \quad 0 \le x \le 1.$$

Solution   For this approximation we need to find the constants a_0 and a_1 that minimize the value of

$$I = \int_0^1 [f(x) - g(x)]^2 \, dx = \int_0^1 (e^x - a_0 - a_1x)^2 \, dx.$$

Evaluating this integral, we have

$$I = \int_0^1 (e^x - a_0 - a_1 x)^2 \, dx$$

$$= \int_0^1 (e^{2x} - 2a_0 e^x - 2a_1 x e^x + a_0^2 + 2a_0 a_1 x + a_1^2 x^2) \, dx$$

$$= \left[\frac{1}{2} e^{2x} - 2a_0 e^x - 2a_1 e^x (x - 1) + a_0^2 x + a_0 a_1 x^2 + a_1^2 \frac{x^3}{3} \right]_0^1$$

$$= \frac{1}{2}(e^2 - 1) - 2a_0(e - 1) - 2a_1 + a_0^2 + a_0 a_1 + \frac{1}{3} a_1^2.$$

Now, considering I to be a function of the variables a_0 and a_1, we use calculus to determine the values of a_0 and a_1 that minimize I. Specifically, by setting the partial derivatives

$$\frac{\partial I}{\partial a_0} = 2a_0 - 2e + 2 + a_1$$

$$\frac{\partial I}{\partial a_1} = a_0 + \frac{2}{3} a_1 - 2$$

equal to zero, we obtain the following two linear equations in a_0 and a_1.

$$2a_0 + a_1 = 2(e - 1)$$

$$3a_0 + 2a_1 = 6$$

The solution of this system is

$$a_0 = 4e - 10 \approx 0.873 \qquad \text{and} \qquad a_1 = 18 - 6e \approx 1.690.$$

Therefore the best *linear approximation* for $f(x) = e^x$ on the interval $[0, 1]$ is given by

$$g(x) = 4e - 10 + (18 - 6e)x$$

$$\approx 0.873 + 1.690x.$$

Figure 5.31 compares the graphs of **f** and **g** on $[0, 1]$.

Figure 5.31

$g(x) \approx 0.87 + 1.69x$

Of course, the approximation obtained in Example 4 depends on the definition of the best approximation. For instance, if the definition of "best" had been the *Taylor polynomial of degree one* centered at 0.5, then the approximating function **g** would have been

$$g(x) = f(0.5) + f'(0.5)(x - 0.5)$$

$$= e^{0.5} + e^{0.5}(x - 0.5)$$

$$\approx 0.824 + 1.649x.$$

Moreover, the function **g** obtained in Example 4 is only the best *linear* approximation of **f** (according to the least squares criterion). In Example 5 we find the best *quadratic* approximation.

EXAMPLE 5 *Finding a Least Squares Approximation*

Find the least squares approximation $g(x) = a_0 + a_1x + a_2x^2$ for

$$f(x) = e^x, \quad 0 \le x \le 1.$$

Solution For this approximation we need to find the values of a_0, a_1, and a_2 that minimize the value of

$$I = \int_0^1 [f(x) - g(x)]^2 \, dx = \int_0^1 (e^x - a_0 - a_1x - a_2x^2)^2 \, dx.$$

Integrating and setting the partial derivatives of I (with respect to a_0, a_1, and a_2) equal to zero produces the following system of linear equations.

$$6a_0 + 3a_1 + 2a_2 = 6(e - 1)$$

$$6a_0 + 4a_1 + 3a_2 = 12$$

$$20a_0 + 15a_1 + 12a_2 = 60(e - 2)$$

The solution of this system is

$$a_0 = -105 + 39e \approx 1.013$$

$$a_1 = 588 - 216e \approx 0.851$$

$$a_2 = -570 + 210e \approx 0.839.$$

Thus the approximating function **g** is

$$g(x) \approx 1.013 + 0.851x + 0.839x^2.$$

The graphs of **f** and **g** are compared in Figure 5.32.

Figure 5.32

$g(x) \approx 1.013 + 0.851x + 0.839x^2$

The integral I (given in the definition of the least squares approximation) may be expressed in vector form. To do this, we use the inner product defined in Example 5 in Section 5.2:

$$\langle \mathbf{f}, \mathbf{g} \rangle = \int_a^b f(x)g(x) \, dx.$$

With this inner product we have

$$I = \int_a^b [f(x) - g(x)]^2 \, dx = \langle \mathbf{f} - \mathbf{g}, \mathbf{f} - \mathbf{g} \rangle = \|\mathbf{f} - \mathbf{g}\|^2.$$

This means that the least squares approximating function $\mathbf{g}$ is the function that minimizes $\|\mathbf{f} - \mathbf{g}\|^2$ or, equivalently, minimizes $\|\mathbf{f} - \mathbf{g}\|$. In other words, the least squares approximation of a function $\mathbf{f}$ is the function $\mathbf{g}$ (in the subspace W) closest to $\mathbf{f}$ in terms of the inner product $\langle \mathbf{f}, \mathbf{g} \rangle$. The following theorem gives us a way of determining the function $\mathbf{g}$.

Theorem 5.19

Least Squares Approximation

Let $\mathbf{f}$ be continuous on $[a, b]$, and let W be a finite-dimensional subspace of $C[a, b]$. The least squares approximating function of $\mathbf{f}$ with respect to W is given by

$$\mathbf{g} = \langle \mathbf{f}, \mathbf{w}_1 \rangle \mathbf{w}_1 + \langle \mathbf{f}, \mathbf{w}_2 \rangle \mathbf{w}_2 + \cdots + \langle \mathbf{f}, \mathbf{w}_n \rangle \mathbf{w}_n,$$

where $B = \{\mathbf{w}_1, \mathbf{w}_2, \ldots, \mathbf{w}_n\}$ is an orthonormal basis for W.

Proof   To show that $\mathbf{g}$ is the least squares approximating function of $\mathbf{f}$, we need to show that the inequality

$$\|\mathbf{f} - \mathbf{g}\| \leq \|\mathbf{f} - \mathbf{w}\|$$

is true for any vector $\mathbf{w}$ in W. By writing $\mathbf{f} - \mathbf{g}$ as

$$\mathbf{f} - \mathbf{g} = \mathbf{f} - \langle \mathbf{f}, \mathbf{w}_1 \rangle \mathbf{w}_1 - \langle \mathbf{f}, \mathbf{w}_2 \rangle \mathbf{w}_2 - \cdots - \langle \mathbf{f}, \mathbf{w}_n \rangle \mathbf{w}_n,$$

we can see that $\mathbf{f} - \mathbf{g}$ is orthogonal to each $\mathbf{w}_i$, which in turn implies that it is orthogonal to each vector in W. In particular, $\mathbf{f} - \mathbf{g}$ is orthogonal to $\mathbf{g} - \mathbf{w}$. This allows us to apply the Pythagorean Theorem to the vector sum

$$\mathbf{f} - \mathbf{w} = (\mathbf{f} - \mathbf{g}) + (\mathbf{g} - \mathbf{w})$$

to conclude that

$$\|\mathbf{f} - \mathbf{w}\|^2 = \|\mathbf{f} - \mathbf{g}\|^2 + \|\mathbf{g} - \mathbf{w}\|^2.$$

Therefore, it follows that $\|\mathbf{f} - \mathbf{g}\|^2 \leq \|\mathbf{f} - \mathbf{w}\|^2$, which then implies that $\|\mathbf{f} - \mathbf{g}\| \leq \|\mathbf{f} - \mathbf{w}\|$.

Now let's see how Theorem 5.19 can be used to produce the least squares approximation obtained in Example 4. First we apply the Gram-Schmidt orthonormalization process to the standard basis $\{1, x\}$ to obtain the orthonormal basis $B = \{1, \sqrt{3}(2x - 1)\}$. Then, by Theorem 5.19, the least squares approximation for e^x in the subspace of all linear functions is given by

$$g(x) = \langle e^x, 1 \rangle (1) + \langle e^x, \sqrt{3}(2x - 1) \rangle \sqrt{3}(2x - 1)$$

$$= \int_0^1 e^x \, dx + \sqrt{3}(2x - 1) \int_0^1 \sqrt{3}e^x(2x - 1) \, dx$$

$$= \int_0^1 e^x dx + 3(2x - 1) \int_0^1 e^x(2x - 1) \, dx$$

$$= (e - 1) + 3(2x - 1)(3 - e)$$

$$= 4e - 10 + (18 - 6e)x,$$

which agrees with the result obtained in Example 4.

EXAMPLE 6   ***Finding a Least Squares Approximation***

Find the least squares approximation for $f(x) = \sin x$, $0 \le x \le \pi$, with respect to the subspace W of quadratic functions.

Solution   To use Theorem 5.19, we apply the Gram-Schmidt orthonormalization process to the standard basis for W, $\{1, x, x^2\}$, to obtain the orthonormal basis

$$B = \{\mathbf{w}_1, \mathbf{w}_2, \mathbf{w}_3\}$$

$$= \left\{ \frac{1}{\sqrt{\pi}}, \frac{\sqrt{3}}{\pi\sqrt{\pi}}(2x - \pi), \frac{\sqrt{5}}{\pi^2\sqrt{\pi}}(6x^2 - 6\pi x + \pi^2) \right\}.$$

The least squares approximating function $\mathbf{g}$ is given by

$$g(x) = \langle \mathbf{f}, \mathbf{w}_1 \rangle \mathbf{w}_1 + \langle \mathbf{f}, \mathbf{w}_2 \rangle \mathbf{w}_2 + \langle \mathbf{f}, \mathbf{w}_3 \rangle \mathbf{w}_3,$$

and we have

$$\langle \mathbf{f}, \mathbf{w}_1 \rangle = \frac{1}{\sqrt{\pi}} \int_0^\pi \sin x \, dx = \frac{2}{\sqrt{\pi}}$$

$$\langle \mathbf{f}, \mathbf{w}_2 \rangle = \frac{\sqrt{3}}{\pi\sqrt{\pi}} \int_0^\pi \sin x \,(2x - \pi) \, dx = 0$$

$$\langle \mathbf{f}, \mathbf{w}_3 \rangle = \frac{\sqrt{5}}{\pi^2\sqrt{\pi}} \int_0^\pi \sin x \,(6x^2 - 6\pi x + \pi^2) \, dx$$

$$= \frac{2\sqrt{5}}{\pi^2\sqrt{\pi}}(\pi^2 - 12).$$

Therefore $\mathbf{g}$ is given by

$$g(x) = \frac{2}{\pi} + \frac{10(\pi^2 - 12)}{\pi^5}(6x^2 - 6\pi x + \pi^2)$$

$$\approx -0.4177x^2 + 1.3122x - 0.0505.$$

The graphs $\mathbf{f}$ and $\mathbf{g}$ are shown in Figure 5.33.

Figure 5.33

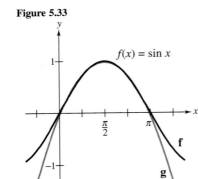

$g(x) \approx -0.4177x^2 + 1.3122x - 0.0505$

Fourier Approximations (Calculus)

We now look at a special type of least squares approximation called a **Fourier approximation.** For this approximation we consider functions of the form

$$g(x) = \frac{a_0}{2} + a_1 \cos x + \cdots + a_n \cos nx + b_1 \sin x + \cdots + b_n \sin nx$$

in the subspace W of $C[0, 2\pi]$ spanned by the basis

$$S = \{1, \cos x, \cos 2x, \ldots, \cos nx, \sin x, \sin 2x, \ldots, \sin nx\}.$$

These $2n + 1$ vectors are *orthogonal* in the inner product space $C[0, 2\pi]$ because

$$\langle \mathbf{f}, \mathbf{g} \rangle = \int_0^{2\pi} f(x)g(x)\, dx = 0, \quad \mathbf{f} \neq \mathbf{g},$$

as demonstrated in Example 3 in Section 5.3. Moreover, by normalizing each function in this basis, we obtain the orthonormal basis

$$B = \{\mathbf{w}_0, \mathbf{w}_1, \ldots, \mathbf{w}_n, \mathbf{w}_{n+1}, \ldots, \mathbf{w}_{2n}\}$$

$$= \left\{ \frac{1}{\sqrt{2\pi}}, \frac{1}{\sqrt{\pi}} \cos x, \ldots, \frac{1}{\sqrt{\pi}} \cos nx, \frac{1}{\sqrt{\pi}} \sin x, \ldots, \frac{1}{\sqrt{\pi}} \sin nx \right\}.$$

With this orthonormal basis we can apply Theorem 5.19 to write

$$g(x) = \langle \mathbf{f}, \mathbf{w}_0 \rangle \mathbf{w}_0 + \langle \mathbf{f}, \mathbf{w}_1 \rangle \mathbf{w}_1 + \cdots + \langle \mathbf{f}, \mathbf{w}_{2n} \rangle \mathbf{w}_{2n}.$$

The coefficients $a_0, a_1, \ldots, a_n, b_1, \ldots, b_n$ for $g(x)$ in the equation

$$g(x) = \frac{a_0}{2} + a_1 \cos x + \cdots + a_n \cos nx + b_1 \sin x + \cdots + b_n \sin nx$$

are given by the following integrals.

$$a_0 = \langle \mathbf{f}, \mathbf{w}_0 \rangle \frac{2}{\sqrt{2\pi}} = \frac{2}{\sqrt{2\pi}} \int_0^{2\pi} f(x) \frac{1}{\sqrt{2\pi}}\, dx = \frac{1}{\pi} \int_0^{2\pi} f(x)\, dx$$

$$a_1 = \langle \mathbf{f}, \mathbf{w}_1 \rangle \frac{1}{\sqrt{\pi}} = \frac{1}{\sqrt{\pi}} \int_0^{2\pi} f(x) \frac{1}{\sqrt{\pi}} \cos x\, dx = \frac{1}{\pi} \int_0^{2\pi} f(x) \cos x\, dx$$

$$\vdots$$

$$a_n = \langle \mathbf{f}, \mathbf{w}_n \rangle \frac{1}{\sqrt{\pi}} = \frac{1}{\sqrt{\pi}} \int_0^{2\pi} f(x) \frac{1}{\sqrt{\pi}} \cos nx\, dx = \frac{1}{\pi} \int_0^{2\pi} f(x) \cos nx\, dx$$

$$b_1 = \langle \mathbf{f}, \mathbf{w}_{n+1} \rangle \frac{1}{\sqrt{\pi}} = \frac{1}{\sqrt{\pi}} \int_0^{2\pi} f(x) \frac{1}{\sqrt{\pi}} \sin x\, dx = \frac{1}{\pi} \int_0^{2\pi} f(x) \sin x\, dx$$

$$\vdots$$

$$b_n = \langle \mathbf{f}, \mathbf{w}_{2n} \rangle \frac{1}{\sqrt{\pi}} = \frac{1}{\sqrt{\pi}} \int_0^{2\pi} f(x) \frac{1}{\sqrt{\pi}} \sin nx\, dx = \frac{1}{\pi} \int_0^{2\pi} f(x) \sin nx\, dx$$

We call $g(x)$ the **nth-order Fourier approximation** of $\mathbf{f}$ on the interval $[0, 2\pi]$, which, like Fourier coefficients, is named after the French mathematician Jean-Baptiste Joseph Fourier (1768–1830). This brings us to Theorem 5.20.

Theorem 5.20

Fourier Approximation

On the interval $[0, 2\pi]$ the least squares approximation of a continuous function $\mathbf{f}$ with respect to the vector space spanned by $\{1, \cos x, \ldots, \cos nx, \sin x, \ldots, \sin nx\}$ is given by

$$g(x) = \frac{a_0}{2} + a_1 \cos x + \cdots + a_n \cos nx + b_1 \sin x + \cdots + b_n \sin nx,$$

where the **Fourier coefficients** $a_0, a_1, \ldots, a_n, b_1, \ldots, b_n$ are

$$a_0 = \frac{1}{\pi} \int_0^{2\pi} f(x)\, dx$$

$$a_j = \frac{1}{\pi} \int_0^{2\pi} f(x) \cos jx\, dx, \quad j = 1, 2, \ldots, n$$

$$b_j = \frac{1}{\pi} \int_0^{2\pi} f(x) \sin jx\, dx, \quad j = 1, 2, \ldots, n$$

EXAMPLE 7   ***Finding a Fourier Approximation***

Find the third-order Fourier approximation of

$$f(x) = x, \quad 0 \le x \le 2\pi.$$

Solution   Using Theorem 5.20, we have

$$g(x) = \frac{a_0}{2} + a_1 \cos x + a_2 \cos 2x + a_3 \cos 3x + b_1 \sin x + b_2 \sin 2x + b_3 \sin 3x,$$

where

$$a_0 = \frac{1}{\pi} \int_0^{2\pi} x\, dx = \frac{1}{\pi} 2\pi^2 = 2\pi$$

$$a_j = \frac{1}{\pi} \int_0^{2\pi} x \cos jx\, dx = \left[\frac{1}{\pi j^2} \cos jx + \frac{x}{\pi j} \sin jx \right]_0^{2\pi} = 0$$

$$b_j = \frac{1}{\pi} \int_0^{2\pi} x \sin jx\, dx = \left[\frac{1}{\pi j^2} \sin jx - \frac{x}{\pi j} \cos jx \right]_0^{2\pi} = -\frac{2}{j}.$$

This implies that $b_1 = -2$, $b_2 = -\frac{2}{2} = -1$, and $b_3 = -\frac{2}{3}$. Therefore we have

$$g(x) = \frac{2\pi}{2} - 2 \sin x - \sin 2x - \frac{2}{3} \sin 3x$$

$$= \pi - 2 \sin x - \sin 2x - \frac{2}{3} \sin 3x.$$

The graphs of $\mathbf{f}$ and $\mathbf{g}$ are compared in Figure 5.34.

Figure 5.34

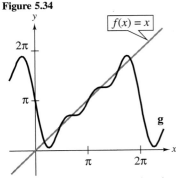

3rd Order Fourier Approximation

In Example 7 the general pattern for the Fourier coefficients appears to be $a_0 = 2\pi, a_1 = a_2 = \cdots = a_n = 0$, and

$$b_1 = -\frac{2}{1}, \ b_2 = -\frac{2}{2}, \ \ldots, \ b_n = -\frac{2}{n}.$$

Thus the nth-order Fourier approximation of $f(x) = x$ is

$$g(x) = \pi - 2\left(\sin x + \frac{1}{2}\sin 2x + \frac{1}{3}\sin 3x + \cdots + \frac{1}{n}\sin nx\right).$$

As n increases, the Fourier approximation improves. For instance, Figure 5.35 shows the fourth- and fifth-order Fourier approximations of $f(x) = x$, $0 \le x \le 2\pi$.

Figure 5.35

4th Order Fourier Approximation

5th Order Fourier Approximation

In advanced courses it is shown that as $n \to \infty$, the approximation error $\|\mathbf{f} - \mathbf{g}\|$ approaches zero for all x in the interval $(0, 2\pi)$. The infinite *series* for $g(x)$ is called a **Fourier series.**

EXAMPLE 8   *Finding a Fourier Approximation*

Find the fourth-order Fourier approximation of

$$f(x) = |x - \pi|, \ 0 \le x \le 2\pi.$$

Solution   Using Theorem 5.20, we find the Fourier coefficients as follows.

$$a_0 = \frac{1}{\pi}\int_0^{2\pi} |x - \pi|\, dx = \pi$$

$$a_j = \frac{1}{\pi}\int_0^{2\pi} |x - \pi|\cos jx\, dx$$

$$= \frac{2}{\pi}\int_0^{\pi} (\pi - x)\cos jx\, dx$$

$$= \frac{2}{\pi j^2}(1 - \cos j\pi)$$

$$b_j = \frac{1}{\pi}\int_0^{2\pi} |x - \pi| \sin jx \, dx = 0$$

Thus $a_1 = 4/\pi$, $a_2 = 0$, $a_3 = 4/9\pi$, and $a_4 = 0$, which means that the fourth-order Fourier approximation of **f** is

$$g(x) = \frac{\pi}{2} + \frac{4}{\pi}\cos x + \frac{4}{9\pi}\cos 3x.$$

The graphs of **f** and **g** are compared in Figure 5.36.

Figure 5.36

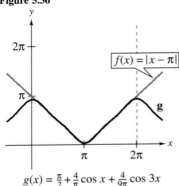

$g(x) = \frac{\pi}{2} + \frac{4}{\pi}\cos x + \frac{4}{9\pi}\cos 3x$

SECTION 5.5 ☐ EXERCISES

The Cross Product of Two Vectors in Space

In Exercises 1–6, find $\mathbf{u} \times \mathbf{v}$ and show that it is orthogonal to both $\mathbf{u}$ and $\mathbf{v}$.

1. $\mathbf{u} = (1, 0, 0), \ \mathbf{v} = (0, 1, 0)$

2. $\mathbf{u} = (0, 1, 0), \ \mathbf{v} = (1, 0, 0)$

3. $\mathbf{u} = \mathbf{j}, \ \mathbf{v} = \mathbf{k}$ **4.** $\mathbf{u} = \mathbf{k}, \ \mathbf{v} = \mathbf{j}$

5. $\mathbf{u} = \mathbf{i} + \mathbf{j} + \mathbf{k}, \ \mathbf{v} = 2\mathbf{i} + \mathbf{j} - \mathbf{k}$

6. $\mathbf{u} = (2, -3, 1), \ \mathbf{v} = (1, -2, 1)$

In Exercises 7–10, find the area of the parallelogram that has the given vectors as adjacent sides.

7. $\mathbf{u} = \mathbf{j}, \ \mathbf{v} = \mathbf{j} + \mathbf{k}$ **8.** $\mathbf{u} = \mathbf{i} + \mathbf{j} + \mathbf{k}, \ \mathbf{v} = \mathbf{j} + \mathbf{k}$

9. $\mathbf{u} = (3, 2, -1), \ \mathbf{v} = (1, 2, 3)$

10. $\mathbf{u} = (2, -1, 0), \ \mathbf{v} = (-1, 2, 0)$

In Exercises 11–13, find $\mathbf{u} \cdot (\mathbf{v} \times \mathbf{w})$. This quantity is called the **triple scalar product** of $\mathbf{u}$, $\mathbf{v}$, and $\mathbf{w}$.

11. $\mathbf{u} = \mathbf{i}, \ \mathbf{v} = \mathbf{j}, \ \mathbf{w} = \mathbf{k}$

12. $\mathbf{u} = (1, 1, 1), \ \mathbf{v} = (2, 1, 0), \ \mathbf{w} = (0, 0, 1)$

13. $\mathbf{u} = (2, 0, 1), \ \mathbf{v} = (0, 3, 0), \ \mathbf{w} = (0, 0, 1)$

14. Show that the volume of a parallelepiped having $\mathbf{u}, \mathbf{v},$ and $\mathbf{w}$ as adjacent sides is given by $|\mathbf{u} \cdot (\mathbf{v} \times \mathbf{w})|$.

15. Use the result of Exercise 14 to find the volume of the parallelepiped with $\mathbf{u} = \mathbf{i} + \mathbf{j}, \ \mathbf{v} = \mathbf{j} + \mathbf{k},$ and $\mathbf{w} = \mathbf{i} + 2\mathbf{k}$ as adjacent edges. (See Figure 5.37.)

Figure 5.37   **Figure 5.38**

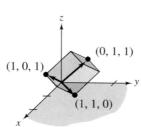

16. Find the volume of the parallelepiped shown in Figure 5.38, with $\mathbf{u} = (1, 1, 0), \ \mathbf{v} = (0, 1, 1),$ and $\mathbf{w} = (1, 0, 1)$ as adjacent sides.

17. Prove that $c\mathbf{u} \times \mathbf{v} = c(\mathbf{u} \times \mathbf{v}) = \mathbf{u} \times c\mathbf{v}$.

18. Prove that $\mathbf{u} \times (\mathbf{v} + \mathbf{w}) = (\mathbf{u} \times \mathbf{v}) + (\mathbf{u} \times \mathbf{w})$.

19. Prove that $\mathbf{u} \times \mathbf{0} = \mathbf{0} \times \mathbf{u} = \mathbf{0}$.

20. Prove that $\mathbf{u} \times \mathbf{u} = \mathbf{0}$.

21. Prove that $\mathbf{u} \cdot (\mathbf{v} \times \mathbf{w}) = (\mathbf{u} \times \mathbf{v}) \cdot \mathbf{w}$.

22. Prove that $\mathbf{u} \times \mathbf{v}$ is orthogonal to both $\mathbf{u}$ and $\mathbf{v}$.

23. Prove that the angle θ between $\mathbf{u}$ and $\mathbf{v}$ is given by
$$\|\mathbf{u} \times \mathbf{v}\| = \|\mathbf{u}\| \, \|\mathbf{v}\| \sin \theta \, .$$

24. Prove that $\mathbf{u} \times \mathbf{v} = \mathbf{0}$ if and only if $\mathbf{u}$ and $\mathbf{v}$ are parallel.

25. Prove **Lagrange's Identity:**
$$\|\mathbf{u} \times \mathbf{v}\|^2 = \|\mathbf{u}\|^2 \|\mathbf{v}\|^2 - (\mathbf{u} \cdot \mathbf{v})^2.$$

26. (a) Prove that $\mathbf{u} \times (\mathbf{v} \times \mathbf{w}) = (\mathbf{u} \cdot \mathbf{w})\mathbf{v} - (\mathbf{u} \cdot \mathbf{v})\mathbf{w}$.

   (b) Find an example for which $\mathbf{u} \times (\mathbf{v} \times \mathbf{w}) \neq (\mathbf{u} \times \mathbf{v}) \times \mathbf{w}$.

Least Squares Approximation (Calculus)

In Exercises 27–32, (a) find the *linear* least squares approximating function $\mathbf{g}$ for the given function and (b) sketch the graphs of $\mathbf{f}$ and $\mathbf{g}$.

27. $f(x) = x^2, \ 0 \le x \le 1$ **28.** $f(x) = \sqrt{x}, \ 1 \le x \le 4$

29. $f(x) = e^{2x}, \ 0 \le x \le 1$

30. $f(x) = \cos x, \ 0 \le x \le \pi$

31. $f(x) = \sin x, \ 0 \le x \le \pi/2$

32. $f(x) = \sin x, \ -\pi/2 \le x \le \pi/2$

In Exercises 33–36, (a) find the quadratic least squares approximating function $\mathbf{g}$ for the given function and (b) sketch the graphs of $\mathbf{f}$ and $\mathbf{g}$.

33. $f(x) = x^3, \ 0 \le x \le 1$ **34.** $f(x) = \sqrt{x}, \ 1 \le x \le 4$

35. $f(x) = \sin x, \ 0 \le x \le \pi$

36. $f(x) = \sin x, \ -\pi/2 \le x \le \pi/2$

Fourier Approximations (Calculus)

In Exercises 37–46, find the Fourier approximation of specified order of the given function on the interval $[0, 2\pi]$.

37. $f(x) = \pi - x, \ $ third order

38. $f(x) = \pi - x, \ $ fourth order

39. $f(x) = (x - \pi)^2, \ $ third order

40. $f(x) = (x - \pi)^2, \ $ fourth order

41. $f(x) = e^{-x}$, first order

42. $f(x) = e^{-x}$, second order

43. $f(x) = 1 + x$, third order

44. $f(x) = 1 + x$, fourth order

45. $f(x) = 2 \sin x \cos x$, fourth order

46. $f(x) = \sin^2 x$, fourth order

47. Use the results of Exercises 37 and 38 to find the nth-order Fourier approximation of $f(x) = \pi - x$ on the interval $[0, 2\pi]$.

48. Use the results of Exercises 39 and 40 to find the nth-order Fourier approximation of $f(x) = (x - \pi)^2$ on the interval $[0, 2\pi]$.

CHAPTER 5 ☐ REVIEW EXERCISES

In Exercises 1–6, find (a) $\|\mathbf{u}\|$, (b) $\|\mathbf{v}\|$, (c) $\mathbf{u} \cdot \mathbf{v}$, and (d) $d(\mathbf{u}, \mathbf{v})$.

1. $\mathbf{u} = (1, 2)$, $\mathbf{v} = (4, 1)$

2. $\mathbf{u} = (0, 3)$, $\mathbf{v} = (2, 0)$

3. $\mathbf{u} = (1, -1, 2)$, $\mathbf{v} = (2, 3, 1)$

4. $\mathbf{u} = (-1, 0, 1)$, $\mathbf{v} = (0, 3, 4)$

5. $\mathbf{u} = (1, -2, 2, 0)$, $\mathbf{v} = (2, -1, 0, 2)$

6. $\mathbf{u} = (1, -1, 0, 1, 1)$, $\mathbf{v} = (0, 1, -2, 2, 1)$

In Exercises 7 and 8, find $\|\mathbf{v}\|$ and find a unit vector in the direction of $\mathbf{v}$.

7. $\mathbf{v} = (5, 3, -2)$ **8.** $\mathbf{v} = (1, -2, 1)$

In Exercises 9–14, find the angle between $\mathbf{u}$ and v.

9. $\mathbf{u} = (1, 5)$, $\mathbf{v} = (3, 6)$

10. $\mathbf{u} = (2, 2)$, $\mathbf{v} = (-3, 3)$

11. $\mathbf{u} = (4, -1, 5)$, $\mathbf{v} = (3, 2, -2)$

12. $\mathbf{u} = \left(\cos \dfrac{3\pi}{4}, \sin \dfrac{3\pi}{4} \right)$, $\mathbf{v} = \left(\cos \dfrac{2\pi}{3}, \sin \dfrac{2\pi}{3} \right)$

13. $\mathbf{u} = (10, -5, 15)$, $\mathbf{v} = (-2, 1, -3)$

14. $\mathbf{u} = (1, 0, -3, 0)$, $\mathbf{v} = (2, -2, 1, 1)$

In Exercises 15–18, find $\text{proj}_{\mathbf{v}}\mathbf{u}$.

15. $\mathbf{u} = (2, 4)$, $\mathbf{v} = (1, -5)$

16. $\mathbf{u} = (2, 3)$, $\mathbf{v} = (0, 4)$

17. $\mathbf{u} = (0, -1, 2)$, $\mathbf{v} = (3, 2, 4)$

18. $\mathbf{u} = (1, 2, -1)$, $\mathbf{v} = (0, 2, 3)$

19. For $\mathbf{u} = (2, -\frac{1}{2}, 1)$ and $\mathbf{v} = (\frac{3}{2}, 2, -1)$, (a) find the inner product given by $\langle \mathbf{u}, \mathbf{v} \rangle = u_1 v_1 + 2u_2 v_2 + 3u_3 v_3$, and (b) use this inner product to find the distance between $\mathbf{u}$ and $\mathbf{v}$.

20. For $\mathbf{u} = (0, 3, \frac{1}{3})$ and $\mathbf{v} = (\frac{4}{3}, 1, -3)$, (a) find the inner product given by $\langle \mathbf{u}, \mathbf{v} \rangle = 2u_1 v_1 + u_2 v_2 + 2u_3 v_3$, and (b) use this inner product to find the distance between $\mathbf{u}$ and $\mathbf{v}$.

21. Verify the Triangle Inequality and the Cauchy-Schwarz Inequality for $\mathbf{u}$ and $\mathbf{v}$ given in Exercise 19. (Use the inner product given in Exercise 19.)

22. Verify the Triangle Inequality and the Cauchy-Schwarz Inequality for $\mathbf{u}$ and $\mathbf{v}$ given in Exercise 20. (Use the inner product given in Exercise 20.)

In Exercises 23 and 24, find all vectors that are orthogonal to the given vector $\mathbf{u}$.

23. $\mathbf{u} = (0, -4, 3)$ **24.** $\mathbf{u} = (1, -2, 2, 1)$

In Exercises 25–28, use the Gram-Schmidt orthonormalization process to transform the given basis into an orthonormal basis. (Use the Euclidean inner product.)

25. $B = \{(1, 1), (0, 1)\}$ **26.** $B = \{(3, 4), (1, 2)\}$

27. $B = \{(0, 3, 4), (1, 0, 0), (1, 1, 0)\}$

28. $B = \{(0, 0, 2), (0, 1, 1), (1, 1, 1)\}$

29. Let $B = \{(0, 2, -2), (1, 0, -2)\}$ be a basis for a subspace of R^3, and let $\mathbf{x} = (-1, 4, -2)$ be a vector in the subspace.

(a) Write $\mathbf{x}$ as a linear combination of the vectors in B. That is, find the coordinates of $\mathbf{x}$ relative to B.

(b) Use the Gram-Schmidt orthonormalization process to transform B into an orthonormal set B'.

(c) Write $\mathbf{x}$ as a linear combination of the vectors in B'. That is, find the coordinates of $\mathbf{x}$ relative to B'.

30. Repeat Exercise 29 for $B = \{(-1, 2, 2), (1, 0, 0)\}$ and $\mathbf{x} = (-3, 4, 4)$.

(Calculus) In Exercises 31–34, let $\mathbf{f}$ and $\mathbf{g}$ be functions in the vector space $C[a, b]$ with inner product

$$\langle \mathbf{f}, \mathbf{g} \rangle = \int_a^b f(x) \, g(x) \, dx.$$

31. Let $f(x) = x$ and $g(x) = x^2$ be vectors in $C[0, 1]$.

(a) Find $\langle \mathbf{f}, \mathbf{g} \rangle$.   (b) Find $\|\mathbf{g}\|$.

(c) Find $d(\mathbf{f}, \mathbf{g})$.

(d) Orthonormalize the set $B = \{\mathbf{f}, \mathbf{g}\}$.

32. Let $f(x) = x + 2$ and $g(x) = 15x - 8$ be vectors in $C[0, 1]$.
   (a) Find $\langle \mathbf{f}, \mathbf{g} \rangle$.   (b) Find $\langle -4\mathbf{f}, \mathbf{g} \rangle$.
   (c) Find $\|\mathbf{f}\|$.
   (d) Orthonormalize the set $B = \{\mathbf{f}, \mathbf{g}\}$.

33. Show that $f(x) = \sqrt{1 - x^2}$ and $g(x) = 2x\sqrt{1 - x^2}$ are orthogonal in $C[-1, 1]$.

34. Apply the Gram-Schmidt orthonormalization process to the following set in $C[-\pi, \pi]$.
$$S = \{1, \cos x, \sin x \cos 2x, \sin 2x, \ldots, \cos nx, \sin nx\}$$

35. Find an orthonormal basis for the following subspace of Euclidean 3-space.
$$W = \{(x_1, x_2, x_3): x_1 + x_2 + x_3 = 0\}$$

36. Find an orthonormal basis for the solution space of the following homogeneous system of linear equations.
$$x + y - z + \ w = 0$$
$$2x - y + z + 2w = 0$$

(Calculus) In Exercises 37 and 38, (a) find the inner product, (b) determine whether the vectors are orthogonal, and (c) verify the Cauchy-Schwarz Inequality for the given vectors.

37. $f(x) = x, g(x) = \dfrac{1}{x^2 + 1}, \langle \mathbf{f}, \mathbf{g} \rangle = \displaystyle\int_{-1}^{1} f(x)g(x)\, dx$

38. $f(x) = x, g(x) = 4x^2, \langle \mathbf{f}, \mathbf{g} \rangle = \displaystyle\int_{0}^{1} f(x)g(x)\, dx$

39. Prove that if $\mathbf{u}$ and $\mathbf{v}$ are vectors in an inner product space such that $\|\mathbf{u}\| \le 1$ and $\|\mathbf{v}\| \le 1$, then $|\langle \mathbf{u}, \mathbf{v} \rangle| \le 1$.

40. Prove that if $\mathbf{u}$ and $\mathbf{v}$ are vectors in an inner product space V, then
$$\big| \|\mathbf{u}\| - \|\mathbf{v}\| \big| \le \|\mathbf{u} \pm \mathbf{v}\|.$$

41. Let V be an m-dimensional subspace of R^n such that $m < n$. Prove that any vector $\mathbf{u}$ in R^n can be uniquely written in the form $\mathbf{u} = \mathbf{v} + \mathbf{w}$, where $\mathbf{v}$ is in V and $\mathbf{w}$ is orthogonal to every vector in V.

42. Let V be the two-dimensional subspace of R^4 spanned by $(0, 1, 0, 1)$ and $(0, 2, 0, 0)$. Write the vector $\mathbf{u} = (1, 1, 1, 1)$ in the form $\mathbf{u} = \mathbf{v} + \mathbf{w}$, where $\mathbf{v}$ is in V and $\mathbf{w}$ is orthogonal to every vector in V.

43. Let $\{\mathbf{u}_1, \mathbf{u}_2, \ldots, \mathbf{u}_m\}$ be an orthonormal subset of R^n, and let $\mathbf{v}$ be any vector in R^n. Prove that
$$\|\mathbf{v}\|^2 \ge \sum_{i=1}^{m} (\mathbf{v} \cdot \mathbf{u}_i)^2.$$

(This inequality is called **Bessel's Inequality.**)

44. Let $\{x_1, x_2, \ldots, x_n\}$ be a set of real numbers. Use the Cauchy Schwarz Inequality to prove that
$$(x_1 + x_2 + \cdots + x_n)^2 \le n(x_1^2 + x_2^2 + \cdots + x_n^2).$$

45. Let $\mathbf{u}$ and $\mathbf{v}$ be vectors in an inner product space V. Prove that $\|\mathbf{u} + \mathbf{v}\| = \|\mathbf{u} - \mathbf{v}\|$ if and only if $\mathbf{u}$ and $\mathbf{v}$ are orthogonal.

46. Let $\{\mathbf{u}_1, \mathbf{u}_2, \ldots, \mathbf{u}_n\}$ be a dependent set of vectors in an inner product space V. Describe the result of applying the Gram-Schmidt orthonormalization process to this set.

47. Find the orthogonal complement $S^\perp$ of the subspace S of R^3 spanned by the two column vectors of the matrix
$$A = \begin{bmatrix} 1 & 2 \\ 2 & 1 \\ 0 & -1 \end{bmatrix}.$$

48. Find the projection of the vector $\mathbf{v} = \begin{bmatrix} 1 & 0 & -2 \end{bmatrix}^T$ onto the subspace
$$S = \operatorname{span}\left\{ \begin{bmatrix} 0 \\ -1 \\ 1 \end{bmatrix}, \begin{bmatrix} 0 \\ 1 \\ 1 \end{bmatrix} \right\}.$$

49. Find bases for the four fundamental subspaces of the matrix
$$A = \begin{bmatrix} 0 & 1 & 0 \\ 0 & -3 & 0 \\ 1 & 0 & 1 \end{bmatrix}.$$

50. Find the least squares regression line for the set of data points
$$\{(-2, 2), (-1, 1), (0, 1), (1, 3)\}.$$
Graph the points and the line on the same set of axes.

The Cross Product of Two Vectors in Space

In Exercises 51 and 52, find $\mathbf{u} \times \mathbf{v}$ and show that it is orthogonal to both $\mathbf{u}$ and $\mathbf{v}$.

51. $\mathbf{u} = (1, 1, 1), \quad \mathbf{v} = (1, 0, 0)$
52. $\mathbf{u} = \mathbf{j} + 6\mathbf{k}, \quad \mathbf{v} = \mathbf{i} - 2\mathbf{j} + \mathbf{k}$
53. Find the area of the parallelogram that has $\mathbf{u} = (1, 3, 0)$ and $\mathbf{v} = (-1, 0, 2)$ as adjacent sides.
54. Prove that $\|\mathbf{u} \times \mathbf{v}\| = \|\mathbf{u}\| \|\mathbf{v}\|$ if and only if $\mathbf{u}$ and $\mathbf{v}$ are orthogonal.

In Exercises 55 and 56, the volume of the parallelepiped having $\mathbf{u}$, $\mathbf{v}$, and $\mathbf{w}$ as adjacent sides is given by the **triple scalar product** $|\mathbf{u} \cdot (\mathbf{v} \times \mathbf{w})|$. Find the volume of the parallelepiped having the three given vectors as adjacent sides.

55. $\mathbf{u} = (1, 0, 0), \quad \mathbf{v} = (0, 0, 1), \quad \mathbf{w} = (0, 1, 0)$

56. u $= (1, 2, 1),$ **v** $= (-1, -1, 0),$ **w** $= (3, 4, -1)$

Least Squares Approximations (Calculus)

In Exercises 57–60, find the *linear* least squares approximating function **g** for the given function **f**. Then sketch the graphs of **f** and **g**.

57. $f(x) = x^3, -1 \leq x \leq 1$ **58.** $f(x) = x^3, 0 \leq x \leq 2$

59. $f(x) = \sin 2x, 0 \leq x \leq \pi/2$

60. $f(x) = \sin x \cos x, 0 \leq x \leq \pi$

In Exercises 61 and 62, find the *quadratic* least squares approxi-

mating function **g** for the given function **f**. Then sketch the graphs of **f** and **g**.

61. $f(x) = \sqrt{x}, 0 \leq x \leq 1$ **62.** $f(x) = \dfrac{1}{x}, 1 \leq x \leq 2$

Fourier Approximations (Calculus)

In Exercises 63 and 64, find the *n*th order Fourier approximation of the given function.

63. $f(x) = x^2, -\pi \leq x \leq \pi,$ first order

64. $f(x) = x, -\pi \leq x \leq \pi,$ second order

CHAPTER 5   PROJECTS

1   The *QR*-factorization

The Gram-Schmidt orthonormalization process leads to an important factorization of matrices called the **QR-factorization**. If A is an $m \times n$ matrix of rank n, then A can be expressed as the product $A = QR$ of an $m \times n$ matrix Q and an $n \times n$ matrix R, where Q has orthonormal columns and R is upper triangular.

The columns of A can be considered a basis for a subspace of R^m, and the columns of Q are the result of applying the Gram-Schmidt orthonormalization process to this set of column vectors.

Recall that in Example 7, Section 5.3, we used the Gram-Schmidt orthonormalization process on the column vectors of the matrix

$$A = \begin{bmatrix} 1 & 1 & 0 \\ 1 & 2 & 1 \\ 0 & 0 & 2 \end{bmatrix}.$$

We obtained an orthonormal basis for R^3, which we will label $\mathbf{q}_1, \mathbf{q}_2, \mathbf{q}_3$.

$$\mathbf{q}_1 = (\sqrt{2}/2, \sqrt{2}/2, 0)$$

$$\mathbf{q}_2 = (-\sqrt{2}/2, \sqrt{2}/2, 0)$$

$$\mathbf{q}_3 = (0, 0, 1)$$

These vectors form the columns of the matrix Q.

$$Q = \begin{bmatrix} \sqrt{2}/2 & -\sqrt{2}/2 & 0 \\ \sqrt{2}/2 & \sqrt{2}/2 & 0 \\ 0 & 0 & 1 \end{bmatrix}$$

The upper triangular matrix R consists of the following dot products.

$$\begin{bmatrix} \mathbf{v}_1 \cdot \mathbf{q}_1 & \mathbf{v}_2 \cdot \mathbf{q}_1 & \mathbf{v}_3 \cdot \mathbf{q}_1 \\ 0 & \mathbf{v}_2 \cdot \mathbf{q}_2 & \mathbf{v}_3 \cdot \mathbf{q}_2 \\ 0 & 0 & \mathbf{v}_3 \cdot \mathbf{q}_3 \end{bmatrix} = \begin{bmatrix} \sqrt{2} & 3\sqrt{2}/2 & \sqrt{2}/2 \\ 0 & \sqrt{2}/2 & \sqrt{2}/2 \\ 0 & 0 & 2 \end{bmatrix}$$

It is now an easy exercise to verify that $A = QR$.

In general if A is an $m \times n$ matrix of rank n, then the QR-factorization of A can be constructed if we keep track of the dot products used in the Gram-Schmidt orthonormalization process as applied to the column of A. The columns of the $m \times n$ matrix Q are the orthonormal vectors that result from the Gram-Schmidt orthonormalization process. The $n \times n$ upper triangular matrix R consists of certain dot products of the original column vectors $\mathbf{v}_i$ and the orthonormal column vectors $\mathbf{q}_i$. If the columns of the matrix A are denoted $\mathbf{v}_1, \mathbf{v}_2, \ldots, \mathbf{v}_n$ and the columns of Q are denoted $\mathbf{q}_1, \mathbf{q}_2, \ldots, \mathbf{q}_n$, then the QR-factorization of A is as follows.

$$A = QR$$

$$[\mathbf{v}_1 \quad \mathbf{v}_2 \quad \cdots \quad \mathbf{v}_n] = [\mathbf{q}_1 \quad \mathbf{q}_2 \quad \cdots \quad \mathbf{q}_n] \begin{bmatrix} \mathbf{v}_1 \cdot \mathbf{q}_1 & \mathbf{v}_2 \cdot \mathbf{q}_1 & \cdots & \mathbf{v}_n \cdot \mathbf{q}_1 \\ 0 & \mathbf{v}_2 \cdot \mathbf{q}_2 & \cdots & \mathbf{v}_n \cdot \mathbf{q}_2 \\ \vdots & \vdots & & \vdots \\ 0 & 0 & \cdots & \mathbf{v}_n \cdot \mathbf{q}_n \end{bmatrix}$$

1. Verify the matrix equation $A = QR$ for the preceding example.
2. Find the QR-factorization of the following matrices.

(a) $A = \begin{bmatrix} 1 & 1 \\ 0 & 1 \\ 1 & 0 \end{bmatrix}$

(b) $A = \begin{bmatrix} 1 & 0 \\ 0 & 0 \\ 1 & 1 \\ 1 & 2 \end{bmatrix}$

(c) $A = \begin{bmatrix} 1 & 0 & 0 \\ 1 & 1 & 0 \\ 1 & 1 & 1 \end{bmatrix}$

(d) $A = \begin{bmatrix} 1 & 0 & -1 \\ 1 & 2 & 0 \\ 1 & 2 & 0 \\ 1 & 0 & 0 \end{bmatrix}$

3. Let $A = QR$ be the QR-factorization of the $m \times n$ matrix A of rank n. Show how the least squares problem can be solved using just matrix multiplication and back substitution.
4. Use the result of Exercise 3 to solve the least squares problem $A\mathbf{x} = \mathbf{b}$ if A is the matrix from Exercise 2 (a) and $\mathbf{b} = [-1 \quad 1 \quad -1]^T$.

The QR-factorization of a matrix forms the basis for many algorithms of linear algebra. Computer routines for the computation of eigenvalues (Chapter 7) are based on this factorization, as are algorithms for computing the least squares regression line for a set of data points. However, it should be mentioned that, in practice, techniques other than the Gram-Schmidt orthonormalization process are actually used to compute the QR-factorization of a matrix.

2 Orthogonal Matrices and Change of Basis

Let $B = \{\mathbf{v}_1, \mathbf{v}_2, \ldots, \mathbf{v}_n\}$ be an ordered basis for the vector space V. Recall that the coordinate matrix of a vector $\mathbf{x} = c_1\mathbf{v}_1 + c_2\mathbf{v}_2 + \cdots + c_n\mathbf{v}_n$ in V is the column vector

$$[\mathbf{x}]_B = \begin{bmatrix} c_1 \\ c_2 \\ \vdots \\ c_n \end{bmatrix}.$$

If B' is another basis for V then the transition matrix P from B' to B changes a coordinate matrix relative to B' into a coordinate matrix relative to B,

$$P[\mathbf{x}]_{B'} = [\mathbf{x}]_B.$$

The question we wish to explore now is whether there are transition matrices P that preserve the length of the coordinate matrix; that is, given $P[\mathbf{x}]_{B'} = [\mathbf{x}]_B$, does $\|[\mathbf{x}]_{B'}\| = \|[\mathbf{x}]_B\|$?

For example, consider the transition matrix from Section 4.7, Example 5,

$$P = \begin{bmatrix} 3 & -2 \\ 2 & -1 \end{bmatrix}$$

relative to the bases for R^2,

$$B = \{(-3, 2), (4, -2)\} \qquad \text{and} \qquad B' = \{(-1, 2), (2, -2)\}.$$

If $\mathbf{x} = (-1, 2)$, then $[\mathbf{x}]_{B'} = [1 \ \ 0]^T$ and $[\mathbf{x}]_B = P[\mathbf{x}]_{B'} = [3 \ \ 2]^T$. Thus, using the Euclidean norm for R^2,

$$\|[\mathbf{x}]_{B'}\| = 1 \neq \sqrt{13} = [\mathbf{x}]_B.$$

We will see in this project that if the transition matrix P is **orthogonal,** then the norm of the coordinate vector will remain unchanged.

Definition of Orthogonal Matrix	The square matrix P is **orthogonal** if it is invertible and $P^{-1} = P^T$.

1. Show that the matrix P defined previously is *not* orthogonal.

2. Show that for any real number θ, the matrix $\begin{bmatrix} \cos\theta & -\sin\theta \\ \sin\theta & \cos\theta \end{bmatrix}$ is orthogonal.

3. Show that a matrix is orthogonal if and only if its columns are pairwise orthogonal.

4. Prove that the inverse of an orthogonal matrix is orthogonal.

5. Is the sum of orthogonal matrices orthogonal? Is the product of orthogonal matrices orthogonal? Illustrate your answers with appropriate examples.

6. What is the determinant of an orthogonal matrix?

7. Prove that if P is an $m \times n$ orthogonal matrix, then $\|P\mathbf{x}\| = \|\mathbf{x}\|$ for all vectors $\mathbf{x}$ in R^n.

8. Verify the result of Exercise 7 using the bases $B = \{(1, 0), (0, 1)\}$ and

$$B' = \left\{ \left(\frac{-2}{\sqrt{5}}, \frac{1}{\sqrt{5}} \right), \left(\frac{1}{\sqrt{5}}, \frac{2}{\sqrt{5}} \right) \right\}.$$

CHAPTER 5 ☐ MATLAB EXERCISES

1. Use the MATLAB command **norm(v)** to find
   (a) the length of the vector $\mathbf{v} = (0, -2, 1, 4, -2)$.
   (b) a unit vector in the direction of $\mathbf{v} = (-3, 2, 4, -5, 0, 1)$.
   (c) the distance between the vectors $\mathbf{u} = (0, 2, 2, -3)$ and $\mathbf{v} = (-4, 7, 10, 1)$.

2. The dot product of the vectors (written as columns)

$$\mathbf{u} = \begin{bmatrix} u_1 \\ u_2 \\ \vdots \\ u_n \end{bmatrix} \quad \text{and} \quad \mathbf{v} = \begin{bmatrix} v_1 \\ v_2 \\ \vdots \\ v_n \end{bmatrix}$$

is given by the matrix product

$$\mathbf{u} \cdot \mathbf{v} = \mathbf{u}^T \mathbf{v} = \begin{bmatrix} u_1 & u_2 & \cdots & u_n \end{bmatrix} \begin{bmatrix} v_1 \\ v_2 \\ \vdots \\ v_n \end{bmatrix}.$$

Hence you can compute the dot product of $\mathbf{u}$ and $\mathbf{v}$ simply by multiplying the transpose of $\mathbf{u}$ times the vector $\mathbf{v}$. Let $\mathbf{u} = (2, -5, 0, 4, 8)$, $\mathbf{v} = (0, -3, 2, -1, 1)$ and $\mathbf{w} = (1, -1, 0, 0, 7)$, and use MATLAB to find the following.
   (a) $\mathbf{u} \cdot \mathbf{v}$
   (b) $(\mathbf{u} \cdot \mathbf{v})\mathbf{w}$
   (c) $\mathbf{u} \cdot (2\mathbf{v} - 3\mathbf{w})$
   (d) $\mathbf{v} \cdot \mathbf{v}$ and $\|\mathbf{v}\|^2$

3. The angle θ between two nonzero vectors is given by

$$\cos \theta = \frac{\mathbf{u} \cdot \mathbf{v}}{\|\mathbf{u}\| \|\mathbf{v}\|}.$$

Use MATLAB to find the angle between $\mathbf{u} = (-3, 4, 0)$ and $\mathbf{v} = (1, 1, 4)$. (Hint: use the built-in inverse cosine function, **acos**).

4. You can find the orthogonal projection of the column vector $\mathbf{x}$ onto the vector $\mathbf{y}$ by computing

$$\frac{\mathbf{x}^T \mathbf{y}}{\mathbf{y}^T \mathbf{y}} \mathbf{y}.$$

Use MATLAB to find the following projections of $\mathbf{x}$ onto $\mathbf{y}$.

(a) $\mathbf{x} = (3, 1, 2)$, $\mathbf{y} = (7, 1, -2)$

(b) $\mathbf{x} = (1, 1, 1)$, $\mathbf{y} = (-1, 1, 1)$

(c) $\mathbf{x} = (0, 1, 3, -3)$, $\mathbf{y} = (4, 0, 0, 1)$

5. Use the MATLAB command **cross(u, v)** to find the cross products of the following vectors.

   (a) $\mathbf{u} = (1, -2, 1)$, $\mathbf{v} = (3, 1, -2)$

   (b) $\mathbf{u} = (0, 1, -2)$, $\mathbf{v} = (-5, 14, 6)$

6. Let $\mathbf{u} = (-3, 2, 4)$, $\mathbf{v} = (5, 0, -7)$, and $\mathbf{w} = (-1, -5, 6)$. Use MATLAB to illustrate the following properties of the cross product.

   (a) $\mathbf{u} \times \mathbf{v} = -(\mathbf{v} \times \mathbf{u})$

   (b) $\mathbf{u} \times \mathbf{u} = \mathbf{0}$

   (c) $\mathbf{u} \times (\mathbf{v} + \mathbf{w}) = (\mathbf{u} \times \mathbf{v}) + (\mathbf{u} \times \mathbf{w})$

   (d) $\mathbf{u} \cdot (\mathbf{v} \times \mathbf{w}) = (\mathbf{u} \times \mathbf{v}) \cdot \mathbf{w}$

7. The MATLAB command **A\b** finds the least squares solution to the linear system of equations $A\mathbf{x} = \mathbf{b}$. For example, if

$$A = \begin{bmatrix} 0 & 2 \\ 3 & 0 \\ 1 & 0 \end{bmatrix} \quad \text{and} \quad \mathbf{b} = \begin{bmatrix} 1 \\ 1 \\ 3 \end{bmatrix},$$

then the command **A\b** gives the answer

$$\begin{bmatrix} 0.6000 \\ 0.5000 \end{bmatrix}.$$

Use MATLAB to solve the least squares problem $A\mathbf{x} = \mathbf{b}$ for the given matrices.

(a) $A = \begin{bmatrix} 1 & 2 \\ 0 & 1 \\ 1 & 3 \\ 1 & 4 \end{bmatrix}$ $\mathbf{b} = \begin{bmatrix} 1 \\ 1 \\ 1 \\ 1 \end{bmatrix}$ (b) $A = \begin{bmatrix} 1 & 2 \\ 0 & 1 \\ 1 & 3 \\ 1 & 4 \end{bmatrix}$ $\mathbf{b} = \begin{bmatrix} 0 \\ 2 \\ 1 \\ 1 \end{bmatrix}$

(c) $A = \begin{bmatrix} 1 & 2 & 1 \\ 3 & 4 & 3 \\ 0 & 0 & 1 \\ 1 & 1 & 0 \\ 1 & 2 & -1 \end{bmatrix}$ $\mathbf{b} = \begin{bmatrix} -1 \\ 2 \\ -1 \\ 0 \\ 1 \end{bmatrix}$

8. MATLAB to find the four fundamental subspaces of the following matrices.

(a) $\begin{bmatrix} 0 & 1 & 0 \\ 1 & 0 & 1 \\ 0 & 0 & 0 \\ 1 & 2 & 1 \end{bmatrix}$ (b) $\begin{bmatrix} 1 & 2 \\ 3 & -1 \\ 1 & 4 \\ 0 & 1 \end{bmatrix}$

(c) $\begin{bmatrix} 2 & 1 & 1 & 0 \\ 0 & 1 & 1 & -1 \\ 0 & 2 & 0 & 0 \\ 1 & 1 & 1 & 1 \end{bmatrix}$ (d) $\begin{bmatrix} 0 & 1 & 1 & 0 \\ 0 & 1 & 1 & 1 \\ 3 & -2 & -1 & 0 \\ 4 & 1 & -1 & 0 \\ 5 & 4 & 3 & 2 \end{bmatrix}$

CUMULATIVE TEST FOR CHAPTERS 4 AND 5

Take this test as you would take a test in class. After you are done, check your work against the answers in the back of the book.

1. Given the vectors $\mathbf{v} = (-1, 2)$ and $\mathbf{w} = (3, -1)$, sketch the following vectors.
   (a) $\mathbf{v} + \mathbf{w}$ (b) $3\mathbf{v}$ (c) $2\mathbf{v} - 4\mathbf{w}$

2. If possible, write $\mathbf{w} = (3, 2, 1)$ as a linear combination of the vectors

   $$\mathbf{v}_1 = (1, 2, 0), \quad \mathbf{v}_2 = (-1, 0, 1), \quad \mathbf{v}_3 = (0, 3, 0)$$

3. Prove that the set of all singular 2×2 matrices is not a vector space.

4. Determine whether the set $\{(x, x + y, y, -y) : x, y \in R\}$ is a subspace of R^4.

5. Determine whether the set $\{(x, xy, y) : x, y \in R\}$ is a subspace of R^3.

6. Determine whether the columns of the following matrix span R^4.

   $$A = \begin{bmatrix} 1 & 2 & -1 & 0 \\ 1 & 3 & 0 & 2 \\ 0 & 0 & 1 & -1 \\ 1 & 0 & 0 & 1 \end{bmatrix}$$

7. (a) Define what it means to say a set of vectors is **linearly independent.**
   (b) Determine whether the following set is linearly dependent or independent.
   $S = \{(1, 0, 1, 0), (0, 3, 0, 1), (1, 1, 2, 2), (3, -4, 2, -3)\}$

8. Find the dimension and a basis for the subspace of $M_{3,3}$ consisting of all the 3×3 symmetric matrices.

9. (a) Define **basis** of a vector space.
   (b) Determine if the following set is a basis for R^3.

   $\{(1, 2, 1), (0, 1, 2), (2, 1, -3)\}$

10. Let $A = \begin{bmatrix} -1 & 0 & 2 \\ 1 & 1 & 0 \end{bmatrix}$.

    (a) Find the rank of A.
    (b) Find a basis for the row space of A.
    (c) Find a basis for the column space of A.

11. Find a basis for the solution space of $A\mathbf{x} = \mathbf{0}$ if

$$A = \begin{bmatrix} 1 & 1 & 0 & 0 \\ -2 & -2 & 0 & 0 \\ 0 & 0 & 1 & 1 \\ -1 & -1 & 0 & 0 \end{bmatrix}.$$

12. Find the coordinates $[\mathbf{v}]_B$ of the vector $\mathbf{v} = (1, 2, -3)$ relative to the basis
$B = \{(0, 1, 1), (1, 1, 0), (1, 0, 1)\}$.

13. Find the transition matrix from the basis $B = \{(2, 1, 0), (1, 0, 0), (0, 1, 1)\}$ to the
basis $B' = \{(1, 0, 2), (1, 1, 1), (0, 1, 3)\}$.

14. Let $\mathbf{u} = (1, 0, 2)$ and $\mathbf{v} = (-2, 1, 3)$.
    (a) Find $\|\mathbf{u}\|$.
    (b) Find the distance between $\mathbf{u}$ and $\mathbf{v}$.
    (c) Find $\mathbf{u} \cdot \mathbf{v}$.

15. Find the inner product of $f(x) = x^2$ and $g(x) = x - 2$ from $C[0, 1]$ using the
integral inner product

$$\langle \mathbf{f}, \mathbf{g} \rangle = \int_0^1 f(x)g(x) \, dx.$$

16. Use the Gram-Schmidt orthonormalization process to transform the following set
of vectors into an orthonormal basis for R^3.
$\{(2, 0, 0), (1, 1, 1), (0, 1, 2)\}$

17. Let $\mathbf{u} = (1, 2)$ and $\mathbf{v} = (-3, 2)$. Find $\text{proj}_\mathbf{v}\mathbf{u}$ and graph $\mathbf{u}$, $\mathbf{v}$, and $\text{proj}_\mathbf{v}\mathbf{u}$ on
the same set of coordinate axes.

18. Find the four fundamental subspaces of the matrix

$$A = \begin{bmatrix} 0 & 1 & 1 & 0 \\ -1 & 0 & 0 & 1 \\ 1 & 1 & 1 & 1 \end{bmatrix}.$$

19. Find the orthogonal complement $S^\perp$ of the set

$$S = \text{span}\left(\begin{bmatrix} 1 \\ 0 \\ 1 \end{bmatrix}, \begin{bmatrix} -1 \\ 1 \\ 0 \end{bmatrix} \right).$$

20. Use the axioms for a vector space to prove that $0\mathbf{v} = \mathbf{0}$ for all vectors $\mathbf{v} \in V$.

21. Suppose that $\mathbf{x}_1, \ldots \mathbf{x}_n$ are linearly independent vectors and $\mathbf{y}$ is a vector not in
their span. Prove that the vectors $\mathbf{x}_1, \ldots, \mathbf{x}_n, \mathbf{y}$ are linearly independent.

22. Let W be a subspace of an inner product space V. Prove that the set
$W^\perp = \{\mathbf{v} \in V : \langle \mathbf{v}, \mathbf{w} \rangle = 0 \text{ for all } \mathbf{w} \in W\}$ is a subspace of V.

23. Find the least squares regression line for the points $\{(1, 1), (3, 0), (5, -3)\}$.
Graph the points and the line.

24. The following two matrices are row equivalent.

$$A = \begin{pmatrix} 2 & -4 & 0 & 1 & 7 & 11 \\ 1 & -2 & -1 & 1 & 9 & 12 \\ -1 & 2 & 1 & 3 & -5 & 16 \\ 4 & -8 & 1 & -1 & 6 & -2 \end{pmatrix}$$

$$B = \begin{pmatrix} 1 & -2 & 0 & 0 & 3 & 2 \\ 0 & 0 & 1 & 0 & -5 & -3 \\ 0 & 0 & 0 & 1 & 1 & 7 \\ 0 & 0 & 0 & 0 & 0 & 0 \end{pmatrix}$$

(a) Find the rank of A.
(b) Find a basis for the row space of A.
(c) Find a basis for the column space of A.
(d) Find a basis for the nullspace of A.
(e) Is the last column of A in the span of the first three columns?
(f) Are the first three columns of A linearly independent?
(g) Is the last column of A in the span of columns 1, 3, and 4?
(h) Are columns 1, 3, and 4 linearly dependent?

25. Let $\mathbf{u}$ and $\mathbf{v}$ be vectors in an inner product space V. Prove that $\|\mathbf{u} + \mathbf{v}\| = \|\mathbf{u} - \mathbf{v}\|$ if and only if $\mathbf{u}$ and $\mathbf{v}$ are orthogonal.

6 LINEAR TRANSFORMATIONS

Emmy
Noether

1 8 8 2 – 1 9 3 5

*E*mmy Noether, generally recognized as the leading woman mathematician in recent history, was born in Erlangen, Germany, where her father was a professor of mathematics.

At the beginning of the twentieth century it was still considered inappropriate for a woman to be interested in mathematics. Emmy Noether's talent for abstract reasoning, however, was so unusual that she was able to overcome the obstacles placed in her way. In 1907 she became the first woman to be granted a doctoral degree from a German university.

After receiving her doctorate, Noether stayed at the University of Göttingen to work with Felix Klein and David Hilbert on the general theory of relativity. In spite of considerable opposition to the idea of granting a professorship to a woman, in 1922,

Noether was finally made a professor at the university.

During the 1920s Noether published several papers on axiomatic systems, differential operators, and the representation of noncommutative algebras as linear transformations. Albert Einstein said of her, "In the realm of algebra in which the most gifted mathematicians have been busy for centuries, she discovered methods which have proved of enormous importance."

The rise of the National Socialist Party forced Noether to leave Germany in 1933. She emigrated to the United States, where she accepted a position as professor of mathematics at Bryn Mawr College in Philadelphia. During her year and a half at Bryn Mawr, Noether often traveled to Princeton University, where she delivered lectures at the Institute for Advanced Study.

6.1 INTRODUCTION TO LINEAR TRANSFORMATIONS

In this chapter we discuss functions that **map** a vector space V into a vector space W. This type of function is denoted by

$$T: V \rightarrow W.$$

We use the standard function terminology for such functions. For instance, V is called the **domain** of T. If $\mathbf{v}$ is in V and $\mathbf{w}$ is in W such that

$$T(\mathbf{v}) = \mathbf{w},$$

then $\mathbf{w}$ is called the **image** of $\mathbf{v}$ under T. The set of all images of vectors in V is called the **range** of T, and the set of all $\mathbf{v}$ in V such that $T(\mathbf{v}) = \mathbf{w}$ is called the **preimage** of $\mathbf{w}$. (See Figure 6.1.)

Figure 6.1

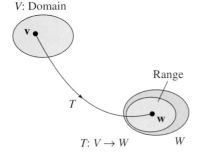

V: Domain

Range

T

$T: V \rightarrow W$

W

316

REMARK: For a vector $\mathbf{v} = (v_1, v_2, \ldots, v_n)$ in R^n, it would be technically correct to use double parentheses to denote $T(\mathbf{v})$ as $T(\mathbf{v}) = T((v_1, v_2, \ldots, v_n))$. For convenience, however, one set of parentheses is dropped, producing

$$T(\mathbf{v}) = T(v_1, v_2, \ldots, v_n).$$

EXAMPLE 1   *A Function from R^2 into R^2*

For any vector $\mathbf{v} = (v_1, v_2)$ in R^2, let $T: R^2 \to R^2$ be defined by

$$T(v_1, v_2) = (v_1 - v_2, v_1 + 2v_2).$$

(a) Find the image of $\mathbf{v} = (-1, 2)$.
(b) Find the preimage of $\mathbf{w} = (-1, 11)$.

Solution   (a) For $\mathbf{v} = (-1, 2)$ we have

$$T(-1, 2) = (-1 - 2, -1 + 2(2)) = (-3, 3).$$

(b) If $T(\mathbf{v}) = (v_1 - v_2, v_1 + 2v_2) = (-1, 11)$, then

$$v_1 - v_2 = -1$$
$$v_1 + 2v_2 = 11.$$

This system of equations has the unique solution $v_1 = 3$ and $v_2 = 4$. Thus the preimage of $(-1, 11)$ is the set in R^2 consisting of the single vector $(3, 4)$.

In this chapter our interest centers on functions (from one vector space to another) that preserve the operations of vector addition and scalar multiplication. We call such functions **linear transformations.**

Definition of a Linear Transformation

Let V and W be vector spaces. The function $T: V \to W$ is called a **linear transformation** of V into W if the following two properties are true for all $\mathbf{u}$ and $\mathbf{v}$ in V and for any scalar c.
1. $T(\mathbf{u} + \mathbf{v}) = T(\mathbf{u}) + T(\mathbf{v})$
2. $T(c\mathbf{u}) = cT(\mathbf{u})$

We say that a linear transformation is *operation preserving,* because the same result occurs whether the operations of addition and scalar multiplication are performed before or after the linear transformation is applied. Although we use the same symbols to denote the vector operations in both V and W, you should note that the operations may be different, as indicated in the following diagram.

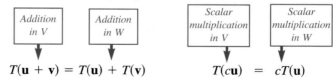

| Addition in V | Addition in W | Scalar multiplication in V | Scalar multiplication in W |

$$T(\mathbf{u} + \mathbf{v}) = T(\mathbf{u}) + T(\mathbf{v}) \qquad\qquad T(c\mathbf{u}) = cT(\mathbf{u})$$

EXAMPLE 2   *Verifying a Linear Transformation from R^2 into R^2*

Show that the function given in Example 1 is a linear transformation from R^2 into R^2.

$$T(v_1, v_2) = (v_1 - v_2, v_1 + 2v_2)$$

Solution   To show that the function T is a linear transformation, we must show that it preserves addition and scalar multiplication. To do this, we let $\mathbf{v} = (v_1, v_2)$ and $\mathbf{u} = (u_1, u_2)$ be vectors in R^2 and c be any real number. Then, using the properties of vector addition and scalar multiplication, we have the following.

1. Since $\mathbf{u} + \mathbf{v} = (u_1, u_2) + (v_1, v_2) = (u_1 + v_1, u_2 + v_2)$, we have

$$
\begin{aligned}
T(\mathbf{u} + \mathbf{v}) &= T(u_1 + v_1, u_2 + v_2) \\
&= ((u_1 + v_1) - (u_2 + v_2), (u_1 + v_1) + 2(u_2 + v_2)) \\
&= ((u_1 - u_2) + (v_1 - v_2), (u_1 + 2u_2) + (v_1 + 2v_2)) \\
&= (u_1 - u_2, u_1 + 2u_2) + (v_1 - v_2, v_1 + 2v_2) \\
&= T(\mathbf{u}) + T(\mathbf{v}).
\end{aligned}
$$

2. Since $c\mathbf{u} = c(u_1, u_2) = (cu_1, cu_2)$, we have

$$
\begin{aligned}
T(c\mathbf{u}) &= T(cu_1, cu_2) = (cu_1 - cu_2, cu_1 + 2cu_2) \\
&= c(u_1 - u_2, u_1 + 2u_2) \\
&= cT(\mathbf{u}).
\end{aligned}
$$

Therefore T is a linear transformation.

REMARK: A linear transformation $T: V \to V$ from a vector space into *itself* (as in Example 2) is called a **linear operator.**

Most of the common functions studied in calculus are not linear transformations.

EXAMPLE 3   *Some Functions That Are Not Linear Transformations*

(a) $f(x) = \sin x$ is not a linear transformation from R into R because, in general,

$$\sin (x_1 + x_2) \neq \sin x_1 + \sin x_2.$$

For instance, $\sin [(\pi/2) + (\pi/3)] \neq \sin(\pi/2) + \sin (\pi/3)$.

(b) $f(x) = x^2$ is not a linear transformation from R into R because, in general,

$$(x_1 + x_2)^2 \neq x_1{}^2 + x_2{}^2.$$

For instance, $(1 + 2)^2 \neq 1^2 + 2^2$.

(c) $f(x) = x + 1$ is not a linear transformation from R into R because

$$f(x_1 + x_2) = x_1 + x_2 + 1$$

whereas

$$f(x_1) + f(x_2) = (x_1 + 1) + (x_2 + 1) = x_1 + x_2 + 2.$$

Thus $f(x_1 + x_2) \neq f(x_1) + f(x_2)$.

REMARK: The function in Example 3(c) points out two uses of the term *linear*. In calculus, $f(x) = x + 1$ is called a linear function because its graph is a line. It is not a linear transformation from the vector space R into R, however, because it preserves neither addition nor scalar multiplication.

Two simple linear transformations are the **zero transformation** and the **identity transformation,** which are defined as follows.

1. $T(\mathbf{v}) = \mathbf{0},$ for all $\mathbf{v}$ Zero transformation $(T: V \rightarrow W)$
2. $T(\mathbf{v}) = \mathbf{v},$ for all $\mathbf{v}$ Identity transformation $(T: V \rightarrow V)$

The verifications of the linearity of these two transformations are left as exercises. (See Exercises 56 and 57.)

Note that the linear transformation in Example 2 has the property that the zero vector is mapped to itself. That is, $T(\mathbf{0}) = \mathbf{0}.$ (Try checking this.) This property is true for all linear transformations, as stated in the next theorem.

Theorem 6.1

Properties of Linear Transformations

Let T be a linear transformation from V into W, where $\mathbf{u}$ and $\mathbf{v}$ are in V. Then the following properties are true.

1. $T(\mathbf{0}) = \mathbf{0}$
2. $T(-\mathbf{v}) = -T(\mathbf{v})$
3. $T(\mathbf{u} - \mathbf{v}) = T(\mathbf{u}) - T(\mathbf{v})$
4. If $\mathbf{v} = c_1\mathbf{v}_1 + c_2\mathbf{v}_2 + \cdots + c_n\mathbf{v}_n$, then

$$T(\mathbf{v}) = T(c_1\mathbf{v}_1 + c_2\mathbf{v}_2 + \cdots + c_n\mathbf{v}_n)$$

$$= c_1T(\mathbf{v}_1) + c_2T(\mathbf{v}_2) + \cdots + c_nT(\mathbf{v}_n).$$

Proof   To prove the first property, note that $0\mathbf{v} = \mathbf{0}.$ Then it follows that

$$T(\mathbf{0}) = T(0\mathbf{v}) = 0T(\mathbf{v}) = \mathbf{0}.$$

The second property follows from $-\mathbf{v} = (-1)\mathbf{v},$ which implies that

$$T(-\mathbf{v}) = T[(-1)\mathbf{v}] = (-1)T(\mathbf{v}) = -T(\mathbf{v}).$$

The third property follows from $\mathbf{u} - \mathbf{v} = \mathbf{u} + (-\mathbf{v})$, which implies that

$$T(\mathbf{u} - \mathbf{v}) = T[\mathbf{u} + (-1)\mathbf{v}] = T(\mathbf{u}) + (-1)T(\mathbf{v}) = T(\mathbf{u}) - T(\mathbf{v}).$$

The proof of the fourth property is left to you.

Property 4 of Theorem 6.1 tells us that a linear transformation $T: V \rightarrow W$ is determined completely by its action on a basis of V. In other words, if $\{\mathbf{v}_1, \mathbf{v}_2, \ldots, \mathbf{v}_n\}$ is a basis for the vector space V and if $T(\mathbf{v}_1), T(\mathbf{v}_2), \ldots, T(\mathbf{v}_n)$ are given, then $T(\mathbf{v})$ is determined for *any* $\mathbf{v}$ in V. The use of this property is demonstrated in Example 4.

EXAMPLE 4   *Linear Transformations and Bases*

Let $T: R^3 \rightarrow R^3$ be a linear transformation such that

$$T(1, 0, 0) = (2, -1, 4)$$
$$T(0, 1, 0) = (1, 5, -2)$$
$$T(0, 0, 1) = (0, 3, 1).$$

Find $T(2, 3, -2)$.

Solution   Since $(2, 3, -2)$ can be written as

$$(2, 3, -2) = 2(1, 0, 0) + 3(0, 1, 0) - 2(0, 0, 1),$$

we can use property 4 of Theorem 6.1 to write

$$T(2, 3, -2) = 2T(1, 0, 0) + 3T(0, 1, 0) - 2T(0, 0, 1)$$
$$= 2(2, -1, 4) + 3(1, 5, -2) - 2(0, 3, 1)$$
$$= (7, 7, 0).$$

Another advantage of Theorem 6.1 is that it provides a quick way to spot functions that are not linear transformations. That is, since all four conditions of the theorem must be true of a linear transformation, it follows that if any one of the properties is not satisfied for a function T, then the function is not a linear transformation. For example, the function given by

$$T(x_1, x_2) = (x_1 + 1, x_2)$$

is not a linear transformation from R^2 to R^2 because $T(0, 0) \neq (0, 0)$.

In the next example we use a matrix to define a linear transformation from R^2 into R^3. The vector $\mathbf{v} = (v_1, v_2)$ is written in the matrix form

$$\mathbf{v} = \begin{bmatrix} v_1 \\ v_2 \end{bmatrix}$$

so that it can be multiplied *on the left* by a matrix of order 3×2.

EXAMPLE 5   *A Linear Transformation Defined by a Matrix*

The function $T: R^2 \to R^3$ is defined as follows.

$$T(\mathbf{v}) = A\mathbf{v} = \begin{bmatrix} 3 & 0 \\ 2 & 1 \\ -1 & -2 \end{bmatrix} \begin{bmatrix} v_1 \\ v_2 \end{bmatrix}$$

(a) Find $T(\mathbf{v})$, where $\mathbf{v} = (2, -1)$.

(b) Show that T is a linear transformation from R^2 into R^3.

Solution   (a) Since $\mathbf{v} = (2, -1)$, we have

$$T(\mathbf{v}) = A\mathbf{v} = \begin{bmatrix} 3 & 0 \\ 2 & 1 \\ -1 & -2 \end{bmatrix} \begin{bmatrix} 2 \\ -1 \end{bmatrix} = \begin{bmatrix} 6 \\ 3 \\ 0 \end{bmatrix}.$$

$\uparrow$ Vector in R^2 $\uparrow$ Vector in R^3

Therefore we have $T(2, -1) = (6, 3, 0)$.

(b) We begin by observing that T does map a vector in R^2 to a vector in R^3. To show that T is a linear transformation, we use the properties of matrix multiplication, as given in Theorem 2.3. For any vectors $\mathbf{u}$ and $\mathbf{v}$ in R^2, the distributive property of matrix multiplication over addition produces

$$T(\mathbf{u} + \mathbf{v}) = A(\mathbf{u} + \mathbf{v}) = A\mathbf{u} + A\mathbf{v} = T(\mathbf{u}) + T(\mathbf{v}).$$

Similarly, for any vector $\mathbf{u}$ in R^2 and any scalar c, the commutative property of scalar multiplication with matrix multiplication produces

$$T(c\mathbf{u}) = A(c\mathbf{u}) = c(A\mathbf{u}) = cT(\mathbf{u}).$$

Example 5 illustrates an important result regarding the representation of linear transformations from R^n into R^m. We present this result in two stages. Theorem 6.2 states that every $m \times n$ matrix represents a linear transformation from R^n into R^m. Then in Section 6.3 we show the converse: that every linear transformation from R^n into R^m can be represented by an $m \times n$ matrix.

Note that in part (b) of Example 5 no reference is made to the specific matrix A. This verification therefore serves as a general proof that the function defined by any $m \times n$ matrix is a linear transformation from R^n into R^m.

Theorem 6.2

The Linear Transformation Given by a Matrix

Let A be an $m \times n$ matrix. The function T defined by

$$T(\mathbf{v}) = A\mathbf{v}$$

is a linear transformation from R^n into R^m. In order to conform to matrix multiplication with an $m \times n$ matrix, the vectors in R^n are represented by $n \times 1$ matrices and the vectors in R^m are represented by $m \times 1$ matrices.

REMARK: The $m \times n$ zero matrix corresponds to the zero transformation from R^n into R^m, and the $n \times n$ identity matrix I_n corresponds to the identity transformation from R^n into R^n.

Be sure you see that an $m \times n$ matrix A defines a linear transformation from R^n into R^m.

$$A\mathbf{v} = \begin{bmatrix} a_{11} & a_{12} & \cdots & a_{1n} \\ a_{21} & a_{22} & \cdots & a_{2n} \\ \vdots & \vdots & & \vdots \\ a_{m1} & a_{m2} & \cdots & a_{mn} \end{bmatrix} \begin{bmatrix} v_1 \\ v_2 \\ \vdots \\ v_n \end{bmatrix} = \begin{bmatrix} a_{11}v_1 + a_{12}v_2 + \cdots + a_{1n}v_n \\ a_{21}v_1 + a_{22}v_2 + \cdots + a_{2n}v_n \\ \vdots & \vdots & & \vdots \\ a_{m1}v_1 + a_{m2}v_2 + \cdots + a_{mn}v_n \end{bmatrix}$$

$\underset{\substack{\text{Vector} \\ \text{in } R^n}}{\uparrow}$ $\underset{\substack{\text{Vector} \\ \text{in } R^m}}{\uparrow}$

EXAMPLE 6   *Linear Transformations Given by Matrices*

The linear transformation $T: R^n \rightarrow R^m$ is defined by $T(\mathbf{v}) = A\mathbf{v}$. Find the dimensions of R^n and R^m for the linear transformations given by the following matrices.

(a) $A = \begin{bmatrix} 0 & 1 & -1 \\ 2 & 3 & 0 \\ 4 & 2 & 1 \end{bmatrix}$ (b) $A = \begin{bmatrix} 2 & -3 \\ -5 & 0 \\ 0 & -2 \end{bmatrix}$ (c) $A = \begin{bmatrix} 1 & 0 & -1 & 2 \\ 3 & 1 & 0 & 0 \end{bmatrix}$

Solution   (a) Since the size of this matrix is 3×3, it defines a linear transformation from R^3 into R^3.

$$A\mathbf{v} = \begin{bmatrix} 0 & 1 & -1 \\ 2 & 3 & 0 \\ 4 & 2 & 1 \end{bmatrix} \begin{bmatrix} v_1 \\ v_2 \\ v_3 \end{bmatrix} = \begin{bmatrix} u_1 \\ u_2 \\ u_3 \end{bmatrix}$$

$\underset{\substack{\text{Vector} \\ \text{in } R^3}}{\uparrow}$ $\underset{\substack{\text{Vector} \\ \text{in } R^3}}{\uparrow}$

(b) Since the size of this matrix is 3×2, it defines a linear transformation from R^2 into R^3.

(c) Since the size of this matrix is 2×4, it defines a linear transformation from R^4 into R^2.

In the next example we discuss a common type of linear transformation from R^2 into R^2.

EXAMPLE 7   *Rotation in the Plane*

Show that the linear transformation $T: R^2 \rightarrow R^2$ given by the matrix

$$A = \begin{bmatrix} \cos\theta & -\sin\theta \\ \sin\theta & \cos\theta \end{bmatrix}$$

has the property that it rotates every vector in R^2 counterclockwise about the origin through the angle θ.

Figure 6.2

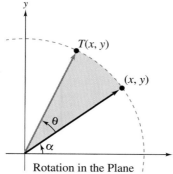

Rotation in the Plane

Figure 6.3

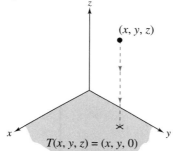

Projection onto xy-plane

Solution   From Theorem 6.2 we know that T is a linear transformation. To show that it rotates every vector in R^2 counterclockwise through the angle θ, we let $\mathbf{v} = (x, y)$ be a vector in R^2. Using polar coordinates, we can write $\mathbf{v}$ as

$$\mathbf{v} = (x, y) = (r \cos \alpha, r \sin \alpha),$$

where r is the length of $\mathbf{v}$ and α is the angle from the positive x-axis counterclockwise to the vector $\mathbf{v}$. Now, applying the linear transformation T to $\mathbf{v}$ produces

$$T(\mathbf{v}) = A\mathbf{v} = \begin{bmatrix} \cos \theta & -\sin \theta \\ \sin \theta & \cos \theta \end{bmatrix} \begin{bmatrix} x \\ y \end{bmatrix}$$

$$= \begin{bmatrix} \cos \theta & -\sin \theta \\ \sin \theta & \cos \theta \end{bmatrix} \begin{bmatrix} r \cos \alpha \\ r \sin \alpha \end{bmatrix}$$

$$= \begin{bmatrix} r \cos \theta \cos \alpha - r \sin \theta \sin \alpha \\ r \sin \theta \cos \alpha + r \cos \theta \sin \alpha \end{bmatrix}$$

$$= \begin{bmatrix} r \cos (\theta + \alpha) \\ r \sin (\theta + \alpha) \end{bmatrix}.$$

Therefore the vector $T(\mathbf{v})$ has the same length as $\mathbf{v}$. Furthermore, since the angle from the positive x-axis to $T(\mathbf{v})$ is $\theta + \alpha$, $T(\mathbf{v})$ is the vector that results from rotating the vector $\mathbf{v}$ counterclockwise through the angle θ, as shown in Figure 6.2.

R E M A R K :   The linear transformation in Example 7 is called a **rotation** in R^2. Rotations in R^2 preserve both vector length and the angle between two vectors. That is, the angle between $\mathbf{u}$ and $\mathbf{v}$ is equal to the angle between $T(\mathbf{u})$ and $T(\mathbf{v})$.

EXAMPLE 8   *A Projection in R^3*

The linear transformation $T: R^3 \rightarrow R^3$ given by

$$A = \begin{bmatrix} 1 & 0 & 0 \\ 0 & 1 & 0 \\ 0 & 0 & 0 \end{bmatrix}$$

is called a **projection** in R^3. If $\mathbf{v} = (x, y, z)$ is a vector in R^3, then $T(\mathbf{v}) = (x, y, 0)$. In other words, T maps every vector in R^3 to its orthogonal projection in the xy-plane, as shown in Figure 6.3.

So far only linear transformations from R^n into R^m have been discussed. In the remainder of this section we consider some linear transformations involving vector spaces other that R^n.

EXAMPLE 9   *A Linear Transformation from $M_{m,n}$ into $M_{n,m}$*

Let $T: M_{m,n} \rightarrow M_{n,m}$ be the function that maps an $m \times n$ matrix A to its transpose. That is,

$$T(A) = A^T.$$

Show that T is a linear transformation.

Solution   Let A and B be $m \times n$ matrices. From Theorem 2.6 we have

$$T(A + B) = (A + B)^T = A^T + B^T = T(A) + T(B)$$

and

$$T(cA) = (cA)^T = c(A^T) = cT(A).$$

Therefore T is a linear transformation from $M_{m,n}$ into $M_{n,m}$.

EXAMPLE 10   *The Differential Operator (Calculus)*

Let $C'[a, b]$ be the set of all functions whose derivatives are continuous on $[a, b]$. Show that the differential operator D_x defines a linear transformation from $C'[a, b]$ into $C[a, b]$.

Solution   Using operator notation, we write

$$D_x(\mathbf{f}) = \frac{d}{dx}[\mathbf{f}],$$

where $\mathbf{f}$ is in $C'[a, b]$. To show that D_x is a linear transformation, we resort to calculus. Specifically, because the derivative of the sum of two functions is equal to the sum of their derivatives and because the sum of two continuous functions is continuous, we have

$$D_x(\mathbf{f} + \mathbf{g}) = \frac{d}{dx}[\mathbf{f} + \mathbf{g}] = \frac{d}{dx}[\mathbf{f}] + \frac{d}{dx}[\mathbf{g}]$$

$$= D_x(\mathbf{f}) + D_x(\mathbf{g}).$$

Similarly, because the derivative of a scalar multiple of a function is equal to the scalar multiple of the derivative and because the scalar multiple of a continuous function is continuous, we have

$$D_x(c\mathbf{f}) = \frac{d}{dx}[c\mathbf{f}] = c\left(\frac{d}{dx}[\mathbf{f}]\right) = cD_x(\mathbf{f}).$$

Therefore D_x is a linear transformation from $C'[a, b]$ into $C[a, b]$.

The linear transformation D_x in Example 10 is called the **differential operator.** For polynomials, the differential operator is a linear transformation from P_n into P_{n-1}, because the derivative of a polynomial function of degree n is a polynomial function of degree $n - 1$ or less. That is

$$D_x(a_n x^n + \cdots + a_1 x + a_0) = na_n x^{n-1} + \cdots + a_1.$$

The next example describes a linear transformation from the vector space of polynomial functions P into the vector space of real numbers R.

EXAMPLE 11   *The Definite Integral as a Linear Transformation (Calculus)*

Let $T: P \to R$ be defined by

$$T(\mathbf{p}) = \int_a^b p(x)\, dx.$$

Show that T is a linear transformation from P, the vector space of polynomial functions, into R, the vector space of real numbers R.

Solution   Using properties of definite integrals, we can write

$$T(\mathbf{p} + \mathbf{q}) = \int_a^b [p(x) + q(x)]\, dx$$

$$= \int_a^b p(x)\, dx + \int_a^b q(x)\, dx$$

$$= T(\mathbf{p}) + T(\mathbf{q})$$

$$T(c\mathbf{p}) = \int_a^b c[p(x)]\, dx = c \int_a^b p(x)\, dx = cT(\mathbf{p}).$$

Therefore T is a linear transformation.

SECTION 6.1 ☐ EXERCISES

In Exercises 1–6, use the given function to find (a) the image of **v** and (b) the preimage of **w**.

1. $T(v_1, v_2) = (v_1 + v_2, v_1 - v_2)$, $\mathbf{v} = (3, -4)$, $\mathbf{w} = (3, 19)$

2. $T(v_1, v_2) = (2v_2 - v_1, v_1, v_2)$, $\mathbf{v} = (0, 6)$, $\mathbf{w} = (3, 1, 2)$

3. $T(v_1, v_2, v_3) = (v_2 - v_1, v_1 + v_2, 2v_1)$, $\mathbf{v} = (2, 3, 0)$, $\mathbf{w} = (-11, -1, 10)$

4. $T(v_1, v_2, v_3) = (2v_1 + v_2, 2v_2 - 3v_1, v_1 - v_3)$, $\mathbf{v} = (-4, 5, 1)$, $\mathbf{w} = (4, 1, -1)$

5. $T(v_1, v_2, v_3) = (4v_2 - v_1, 4v_1 + 5v_2)$, $\mathbf{v} = (2, -3, -1)$, $\mathbf{w} = (3, 9)$

6. $T(v_1, v_2) = \left(\dfrac{\sqrt{2}}{2} v_1 - \dfrac{\sqrt{2}}{2} v_2, v_1 + v_2, 2v_1 - v_2 \right)$, $\mathbf{v} = (1, 1)$ $\mathbf{w} = (-5\sqrt{2}, -2, -16)$

In Exercises 7–16, determine whether the given function is a linear transformation.

7. $T: R^2 \to R^2$, $T(x, y) = (x, 1)$

8. $T: R^3 \to R^3$, $T(x, y, z) = (x + y, x - y, z)$

9. $T: R^2 \to R^2$, $T(x, y) = (x + 3, y)$

10. $T: R^2 \to R^3$, $T(x, y) = (\sqrt{x}, xy, \sqrt{y})$

11. $T: M_{2,2} \to R$, $T(A) = |A|$

12. $T: M_{3,3} \to M_{3,3}$, $T(A) = \begin{bmatrix} 0 & 0 & 1 \\ 0 & 1 & 0 \\ 1 & 0 & 0 \end{bmatrix} A$

13. $T: M_{2,2} \to M_{2,4}$, $T(A) = AB$, B is in $M_{2,4}$

14. $T: M_{2,2} \to M_{2,2}$, $T(A) = A^T$

15. $T: P_2 \rightarrow P_2, T(a_0 + a_1 x + a_2 x^2) =$
$(a_0 + a_1 + a_2) + (a_1 + a_2)x + a_2 x^2$

16. $T: P_2 \rightarrow P_2, T(a_0 + a_1 x + a_2 x^2) = a_1 + 2a_2 x$

In Exercises 17–22, the linear transformation $T: R^n \rightarrow R^m$ is defined by $T(\mathbf{v}) = A\mathbf{v}$. Find the dimensions of R^n and R^m.

17. $A = \begin{bmatrix} 0 & 1 & -2 & 1 \\ -1 & 4 & 5 & 0 \\ 0 & 1 & 3 & 1 \end{bmatrix}$

18. $A = \begin{bmatrix} 1 & 0 & 0 & -1 & 0 \\ 0 & 1 & 0 & 2 & 0 \\ 0 & 0 & 1 & 0 & 1 \end{bmatrix}$

19. $A = \begin{bmatrix} 1 & 2 \\ -2 & 4 \\ -2 & 2 \end{bmatrix}$

20. $A = \begin{bmatrix} -1 & 2 & 1 & 3 & 4 \\ 0 & 0 & 2 & -1 & 0 \end{bmatrix}$

21. $A = \begin{bmatrix} -1 & 0 & 0 & 0 \\ 0 & 1 & 0 & 0 \\ 0 & 0 & 2 & 0 \\ 0 & 0 & 0 & 1 \end{bmatrix}$

22. $A = \begin{bmatrix} 0 & -1 \\ -1 & 0 \end{bmatrix}$

23. For the linear transformation given in Exercise 17, find (a) $T(1, 0, 2, 3)$ and (b) the preimage of $(0, 0, 0)$.

24. For the linear transformation given in Exercise 18, find (a) $T(1, -1, -2, 0, 2)$ and (b) the preimage of $(0, 0, 0)$.

25. For the linear transformation given in Exercise 19, find (a) $T(2, 4)$ and (b) the preimage of $(-1, 2, 2)$. Then explain why the vector $(1, 1, 1)$ has no preimage under this transformation.

26. For the linear transformation given in Exercise 20, find (a) $T(1, 0, -1, 3, 0)$ and (b) the preimage of $(-1, 8)$.

27. For the linear transformation given in Exercise 21, find (a) $T(1, 1, 1, 1)$ and (b) the preimage of $(1, 1, 1, 1)$.

28. For the linear transformation given in Exercise 22, find (a) $T(1, 1)$, (b) the preimage of $(1, 1)$, and (c) the preimage of $(0, 0)$.

29. Let T be the linear transformation from R^2 into R^2 given by
$T(x, y) = (x \cos \theta - y \sin \theta, x \sin \theta + y \cos \theta)$.
Find (a) $T(4, 4)$ for $\theta = 45°$, (b) $T(4, 4)$ for $\theta = 30°$, and (c) $T(5, 0)$ for $\theta = 120°$.

30. For the linear transformation in Exercise 29, let $\theta = 45°$ and find the preimage of $\mathbf{v} = (1, 1)$.

31. (Calculus) Let D_x be the linear transformation from $C'[a, b]$ into $C[a, b]$ given in Example 10. Which of the following are true?
(a) $D_x(e^{x^2} + 2x) = D_x(e^{x^2}) + 2D_x(x)$
(b) $D_x(x^2 - \ln x) = D_x(x^2) - D_x(\ln x)$
(c) $D_x(\sin 2x) = 2D_x(\sin x)$

32. (Calculus) For the linear transformation in Example 10, find the preimage of the following functions.
(a) $f(x) = 2x + 1$ (b) $f(x) = e^x$ (c) $f(x) = \sin x$

33. (Calculus) Let T be the linear transformation from P into R given by
$$T(\mathbf{p}) = \int_0^1 p(x)\, dx.$$
Find (a) $T(3x^2 - 2)$, (b) $T(x^3 - x^5)$, and (c) $T(4x - 6)$.

34. (Calculus) Let T be the linear transformation from P_2 into R given by the integral in Exercise 33. Find the preimage of 1. That is, find the polynomial function(s) of degree two or less such that $T(\mathbf{p}) = 1$.

35. Let T be a linear transformation from R^2 into R^2 such that $T(1, 1) = (1, 0)$ and $T(1, -1) = (0, 1)$.
Find $T(1, 0)$ and $T(0, 2)$.

36. Let T be a linear transformation from R^2 into R^2 such that $T(1, 0) = (1, 1)$ and $T(0, 1) = (-1, 1)$. Find $T(1, 4)$ and $T(-2, 1)$.

37. Let T be a linear transformation from P_2 into P_2 such that $T(1) = x$, $T(x) = 1 + x$, and $T(x^2) = 1 + x + x^2$. Find $T(2 - 6x + x^2)$.

38. Let T be a linear transformation from $M_{2,2}$ into $M_{2,2}$ such that
$T\left(\begin{bmatrix} 1 & 0 \\ 0 & 0 \end{bmatrix}\right) = \begin{bmatrix} 1 & -1 \\ 0 & 2 \end{bmatrix}$, $T\left(\begin{bmatrix} 0 & 1 \\ 0 & 0 \end{bmatrix}\right) = \begin{bmatrix} 0 & 2 \\ 1 & 1 \end{bmatrix}$,
$T\left(\begin{bmatrix} 0 & 0 \\ 1 & 0 \end{bmatrix}\right) = \begin{bmatrix} 1 & 2 \\ 0 & 1 \end{bmatrix}$, $T\left(\begin{bmatrix} 0 & 0 \\ 0 & 1 \end{bmatrix}\right) = \begin{bmatrix} 3 & -1 \\ 1 & 0 \end{bmatrix}$.
Find $T\left(\begin{bmatrix} 1 & 3 \\ -1 & 4 \end{bmatrix}\right)$.

39. Suppose $T: R^2 \rightarrow R^2$ such that $T(1, 0) = (1, 0)$ and $T(0, 1) = (0, 0)$.
(a) Determine $T(x, y)$ for (x, y) in R^2.
(b) Give a geometric description of T.

40. Suppose $T: R^2 \to R^2$ such that $T(1, 0) = (0, 1)$ and $T(0, 1) = (1, 0)$.

    (a) Determine $T(x, y)$ for (x, y) in R^2.

    (b) Give a geometric description of T.

In Exercises 41–46, let T be the function from R^2 into R^2 such that $T(\mathbf{u}) = \text{proj}_{\mathbf{v}}\mathbf{u}$, where $\mathbf{v} = (1, 1)$.

41. Find $T(x, y)$.   **42.** Find $T(5, 0)$.

43. Prove that $T(\mathbf{u} + \mathbf{w}) = T(\mathbf{u}) + T(\mathbf{w})$ for every $\mathbf{u}$ and $\mathbf{w}$ in R^2.

44. Prove that $T(c\mathbf{u}) = cT(\mathbf{u})$ for every $\mathbf{u}$ in R^2. This result and the one in Exercise 43 prove that T is a linear transformation from R^2 into R^2.

45. Find $T(3, 4)$ and $T(T(3, 4))$ and give a geometric interpretation of the result.

46. Show that T is given by the matrix
$$A = \begin{bmatrix} \frac{1}{2} & \frac{1}{2} \\ \frac{1}{2} & \frac{1}{2} \end{bmatrix}.$$

In Exercises 47–50, we use the concept of a fixed point of a linear transformation $T: V \to V$. A vector $\mathbf{u}$ is a **fixed point** if $T(\mathbf{u}) = \mathbf{u}$.

47. Prove that $\mathbf{0}$ is a fixed point of any linear transformation $T: V \to V$.

48. Prove that the set of fixed points of a linear transformation $T: V \to V$ is a subspace of V.

49. Determine all fixed points of the linear transformation $T: R^2 \to R^2$ given by
$$T(x, y) = (x, 2y).$$

50. Determine all fixed points of the linear transformation $T: R^2 \to R^2$ given by
$$T(x, y) = (y, x).$$

Exercises 51–53 deal with translations in the plane. A **translation** is a function of the form $T(x, y) = (x - h, y - k)$, where at least one of the constants h and k is nonzero.

51. Show that a translation in the plane is not a linear transformation.

52. For the translation $T(x, y) = (x - 2, y + 1)$, determine the images of $(0, 0)$, $(2, -1)$, and $(5, 4)$.

53. Show that a translation in the plane has no fixed points.

54. Let $S = \{\mathbf{v}_1, \mathbf{v}_2, \ldots, \mathbf{v}_n\}$ be a set of linearly dependent vectors in V, and let T be a linear transformation from V into V. Prove that the set
$$\{T(\mathbf{v}_1), T(\mathbf{v}_2), \ldots, T(\mathbf{v}_n)\}$$
is linearly dependent.

55. Let $S = \{\mathbf{v}_1, \mathbf{v}_2, \mathbf{v}_3\}$ be a set of linearly independent vectors in R^3. Find a linear transformation T from R^3 into R^3 such that the set $\{T(\mathbf{v}_1), T(\mathbf{v}_2), T(\mathbf{v}_3)\}$ is linearly dependent.

56. Prove that the zero transformation $T: V \to W$ is a linear transformation.

57. Prove that the identity transformation $T: V \to V$ is a linear transformation.

58. Let V be an inner product space. For a fixed vector $\mathbf{v}_0$ in V, define $T: V \to R$ by $T(\mathbf{v}) = \langle \mathbf{v}, \mathbf{v}_0 \rangle$. Prove that T is a linear transformation.

59. Let $T: M_{n,n} \to R$ be defined by $T(A) = a_{11} + a_{22} + \cdots + a_{nn}$ (the trace of A). Prove that T is a linear transformation.

60. Let V be an inner product space with a subspace W having $B = \{\mathbf{w}_1, \mathbf{w}_2, \ldots, \mathbf{w}_n\}$ as an orthonormal basis. Show that the function $T: V \to W$ given by
$$T(\mathbf{v}) = \langle \mathbf{v}, \mathbf{w}_1 \rangle \mathbf{w}_1 + \langle \mathbf{v}, \mathbf{w}_2 \rangle \mathbf{w}_2 + \cdots + \langle \mathbf{v}, \mathbf{w}_n \rangle \mathbf{w}_n$$
is a linear transformation. T is called the **orthogonal projection of V onto W**.

61. Let $\{\mathbf{v}_1, \mathbf{v}_2, \ldots, \mathbf{v}_n\}$ be a basis for a vector space V. Prove that if a linear transformation $T: V \to W$ satisfies $T(\mathbf{v}_i) = \mathbf{0}$ for $i = 1, 2, \ldots, n$, then T is the zero transformation.

62. Prove that $T: V \to W$ is a linear transformation if and only if $T(a\mathbf{u} + b\mathbf{v}) = aT(\mathbf{u}) + bT(\mathbf{v})$ for all vectors $\mathbf{u}$ and $\mathbf{v}$, and all scalars a and b.

6.2 THE KERNEL AND RANGE OF A LINEAR TRANSFORMATION

We know from Theorem 6.1 that for any linear transformation $T: V \rightarrow W$, the zero vector in V is mapped to the zero vector in W. That is,

$$T(\mathbf{0}) = \mathbf{0}.$$

The question we will consider first in this section is whether there are *other* vectors $\mathbf{v}$ such that $T(\mathbf{v}) = \mathbf{0}$. The collection of all such elements is called the **kernel** of T. Note that we use the symbol $\mathbf{0}$ to represent the zero vector in both V and W, although these two zero vectors are often different.

Definition of Kernel of a Linear Transformation

Let $T: V \rightarrow W$ be a linear transformation. Then the set of all vectors $\mathbf{v}$ in V that satisfy $T(\mathbf{v}) = \mathbf{0}$ is called the **kernel** of T and is denoted by $\ker(T)$.

Sometimes the kernel of a transformation is obvious and can be found by inspection, as demonstrated in Examples 1, 2, and 3.

EXAMPLE 1   *Finding the Kernel of a Linear Transformation*

Let $T: M_{3,2} \rightarrow M_{2,3}$ be the linear transformation that maps a 3×2 matrix A to its transpose. That is, $T(A) = A^T$. Find the kernel of T.

Solution   For this linear transformation, the 3×2 zero matrix is clearly the only matrix in $M_{3,2}$ whose transpose is the zero matrix in $M_{2,3}$.

Zero Matrix in $M_{3,2}$

$$\mathbf{0} = \begin{bmatrix} 0 & 0 \\ 0 & 0 \\ 0 & 0 \end{bmatrix}$$

Zero Matrix in $M_{2,3}$

$$\mathbf{0} = \begin{bmatrix} 0 & 0 & 0 \\ 0 & 0 & 0 \end{bmatrix}$$

Therefore the kernel of T consists of a single element: the zero matrix in $M_{3,2}$.

EXAMPLE 2   *The Kernel of the Zero and Identity Transformations*

(a) The kernel of the zero transformation $T: V \rightarrow W$ consists of all of V because $T(\mathbf{v}) = \mathbf{0}$ for every $\mathbf{v}$ in V. That is,

$$\ker(T) = V.$$

(b) The kernel of the identity transformation $T: V \rightarrow V$ consists of the single element $\mathbf{0}$. That is,

$$\ker(T) = \{\mathbf{0}\}.$$

EXAMPLE 3   *Finding the Kernel of a Linear Transformation*

Find the kernel of the projection $T: R^3 \to R^3$ given by

$$T(x, y, z) = (x, y, 0).$$

Solution   This linear transformation projects the vector (x, y, z) in R^3 to the vector $(x, y, 0)$ in the xy-plane. Therefore the kernel consists of all vectors lying on the z-axis. That is,

$$\ker(T) = \{(0, 0, z): z \text{ is a real number}\}.$$

(See Figure 6.4.)

Figure 6.4

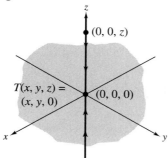

The kernel of T is the set
of all vectors on the z-axis.

Finding the kernels of the linear transformations in Examples 1, 2, and 3 was fairly easy. Generally the kernel of a linear transformation is not so obvious, and finding it requires a little work, as illustrated in the next two examples.

EXAMPLE 4   *Finding the Kernel of a Linear Transformation*

Find the kernel of the linear transformation $T: R^2 \to R^3$ given by

$$T(x_1, x_2) = (x_1 - 2x_2, 0, -x_1).$$

Solution   To find $\ker(T)$, we need to find all $\mathbf{x} = (x_1, x_2)$ in R^2 such that

$$T(x_1, x_2) = (x_1 - 2x_2, 0, -x_1) = (0, 0, 0).$$

This leads to the homogeneous system

$$
\begin{aligned}
x_1 - 2x_2 &= 0 \\
0 &= 0 \\
-x_1 \quad\;\; &= 0,
\end{aligned}
$$

which has only the trivial solution $(x_1, x_2) = (0, 0)$. Thus we have

$$\ker(T) = \{(0, 0)\} = \{\mathbf{0}\}.$$

EXAMPLE 5   *Finding the Kernel of a Linear Transformation*

Find the kernel of the linear transformation $T: R^3 \to R^2$ defined by $T(\mathbf{x}) = A\mathbf{x}$, where

$$A = \begin{bmatrix} 1 & -1 & -2 \\ -1 & 2 & 3 \end{bmatrix}.$$

Solution   The kernel of T is the set of all $\mathbf{x} = (x_1, x_2, x_3)$ in R^3 such that

$$T(x_1, x_2, x_3) = (0, 0).$$

From this equation we obtain the following homogeneous system.

$$\begin{bmatrix} 1 & -1 & -2 \\ -1 & 2 & 3 \end{bmatrix} \begin{bmatrix} x_1 \\ x_2 \\ x_3 \end{bmatrix} = \begin{bmatrix} 0 \\ 0 \end{bmatrix} \quad \longrightarrow \quad \begin{aligned} x_1 - x_2 - 2x_3 &= 0 \\ -x_1 + 2x_2 + 3x_3 &= 0 \end{aligned}$$

Figure 6.5

Kernel:
$t(1, -1, 1)$

Writing the augmented matrix of this system in reduced row-echelon form produces

$$\begin{bmatrix} 1 & 0 & -1 & 0 \\ 0 & 1 & 1 & 0 \end{bmatrix} \quad \longrightarrow \quad \begin{aligned} x_1 &= x_3 \\ x_2 &= -x_3. \end{aligned}$$

Using the parameter $t = x_3$ produces the family of solutions

$$\begin{bmatrix} x_1 \\ x_2 \\ x_3 \end{bmatrix} = \begin{bmatrix} t \\ -t \\ t \end{bmatrix} = t \begin{bmatrix} 1 \\ -1 \\ 1 \end{bmatrix}.$$

Thus the kernel of T is given by

$$\ker(T) = \{t(1, -1, 1): t \text{ is a real number}\}$$
$$= \text{span}\{(1, -1, 1)\}.$$

Note that in Example 5 the kernel of T contains an infinite number of vectors. Of course, the zero vector is in $\ker(T)$, but the kernel also contains such nonzero vectors as $(1, -1, 1)$ and $(2, -2, 2)$, as shown in Figure 6.5. Figure 6.5 shows that this particular kernel is a line passing through the origin, which implies that it is a subspace of R^3. In the following theorem we show that the kernel of every linear transformation $T: V \to W$ is a subspace of V.

Theorem 6.3 The Kernel Is a Subspace of V	The kernel of a linear transformation $T: V \to W$ is a subspace of the domain V.

Proof From Theorem 6.1 we know that ker(T) is a nonempty subset of V. Therefore, by Theorem 4.5, we can show that ker(T) is a subspace of V by showing that it is closed under addition and scalar multiplication. To do so, we let **u** and **v** be vectors in the kernel of T. Then

$$T(\mathbf{u} + \mathbf{v}) = T(\mathbf{u}) + T(\mathbf{v}) = \mathbf{0} + \mathbf{0} = \mathbf{0},$$

which implies that $\mathbf{u} + \mathbf{v}$ is in the kernel. Moreover, if c is any scalar, then

$$T(c\mathbf{u}) = cT(\mathbf{u}) = c\mathbf{0} = \mathbf{0},$$

which implies that $c\mathbf{u}$ is in the kernel.

REMARK: As a result of Theorem 6.3, the kernel of T is sometimes called the **nullspace** of T.

The next example shows how to find a basis for the kernel of a transformation defined by a matrix.

EXAMPLE 6 *Finding a Basis for the Kernel*

Let $T: R^5 \to R^4$ be defined by $T(\mathbf{x}) = A\mathbf{x}$, where $\mathbf{x}$ is in R^5 and

$$A = \begin{bmatrix} 1 & 2 & 0 & 1 & -1 \\ 2 & 1 & 3 & 1 & 0 \\ -1 & 0 & -2 & 0 & 1 \\ 0 & 0 & 0 & 2 & 8 \end{bmatrix}.$$

Find a basis for ker(T) as a subspace of R^5.

Solution Following the procedure shown in Example 5, we reduce the augmented matrix $[A : \mathbf{0}]$ to echelon form as follows.

$$\begin{bmatrix} 1 & 0 & 2 & 0 & -1 & 0 \\ 0 & 1 & -1 & 0 & -2 & 0 \\ 0 & 0 & 0 & 1 & 4 & 0 \\ 0 & 0 & 0 & 0 & 0 & 0 \end{bmatrix} \longrightarrow \begin{matrix} x_1 = -2x_3 + x_5 \\ x_2 = x_3 + 2x_5 \\ x_4 = -4x_5 \end{matrix}$$

DISCOVERY

What is the rank of the matrix A in Example 6? Formulate a conjecture relating the dimension of the kernel, the rank, and the number of columns of A. Verify your conjecture for the matrix in Example 5.

Letting $x_3 = s$ and $x_5 = t$, we have

$$\mathbf{x} = \begin{bmatrix} x_1 \\ x_2 \\ x_3 \\ x_4 \\ x_5 \end{bmatrix} = \begin{bmatrix} -2s + t \\ s + 2t \\ s + 0t \\ 0s - 4t \\ 0s + t \end{bmatrix} = s\begin{bmatrix} -2 \\ 1 \\ 1 \\ 0 \\ 0 \end{bmatrix} + t\begin{bmatrix} 1 \\ 2 \\ 0 \\ -4 \\ 1 \end{bmatrix}.$$

Thus one basis for the kernel of T is given by

$$B = \{(-2, 1, 1, 0, 0), (1, 2, 0, -4, 1)\}.$$

In the solution given in Example 6, we found a basis for the kernel of T by solving the homogeneous system given by $A\mathbf{x} = \mathbf{0}$. This procedure is a familiar one—it is the same procedure used to find the *solution space* of $A\mathbf{x} = \mathbf{0}$. In other words, the kernel of T is the nullspace of the matrix A, as given in the following corollary of Theorem 6.3.

Corollary of Theorem 6.3

Let $T: R^n \to R^m$ be the linear transformation given by $T(\mathbf{x}) = A\mathbf{x}$. Then the kernel of T is equal to the solution space of $A\mathbf{x} = \mathbf{0}$.

The Range of a Linear Transformation

The kernel is one of two critical subspaces associated with a linear transformation. The second is the **range** of T, denoted by range(T). Recall from Section 6.1 that the range of $T: V \to W$ is the set of all vectors $\mathbf{w}$ in W that are images of vectors in V. That is, range $(T) = \{T(\mathbf{v}) : \mathbf{v} \text{ is in } V\}$.

Theorem 6.4

The Range of T Is a Subspace of W

The range of a linear transformation $T: V \to W$ is a subspace of W.

Proof

The range of T is nonempty because $T(\mathbf{0}) = \mathbf{0}$ implies that the range contains the zero vector. To show that it is closed under addition, we let $T(\mathbf{u})$ and $T(\mathbf{v})$ be vectors in the range of T. Since $\mathbf{u}$ and $\mathbf{v}$ are in V, it follows that $\mathbf{u} + \mathbf{v}$ is also in V. Hence, the sum $T(\mathbf{u}) + T(\mathbf{v}) = T(\mathbf{u} + \mathbf{v})$ is in the range of T.

To show closure under scalar multiplication, we let $T(\mathbf{u})$ be a vector in the range of T and c be a scalar. Since $\mathbf{u}$ is in V, it follows that $c\mathbf{u}$ is also in V. Hence, the scalar multiple $cT(\mathbf{u}) = T(c\mathbf{u})$ is in the range of T.

Note that the kernel and range of a linear transformation $T: V \to W$ are subspaces of V and W, respectively, as illustrated in Figure 6.6.

To find a basis for the range of a linear transformation defined by $T(\mathbf{x}) = A\mathbf{x}$, we observe that the range consists of all vectors $\mathbf{b}$ such that the system $A\mathbf{x} = \mathbf{b}$ is consistent. By writing the system

$$
\begin{bmatrix}
a_{11} & a_{12} & \cdots & a_{1n} \\
a_{21} & a_{22} & \cdots & a_{2n} \\
\vdots & \vdots & & \vdots \\
a_{m1} & a_{m2} & \cdots & a_{mn}
\end{bmatrix}
\begin{bmatrix}
x_1 \\
x_2 \\
\vdots \\
x_n
\end{bmatrix}
=
\begin{bmatrix}
b_1 \\
b_2 \\
\vdots \\
b_m
\end{bmatrix}
$$

in the form

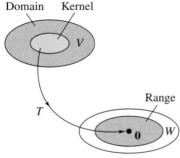

Figure 6.6
Domain   Kernel
Range

$$A\mathbf{x} = x_1 \begin{bmatrix} a_{11} \\ a_{21} \\ \vdots \\ a_{m1} \end{bmatrix} + x_2 \begin{bmatrix} a_{12} \\ a_{22} \\ \vdots \\ a_{m2} \end{bmatrix} + \cdots + x_n \begin{bmatrix} a_{1n} \\ a_{2n} \\ \vdots \\ a_{mn} \end{bmatrix} = \begin{bmatrix} b_1 \\ b_2 \\ \vdots \\ b_m \end{bmatrix} = \mathbf{b}$$

we see that $\mathbf{b}$ is in the range of T if and only if $\mathbf{b}$ is a linear combination of the column vectors of A. Thus *the column space of the matrix A is the same as the range of T.*

Corollary of Theorem 6.4	Let $T: R^n \rightarrow R^m$ be the linear transformation given by $T(\mathbf{x}) = A\mathbf{x}$. Then the column space of A is equal to the range of T.

In Example 4 of Section 4.6, we demonstrated two procedures for finding a basis for the column space of a matrix. In the following example, we use the second procedure given in that example to find a basis for the range of a linear transformation defined by a matrix.

EXAMPLE 7   ***Finding a Basis for the Range of a Linear Transformation***

Let $T: R^5 \rightarrow R^4$ be the linear transformation given in Example 6. Find a basis for the range of T.

Solution   The echelon form of A was calculated in Example 6.

$$A = \begin{bmatrix} 1 & 2 & 0 & 1 & -1 \\ 2 & 1 & 3 & 1 & 0 \\ -1 & 0 & -2 & 0 & 1 \\ 0 & 0 & 0 & 2 & 8 \end{bmatrix} \Rightarrow \begin{bmatrix} 1 & 0 & 2 & 0 & -1 \\ 0 & 1 & -1 & 0 & -2 \\ 0 & 0 & 0 & 1 & 4 \\ 0 & 0 & 0 & 0 & 0 \end{bmatrix}$$

Since the leading ones appear in columns 1, 2, and 4 of the reduced matrix on the right, the corresponding column vectors of A form a basis for the column space of A. Therefore, one basis for the range of T is

$$B = \{(1, 2, -1, 0), (2, 1, 0, 0), (1, 1, 0, 2)\}.$$

The dimensions of the kernel and range of a linear transformation are given the following names.

Definition of Rank and Nullity of a Linear Transformation	Let $T: V \rightarrow W$ be a linear transformation. The dimension of the kernel of T is called the **nullity** of T and is denoted by **nullity**(T). The dimension of the range of T is called the **rank** of T and is denoted by **rank**(T).

REMARK: If T is given by a matrix A, then the rank of T is equal to the rank of A, as defined in Section 4.6.

In Examples 6 and 7 the nullity and rank of T are related to the dimension of the domain as follows.

$$\text{rank}(T) + \text{nullity}(T) = 3 + 2 = 5 = \text{dimension of domain}$$

This relationship is true for any linear transformation from a finite-dimensional vector space, as stated in the following theorem.

Theorem 6.5

Sum of Rank and Nullity

Let $T: V \rightarrow W$ be a linear transformation from an n-dimensional vector space V into a vector space W. Then the sum of the dimensions of the range and kernel is equal to the dimension of the domain. That is,

$$\text{rank}(T) + \text{nullity}(T) = n$$

or

$$\text{dim(range)} + \text{dim(kernel)} = \text{dim(domain)}.$$

Proof   For now we give a proof for the case in which T is represented by an $m \times n$ matrix A. In Section 6.3 we show that any linear transformation from an n-dimensional space to an m-dimensional space can be represented by a matrix. To prove this theorem, we assume that the matrix A has a rank of r. Then we have

$$\text{rank}(T) = \text{dim(range of } T) = \text{dim(column space)} = \text{rank}(A) = r.$$

From Theorem 4.17, however, we know that

$$\text{nullity}(T) = \text{dim(kernel of } T) = \text{dim(solution space)} = n - r.$$

Thus it follows that

$$\text{rank}(T) + \text{nullity}(T) = r + (n - r) = n.$$

EXAMPLE 8   ***Finding the Rank and Nullity of a Linear Transformation***

Find the rank and nullity of the linear transformation $T: R^3 \rightarrow R^3$ defined by the matrix

$$A = \begin{bmatrix} 1 & 0 & -2 \\ 0 & 1 & 1 \\ 0 & 0 & 0 \end{bmatrix}.$$

Solution   Since A is in row-echelon form and has two nonzero rows, it has a rank of 2. Thus the rank of T is 2, and the nullity is $\text{dim(domain)} - \text{rank} = 3 - 2 = 1$.

REMARK: One way to visualize the relationship between the rank and the nullity of a linear transformation given by a matrix is to observe that the rank is determined by the number of leading ones, and the nullity by the number of free variables (columns without leading ones). Their sum must be the total number of columns of the matrix, which is the dimension of the domain. In Example 8, the first two columns have leading ones, indicating that the rank is two. The third column corresponds to a free variable, indicating that the nullity is one.

EXAMPLE 9   *Finding the Rank and Nullity of a Linear Transformation*

Let $T: R^5 \to R^7$ be a linear transformation.

(a) Find the dimension of the kernel of T if the dimension of the range is 2.
(b) Find the rank of T if the nullity of T is 4.
(c) Find the rank of T if $\ker(T) = \{\mathbf{0}\}$.

Solution   (a) By Theorem 6.5, with $n = 5$, we have

$$\dim(\text{kernel}) = n - \dim(\text{range}) = 5 - 2 = 3.$$

(b) Again by Theorem 6.5, we have

$$\text{rank}(T) = n - \text{nullity}(T) = 5 - 4 = 1.$$

(c) In this case, the nullity of T is 0. Hence

$$\text{rank}(T) = n - \text{nullity}(T) = 5 - 0 = 5.$$

One-to-One and Onto Linear Transformations

This section began with a question: How many vectors in the domain of a linear transformation are mapped to the zero vector? Theorem 6.6 shows that if the zero vector is the only vector $\mathbf{v}$ such that $T(\mathbf{v}) = \mathbf{0}$, then T is one-to-one. A function $T: V \to W$ is called **one-to-one** if the preimage of every $\mathbf{w}$ in the range consists of a single vector, as shown in Figure 6.7. This is equivalent to saying that T is one-to-one if and only if for all $\mathbf{u}$ and $\mathbf{v}$ in V, $T(\mathbf{u}) = T(\mathbf{v})$ implies that $\mathbf{u} = \mathbf{v}$.

Figure 6.7

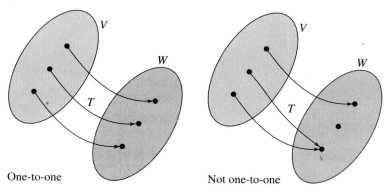

One-to-one   Not one-to-one

Theorem 6.6

One-to-One Linear Transformations

Let $T: V \rightarrow W$ be a linear transformation. Then T is one-to-one if and only if $\ker(T) = \{\mathbf{0}\}$.

Proof   Suppose T is one-to-one. Then $T(\mathbf{v}) = \mathbf{0}$ can have only one solution: $\mathbf{v} = \mathbf{0}$. In that case, $\ker(T) = \{\mathbf{0}\}$. Conversely, suppose $\ker(T) = \{\mathbf{0}\}$ and $T(\mathbf{u}) = T(\mathbf{v})$. Since T is a linear transformation, it follows that

$$T(\mathbf{u} - \mathbf{v}) = T(\mathbf{u}) - T(\mathbf{v}) = \mathbf{0}.$$

This implies that the vector $\mathbf{u} - \mathbf{v}$ lies in the kernel of T and must therefore equal $\mathbf{0}$. Hence $\mathbf{u} - \mathbf{v} = \mathbf{0}$ and $\mathbf{u} = \mathbf{v}$, and we conclude that T is one-to-one.

EXAMPLE 10   ***One-to-One and Not One-to-One Linear Transformations***

(a) The linear transformation $T: M_{m,n} \rightarrow M_{n,m}$, given by $T(A) = A^T$ is one-to-one since its kernel consists of only the $m \times n$ zero matrix.
(b) The zero transformation $T: R^3 \rightarrow R^3$ is not one-to-one since its kernel is all of R^3.

A function $T: V \rightarrow W$ is said to be **onto** if every element in W has a preimage in V. In other words, T is onto W when W is equal to the range of T. Hence we have the following theorem.

Theorem 6.7

Onto Linear Transformations

Let $T: V \rightarrow W$ be a linear transformation, where W is finite dimensional. Then T is onto if and only if the rank of T is equal to the dimension of W.

For vector spaces of equal dimensions, we can combine the results of Theorem 6.5, 6.6, and 6.7 to obtain the following theorem relating the concepts of one-to-one and onto.

Theorem 6.8

One-to-One and Onto Linear Transformations

Let $T: V \rightarrow W$ be a linear transformation with vector spaces V and W *both* of dimension n. Then T is one-to-one if and only if it is onto.

Proof   If T is one-to-one, then by Theorem 6.6 $\ker(T) = \{\mathbf{0}\}$, and $\dim(\ker(T)) = 0$. In that case, Theorem 6.5 produces

$$\dim(\text{range of } T) = n - \dim(\ker(T))$$

$$= n$$

$$= \dim(W).$$

Consequently, by Theorem 6.7, T is onto. Similarly, if T is onto, then

$$\dim(\text{range of } T) = \dim(W) = n,$$

which by Theorem 6.5 implies that $\dim(\ker(T)) = 0$. Therefore, by Theorem 6.6, T is one-to-one.

The next example brings together several ideas related to the kernel and range of a linear transformation.

EXAMPLE 11   *Summarizing Several Results*

The linear transformation $T: R^n \to R^m$ is given by $T(\mathbf{x}) = A\mathbf{x}.$. Find the nullity and rank of T and determine whether T is one-to-one, onto, or neither.

(a) $A = \begin{bmatrix} 1 & 2 & 0 \\ 0 & 1 & 1 \\ 0 & 0 & 1 \end{bmatrix}$ (b) $A = \begin{bmatrix} 1 & 2 \\ 0 & 1 \\ 0 & 0 \end{bmatrix}$

(c) $A = \begin{bmatrix} 1 & 2 & 0 \\ 0 & 1 & -1 \end{bmatrix}$ (d) $A = \begin{bmatrix} 1 & 2 & 0 \\ 0 & 1 & 1 \\ 0 & 0 & 0 \end{bmatrix}$

Solution   Note that each matrix is already in echelon form, so that its rank can be determined by inspection.

$T: R^n \to R^m$	Dim(domain)	Dim(range) Rank(T)	Dim(kernel) Nullity(T)	One-to-One	Onto
(a) $T: R^3 \to R^3$	3	3	0	Yes	Yes
(b) $T: R^2 \to R^3$	2	2	0	Yes	No
(c) $T: R^3 \to R^2$	3	2	1	No	Yes
(d) $T: R^3 \to R^3$	3	2	1	No	No

Isomorphisms of Vector Spaces

This section ends with a very important result that can greatly aid in the understanding of vector spaces. The result describes a way to think of distinct vector spaces as being "essentially the same"—at least with respect to the operations of vector addition and scalar multiplication. For example, the vector spaces R^3 and $M_{3,1}$ are essentially the same with respect to their standard operations. We call such spaces **isomorphic** to each other. (The Greek word *isos* means "equal.")

Definition of Isomorphism

A linear transformation $T: V \to W$ that is one-to-one and onto is called an **isomorphism**. Moreover, if V and W are vector spaces such that there exists an isomorphism from V to W, then V and W are said to be **isomorphic** to each other.

One way in which isomorphic spaces are "essentially the same" is that they have the same dimensions, as stated in the following theorem. In fact, the theorem goes even further, stating that if two vector spaces have the same finite dimension then they must be isomorphic.

Theorem 6.9
Isomorphic Spaces and Dimension

Two finite-dimensional vector spaces V and W are isomorphic if and only if they are of the same dimension.

Proof   Assume that V is isomorphic to W, where V has dimension n. By definition of isomorphic spaces, we know that there exists a linear transformation $T: V \rightarrow W$ that is one-to-one and onto. Since T is one-to-one, it follows that dim(kernel) $= 0$, which also implies that

$$\dim(\text{range}) = \dim(\text{domain}) = n.$$

In addition, because T is onto, we can conclude that

$$\dim(\text{range}) = \dim(W) = n.$$

To prove the theorem in the other direction, we assume that V and W both have dimension n. Let $B = \{\mathbf{v}_1, \mathbf{v}_2, \ldots, \mathbf{v}_n\}$ be a basis of V, and $B' = \{\mathbf{w}_1, \mathbf{w}_2, \ldots, \mathbf{w}_n\}$ be a basis of W. Then an arbitrary vector in V can be represented as

$$\mathbf{v} = c_1 \mathbf{v}_1 + c_2 \mathbf{v}_2 + \cdots + c_n \mathbf{v}_n,$$

and we may define a linear transformation $T: V \rightarrow W$ as follows.

$$T(\mathbf{v}) = c_1 \mathbf{w}_1 + c_2 \mathbf{w}_2 + \cdots + c_n \mathbf{w}_n$$

It can be shown that this linear transformation is both one-to-one and onto. Thus V and W are isomorphic.

Our study of vector spaces has given much greater coverage to R^n than to other vector spaces. This preference for R^n stems from its notational convenience and from the geometric models available for R^2 and R^3. Theorem 6.9 tells us that R^n is a perfect model for every n-dimensional vector space. Example 12 lists some vector spaces that are isomorphic to R^4.

EXAMPLE 12   *Isomorphic Vector Spaces*

The following vector spaces are isomorphic to each other.
(a) $R^4 = $ 4-space
(b) $M_{4,1} = $ space of all 4×1 matrices
(c) $M_{2,2} = $ space of all 2×2 matrices
(d) $P_3 = $ space of all polynomials of degree 3 or less
(e) $V = \{(x_1, x_2, x_3, x_4, 0): x_i \text{ is a real number}\}$ (Subspace of R^5)

Example 12 tells us that the elements in these spaces behave the same way *as vectors* even though they are distinct mathematical entities. Thus the convention of using the notation for an n-tuple and an $n \times 1$ matrix interchangeably is justified.

SECTION 6.2 □ EXERCISES

In Exercises 1–6, find the kernel of the given linear transformation.

1. $T: R^3 \to R^3, T(x, y, z) = (0, 0, 0)$

2. $T: R^4 \to R^4, T(x, y, z, w) = (y, x, w, z)$

3. $T: P_3 \to R, T(a_0 + a_1x + a_2x^2 + a_3x^3) = a_0$

4. $T: P_2 \to P_1, T(a_0 + a_1x + a_2x^2) = a_1 + 2a_2x$

5. $T: R^2 \to R^2, T(x, y) = (x + 2y, y - x)$

6. $T: R^2 \to R^2, T(x, y) = (x - y, y - x)$

In Exercises 7–12, the linear transformation T is given by $T(\mathbf{v}) = A\mathbf{v}$. Find a basis for (a) the kernel of T and (b) the range of T.

7. $A = \begin{bmatrix} 1 & 2 \\ 3 & 4 \end{bmatrix}$

8. $A = \begin{bmatrix} 1 & 2 \\ -2 & -4 \end{bmatrix}$

9. $A = \begin{bmatrix} 1 & -1 & 2 \\ 0 & 1 & 2 \end{bmatrix}$

10. $A = \begin{bmatrix} 1 & 2 \\ -1 & -2 \\ 1 & 1 \end{bmatrix}$

11. $A = \begin{bmatrix} 1 & 2 & -1 & 4 \\ 3 & 1 & 2 & -1 \\ -4 & -3 & -1 & -3 \\ -1 & -2 & 1 & 1 \end{bmatrix}$

12. $A = \begin{bmatrix} -1 & 3 & 2 & 1 & 4 \\ 2 & 3 & 5 & 0 & 0 \\ 2 & 1 & 2 & 1 & 0 \end{bmatrix}$

In Exercises 13–24, the linear transformation T is given by $T(\mathbf{x}) = A\mathbf{x}$. Find (a) $\ker(T)$, (b) $\text{nullity}(T)$, (c) $\text{range}(T)$, and (d) $\text{rank}(T)$.

13. $A = \begin{bmatrix} 1 & 1 \\ 1 & -1 \end{bmatrix}$

14. $A = \begin{bmatrix} 3 & 2 \\ -9 & -6 \end{bmatrix}$

15. $A = \begin{bmatrix} 5 & -3 \\ 1 & 1 \\ 1 & -1 \end{bmatrix}$

16. $A = \begin{bmatrix} 4 & 1 \\ 0 & 0 \\ 2 & -3 \end{bmatrix}$

17. $A = \begin{bmatrix} 0 & -2 & 3 \\ 4 & 0 & 11 \end{bmatrix}$

18. $A = \begin{bmatrix} 1 & 1 & 0 & 0 \\ 0 & 0 & 1 & 1 \end{bmatrix}$

19. $A = \begin{bmatrix} \frac{9}{10} & \frac{3}{10} \\ \frac{3}{10} & \frac{1}{10} \end{bmatrix}$

20. $A = \begin{bmatrix} \frac{1}{26} & -\frac{5}{26} \\ -\frac{5}{26} & \frac{25}{26} \end{bmatrix}$

21. $A = \begin{bmatrix} 2 & 2 & -3 & 1 & 13 \\ 1 & 1 & 1 & 1 & -1 \\ 3 & 3 & -5 & 0 & 14 \\ 6 & 6 & -2 & 4 & 16 \end{bmatrix}$

22. $A = \begin{bmatrix} 3 & -2 & 6 & -1 & 15 \\ 4 & 3 & 8 & 10 & -14 \\ 2 & -3 & 4 & -4 & 20 \end{bmatrix}$

23. $A = \begin{bmatrix} \frac{4}{9} & -\frac{4}{9} & \frac{2}{9} \\ -\frac{4}{9} & \frac{4}{9} & -\frac{2}{9} \\ \frac{2}{9} & -\frac{2}{9} & \frac{1}{9} \end{bmatrix}$

24. $A = \begin{bmatrix} 1 & 0 & 0 \\ 0 & 0 & 0 \\ 0 & 0 & 1 \end{bmatrix}$

In Exercises 25–32, let $T: R^3 \to R^3$ be a linear transformation. Use the given information to find the nullity of T and give a geometric description of the kernel and range of T.

25. $\text{rank}(T) = 2$

26. $\text{rank}(T) = 1$

27. $\text{rank}(T) = 0$

28. $\text{rank}(T) = 3$

29. T is the counterclockwise rotation of $45°$ about the z-axis:
$$T(x, y, z) = \left(\frac{\sqrt{2}}{2}x - \frac{\sqrt{2}}{2}y, \frac{\sqrt{2}}{2}x + \frac{\sqrt{2}}{2}y, z \right)$$

30. T is the reflection through the yz-coordinate plane:
$$T(x, y, z) = (-x, y, z)$$

31. T is the projection onto the vector $\mathbf{v} = (1, 2, 2)$:
$$T(x, y, z) = \frac{x + 2y + 2z}{9}(1, 2, 2)$$

32. T is the projection onto the xy-coordinate plane:
$$T(x, y, z) = (x, y, 0)$$

In Exercises 33–36, find the nullity of T.

33. $T: R^4 \to R^2$, $\text{rank}(T) = 1$

34. $T: R^5 \to R^2$, $\text{rank}(T) = 1$

35. $T: R^5 \to R^5$, $\text{rank}(T) = 0$

36. $T: P_3 \to P_1$, $\text{rank}(T) = 2$

37. Identify the zero element and standard basis for each of the isomorphic vector spaces in Example 12.

38. Which of the following vector spaces are isomorphic to R^6?

(a) $M_{2,3}$ (b) P_6 (c) $C[0, 6]$

(d) $M_{6,1}$ (e) P_5

(f) $\{(x_1, x_2, x_3, 0, x_5, x_6, x_7): x_i \text{ is a real number}\}$

39. (Calculus) Let $T: P_4 \to P_3$ be given by $T(\mathbf{p}) = \mathbf{p}'$. What is the kernel of T?

40. (Calculus) Let $T: P_2 \to R$ be given by
$$T(\mathbf{p}) = \int_0^1 p(x)\, dx.$$

What is the kernel of T?

41. Let $T: R^3 \rightarrow R^3$ be the linear transformation that projects $\mathbf{u}$ onto $\mathbf{v} = (2, -1, 1)$.

(a) Find the rank and nullity of T.

(b) Find a basis for the kernel of T.

42. Repeat Exercise 41 for $\mathbf{v} = (3, 0, 4)$.

In Exercises 43–46, verify that the given matrix defines a linear function T that is one-to-one and onto.

43. $A = \begin{bmatrix} -1 & 0 \\ 0 & 1 \end{bmatrix}$ **44.** $A = \begin{bmatrix} 1 & 0 \\ 0 & -1 \end{bmatrix}$

45. $A = \begin{bmatrix} 1 & 0 & 0 \\ 0 & 0 & 1 \\ 0 & 1 & 0 \end{bmatrix}$ **46.** $A = \begin{bmatrix} 1 & 2 & 3 \\ -1 & 2 & 4 \\ 0 & 4 & 1 \end{bmatrix}$

47. For the transformation $T: R^n \rightarrow R^n$ given by $T(\mathbf{v}) = A\mathbf{v}$, what can be said about the rank of T if (a) $\det(A) \neq 0$ and (b) $\det(A) = 0$?

48. Let $T: M_{n,n} \rightarrow M_{n,n}$ be given by $T(A) = A - A^T$. Show that the kernel of T is the set of $n \times n$ symmetric matrices.

49. Determine a relationship between m, n, j, and k such that $M_{m,n}$ is isomorphic to $M_{j,k}$.

50. Let B be an invertible $n \times n$ matrix. Prove that the linear transformation $T: M_{n,n} \rightarrow M_{n,n}$, given by $T(A) = AB$, is an isomorphism.

51. Let $T: V \rightarrow W$ be a linear transformation. Prove that T is one-to-one if and only if the rank of T equals the dimension of V.

52. Let $T: V \rightarrow W$ be a linear transformation, and let U be a subspace of W. Prove that the set $T^{-1}(U) = \{\mathbf{v} \in V : T(\mathbf{v}) \in U\}$ is a subspace of V. What is $T^{-1}(U)$ if $U = \{\mathbf{0}\}$?

53. Are the vector spaces R^4, $M_{2,2}$, and $M_{1,4}$ exactly the same? Describe their similarities and differences.

54. Let $T: R^m \rightarrow R^n$ be a linear transformation. Explain the differences between the concepts of one-to-one and onto. What can you say about m and n if T is onto? What can you say about m and n if T is one-to-one?

6.3 MATRICES FOR LINEAR TRANSFORMATIONS

Which of the following representations of $T: R^3 \rightarrow R^3$ is better?

$$T(x_1, x_2, x_3) = (2x_1 + x_2 - x_3, -x_1 + 3x_2 - 2x_3, 3x_2 + 4x_3)$$

or

$$T(\mathbf{x}) = A\mathbf{x} = \begin{bmatrix} 2 & 1 & -1 \\ -1 & 3 & -2 \\ 0 & 3 & 4 \end{bmatrix} \begin{bmatrix} x_1 \\ x_2 \\ x_3 \end{bmatrix}$$

The second representation is better than the first for at least three reasons: It is simpler to write, simpler to read, and more easily adapted for computer use. Later we will see that matrix representation of a linear transformation also has some theoretical advantages. In this section we will see that for linear transformations involving finite-dimensional vector spaces, matrix representation is always possible.

The key to representing a linear transformation $T: V \rightarrow W$ by a matrix is to determine how it acts on a basis of V. Once we know the image of every vector in the basis, we can use the properties of linear transformations to determine $T(\mathbf{v})$ for any $\mathbf{v}$ in V.

For convenience, the first three theorems in this section are stated in terms of linear transformations from R^n into R^m, relative to the standard bases in R^n and R^m. At the end of the section we generalize the results to include nonstandard bases and general vector spaces.

Recall that the standard basis for R^n, written in column vector notation, is given by

$$B = \{\mathbf{e}_1, \mathbf{e}_2, \ldots, \mathbf{e}_n\} = \left\{ \begin{bmatrix} 1 \\ 0 \\ \vdots \\ 0 \end{bmatrix}, \begin{bmatrix} 0 \\ 1 \\ \vdots \\ 0 \end{bmatrix}, \ldots, \begin{bmatrix} 0 \\ 0 \\ \vdots \\ 1 \end{bmatrix} \right\}.$$

Theorem 6.10

Standard Matrix for a Linear Transformation

Let $T: R^n \to R^m$ be a linear transformation such that

$$T(\mathbf{e}_1) = \begin{bmatrix} a_{11} \\ a_{21} \\ \vdots \\ a_{m1} \end{bmatrix}, \quad T(\mathbf{e}_2) = \begin{bmatrix} a_{12} \\ a_{22} \\ \vdots \\ a_{m2} \end{bmatrix}, \quad \ldots, \quad T(\mathbf{e}_n) = \begin{bmatrix} a_{1n} \\ a_{2n} \\ \vdots \\ a_{mn} \end{bmatrix}.$$

Then the $m \times n$ matrix whose n columns correspond to $T(\mathbf{e}_i)$,

$$A = \begin{bmatrix} a_{11} & a_{12} & \cdots & a_{1n} \\ a_{21} & a_{22} & \cdots & a_{2n} \\ \vdots & \vdots & & \vdots \\ a_{m1} & a_{m2} & \cdots & a_{mn} \end{bmatrix},$$

is such that $T(\mathbf{v}) = A\mathbf{v}$ for every $\mathbf{v}$ in R^n. A is called the **standard matrix** for T.

Proof   To show that $T(\mathbf{v}) = A\mathbf{v}$ for any $\mathbf{v}$ in R^n, we write

$$\mathbf{v} = \begin{bmatrix} v_1 \\ v_2 \\ \vdots \\ v_n \end{bmatrix} = v_1\mathbf{e}_1 + v_2\mathbf{e}_2 + \cdots + v_n\mathbf{e}_n.$$

Since T is a linear transformation, we have

$$T(\mathbf{v}) = T(v_1\mathbf{e}_1 + v_2\mathbf{e}_2 + \cdots + v_n\mathbf{e}_n)$$
$$= T(v_1\mathbf{e}_1) + T(v_2\mathbf{e}_2) + \cdots + T(v_n\mathbf{e}_n)$$
$$= v_1 T(\mathbf{e}_1) + v_2 T(\mathbf{e}_2) + \cdots + v_n T(\mathbf{e}_n).$$

On the other hand, the matrix product $A\mathbf{v}$ is given by

$$A\mathbf{v} = \begin{bmatrix} a_{11} & a_{12} & \cdots & a_{1n} \\ a_{21} & a_{22} & \cdots & a_{2n} \\ \vdots & \vdots & & \vdots \\ a_{m1} & a_{m2} & \cdots & a_{mn} \end{bmatrix} \begin{bmatrix} v_1 \\ v_2 \\ \vdots \\ v_n \end{bmatrix} = \begin{bmatrix} a_{11}v_1 + a_{12}v_2 + \cdots + a_{1n}v_n \\ a_{21}v_1 + a_{22}v_2 + \cdots + a_{2n}v_n \\ \vdots & \vdots & \vdots \\ a_{m1}v_1 + a_{m2}v_2 + \cdots + a_{mn}v_n \end{bmatrix}$$

$$= v_1 \begin{bmatrix} a_{11} \\ a_{21} \\ \vdots \\ a_{m1} \end{bmatrix} + v_2 \begin{bmatrix} a_{12} \\ a_{22} \\ \vdots \\ a_{m2} \end{bmatrix} + \cdots + v_n \begin{bmatrix} a_{1n} \\ a_{2n} \\ \vdots \\ a_{mn} \end{bmatrix}$$

$$= v_1 T(\mathbf{e}_1) + v_2 T(\mathbf{e}_2) + \cdots + v_n T(\mathbf{e}_n).$$

Therefore $T(\mathbf{v}) = A\mathbf{v}$ for each $\mathbf{v}$ in R^n.

EXAMPLE 1   ***Finding the Standard Matrix of a Linear Transformation***

Find the standard matrix for the linear transformation $T: R^3 \rightarrow R^2$ defined by

$$T(x, y, z) = (x - 2y, 2x + y).$$

Solution   We begin by finding the images of $\mathbf{e}_1, \mathbf{e}_2,$ and $\mathbf{e}_3$.

Vector Notation   *Matrix Notation*

$$T(\mathbf{e}_1) = T(1, 0, 0) = (1, 2) \qquad T(\mathbf{e}_1) = T\left(\begin{bmatrix} 1 \\ 0 \\ 0 \end{bmatrix} \right) = \begin{bmatrix} 1 \\ 2 \end{bmatrix}$$

$$T(\mathbf{e}_2) = T(0, 1, 0) = (-2, 1) \qquad T(\mathbf{e}_2) = T\left(\begin{bmatrix} 0 \\ 1 \\ 0 \end{bmatrix} \right) = \begin{bmatrix} -2 \\ 1 \end{bmatrix}$$

$$T(\mathbf{e}_3) = T(0, 0, 1) = (0, 0) \qquad T(\mathbf{e}_3) = T\left(\begin{bmatrix} 0 \\ 0 \\ 1 \end{bmatrix} \right) = \begin{bmatrix} 0 \\ 0 \end{bmatrix}$$

By Theorem 6.10, the columns of A consist of $T(\mathbf{e}_1), T(\mathbf{e}_2)$ and $T(\mathbf{e}_3)$, and we have

$$A = [T(\mathbf{e}_1) \vdots T(\mathbf{e}_2) \vdots T(\mathbf{e}_3)] = \begin{bmatrix} 1 & -2 & 0 \\ 2 & 1 & 0 \end{bmatrix}.$$

As a check, we note that

$$A \begin{bmatrix} x \\ y \\ z \end{bmatrix} = \begin{bmatrix} 1 & -2 & 0 \\ 2 & 1 & 0 \end{bmatrix} \begin{bmatrix} x \\ y \\ z \end{bmatrix} = \begin{bmatrix} x - 2y \\ 2x + y \end{bmatrix},$$

which is equivalent to $T(x, y, z) = (x - 2y, 2x + y)$.

A little practice will enable you to determine the standard matrix for a linear transformation, such as the one in Example 1, by inspection. For instance, the standard matrix for the linear transformation given by

$$T(x_1, x_2, x_3) = (x_1 - 2x_2 + 5x_3, 2x_1 + 3x_3, 4x_1 + x_2 - 2x_3)$$

is found by using the coefficients of x_1, x_2, and x_3 to form the rows of A as follows.

$$A = \begin{bmatrix} 1 & -2 & 5 \\ 2 & 0 & 3 \\ 4 & 1 & -2 \end{bmatrix} \quad \begin{matrix} \longleftarrow \\ \longleftarrow \\ \longleftarrow \end{matrix} \quad \begin{matrix} 1x_1 - 2x_2 + 5x_3 \\ 2x_1 + 0x_2 + 3x_3 \\ 4x_1 + 1x_2 - 2x_3 \end{matrix}$$

EXAMPLE 2   *Finding the Standard Matrix of a Linear Transformation*

The linear transformation $T: R^2 \to R^2$ is given by projecting each point in R^2 onto the x-axis, as shown in Figure 6.8. Find the standard matrix for T.

Solution   This linear transformation is given by

$$T(x, y) = (x, 0).$$

Therefore the standard matrix for T is

$$A = [T(1, 0) \vdots T(0, 1)] = \begin{bmatrix} 1 & 0 \\ 0 & 0 \end{bmatrix}.$$

Figure 6.8

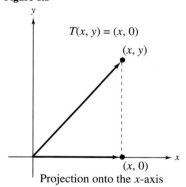

Projection onto the x-axis

The standard matrix for the zero transformation from R^n into R^m is the $m \times n$ zero matrix, and the standard matrix for the identity transformation from R^n into R^n is I_n.

Composition of Linear Transformations

The **composition,** T, of $T_1: R^n \to R^m$ with $T_2: R^m \to R^p$ is defined by

$$T(\mathbf{v}) = T_2(T_1(\mathbf{v})),$$

where $\mathbf{v}$ is a vector in R^n. This composition is denoted by $T = T_2 \circ T_1$. The domain of T is defined to be the domain of T_1. Moreover, the composition is not defined unless the range of T_1 lies within the domain of T_2, as shown in Figure 6.9.

The following theorem emphasizes the usefulness of matrices for representing linear transformations. The theorem not only states that the composition of two linear transformations is a linear transformation, but also says that the standard matrix of the composition is the product of the standard matrices for the two original linear transformations.

Theorem 6.11 Composition of Linear Transformations	Let $T_1: R^n \rightarrow R^m$ and $T_2: R^m \rightarrow R^p$ be linear transformations with standard matrices A_1 and A_2. The **composition** $T: R^n \rightarrow R^p$, defined by $T(\mathbf{v}) = T_2(T_1(\mathbf{v}))$, is a linear transformation. Moreover, the standard matrix A for T is given by the matrix product $A = A_2 A_1.$

Proof

To show that T is a linear transformation, we let $\mathbf{u}$ and $\mathbf{v}$ be vectors in R^n and c be any scalar. Then, since T_1 and T_2 are linear transformations, we can write

$$T(\mathbf{u} + \mathbf{v}) = T_2(T_1(\mathbf{u} + \mathbf{v}))$$
$$= T_2(T_1(\mathbf{u}) + T_1(\mathbf{v}))$$
$$= T_2(T_1(\mathbf{u})) + T_2(T_1(\mathbf{v})) = T(\mathbf{u}) + T(\mathbf{v})$$

$$T(c\mathbf{v}) = T_2(T_1(c\mathbf{v}))$$
$$= T_2(cT_1(\mathbf{v}))$$
$$= cT_2(T_1(\mathbf{v})) = cT(\mathbf{v}).$$

Figure 6.9

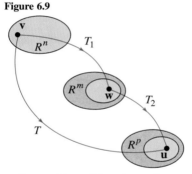

Composition of Transformations

Now, to show that $A_2 A_1$ is the standard matrix for T, we use the associative property of matrix multiplication to write

$$T(\mathbf{v}) = T_2(T_1(\mathbf{v})) = T_2(A_1\mathbf{v}) = A_2(A_1\mathbf{v}) = (A_2 A_1)\mathbf{v}.$$

REMARK: Theorem 6.11 can be generalized to cover the composition of n linear transformations. That is, if the standard matrices of $T_1, T_2, \ldots, T_n$ are $A_1, A_2, \ldots, A_n$, then the standard matrix of the composition T is given by

$$A = A_n A_{n-1} \cdots A_2 A_1.$$

Since matrix multiplication is not commutative, the order is important when the composition of linear transformations is formed. In general, the composition $T_2 \circ T_1$ is not the same as $T_1 \circ T_2$, as demonstrated in the next example.

EXAMPLE 3   *The Standard Matrix of a Composition*

Let T_1 and T_2 be linear transformations from R^3 into R^3 such that

$$T_1(x, y, z) = (2x + y, 0, x + z)$$

and

$$T_2(x, y, z) = (x - y, z, y).$$

Find the standard matrices for the compositions $T = T_2 \circ T_1$ and $T' = T_1 \circ T_2$.

Solution   The standard matrices for T_1 and T_2 are

$$A_1 = \begin{bmatrix} 2 & 1 & 0 \\ 0 & 0 & 0 \\ 1 & 0 & 1 \end{bmatrix} \quad \text{and} \quad A_2 = \begin{bmatrix} 1 & -1 & 0 \\ 0 & 0 & 1 \\ 0 & 1 & 0 \end{bmatrix}.$$

Thus by Theorem 6.11, the standard matrix for T is given by

$$A = A_2A_1 = \begin{bmatrix} 1 & -1 & 0 \\ 0 & 0 & 1 \\ 0 & 1 & 0 \end{bmatrix}\begin{bmatrix} 2 & 1 & 0 \\ 0 & 0 & 0 \\ 1 & 0 & 1 \end{bmatrix} = \begin{bmatrix} 2 & 1 & 0 \\ 1 & 0 & 1 \\ 0 & 0 & 0 \end{bmatrix},$$

and the standard matrix for T' is given by

$$A' = A_1A_2 = \begin{bmatrix} 2 & 1 & 0 \\ 0 & 0 & 0 \\ 1 & 0 & 1 \end{bmatrix}\begin{bmatrix} 1 & -1 & 0 \\ 0 & 0 & 1 \\ 0 & 1 & 0 \end{bmatrix} = \begin{bmatrix} 2 & -2 & 1 \\ 0 & 0 & 0 \\ 1 & 0 & 0 \end{bmatrix}.$$

Another benefit of matrix representation is that it can represent the **inverse** of a linear transformation. Before showing how this works, we give the following definition.

Definition of Inverse Linear Transformation

If $T_1: R^n \rightarrow R^n$ and $T_2: R^n \rightarrow R^n$ are linear transformations such that for every **v** in R^n

$$T_2(T_1(\mathbf{v})) = \mathbf{v} \quad \text{and} \quad T_1(T_2(\mathbf{v})) = \mathbf{v},$$

then T_2 is called the **inverse** of T_1 and we say that T_1 is **invertible.**

Not every linear transformation has an inverse. However, if the transformation T_1 is invertible, then the inverse is unique and denoted by T_1^{-1}.

Just as the inverse of a function of a real variable may be thought of as undoing what the function did, the inverse of a linear transformation T may be thought of as undoing the mapping done by T. For instance, if T is a linear transformation from R^3 onto R^3 such that

$$T(1, 4, -5) = (2, 3, 1)$$

and if T^{-1} exists, then T^{-1} maps $(2, 3, 1)$ back to its preimage under T. That is,

$$T^{-1}(2, 3, 1) = (1, 4, -5).$$

The following theorem states that a linear transformation is invertible if and only if it is an isomorphism (one-to-one and onto). You are asked to prove the theorem in Exercise 56.

Theorem 6.12

Existence of an Inverse Transformation

Let $T: R^n \to R^n$ be a linear transformation with standard matrix A. Then the following conditions are equivalent.
1. T is invertible.
2. T is an isomorphism.
3. A is invertible.

Moreover, if T is invertible with standard matrix A, then the standard matrix for T^{-1} is A^{-1}.

REMARK: Several other conditions are equivalent to the three given in this theorem; see the summary of equivalent conditions given in Section 4.6.

EXAMPLE 4   *Finding the Inverse of a Linear Transformation*

The linear transformation $T: R^3 \to R^3$ is defined by

$$T(x_1, x_2, x_3) = (2x_1 + 3x_2 + x_3, 3x_1 + 3x_2 + x_3, 2x_1 + 4x_2 + x_3).$$

Show that T is invertible, and find its inverse.

Solution   The standard matrix for T is

$$A = \begin{bmatrix} 2 & 3 & 1 \\ 3 & 3 & 1 \\ 2 & 4 & 1 \end{bmatrix}.$$

Using the techniques for matrix inversion (See Section 2.3.), we find that A is invertible and its inverse is given by

$$A^{-1} = \begin{bmatrix} -1 & 1 & 0 \\ -1 & 0 & 1 \\ 6 & -2 & -3 \end{bmatrix}.$$

Therefore T is invertible and its standard matrix is A^{-1}.

Using the standard matrix for the inverse, we can find the rule for T^{-1} by computing the image of an arbitrary vector $\mathbf{v} = (x_1, x_2, x_3)$.

$$T^{-1}(\mathbf{v}) = \begin{bmatrix} -1 & 1 & 0 \\ -1 & 0 & 1 \\ 6 & -2 & -3 \end{bmatrix} \begin{bmatrix} x_1 \\ x_2 \\ x_3 \end{bmatrix} = \begin{bmatrix} -x_1 + x_2 \\ -x_1 + x_3 \\ 6x_1 - 2x_2 - 3x_3 \end{bmatrix}$$

In other words,

$$T^{-1}(x_1, x_2, x_3) = (-x_1 + x_2, -x_1 + x_3, 6x_1 - 2x_2 - 3x_3).$$

Nonstandard Bases and General Vector Spaces

We now consider the more general problem of finding a matrix for a linear transformation $T: V \rightarrow W$, where B and B' are ordered bases for V and W, respectively. Recall that the coordinate matrix of $\mathbf{v}$ relative to B is denoted by $[\mathbf{v}]_B$. In order to represent the linear transformation T, A must be multiplied by a *coordinate matrix relative to B*. The result of the multiplication will be a *coordinate matrix relative to B'*. That is,

$$[T(\mathbf{v})]_{B'} = A[\mathbf{v}]_B.$$

A is called the **matrix of T relative to the bases B and B'.**

To find the matrix A, we use a procedure similar to the one used to find the standard matrix for T. That is, the images of the vectors in B are written as coordinate matrices relative to the basis B'. These coordinate matrices form the columns of A.

Transformation Matrix for Nonstandard Bases

Let V and W be finite-dimensional vector spaces with bases B and B', respectively, where

$$B = \{\mathbf{v}_1, \mathbf{v}_2, \ldots, \mathbf{v}_n\}.$$

If $T: V \rightarrow W$ is a linear transformation such that

$$[T(\mathbf{v}_1)]_{B'} = \begin{bmatrix} a_{11} \\ a_{21} \\ \vdots \\ a_{m1} \end{bmatrix}, [T(\mathbf{v}_2)]_{B'} = \begin{bmatrix} a_{12} \\ a_{22} \\ \vdots \\ a_{m2} \end{bmatrix}, \ldots, [T(\mathbf{v}_n)]_{B'} = \begin{bmatrix} a_{1n} \\ a_{2n} \\ \vdots \\ a_{mn} \end{bmatrix},$$

then the $m \times n$ matrix whose n columns correspond to $[T(\mathbf{v}_i)]_{B'}$,

$$A = \begin{bmatrix} a_{11} & a_{12} & \cdots & a_{1n} \\ a_{21} & a_{22} & \cdots & a_{2n} \\ \vdots & \vdots & & \vdots \\ a_{m1} & a_{m2} & \cdots & a_{mn} \end{bmatrix},$$

is such that $[T(\mathbf{v})]_{B'} = A[\mathbf{v}]_B$ for every $\mathbf{v}$ in V.

EXAMPLE 5   *Finding a Matrix Relative to Nonstandard Bases*

Let $T: R^2 \rightarrow R^2$ be a linear transformation defined by

$$T(x_1, x_2) = (x_1 + x_2, 2x_1 - x_2).$$

Find the matrix of T relative to the bases

$$\overset{\mathbf{v}_1 \qquad \mathbf{v}_2}{B = \{(1, 2), (-1, 1)\}} \qquad \text{and} \qquad \overset{\mathbf{w}_1 \qquad \mathbf{w}_2}{B' = \{(1, 0), (0, 1)\}}.$$

Solution   By definition of T, we have

$$T(\mathbf{v}_1) = T(1, 2) = (3, 0) = 3\mathbf{w}_1 + 0\mathbf{w}_2$$

$$T(\mathbf{v}_2) = T(-1, 1) = (0, -3) = 0\mathbf{w}_1 - 3\mathbf{w}_2.$$

Therefore the coordinate matrices of $T(\mathbf{v}_1)$ and $T(\mathbf{v}_2)$ relative to B' are

$$[T(\mathbf{v}_1)]_{B'} = \begin{bmatrix} 3 \\ 0 \end{bmatrix} \qquad \text{and} \qquad [T(\mathbf{v}_2)]_{B'} = \begin{bmatrix} 0 \\ -3 \end{bmatrix}.$$

The matrix for T relative to B and B' is formed by using these coordinate matrices as columns to produce

$$A = \begin{bmatrix} 3 & 0 \\ 0 & -3 \end{bmatrix}.$$

EXAMPLE 6   *Using a Matrix to Represent a Linear Transformation*

For the linear transformation $T: R^2 \rightarrow R^2$ given in Example 5, use the matrix A to find $T(\mathbf{v})$, where $\mathbf{v} = (2, 1)$.

Solution   Using the basis $B = \{(1, 2), (-1, 1)\}$, we find that

$$\mathbf{v} = (2, 1) = 1(1, 2) - 1(-1, 1),$$

which implies that

$$[\mathbf{v}]_B = \begin{bmatrix} 1 \\ -1 \end{bmatrix}.$$

Therefore $[T(\mathbf{v})]_{B'}$ is given by

$$A[\mathbf{v}]_B = \begin{bmatrix} 3 & 0 \\ 0 & -3 \end{bmatrix} \begin{bmatrix} 1 \\ -1 \end{bmatrix} = \begin{bmatrix} 3 \\ 3 \end{bmatrix} = [T(\mathbf{v})]_{B'}.$$

Finally, since $B' = \{(1, 0), (0, 1)\}$, it follows that

$$T(\mathbf{v}) = 3(1, 0) + 3(0, 1) = (3, 3).$$

You can check this result by directly calculating $T(\mathbf{v})$ using the definition of T given in Example 5:

$$T(2, 1) = (2 + 1, 2(2) - 1) = (3, 3).$$

In the special case where $V = W$ and $B = B'$, the matrix A is called the **matrix of T relative to the basis B.** In such cases the matrix of the identity transformation is simply I_n. To see this, let $B = \{\mathbf{v}_1, \mathbf{v}_2, \ldots, \mathbf{v}_n\}$. Since the identity transformation maps each $\mathbf{v}_i$ to itself, we have

$$[T(\mathbf{v}_1)]_B = \begin{bmatrix} 1 \\ 0 \\ \vdots \\ 0 \end{bmatrix}, [T(\mathbf{v}_2)]_B = \begin{bmatrix} 0 \\ 1 \\ \vdots \\ 0 \end{bmatrix}, \ldots, [T(\mathbf{v}_n)]_B = \begin{bmatrix} 0 \\ 0 \\ \vdots \\ 1 \end{bmatrix},$$

and it follows that $A = I_n$.

In the next example we construct a matrix representing the differential operator discussed in Example 10 of Section 6.1.

EXAMPLE 7   *A Matrix for the Differential Operator (Calculus)*

Let $D_x: P_2 \to P_1$ be the differential operator that maps a quadratic polynomial $\mathbf{p}$ onto its derivative $\mathbf{p}'$. Find the matrix for D_x using the bases $B = \{1, x, x^2\}$ and $B' = \{1, x\}$.

Solution   The derivatives of the basis vectors are

$$D_x(1) = 0 = 0(1) + 0(x)$$
$$D_x(x) = 1 = 1(1) + 0(x)$$
$$D_x(x^2) = 2x = 0(1) + 2(x).$$

Thus the coordinate matrices relative to B' are

$$[D_x(1)]_{B'} = \begin{bmatrix} 0 \\ 0 \end{bmatrix}, \quad [D_x(x)]_{B'} = \begin{bmatrix} 1 \\ 0 \end{bmatrix}, \quad [D_x(x^2)]_{B'} = \begin{bmatrix} 0 \\ 2 \end{bmatrix},$$

and the matrix for D_x is

$$A = \begin{bmatrix} 0 & 1 & 0 \\ 0 & 0 & 2 \end{bmatrix}.$$

Note that this matrix *does* produce the derivative of a quadratic polynomial $p(x) = a + bx + cx^2$.

$$A\mathbf{p} = \begin{bmatrix} 0 & 1 & 0 \\ 0 & 0 & 2 \end{bmatrix} \begin{bmatrix} a \\ b \\ c \end{bmatrix} = \begin{bmatrix} b \\ 2c \end{bmatrix} = b + 2cx = D_x[a + bx + cx^2]$$

SECTION 6.3 ☐ EXERCISES

In Exercises 1–8, find the standard matrix for the linear transformation T.

1. $T(x, y) = (x + y, x - y)$
2. $T(x, y) = (3x + 2y, 2y - x)$
3. $T(x, y) = (5x - 3y, x + y, y - 4x)$
4. $T(x, y) = (4x + y, 0, 2x - 3y)$
5. $T(x, y, z) = (x + y, x - y, z)$
6. $T(x, y, z) = (5x - 3y + z, 2z + 4y, 5x + 3y)$
7. $T(x, y, z) = (3z - 2y, 4x + 11z)$
8. $T(x_1, x_2, x_3, x_4) = (0, 0, 0, 0)$

In Exercises 9–12, use the standard matrix for the linear transformation T to find the image of the vector $\mathbf{v}$.

9. $T(x, y, z) = (13x - 9y + 4z, 6x + 5y - 3z)$, $\mathbf{v} = (1, -2, 1)$
10. $T(x, y) = (x + y, x - y, 2x, 2y)$, $\mathbf{v} = (3, -3)$
11. $T(x_1, x_2, x_3, x_4) = (x_1 + x_2, x_3 + x_4)$, $\mathbf{v} = (1, -1, 1, -1)$
12. $T(x_1, x_2, x_3, x_4) = (2x_1 - x_3, 3x_2 - 4x_4, 4x_3 - x_1, x_2 + x_4)$, $\mathbf{v} = (1, 2, 3, -2)$

In Exercises 13–24, (a) find the standard matrix A for the linear transformation T, (b) use A to find the image of the vector $\mathbf{v}$, and (c) sketch the graph of $\mathbf{v}$ and its image.

13. T is the reflection through the origin in R^2: $T(x, y) = (-x, -y)$, $\mathbf{v} = (3, 4)$.
14. T is the reflection in the line $y = x$ in R^2: $T(x, y) = (y, x)$, $\mathbf{v} = (3, 4)$.
15. T is the counterclockwise rotation of $135°$ in R^2, $\mathbf{v} = (4, 4)$.
16. T is the clockwise rotation (θ is negative) of $60°$ in R^2, $\mathbf{v} = (1, 2)$.
17. T is the reflection through the xy-coordinate plane in R^3: $T(x, y, z) = (x, y, -z)$, $\mathbf{v} = (3, 2, 2)$.
18. T is the reflection through the yz-coordinate plane in R^3: $T(x, y, z) = (-x, y, z)$, $\mathbf{v} = (2, 3, 4)$.
19. T is the counterclockwise rotation of $180°$ in R^2, $\mathbf{v} = (1, 2)$.
20. T is the counterclockwise rotation of $45°$ in R^2, $\mathbf{v} = (2, 2)$.
21. T is the projection onto the vector $\mathbf{w} = (3, 1)$ in R^2: $T(\mathbf{v}) = \text{proj}_\mathbf{w}\mathbf{v}$, $\mathbf{v} = (1, 4)$.
22. T is the projection onto the vector $\mathbf{w} = (-1, 5)$ in R^2: $T(\mathbf{v}) = \text{proj}_\mathbf{w}\mathbf{v}$, $\mathbf{v} = (2, -3)$.

23. T is the reflection through the vector $\mathbf{w} = (3, 1)$ in R^2, $\mathbf{v} = (1, 4)$. (The reflection of a vector $\mathbf{v}$ through $\mathbf{w}$ is given by $T(\mathbf{v}) = 2 \text{ proj}_\mathbf{w}\mathbf{v} - \mathbf{v}$.)
24. Repeat Exercise 23 for $\mathbf{w} = (4, -2)$ and $\mathbf{v} = (5, 0)$.

In Exercises 25–30, find the standard matrices for $T = T_2 \circ T_1$ and $T' = T_1 \circ T_2$.

25. $T_1: R^2 \to R^2$, $T_1(x, y) = (x - 2y, 2x + 3y)$
    $T_2: R^2 \to R^2$, $T_2(x, y) = (2x, x - y)$
26. $T_1: R^2 \to R^2$, $T_1(x, y) = (x - 2y, 2x + 3y)$
    $T_2: R^2 \to R^2$, $T_2(x, y) = (y, 0)$
27. $T_1: R^3 \to R^3$, $T_1(x, y, z) = (x, y, z)$
    $T_2: R^3 \to R^3$, $T_2(x, y, z) = (0, x, 0)$
28. $T_1: R^3 \to R^3$, $T_1(x, y, z) = (x + 2y, y - z, -2x + y + 2z)$
    $T_2: R^3 \to R^3$, $T_2(x, y, z) = (y + z, x + z, 2y - 2z)$
29. $T_1: R^2 \to R^3$, $T_1(x, y) = (-x + 2y, x + y, x - y)$
    $T_2: R^3 \to R^2$, $T_2(x, y, z) = (x - 3y, z + 3x)$
30. $T_1: R^2 \to R^3$, $T_1(x, y) = (x, y, y)$
    $T_2: R^3 \to R^2$, $T_2(x, y, z) = (y, z)$

In Exercises 31–36, determine whether the given linear transformation is invertible. If it is, find its inverse.

31. $T(x, y) = (x + y, x - y)$
32. $T(x_1, x_2, x_3) = (x_1, x_1 + x_2, x_1 + x_2 + x_3)$
33. $T(x, y) = (2x, 0)$
34. $T(x, y) = (x + y, 3x + 3y)$
35. $T(x, y) = (5x, 5y)$
36. $T(x_1, x_2, x_3, x_4) = (x_1 - 2x_2, x_2, x_3 + x_4, x_3)$

In Exercises 37–44, find $T(\mathbf{v})$ by using (a) the standard matrix and (b) the matrix relative to B and B'.

37. $T: R^2 \to R^3$, $T(x, y) = (x + y, x, y)$, $\mathbf{v} = (5, 4)$,
    $B = \{(1, -1), (0, 1)\}$, $B' = \{(1, 1, 0), (0, 1, 1), (1, 0, 1)\}$
38. $T: R^2 \to R^3$, $T(x, y) = (x - y, 0, x + y)$, $\mathbf{v} = (-3, 2)$,
    $B = \{(1, 2), (1, 1)\}$, $B' = \{(1, 1, 1), (1, 1, 0), (0, 1, 1)\}$
39. $T: R^3 \to R^2$, $T(x, y, z) = (x - y, y - z)$, $\mathbf{v} = (1, 2, -3)$,
    $B = \{(1, 1, 1), (1, 1, 0), (0, 1, 1)\}$, $B' = \{(1, 2), (1, 1)\}$
40. $T: R^3 \to R^2$, $T(x, y, z) = (2x - z, y - 2x)$, $\mathbf{v} = (0, -5, 7)$,
    $B = \{(2, 0, 1), (0, 2, 1), (1, 2, 1)\}$, $B' = \{(1, 1), (2, 0)\}$

41. $T: R^3 \to R^4$, $T(x, y, z) = (2x, x + y, y + z, x + z)$,
$\mathbf{v} = (1, -5, 2)$,
$B = \{(2, 0, 1), (0, 2, 1), (1, 2, 1)\}$,
$B' = \{(1, 0, 0, 1), (0, 1, 0, 1), (1, 0, 1, 0), (1, 1, 0, 0)\}$

42. $T: R^4 \to R^2$, $T(x_1, x_2, x_3, x_4) = (x_1 + x_2 + x_3 + x_4, x_4 - x_1)$,
$\mathbf{v} = (4, -3, 1, 1)$,
$B = \{(1, 0, 0, 1), (0, 1, 0, 1), (1, 0, 1, 0), (1, 1, 0, 0)\}$,
$B' = \{(1, 1), (2, 0)\}$

43. $T: R^3 \to R^3$, $T(x, y, z) = (x + y + z, 2z - x, 2y - z)$,
$\mathbf{v} = (4, -5, 10)$,
$B = \{(2, 0, 1), (0, 2, 1), (1, 2, 1)\}$,
$B' = \{(1, 1, 1), (1, 1, 0), (0, 1, 1)\}$

44. $T: R^2 \to R^2$, $T(x, y) = (2x - 12y, x - 5y)$, $\mathbf{v} = (10, 5)$,
$B = B' = \{(4, 1), (3, 1)\}$

45. Let $T: P_2 \to P_3$ be given by $T(\mathbf{p}) = x\mathbf{p}$. Find the matrix of T relative to the bases $B = \{1, x, x^2\}$ and $B' = \{1, x, x^2, x^3\}$.

46. Let $T: P_2 \to P_4$ be given by $T(\mathbf{p}) = x^2\mathbf{p}$. Find the matrix of T relative to the bases $B = \{1, x, x^2\}$ and $B' = \{1, x, x^2, x^3, x^4\}$.

47. (Calculus) Let $B = \{1, x, e^x, xe^x\}$ be a basis of a subspace W of the space of continuous functions, and let D_x be the differential operator on W. Find the matrix for D_x relative to the basis B.

48. (Calculus) Repeat Exercise 47 for $B = \{e^{2x}, xe^{2x}, x^2e^{2x}\}$.

49. (Calculus) Use the matrix from Exercise 47 to evaluate $D_x[3x - 2xe^x]$.

50. (Calculus) Use the matrix from Exercise 48 to evaluate $D_x[5e^{2x} - 3xe^{2x} + x^2e^{2x}]$.

51. (Calculus) Let $B = \{1, x, x^2, x^3\}$ be a basis for P_3, and let $T: P_3 \to P_4$ be the linear transformation given by

$$T(x^k) = \int_0^x t^k \, dt.$$

(a) Find the matrix A for T with respect to B and the standard basis for P_4.

(b) Use A to integrate $p(x) = 6 - 2x + 3x^3$.

52. Let T be a linear transformation such that $T(\mathbf{v}) = k\mathbf{v}$ for $\mathbf{v}$ in R^n. Find the standard matrix for T.

53. Let $T: M_{2,3} \to M_{3,2}$ be given by $T(A) = A^T$. Find the matrix for T relative to the standard bases for $M_{2,3}$ and $M_{3,2}$.

54. Show that the linear transformation T given in Exercise 53 is an isomorphism and find the matrix for the inverse of T.

55. Let $T_1: V \to V$ and $T_2: V \to V$ be one-to-one linear transformations. Prove that the composition $T_2 \circ T_1$ is one-to-one and that $(T_2 \circ T_1)^{-1} = T_1^{-1} \circ T_2^{-1}$.

56. Prove Theorem 6.12.

57. Is it always preferable to use the standard basis for R^n? Discuss the advantages and disadvantages of using different bases.

58. Look back at Theorem 4.19 and rephrase it in terms of what you have learned in this chapter.

6.4 TRANSITION MATRICES AND SIMILARITY

In Section 6.3 we saw that the matrix of a linear transformation

$$T: V \to V$$

depends on the basis of V. In other words, the matrix of T relative to a basis B is different from the matrix of T relative to another basis B'.

A classical problem in linear algebra is this: Is it possible to find a basis B such that the matrix of T relative to B is diagonal? The solution of this problem is discussed in Chapter 7. This section lays a foundation for solving the problem. We will see how the matrices of a linear transformation relative to two different bases are related. In this section A, A', P, and P^{-1} represent the following four *square* matrices.

1. Matrix of T relative to B: A

2. Matrix of T relative to B': A'

3. Transition matrix from B' to B: P

4. Transition matrix from B to B': P^{-1}

Note that in Figure 6.10 there are two ways to get from the coordinate matrix $[\mathbf{v}]_B$ to the coordinate matrix $[T(\mathbf{v})]_{B'}$. One way is direct, using the matrix A' to obtain

$$A'[\mathbf{v}]_{B'} = [T(\mathbf{v})]_{B'}.$$

The other way is indirect, using the matrices P, A, and P^{-1} to obtain

$$P^{-1}AP[\mathbf{v}]_{B'} = [T(\mathbf{v})]_{B'}.$$

But by definition of the matrix of a linear transformation relative to a basis, this implies

$$A' = P^{-1}AP.$$

This relationship is demonstrated in Example 1.

Figure 6.10

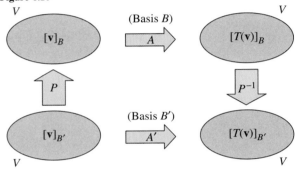

EXAMPLE 1   *Finding a Matrix for a Linear Transformation*

Find the matrix A' for $T: R^2 \rightarrow R^2$,
$$T(x_1, x_2) = (2x_1 - 2x_2, -x_1 + 3x_2),$$

relative to the basis $B' = \{(1, 0), (1, 1)\}$.

Solution   The standard matrix for T is

$$A = \begin{bmatrix} 2 & -2 \\ -1 & 3 \end{bmatrix}.$$

Furthermore, using the techniques of Section 4.7, we find that the transition matrix from B' to the standard basis $B = \{(1, 0), (0, 1)\}$ is

$$P = \begin{bmatrix} 1 & 1 \\ 0 & 1 \end{bmatrix}.$$

The inverse of this matrix is the transition matrix from B to B',

$$P^{-1} = \begin{bmatrix} 1 & -1 \\ 0 & 1 \end{bmatrix}.$$

Therefore the matrix for T relative to B' is

$$A' = P^{-1}AP = \begin{bmatrix} 1 & -1 \\ 0 & 1 \end{bmatrix} \begin{bmatrix} 2 & -2 \\ -1 & 3 \end{bmatrix} \begin{bmatrix} 1 & 1 \\ 0 & 1 \end{bmatrix} = \begin{bmatrix} 3 & -2 \\ -1 & 2 \end{bmatrix}.$$

In Example 1 the basis B is the standard basis for R^2. In the next example both B and B' are nonstandard bases.

EXAMPLE 2   *Finding a Matrix for a Linear Transformation*

Let $B = \{(-3, 2), (4, -2)\}$ and $B' = \{(-1, 2), (2, -2)\}$ be bases for R^2, and let

$$A = \begin{bmatrix} -2 & 7 \\ -3 & 7 \end{bmatrix}$$

be the matrix for $T: R^2 \to R^2$ relative to B. Find A', the matrix of T relative to B'.

Solution In Example 5 of Section 4.7 we found that

$$P = \begin{bmatrix} 3 & -2 \\ 2 & -1 \end{bmatrix} \quad \text{and} \quad P^{-1} = \begin{bmatrix} -1 & 2 \\ -2 & 3 \end{bmatrix}.$$

Therefore the matrix of T relative to B' is given by

$$A' = P^{-1}AP = \begin{bmatrix} -1 & 2 \\ -2 & 3 \end{bmatrix} \begin{bmatrix} -2 & 7 \\ -3 & 7 \end{bmatrix} \begin{bmatrix} 3 & -2 \\ 2 & -1 \end{bmatrix} = \begin{bmatrix} 2 & 1 \\ -1 & 3 \end{bmatrix}.$$

The diagram in Figure 6.10 should help you to remember the roles of the matrices $A, A', P,$ and P^{-1}.

EXAMPLE 3   *Using a Matrix for a Linear Transformation*

For the linear transformation $T: R^2 \to R^2$ given in Example 2, find $[\mathbf{v}]_B, [T(\mathbf{v})]_B$, and $[T(\mathbf{v})]_{B'}$ for the vector $\mathbf{v}$ whose coordinate matrix is

$$[\mathbf{v}]_{B'} = \begin{bmatrix} -3 \\ -1 \end{bmatrix}.$$

Solution   To find $[\mathbf{v}]_B$, we use the transition matrix P from B' to B.

$$[\mathbf{v}]_B = P[\mathbf{v}]_{B'} = \begin{bmatrix} 3 & -2 \\ 2 & -1 \end{bmatrix} \begin{bmatrix} -3 \\ -1 \end{bmatrix} = \begin{bmatrix} -7 \\ -5 \end{bmatrix}$$

To find $[T(\mathbf{v})]_B$, we multiply $[\mathbf{v}]_B$ by the matrix A to obtain

$$[T(\mathbf{v})]_B = A[\mathbf{v}]_B = \begin{bmatrix} -2 & 7 \\ -3 & 7 \end{bmatrix} \begin{bmatrix} -7 \\ -5 \end{bmatrix} = \begin{bmatrix} -21 \\ -14 \end{bmatrix}.$$

To find $[T(\mathbf{v})]_{B'}$, we may now multiply $[T(\mathbf{v})]_B$ by P^{-1} to obtain

$$[T(\mathbf{v})]_{B'} = P^{-1}[T(\mathbf{v})]_B = \begin{bmatrix} -1 & 2 \\ -2 & 3 \end{bmatrix} \begin{bmatrix} -21 \\ -14 \end{bmatrix} = \begin{bmatrix} -7 \\ 0 \end{bmatrix}$$

or multiply $[\mathbf{v}]_{B'}$ by A' to obtain

$$[T(\mathbf{v})]_{B'} = A'[\mathbf{v}]_{B'} = \begin{bmatrix} 2 & 1 \\ -1 & 3 \end{bmatrix} \begin{bmatrix} -3 \\ -1 \end{bmatrix} = \begin{bmatrix} -7 \\ 0 \end{bmatrix}.$$

REMARK: It is instructive to note that the transformation T in Examples 2 and 3 is given by the rule $T(x, y) = (x - \frac{3}{2}y, 2x + 4y)$. Verify the results of Example 3 by showing that $\mathbf{v} = (1, -4)$ and $T(\mathbf{v}) = (7, -14)$.

Similar Matrices

Two square matrices A and A' that are related by an equation $A' = P^{-1}AP$ are called **similar** matrices, as indicated in the following definition.

Definition of Similar Matrices

For square matrices A and A' of order n, A' is said to be **similar** to A if there exists an invertible matrix P such that

$$A' = P^{-1}AP.$$

If A' is similar to A, then it is also true that A is similar to A', as stated in the following theorem. Thus it makes sense to say simply that **A and A' are similar.**

Theorem 6.13

Properties of Similar Matrices

Let A, B, and C be square matrices of order n. Then the following properties are true.
1. A is similar to A.
2. If A is similar to B, then B is similar to A.
3. If A is similar to B and B is similar to C, then A is similar to C.

Proof   The first property follows from the fact that $A = I_n A I_n$. To prove the second property, we write

$$A = P^{-1}BP$$
$$PAP^{-1} = P(P^{-1}BP)P^{-1}$$
$$PAP^{-1} = B$$
$$Q^{-1}AQ = B, \qquad\qquad \text{where } Q = P^{-1}.$$

The proof of the third property is left to you. (See Exercise 21.)

From the definition of similarity it follows that any two matrices that represent the same linear transformation $T : V \to V$ with respect to different bases must be similar.

EXAMPLE 4   **Similar Matrices**

(a) From Example 1, the matrices

$$A = \begin{bmatrix} 2 & -2 \\ -1 & 3 \end{bmatrix} \quad \text{and} \quad A' = \begin{bmatrix} 3 & -2 \\ -1 & 2 \end{bmatrix}$$

are similar because $A' = P^{-1}AP$, where

$$P = \begin{bmatrix} 1 & 1 \\ 0 & 1 \end{bmatrix}.$$

(b) From Example 2, the matrices

$$A = \begin{bmatrix} -2 & 7 \\ -3 & 7 \end{bmatrix} \quad \text{and} \quad A' = \begin{bmatrix} 2 & 1 \\ -1 & 3 \end{bmatrix}$$

are similar because $A' = P^{-1}AP$ where

$$P = \begin{bmatrix} 3 & -2 \\ 2 & -1 \end{bmatrix}.$$

We have seen that the matrix for a linear transformation $T: V \to V$ depends on the basis used for V. This observation leads naturally to the question: What choice of basis will make the matrix for T as simple as possible? Is it always the *standard* basis? Not necessarily, as the following example demonstrates.

EXAMPLE 5   **A Comparison of Two Matrices for a Linear Transformation**

Suppose

$$A = \begin{bmatrix} 1 & 3 & 0 \\ 3 & 1 & 0 \\ 0 & 0 & -2 \end{bmatrix}$$

is the matrix for $T: R^3 \to R^3$ relative to the standard basis. Find the matrix for T relative to the basis

$$B' = \{(1, 1, 0), (1, -1, 0), (0, 0, 1)\}.$$

Solution   The transition matrix from B' to the standard matrix has columns consisting of the vectors in B',

$$P = \begin{bmatrix} 1 & 1 & 0 \\ 1 & -1 & 0 \\ 0 & 0 & 1 \end{bmatrix},$$

and it follows that

$$
P^{-1} = \begin{bmatrix} \frac{1}{2} & \frac{1}{2} & 0 \\ \frac{1}{2} & -\frac{1}{2} & 0 \\ 0 & 0 & 1 \end{bmatrix}.
$$

Therefore the matrix for T relative to B' is

$$
A' = P^{-1}AP = \begin{bmatrix} \frac{1}{2} & \frac{1}{2} & 0 \\ \frac{1}{2} & -\frac{1}{2} & 0 \\ 0 & 0 & 1 \end{bmatrix} \begin{bmatrix} 1 & 3 & 0 \\ 3 & 1 & 0 \\ 0 & 0 & -2 \end{bmatrix} \begin{bmatrix} 1 & 1 & 0 \\ 1 & -1 & 0 \\ 0 & 0 & 1 \end{bmatrix}
$$

$$
= \begin{bmatrix} 4 & 0 & 0 \\ 0 & -2 & 0 \\ 0 & 0 & -2 \end{bmatrix}.
$$

Note that matrix A' is diagonal.

Diagonal matrices have many computational advantages over nondiagonal ones. For instance, the kth power of a diagonal matrix is given as follows.

$$
D = \begin{bmatrix} d_1 & 0 & \cdots & 0 \\ 0 & d_2 & \cdots & 0 \\ \vdots & \vdots & & \vdots \\ 0 & 0 & \cdots & d_n \end{bmatrix} \qquad D^k = \begin{bmatrix} d_1^{\,k} & 0 & \cdots & 0 \\ 0 & d_2^{\,k} & \cdots & 0 \\ \vdots & \vdots & & \vdots \\ 0 & 0 & \cdots & d_n^{\,k} \end{bmatrix}
$$

A diagonal matrix is its own transpose. Moreover, if all the diagonal elements are nonzero, then the inverse of a diagonal matrix is the matrix whose main diagonal elements are the reciprocals of corresponding elements in the original matrix. Given such computational advantages, it is important to find ways (if possible) to choose a basis for V such that the transformation matrix is diagonal, as it is in Example 5. We will pursue this problem in the next chapter.

SECTION 6.4   □   EXERCISES

In Exercises 1–8, (a) find the matrix A' for T relative to the basis B' and (b) show that A' is similar to A, the standard matrix for T.

1. $T : R^2 \rightarrow R^2$, $T(x, y) = (2x - y, y - x)$, $B' = \{(1, -2), (0, 3)\}$
2. $T : R^2 \rightarrow R^2$, $T(x, y) = (x + y, 4y)$, $B' = \{(-4, 1), (1, -1)\}$
3. $T : R^2 \rightarrow R^2$, $T(x, y) = (y, x)$, $B' = \{(1, -1), (1, 1)\}$
4. $T : R^2 \rightarrow R^2$, $T(x, y) = (x + y, x - y)$, $B' = \{(0, 1), (1, 0)\}$
5. $T : R^3 \rightarrow R^3$, $T(x, y, z) = (x, y, z)$,
   $B' = \{(1, 1, 0), (1, 0, 1), (0, 1, 1)\}$
6. $T : R^3 \rightarrow R^3$, $T(x, y, z) = (0, 0, 0)$,
   $B' = \{(1, 1, 0), (1, 0, 1), (0, 1, 1)\}$
7. $T : R^3 \rightarrow R^3$, $T(x, y, z) = (x - y + 2z, 2x + y - z, x + 2y + z)$, $B' = \{(1, 0, 1), (0, 2, 2), (1, 2, 0)\}$
8. $T : R^3 \rightarrow R^3$, $T(x, y, z) = (x, x + 2y, x + y + 3z)$,
   $B' = \{(1, -1, 0), (0, 0, 1), (0, 1, -1)\}$

9. Let $B = \{(1, 3), (-2, -2)\}$ and $B' = \{(-12, 0), (-4, 4)\}$ be bases for R^2, and let
$$A = \begin{bmatrix} 3 & 2 \\ 0 & 4 \end{bmatrix}$$
   be the matrix for $T : R^2 \rightarrow R^2$ relative to B.
   (a) Find the transition matrix P from B' to B.
   (b) Use the matrices A and P to find $[\mathbf{v}]_B$ and $[T(\mathbf{v})]_B$, where
   $$[\mathbf{v}]_{B'} = \begin{bmatrix} -1 \\ 2 \end{bmatrix}.$$
   (c) Find A' (the matrix of T relative to B') and P^{-1}.
   (d) Find $[T(\mathbf{v})]_{B'}$ in two ways: first as $P^{-1}[T(\mathbf{v})]_B$ and then as $A'[\mathbf{v}]_{B'}$.

10. Repeat Exercise 9 for $B = \{(1, 1), (-2, 3)\}$, $B' = \{(1, -1), (0, 1)\}$, and
   $$[\mathbf{v}]_{B'} = \begin{bmatrix} 1 \\ -3 \end{bmatrix}.$$

11. Let $B = \{(1, 1, 0), (1, 0, 1), (0, 1, 1)\}$ and $B' = \{(1, 0, 0), (0, 1, 0), (0, 0, 1)\}$ be bases for R^3, and let
$$A = \begin{bmatrix} \frac{3}{2} & -1 & -\frac{1}{2} \\ -\frac{1}{2} & 2 & \frac{1}{2} \\ \frac{1}{2} & 1 & \frac{5}{2} \end{bmatrix}$$
   be the matrix for $T : R^3 \rightarrow R^3$ relative to B.
   (a) Find the transition matrix P from B' to B.

(b) Use the matrices A and P to find $[\mathbf{v}]_B$ and $[T(\mathbf{v})]_B$, where
$$[\mathbf{v}]_{B'} = \begin{bmatrix} 1 \\ 0 \\ -1 \end{bmatrix}.$$
(c) Find A' (the matrix of T relative to B') and P^{-1}.
(d) Find $[T(\mathbf{v})]_{B'}$ in two ways: first as $P^{-1}[T(\mathbf{v})]_B$ and then as $A'[\mathbf{v}]_{B'}$.

12. Repeat Exercise 11 for $B = \{(1, 0, 0), (0, 1, 0), (0, 0, 1)\}$, $B' = \{(1, 1, -1), (1, -1, 1), (-1, 1, 1)\}$, and
$$[\mathbf{v}]_{B'} = \begin{bmatrix} 2 \\ 1 \\ 1 \end{bmatrix}.$$

13. Prove that if A and B are similar, then $|A| = |B|$. Is the converse true?

14. Illustrate the result of Exercise 13 using the matrices
$$A = \begin{bmatrix} 1 & 0 & 0 \\ 0 & -2 & 0 \\ 0 & 0 & 3 \end{bmatrix}, \quad B = \begin{bmatrix} 11 & 7 & 10 \\ 10 & 8 & 10 \\ -18 & -12 & -17 \end{bmatrix},$$
$$P = \begin{bmatrix} -1 & 1 & 0 \\ 2 & 1 & 2 \\ 1 & 1 & 1 \end{bmatrix},$$
$$P^{-1} = \begin{bmatrix} -1 & -1 & 2 \\ 0 & -1 & 2 \\ 1 & 2 & -3 \end{bmatrix}, \quad \text{where } B = P^{-1}AP.$$

15. Let A and B be similar matrices.
   (a) Prove that A^T and B^T are similar.
   (b) Prove that if A is nonsingular, then so is B and A^{-1} and B^{-1} are similar.
   (c) Prove that there exists a matrix P such that $B^k = P^{-1}A^kP$.

16. Use the result of Exercise 15 to find B^4, where $B = P^{-1}AP$ for the matrices
$$A = \begin{bmatrix} 1 & 0 \\ 0 & 2 \end{bmatrix}, \quad B = \begin{bmatrix} -4 & -15 \\ 2 & 7 \end{bmatrix},$$
$$P = \begin{bmatrix} 2 & 5 \\ 1 & 3 \end{bmatrix}, \quad P^{-1} = \begin{bmatrix} 3 & -5 \\ -1 & 2 \end{bmatrix}.$$

17. Determine all $n \times n$ matrices that are similar to I_n.

18. Prove that if A is idempotent and B is similar to A, then B is idempotent. (An $n \times n$ matrix A is idempotent if $A = A^2$.)

19. Let A be an $n \times n$ matrix such that $A^2 = O$. Prove that if B is similar to A, then $B^2 = O$.

20. Let $B = P^{-1}AP$. Prove that if $A\mathbf{x} = \mathbf{x}$, then $PBP^{-1}\mathbf{x} = \mathbf{x}$.

21. Complete the proof of Theorem 6.13 by proving that if A is similar to B and B is similar to C, then A is similar to C.

22. Prove that if A and B are similar, then they have the same rank.

23. Prove that if A and B are similar, then A^2 is similar to B^2.

24. Prove that if A and B are similar, then A^k is similar to B^k for any positive integer k.

25. Let $A = CD$, where C is an invertible $n \times n$ matrix. Prove that the matrix DC is similar to A.

26. Let $B = P^{-1}AP$, where B is a diagonal matrix with main diagonal entries $b_{11}, b_{22}, \ldots, b_{nn}$. Prove that

$$
\begin{bmatrix}
a_{11} & a_{12} & \cdots & a_{1n} \\
a_{21} & a_{22} & \cdots & a_{2n} \\
\vdots & \vdots & & \vdots \\
a_{n1} & a_{n2} & \cdots & a_{nn}
\end{bmatrix}
\begin{bmatrix}
p_{1i} \\
p_{2i} \\
\vdots \\
p_{ni}
\end{bmatrix}
= b_{ii}
\begin{bmatrix}
p_{1i} \\
p_{2i} \\
\vdots \\
p_{ni}
\end{bmatrix},
$$

for $i = 1, 2, \ldots, n$.

27. Let $B = \{\mathbf{v}_1, \mathbf{v}_2, \ldots, \mathbf{v}_n\}$ be a basis for the vector space V, let B' be the standard basis and consider the identity transformation $I : V \rightarrow V$. What can you say about the matrix of I relative to B and B'? What can you say about the matrix of I relative to B? Relative to B'?

6.5 APPLICATIONS OF LINEAR TRANSFORMATIONS

The Geometry of Linear Transformations in the Plane

This section gives geometrical interpretations for linear transformations represented by 2×2 elementary matrices. A summary of the various types of 2×2 elementary matrices is followed by examples in which each type is examined in more detail.

Elementary Matrices for Linear Transformations in the Plane

Reflection in y-Axis
$$A = \begin{bmatrix} -1 & 0 \\ 0 & 1 \end{bmatrix}$$

Reflection in x-Axis
$$A = \begin{bmatrix} 1 & 0 \\ 0 & -1 \end{bmatrix}$$

Reflection in Line $y = x$
$$A = \begin{bmatrix} 0 & 1 \\ 1 & 0 \end{bmatrix}$$

Horizontal Expansion $(k > 1)$ or Contraction $(0 < k < 1)$
$$A = \begin{bmatrix} k & 0 \\ 0 & 1 \end{bmatrix}$$

Vertical Expansion $(k > 1)$ or Contraction $(0 < k < 1)$
$$A = \begin{bmatrix} 1 & 0 \\ 0 & k \end{bmatrix}$$

Horizontal Shear
$$A = \begin{bmatrix} 1 & k \\ 0 & 1 \end{bmatrix}$$

Vertical Shear
$$A = \begin{bmatrix} 1 & 0 \\ k & 1 \end{bmatrix}$$

EXAMPLE 1   *Reflections in the Plane*

The transformations defined by the following matrices are called **reflections.** Reflections have the effect of mapping a point in the *xy*-plane to its "mirror image" with respect to one of the coordinate axes or the line given by $y = x$, as shown in Figure 6.11.

(a) Reflection in the *y*-axis:

$$T(x, y) = (-x, y)$$

$$\begin{bmatrix} -1 & 0 \\ 0 & 1 \end{bmatrix} \begin{bmatrix} x \\ y \end{bmatrix} = \begin{bmatrix} -x \\ y \end{bmatrix}$$

(b) Reflection in the *x*-axis:

$$T(x, y) = (x, -y)$$

$$\begin{bmatrix} 1 & 0 \\ 0 & -1 \end{bmatrix} \begin{bmatrix} x \\ y \end{bmatrix} = \begin{bmatrix} x \\ -y \end{bmatrix}$$

(c) Reflection in the line $y = x$:

$$T(x, y) = (y, x)$$

$$\begin{bmatrix} 0 & 1 \\ 1 & 0 \end{bmatrix} \begin{bmatrix} x \\ y \end{bmatrix} = \begin{bmatrix} y \\ x \end{bmatrix}$$

Figure 6.11

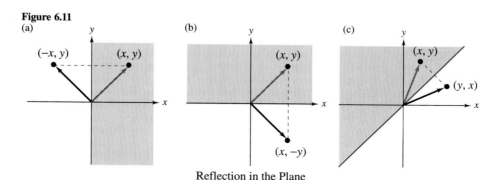

Reflection in the Plane

EXAMPLE 2   *Expansions and Contractions in the Plane*

The transformations defined by the following matrices are called **expansions** or **contractions,** depending on the value of the positive scalar *k*.

(a) Horizontal contractions and expansions:

$$T(x, y) = (kx, y)$$

$$\begin{bmatrix} k & 0 \\ 0 & 1 \end{bmatrix} \begin{bmatrix} x \\ y \end{bmatrix} = \begin{bmatrix} kx \\ y \end{bmatrix}$$

(b) Vertical contractions and expansions:

$$T(x, y) = (x, ky)$$

$$\begin{bmatrix} 1 & 0 \\ 0 & k \end{bmatrix} \begin{bmatrix} x \\ y \end{bmatrix} = \begin{bmatrix} x \\ ky \end{bmatrix}$$

Note that in Figures 6.12 and 6.13 the distance the point (x, y) is moved by a contraction or an expansion is proportional to its x- or y-coordinate. For instance, under the transformation given by $T(x, y) = (2x, y)$, the point $(1, 3)$ would be moved 1 unit to the right, but the point $(4, 3)$ would be moved 4 units to the right.

Figure 6.12

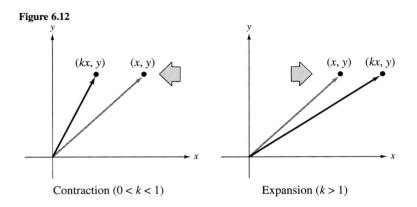

Contraction $(0 < k < 1)$ Expansion $(k > 1)$

Figure 6.13

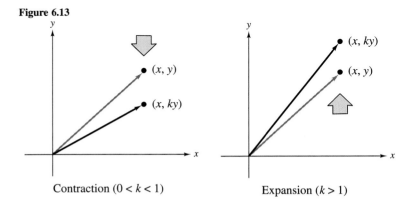

Contraction $(0 < k < 1)$ Expansion $(k > 1)$

The third type of linear transformation in the plane corresponding to an elementary matrix is called a **shear,** as described in Example 3.

EXAMPLE 3   *Shears in the Plane*

Figure 6.14

The transformations defined by the following matrices are shears.

$$T(x, y) = (x + ky, y) \qquad\qquad T(x, y) = (x, y + kx)$$

$$\begin{bmatrix} 1 & k \\ 0 & 1 \end{bmatrix}\begin{bmatrix} x \\ y \end{bmatrix} = \begin{bmatrix} x + ky \\ y \end{bmatrix} \qquad \begin{bmatrix} 1 & 0 \\ k & 1 \end{bmatrix}\begin{bmatrix} x \\ y \end{bmatrix} = \begin{bmatrix} x \\ kx + y \end{bmatrix}$$

(a) The horizontal shear given by $T(x, y) = (x + 2y, y)$ is shown in Figure 6.14. Under this transformation, points in the upper half-plane are "sheared" to the right by an amount proportional to their y-coordinate. Points in the lower half-plane are "sheared" to the left by an amount proportional to the absolute value of their y-coordinate. Points on the x-axis are unmoved by this transformation.

Figure 6.15

(b) The vertical shear given by $T(x, y) = (x, y + 2x)$ is shown in Figure 6.15. Here, points in the right half-plane are "sheared" upward by an amount proportional to their x-coordinate. Points in the left half-plane are "sheared" downward by an amount proportional to the absolute value of their x-coordinate. Points on the y-axis are unmoved.

Computer Graphics

Linear transformations are useful in computer graphics. In Example 7 of Section 6.1 we saw how a linear transformation could be used to rotate figures in the plane. Here we will see how linear transformations can be used to rotate figures in three-dimensional space.

Suppose we want to rotate the point (x, y, z) counterclockwise about the z-axis through an angle θ, as shown in Figure 6.16. Letting the coordinates of the rotated point be (x', y', z'), we have

Figure 6.16

$$\begin{bmatrix} x' \\ y' \\ z' \end{bmatrix} = \begin{bmatrix} \cos\theta & -\sin\theta & 0 \\ \sin\theta & \cos\theta & 0 \\ 0 & 0 & 1 \end{bmatrix}\begin{bmatrix} x \\ y \\ z \end{bmatrix} = \begin{bmatrix} x\cos\theta - y\sin\theta \\ x\sin\theta + y\cos\theta \\ z \end{bmatrix}.$$

Example 4 shows how to use this matrix to rotate a figure in three-dimensional space.

EXAMPLE 4   *Rotation About the z-Axis*

The eight vertices of a rectangular box having sides of lengths 1, 2, and 3 are as follows.

$$V_1 = (0, 0, 0), \qquad V_2 = (1, 0, 0), \qquad V_3 = (1, 2, 0,), \qquad V_4 = (0, 2, 0),$$

$$V_5 = (0, 0, 3), \qquad V_6 = (1, 0, 3), \qquad V_7 = (1, 2, 3), \qquad V_8 = (0, 2, 3)$$

Find the coordinates of the box when it is rotated counterclockwise about the z-axis through the following angles.

(a) $\theta = 60°$ (b) $\theta = 90°$ (c) $\theta = 120°$

Solution   The original box is shown in Figure 6.17.

Figure 6.17

(a) The matrix that yields a rotation of $60°$ is

$$A = \begin{bmatrix} \cos 60° & -\sin 60° & 0 \\ \sin 60° & \cos 60° & 0 \\ 0 & 0 & 1 \end{bmatrix} = \begin{bmatrix} 1/2 & -\sqrt{3}/2 & 0 \\ \sqrt{3}/2 & 1/2 & 0 \\ 0 & 0 & 1 \end{bmatrix}.$$

Multiplying this matrix by the eight vertices of the box produces the following vertices of the rotated box.

Original Vertex	Rotated Vertex
$V_1 = (0, 0, 0)$	$(\ 0.00, 0.00, 0)$
$V_2 = (1, 0, 0)$	$(\ 0.50, 0.87, 0)$
$V_3 = (1, 2, 0)$	$(-1.23, 1.87, 0)$
$V_4 = (0, 2, 0)$	$(-1.73, 1.00, 0)$
$V_5 = (0, 0, 3)$	$(\ 0.00, 0.00, 3)$
$V_6 = (1, 0, 3)$	$(\ 0.50, 0.87, 3)$
$V_7 = (1, 2, 3)$	$(-1.23, 1.87, 3)$
$V_8 = (0, 2, 3)$	$(-1.73, 1.00, 3)$

Figure 6.18

(a)

A computer-generated graph of the rotated box is shown in Figure 6.18(a). Note that in this graph line segments representing the sides of the box are drawn between images of pairs of vertices that are connected in the original box. For instance, since V_1 and V_2 are connected in the original box, the computer is told to connect the images of V_1 and V_2 in the rotated box.

(b) The matrix that yields a rotation of $90°$ is

(b)

$$A = \begin{bmatrix} \cos 90° & -\sin 90° & 0 \\ \sin 90° & \cos 90° & 0 \\ 0 & 0 & 1 \end{bmatrix} = \begin{bmatrix} 0 & -1 & 0 \\ 1 & 0 & 0 \\ 0 & 0 & 1 \end{bmatrix},$$

and the graph of the rotated box is shown in Figure 6.18(b).

(c) The matrix that yields a rotation of $120°$ is

(c)

$$A = \begin{bmatrix} \cos 120° & -\sin 120° & 0 \\ \sin 120° & \cos 120° & 0 \\ 0 & 0 & 1 \end{bmatrix} = \begin{bmatrix} -1/2 & -\sqrt{3}/2 & 0 \\ \sqrt{3}/2 & -1/2 & 0 \\ 0 & 0 & 1 \end{bmatrix},$$

and the graph of the rotated box is shown in Figure 6.18(c).

In Example 4 we used a matrix to perform a rotation about the z-axis. Similarly, we can use matrices to rotate figures about the x- or y-axis. All three types of rotations are summarized as follows.

Rotation About the x-Axis   *Rotation About the y-Axis*   *Rotation About the z-Axis*

$$
\begin{bmatrix} 1 & 0 & 0 \\ 0 & \cos\theta & -\sin\theta \\ 0 & \sin\theta & \cos\theta \end{bmatrix}
\quad
\begin{bmatrix} \cos\theta & 0 & \sin\theta \\ 0 & 1 & 0 \\ -\sin\theta & 0 & \cos\theta \end{bmatrix}
\quad
\begin{bmatrix} \cos\theta & -\sin\theta & 0 \\ \sin\theta & \cos\theta & 0 \\ 0 & 0 & 1 \end{bmatrix}
$$

In each case the rotation is oriented counterclockwise relative to a person facing the negative direction of the indicated axis, as shown in Figure 6.19.

Figure 6.19

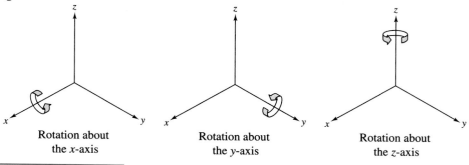

Rotation about   Rotation about   Rotation about
the x-axis   the y-axis   the z-axis

EXAMPLE 5   ***Rotations About the x-Axis and y-Axis***

(a) The matrix that rotates a point $90°$ about the x-axis is

$$
A = \begin{bmatrix} 1 & 0 & 0 \\ 0 & 0 & -1 \\ 0 & 1 & 0 \end{bmatrix}.
$$

(b) The matrix that rotates a point $90°$ about the y-axis is

$$
A = \begin{bmatrix} 0 & 0 & 1 \\ 0 & 1 & 0 \\ -1 & 0 & 0 \end{bmatrix}.
$$

Figure 6.20 shows the result of multiplying these two matrices by the vertices of the box in Example 4.

Figure 6.20

(a)   (b)

Figure 6.21

Rotations about the coordinate axes can be combined to produce any desired view of a figure. For instance, Figure 6.21 shows the rotation produced first by rotating the box (from Example 4) 90° about the *y*-axis, then further rotating the box 120° about the *z*-axis.

The use of computer graphics has become common among designers in many fields. Simply by entering into a computer the coordinates that form the outline of an object, a designer can see the object before it is created. As a simple example, the image of the toy boat shown in Figure 6.22 was created using only 27 points in space. Once the points have been stored in the computer, the boat can be viewed from any perspective.

Figure 6.22

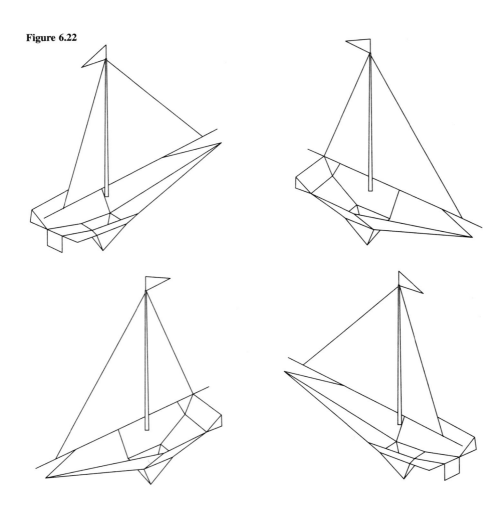

SECTION 6.5 □ EXERCISES

The Geometry of Linear Transformations in the Plane

1. Let $T: R^2 \to R^2$ be a reflection in the x-axis. Find the images of the following vectors.

(a) $(3, 5)$ (b) $(2, -1)$

(c) $(a, 0)$ (d) $(0, b)$

2. Let $T: R^2 \to R^2$ be a reflection in the line $y = x$. Find the images of the following vectors.

(a) $(0, 1)$ (b) $(-1, 3)$

(c) $(a, 0)$ (d) $(0, b)$

3. Let $T(1, 0) = (0, 1)$ and $T(0, 1) = (1, 0)$.

(a) Determine $T(x, y)$ for any (x, y).

(b) Give a geometric description of T.

4. Let $T(1, 0) = (2, 0)$ and $T(0, 1) = (0, 1)$.

(a) Determine $T(x, y)$ for any (x, y).

(b) Give a geometric description of T.

In Exercises 5–8, (a) identify the transformation and (b) graphically represent the transformation for an arbitrary vector in the plane.

5. $T(x, y) = (x, y/2)$ **6.** $T(x, y) = (4x, y)$

7. $T(x, y) = (x + 3y, y)$ **8.** $T(x, y) = (x, 2x + y)$

In Exercises 9–12, find all fixed points of the given linear transformation. The vector $\mathbf{v}$ is a fixed point of T if $T(\mathbf{v}) = \mathbf{v}$.

9. A reflection in the y-axis

10. A reflection in the line $y = x$

11. A vertical contraction

12. A horizontal shear

In Exercises 13–18, sketch the image of the unit square with vertices at $(0, 0)$, $(1, 0)$, $(1, 1)$, and $(0, 1)$ under the given transformation.

13. T is a reflection in the x-axis.

14. T is a reflection in the line $y = x$.

15. T is the contraction given by $T(x, y) = (x/2, y)$.

16. T is the expansion given by $T(x, y) = (x, 3y)$.

17. T is the shear given by $T(x, y) = (x + 2y, y)$.

18. T is the shear given by $T(x, y) = (x, y + 3x)$.

In Exercises 19–24, sketch the image of the rectangle with vertices at $(0, 0)$, $(0, 2)$, $(1, 2)$, and $(1, 0)$ under the given transformation.

19. T is a reflection in the y-axis.

20. T is a reflection in the line $y = x$.

21. T is the contraction given by $T(x, y) = (x, y/2)$.

22. T is the expansion given by $T(x, y) = (2x, y)$.

23. T is the shear given by $T(x, y) = (x + y, y)$.

24. T is the shear given by $T(x, y) = (x, y + 2x)$.

25. The linear transformation defined by a diagonal matrix with positive main diagonal elements is called a **magnification.** Find the images of $(1, 0)$, $(0, 1)$, and $(2, 2)$ under the linear transformation defined by

$$A = \begin{bmatrix} 2 & 0 \\ 0 & 3 \end{bmatrix}$$

and graphically interpret your results.

26. Repeat Exercise 25 for the linear transformation defined by

$$A = \begin{bmatrix} 3 & 0 \\ 0 & 3 \end{bmatrix}.$$

In Exercises 27–30, give a geometric description of the linear transformation defined by the given elementary matrix.

27. $A = \begin{bmatrix} 2 & 0 \\ 0 & 1 \end{bmatrix}$ **28.** $A = \begin{bmatrix} 1 & 0 \\ 2 & 1 \end{bmatrix}$

29. $A = \begin{bmatrix} 0 & 1 \\ 1 & 0 \end{bmatrix}$ **30.** $A = \begin{bmatrix} 1 & 3 \\ 0 & 1 \end{bmatrix}$

In Exercises 31 and 32, give a geometric description of the linear transformation defined by the given matrix product.

31. $A = \begin{bmatrix} 2 & 0 \\ 2 & 1 \end{bmatrix} = \begin{bmatrix} 2 & 0 \\ 0 & 1 \end{bmatrix}\begin{bmatrix} 1 & 0 \\ 2 & 1 \end{bmatrix}$

32. $A = \begin{bmatrix} 0 & 3 \\ 1 & 0 \end{bmatrix} = \begin{bmatrix} 0 & 1 \\ 1 & 0 \end{bmatrix}\begin{bmatrix} 1 & 0 \\ 0 & 3 \end{bmatrix}$

Computer Graphics

In Exercises 33–36. find the matrix that will produce the indicated rotation.

33. 30° about the z-axis   **34.** 60° about the x-axis

35. 60° about the y-axis   **36.** 120° about the x-axis

In Exercises 37–40, find the image of the vector $(1, 1, 1)$ for the indicated rotation.

37. 30° about the z-axis   **38.** 60° about the x-axis

39. 60° about the y-axis   **40.** 120° about the x-axis

In Exercises 41–46, determine which single counterclockwise rotation about the *x*-, *y*-, or *z*-axis will produce the indicated tetrahedron. The original tetrahedron position is illustrated in Figure 6.23.

Figure 6.23

41.

42.

43.

44.

45.

46.

In Exercises 47–50, determine the matrix that will produce the indicated pair of rotations. Then find the image of the line segment from $(0, 0, 0)$ to $(1, 1, 1)$ under this composition.

47. 90° about the *x*-axis followed by 90° about the *y*-axis

48. 45° about the *y*-axis followed by 90° about the *z*-axis

49. 30° about the *z*-axis followed by 60° about the *y*-axis

50. 45° about the *z*-axis followed by 135° about the *x*-axis

CHAPTER 6 ☐ REVIEW EXERCISES

In Exercises 1–4, find (a) the image of **v** and (b) the preimage of **w** for the given linear transformation.

1. $T: R^2 \to R^2$, $T(v_1, v_2) = (v_1, v_1 + 2v_2)$, $\mathbf{v} = (2, -3)$, $\mathbf{w} = (4, 12)$

2. $T: R^2 \to R^2$, $T(v_1, v_2) = (v_1 - 2v_2, 2v_1 + v_2)$, $\mathbf{v} = (6, 4)$, $\mathbf{w} = (-7, 0)$

3. $T: R^3 \to R^3$, $T(v_1, v_2, v_3) = (v_2, v_1 + v_2, v_3)$, $\mathbf{v} = (0, 1, 1)$, $\mathbf{w} = (4, 4, 4)$

4. $T: R^3 \to R^3$, $T(v_1, v_2, v_3) = (0, v_1 + v_2, v_2 + v_3)$, $\mathbf{v} = (-3, 2, 5)$, $\mathbf{w} = (0, 2, 5)$

In Exercises 5–12, determine whether the given function is a linear transformation. If it is, find its standard matrix A.

5. $T: R^2 \to R^2$, $T(x_1, x_2) = (x_1 + 2x_2, -x_1 - x_2)$

6. $T: R^2 \to R^2$, $T(x_1, x_2) = (x_1 + 3, x_2)$

7. $T: R^2 \to R^2$, $T(x, y) = (x + h, y + k)$, $h \neq 0$ or $k \neq 0$ (translation in the plane)

8. $T: R^2 \to R^2$, $T(x, y) = (|x|, |y|)$

9. $T: R^2 \to R^3$, $T(x_1, x_2) = (x_2, x_2, x_1)$

10. $T: R^3 \to R^2$, $T(x, y, z) = (y, y)$

11. $T: R^3 \to R^3$, $T(x_1, x_2, x_3) = (x_1 - x_2, x_2 - x_3, x_3 - x_1)$

12. $T: R^3 \to R^3$, $T(x, y, z) = (z, y, x)$

13. Let T be a linear transformation from R^2 to R^2 such that $T(2, 0) = (1, 1)$ and $T(0, 3) = (3, 3)$. Find $T(1, 1)$ and $T(0, 1)$.

14. Let T be a linear transformation from R^3 to R such that $T(1, 1, 1) = 1$, $T(1, 1, 0) = 2$, and $T(1, 0, 0) = 3$. Find $T(0, 1, 1)$.

In Exercises 15–18, find the indicated power of A, the standard matrix for T.

15. $T: R^3 \rightarrow R^3$, reflection in the xy-plane. Find A^2.

16. $T: R^3 \rightarrow R^3$, projection onto the xy-plane. Find A^2.

17. $T: R^2 \rightarrow R^2$, counterclockwise rotation through the angle θ. Find A^3.

18. (Calculus) $T: P_3 \rightarrow P_3$, differential operator. Find A^2.

In Exercises 19–22, the linear transformation $T: R^n \rightarrow R^m$ is defined by $T(\mathbf{v}) = A\mathbf{v}$. For each matrix A, (a) determine the dimensions of R^n and R^m, (b) find the image $T(\mathbf{v})$ of the given vector $\mathbf{v}$, and (c) find the preimage of the given vector $\mathbf{w}$.

19. $A = \begin{bmatrix} 0 & 1 & 2 \\ -2 & 0 & 0 \end{bmatrix}$, $\mathbf{v} = (6, 1, 1)$, $\mathbf{w} = (3, 5)$

20. $A = [1, 1]$, $\mathbf{v} = (2, 3)$, $\mathbf{w} = (4)$

21. $A = \begin{bmatrix} 1 & 1 & 1 \\ 0 & 1 & 1 \\ 0 & 0 & 1 \end{bmatrix}$, $\mathbf{v} = (2, 1, -5)$, $\mathbf{w} = (6, 4, 2)$

22. $A = \begin{bmatrix} 4 & 0 \\ 0 & 5 \\ 1 & 1 \end{bmatrix}$, $\mathbf{v} = (2, 2)$, $\mathbf{w} = (4, -5, 0)$

In Exercises 23 and 24, find a basis for (a) ker(T) and (b) range(T).

23. $T: R^4 \rightarrow R^3$, $T(w, x, y, z) = (2w + 4x + 6y + 5z, -w - 2x + 2y, 8y + 4z)$

24. $T: R^3 \rightarrow R^3$, $T(x, y, z) = (x + 2y, y + 2z, z + 2x)$

In Exercises 25 and 26, the linear transformation T is given by $T(\mathbf{v}) = A\mathbf{v}$. Find a basis for (a) the kernel of T and (b) the range of T. What are the rank and the nullity of T?

25. $A = \begin{bmatrix} 1 & 2 \\ -1 & 0 \\ 1 & 1 \end{bmatrix}$ **26.** $A = \begin{bmatrix} 2 & 1 & 3 \\ 1 & 1 & 0 \\ 0 & 1 & -3 \end{bmatrix}$

27. Given $T: R^5 \rightarrow R^3$ and nullity(T) $= 2$, find rank(T).

28. Given $T: P_5 \rightarrow P_3$ and nullity(T) $= 3$, find rank(T).

29. Given $T: P_4 \rightarrow R^5$ and rank(T) $= 4$, find nullity(T).

30. Given $T: M_{2,2} \rightarrow M_{2,2}$ and rank(T) $= 3$, find nullity(T).

In Exercises 31–36, determine whether the transformation T has an inverse. If it does, find A and A^{-1}.

31. $T: R^2 \rightarrow R^2$, $T(x, y) = (y, x)$

32. $T: R^2 \rightarrow R^2$, $T(x, y) = (2x, y)$

33. $T: R^2 \rightarrow R^2$, $T(x, y) = (x, y + kx)$

34. $T: R^2 \rightarrow R^2$, $T(x, y) = (x \cos \theta - y \sin \theta, x \sin \theta + y \cos \theta)$

35. $T: R^3 \rightarrow R^3$, $T(x, y, z) = (x, y, 0)$

36. $T: R^3 \rightarrow R^2$, $T(x, y, z) = (x + y, y - z)$

In Exercises 37 and 38, find the standard matrices for $T = T_1 \circ T_2$ and $T' = T_2 \circ T_1$.

37. $T_1: R^2 \rightarrow R^3$, $T_1(x, y) = (x, x + y, y)$
$T_2: R^3 \rightarrow R^2$, $T_2(x, y, z) = (0, y)$

38. $T_1: R \rightarrow R^2$, $T(x) = (x, 3x)$
$T_2: R^2 \rightarrow R$, $T(x, y) = (y + 2x)$

39. Use the standard matrix for counterclockwise rotation in R^2 to rotate the triangle with vertices $(3, 5)$, $(5, 3)$, and $(3, 0)$ counterclockwise $90°$ about the origin. Graph the triangles.

40. Rotate the triangle in Exercise 39 counterclockwise $90°$ about the point $(5, 3)$. Graph the triangles. [Hint: Translate the axes so that the vertex $(5, 3)$ is at the origin of the new coordinate system. Use the matrix to rotate the triangle and then translate back to the original coordinate system.]

In Exercises 41–44, determine whether the linear transformation represented by the matrix A is (a) one-to-one, (b) onto, and (c) invertible.

41. $A = \begin{bmatrix} 2 & 0 \\ 0 & 3 \end{bmatrix}$ **42.** $A = \begin{bmatrix} 1 & 1 & 1 \\ 0 & 1 & 1 \end{bmatrix}$

43. $A = \begin{bmatrix} 1 & \frac{1}{4} \\ 0 & 1 \end{bmatrix}$ **44.** $A = \begin{bmatrix} 4 & 0 & 7 \\ 5 & 5 & 1 \\ 0 & 0 & 2 \end{bmatrix}$

In Exercises 45 and 46, find $T(\mathbf{v})$ by using (a) the standard matrix and (b) the matrix relative to B and B'.

45. $T: R^2 \rightarrow R^3$, $T(x, y) = (-x, y, x + y)$, $\mathbf{v} = (0, 1)$,
$B = \{(1, 1), (1, -1)\}$, $B' = \{(0, 1, 0), (0, 0, 1), (1, 0, 0)\}$

46. $T: R^2 \rightarrow R^2$, $T(x, y) = (2y, 0)$, $\mathbf{v} = (-1, 3)$,
$B = \{(2, 1), (-1, 0)\}$, $B' = \{(-1, 0), (2, 2)\}$

In Exercises 47 and 48, find the matrix A' for T relative to the basis B' and show that A' is similar to A, the standard matrix for T.

47. $T: R^2 \rightarrow R^2$, $T(x, y) = (x - 3y, y - x)$, $B' = \{(1, -1), (1, 1)\}$

48. $T: R^3 \rightarrow R^3$, $T(x, y, z) = (x + 3y, 3x + y, -2z)$,
$B' = \{(1, 1, 0), (1, -1, 0), (0, 0, 1)\}$

49. Let $T: R^3 \rightarrow R^3$ be given by $T(\mathbf{v}) = \text{proj}_\mathbf{u}\mathbf{v}$, where $\mathbf{u} = (0, 1, 2)$.

(a) Find A, the standard matrix for T.

(b) Let S be the linear transformation represented by $I - A$. Show that S is of the form $S(\mathbf{v}) = \text{proj}_{\mathbf{w}_1}\mathbf{v} + \text{proj}_{\mathbf{w}_2}\mathbf{v}$, where $\mathbf{w}_1$ and $\mathbf{w}_2$ are fixed vectors in R^3.

(c) Show that the kernel of T is equal to the range of S.

50. Let $T: R^2 \rightarrow R^2$ be given by $T(\mathbf{v}) = \text{proj}_\mathbf{u}\mathbf{v}$, where $\mathbf{u} = (4, 3)$.

(a) Find A, the standard matrix for T, and show that $A^2 = A$.

(b) Show that $(I - A)^2 = I - A$.

(c) Find $A\mathbf{v}$ and $(I - A)\mathbf{v}$ for $\mathbf{v} = (5, 0)$.

(d) Sketch the graph of $\mathbf{u}$, $\mathbf{v}$, $A\mathbf{v}$, and $(I - A)\mathbf{v}$.

51. Let S and T be linear transformations from V into W. Show that $S + T$ and kT are both linear transformations, where $(S + T)(\mathbf{v}) = S(\mathbf{v}) + T(\mathbf{v})$ and $(kT)(\mathbf{v}) = kT(\mathbf{v})$.

52. Assume the A and B are similar matrices and that A is invertible.

(a) Prove that B is invertible.

(b) Prove that A^{-1} and B^{-1} are similar.

In Exercises 53 and 54, the **sum** $S + T$ of two linear transformations $S: V \rightarrow W$ and $T: V \rightarrow W$ is defined as $(S + T)(\mathbf{v}) = S(\mathbf{v}) + T(\mathbf{v})$.

53. Prove that $\text{rank}(S + T) \leq \text{rank}(S) + \text{rank}(T)$.

54. Give an example for each of the following.

(a) $\text{Rank}(S + T) = \text{rank}(S) + \text{rank}(T)$

(b) $\text{Rank}(S + T) < \text{rank}(S) + \text{rank}(T)$

55. Let $T: P_3 \rightarrow R$ such that $T(a_0 + a_1x + a_2x^2 + a_3x^3) = a_0 + a_1 + a_2 + a_3$.

(a) Prove that T is linear.

(b) Find the rank and nullity of T.

(c) Find a basis for the kernel of T.

56. Let $T: V \rightarrow U$ and $S: U \rightarrow W$ be linear transformations.

(a) Prove that if S and T are both one-to-one, then so is $S \circ T$.

(b) Prove that the kernel of T is contained in the kernel of $S \circ T$.

(c) Prove that if $S \circ T$ is onto, then so is S.

57. Let V be an inner product space. For a fixed nonzero vector $\mathbf{v}_0$ in V, let $T: V \rightarrow R$ be the linear transformation $T(\mathbf{v}) = \langle \mathbf{v}, \mathbf{v}_0 \rangle$. Find the kernel and range of T. Then determine the rank and nullity of T.

58. (Calculus) Let $B = \{1, x, \sin x, \cos x\}$ be a basis for a subspace W of the space of continuous functions, and let D_x be the differential operator on W. Find the matrix for D_x relative to the basis B. Find the range and kernel of D_x.

▶ **59.** Under what conditions are the spaces $M_{m,n}$ and $M_{p,q}$ isomorphic? Describe an isomorphism T in this case.

60. (Calculus) Let $T: P_3 \rightarrow P_3$ be given by $T(\mathbf{p}) = p(x) + p'(x)$. Find the rank and nullity of T.

The Geometry of Linear Transformations in the Plane

In Exercises 61–64, (a) identify the transformations and (b) graphically represent the transformation for an arbitrary vector in the plane.

61. $T(x, y) = (x, 2y)$

62. $T(x, y) = (x + y, y)$

63. $T(x, y) = (x, y + 3x)$

64. $T(x, y) = (5x, y)$

In Exercises 65–68, sketch the image of the triangle with vertices $(0, 0)$, $(1, 0)$, and $(0, 1)$ under the given transformation.

65. T is a reflection in the x-axis.

66. T is the expansion given by $T(x, y) = (2x, y)$.

67. T is the shear given by $T(x, y) = (x + 3y, y)$.

68. T is the shear given by $T(x, y) = (x, y + 2x)$.

In Exercises 69 and 70, give a geometric description of the linear transformation defined by the matrix product.

69. $\begin{bmatrix} 0 & 2 \\ 1 & 0 \end{bmatrix} = \begin{bmatrix} 2 & 0 \\ 0 & 1 \end{bmatrix}\begin{bmatrix} 0 & 1 \\ 1 & 0 \end{bmatrix}$

70. $\begin{bmatrix} 1 & 0 \\ 6 & 2 \end{bmatrix} = \begin{bmatrix} 1 & 0 \\ 0 & 2 \end{bmatrix}\begin{bmatrix} 1 & 0 \\ 3 & 1 \end{bmatrix}$

Computer Graphics

In Exercises 71 and 72, find the matrix that will produce the indicated rotation and then find the image of the vector $(1, -1, 1)$.

71. 45° about the z-axis

72. 90° about the x-axis

In Exercises 73 and 74, determine the matrix that will produce the indicated pair of rotations.

73. $60°$ about the x-axis followed by $30°$ about the z-axis

74. $120°$ about the y-axis followed by $45°$ about the z-axis

In Exercises 75 and 76, find the image of the unit cube with vertices $(0, 0, 0)$, $(1, 0, 0)$, $(1, 1, 0)$, $(0, 1, 0)$, $(0, 0, 1)$, $(1, 0, 1)$, $(1, 1, 1)$ and $(0, 1, 1)$ when it is rotated by the given angle.

75. $45°$ about the z-axis   **76.** $90°$ about the x-axis

CHAPTER 6   PROJECTS

1 Reflections in the Plane-I.

Figure 6.24

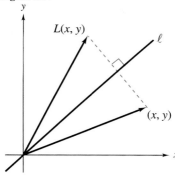

Let ℓ be the line $ax + by = 0$ in the plane. The linear transformation $L\colon R^2 \to R^2$ that sends a point (x, y) to its mirror image in ℓ is called the **reflection** in ℓ. (See Figure 6.24.)

The goal of these two projects is to find the matrix of this reflection relative to the standard basis. The first project is based on transition matrices, and the second project uses projections.

1. Find the standard matrix of L for the line $x = 0$.
2. Find the standard matrix of L for the line $y = 0$.
3. Find the standard matrix of L for the line $x - y = 0$.
4. Consider the line ℓ given by $x - 2y = 0$. Find a vector $\mathbf{v}$ parallel to ℓ and another vector $\mathbf{w}$ orthogonal to ℓ. Determine the matrix A of the reflection in ℓ relative to the ordered basis $\{\mathbf{v}, \mathbf{w}\}$.   Finally, use the appropriate transition matrix to find the matrix of the reflection relative to the standard basis. Use this matrix to find $L(2, 1)$, $L(-1, 2)$, and $L(5, 0)$.
5. Consider the general line $ax + by = 0$. Let $\mathbf{v}$ be a vector parallel to ℓ, and let $\mathbf{w}$ be a vector orthogonal to ℓ. Determine the matrix A of the reflection in ℓ relative to the ordered basis $\{\mathbf{v}, \mathbf{w}\}$. Finally, use the appropriate transition matrix to find the matrix of L relative to the standard basis.
6. Find the standard matrix of the reflection in the line $3x + 4y = 0$. Use this matrix to find the images of the points $(3, 4)$, $(-4, 3)$, and $(0, 5)$.

2 Reflections in the Plane-II.

Figure 6.25

In this second project, you will use projections to determine the standard matrix for the reflection L in the line $ax + by = 0$. (See Figure 6.25.) Recall that the projection of the vector $\mathbf{u}$ onto the vector $\mathbf{v}$ is given by

$$\text{proj}_\mathbf{v}\mathbf{u} = \frac{\mathbf{u} \cdot \mathbf{v}}{\mathbf{v} \cdot \mathbf{v}}\,\mathbf{v}.$$

1. Find the standard matrix for the projection onto the y-axis. That is, find the standard matrix for $\text{proj}_\mathbf{v}\mathbf{u}$ if $\mathbf{v} = (0, 1)$.
2. Find the standard matrix for the projection onto the x-axis.

Figure 6.26

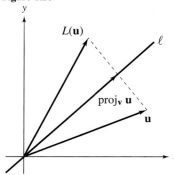

3. Consider the line ℓ given by $x - 2y = 0$. Find a vector $\mathbf{v}$ parallel to ℓ and another vector $\mathbf{w}$ orthogonal to ℓ. Determine the matrix A of the projection onto ℓ relative to the ordered basis $\{\mathbf{v}, \mathbf{w}\}$. Finally, use the appropriate transition matrix to find the matrix of the projection relative to the standard basis. Use this matrix to find $\text{proj}_\ell\mathbf{u}$ for the cases $\mathbf{u} = (2, 1)$, $\mathbf{u} = (-1, 2)$ and $\mathbf{u} = (5, 0)$.

4. Consider the general line $ax + by = 0$. Let $\mathbf{v}$ be a vector parallel to ℓ, and let $\mathbf{w}$ be a vector orthogonal to ℓ. Determine the matrix A of the projection onto ℓ relative to the ordered basis $\{\mathbf{v}, \mathbf{w}\}$. Finally, use the appropriate transition matrix to find the matrix of the projection relative to the standard basis.

5. Use Figure 6.26 to show that

$$\text{proj}_\mathbf{v}\mathbf{u} = \frac{1}{2}(\mathbf{u} + L(\mathbf{u}))$$

where L is the reflection in the line ℓ. Solve this equation for L and compare your answer with the formula from the first project.

CHAPTER 6   ▢   MATLAB EXERCISES

1. Find the kernel and range of the linear transformation given by $T(\mathbf{x}) = A\mathbf{x}$ for these matrices A.

(a) $A = \begin{bmatrix} 1 & 0 & 0 \\ 1 & 1 & 0 \\ -1 & -1 & 1 \\ -2 & 0 & -2 \end{bmatrix}$

(b) $A = \begin{bmatrix} 1 & 0 & -3 & 2 \\ 0 & -1 & -2 & 2 \\ 1 & 2 & 4 & -5 \end{bmatrix}$

(c) $A = \begin{bmatrix} 1 & 2 & 3 & 4 \\ 9 & 10 & 11 & 12 \\ 5 & 6 & 7 & 8 \\ -13 & -14 & -15 & -16 \end{bmatrix}$

(d) $A = \begin{bmatrix} 1 & -1 & 1 & -1 & 1 \\ -1 & 1 & -1 & 1 & -1 \end{bmatrix}$

2. Let B be the upper trianglular matrix generated by the MATLAB command $\mathbf{B} = \textbf{triu(ones(6))}$. Let $A = BB^T - B$ and determine the rank and nullity of the linear transformation $L: R^6 \rightarrow R^6$, $L(\mathbf{x}) = A\mathbf{x}$.

3. Which of these linear transformations defined by $T(\mathbf{x}) = A\mathbf{x}$ are one-to-one? Which are onto?
   (a) $A = $ magic(6)   (b) $A = $ hilb(6)   (c) $A = $ tril(ones (6))

4. Let $T: R^n \rightarrow R^m$ be a linear transformation. Let $B = \{\mathbf{v}_1, \mathbf{v}_2, \ldots, \mathbf{v}_n\}$ and $B1 = \{\mathbf{w}_1, \mathbf{w}_2, \ldots, \mathbf{w}_m\}$ be bases for R^n and R^m, respectively. You can use MATLAB to find the matrix of T relative to the bases B and $B1$ as follows.
   (a) Form the matrices B and $B1$ whose *columns* are the given basis vectors.
   (b) Let A be the $m \times n$ standard matrix of T.
   (c) Adjoin $B1$ to AB to form the $m \times (m + n)$ matrix C: $\mathbf{C} = [\mathbf{B1}\ \ \mathbf{A^*B}]$.
   (d) Use $\textbf{rref(C)}$ to calculate the reduced row-echelon form of C. The $m \times n$ matrix composed of the right-hand n columns of C form the matrix of T relative to the bases B and $B1$.

Use this algorithm to find the matrix of the following linear transformations relative to the given bases.

(a) $T: R^2 \to R^3, T(x, y) = (x + y, x, y)$,
   $B = \{(1, -1), (0, 1)\}, B1 = \{(1, 1, 0), (0, 1, 1), (1, 0, 1)\}$

(b) $T: R^3 \to R^2, T(x, y, z) = (2x - z, y - 2x)$,
   $B = \{(2, 0, 1), (0, 2, 1), (1, 2, 1)\}, B1 = \{(1, 1), (2, 0)\}$

(c) $T: R^3 \to R^4, T(x, y, z) = (2x, x + y, y + z, x + z)$,
   $B = \{(2, 0, 1), (0, 2, 1), (1, 2, 1)\}$,
   $B1 = \{(1, 0, 0, 1), (0, 1, 0, 1), (1, 0, 1, 0), (1, 1, 0, 0)\}$

5. Use the results of Exercise 4 to find the image of the given vector $\mathbf{v}$ two ways: first by calculating $T(\mathbf{v}) = A\mathbf{v}$, and second by using the matrix of T relative to the bases B and $B1$.

(a) $\mathbf{v} = (5, 4)$
(b) $\mathbf{v} = (0, -5, 7)$
(c) $\mathbf{v} = (1, -5, 2)$

6. Let $B = \{\mathbf{v}_1, \mathbf{v}_2, \ldots, \mathbf{v}_n\}$ and $B1 = \{\mathbf{w}_1, \mathbf{w}_2, \ldots, \mathbf{w}_n\}$ be two ordered bases for R^n. Recall from Section 4.7 that you find the transition matrix P^{-1} from B to $B1$ as follows.

(a) Form the matrices B and $B1$ whose columns are the given basis vectors.
(b) Adjoin B to $B1$, forming the $n \times 2n$ matrix C, $\mathbf{C} = [\mathbf{B1}\ \mathbf{B}]$.
(c) Let D be the reduced row-echelon form of C, $\mathbf{D} = \text{rref}(\mathbf{C})$.
(d) P^{-1} is the $n \times n$ matrix consisting of the right-hand n columns of D.

Use MATLAB to find the matrix $A1$ of the linear transformation $T: R^n \to R^n$ relative to the basis $B1$.

(a) $T: R^2 \to R^2, T(x, y) = (2x - y, y - x)$,
   $B1 = \{(1, -2), (0, 3)\}$

(b) $T: R^3 \to R^3, T(x, y, z) = (x, x + 2y, x + y + 3z)$,
   $B1 = \{(1 - 1, 0), (0, 0, 1), (0, 1, -1)\}$

7. Let $B = \{1, 0, 0), (0, 1, 0), (0, 0, 1)\}$ and $B1 = \{(1, 1, 0), (1, -1, 0), (0, 0, 1)\}$ be bases for R^3, and let

$$A = \begin{bmatrix} 1 & 3 & 0 \\ 3 & 1 & 0 \\ 0 & 0 & -2 \end{bmatrix}$$

be the matrix of $T: R^3 \to R^3$ relative to B, the standard basis.

(a) Find the transition matrix P from $B1$ to B.
(b) Find the transition matrix P^{-1} from B to $B1$.
(c) Find $A1$, the matrix of T relative to $B1$.
(d) Let

$$[\mathbf{v}]_{B1} = \begin{bmatrix} 1 \\ 2 \\ 3 \end{bmatrix}$$

and find $[\mathbf{v}]_B$ and $[T(\mathbf{v})]_B$.

(e) Find $[T(\mathbf{v})]_{B1}$ two ways: first as $P^{-1}[T(\mathbf{v})]_B$ and then as $A1[\mathbf{v}]_{B1}$.

7 EIGENVALUES AND EIGENVECTORS

James Joseph
Sylvester
1 8 1 4 – 1 8 9 7

*J*ames Joseph Sylvester, founder of the *American Journal of Mathematics*, was born in London. Although little is known of his early life, his mathematical ability must have been recognized early because by the age of fourteen he was studying at the University of London under Augustus DeMorgan, a well-known English mathematician. At fifteen, Sylvester entered the Royal Institute at Liverpool, where he won several prizes in mathematics.

After receiving his degree from Cambridge University in 1837, Sylvester embarked upon a series of careers in England and the United States. These included a professorship at the University of Virginia, an actuarial position in England, enrollment at law school (with subsequent work as a lawyer), a professorship at a military academy, a return to America as a professor of mathematics at Johns Hopkins University, and finally a professorship of mathematics at Oxford University, a position he held until his death in 1897.

In 1850 Sylvester met Arthur Cayley and the two began a life-long friendship. Sylvester attributed his "restoration to the enjoyment of mathematical life" to this meeting, and during the next half century he contributed much to the theory of determinants. His mathematical papers tended to be emotional discourses rather than systematic developments of theory, and he often claimed results to be "self-evident." Although his exuberance occasionally led to incorrect conjectures, Sylvester's intuition was usually right, probably because, as he said, "I really love my subject."

7.1 EIGENVALUES AND EIGENVECTORS

This section presents one of the most important problems in linear algebra, the **eigenvalue problem.** Its central question can be stated as follows. If A is an $n \times n$ matrix, do there exist nonzero vectors $\mathbf{x}$ in R^n such that $A\mathbf{x}$ is a scalar multiple of $\mathbf{x}$? The scalar, denoted by the Greek letter lambda (λ), is called an **eigenvalue** of the matrix A, and the nonzero vector $\mathbf{x}$ is called an **eigenvector** of A corresponding to λ. The terms *eigenvalue* and *eigenvector* are derived from the German word *Eigenwert*, meaning "proper value." Thus we have

$$A\mathbf{x} = \lambda\mathbf{x}.$$

Although we briefly looked at the eigenvalue problem in Section 3.4, our approach in this chapter will not depend on that material.

Eigenvalues and eigenvectors have many important applications, some of which are discussed in Section 7.4. For now we will give a geometric interpretation of the problem in R^2. If λ is an eigenvalue of a matrix A and $\mathbf{x}$ is an eigenvector of A corresponding to λ, then multiplication of $\mathbf{x}$ by the matrix A produces a vector $\lambda\mathbf{x}$ that is parallel to $\mathbf{x}$, as shown in Figure 7.1.

Figure 7.1

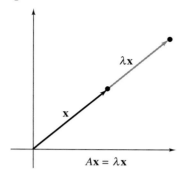

$$A\mathbf{x} = \lambda\mathbf{x}$$

Definition of Eigenvalue and Eigenvector	Let A be an $n \times n$ matrix. The scalar λ is called an **eigenvalue** of A if there is a *nonzero* vector $\mathbf{x}$ such that $$A\mathbf{x} = \lambda\mathbf{x}.$$ The vector $\mathbf{x}$ is called an **eigenvector** of A corresponding to λ.

In this chapter we are concerned only with real eigenvalues. In Chapter 8, we will discuss complex eigenvalues.

REMARK: Note that an eigen*vector* cannot be zero. Allowing $\mathbf{x}$ to be the zero vector would render the definition meaningless, because $A\mathbf{0} = \lambda\mathbf{0}$ is true for all real values of λ. An eigenvalue of $\lambda = 0$, however, is possible. (See Example 2.)

A matrix can have more than one eigenvalue, as demonstrated in Examples 1 and 2.

EXAMPLE 1   *Verifying Eigenvalues and Eigenvectors*

For the matrix

$$A = \begin{bmatrix} 2 & 0 \\ 0 & -1 \end{bmatrix},$$

verify that $\mathbf{x}_1 = (1, 0)$ is an eigenvector of A corresponding to the eigenvalue $\lambda_1 = 2$, and $\mathbf{x}_2 = (0, 1)$ is an eigenvector of A corresponding to the eigenvalue $\lambda_2 = -1$.

Solution   Multiplying $\mathbf{x}_1$ by A produces

$$A\mathbf{x}_1 = \begin{bmatrix} 2 & 0 \\ 0 & -1 \end{bmatrix}\begin{bmatrix} 1 \\ 0 \end{bmatrix}$$

$$= \begin{bmatrix} 2 \\ 0 \end{bmatrix}$$

$$= 2\begin{bmatrix} 1 \\ 0 \end{bmatrix}.$$

| Eigenvalue | Eigenvector |

Thus $\mathbf{x}_1 = (1, 0)$ is an eigenvector of A corresponding to the eigenvalue $\lambda_1 = 2$. Similarly, multiplying $\mathbf{x}_2$ by A produces

$$A\mathbf{x}_2 = \begin{bmatrix} 2 & 0 \\ 0 & -1 \end{bmatrix}\begin{bmatrix} 0 \\ 1 \end{bmatrix}$$

$$= \begin{bmatrix} 0 \\ -1 \end{bmatrix}$$

$$= -1\begin{bmatrix} 0 \\ 1 \end{bmatrix}.$$

Thus $\mathbf{x}_2 = (0, 1)$ is an eigenvector of A corresponding to the eigenvalue $\lambda_2 = -1$.

EXAMPLE 2   *Verifying Eigenvalues and Eigenvectors*

For the matrix

$$A = \begin{bmatrix} 1 & -2 & 1 \\ 0 & 0 & 0 \\ 0 & 1 & 1 \end{bmatrix},$$

verify that $\mathbf{x}_1 = (-3, -1, 1)$ and $\mathbf{x}_2 = (1, 0, 0)$ are eigenvectors of A and find their corresponding eigenvalues.

Solution   Multiplying $\mathbf{x}_1$ by A produces

$$A\mathbf{x}_1 = \begin{bmatrix} 1 & -2 & 1 \\ 0 & 0 & 0 \\ 0 & 1 & 1 \end{bmatrix}\begin{bmatrix} -3 \\ -1 \\ 1 \end{bmatrix} = \begin{bmatrix} 0 \\ 0 \\ 0 \end{bmatrix} = 0\begin{bmatrix} -3 \\ -1 \\ 1 \end{bmatrix}.$$

Thus $\mathbf{x}_1 = (-3, -1, 1)$ is an eigenvector of A corresponding to the eigenvalue $\lambda_1 = 0$. Similarly, multiplying $\mathbf{x}_2$ by A produces

$$A\mathbf{x}_2 = \begin{bmatrix} 1 & -2 & 1 \\ 0 & 0 & 0 \\ 0 & 1 & 1 \end{bmatrix} \begin{bmatrix} 1 \\ 0 \\ 0 \end{bmatrix} = \begin{bmatrix} 1 \\ 0 \\ 0 \end{bmatrix} = 1 \begin{bmatrix} 1 \\ 0 \\ 0 \end{bmatrix}.$$

Thus $\mathbf{x}_2 = (1, 0, 0)$ is an eigenvector of A corresponding to the eigenvalue $\lambda_2 = 1$.

Eigenspaces

DISCOVERY

In Example 2, $\lambda_2 = 1$ is an eigenvalue of the matrix A. Calculate the determinant of the matrix $A - \lambda_2 I$, where I is the 3×3 identity matrix. Repeat this experiment for the other eigenvalue, $\lambda_1 = 0$. In general, if λ is an eigenvalue of the matrix A, what is the value of $|A - \lambda I|$?

Although Examples 1 and 2 list only one eigenvector for each eigenvalue, each of the four eigenvalues in Examples 1 and 2 has an infinite number of eigenvectors. For instance, in Example 1 the vectors $(2, 0)$ and $(-3, 0)$ are eigenvectors of A corresponding to the eigenvalue 2. In fact, if A is an $n \times n$ matrix with an eigenvalue λ and a corresponding eigenvector $\mathbf{x}$, then every nonzero scalar multiple of $\mathbf{x}$ is also an eigenvector of A. This may be seen by letting c be a nonzero scalar, which then produces

$$A(c\mathbf{x}) = c(A\mathbf{x}) = c(\lambda\mathbf{x}) = \lambda(c\mathbf{x}).$$

It is also true that if $\mathbf{x}_1$ and $\mathbf{x}_2$ are eigenvectors corresponding to the *same* eigenvalue λ, then their sum is also an eigenvector corresponding to λ, because

$$A(\mathbf{x}_1 + \mathbf{x}_2) = A\mathbf{x}_1 + A\mathbf{x}_2 = \lambda\mathbf{x}_1 + \lambda\mathbf{x}_2 = \lambda(\mathbf{x}_1 + \mathbf{x}_2).$$

In other words, the set of all eigenvectors of a given eigenvalue λ, together with the zero vector, is a subspace of R^n. This special subspace of R^n is called the **eigenspace** of λ.

Theorem 7.1

Eigenvectors of λ Form a Subspace

If A is an $n \times n$ matrix with an eigenvalue λ, then the set of all eigenvectors of λ, together with the zero vector

$$\{\mathbf{0}\} \cup \{\mathbf{x}: \mathbf{x} \text{ is an eigenvector of } \lambda\},$$

is a subspace of R^n. We call this subspace the **eigenspace** of λ.

Determining the eigenvalues and corresponding eigenspaces for a matrix can be difficult. Occasionally, however, we can find eigenvalues and eigenspaces by simple inspection, as demonstrated in Example 3.

EXAMPLE 3   *An Example of Eigenspaces in the Plane*

Find the eigenvalues and corresponding eigenspaces of

$$A = \begin{bmatrix} -1 & 0 \\ 0 & 1 \end{bmatrix}.$$

Solution   Geometrically, multiplying a vector (x, y) in R^2 by the matrix A corresponds to a reflection in the y-axis. That is, if $\mathbf{v} = (x, y)$, then

$$A\mathbf{v} = \begin{bmatrix} -1 & 0 \\ 0 & 1 \end{bmatrix} \begin{bmatrix} x \\ y \end{bmatrix} = \begin{bmatrix} -x \\ y \end{bmatrix}.$$

Figure 7.2 illustrates that the only vectors reflected onto scalar multiples of themselves are those lying on either the x-axis or the y-axis.

Figure 7.2

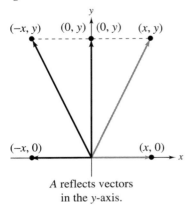

A reflects vectors in the y-axis.

For a Vector on the x-Axis

$$\begin{bmatrix} -1 & 0 \\ 0 & 1 \end{bmatrix} \begin{bmatrix} x \\ 0 \end{bmatrix} = \begin{bmatrix} -x \\ 0 \end{bmatrix} = -1 \begin{bmatrix} x \\ 0 \end{bmatrix}$$

Eigenvalue is $\lambda_1 = -1$

For a Vector on the y-Axis

$$\begin{bmatrix} -1 & 0 \\ 0 & 1 \end{bmatrix} \begin{bmatrix} 0 \\ y \end{bmatrix} = \begin{bmatrix} 0 \\ y \end{bmatrix} = 1 \begin{bmatrix} 0 \\ y \end{bmatrix}$$

Eigenvalue is $\lambda_2 = 1$

Thus the eigenvectors corresponding to $\lambda_1 = -1$ are the nonzero vectors on the x-axis, and the eigenvectors corresponding to $\lambda_2 = 1$ are the nonzero vectors on the y-axis. This implies that the eigenspace corresponding to $\lambda_1 = -1$ is the x-axis, and the eigenspace corresponding to $\lambda_2 = 1$ is the y-axis.

Finding Eigenvalues and Eigenvectors

The geometric solution given in Example 3 is not typical of the general eigenvalue problem. We now describe a general approach.

To find the eigenvalues and eigenvectors for an $n \times n$ matrix A, we let I be the $n \times n$ identity matrix. Writing the equation $A\mathbf{x} = \lambda\mathbf{x}$ in the form $\lambda I\mathbf{x} = A\mathbf{x}$ then produces

$$(\lambda I - A)\mathbf{x} = \mathbf{0}.$$

This homogeneous system of equations has nonzero solutions if and only if the coefficient matrix $(\lambda I - A)$ is *not* invertible—that is, if and only if the determinant of $(\lambda I - A)$ is zero. Thus we can establish the following theorem.

Theorem 7.2

Eigenvalues and Eigenvectors of a Matrix

Let A be an $n \times n$ matrix.
1. An eigenvalue of A is a scalar λ such that $\det(\lambda I - A) = 0$.
2. The eigenvectors of A corresponding to λ are the nonzero solutions of $(\lambda I - A)\mathbf{x} = \mathbf{0}$.

The equation $\det(\lambda I - A) = 0$ is called the **characteristic equation** of A. Moreover, when expanded to polynomial form, the polynomial

$$|\lambda I - A| = \lambda^n + c_{n-1}\lambda^{n-1} + \cdots + c_1\lambda + c_0$$

is called the **characteristic polynomial** of A. This definition tells us that the eigenvalues of an $n \times n$ matrix A correspond to the roots of the characteristic polynomial of A. Because the characteristic polynomial of A is of degree n, A can have at most n distinct eigenvalues.*

EXAMPLE 4   *Finding Eigenvalues and Eigenvectors*

Find the eigenvalues and corresponding eigenvectors of

$$A = \begin{bmatrix} 2 & -12 \\ 1 & -5 \end{bmatrix}.$$

Solution   The characteristic equation of A is

$$\begin{aligned}
|\lambda I - A| &= \begin{vmatrix} \lambda - 2 & 12 \\ -1 & \lambda + 5 \end{vmatrix} \\
&= (\lambda - 2)(\lambda + 5) - (-12) \\
&= \lambda^2 + 3\lambda - 10 + 12 \\
&= \lambda^2 + 3\lambda + 2 \\
&= (\lambda + 1)(\lambda + 2) = 0,
\end{aligned}$$

which gives $\lambda_1 = -1$ and $\lambda_2 = -2$ as the eigenvalues of A. To find the corresponding eigenvectors, we use Gauss-Jordan elimination to solve the homogeneous linear system given by $(\lambda I - A)\mathbf{x} = \mathbf{0}$ twice: first for $\lambda = \lambda_1 = -1$, and then for $\lambda = \lambda_2 = -2$. For $\lambda_1 = -1$, the coefficient matrix is

$$(-1)I - A = \begin{bmatrix} -1 - 2 & 12 \\ -1 & -1 + 5 \end{bmatrix} = \begin{bmatrix} -3 & 12 \\ -1 & 4 \end{bmatrix},$$

which row-reduces to

$$\begin{bmatrix} 1 & -4 \\ 0 & 0 \end{bmatrix}.$$

Therefore $x_1 - 4x_2 = 0$. Letting $x_2 = t$, we conclude that every eigenvector of λ_1 is of the form

$$\mathbf{x} = \begin{bmatrix} x_1 \\ x_2 \end{bmatrix} = \begin{bmatrix} 4t \\ t \end{bmatrix} = t \begin{bmatrix} 4 \\ 1 \end{bmatrix}, \quad t \neq 0.$$

For $\lambda_2 = -2$, we have

$$(-2)I - A = \begin{bmatrix} -2 - 2 & 12 \\ -1 & -2 + 5 \end{bmatrix} = \begin{bmatrix} -4 & 12 \\ -1 & 3 \end{bmatrix} \longrightarrow \begin{bmatrix} 1 & -3 \\ 0 & 0 \end{bmatrix}.$$

---

*The Fundamental Theorem of Algebra states that an nth-degree polynomial has precisely n roots. These n roots however, include both repeated and complex roots. In this chapter we are concerned only with the real roots of characteristic polynomials—that is, real eigenvalues. (In Chapter 8, we discuss complex eigenvalues.)

Letting $x_2 = t$, we conclude that every eigenvector of λ_2 is of the form

$$\mathbf{x} = \begin{bmatrix} x_1 \\ x_2 \end{bmatrix} = \begin{bmatrix} 3t \\ t \end{bmatrix} = t \begin{bmatrix} 3 \\ 1 \end{bmatrix}, \quad t \neq 0.$$

Try checking that $A\mathbf{x} = \lambda_i \mathbf{x}$ for the eigenvalues and eigenvectors found in this example.

The homogeneous systems that arise when we are finding eigenvectors will always row-reduce to a matrix having at least one row of zeros, since the system must have nontrivial solutions. The steps used to find the eigenvalues and corresponding eigenvectors of a matrix are summarized as follows.

Finding Eigenvalues and Eigenvectors

Let A be an $n \times n$ matrix.

1. Form the characteristic equation $|\lambda I - A| = 0$. It will be a polynomial equation of degree n in the variable λ.
2. Find the real roots of the characteristic equation. These are the eigenvalues of A.
3. For each eigenvalue λ_i, find the eigenvectors corresponding to λ_i by solving the homogeneous system $(\lambda_i I - A)\mathbf{x} = \mathbf{0}$. This requires row-reducing an $n \times n$ matrix. The resulting reduced row-echelon form must have at least one row of zeros.

Finding the eigenvalues for an $n \times n$ matrix can be difficult because it involves the factorization of an nth-degree polynomial. Once an eigenvalue has been found, however, finding the corresponding eigenvectors is a straightforward application of Gauss-Jordan reduction.

EXAMPLE 5   *Finding Eigenvalues and Eigenvectors*

Find the eigenvalues and corresponding eigenvectors for

$$A = \begin{bmatrix} 2 & 1 & 0 \\ 0 & 2 & 0 \\ 0 & 0 & 2 \end{bmatrix}.$$

What is the dimension of the eigenspace of each eigenvalue?

Solution   The characteristic equation of A is

$$|\lambda I - A| = \begin{vmatrix} \lambda - 2 & -1 & 0 \\ 0 & \lambda - 2 & 0 \\ 0 & 0 & \lambda - 2 \end{vmatrix} = (\lambda - 2)^3 = 0.$$

Thus the only eigenvalue is $\lambda = 2$. To find the eigenvectors for $\lambda = 2$, we solve the homogeneous linear system represented by $(2I - A)\mathbf{x} = \mathbf{0}$.

$$2I - A = \begin{bmatrix} 0 & -1 & 0 \\ 0 & 0 & 0 \\ 0 & 0 & 0 \end{bmatrix}$$

This implies that $x_2 = 0$. Using the parameters $s = x_1$ and $t = x_3$, we find that the eigen-vectors of $\lambda = 2$ are of the form

$$\mathbf{x} = \begin{bmatrix} x_1 \\ x_2 \\ x_3 \end{bmatrix} = \begin{bmatrix} s \\ 0 \\ t \end{bmatrix} = s \begin{bmatrix} 1 \\ 0 \\ 0 \end{bmatrix} + t \begin{bmatrix} 0 \\ 0 \\ 1 \end{bmatrix}, \quad s \text{ and } t \text{ are not both zero.}$$

Since $\lambda = 2$ has two linearly independent eigenvectors, the dimension of its eigenspace is 2.

If an eigenvalue λ_1 occurs as a *multiple root* (k times) for the characteristic polynomial, then we say that λ_1 has **multiplicity** k. This implies that $(\lambda - \lambda_1)^k$ is a factor of the characteristic polynomial and $(\lambda - \lambda_1)^{k+1}$ is not a factor of the characteristic polynomial. For instance, in Example 5 the eigenvalue $\lambda = 2$ has a multiplicity of 3.

Note also that in Example 5 the dimension of the eigenspace of $\lambda = 2$ is 2. In general, the multiplicity of an eigenvalue is greater than or equal to the dimension of its eigenspace.

EXAMPLE 6   ***Finding Eigenvalues and Eigenvectors***

Find the eigenvalues of

$$A = \begin{bmatrix} 1 & 0 & 0 & 0 \\ 0 & 1 & 5 & -10 \\ 1 & 0 & 2 & 0 \\ 1 & 0 & 0 & 3 \end{bmatrix}$$

and find a basis for each of the corresponding eigenspaces.

Solution   The characteristic equation of A is

$$|\lambda I - A| = \begin{vmatrix} \lambda - 1 & 0 & 0 & 0 \\ 0 & \lambda - 1 & -5 & 10 \\ -1 & 0 & \lambda - 2 & 0 \\ -1 & 0 & 0 & \lambda - 3 \end{vmatrix}$$

$$= (\lambda - 1)^2(\lambda - 2)(\lambda - 3) = 0.$$

Thus the eigenvalues are $\lambda_1 = 1$, $\lambda_2 = 2$, and $\lambda_3 = 3$. (Note that $\lambda_1 = 1$ has a multiplicity of 2.) We find a basis for the eigenspace of $\lambda_1 = 1$ as follows.

$$(1)I - A = \begin{bmatrix} 0 & 0 & 0 & 0 \\ 0 & 0 & -5 & 10 \\ -1 & 0 & -1 & 0 \\ -1 & 0 & 0 & -2 \end{bmatrix} \longrightarrow \begin{bmatrix} 1 & 0 & 0 & 2 \\ 0 & 0 & 1 & -2 \\ 0 & 0 & 0 & 0 \\ 0 & 0 & 0 & 0 \end{bmatrix}$$

Letting $s = x_2$ and $t = x_4$ produces

$$\mathbf{x} = \begin{bmatrix} x_1 \\ x_2 \\ x_3 \\ x_4 \end{bmatrix} = \begin{bmatrix} 0s - 2t \\ s + 0t \\ 0s + 2t \\ 0s + t \end{bmatrix} = s \begin{bmatrix} 0 \\ 1 \\ 0 \\ 0 \end{bmatrix} + t \begin{bmatrix} -2 \\ 0 \\ 2 \\ 1 \end{bmatrix}.$$

Therefore a basis for the eigenspace corresponding to $\lambda_1 = 1$ is

$$B_1 = \{(0, 1, 0, 0), (-2, 0, 2, 1)\}. \qquad \textbf{Basis for } \lambda_1 = 1$$

For $\lambda_2 = 2$ and $\lambda_3 = 3$, we follow the same pattern to obtain the eigenspace bases

$$B_2 = \{(0, 5, 1, 0)\} \qquad \textbf{Basis for } \lambda_2 = 2$$

$$B_3 = \{(0, -5, 0, 1)\}. \qquad \textbf{Basis for } \lambda_3 = 3$$

Finding eigenvalues and eigenvectors for matrices of order $n \geq 4$ can be tedious. Moreover, the procedure followed in Example 6 is generally inefficient when used on a computer because root-finding on a computer is both time consuming and subject to round-off error. Consequently, some numerical methods for approximating the eigenvalues of large matrices are included in Chapter 10.

TECHNOLOGY NOTE

Many computers and graphing calculators have built-in programs to approximate the eigenvalues and eigenvectors of an $n \times n$ matrix. If you enter the matrix A from Example 6, you should obtain the four eigenvalues

$$\{1 \quad 1 \quad 2 \quad 3\}.$$

Your computer or graphing calculator should also be able to produce a matrix in which the columns are the corresponding eigenvectors.

There are a few types of matrices for which eigenvalues are easy to find. The following theorem says that the eigenvalues of an $n \times n$ triangular matrix are the entries on the main diagonal. Its proof follows from the fact that the determinant of a triangular matrix is the product of its diagonal elements.

Theorem 7.3

Eigenvalues for Triangular Matrices

If A is an $n \times n$ triangular matrix, then its eigenvalues are the entries on its main diagonal.

EXAMPLE 7   *Finding Eigenvalues for Diagonal and Triangular Matrices*

Find the eigenvalues for the following matrices.

(a) $A = \begin{bmatrix} 2 & 0 & 0 \\ -1 & 1 & 0 \\ 5 & 3 & -3 \end{bmatrix}$ (b) $A = \begin{bmatrix} -1 & 0 & 0 & 0 & 0 \\ 0 & 2 & 0 & 0 & 0 \\ 0 & 0 & 0 & 0 & 0 \\ 0 & 0 & 0 & -4 & 0 \\ 0 & 0 & 0 & 0 & 3 \end{bmatrix}$

Solution   (a) Without using Theorem 7.3, we find that

$$|\lambda I - A| = \begin{vmatrix} \lambda - 2 & 0 & 0 \\ 1 & \lambda - 1 & 0 \\ -5 & -3 & \lambda + 3 \end{vmatrix}$$

$$= (\lambda - 2)(\lambda - 1)(\lambda + 3).$$

Thus the eigenvalues are $\lambda_1 = 2$, $\lambda_2 = 1$, and $\lambda_3 = -3$, which are simply the main diagonal entries of A.

(b) In this case, we use Theorem 7.3 to conclude that the eigenvalues are the main diagonal entries $\lambda_1 = -1$, $\lambda_2 = 2$, $\lambda_3 = 0$, $\lambda_4 = -4$, and $\lambda_5 = 3$.

Eigenvalues and Eigenvectors of Linear Transformations

We began this section by defining eigenvalues and eigenvectors in terms of matrices. We could, however, have defined them in terms of linear transformations. A number λ is called an **eigenvalue** of a linear transformation $T: V \rightarrow V$ if there is a nonzero vector $\mathbf{x}$ such that $T(\mathbf{x}) = \lambda \mathbf{x}$. The vector $\mathbf{x}$ is called an **eigenvector** of T corresponding to λ, and the set of all eigenvectors of λ (with the zero vector) is called the **eigenspace** of λ.

Consider the linear transformation $T: R^3 \rightarrow R^3$, whose matrix relative to the standard basis is

$$A = \begin{bmatrix} 1 & 3 & 0 \\ 3 & 1 & 0 \\ 0 & 0 & -2 \end{bmatrix}.$$ **Standard basis:**
$B = \{(1, 0, 0), (0, 1, 0), (0, 0, 1)\}$

In Example 5 of Section 6.4 we found that the matrix of T relative to the basis B' is the diagonal matrix

$$A' = \begin{bmatrix} 4 & 0 & 0 \\ 0 & -2 & 0 \\ 0 & 0 & -2 \end{bmatrix}.$$ **Nonstandard basis:**
$B' = \{(1, 1, 0), (0, -1, 0), (0, 0, 1)\}$

The question now is this: "For a given transformation T, can we find a basis B' whose corresponding matrix is diagonal?" The next example gives an indication of the answer.

EXAMPLE 8   *Finding Eigenvalues and Eigenspaces*

Find the eigenvalues and corresponding eigenspaces of

$$A = \begin{bmatrix} 1 & 3 & 0 \\ 3 & 1 & 0 \\ 0 & 0 & -2 \end{bmatrix}.$$

Solution   Since

$$|\lambda I - A| = \begin{vmatrix} \lambda - 1 & -3 & 0 \\ -3 & \lambda - 1 & 0 \\ 0 & 0 & \lambda + 2 \end{vmatrix}$$

$$= (\lambda + 2)[(\lambda - 1)^2 - 9]$$

$$= (\lambda + 2)(\lambda^2 - 2\lambda - 8) = (\lambda + 2)^2(\lambda - 4),$$

the eigenvalues of A are $\lambda_1 = 4$ and $\lambda_2 = -2$. The eigenspaces for these two eigenvalues are as follows.

$$B_1 = \{(1, 1, 0)\} \qquad \text{**Basis for } \lambda_1 = 4\text{**}$$

$$B_2 = \{(1, -1, 0), (0, 0, 1)\} \qquad \text{**Basis for } \lambda_2 = -2\text{**}$$

Example 8 illustrates two important and perhaps surprising results.

1. Let $T: R^3 \rightarrow R^3$ be the linear transformation whose standard matrix is A, and let B' be the basis of R^3 made up of the three linearly independent eigenvectors found in Example 8. Then A', the matrix of T relative to the basis B', is diagonal.

$$A' = \begin{bmatrix} 4 & 0 & 0 \\ 0 & -2 & 0 \\ 0 & 0 & -2 \end{bmatrix}$$

Nonstandard basis:
$$B' = \{(1, 1, 0), (0, -1, 0), (0, 0, 1)\}$$

Eigenvalues of A Eigenvectors of A

2. The main diagonal entries of the matrix A' are the eigenvalues of A.

The next section formalizes these two results and also characterizes linear transformations that can be represented by diagonal matrices.

SECTION 7.1 ☐ EXERCISES

In Exercises 1–8, verify that λ_i is an eigenvalue of A and that $\mathbf{x}_i$ is a corresponding eigenvector.

1. $A = \begin{bmatrix} 0 & 1 \\ 1 & 0 \end{bmatrix}$, $\lambda_1 = 1,\ \mathbf{x}_1 = (1, 1)$
   $\lambda_2 = -1,\ \mathbf{x}_2 = (1, -1)$

2. $A = \begin{bmatrix} 1 & 0 \\ 0 & -1 \end{bmatrix}$, $\lambda_1 = 1,\ \mathbf{x}_1 = (1, 0)$
   $\lambda_2 = -1,\ \mathbf{x}_2 = (0, 1)$

3. $A = \begin{bmatrix} 1 & k \\ 0 & -1 \end{bmatrix}$, $\lambda_1 = 1, \mathbf{x}_1 = (1, 0)$

4. $A = \begin{bmatrix} 4 & -5 \\ 2 & -3 \end{bmatrix}$, $\lambda_1 = -1,\ \mathbf{x}_1 = (1, 1)$
   $\lambda_2 = 2,\ \mathbf{x}_2 = (5, 2)$

5. $A = \begin{bmatrix} 1 & 1 \\ 1 & 1 \end{bmatrix}$, $\lambda_1 = 0,\ \mathbf{x}_1 = (1, -1)$
   $\lambda_2 = 2,\ \mathbf{x}_2 = (1, 1)$

6. $A = \begin{bmatrix} 2 & 3 & 1 \\ 0 & -1 & 2 \\ 0 & 0 & 3 \end{bmatrix}$, $\lambda_1 = 2,\ \mathbf{x}_1 = (1, 0, 0)$
   $\lambda_2 = -1,\ \mathbf{x}_2 = (1, -1, 0)$
   $\lambda_3 = 3,\ \mathbf{x}_3 = (5, 1, 2)$

7. $A = \begin{bmatrix} -2 & 2 & -3 \\ 2 & 1 & -6 \\ -1 & -2 & 0 \end{bmatrix}$, $\lambda_1 = 5,\ \mathbf{x}_1 = (1, 2, -1)$
   $\lambda_2 = -3,\ \mathbf{x}_2 = (-2, 1, 0)$
   $\lambda_3 = -3,\ \mathbf{x}_3 = (3, 0, 1)$

8. $A = \begin{bmatrix} 0 & 1 & 0 \\ 0 & 0 & 1 \\ 1 & 0 & 0 \end{bmatrix}$, $\lambda_1 = 1, \mathbf{x}_1 = (1, 1, 1)$

9. Use A, λ_i, and $\mathbf{x}_i$ from Exercise 5 for the following.
   (a) Show that $A(c\mathbf{x}_1) = 0(c\mathbf{x}_1)$ for any real number c.
   (b) Show that $A(c\mathbf{x}_2) = 2(c\mathbf{x}_2)$ for any real number c.

10. Use A, λ_i, and $\mathbf{x}_i$ from Exercise 6 for the following.
   (a) Show that $A(c\mathbf{x}_1) = 2(c\mathbf{x}_1)$ for any real number c.
   (b) Show that $A(c\mathbf{x}_2) = -(c\mathbf{x}_2)$ for any real number c.
   (c) Show that $A(c\mathbf{x}_3) = 3(c\mathbf{x}_3)$ for any real number c.

In Exercises 11–14, determine whether $\mathbf{x}$ is an eigenvector of A.

11. $A = \begin{bmatrix} 7 & 2 \\ 2 & 4 \end{bmatrix}$
   (a) $\mathbf{x} = (1, 2)$
   (b) $\mathbf{x} = (2, 1)$
   (c) $\mathbf{x} = (1, -2)$
   (d) $\mathbf{x} = (-1, 0)$

12. $A = \begin{bmatrix} -3 & 10 \\ 5 & 2 \end{bmatrix}$
   (a) $\mathbf{x} = (4, 4)$
   (b) $\mathbf{x} = (-8, 4)$
   (c) $\mathbf{x} = (-4, 8)$
   (d) $\mathbf{x} = (5, -3)$

13. $A = \begin{bmatrix} -1 & -1 & 1 \\ -2 & 0 & -2 \\ 3 & -3 & 1 \end{bmatrix}$
   (a) $\mathbf{x} = (2, -4, 6)$
   (b) $\mathbf{x} = (2, 0, 6)$
   (c) $\mathbf{x} = (2, 2, 0)$
   (d) $\mathbf{x} = (-1, 0, 1)$

14. $A = \begin{bmatrix} 1 & 0 & 5 \\ 0 & -2 & 4 \\ 1 & -2 & 9 \end{bmatrix}$
   (a) $\mathbf{x} = (1, 1, 0)$
   (b) $\mathbf{x} = (-5, 2, 1)$
   (c) $\mathbf{x} = (0, 0, 0)$
   (d) $\mathbf{x} = (2\sqrt{6} - 3, -2\sqrt{6} + 6, 3)$

In Exercises 15–30, find (a) the characteristic equation and (b) the eigenvalues (and corresponding eigenvectors) of the matrix.

15. $\begin{bmatrix} 2 & 1 \\ 0 & 3 \end{bmatrix}$

16. $\begin{bmatrix} 1 & -4 \\ -2 & 8 \end{bmatrix}$

17. $\begin{bmatrix} 6 & -3 \\ -2 & 1 \end{bmatrix}$

18. $\begin{bmatrix} 1 & 3 \\ 2 & 0 \end{bmatrix}$

19. $\begin{bmatrix} 2 & 3 \\ 1 & 4 \end{bmatrix}$

20. $\begin{bmatrix} 4 & 0 \\ 3 & -4 \end{bmatrix}$

21. $\begin{bmatrix} 2 & 0 & 1 \\ 0 & 3 & 4 \\ 0 & 0 & 1 \end{bmatrix}$

22. $\begin{bmatrix} -5 & 0 & 0 \\ 3 & 7 & 0 \\ 4 & -2 & 3 \end{bmatrix}$

23. $\begin{bmatrix} 1 & 2 & -2 \\ -2 & 5 & -2 \\ -6 & 6 & -3 \end{bmatrix}$

24. $\begin{bmatrix} 3 & 2 & -3 \\ -3 & -4 & 9 \\ -1 & -2 & 5 \end{bmatrix}$

25. $\begin{bmatrix} 1 & -2 & 1 \\ 0 & 1 & 4 \\ 0 & 0 & 2 \end{bmatrix}$

26. $\begin{bmatrix} 2 & 1 & -1 \\ 0 & -1 & 2 \\ 0 & 0 & -1 \end{bmatrix}$

27. $\begin{bmatrix} 0 & -3 & 5 \\ -4 & 4 & -10 \\ 0 & 0 & 4 \end{bmatrix}$

28. $\begin{bmatrix} 1 & -\frac{3}{2} & \frac{5}{2} \\ -2 & \frac{13}{2} & -10 \\ \frac{3}{2} & -\frac{9}{2} & 8 \end{bmatrix}$

29. $\begin{bmatrix} 1 & 0 & -1 & 1 \\ 0 & 1 & 0 & 1 \\ -2 & 0 & 2 & -2 \\ 0 & 2 & 0 & 2 \end{bmatrix}$ **30.** $\begin{bmatrix} 1 & -3 & 3 & 3 \\ -1 & 4 & -3 & -3 \\ -2 & 0 & 1 & 1 \\ 1 & 0 & 0 & 0 \end{bmatrix}$

In Exercises 31–34, demonstrate the Cayley-Hamilton Theorem for the given matrix. The **Cayley-Hamilton Theorem** states that a matrix satisfies its characteristic equation. For example, the characteristic equation of

$$A = \begin{bmatrix} 1 & -3 \\ 2 & 5 \end{bmatrix}$$

is $\lambda^2 - 6\lambda + 11 = 0$, and therefore, by the theorem, we have $A^2 - 6A + 11I_2 = O$.

31. $\begin{bmatrix} 4 & 0 \\ -3 & 2 \end{bmatrix}$ **32.** $\begin{bmatrix} 6 & -1 \\ 1 & 5 \end{bmatrix}$

33. $\begin{bmatrix} 1 & 0 & -4 \\ 0 & 3 & 1 \\ 2 & 0 & 1 \end{bmatrix}$ **34.** $\begin{bmatrix} -3 & 1 & 0 \\ -1 & 3 & 2 \\ 0 & 4 & 3 \end{bmatrix}$

35. Use the following computational checks on the eigenvalues found in Exercises 15–30.

(a) The sum of the n eigenvalues equals the sum of the diagonal entries of the matrix. (This sum is called the **trace** of A.)

(b) The product of the n eigenvalues equals $|A|$.

(If λ is an eigenvalue of multiplicity k, remember to enter it k times in the sum or product of these checks.)

36. Prove that $\lambda = 0$ is an eigenvalue of A if and only if A is singular.

▶ **37.** For an invertible matrix A, prove that A and A^{-1} have the same eigenvectors. How are the eigenvalues of A related to the eigenvalues of A^{-1}?

▶ **38.** Prove that A and A^T have the same eigenvalues. Are the eigenspaces the same?

39. Prove that the constant term of the characteristic polynomial is $\pm |A|$.

40. Let $T: R^2 \rightarrow R^2$ be given by $T(\mathbf{v}) = \text{proj}_{\mathbf{u}}\mathbf{v}$, where $\mathbf{u}$ is a fixed vector in R^2. Show that the eigenvalues of A (the standard matrix of T) are 0 and 1.

41. Prove that a triangular matrix is nonsingular if and only if its eigenvalues are real and nonzero.

42. Prove that if $A^2 = O$, then 0 is the only eigenvalue of A.

43. If the eigenvalues of

$$A = \begin{bmatrix} a & b \\ 0 & d \end{bmatrix}$$

are $\lambda_1 = 0$ and $\lambda_2 = 1$, what are the possible values of a and d?

44. Show that

$$A = \begin{bmatrix} 0 & 1 \\ -1 & 0 \end{bmatrix}$$

has no real eigenvalues.

In Exercises 45–48, find the dimension of the eigenspace corresponding to the eigenvalue 3.

45. $A = \begin{bmatrix} 3 & 0 & 0 \\ 0 & 3 & 0 \\ 0 & 0 & 3 \end{bmatrix}$ **46.** $A = \begin{bmatrix} 3 & 1 & 0 \\ 0 & 3 & 0 \\ 0 & 0 & 3 \end{bmatrix}$

47. $A = \begin{bmatrix} 3 & 1 & 0 \\ 0 & 3 & 1 \\ 0 & 0 & 3 \end{bmatrix}$ **48.** $A = \begin{bmatrix} 3 & 1 & 1 \\ 0 & 3 & 1 \\ 0 & 0 & 3 \end{bmatrix}$

49. (Calculus) Let $T: C'[0, 1] \rightarrow C[0, 1]$ be given by $T(\mathbf{f}) = \mathbf{f}'$. Show that $\lambda = 1$ is an eigenvalue of $f(x) = e^x$.

50. (Calculus) For the linear transformation given in Exercise 49, find the eigenvalue corresponding to the eigenvector $f(x) = e^{-2x}$.

51. Let $T: P_2 \rightarrow P_2$ be given by

$$T(a_0 + a_1x + a_2x^2) = (-3a_1 + 5a_2)$$
$$+ (-4a_0 + 4a_1 - 10a_2)x + 4a_2x^2.$$

Find the eigenvalues and the eigenvectors of T relative to the standard basis $\{1, x, x^2\}$.

52. Let $T: P_2 \rightarrow P_2$ be given by

$$T(a_0 + a_1x + a_2x^2) = (2a_0 + a_1 - a_2)$$
$$+ (-a_1 + 2a_2)x - a_2x^2.$$

Find the eigenvalues and eigenvectors of T relative to the standard basis $\{1, x, x^2\}$.

53. Let $T: M_{2,2} \rightarrow M_{2,2}$ be given by

$$T\left(\begin{bmatrix} a & b \\ c & d \end{bmatrix}\right) = \begin{bmatrix} a - c + d & b + d \\ -2a + 2c - 2d & 2b + 2d \end{bmatrix}.$$

Find the eigenvalues and eigenvectors of T relative to the standard basis

$$B = \left\{\begin{bmatrix} 1 & 0 \\ 0 & 0 \end{bmatrix}, \begin{bmatrix} 0 & 1 \\ 0 & 0 \end{bmatrix}, \begin{bmatrix} 0 & 0 \\ 1 & 0 \end{bmatrix}, \begin{bmatrix} 0 & 0 \\ 0 & 1 \end{bmatrix}\right\}.$$

54. A square matrix A is called **idempotent** if $A^2 = A$. What are the possible eigenvalues of an idempotent matrix?

55. A square matrix A is called **nilpotent** if there exists a positive integer k such that $A^k = 0$. What are the possible eigenvalues of a nilpotent matrix?

56. Find all values of the angle θ for which the matrix
$$A = \begin{bmatrix} \cos\theta & -\sin\theta \\ \sin\theta & \cos\theta \end{bmatrix}$$
has real eigenvalues. Interpret your answer geometrically.

57. Let A be an $n \times n$ matrix such that the sum of the entries in each row is a fixed constant r. Prove that r is an eigenvalue of A. Illustrate this result with a particular example.

7.2 DIAGONALIZATION

The previous section discussed the *eigenvalue* problem. In this section we look at another classic problem in linear algebra called the **diagonalization problem.** Expressed in terms of matrices,* the problem is this: For a square matrix A, does there exist an invertible matrix P such that $P^{-1}AP$ is diagonal?

Recall from Section 6.4 that two square matrices A and B are called **similar** if there exists an invertible matrix P such that

$$B = P^{-1}AP.$$

Matrices that are similar to diagonal matrices are called **diagonalizable.**

Definition of a Diagonalizable Matrix

An $n \times n$ matrix A is **diagonalizable** if A is similar to a diagonal matrix. That is, A is diagonalizable if there exists an invertible matrix P such that

$$P^{-1}AP$$

is a diagonal matrix.

Given this definition, the diagonalization problem can be stated as follows. Which square matrices are diagonalizable? Clearly, every diagonal matrix D is diagonalizable, since the identity matrix I can play the role of P to give $D = I^{-1}DI$. Example 1 shows another example of a diagonalizable matrix.

EXAMPLE 1   *A Diagonalizable Matrix*

The matrix from Example 5 of Section 6.4,

$$A = \begin{bmatrix} 1 & 3 & 0 \\ 3 & 1 & 0 \\ 0 & 0 & -2 \end{bmatrix},$$

---

* At the end of this section, we consider the diagonalization problem expressed in terms of linear transformations.

is diagonalizable, since

$$P = \begin{bmatrix} 1 & 1 & 0 \\ 1 & -1 & 0 \\ 0 & 0 & 1 \end{bmatrix}$$

has the property that

$$P^{-1}AP = \begin{bmatrix} 4 & 0 & 0 \\ 0 & -2 & 0 \\ 0 & 0 & -2 \end{bmatrix}.$$

As indicated in Example 8 of the previous section, the eigenvalue problem is related closely to the diagonalization problem. The next two theorems shed more light on this relationship. The first theorem tells us that similar matrices must have the same eigenvalues.

Theorem 7.4

Similar Matrices Have the Same Eigenvalues

If A and B are similar $n \times n$ matrices, then they have the same eigenvalues.

Proof   Since A and B are similar, there exists an invertible matrix P such that $B = P^{-1}AP$. By the properties of determinants, it follows that

$$|\lambda I - B| = |\lambda I - P^{-1}AP| = |P^{-1}\lambda IP - P^{-1}AP|$$

$$= |P^{-1}(\lambda I - A)P|$$

$$= |P^{-1}| \, |\lambda I - A| \, |P|$$

$$= |P^{-1}| \, |P| \, |\lambda I - A|$$

$$= |P^{-1}P| \, |\lambda I - A|$$

$$= |\lambda I - A|.$$

But this means that A and B have the same characteristic polynomial. Hence they must have the same eigenvalues.

EXAMPLE 2   *Finding Eigenvalues of Similar Matrices*

The following matrices are similar.

$$A = \begin{bmatrix} 1 & 0 & 0 \\ -1 & 1 & 1 \\ -1 & -2 & 4 \end{bmatrix} \quad \text{and} \quad D = \begin{bmatrix} 1 & 0 & 0 \\ 0 & 2 & 0 \\ 0 & 0 & 3 \end{bmatrix}$$

Use Theorem 7.4 to find the eigenvalues of A and D.

Solution   Since D is a diagonal matrix, its eigenvalues are simply the entries on its main diagonal—that is,

$$\lambda_1 = 1, \quad \lambda_2 = 2, \quad \lambda_3 = 3.$$

Moreover, since A is given to be similar to D, we know from Theorem 7.4 that A has the same eigenvalues. This can be checked by showing that the characteristic polynomial for A is

$$|\lambda I - A| = (\lambda - 1)(\lambda - 2)(\lambda - 3).$$

REMARK: Example 2 simply states that the matrices A and D are similar. Try checking that $D = P^{-1}AP$ using the matrices

$$P = \begin{bmatrix} 1 & 0 & 0 \\ 1 & 1 & 1 \\ 1 & 1 & 2 \end{bmatrix} \quad \text{and} \quad P^{-1} = \begin{bmatrix} 1 & 0 & 0 \\ -1 & 2 & -1 \\ 0 & -1 & 1 \end{bmatrix}.$$

In fact, the columns of P are precisely the eigenvectors of A corresponding to the eigenvalues 1, 2, and 3.

The two diagonalizable matrices given in Examples 1 and 2 provide a clue to the diagonalization problem. Both matrices possess a set of three linearly independent eigenvectors. (See Example 3.) This is characteristic of diagonalizable matrices, as stated in the following important theorem.

Theorem 7.5 Condition for Diagonalization	An $n \times n$ matrix A is diagonalizable if and only if it has n linearly independent eigenvectors.

Proof   First we assume that A is diagonalizable. Then there exists an invertible matrix P such that $P^{-1}AP = D$ is diagonal. Letting the main entries of D be $\lambda_1, \lambda_2, \ldots, \lambda_n$ and the column vectors of P be $\mathbf{p}_1, \mathbf{p}_2, \ldots, \mathbf{p}_n$ produces

$$PD = [\mathbf{p}_1 \vdots \mathbf{p}_2 \vdots \ldots \vdots \mathbf{p}_n] \begin{bmatrix} \lambda_1 & 0 & \cdots & 0 \\ 0 & \lambda_2 & \cdots & 0 \\ \vdots & \vdots & & \vdots \\ 0 & 0 & \cdots & \lambda_n \end{bmatrix}$$

$$= [\lambda_1 \mathbf{p}_1 \vdots \lambda_2 \mathbf{p}_2 \vdots \ldots \vdots \lambda_n \mathbf{p}_n].$$

But since $AP = [A\mathbf{p}_1 \vdots A\mathbf{p}_2 \vdots \ldots \vdots A\mathbf{p}_n]$ and $P^{-1}AP = D$, we have $AP = PD$, which implies that

$$[A\mathbf{p}_1 \vdots A\mathbf{p}_2 \vdots \ldots \vdots A\mathbf{p}_n] = [\lambda_1\mathbf{p}_1 \vdots \lambda_2\mathbf{p}_2 \vdots \ldots \vdots \lambda_n\mathbf{p}_n].$$

In other words, $A\mathbf{p}_i = \lambda_i\mathbf{p}_i$ for each column vector $\mathbf{p}_i$. This means that the column vectors $\mathbf{p}_i$ of P are eigenvectors of A. Moreover, since P is invertible, its column vectors are linearly independent. Thus A has n linearly independent eigenvectors.

Conversely, assume A has n linearly independent eigenvectors $\mathbf{p}_1, \mathbf{p}_2, \ldots, \mathbf{p}_n$ with corresponding eigenvalues $\lambda_1, \lambda_2, \ldots, \lambda_n$. We let P be the matrix whose columns are these n eigenvectors. That is, $P = [\mathbf{p}_1 \vdots \mathbf{p}_2 \vdots \ldots \vdots \mathbf{p}_n]$. Since each $\mathbf{p}_i$ is an eigenvector of A, we have $A\mathbf{p}_i = \lambda_i\mathbf{p}_i$ and

$$AP = A[\mathbf{p}_1 \vdots \mathbf{p}_2 \vdots \ldots \vdots \mathbf{p}_n] = [\lambda_1\mathbf{p}_1 \vdots \lambda_2\mathbf{p}_2 \vdots \ldots \vdots \lambda_n\mathbf{p}_n].$$

The right-hand matrix in this equation can be written as the following matrix product.

$$AP = [\mathbf{p}_1 \vdots \mathbf{p}_2 \vdots \ldots \vdots \mathbf{p}_n]\begin{bmatrix} \lambda_1 & 0 & \cdots & 0 \\ 0 & \lambda_2 & \cdots & 0 \\ \vdots & \vdots & & \vdots \\ 0 & 0 & \cdots & \lambda_n \end{bmatrix} = PD$$

Finally, since the vectors $\mathbf{p}_1, \mathbf{p}_2, \ldots, \mathbf{p}_n$ are linearly independent, P is invertible and we can write the equation $AP = PD$ as $P^{-1}AP = D$, which means that A is diagonalizable.

A key result from this proof is the fact that for diagonalizable matrices, *the columns of P consist of the n linearly independent eigenvectors.* The following example verifies this important property for the matrices from Examples 1 and 2.

EXAMPLE 3   *Diagonalizable Matrices*

(a) The matrix in Example 1 has the following eigenvalues and corresponding eigenvectors.

$$\lambda_1 = 4, \mathbf{p}_1 = \begin{bmatrix} 1 \\ 1 \\ 0 \end{bmatrix}; \quad \lambda_2 = -2, \mathbf{p}_2 = \begin{bmatrix} 1 \\ -1 \\ 0 \end{bmatrix}; \quad \lambda_3 = -2, \mathbf{p}_3 = \begin{bmatrix} 0 \\ 0 \\ 1 \end{bmatrix}$$

The matrix P whose columns correspond to these eigenvectors is

$$P = \begin{bmatrix} 1 & 1 & 0 \\ 1 & -1 & 0 \\ 0 & 0 & 1 \end{bmatrix}.$$

Moreover, since P is row-equivalent to the identity matrix, the eigenvectors $\mathbf{p}_1, \mathbf{p}_2,$ and $\mathbf{p}_3$ are linearly independent.

(b) The matrix in Example 2 has the following eigenvalues and corresponding eigenvectors.

$$\lambda_1 = 1, \mathbf{p}_1 = \begin{bmatrix} 1 \\ 1 \\ 1 \end{bmatrix}; \quad \lambda_2 = 2, \mathbf{p}_2 = \begin{bmatrix} 0 \\ 1 \\ 1 \end{bmatrix}; \quad \lambda_3 = 3, \mathbf{p}_3 = \begin{bmatrix} 0 \\ 1 \\ 2 \end{bmatrix}$$

The matrix P whose columns correspond to these eigenvectors is

$$P = \begin{bmatrix} 1 & 0 & 0 \\ 1 & 1 & 1 \\ 1 & 1 & 2 \end{bmatrix}.$$

Again, since P is row-equivalent to the identity matrix, the eigenvectors $\mathbf{p}_1$, $\mathbf{p}_2$, and $\mathbf{p}_3$ are linearly independent.

The second part of the proof of Theorem 7.5 and Example 3 suggest the following steps for diagonalizing a matrix.

Steps for Diagonalizing an $n \times n$ Square Matrix

Let A be an $n \times n$ matrix.
1. Find n linearly independent eigenvectors $\mathbf{p}_1$, $\mathbf{p}_2$, ..., $\mathbf{p}_n$ for A, with corresponding eigenvalues λ_1, λ_2, ..., λ_n. If n linearly independent eigenvectors do not exist, then A is not diagonalizable.
2. If A has n linearly independent eigenvectors, let P be the $n \times n$ matrix whose columns consist of these eigenvectors. That is,

$$P = [\mathbf{p}_1 \vdots \mathbf{p}_2 \vdots \ldots \vdots \mathbf{p}_n].$$

3. The diagonal matrix $D = P^{-1}AP$ will have the eigenvalues λ_1, λ_2, ..., λ_n on its main diagonal (and zeros elsewhere). Note that the order of eigenvectors used to form P will determine the order in which the eigenvalues appear on the main diagonal of D.

EXAMPLE 4   *A Matrix That Is Not Diagonalizable*

Show that the following matrix is not diagonalizable.

$$A = \begin{bmatrix} 1 & 2 \\ 0 & 1 \end{bmatrix}$$

Solution   Since A is triangular, the eigenvalues are simply the entries on the main diagonal. Thus the only eigenvalue is $\lambda = 1$. The matrix $(I - A)$ has the following reduced row-echelon form.

$$I - A = \begin{bmatrix} 0 & -2 \\ 0 & 0 \end{bmatrix} \longrightarrow \begin{bmatrix} 0 & 1 \\ 0 & 0 \end{bmatrix}$$

This implies that $x_2 = 0$, and letting $x_1 = t$, we find that every eigenvector of A has the form

$$\mathbf{x} = \begin{bmatrix} x_1 \\ x_2 \end{bmatrix} = \begin{bmatrix} t \\ 0 \end{bmatrix} = t \begin{bmatrix} 1 \\ 0 \end{bmatrix}.$$

Hence A does not have two linearly independent eigenvectors, and we conclude that A is not diagonalizable.

EXAMPLE 5   *Diagonalizing a Matrix*

Show that the following matrix is diagonalizable.

$$A = \begin{bmatrix} 1 & -1 & -1 \\ 1 & 3 & 1 \\ -3 & 1 & -1 \end{bmatrix}$$

Then find a matrix P such that $P^{-1}AP$ is diagonal.

Solution   The characteristic polynomial for A is

$$|\lambda I - A| = \begin{vmatrix} \lambda - 1 & 1 & 1 \\ -1 & \lambda - 3 & -1 \\ 3 & -1 & \lambda + 1 \end{vmatrix} = (\lambda - 2)(\lambda + 2)(\lambda - 3).$$

Thus the eigenvalues of A are $\lambda_1 = 2$, $\lambda_2 = -2$, and $\lambda_3 = 3$. From these eigenvalues we obtain the following reduced row echelon forms and corresponding eigenvectors.

Eigenvector

$$2I - A = \begin{bmatrix} 1 & 1 & 1 \\ -1 & -1 & -1 \\ 3 & -1 & 3 \end{bmatrix} \longrightarrow \begin{bmatrix} 1 & 0 & 1 \\ 0 & 1 & 0 \\ 0 & 0 & 0 \end{bmatrix} \qquad \begin{bmatrix} -1 \\ 0 \\ 1 \end{bmatrix}$$

$$-2I - A = \begin{bmatrix} -3 & 1 & 1 \\ -1 & -5 & -1 \\ 3 & -1 & -1 \end{bmatrix} \longrightarrow \begin{bmatrix} 1 & 0 & -\frac{1}{4} \\ 0 & 1 & \frac{1}{4} \\ 0 & 0 & 0 \end{bmatrix} \qquad \begin{bmatrix} 1 \\ -1 \\ 4 \end{bmatrix}$$

$$3I - A = \begin{bmatrix} 2 & 1 & 1 \\ -1 & 0 & -1 \\ 3 & -1 & 4 \end{bmatrix} \longrightarrow \begin{bmatrix} 1 & 0 & 1 \\ 0 & 1 & -1 \\ 0 & 0 & 0 \end{bmatrix} \qquad \begin{bmatrix} -1 \\ 1 \\ 1 \end{bmatrix}$$

We form the matrix P whose columns are the eigenvectors just obtained.

$$P = \begin{bmatrix} -1 & 1 & -1 \\ 0 & -1 & 1 \\ 1 & 4 & 1 \end{bmatrix}$$

This matrix is nonsingular, which implies that the eigenvalues are linearly independent and A is diagonalizable. The inverse of P is

$$P^{-1} = \begin{bmatrix} -1 & -1 & 0 \\ \frac{1}{5} & 0 & \frac{1}{5} \\ \frac{1}{5} & 1 & \frac{1}{5} \end{bmatrix},$$

and it follows that

$$P^{-1}AP = \begin{bmatrix} 2 & 0 & 0 \\ 0 & -2 & 0 \\ 0 & 0 & 3 \end{bmatrix}.$$

EXAMPLE 6   *Diagonalizing a Matrix*

Show that the following matrix is diagonalizable.

$$A = \begin{bmatrix} 1 & 0 & 0 & 0 \\ 0 & 1 & 5 & -10 \\ 1 & 0 & 2 & 0 \\ 1 & 0 & 0 & 3 \end{bmatrix}$$

Then find a matrix P such that $P^{-1}AP$ is diagonal.

Solution   In Example 6 of Section 7.1, we found that the three eigenvalues $\lambda_1 = 1$, $\lambda_2 = 2$, and $\lambda_3 = 3$ have the following eigenvectors.

$$\lambda_1: \begin{bmatrix} 0 \\ 1 \\ 0 \\ 0 \end{bmatrix}, \begin{bmatrix} -2 \\ 0 \\ 2 \\ 1 \end{bmatrix} \qquad \lambda_2: \begin{bmatrix} 0 \\ 5 \\ 1 \\ 0 \end{bmatrix} \qquad \lambda_3: \begin{bmatrix} 0 \\ -5 \\ 0 \\ 1 \end{bmatrix}$$

The matrix whose columns consist of these eigenvectors is

$$P = \begin{bmatrix} 0 & -2 & 0 & 0 \\ 1 & 0 & 5 & -5 \\ 0 & 2 & 1 & 0 \\ 0 & 1 & 0 & 1 \end{bmatrix}.$$

Since P is invertible (check this), its column vectors form a linearly independent set. Hence A is diagonalizable, and we have

$$P^{-1}AP = \begin{bmatrix} 1 & 0 & 0 & 0 \\ 0 & 1 & 0 & 0 \\ 0 & 0 & 2 & 0 \\ 0 & 0 & 0 & 3 \end{bmatrix}.$$

For a square matrix A of order n to be diagonalizable, the sum of the dimensions of the eigenspaces must be equal to n. One way this can happen is if A has n distinct eigenvalues. Thus we have the next theorem.

Theorem 7.6

Sufficient Condition for Diagonalization

If an $n \times n$ matrix A has n *distinct* eigenvalues, then the corresponding eigenvectors are linearly independent and A is diagonalizable.

Proof   Let $\lambda_1, \lambda_2, \ldots, \lambda_n$ be n distinct eigenvalues of A corresponding to the eigenvectors $\mathbf{x}_1, \mathbf{x}_2, \ldots, \mathbf{x}_n$. To begin, we assume that the set of eigenvectors is linearly dependent.

Moreover, we consider the eigenvectors to be ordered so that the first m eigenvectors are linearly independent, but the first $m + 1$ are dependent, where $m < n$. Then we can write $\mathbf{x}_{m+1}$ as a linear combination of the first m eigenvectors:

$$\mathbf{x}_{m+1} = c_1\mathbf{x}_1 + c_2\mathbf{x}_2 + \cdots + c_m\mathbf{x}_m, \qquad \text{Equation 1}$$

where the c_i's are not all zero. Multiplication of both sides of Equation 1 by A yields

$$A\mathbf{x}_{m+1} = Ac_1\mathbf{x}_1 + Ac_2\mathbf{x}_2 + \cdots + Ac_m\mathbf{x}_m$$

$$\lambda_{m+1}\mathbf{x}_{m+1} = c_1\lambda_1\mathbf{x}_1 + c_2\lambda_2\mathbf{x}_2 + \cdots + c_m\lambda_m\mathbf{x}_m, \qquad \text{Equation 2}$$

whereas multiplication of Equation 1 by λ_{m+1} yields

$$\lambda_{m+1}\mathbf{x}_{m+1} = c_1\lambda_{m+1}\mathbf{x}_1 + c_2\lambda_{m+1}\mathbf{x}_2 + \cdots + c_m\lambda_{m+1}\mathbf{x}_m. \qquad \text{Equation 3}$$

Now subtracting Equation 2 from Equation 3 produces

$$c_1(\lambda_{m+1} - \lambda_1)\mathbf{x}_1 + c_2(\lambda_{m+1} - \lambda_2)\mathbf{x}_2 + \cdots + c_m(\lambda_{m+1} - \lambda_m)\mathbf{x}_m = \mathbf{0},$$

and, using the fact that the first m eigenvectors are linearly independent, we conclude that all coefficients of this equation must be zero. That is,

$$c_1(\lambda_{m+1} - \lambda_1) = c_2(\lambda_{m+1} - \lambda_2) = \cdots = c_m(\lambda_{m+1} - \lambda_m) = 0.$$

Since all the eigenvalues are distinct, it follows that $c_i = 0$, $i = 1, 2, \ldots, m$. But this result contradicts our assumption that $\mathbf{x}_{m+1}$ can be written as a linear combination of the first m eigenvectors. Hence the set of eigenvectors is linearly independent, and from Theorem 7.5 we conclude that A is diagonalizable.

EXAMPLE 7   *Determining Whether a Matrix Is Diagonalizable*

Determine whether the following matrix is diagonalizable.

$$A = \begin{bmatrix} 1 & -2 & 1 \\ 0 & 0 & 1 \\ 0 & 0 & -3 \end{bmatrix}$$

Solution   Since A is a triangular matrix, its eigenvalues are the main diagonal entries

$$\lambda_1 = 1, \qquad \lambda_2 = 0, \qquad \lambda_3 = -3.$$

Moreover, because these three values are distinct, we conclude from Theorem 7.6 that A is diagonalizable.

REMARK: Remember that the condition in Theorem 7.6 is sufficient but not necessary for diagonalization, as demonstrated in Example 6. In other words, a diagonalizable matrix need not have distinct eigenvalues.

Diagonalization and Linear Transformations

So far in this section we have considered the diagonalization problem in terms of matrices. In terms of linear transformations, the diagonalization problem can be stated as follows. For a linear transformation

$$T: V \to V$$

does there exist a basis B for V such that the matrix for T relative to B is diagonal? The answer is "yes," provided the standard matrix for T is diagonalizable.

EXAMPLE 8   *Finding a Diagonal Matrix for a Linear Transformation*

Let $T: R^3 \to R^3$ be the linear transformation given by

$$T(x_1, x_2, x_3) = (x_1 - x_2 - x_3, x_1 + 3x_2 + x_3, -3x_1 + x_2 - x_3).$$

If possible, find a basis B for R^3 such that the matrix for T relative to B is diagonal.

Solution   The standard matrix for T is given by

$$A = \begin{bmatrix} 1 & -1 & -1 \\ 1 & 3 & 1 \\ -3 & 1 & -1 \end{bmatrix}.$$

From Example 5 we know that A is diagonalizable. Thus the three linearly independent eigenvectors found in Example 5 can be used to form the basis B. That is,

$$B = \{(-1, 0, 1), (1, -1, 4), (-1, 1, 1)\}.$$

The matrix for T relative to this basis is

$$D = \begin{bmatrix} 2 & 0 & 0 \\ 0 & -2 & 0 \\ 0 & 0 & 3 \end{bmatrix}.$$

SECTION 7.2 ▢ EXERCISES

In Exercises 1–4, verify that A is diagonalizable by computing $P^{-1}AP$.

1. $A = \begin{bmatrix} -11 & 36 \\ -3 & 10 \end{bmatrix}$, $P = \begin{bmatrix} -3 & -4 \\ -1 & -1 \end{bmatrix}$

2. $A = \begin{bmatrix} 1 & 3 \\ -1 & 5 \end{bmatrix}$, $P = \begin{bmatrix} 3 & 1 \\ 1 & 1 \end{bmatrix}$

3. $A = \begin{bmatrix} -1 & 1 & 0 \\ 0 & 3 & 0 \\ 4 & -2 & 5 \end{bmatrix}$, $P = \begin{bmatrix} 0 & 1 & -3 \\ 0 & 4 & 0 \\ 1 & 2 & 2 \end{bmatrix}$

4. $A = \begin{bmatrix} 2 & 0 & -2 \\ 0 & 2 & -2 \\ 3 & 0 & -3 \end{bmatrix}$, $P = \begin{bmatrix} 1 & 0 & 2 \\ 1 & 1 & 2 \\ 1 & 0 & 3 \end{bmatrix}$

In Exercises 5–10, show that the given matrix is not diagonalizable.

5. $\begin{bmatrix} 0 & 0 \\ 3 & 0 \end{bmatrix}$

6. $\begin{bmatrix} 1 & k \\ 0 & 1 \end{bmatrix}$, $k \neq 0$

7. $\begin{bmatrix} 1 & -2 & 1 \\ 0 & 1 & 4 \\ 0 & 0 & 2 \end{bmatrix}$
(See Exercise 25, Section 7.1.)

8. $\begin{bmatrix} 2 & 1 & -1 \\ 0 & -1 & 2 \\ 0 & 0 & -1 \end{bmatrix}$
(See Exercise 26, Section 7.1.)

9. $\begin{bmatrix} 1 & 0 & -1 & 1 \\ 0 & 1 & 0 & 1 \\ -2 & 0 & 2 & -2 \\ 0 & 2 & 0 & 2 \end{bmatrix}$
(See Exercise 29, Section 7.1.)

10. $\begin{bmatrix} 1 & -3 & 3 & 3 \\ -1 & 4 & -3 & -3 \\ -2 & 0 & 1 & 1 \\ 1 & 0 & 0 & 0 \end{bmatrix}$
(See Exercise 30, Section 7.1.)

In Exercises 11–14, find the eigenvalues of the matrix and determine whether there are a sufficient number to guarantee that the matrix is diagonalizable. (Recall that the matrix may be diagonalizable even though it is not guaranteed by Theorem 7.6.)

11. $\begin{bmatrix} 1 & 1 \\ 1 & 1 \end{bmatrix}$

12. $\begin{bmatrix} 2 & 0 \\ 5 & 2 \end{bmatrix}$

13. $\begin{bmatrix} 3 & 2 & -3 \\ -3 & -4 & 9 \\ -1 & -2 & 5 \end{bmatrix}$

14. $\begin{bmatrix} 4 & 3 & -2 \\ 0 & 1 & 1 \\ 0 & 0 & -2 \end{bmatrix}$

In Exercises 15–28, for each matrix A find (if possible) a nonsingular matrix P such that $P^{-1}AP$ is diagonal. Verify that $P^{-1}AP$ is a diagonal matrix with the eigenvalues on the diagonal.

15. $A = \begin{bmatrix} 0 & 1 \\ 1 & 0 \end{bmatrix}$

16. $A = \begin{bmatrix} 1 & 0 \\ -2 & 2 \end{bmatrix}$

17. $A = \begin{bmatrix} 2 & 3 \\ 1 & 4 \end{bmatrix}$
(See Exercise 19, Section 7.1.)

18. $A = \begin{bmatrix} 3 & 3 \\ -1 & -1 \end{bmatrix}$

19. $A = \begin{bmatrix} 2 & 0 & 1 \\ 0 & 3 & 4 \\ 0 & 0 & 1 \end{bmatrix}$
(See Exercise 21, Section 7.1.)

20. $A = \begin{bmatrix} -5 & 0 & 0 \\ 3 & 7 & 0 \\ 4 & -2 & 3 \end{bmatrix}$
(See Exercise 22, Section 7.1.)

21. $A = \begin{bmatrix} 1 & 2 & -2 \\ -2 & 5 & -2 \\ -6 & 6 & -3 \end{bmatrix}$
(See Exercise 23, Section 7.1.)

22. $A = \begin{bmatrix} 3 & 2 & -3 \\ -3 & -4 & 9 \\ -1 & -2 & 5 \end{bmatrix}$
(See Exercise 24, Section 7.1.)

23. $A = \begin{bmatrix} 0 & -3 & 5 \\ -4 & 4 & -10 \\ 0 & 0 & 4 \end{bmatrix}$
(See Exercise 27, Section 7.1.)

24. $A = \begin{bmatrix} 1 & -\frac{3}{2} & \frac{5}{2} \\ -2 & \frac{13}{2} & -10 \\ \frac{3}{2} & -\frac{9}{2} & 8 \end{bmatrix}$
(See Exercise 28, Section 7.1.)

25. $A = \begin{bmatrix} 1 & 0 & 0 \\ 1 & 2 & 1 \\ 1 & 0 & 2 \end{bmatrix}$

26. $A = \begin{bmatrix} 4 & 0 & 0 \\ 2 & 2 & 0 \\ 0 & 2 & 2 \end{bmatrix}$

27. $A = \begin{bmatrix} 2 & 0 & 0 & 0 \\ 3 & -1 & 0 & 0 \\ 0 & 1 & 1 & 0 \\ 0 & 0 & 1 & -2 \end{bmatrix}$

28. $A = \begin{bmatrix} 1 & 0 & 0 & 0 \\ 1 & 0 & 1 & 0 \\ 0 & 0 & 1 & 0 \\ 0 & 1 & 0 & 1 \end{bmatrix}$

In Exercises 29–32, find a basis B for the domain of T such that the matrix of T relative to B is diagonal.

29. $T: R^2 \rightarrow R^2$: $T(x, y) = (x + y, x + y)$
30. $T: R^3 \rightarrow R^3$: $T(x, y, z) = (-2x + 2y - 3z, 2x + y - 6z, -x - 2y)$
31. $T: P_1 \rightarrow P_1$: $T(a + bx) = a + (a + 2b)x$
32. $T: P_2 \rightarrow P_2$: $T(a_0 + a_1x + a_2x^2) = (2a_0 + a_2) + (3a_1 + 4a_2)x + a_2x^2$

33. Let A be an $n \times n$ diagonalizable matrix and P an invertible $n \times n$ matrix such that $B = P^{-1}AP$ is the diagonal form of A. Prove the following.

    (a) $B^k = P^{-1}A^kP$, where k is a positive integer.
    (b) $A^k = PB^kP^{-1}$, where k is a positive integer.

34. Let $\lambda_1, \lambda_2, \ldots, \lambda_n$ be n distinct eigenvalues of the $n \times n$ matrix A. Use the result of Exercise 33 to find the eigenvalues of A^k.

In Exercises 35–38, use the result of Exercise 33 to find the indicated power of A.

35. $A = \begin{bmatrix} 10 & 18 \\ -6 & -11 \end{bmatrix}$, A^6

36. $A = \begin{bmatrix} 1 & 3 \\ 2 & 0 \end{bmatrix}$, A^7

37. $A = \begin{bmatrix} 3 & 2 & -3 \\ -3 & -4 & 9 \\ -1 & -2 & 5 \end{bmatrix}$, A^8

38. $A = \begin{bmatrix} 2 & 0 & -2 \\ 0 & 2 & -2 \\ 3 & 0 & -3 \end{bmatrix}$, A^5

39. Can a matrix be similar to two different diagonal matrices? Explain your answer.

40. Are the following two matrices similar? If so, find a matrix P such that $B = P^{-1}AP$.

    (a) $A = \begin{bmatrix} 1 & 0 & 0 \\ 0 & 2 & 0 \\ 0 & 0 & 3 \end{bmatrix}$

    (b) $B = \begin{bmatrix} 3 & 0 & 0 \\ 0 & 2 & 0 \\ 0 & 0 & 1 \end{bmatrix}$

41. Prove that if A is diagonalizable, then A^T is diagonalizable.
42. Prove that the matrix

$$A = \begin{bmatrix} a & b \\ c & d \end{bmatrix}$$

    is diagonalizable if $-4bc < (a - d)^2$, and not diagonalizable if $-4bc > (a - d)^2$.

43. Prove that if A is diagonalizable with n real eigenvalues $\lambda_1, \lambda_2, \ldots,$ and λ_n, then

$$|A| = \lambda_1\lambda_2 \cdots \lambda_n.$$

44. (Calculus) If x is a real number, then e^x can be defined by the series

$$e^x = 1 + x + \frac{x^2}{2!} + \frac{x^3}{3!} + \frac{x^4}{4!} + \cdots.$$

In a similar way, if X is a square matrix, we can define e^X by the series

$$e^X = I + X + \frac{1}{2!}X^2 + \frac{1}{3!}X^3 + \frac{1}{4!}X^4 + \cdots.$$

Evaluate e^X, where X is the following square matrix.

    (a) $X = \begin{bmatrix} 1 & 0 \\ 0 & 1 \end{bmatrix}$

    (b) $X = \begin{bmatrix} 0 & 0 \\ 0 & 0 \end{bmatrix}$

    (c) $X = \begin{bmatrix} 1 & 0 \\ 1 & 0 \end{bmatrix}$

    (d) $X = \begin{bmatrix} 0 & 1 \\ 1 & 0 \end{bmatrix}$

    (e) $X = \begin{bmatrix} 2 & 0 \\ 0 & -2 \end{bmatrix}$

45. Prove that if the eigenvalues of a diagonalizable matrix are all ± 1, then the matrix is equal to its inverse.

46. Prove that nonzero nilpotent matrices are not diagonalizable.

47. Prove that if A is a nonsingular diagonalizable matrix, then A^{-1} is also diagonalizable.

7.3 SYMMETRIC MATRICES AND ORTHOGONAL DIAGONALIZATION

For most matrices we must go through much of the diagonalization process before we can finally determine whether diagonalization is possible. One exception is a triangular matrix with distinct entries on the main diagonal. These can be recognized as diagonalizable by simple inspection. In this section we study another type of matrix that is guaranteed to be diagonalizable: a **symmetric** matrix.

Definition of Symmetric Matrix	A square matrix A is **symmetric** if it is equal to its transpose: $$A = A^T.$$

We can determine easily whether a matrix is symmetric by checking to see whether it is symmetrical with respect to its main diagonal.

EXAMPLE 1   ***Symmetric Matrices and Nonsymmetric Matrices***

The matrices A and B *are* symmetric, but the matrix C is *not*.

$$A = \begin{bmatrix} 0 & 1 & -2 \\ 1 & 3 & 0 \\ -2 & 0 & 5 \end{bmatrix} \qquad \text{Symmetric}$$

$$B = \begin{bmatrix} 4 & 3 \\ 3 & 1 \end{bmatrix} \qquad \text{Symmetric}$$

$$C = \begin{bmatrix} 3 & 2 & 1 \\ 1 & -4 & 0 \\ 1 & 0 & 5 \end{bmatrix} \qquad \text{Not symmetric}$$

DISCOVERY

If you have access to a computer or calculator that can find eigenvalues, try the following experiment. Pick an arbitrary square matrix and calculate its eigenvalues. Can you find a matrix for which the eigenvalues are not real?

Now pick an arbitrary *symmetric* matrix and calculate its eigenvalues. Can you find a symmetric matrix for which the eigenvalues are not real? What can you conclude about the eigenvalues of a symmetric matrix?

Symmetric matrices have some special properties that are not generally possessed by nonsymmetric matrices. To see this, consider the following.

1. A nonsymmetric matrix may not be diagonalizable.
2. A nonsymmetric matrix can have eigenvalues that are not real. For instance, the matrix

$$A = \begin{bmatrix} 0 & -1 \\ 1 & 0 \end{bmatrix}$$

has a characteristic equation of $\lambda^2 + 1 = 0$. Hence its eigenvalues are the imaginary numbers $\lambda_1 = i$ and $\lambda_2 = -i$.
3. For a nonsymmetric matrix, the number of linearly independent eigenvectors corresponding to an eigenvalue can be less than the multiplicity of the eigenvalue. (See Example 4, Section 7.2.)

None of these three is possible with a symmetric matrix.

Theorem 7.7

Eigenvalues of Symmetric Matrices

If A is an $n \times n$ symmetric matrix, then the following properties are true.
1. A is diagonalizable.
2. All eigenvalues of A are real.
3. If λ is an eigenvalue of A with multiplicity k, then λ has k linearly independent eigenvectors. That is, the eigenspace of λ has dimension k.

REMARK: Theorem 7.7 is called the **Real Spectral Theorem,** and the set of eigenvalues of A is called the **spectrum** of A.

A general proof of Theorem 7.7 is beyond the scope of this text. However, part 2 will be proved in Chapter 8, in the section on complex vector spaces, as a special case of Theorem 8.10. The following example verifies that every 2×2 symmetric matrix is diagonalizable.

EXAMPLE 2   *The Eigenvalues and Eigenvectors of a 2 × 2 Symmetric Matrix*

Prove that a symmetric matrix

$$A = \begin{bmatrix} a & c \\ c & b \end{bmatrix}$$

is diagonalizable.

Solution   The characteristic polynomial of A is

$$|\lambda I - A| = \begin{vmatrix} \lambda - a & -c \\ -c & \lambda - b \end{vmatrix} = \lambda^2 - (a + b)\lambda + ab - c^2.$$

As a quadratic in λ, this polynomial has a discriminant of

$$(a + b)^2 - 4(ab - c^2) = a^2 + 2ab + b^2 - 4ab + 4c^2$$
$$= a^2 - 2ab + b^2 + 4c^2$$
$$= (a - b)^2 + 4c^2.$$

Since this discriminant is the sum of two squares, it must be either zero or positive. If $(a - b)^2 + 4c^2 = 0$, then $a = b$ and $c = 0$, which implies that A is already diagonal. That is,

$$A = \begin{bmatrix} a & 0 \\ 0 & a \end{bmatrix}.$$

On the other hand, if $(a - b)^2 + 4c^2 > 0$, then by the Quadratic Formula the characteristic polynomial of A has two distinct real roots, which implies that A has two distinct real eigenvalues. Thus A is diagonalizable in this case also.

EXAMPLE 3   ***Dimensions of the Eigenspaces of a Symmetric Matrix***

Find the eigenvalues of the symmetric matrix

$$A = \begin{bmatrix} 1 & -2 & 0 & 0 \\ -2 & 1 & 0 & 0 \\ 0 & 0 & 1 & -2 \\ 0 & 0 & -2 & 1 \end{bmatrix}$$

and determine the dimensions of the corresponding eigenspaces.

Solution   The characteristic polynomial for A is given by

$$|\lambda I - A| = \begin{vmatrix} \lambda - 1 & 2 & 0 & 0 \\ 2 & \lambda - 1 & 0 & 0 \\ 0 & 0 & \lambda - 1 & 2 \\ 0 & 0 & 2 & \lambda - 1 \end{vmatrix} = (\lambda + 1)^2(\lambda - 3)^2.$$

Thus the eigenvalues of A are $\lambda_1 = -1$ and $\lambda_2 = 3$. Since each of these eigenvalues has a multiplicity of 2, we know from Theorem 7.7 that the corresponding eigenspaces also have dimension 2. Specifically, the eigenspace of $\lambda_1 = -1$ has a basis of $B_1 = \{(1, 1, 0, 0), (0, 0, 1, 1)\}$ and the eigenspace of $\lambda_2 = 3$ has a basis of $B_2 = \{(1, -1, 0, 0), (0, 0, 1, -1)\}$.

Orthogonal Matrices

To diagonalize a square matrix A, we need to find an *invertible* matrix P such that $P^{-1}AP$ is diagonal. For symmetric matrices, we will show that the matrix P can be chosen to have the special property that $P^{-1} = P^T$. We define this unusual matrix property as follows.

Definition of an Orthogonal Matrix   A square matrix P is called **orthogonal** if it is invertible and

$$P^{-1} = P^T.$$

EXAMPLE 4   ***Orthogonal Matrices***

(a) The matrix

$$P = \begin{bmatrix} 0 & 1 \\ -1 & 0 \end{bmatrix}$$

is orthogonal because

$$P^{-1} = P^T = \begin{bmatrix} 0 & -1 \\ 1 & 0 \end{bmatrix}.$$

(b) The matrix

$$P = \begin{bmatrix} \frac{3}{5} & 0 & -\frac{4}{5} \\ 0 & 1 & 0 \\ \frac{4}{5} & 0 & \frac{3}{5} \end{bmatrix}$$

is orthogonal because

$$P^{-1} = P^T = \begin{bmatrix} \frac{3}{5} & 0 & \frac{4}{5} \\ 0 & 1 & 0 \\ -\frac{4}{5} & 0 & \frac{3}{5} \end{bmatrix}.$$

In parts (a) and (b) of Example 4, the columns of the matrices P form orthonormal sets in R^2 and R^3, respectively. This result suggests the following theorem, which you are asked to prove in Exercise 36.

Theorem 7.8

Property of Orthogonal Matrices

An $n \times n$ matrix P is orthogonal if and only if its column vectors form an orthonormal set.

EXAMPLE 5   *An Orthogonal Matrix*

Show that

$$P = \begin{bmatrix} \dfrac{1}{3} & \dfrac{2}{3} & \dfrac{2}{3} \\ \dfrac{-2}{\sqrt{5}} & \dfrac{1}{\sqrt{5}} & 0 \\ \dfrac{-2}{3\sqrt{5}} & \dfrac{-4}{3\sqrt{5}} & \dfrac{5}{3\sqrt{5}} \end{bmatrix}$$

is orthogonal by showing that $PP^T = I$. Then show that the column vectors of P form an orthonormal set.

Solution   Since

$$PP^T = \begin{bmatrix} \dfrac{1}{3} & \dfrac{2}{3} & \dfrac{2}{3} \\ \dfrac{-2}{\sqrt{5}} & \dfrac{1}{\sqrt{5}} & 0 \\ \dfrac{-2}{3\sqrt{5}} & \dfrac{-4}{3\sqrt{5}} & \dfrac{5}{3\sqrt{5}} \end{bmatrix} \begin{bmatrix} \dfrac{1}{3} & \dfrac{-2}{\sqrt{5}} & \dfrac{-2}{3\sqrt{5}} \\ \dfrac{2}{3} & \dfrac{1}{\sqrt{5}} & \dfrac{-4}{3\sqrt{5}} \\ \dfrac{2}{3} & 0 & \dfrac{5}{3\sqrt{5}} \end{bmatrix} = \begin{bmatrix} 1 & 0 & 0 \\ 0 & 1 & 0 \\ 0 & 0 & 1 \end{bmatrix} = I_3,$$

it follows that $P^T = P^{-1}$, and we conclude that P is orthogonal. Moreover, letting

$$
\mathbf{p}_1 = \begin{bmatrix} \dfrac{1}{3} \\[2mm] \dfrac{-2}{\sqrt{5}} \\[2mm] \dfrac{-2}{3\sqrt{5}} \end{bmatrix}, \quad \mathbf{p}_2 = \begin{bmatrix} \dfrac{2}{3} \\[2mm] \dfrac{1}{\sqrt{5}} \\[2mm] \dfrac{-4}{3\sqrt{5}} \end{bmatrix}, \text{ and } \quad \mathbf{p}_3 = \begin{bmatrix} \dfrac{2}{3} \\[2mm] 0 \\[2mm] \dfrac{5}{3\sqrt{5}} \end{bmatrix},
$$

produces

$$
\mathbf{p}_1 \cdot \mathbf{p}_2 = \mathbf{p}_1 \cdot \mathbf{p}_3 = \mathbf{p}_2 \cdot \mathbf{p}_3 = 0
$$

and

$$
\| \mathbf{p}_1 \| = \| \mathbf{p}_2 \| = \| \mathbf{p}_3 \| = 1.
$$

Therefore $\{\mathbf{p}_1, \mathbf{p}_2, \mathbf{p}_3\}$ is an orthonormal set, as guaranteed by Theorem 7.8.

Before presenting the main result of this section, we give the following preliminary result, which states that for symmetric matrices eigenvectors corresponding to distinct eigenvalues are orthogonal.

Theorem 7.9

Property of Symmetric Matrices

Let A be an $n \times n$ symmetric matrix. If λ_1 and λ_2 are distinct eigenvalues of A, then their corresponding eigenvectors $\mathbf{x}_1$ and $\mathbf{x}_2$ are orthogonal.

Proof   Let λ_1 and λ_2 be distinct eigenvalues of A with corresponding eigenvectors $\mathbf{x}_1$ and $\mathbf{x}_2$. Thus $A\mathbf{x}_1 = \lambda_1 \mathbf{x}_1$ and $A\mathbf{x}_2 = \lambda_2 \mathbf{x}_2$. To prove the theorem, we use the following matrix form for the dot product.

$$
\mathbf{x}_1 \cdot \mathbf{x}_2 = [x_{11} \; x_{12} \; \cdots \; x_{1n}] \begin{bmatrix} x_{21} \\ x_{22} \\ \vdots \\ x_{2n} \end{bmatrix} = \mathbf{x}_1^T \mathbf{x}_2
$$

Now we can write

$$
\begin{aligned}
\lambda_1 (\mathbf{x}_1 \cdot \mathbf{x}_2) &= (\lambda_1 \mathbf{x}_1) \cdot \mathbf{x}_2 \\
&= (A\mathbf{x}_1) \cdot \mathbf{x}_2 \\
&= (A\mathbf{x}_1)^T \mathbf{x}_2 \\
&= (\mathbf{x}_1^T A^T) \mathbf{x}_2 \\
&= (\mathbf{x}_1^T A) \mathbf{x}_2 \qquad \text{\textit{Since A is symmetric, } } A = A^T. \\
&= \mathbf{x}_1^T (A\mathbf{x}_2) \\
&= \mathbf{x}_1^T (\lambda_2 \mathbf{x}_2) \\
&= \mathbf{x}_1 \cdot (\lambda_2 \mathbf{x}_2) = \lambda_2 (\mathbf{x}_1 \cdot \mathbf{x}_2).
\end{aligned}
$$

This implies that $(\lambda_1 - \lambda_2)(\mathbf{x}_1 \cdot \mathbf{x}_2) = 0$, and because $\lambda_1 \neq \lambda_2$ it follows that $\mathbf{x}_1 \cdot \mathbf{x}_2 = 0$. Therefore $\mathbf{x}_1$ and $\mathbf{x}_2$ are orthogonal.

EXAMPLE 6   *Eigenvectors of a Symmetric Matrix*

Show that any two eigenvectors of

$$A = \begin{bmatrix} 3 & 1 \\ 1 & 3 \end{bmatrix}$$

corresponding to distinct eigenvalues are orthogonal.

Solution   The characteristic polynomial of A is

$$|\lambda I - A| = \begin{vmatrix} \lambda - 3 & -1 \\ -1 & \lambda - 3 \end{vmatrix} = (\lambda - 2)(\lambda - 4),$$

which implies that the eigenvalues of A are $\lambda_1 = 2$ and $\lambda_2 = 4$. Every eigenvector corresponding to $\lambda_1 = 2$ is of the form

$$\mathbf{x}_1 = \begin{bmatrix} s \\ -s \end{bmatrix}, \ s \neq 0$$

and every eigenvector corresponding to $\lambda_2 = 4$ is of the form

$$\mathbf{x}_2 = \begin{bmatrix} t \\ t \end{bmatrix}, \ t \neq 0.$$

Therefore,

$$\mathbf{x}_1 \cdot \mathbf{x}_2 = \begin{bmatrix} s \\ -s \end{bmatrix} \cdot \begin{bmatrix} t \\ t \end{bmatrix} = st - st = 0,$$

and we conclude that $\mathbf{x}_1$ and $\mathbf{x}_2$ are orthogonal.

Orthogonal Diagonalization

A matrix A is **orthogonally diagonalizable** if there exists an orthogonal matrix P such that $P^{-1}AP = D$ is diagonal. The following important theorem states that the set of orthogonally diagonalizable matrices is precisely the set of symmetric matrices.

Theorem 7.10

Fundamental Theorem of Symmetric Matrices

Let A be an $n \times n$ matrix. Then A is orthogonally diagonalizable and has real eigenvalues if and only if A is symmetric.

Proof   The proof of the theorem in one direction is fairly straightforward. That is, if we assume that A is orthogonally diagonalizable, then there exists an orthogonal matrix P such that $D = P^{-1}AP$ is diagonal. Moreover, since $P^{-1} = P^T$, we have

$$A = PDP^{-1} = PDP^T,$$

which implies that

$$A^T = (PDP^T)^T = (P^T)^T D^T P^T = PDP^T = A.$$

Therefore A is symmetric.

The proof of the theorem in the other direction is more involved, but it is important because it is constructive. Assume that A is symmetric. If A has an eigenvalue λ of multiplicity k, then by Theorem 7.7, λ has k linearly independent eigenvectors. Through the Gram-Schmidt orthonormalization process, this set of k vectors can be used to form an orthonormal basis of eigenvectors for the eigenspace corresponding to λ. This procedure is repeated for each eigenvalue of A. The collection of all resulting eigenvectors is orthogonal by Theorem 7.9, and we know from the normalization process that the collection is also orthonormal. Now we let P be the matrix whose columns consist of these n orthonormal eigenvectors. By Theorem 7.8, P is an orthogonal matrix. Finally, by Theorem 7.5, we can conclude that $P^{-1}AP$ is diagonal. Hence A is orthogonally diagonalizable.

EXAMPLE 7   *Determining Whether a Matrix Is Orthogonally Diagonalizable*

Which of the following are orthogonally diagonalizable?

$$A_1 = \begin{bmatrix} 1 & 1 & 1 \\ 1 & 0 & 1 \\ 1 & 1 & 1 \end{bmatrix} \qquad A_2 = \begin{bmatrix} 5 & 2 & 1 \\ 2 & 1 & 8 \\ -1 & 8 & 0 \end{bmatrix}$$

$$A_3 = \begin{bmatrix} 3 & 2 & 0 \\ 2 & 0 & 1 \end{bmatrix} \qquad A_4 = \begin{bmatrix} 0 & 0 \\ 0 & -2 \end{bmatrix}$$

Solution   By Theorem 7.10, the only orthogonally diagonalizable matrices are the symmetric ones: A_1 and A_4.

We mentioned that the second part of the proof of Theorem 7.10 is *constructive*. That is, it gives us steps to follow to orthogonally diagonalize a symmetric matrix. These steps are summarized as follows.

Orthogonal Diagonalization of a Symmetric Matrix

Let A be an $n \times n$ symmetric matrix.
1. Find all eigenvalues of A and determine the multiplicity of each.
2. For *each* eigenvalue of multiplicity 1, choose a unit eigenvector. (Choose any eigenvector and then normalize it.)
3. For each eigenvalue of multiplicity $k \geq 2$, find a set of k linearly independent eigenvectors. (We know from Theorem 7.7 that this is possible.) If this set is not orthonormal, apply the Gram-Schmidt orthonormalization process.
4. The composite of steps 2 and 3 produces an orthonormal set of n eigenvectors. Use these eigenvectors to form the columns of P. The matrix $P^{-1}AP = P^TAP = D$ will be diagonal. (The main diagonal entries of D are the eigenvalues of A.)

EXAMPLE 8   *Orthogonal Diagonalization*

Find an orthogonal matrix P that orthogonally diagonalizes

$$A = \begin{bmatrix} -2 & 2 \\ 2 & 1 \end{bmatrix}.$$

Solution   1. The characteristic polynomial of A is

$$|\lambda I - A| = \begin{vmatrix} \lambda + 2 & -2 \\ -2 & \lambda - 1 \end{vmatrix} = (\lambda + 3)(\lambda - 2).$$

Thus the eigenvalues are $\lambda_1 = -3$ and $\lambda_2 = 2$.

2. For each eigenvalue we find an eigenvector by converting the matrix $\lambda I - A$ to reduced row-echelon form.

Eigenvector

$$-3I - A = \begin{bmatrix} -1 & -2 \\ -2 & -4 \end{bmatrix} \longrightarrow \begin{bmatrix} 1 & 2 \\ 0 & 0 \end{bmatrix} \longrightarrow \begin{bmatrix} -2 \\ 1 \end{bmatrix}$$

$$2I - A = \begin{bmatrix} 4 & -2 \\ -2 & 1 \end{bmatrix} \longrightarrow \begin{bmatrix} 1 & -\frac{1}{2} \\ 0 & 0 \end{bmatrix} \longrightarrow \begin{bmatrix} 1 \\ 2 \end{bmatrix}$$

The eigenvectors $(-2, 1)$ and $(1, 2)$ form an *orthogonal* basis for R^2. Each of these is normalized to produce an *orthonormal* basis.

$$\mathbf{p}_1 = \frac{(-2, 1)}{\|(-2, 1)\|} = \frac{1}{\sqrt{5}}(-2, 1) = \left(\frac{-2}{\sqrt{5}}, \frac{1}{\sqrt{5}} \right)$$

$$\mathbf{p}_2 = \frac{(1, 2)}{\|(1, 2)\|} = \frac{1}{\sqrt{5}}(1, 2) = \left(\frac{1}{\sqrt{5}}, \frac{2}{\sqrt{5}} \right)$$

3. Because each eigenvalue has a multiplicity of 1, we go directly to step 4.
4. Using $\mathbf{p}_1$ and $\mathbf{p}_2$ as column vectors, we construct the matrix P.

$$P = \begin{bmatrix} \dfrac{-2}{\sqrt{5}} & \dfrac{1}{\sqrt{5}} \\ \dfrac{1}{\sqrt{5}} & \dfrac{2}{\sqrt{5}} \end{bmatrix}$$

We verify that P is correct by computing $P^{-1}AP = P^TAP$.

$$P^TAP = \begin{bmatrix} \dfrac{-2}{\sqrt{5}} & \dfrac{1}{\sqrt{5}} \\ \dfrac{1}{\sqrt{5}} & \dfrac{2}{\sqrt{5}} \end{bmatrix} \begin{bmatrix} -2 & 2 \\ 2 & 1 \end{bmatrix} \begin{bmatrix} \dfrac{-2}{\sqrt{5}} & \dfrac{1}{\sqrt{5}} \\ \dfrac{1}{\sqrt{5}} & \dfrac{2}{\sqrt{5}} \end{bmatrix} = \begin{bmatrix} -3 & 0 \\ 0 & 2 \end{bmatrix}$$

EXAMPLE 9   *Orthogonal Diagonalization*

Find an orthogonal matrix P that diagonalizes

$$A = \begin{bmatrix} 2 & 2 & -2 \\ 2 & -1 & 4 \\ -2 & 4 & -1 \end{bmatrix}.$$

Solution   1. The characteristic polynomial of A,

$$|\lambda I - A| = (\lambda - 3)^2(\lambda + 6),$$

yields the eigenvalues $\lambda_1 = -6$ and $\lambda_2 = 3$. λ_1 has a multiplicity of 1 and λ_2 has a multiplicity of 2.

2. An eigenvector for λ_1 is $\mathbf{v}_1 = (1, -2, 2)$, which normalizes to

$$\mathbf{u}_1 = \frac{\mathbf{v}_1}{\|\mathbf{v}_1\|} = \left(\frac{1}{3}, -\frac{2}{3}, \frac{2}{3} \right).$$

3. Two eigenvectors for λ_2 are

$$\mathbf{v}_2 = (2, 1, 0) \quad \text{and} \quad \mathbf{v}_3 = (-2, 0, 1).$$

Note that $\mathbf{v}_1$ is orthogonal to $\mathbf{v}_2$ and $\mathbf{v}_3$, as guaranteed by Theorem 7.9. The eigenvectors $\mathbf{v}_2$ and $\mathbf{v}_3$, however, are not orthogonal to each other. To find two orthonormal eigenvectors for λ_2, we use the Gram-Schmidt process as follows.

$$\mathbf{w}_2 = \mathbf{v}_2 = (2, 1, 0)$$

$$\mathbf{w}_3 = \mathbf{v}_3 - \left(\frac{\mathbf{v}_3 \cdot \mathbf{w}_2}{\mathbf{w}_2 \cdot \mathbf{w}_2} \right) \mathbf{w}_2 = \left(-\frac{2}{5}, \frac{4}{5}, 1 \right)$$

These vectors normalize to

$$\mathbf{u}_2 = \frac{\mathbf{w}_2}{\|\mathbf{w}_2\|} = \left(\frac{2}{\sqrt{5}}, \frac{1}{\sqrt{5}}, 0 \right)$$

$$\mathbf{u}_3 = \frac{\mathbf{w}_3}{\|\mathbf{w}_3\|} = \left(\frac{-2}{3\sqrt{5}}, \frac{4}{3\sqrt{5}}, \frac{5}{3\sqrt{5}} \right).$$

4. The matrix P has $\mathbf{u}_1$, $\mathbf{u}_2$, and $\mathbf{u}_3$ as its column vectors.

$$P = \begin{bmatrix} \dfrac{1}{3} & \dfrac{2}{\sqrt{5}} & \dfrac{-2}{3\sqrt{5}} \\ \dfrac{-2}{3} & \dfrac{1}{\sqrt{5}} & \dfrac{4}{3\sqrt{5}} \\ \dfrac{2}{3} & 0 & \dfrac{5}{3\sqrt{5}} \end{bmatrix}$$

A check shows that $P^{-1}AP = P^TAP = \begin{bmatrix} -6 & 0 & 0 \\ 0 & 3 & 0 \\ 0 & 0 & 3 \end{bmatrix}.$

SECTION 7.3 ☐ EXERCISES

In Exercises 1–6, determine whether the given matrix is symmetric.

1. $\begin{bmatrix} 1 & -1 \\ -1 & 4 \end{bmatrix}$

2. $\begin{bmatrix} 2 & 0 \\ 0 & -4 \end{bmatrix}$

3. $\begin{bmatrix} 4 & -2 & 1 \\ 3 & 1 & 2 \\ 1 & 2 & 1 \end{bmatrix}$

4. $\begin{bmatrix} 1 & -5 & 4 \\ -5 & 3 & 6 \\ -4 & 6 & 2 \end{bmatrix}$

5. $\begin{bmatrix} 0 & 1 & 2 \\ 1 & 0 & -3 \\ 2 & -3 & 0 \end{bmatrix}$

6. $\begin{bmatrix} 2 & 0 & 3 \\ 0 & 11 & 0 \\ 3 & 0 & 5 \end{bmatrix}$

In Exercises 7–12, find the eigenvalues of the given symmetric matrix. For each eigenvalue, find the dimension of the corresponding eigenspace.

7. $\begin{bmatrix} 1 & 2 \\ 2 & 1 \end{bmatrix}$

8. $\begin{bmatrix} 2 & 0 \\ 0 & 2 \end{bmatrix}$

9. $\begin{bmatrix} 3 & 0 & 0 \\ 0 & 2 & 0 \\ 0 & 0 & 2 \end{bmatrix}$

10. $\begin{bmatrix} 2 & 1 & 1 \\ 1 & 2 & 1 \\ 1 & 1 & 2 \end{bmatrix}$

11. $\begin{bmatrix} 0 & 2 & 2 \\ 2 & 0 & 2 \\ 2 & 2 & 0 \end{bmatrix}$

12. $\begin{bmatrix} 0 & 4 & 4 \\ 4 & 2 & 0 \\ 4 & 0 & -2 \end{bmatrix}$

In Exercises 13–20, determine whether the given matrix is orthogonal.

13. $\begin{bmatrix} \dfrac{\sqrt{2}}{2} & \dfrac{\sqrt{2}}{2} \\ -\dfrac{\sqrt{2}}{2} & \dfrac{\sqrt{2}}{2} \end{bmatrix}$

14. $\begin{bmatrix} \frac{2}{3} & -\frac{2}{3} & \frac{1}{3} \\ \frac{2}{3} & \frac{1}{3} & -\frac{2}{3} \\ \frac{1}{3} & \frac{2}{3} & \frac{2}{3} \end{bmatrix}$

15. $\begin{bmatrix} -4 & 0 & 3 \\ 0 & 1 & 0 \\ 3 & 0 & 4 \end{bmatrix}$

16. $\begin{bmatrix} -\frac{4}{5} & 0 & \frac{3}{5} \\ 0 & 1 & 0 \\ \frac{3}{5} & 0 & \frac{4}{5} \end{bmatrix}$

17. $\begin{bmatrix} \dfrac{\sqrt{2}}{2} & -\dfrac{\sqrt{6}}{6} & \dfrac{\sqrt{3}}{3} \\ 0 & \dfrac{\sqrt{6}}{3} & \dfrac{\sqrt{3}}{3} \\ \dfrac{\sqrt{2}}{2} & \dfrac{\sqrt{6}}{6} & -\dfrac{\sqrt{3}}{3} \end{bmatrix}$

18. $\begin{bmatrix} \dfrac{\sqrt{2}}{3} & 0 & \dfrac{\sqrt{5}}{2} \\ 0 & \dfrac{2\sqrt{5}}{5} & 0 \\ -\dfrac{\sqrt{2}}{6} & -\dfrac{\sqrt{5}}{5} & \dfrac{1}{2} \end{bmatrix}$

19. $\begin{bmatrix} \dfrac{1}{10}\sqrt{10} & 0 & 0 & -\dfrac{3}{10}\sqrt{10} \\ 0 & 0 & 1 & 0 \\ 0 & 1 & 0 & 0 \\ \dfrac{3}{10}\sqrt{10} & 0 & 0 & \dfrac{1}{10}\sqrt{10} \end{bmatrix}$

20. $\begin{bmatrix} 4 & -1 & -4 \\ -1 & 0 & -17 \\ 1 & 4 & -1 \end{bmatrix}$

In Exercises 21–28, find an orthogonal matrix P such that $P^T AP$ diagonalizes A. Verify that $P^T AP$ gives the proper diagonal form.

21. $A = \begin{bmatrix} 1 & 1 \\ 1 & 1 \end{bmatrix}$

22. $A = \begin{bmatrix} 4 & 2 \\ 2 & 4 \end{bmatrix}$

23. $A = \begin{bmatrix} 2 & \sqrt{2} \\ \sqrt{2} & 1 \end{bmatrix}$

24. $A = \begin{bmatrix} 0 & 1 & 1 \\ 1 & 0 & 1 \\ 1 & 1 & 0 \end{bmatrix}$

25. $A = \begin{bmatrix} 0 & 10 & 10 \\ 10 & 5 & 0 \\ 10 & 0 & -5 \end{bmatrix}$

26. $A = \begin{bmatrix} 0 & 3 & 0 \\ 3 & 0 & 4 \\ 0 & 4 & 0 \end{bmatrix}$

27. $A = \begin{bmatrix} 4 & 2 & 0 & 0 \\ 2 & 4 & 0 & 0 \\ 0 & 0 & 4 & 2 \\ 0 & 0 & 2 & 4 \end{bmatrix}$ **28.** $A = \begin{bmatrix} 1 & 1 & 0 & 0 \\ 1 & 1 & 0 & 0 \\ 0 & 0 & 1 & 1 \\ 0 & 0 & 1 & 1 \end{bmatrix}$

29. Prove that if A is an $m \times n$ matrix, then A^TA and AA^T are symmetric.

30. Find A^TA and AA^T for the following matrix.

$$A = \begin{bmatrix} 1 & -3 & 2 \\ 4 & -6 & 1 \end{bmatrix}$$

31. Prove that if A is an orthogonal matrix, then $|A| = \pm 1$.

32. Prove that if A and B are $n \times n$ orthogonal matrices, then AB and BA are orthogonal.

33. Show that the following matrix is orthogonal for any value of θ.

$$A = \begin{bmatrix} \cos \theta & -\sin \theta \\ \sin \theta & \cos \theta \end{bmatrix}$$

34. Prove that if a symmetric matrix A has only one eigenvalue λ, then $A = \lambda I$.

35. Prove that if A is an orthogonal matrix, then so are A^T and A^{-1}.

36. Prove Theorem 7.8: An $n \times n$ matrix P is orthogonal if and only if its column vectors form an orthonormal set.

7.4 APPLICATIONS OF EIGENVALUES AND EIGENVECTORS

Population Growth

Matrices can be used to form models for population growth. The first step in this process is to group the population into age classes of equal duration. For instance, if the maximum life span of a member is L years, then the age classes are represented by the following n intervals.

First age   Second age nth age
class   class   class

$$\left[0, \frac{L}{n} \right), \quad \left[\frac{L}{n}, \frac{2L}{n} \right), \dots, \left[\frac{(n-1)L}{n}, L \right]$$

The number of population members in each age class is then represented by the **age distribution** vector

$$\mathbf{x} = \begin{bmatrix} x_1 \\ x_2 \\ \vdots \\ x_n \end{bmatrix}.$$

Number in first age class

Number in second age class

Number in nth age class

Over a period of L/n years, the *probability* that a member of the ith age class will survive to become a member of the $(i + 1)$th age class is given by p_i, where

$$0 \le p_i \le 1, \ i = 1, 2, \dots, n - 1.$$

The *average number* of offspring produced by a member of the ith age class is given by b_i, where

$$0 \le b_i, \ i = 1, 2, \dots, n.$$

These numbers can be written in matrix form as follows.

$$A = \begin{bmatrix} b_1 & b_2 & b_3 & \cdots & b_{n-1} & b_n \\ p_1 & 0 & 0 & \cdots & 0 & 0 \\ 0 & p_2 & 0 & \cdots & 0 & 0 \\ \vdots & \vdots & \vdots & & \vdots & \vdots \\ 0 & 0 & 0 & \cdots & p_{n-1} & 0 \end{bmatrix}$$

Multiplying this **age transition** matrix by the age distribution vector for a given time period produces the age distribution vector for the next time period. That is,

$$A\mathbf{x}_i = \mathbf{x}_{i+1}.$$

This procedure is illustrated in Example 1.

EXAMPLE 1   ***A Population Growth Model***

A population of rabbits raised in a research laboratory has the following characteristics.
(a) Half of the rabbits survive their first year. Of those, half survive their second year. The maximum life span is three years.
(b) During the first year the rabbits produce no offspring. The average number of offspring is 6 during the second year and 8 during the third year.
The laboratory population now consists of 24 rabbits in the first age class, 24 in the second, and 20 in the third. How many will be in each age class in one year?

Solution   The current age distribution vector is

$$\mathbf{x}_1 = \begin{bmatrix} 24 \\ 24 \\ 20 \end{bmatrix} \qquad \begin{array}{l} 0 \le \text{age} < 1 \\ 1 \le \text{age} < 2 \\ 2 \le \text{age} \le 3 \end{array}$$

and the age transition matrix is

$$A = \begin{bmatrix} 0 & 6 & 8 \\ 0.5 & 0 & 0 \\ 0 & 0.5 & 0 \end{bmatrix}.$$

After one year the age distribution vector will be

$$\mathbf{x}_2 = A\mathbf{x}_1 = \begin{bmatrix} 0 & 6 & 8 \\ 0.5 & 0 & 0 \\ 0 & 0.5 & 0 \end{bmatrix} \begin{bmatrix} 24 \\ 24 \\ 20 \end{bmatrix} = \begin{bmatrix} 304 \\ 12 \\ 12 \end{bmatrix}. \qquad \begin{array}{l} 0 \le \text{age} < 1 \\ 1 \le \text{age} < 2 \\ 2 \le \text{age} \le 3 \end{array}$$

If the pattern of growth in Example 1 continued for another year, the rabbit population would be

$$\mathbf{x}_3 = A\mathbf{x}_2 = \begin{bmatrix} 0 & 6 & 8 \\ 0.5 & 0 & 0 \\ 0 & 0.5 & 0 \end{bmatrix} \begin{bmatrix} 304 \\ 12 \\ 12 \end{bmatrix} = \begin{bmatrix} 168 \\ 152 \\ 6 \end{bmatrix}. \qquad \begin{array}{l} 0 \le \text{age} < 1 \\ 1 \le \text{age} < 2 \\ 2 \le \text{age} \le 3 \end{array}$$

From the age distribution vectors $\mathbf{x}_1$, $\mathbf{x}_2$, and $\mathbf{x}_3$ we see that the percentage of rabbits in the three age classes changes each year. Suppose that the laboratory prefers a stable growth pattern, one in which the percentage in each age class remains the same each year. For this stable growth pattern to be achieved, the $(n + 1)$th age distribution vector must be a scalar multiple of the nth age distribution vector. That is $A\mathbf{x}_n = \mathbf{x}_{n+1} = \lambda\mathbf{x}_n$. Thus the laboratory can obtain a growth pattern in which the percentage in each age class remains the same each year by finding an eigenvector of A. Example 2 shows how to solve this problem.

EXAMPLE 2   ***Finding a Stable Age Distribution***

Find a stable age distribution for the population given in Example 1.

Solution   To solve this problem, we need to find an eigenvalue λ and corresponding eigenvector $\mathbf{x}$ such that

$$A\mathbf{x} = \lambda\mathbf{x}.$$

The characteristic polynomial for A is

$$|\lambda I - A| = \begin{vmatrix} \lambda & -6 & -8 \\ -0.5 & \lambda & 0 \\ 0 & -0.5 & \lambda \end{vmatrix}$$

$$= \lambda^3 - 3\lambda - 2$$

$$= (\lambda + 1)^2(\lambda - 2),$$

which implies that the eigenvalues are -1 and 2. Choosing the positive value, we let $\lambda = 2$. To find a corresponding eigenvector, we row-reduce the matrix $2I - A$ to obtain

$$\begin{bmatrix} 2 & -6 & -8 \\ -0.5 & 2 & 0 \\ 0 & -0.5 & 2 \end{bmatrix} \longrightarrow \begin{bmatrix} 1 & 0 & -16 \\ 0 & 1 & -4 \\ 0 & 0 & 0 \end{bmatrix}$$

Thus the eigenvectors of $\lambda = 2$ are of the form

$$\mathbf{x} = \begin{bmatrix} x_1 \\ x_2 \\ x_3 \end{bmatrix} = \begin{bmatrix} 16t \\ 4t \\ t \end{bmatrix} = t \begin{bmatrix} 16 \\ 4 \\ 1 \end{bmatrix}.$$

For instance, if $t = 2$, then the initial age distribution vector would be

$$\mathbf{x}_1 = \begin{bmatrix} 32 \\ 8 \\ 2 \end{bmatrix} \qquad \begin{array}{l} 0 \le \text{age} < 1 \\ 1 \le \text{age} < 2 \\ 2 \le \text{age} \le 3 \end{array}$$

and the age distribution vector for the next year would be

$$\mathbf{x}_2 = A\mathbf{x}_1 = \begin{bmatrix} 0 & 6 & 8 \\ 0.5 & 0 & 0 \\ 0 & 0.5 & 0 \end{bmatrix} \begin{bmatrix} 32 \\ 8 \\ 2 \end{bmatrix} = \begin{bmatrix} 64 \\ 16 \\ 4 \end{bmatrix}. \qquad \begin{array}{l} 0 \le \text{age} < 1 \\ 1 \le \text{age} < 2 \\ 2 \le \text{age} \le 3 \end{array}$$

Notice that the ratio of the three age classes is still 16:8:1, and hence the percentage in each age class remains the same.

Systems of Linear Differential Equations (Calculus)

A **system of first-order linear differential equations** has the form

$$y_1' = a_{11}y_1 + a_{12}y_2 + \cdots + a_{1n}y_n$$

$$y_2' = a_{21}y_1 + a_{22}y_2 + \cdots + a_{2n}y_n$$

$$\vdots$$

$$y_n' = a_{n1}y_1 + a_{n2}y_2 + \cdots + a_{nn}y_n,$$

where each y_i is a function of t and $y_i' = dy_i/dt$. If we let

$$\mathbf{y} = \begin{bmatrix} y_1 \\ y_2 \\ \vdots \\ y_n \end{bmatrix} \quad \text{and} \quad \mathbf{y}' = \begin{bmatrix} y_1' \\ y_2' \\ \vdots \\ y_n' \end{bmatrix},$$

then the system can be written in matrix form as

$$\mathbf{y}' = A\mathbf{y}.$$

EXAMPLE 3   *Solving a System of Linear Differential Equations*

Solve the following system of linear differential equations.

$$y_1' = 4y_1$$

$$y_2' = -y_2$$

$$y_3' = 2y_3$$

Solution   From calculus we know that the solution of the differential equation

$$y' = ky$$

is

$$y = Ce^{kt}.$$

Therefore the solution of the given system is

$$y_1 = C_1 e^{4t}$$

$$y_2 = C_2 e^{-t}$$

$$y_3 = C_3 e^{2t}.$$

The matrix form of the system of linear differential equations in Example 3 is $\mathbf{y}' = A\mathbf{y}$, or

$$\begin{bmatrix} y_1' \\ y_2' \\ y_3' \end{bmatrix} = \begin{bmatrix} 4 & 0 & 0 \\ 0 & -1 & 0 \\ 0 & 0 & 2 \end{bmatrix} \begin{bmatrix} y_1 \\ y_2 \\ y_3 \end{bmatrix}.$$

Thus the coefficients of t in the solutions $y_i = C_i e^{\lambda_i t}$ are given by the *eigenvalues* of the matrix A.

If A is a *diagonal* matrix, then the solution of

$$\mathbf{y}' = A\mathbf{y}$$

can be obtained immediately, as in Example 3. If A is *not* diagonal, then the solution requires a little more work. First we attempt to find a matrix P that diagonalizes A. Then the change of variables given by $\mathbf{y} = P\mathbf{w}$ and $\mathbf{y}' = P\mathbf{w}'$ produces

$$P\mathbf{w}' = \mathbf{y}' = A\mathbf{y} = AP\mathbf{w} \Rightarrow \mathbf{w}' = P^{-1}AP\mathbf{w},$$

where $P^{-1}AP$ is a diagonal matrix. This procedure is demonstrated in Example 4.

EXAMPLE 4   *Solving a System of Linear Differential Equations*

Solve the following system of linear differential equations.

$$y_1' = 3y_1 + 2y_2$$

$$y_2' = 6y_1 - y_2$$

Solution   First we find a matrix P that diagonalizes

$$A = \begin{bmatrix} 3 & 2 \\ 6 & -1 \end{bmatrix}.$$

The eigenvalues of A are $\lambda_1 = -3$ and $\lambda_2 = 5$, with corresponding eigenvectors

$$\mathbf{p}_1 = \begin{bmatrix} 1 \\ -3 \end{bmatrix} \quad \text{and} \quad \mathbf{p}_2 = \begin{bmatrix} 1 \\ 1 \end{bmatrix}.$$

We can diagonalize A using the matrix P whose columns consist of $\mathbf{p}_1$ and $\mathbf{p}_2$.

$$P = \begin{bmatrix} 1 & 1 \\ -3 & 1 \end{bmatrix} \quad \text{and} \quad P^{-1}AP = \begin{bmatrix} -3 & 0 \\ 0 & 5 \end{bmatrix}.$$

The system represented by $\mathbf{w}' = P^{-1}AP\mathbf{w}$ has the following form.

$$\begin{bmatrix} w_1' \\ w_2' \end{bmatrix} = \begin{bmatrix} -3 & 0 \\ 0 & 5 \end{bmatrix} \begin{bmatrix} w_1 \\ w_2 \end{bmatrix} \quad \longrightarrow \quad \begin{matrix} w_1' = -3w_1 \\ w_2' = 5w_2 \end{matrix}$$

The solution to this system of equations is

$$w_1 = C_1 e^{-3t}$$

$$w_2 = C_2 e^{5t}.$$

To return to the original variables y_1 and y_2, we use the substitution $\mathbf{y} = P\mathbf{w}$ and write

$$\begin{bmatrix} y_1 \\ y_2 \end{bmatrix} = \begin{bmatrix} 1 & 1 \\ -3 & 1 \end{bmatrix} \begin{bmatrix} w_1 \\ w_2 \end{bmatrix},$$

which implies that the solution is

$$y_1 = \quad w_1 + w_2 = \quad C_1 e^{-3t} + C_2 e^{5t}$$
$$y_2 = -3w_1 + w_2 = -3C_1 e^{-3t} + C_2 e^{5t}.$$

For the systems of linear differential equations in Examples 3 and 4, we found that each y_i can be written as a linear combination of $e^{\lambda_1 t}, e^{\lambda_2 t}, \ldots, e^{\lambda_n t}$, where $\lambda_1, \lambda_2, \ldots, \lambda_n$ are *distinct real eigenvalues* of the $n \times n$ matrix A. If A has eigenvalues with multiplicity greater than 1 or if A has complex eigenvalues, then the technique for solving the system must be modified. If you take a course on differential equations you will cover these two cases. For now, you can get an idea of the type of modification that is required from the following two systems of linear differential equations.

1. *Eigenvalue with multiplicity greater than* 1: The coefficient matrix of the system

$$y_1' = \qquad y_2$$
$$y_2' = -4y_1 + 4y_2$$

is

$$A = \begin{bmatrix} 0 & 1 \\ -4 & 4 \end{bmatrix}.$$

The only eigenvalue of A is $\lambda = 2$, and the solution of the system of linear differential equations is

$$y_1 = \qquad C_1 e^{2t} + \quad C_2 t e^{2t}$$
$$y_2 = (2C_1 + C_2)e^{2t} + 2C_2 t e^{2t}.$$

2. *Complex eigenvalues*: The coefficient matrix of the system

$$y_1' = -y_2$$
$$y_2' = \quad y_1$$

is

$$A = \begin{bmatrix} 0 & -1 \\ 1 & 0 \end{bmatrix}.$$

The eigenvalues of A are $\lambda_1 = i$ and $\lambda_2 = -i$, and the solution of the system of linear differential equations is

$$y_1 = \quad C_1 \cos t + C_2 \sin t$$
$$y_2 = -C_2 \cos t + C_1 \sin t.$$

Try checking these solutions by differentiating and substituting into the original system of equations.

Quadratic Forms

Eigenvalues and eigenvectors can be used to solve the rotation of axes problem introduced in Section 4.8. (You may want to review the discussion presented there.) Recall that classifying the graph of the quadratic equation

$$ax^2 + bxy + cy^2 + dx + ey + f = 0 \qquad \text{Quadratic equation}$$

is fairly straightforward as long as the equation has no xy-term (that is, $b = 0$). If the equation has an xy-term, however, then the classification is most easily accomplished by first performing a rotation of axes that eliminates the xy-term. The resulting equation (relative to the new $x'y'$-axes) will then be the form

$$a'(x')^2 + c'(y')^2 + d'x' + e'y' + f' = 0.$$

We will see that the coefficients a' and c' are eigenvalues of the matrix

$$A = \begin{bmatrix} a & b/2 \\ b/2 & c \end{bmatrix}.$$

We call the expression

$$ax^2 + bxy + cy^2 \qquad \text{Quadratic form}$$

the **quadratic form** associated with the quadratic equation $ax^2 + bxy + cy^2 + dx + ey + f = 0$, and the matrix A is called the **matrix of the quadratic form.** Note that the matrix A is *symmetric* by definition. Moreover, the matrix A will be diagonal if and only if its corresponding quadratic form has no xy-term, as illustrated in Example 5.

EXAMPLE 5   *Finding the Matrix of a Quadratic Form*

Find the matrix of the quadratic form associated with each of the following quadratic equations.

(a) $4x^2 + 9y^2 - 36 = 0$

(b) $13x^2 - 10xy + 13y^2 - 72 = 0$

Solution   (a) Since $a = 4$, $b = 0$, and $c = 9$, the matrix is

$$A = \begin{bmatrix} 4 & 0 \\ 0 & 9 \end{bmatrix}. \qquad \text{Diagonal matrix (no } xy\text{-term)}$$

(b) Since $a = 13$, $b = -10$, and $c = 13$, the matrix is

$$A = \begin{bmatrix} 13 & -5 \\ -5 & 13 \end{bmatrix}. \qquad \text{Nondiagonal matrix (} xy\text{-term)}$$

Figure 7.3

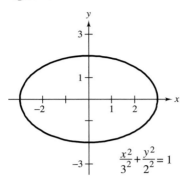

In standard form, the equation $4x^2 + 9y^2 - 36 = 0$ is

$$\frac{x^2}{3^2} + \frac{y^2}{2^2} = 1,$$

which we recognize to be the equation of the ellipse shown in Figure 7.3. Although it is not apparent by simple inspection, the graph of the equation $13x^2 - 10xy + 13y^2 - 72 = 0$ is similar. In fact, if we rotate the x- and y-axes counterclockwise $45°$ to form a new $x'y'$ coordinate system, this equation takes the form

$$\frac{(x')^2}{3^2} + \frac{(y')^2}{2^2} = 1,$$

which we recognize as the equation of the ellipse shown in Figure 7.4.

To see how the matrix of a quadratic form can be used to perform a rotation of axes, we let

$$X = \begin{bmatrix} x \\ y \end{bmatrix}.$$

Then the quadratic expression $ax^2 + bxy + cy^2 + dx + ey + f$ can be written in matrix form as follows.

$$X^T A X + [d \ e] X + f = [x \ y] \begin{bmatrix} a & b/2 \\ b/2 & c \end{bmatrix} \begin{bmatrix} x \\ y \end{bmatrix} + [d \ e] \begin{bmatrix} x \\ y \end{bmatrix} + f$$

$$= ax^2 + bxy + cy^2 + dx + ey + f$$

Figure 7.4

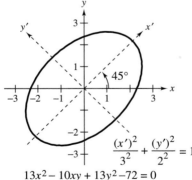

$$\frac{(x')^2}{3^2} + \frac{(y')^2}{2^2} = 1$$

$$13x^2 - 10xy + 13y^2 - 72 = 0$$

If $b = 0$, then no rotation is necessary. But if $b \neq 0$, then, since A is symmetric, we can apply Theorem 7.10 to conclude that there exists an orthogonal matrix P such that

$$P^T A P = D$$

is diagonal. Thus if we let

$$P^T X = X' = \begin{bmatrix} x' \\ y' \end{bmatrix}$$

it follows that $X = PX'$, and we have

$$X^T A X = (PX')^T A (PX')$$

$$= (X')^T P^T A P X'$$

$$= (X')^T D X'.$$

The choice of the matrix P must be made with care. Because P is orthogonal, its determinant will be ± 1. It can be shown (see Exercise 49) that if P is chosen so that $|P| = 1$, then P will be of the form

$$P = \begin{bmatrix} \cos \theta & -\sin \theta \\ \sin \theta & \cos \theta \end{bmatrix},$$

where θ gives the angle of rotation of the conic measured from the positive x-axis to the positive x'-axis. This brings us to the following theorem, the **Principal Axes Theorem.**

Principal Axes Theorem

For a conic whose equation is $ax^2 + bxy + cy^2 + dx + ey + f = 0$, the rotation given by $X = PX'$ eliminates the xy-term if P is an orthogonal matrix, with $|P| = 1$, that diagonalizes A. That is,

$$P^T A P = \begin{bmatrix} \lambda_1 & 0 \\ 0 & \lambda_2 \end{bmatrix},$$

where λ_1 and λ_2 are eigenvalues of A. The equation of the rotated conic is given by

$$\lambda_1 (x')^2 + \lambda_2 (y')^2 + [d \ \ e]PX' + f = 0.$$

REMARK: Note that the matrix product $[d \ \ e]PX'$ has the form

$$[d \ \ e]PX' = (d \cos \theta + e \sin \theta)x' + (-d \sin \theta + e \cos \theta)y'.$$

EXAMPLE 6   *Rotation of a Conic*

Perform a rotation of axes to eliminate the xy-term in the quadratic equation $13x^2 - 10xy + 13y^2 - 72 = 0$.

Solution   The matrix of the quadratic form associated with this equation is

$$A = \begin{bmatrix} 13 & -5 \\ -5 & 13 \end{bmatrix}.$$

Since the characteristic polynomial of A is

$$\begin{vmatrix} \lambda - 13 & 5 \\ 5 & \lambda - 13 \end{vmatrix} = (\lambda - 13)^2 - 25 = (\lambda - 8)(\lambda - 18),$$

it follows that the eigenvalues of A are $\lambda_1 = 8$ and $\lambda_2 = 18$. Thus the equation of the rotated conic is

$$8(x')^2 + 18(y')^2 - 72 = 0,$$

which, when written in the standard form

$$\frac{(x')^2}{3^2} + \frac{(y')^2}{2^2} = 1,$$

we recognize as the equation of an ellipse. (See Figure 7.4.)

In Example 6, the eigenvalues of the matrix A are $\mathbf{x}_1 = \begin{bmatrix} 1 \\ 1 \end{bmatrix}$ and $\mathbf{x}_2 = \begin{bmatrix} -1 \\ 1 \end{bmatrix}$, which we can normalize to form the columns of P as follows.

$$P = \begin{bmatrix} \dfrac{1}{\sqrt{2}} & -\dfrac{1}{\sqrt{2}} \\ \dfrac{1}{\sqrt{2}} & \dfrac{1}{\sqrt{2}} \end{bmatrix} = \begin{bmatrix} \cos\theta & -\sin\theta \\ \sin\theta & \cos\theta \end{bmatrix}.$$

Note first that $|P| = 1$, which implies that P is a rotation. Moreover, since $\cos 45° = 1/\sqrt{2} = \sin 45°$, we conclude that $\theta = 45°$, as shown in Figure 7.4.

The orthogonal matrix P specified in the Principal Axes Theorem is not unique. Its entries depend on the ordering of the eigenvalues λ_1 and λ_2 *and* on the subsequent choice of eigenvectors $\mathbf{x}_1$ and $\mathbf{x}_2$. For instance, in the solution of Example 6, any of the following choices of P would have worked.

$$\begin{matrix} \mathbf{x}_1 & \mathbf{x}_2 \end{matrix}$$
$$\begin{bmatrix} -\dfrac{1}{\sqrt{2}} & \dfrac{1}{\sqrt{2}} \\ -\dfrac{1}{\sqrt{2}} & -\dfrac{1}{\sqrt{2}} \end{bmatrix}$$
$$\lambda_1 = 8, \lambda_2 = 18$$
$$\theta = 225°$$

$$\begin{matrix} \mathbf{x}_1 & \mathbf{x}_2 \end{matrix}$$
$$\begin{bmatrix} -\dfrac{1}{\sqrt{2}} & -\dfrac{1}{\sqrt{2}} \\ \dfrac{1}{\sqrt{2}} & -\dfrac{1}{\sqrt{2}} \end{bmatrix}$$
$$\lambda_1 = 18, \lambda_2 = 8$$
$$\theta = 135°$$

$$\begin{matrix} \mathbf{x}_1 & \mathbf{x}_2 \end{matrix}$$
$$\begin{bmatrix} \dfrac{1}{\sqrt{2}} & \dfrac{1}{\sqrt{2}} \\ -\dfrac{1}{\sqrt{2}} & \dfrac{1}{\sqrt{2}} \end{bmatrix}$$
$$\lambda_1 = 18, \lambda_2 = 8$$
$$\theta = 315°$$

For any of these choices of P, the graph of the rotated conic will, of course, be the same. (See Figure 7.5.)

Figure 7.5

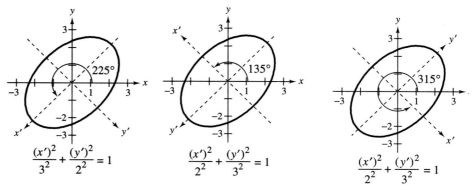

$$\frac{(x')^2}{3^2} + \frac{(y')^2}{2^2} = 1 \qquad \frac{(x')^2}{2^2} + \frac{(y')^2}{3^2} = 1 \qquad \frac{(x')^2}{2^2} + \frac{(y')^2}{3^2} = 1$$

We summarize the steps used to apply the Principal Axes Theorem as follows.
1. Form the matrix A and find its eigenvalues λ_1 and λ_2.
2. Find eigenvectors corresponding to λ_1 and λ_2. Normalize these eigenvectors to form the columns of P.

3. If $|P| = -1$, then multiply one of the columns of P by -1 to obtain a matrix of the form

$$P = \begin{bmatrix} \cos \theta & -\sin \theta \\ \sin \theta & \cos \theta \end{bmatrix}$$

4. The angle θ represents the angle of rotation of the conic.
5. The equation of the rotated conic is

$$\lambda_1 (x')^2 + \lambda_2 (y')^2 + [d \ \ e] PX' + f = 0.$$

Example 7 shows how to apply the Principal Axes Theorem to rotate a conic whose center has been translated away from the origin.

EXAMPLE 7   ***Rotation of a Conic***

Perform a rotation of axes to eliminate the xy-term in the quadratic equation

$$3x^2 - 10xy + 3y^2 + 16\sqrt{2}x - 32 = 0.$$

Solution   The matrix of the quadratic form associated with this equation is

$$A = \begin{bmatrix} 3 & -5 \\ -5 & 3 \end{bmatrix}.$$

The eigenvalues of A are $\lambda_1 = 8$ and $\lambda_2 = -2$, with corresponding eigenvectors of $\mathbf{x}_1 = (-1, 1)$ and $\mathbf{x}_2 = (-1, -1)$. This implies that the matrix P is

$$P = \begin{bmatrix} -\dfrac{1}{\sqrt{2}} & -\dfrac{1}{\sqrt{2}} \\ \dfrac{1}{\sqrt{2}} & -\dfrac{1}{\sqrt{2}} \end{bmatrix} = \begin{bmatrix} \cos \theta & -\sin \theta \\ \sin \theta & \cos \theta \end{bmatrix}, \text{ where } |P| = 1.$$

Since $\cos 135° = -1/\sqrt{2}$ and $\sin 135° = 1/\sqrt{2}$, we conclude that the angle of rotation is $135°$. Finally, from the matrix product

$$[d \ \ e]PX' = [16\sqrt{2} \ \ 0] \begin{bmatrix} -\dfrac{1}{\sqrt{2}} & -\dfrac{1}{\sqrt{2}} \\ \dfrac{1}{\sqrt{2}} & -\dfrac{1}{\sqrt{2}} \end{bmatrix} \begin{bmatrix} x' \\ y' \end{bmatrix}$$

$$= -16x' - 16y'$$

we conclude that the equation of the rotated conic is

$$8(x')^2 - 2(y')^2 - 16x' - 16y' - 32 = 0.$$

Figure 7.6

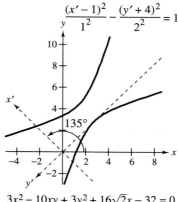

$$\frac{(x'-1)^2}{1^2} - \frac{(y'+4)^2}{2^2} = 1$$

$$3x^2 - 10xy + 3y^2 + 16\sqrt{2}x - 32 = 0$$

In standard form, the equation

$$\frac{(x'-1)^2}{1^2} - \frac{(y'+4)^2}{2^2} = 1$$

is recognizable as the equation of a hyperbola. Its graph is shown in Figure 7.6.

Quadratic forms can also be used to analyze equations of quadric surfaces in space, which are the three-dimensional analogues of conic sections. The equation of a quadric surface in space is a second-degree polynomial of the form

$$ax^2 + by^2 + cz^2 + dxy + exz + fyz + gx + hy + iz + j = 0.$$

There are six basic types of quadric surfaces: ellipsoids, hyperboloids of one sheet, hyperboloids of two sheets, elliptic cones, elliptic paraboloids, and hyperbolic paraboloids. The intersection of a surface with a plane, called the **trace** of the surface in the plane, is useful to help visualize the graph of the surface in space. The six basic types of quadric surfaces, together with their traces, are shown on the following pages.

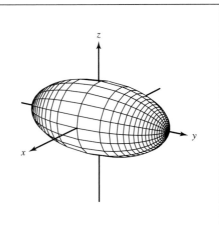

Ellipsoid

$$\frac{x^2}{a^2} + \frac{y^2}{b^2} + \frac{z^2}{c^2} = 1$$

Trace	*Plane*
Ellipse	Parallel to xy-plane
Ellipse	Parallel to xz-plane
Ellipse	Parallel to yz-plane

The surface is a sphere if $a = b = c \neq 0$.

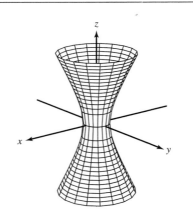

Hyperboloid of One Sheet

$$\frac{x^2}{a^2} + \frac{y^2}{b^2} - \frac{z^2}{c^2} = 1$$

Trace	*Plane*
Ellipse	Parallel to xy-plane
Hyperbola	Parallel to xz-plane
Hyperbola	Parallel to yz-plane

The axis of the hyperboloid corresponds to the variable whose coefficient is negative.

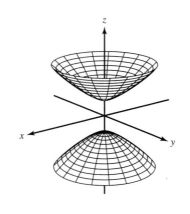

Hyperboloid of Two Sheets

$$\frac{z^2}{c^2} - \frac{x^2}{a^2} - \frac{y^2}{b^2} = 1$$

Trace	*Plane*
Ellipse	Parallel to xy-plane
Hyperbola	Parallel to xz-plane
Hyperbola	Parallel to yz-plane

The axis of the hyperboloid corresponds to the variable whose coefficient is positive. There is no trace in the coordinate plane perpendicular to this axis.

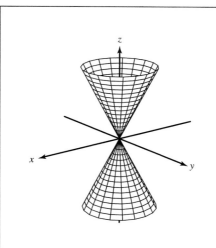

Elliptic Cone

$$\frac{x^2}{a^2} + \frac{y^2}{b^2} - \frac{z^2}{c^2} = 0$$

Trace	Plane
Ellipse	Parallel to xy-plane
Hyperbola	Parallel to xz-plane
Hyperbola	Parallel to yz-plane

The axis of the cone corresponds to the variable whose coefficient is negative. The traces in the coordinate planes parallel to this axis are intersecting lines.

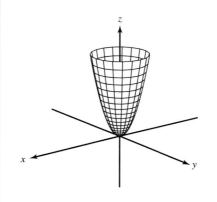

Elliptic Paraboloid

$$z = \frac{x^2}{a^2} + \frac{y^2}{b^2}$$

Trace	Plane
Ellipse	Parallel to xy-plane
Parabola	Parallel to xz-plane
Parabola	Parallel to yz-plane

The axis of the paraboloid corresponds to the variable raised to the first power.

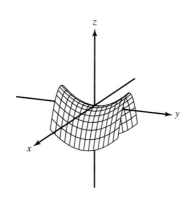

Hyperbolic Paraboloid

$$z = \frac{y^2}{b^2} - \frac{x^2}{a^2}$$

Trace	Plane
Hyperbola	Parallel to xy-plane
Parabola	Parallel to xz-plane
Parabola	Parallel to yz-plane

The axis of the paraboloid corresponds to the variable raised to the first power.

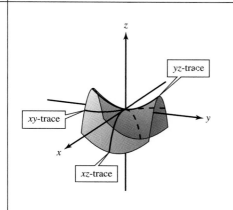

We define the quadratic form of the equation

$$ax^2 + by^2 + cz^2 + dxy + exz + fyz + gx + hy + iz + j = 0 \quad \text{Quadric surface}$$

to be

$$ax^2 + by^2 + cz^2 + dxy + exz + fyz. \qquad\qquad \text{Quadratic form}$$

The corresponding matrix is

$$\begin{bmatrix} a & \dfrac{d}{2} & \dfrac{e}{2} \\[2ex] \dfrac{d}{2} & b & \dfrac{f}{2} \\[2ex] \dfrac{e}{2} & \dfrac{f}{2} & c \end{bmatrix}.$$

In its three-dimensional version, the Principal Axes Theorem relates the eigenvalues and eigenvectors of A to the equation of the rotated surface. For instance, the matrix A associated with the quadratic equation

$$5x^2 + 4y^2 + 5z^2 + 8xz - 36 = 0$$

is

$$A = \begin{bmatrix} 5 & 0 & 4 \\ 0 & 4 & 0 \\ 4 & 0 & 5 \end{bmatrix},$$

which has eigenvalues of $\lambda_1 = 1$, $\lambda_2 = 4$, and $\lambda_3 = 9$. Thus, in the rotated $x'y'z'$-system, the quadratic equation is

$$(x')^2 + 4(y')^2 + 9(z')^2 - 36 = 0,$$

Figure 7.7

which in standard form is

$$\frac{(x')^2}{6^2} + \frac{(y')^2}{3^2} + \frac{(z')^2}{2^2} = 1.$$

The graph of this equation is an ellipsoid. As shown in Figure 7.7, the $x'y'z'$-axes represent a counterclockwise rotation of $45°$ about the y-axis. Moreover, the orthogonal matrix

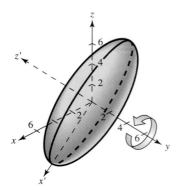

$$P = \begin{bmatrix} \dfrac{1}{\sqrt{2}} & 0 & \dfrac{1}{\sqrt{2}} \\[2ex] 0 & 1 & 0 \\[2ex] -\dfrac{1}{\sqrt{2}} & 0 & \dfrac{1}{\sqrt{2}} \end{bmatrix},$$

whose columns are the eigenvectors of A, has the property that $P^T A P$ is diagonal.

SECTION 7.4 ☐ EXERCISES

Population Growth

In Exercises 1–4, use the given age transition matrix A and age distribution vector $\mathbf{x}_1$ to find the age distribution vectors $\mathbf{x}_2$ and $\mathbf{x}_3$.

1. $A = \begin{bmatrix} 0 & 2 \\ \frac{1}{2} & 0 \end{bmatrix}$, $\mathbf{x}_1 = \begin{bmatrix} 10 \\ 10 \end{bmatrix}$

2. $A = \begin{bmatrix} 0 & 4 \\ \frac{1}{16} & 0 \end{bmatrix}$, $\mathbf{x}_1 = \begin{bmatrix} 160 \\ 160 \end{bmatrix}$

3. $A = \begin{bmatrix} 0 & 3 & 4 \\ 1 & 0 & 0 \\ 0 & \frac{1}{2} & 0 \end{bmatrix}$, $\mathbf{x}_1 = \begin{bmatrix} 12 \\ 12 \\ 12 \end{bmatrix}$

4. $A = \begin{bmatrix} 0 & 2 & 2 & 0 \\ \frac{1}{4} & 0 & 0 & 0 \\ 0 & 1 & 0 & 0 \\ 0 & 0 & \frac{1}{2} & 0 \end{bmatrix}$, $\mathbf{x}_1 = \begin{bmatrix} 100 \\ 100 \\ 100 \\ 100 \end{bmatrix}$

5. Find a stable age distribution for the age transition matrix in Exercise 1.

6. Find a stable age distribution for the age transition matrix in Exercise 2.

7. Find a stable age distribution for the age transition matrix in Exercise 3.

8. Find a stable age distribution for the age transition matrix in Exercise 4.

9. A population has the following characteristics.

   (a) A total of 75% of the population survives its first year. Of that 75%, 25% survives the second year. The maximum life span is three years.

   (b) The average number of offspring for each member of the population is 2 the first year, 4 the second year, and 2 the third year.

   The population now consists of 120 members in each of the three age classes. How many will there be in each age class in one year? In two years?

10. Find the limit (if it exists) of $A^n\mathbf{x}_1$ as n approaches infinity for the following matrix.

$$A = \begin{bmatrix} 0 & 2 \\ \frac{1}{2} & 0 \end{bmatrix} \quad \text{and} \quad \mathbf{x}_1 = \begin{bmatrix} a \\ a \end{bmatrix}$$

Systems of Linear Differential Equations (Calculus)

In Exercises 11–14, solve the given system of first-order linear differential equations.

11. $\begin{aligned} y_1{}' &= 2y_1 \\ y_2{}' &= y_2 \end{aligned}$

12. $\begin{aligned} y_1{}' &= -3y_1 \\ y_2{}' &= 4y_2 \end{aligned}$

13. $\begin{aligned} y_1{}' &= -y_1 \\ y_2{}' &= 6y_2 \\ y_3{}' &= y_3 \end{aligned}$

14. $\begin{aligned} y_1{}' &= 5y_1 \\ y_2{}' &= -2y_2 \\ y_3{}' &= -3y_3 \end{aligned}$

In Exercises 15–22, solve the given system of first-order linear differential equations.

15. $\begin{aligned} y_1{}' &= y_1 - 4y_2 \\ y_2{}' &= 2y_2 \end{aligned}$

16. $\begin{aligned} y_1{}' &= y_1 - 4y_2 \\ y_2{}' &= -2y_1 + 8y_2 \end{aligned}$

17. $\begin{aligned} y_1{}' &= y_1 + 2y_2 \\ y_2{}' &= 2y_1 + y_2 \end{aligned}$

18. $\begin{aligned} y_1{}' &= y_1 - y_2 \\ y_2{}' &= 2y_1 + 4y_2 \end{aligned}$

19. $\begin{aligned} y_1{}' &= -3y_2 + 5y_3 \\ y_2{}' &= -4y_1 + 4y_2 - 10y_3 \\ y_3{}' &= 4y_3 \end{aligned}$

20. $\begin{aligned} y_1{}' &= -2y_1 + y_3 \\ y_2{}' &= 3y_2 + 4y_3 \\ y_3{}' &= y_3 \end{aligned}$

21. $\begin{aligned} y_1{}' &= y_1 - 2y_2 + y_3 \\ y_2{}' &= 2y_2 + 4y_3 \\ y_3{}' &= 3y_3 \end{aligned}$

22. $\begin{aligned} y_1{}' &= 2y_1 + y_2 + y_3 \\ y_2{}' &= y_1 + y_2 \\ y_3{}' &= y_1 + y_3 \end{aligned}$

In Exercises 23–26, write out the system of first-order linear differential equations represented by the matrix equation $\mathbf{y}' = A\mathbf{y}$. Then verify the indicated general solution.

23. $A = \begin{bmatrix} 1 & 1 \\ 0 & 1 \end{bmatrix}$, $\begin{aligned} y_1 &= C_1e^t + C_2te^t \\ y_2 &= C_2e^t \end{aligned}$

24. $A = \begin{bmatrix} 1 & -1 \\ 1 & 1 \end{bmatrix}$, $\begin{aligned} y_1 &= C_1e^t \cos t + C_2e^t \sin t \\ y_2 &= -C_2e^t \cos t + C_1e^t \sin t \end{aligned}$

25. $A = \begin{bmatrix} 0 & 1 & 0 \\ 0 & 0 & 1 \\ 0 & -4 & 0 \end{bmatrix}$, $\begin{aligned} y_1 &= C_1 + C_2 \cos 2t + C_3 \sin 2t \\ y_2 &= 2C_3 \cos 2t - 2C_2 \sin 2t \\ y_3 &= -4C_2 \cos 2t - 4C_3 \sin 2t \end{aligned}$

26. $A = \begin{bmatrix} 0 & 1 & 0 \\ 0 & 0 & 1 \\ 1 & -3 & 3 \end{bmatrix}$,

$$y_1 = \qquad C_1 e^t + \qquad C_2 t e^t + C_3 t^2 e^t$$
$$y_2 = \qquad (C_1 + C_2)e^t + (C_2 + 2C_3)t e^t + C_3 t^2 e^t$$
$$y_3 = (C_1 + 2C_2 + 2C_3)e^t + (C_2 + 4C_3)t e^t + C_3 t^2 e^t$$

Quadratic Forms

In Exercises 27–32, find the matrix of the quadratic form associated with the given equation.

27. $x^2 + y^2 - 4 = 0$ **28.** $x^2 - 4xy + y^2 - 4 = 0$

29. $9x^2 + 10xy - 4y^2 - 36 = 0$

30. $12x^2 - 5xy - x + 2y - 20 = 0$

31. $10xy - 10y^2 + 4x - 48 = 0$

32. $16x^2 - 4xy + 20y^2 - 72 = 0$

In Exercises 33–38, find the matrix A of the quadratic form associated with the given equation. In each case, find the eigenvalues of A and an orthogonal matrix P such that $P^T A P$ is diagonal.

33. $2x^2 - 3xy - 2y^2 + 10 = 0$

34. $5x^2 - 2xy + 5y^2 + 10x - 17 = 0$

35. $13x^2 + 6\sqrt{3}xy + 7y^2 - 16 = 0$

36. $3x^2 - 2\sqrt{3}xy + y^2 + 2x + 2\sqrt{3}y = 0$

37. $16x^2 - 24xy + 9y^2 - 60x - 80y + 100 = 0$

38. $17x^2 + 32xy - 7y^2 - 75 = 0$

In Exercises 39–46, use the Principal Axes Theorem to perform a rotation of axes to eliminate the xy-term in the given quadratic equation. Identify the resulting rotated conic and give its equation in the new coordinate system.

39. $13x^2 - 8xy + 7y^2 - 45 = 0$

40. $x^2 + 4xy + y^2 - 9 = 0$

41. $7x^2 + 32xy - 17y^2 - 50 = 0$

42. $2x^2 - 4xy + 5y^2 - 36 = 0$

43. $2x^2 + 4xy + 2y^2 + 6\sqrt{2}x + 2\sqrt{2}y + 4 = 0$

44. $8x^2 + 8xy + 8y^2 + 10\sqrt{2}x + 26\sqrt{2}y + 31 = 0$

45. $xy + x - 2y + 3 = 0$

46. $5x^2 - 2xy + 5y^2 + 10\sqrt{2}x = 0$

In Exercises 47 and 48, find the matrix A of the quadratic form associated with the given equation. Then find the equation of the rotated quadric surface in which the xy, xz, and yz terms have been eliminated.

47. $3x^2 - 2xy + 3y^2 + 8z^2 - 16 = 0$

48. $2x^2 + 2y^2 + 2z^2 + 2xy + 2xz + 2yz - 1 = 0$

49. Let P be a 2×2 orthogonal matrix such that $|P| = 1$. Show that there exists a number θ, $0 \le \theta < 2\pi$, such that

$$P = \begin{bmatrix} \cos\theta & -\sin\theta \\ \sin\theta & \cos\theta \end{bmatrix}.$$

CHAPTER 7 ☐ REVIEW EXERCISES

In Exercises 1–6, find (a) the characteristic equation of A, (b) the real eigenvalues of A, and (c) a basis for the eigenspace corresponding to each eigenvalue.

1. $A = \begin{bmatrix} 2 & 1 \\ 5 & -2 \end{bmatrix}$ **2.** $A = \begin{bmatrix} 2 & 1 \\ -4 & -2 \end{bmatrix}$

3. $A = \begin{bmatrix} 9 & 4 & -3 \\ -2 & 0 & 6 \\ -1 & -4 & 11 \end{bmatrix}$ **4.** $A = \begin{bmatrix} -4 & 1 & 2 \\ 0 & 1 & 1 \\ 0 & 0 & 3 \end{bmatrix}$

5. $A = \begin{bmatrix} 2 & 0 & 1 \\ 0 & 3 & 4 \\ 0 & 0 & 1 \end{bmatrix}$ **6.** $A = \begin{bmatrix} 2 & 1 & 0 & 0 \\ 1 & 2 & 0 & 0 \\ 0 & 0 & 2 & 1 \\ 0 & 0 & 1 & 2 \end{bmatrix}$

In Exercises 7–10, determine whether A is diagonalizable. If it is, find a nonsingular matrix P such that $P^{-1}AP$ is diagonal.

7. $A = \begin{bmatrix} -2 & -1 & 3 \\ 0 & 1 & 2 \\ 0 & 0 & 1 \end{bmatrix}$ **8.** $A = \begin{bmatrix} 3 & -2 & 2 \\ -2 & 0 & -1 \\ 2 & -1 & 0 \end{bmatrix}$

9. $A = \begin{bmatrix} 1 & 0 & 2 \\ 0 & 1 & 0 \\ 2 & 0 & 1 \end{bmatrix}$ **10.** $A = \begin{bmatrix} 2 & -1 & 1 \\ -2 & 3 & -2 \\ -1 & 1 & 0 \end{bmatrix}$

11. Show that if $0 < \theta < \pi$, then the transformation for a counterclockwise rotation through an angle θ has no real eigenvalues.

12. For what value(s) of a does the matrix

$$A = \begin{bmatrix} 0 & 1 \\ a & 1 \end{bmatrix}$$

have the following characteristics?

(a) A has an eigenvalue of multiplicity 2.

(b) A has -1 and 2 as eigenvalues.

(c) A has real eigenvalues.

In Exercises 13 and 14, show that the given matrix is not diagonalizable.

13. $A = \begin{bmatrix} 3 & 0 & 0 \\ 1 & 3 & 0 \\ 0 & 0 & 3 \end{bmatrix}$ **14.** $A = \begin{bmatrix} 0 & 2 \\ 0 & 0 \end{bmatrix}$

In Exercises 15 and 16, determine whether the given matrices are similar. If they are, find a matrix P such that $A = P^{-1}BP$.

15. $A = \begin{bmatrix} 1 & 0 \\ 0 & 2 \end{bmatrix}$, $B = \begin{bmatrix} 2 & 0 \\ 0 & 1 \end{bmatrix}$

16. $A = \begin{bmatrix} 1 & 1 & 0 \\ 0 & 1 & 1 \\ 0 & 0 & 1 \end{bmatrix}$, $B = \begin{bmatrix} 1 & 1 & 0 \\ 0 & 1 & 0 \\ 0 & 0 & 1 \end{bmatrix}$

In Exercises 17–20, determine whether the given matrix is symmetric, orthogonal, both, or neither.

17. $A = \begin{bmatrix} -\dfrac{\sqrt{2}}{2} & \dfrac{\sqrt{2}}{2} \\ \dfrac{\sqrt{2}}{2} & \dfrac{\sqrt{2}}{2} \end{bmatrix}$ **18.** $A = \begin{bmatrix} -\dfrac{2}{3} & \dfrac{1}{3} & -\dfrac{2}{3} \\ \dfrac{2}{3} & \dfrac{2}{3} & -\dfrac{1}{3} \\ \dfrac{1}{3} & -\dfrac{2}{3} & \dfrac{2}{3} \end{bmatrix}$

19. $A = \begin{bmatrix} 0 & 0 & 1 \\ 0 & 1 & 0 \\ 1 & 0 & 1 \end{bmatrix}$ **20.** $A = \begin{bmatrix} \dfrac{4}{5} & 0 & \dfrac{3}{5} \\ 0 & 1 & 0 \\ -\dfrac{3}{5} & 0 & \dfrac{4}{5} \end{bmatrix}$

In Exercises 21–24, find an orthogonal matrix P that diagonalizes A.

21. $A = \begin{bmatrix} 3 & 4 \\ 4 & -3 \end{bmatrix}$ **22.** $A = \begin{bmatrix} 8 & 15 \\ 15 & -8 \end{bmatrix}$

23. $A = \begin{bmatrix} 2 & 0 & -1 \\ 0 & 1 & 0 \\ -1 & 0 & 2 \end{bmatrix}$ **24.** $A = \begin{bmatrix} 1 & 2 & 0 \\ 2 & 1 & 0 \\ 0 & 0 & 5 \end{bmatrix}$

In Exercises 25–30, find the steady-state probability vector (if it exists) for the given matrix. An eigenvector $\mathbf{v}$ of an $n \times n$ matrix A is called a **steady-state probability vector** if $A\mathbf{v} = \mathbf{v}$ and the components of $\mathbf{v}$ add up to 1.

25. $A = \begin{bmatrix} \dfrac{2}{3} & \dfrac{1}{2} \\ \dfrac{1}{3} & \dfrac{1}{2} \end{bmatrix}$ **26.** $A = \begin{bmatrix} \dfrac{1}{2} & 1 \\ \dfrac{1}{2} & 0 \end{bmatrix}$

27. $A = \begin{bmatrix} \dfrac{1}{2} & \dfrac{1}{4} & 0 \\ \dfrac{1}{2} & \dfrac{1}{2} & \dfrac{1}{2} \\ 0 & \dfrac{1}{4} & \dfrac{1}{2} \end{bmatrix}$ **28.** $A = \begin{bmatrix} \dfrac{1}{3} & \dfrac{2}{3} & \dfrac{1}{3} \\ \dfrac{1}{3} & \dfrac{1}{3} & 0 \\ \dfrac{1}{3} & 0 & \dfrac{2}{3} \end{bmatrix}$

29. $A = \begin{bmatrix} 0.7 & 0.1 & 0.1 \\ 0.2 & 0.7 & 0.1 \\ 0.1 & 0.2 & 0.8 \end{bmatrix}$ **30.** $A = \begin{bmatrix} 0.8 & 0.3 \\ 0.2 & 0.7 \end{bmatrix}$

31. Prove that if A is an $n \times n$ symmetric matrix, then $P^T A P$ is symmetric for any $n \times n$ matrix P.

32. Show that the characteristic equation of

$$A = \begin{bmatrix} 0 & 1 & 0 & 0 & \cdots & 0 \\ 0 & 0 & 1 & 0 & \cdots & 0 \\ \vdots & \vdots & \vdots & \vdots & & \vdots \\ 0 & 0 & 0 & 0 & \cdots & 1 \\ -a_0/a_n & -a_1/a_n & -a_2/a_n & -a_3/a_n & \cdots & -a_{n-1}/a_n \end{bmatrix},$$

$a_n \neq 0$, is $p(\lambda) = a_n\lambda^n + a_{n-1}\lambda^{n-1} + \cdots + a_3\lambda^3 + a_2\lambda^2 + a_1\lambda + a_0 = 0$. A is called the **companion matrix** of the polynomial p.

In Exercises 33 and 34, use the result of Exercise 32 to find the companion matrix A of the given polynomial and find the eigenvalues of A.

33. $p(\lambda) = -9\lambda + 4\lambda^2$

34. $p(\lambda) = 189 - 120\lambda - 7\lambda^2 + 2\lambda^3$

35. The characteristic equation of the matrix

$$A = \begin{bmatrix} 8 & -4 \\ 2 & 2 \end{bmatrix}$$

is $\lambda^2 - 10\lambda + 24 = 0$. Since $A^2 - 10A + 24I_2 = O$, we can find powers of A by the following process.

$$A^2 = 10A - 24I_2, \quad A^3 = 10A^2 - 24A,$$
$$A^4 = 10A^3 - 24A^2, \ldots$$

Use this process to find A^2 and A^3.

36. Repeat Exercise 35 for the matrix

$$A = \begin{bmatrix} 9 & 4 & -3 \\ -2 & 0 & 6 \\ -1 & -4 & 11 \end{bmatrix}.$$

37. Let A be an $n \times n$ matrix.

(a) Prove or disprove that an eigenvector of A is also an eigenvector of A^2.

(b) Prove or disprove that an eigenvector of A^2 is also an eigenvector of A.

38. Let A be an $n \times n$ matrix. Prove that if $A\mathbf{x} = \lambda\mathbf{x}$, then $\mathbf{x}$ is an eigenvector of $(A + cI)$. What is the corresponding eigenvalue?

39. Let A and B be $n \times n$ matrices. Prove that if A is nonsingular, then AB is similar to BA.

40. (a) Find a symmetric matrix B such that $B^2 = A$ for the matrix

$$A = \begin{bmatrix} 2 & 1 \\ 1 & 2 \end{bmatrix}.$$

(b) Generalize the result of part (a) by proving that if A is an $n \times n$ symmetric matrix with positive eigenvalues, then there exists a symmetric matrix B such that $B^2 = A$.

41. Find an orthogonal matrix P such that $P^{-1}AP$ is diagonal for the matrix

$$A = \begin{bmatrix} a & b \\ b & a \end{bmatrix}.$$

42. Let A be an $n \times n$ idempotent matrix (that is, $A^2 = A$). Describe the eigenvalues of A.

43. The following matrix has an eigenvalue $\lambda = 2$ of multiplicity 4.

$$A = \begin{bmatrix} 2 & a & 0 & 0 \\ 0 & 2 & b & 0 \\ 0 & 0 & 2 & c \\ 0 & 0 & 0 & 2 \end{bmatrix}$$

(a) Under what conditions is A diagonalizable?

(b) Under what conditions does the eigenspace of $\lambda = 2$ have dimension 1? 2? 3?

44. Determine all $n \times n$ symmetric matrices that have 0 as their only eigenvalue.

Population Growth

In Exercises 45–48, use the given age transition matrix A and the age distribution vector $\mathbf{x}_1$ to find the age distribution vectors $\mathbf{x}_2$ and $\mathbf{x}_3$. Then find a stable age distribution for the population.

45. $A = \begin{bmatrix} 0 & 1 \\ \frac{1}{4} & 0 \end{bmatrix}$, $\mathbf{x}_1 = \begin{bmatrix} 100 \\ 100 \end{bmatrix}$

46. $A = \begin{bmatrix} 0 & 1 \\ \frac{3}{4} & 0 \end{bmatrix}$, $\mathbf{x}_1 = \begin{bmatrix} 32 \\ 32 \end{bmatrix}$

47. $A = \begin{bmatrix} 0 & 3 & 12 \\ 1 & 0 & 0 \\ 0 & \frac{1}{6} & 0 \end{bmatrix}$, $\mathbf{x}_1 = \begin{bmatrix} 300 \\ 300 \\ 300 \end{bmatrix}$

48. $A = \begin{bmatrix} 0 & 2 & 2 \\ \frac{1}{2} & 0 & 0 \\ 0 & 0 & 0 \end{bmatrix}$, $\mathbf{x}_1 = \begin{bmatrix} 240 \\ 240 \\ 240 \end{bmatrix}$

Systems of Linear Differential Equations (Calculus)

In Exercises 49–52, solve the given system of first-order linear differential equations.

49. $y_1' = y_1 + 2y_2$
$\quad\ y_2' = 0$

50. $y_1' = 3y_1$
$\quad\ y_2' = y_1 - y_2$

51. $y_1' = y_2$
$\quad\ y_2' = y_1$

52. $y_1' = 6y_1 - y_2 + 2y_3$
$\quad\ y_2' = \quad\ \ 3y_2 - y_3$
$\quad\ y_3' = \quad\quad\quad\quad y_3$

Quadratic Forms

In Exercises 53–56, find the matrix A of the quadratic form associated with the given equation. In each case, find an orthogonal matrix P such that P^TAP is diagonal. Sketch the graph of each equation.

53. $x^2 + 3xy + y^2 - 3 = 0$

54. $x^2 - \sqrt{3}xy + 2y^2 - 10 = 0$

55. $xy - 2 = 0$

56. $9x^2 - 24xy + 16y^2 - 400x - 300y = 0$

CHAPTER 7   PROJECTS

1   Population Growth and Dynamical Systems-I

Systems of differential equations often arise in biological applications of population growth of various species of animals. These equations are called **dynamical systems** because they describe the changes in a system as a function of time. Suppose that over time t you are studying the populations of predator sharks $y_1(t)$ and their small fish prey, $y_2(t)$. One simple model for the relative growth of these populations is

$$y'_1(t) = ay_1(t) + by_2(t) \qquad \text{Predator}$$
$$y'_2(t) = cy_1(t) + dy_2(t) \qquad \text{Prey}$$

where a, b, c, and d are constants that depend on the particular species being studied and on factors such as environment, available food, other competing species, and so on. Generally, the constants a and d are positive, reflecting the growth rates of the individual species. If the species are in a predator–prey relationship, then $b > 0$ and $c < 0$ indicate that increases in prey fish y_2 would cause an increase in y_1, whereas an increase in the predator y_1 would cause a decrease in y_2.

Suppose that the following system of linear differential equations models the populations of sharks $y_1(t)$ and prey fish $y_2(t)$.

$$y'_1(t) = \quad 0.5y_1(t) + 0.6y_2(t) \qquad y_1(0) = 36$$
$$y'_2(t) = -0.4y_1(t) + 3.0y_2(t) \qquad y_2(0) = 121$$

1. Use the diagonalization techniques of this chapter to find the populations $y_1(t)$ and $y_2(t)$ at any time $t > 0$.
2. Interpret the solution in terms of the long-term population trend for the two species. Does one species ultimately disappear? Why or why not?
3. If you have access to a computer or graphing calculator, graph the solutions $y_1(t)$ and $y_2(t)$ over the domain $0 \le t \le 3$.
4. Use the explicit solution found in part (1) to explain why the quotient $y_2(t)/y_1(t)$ approaches a limit as t increases.
5. If you have access to a computer or graphing calculator that can numerically solve differential equations, use it to graph the solution to the original system of equations. Does this numerical approximation appear to be accurate?

(In the project for Chapter 8, you are asked to analyze another population model for which the long-term trend is quite different.)

For Further Reference You can learn more about dynamical systems and population modeling in most books on differential equations. For example, *Differential Equations and Their Applications*, fourth edition, by Martin Braun, Springer-Verlag, 1992, discusses the theory and applications of systems of linear differential equations. An especially interesting application of *nonlinear* differential equations is section 4.10: "Predator–prey problems; or why the percentage of sharks caught in the Mediterranean Sea rose dramatically during World War I."

2 The Fibonacci Sequence

The **Fibonacci sequence** is named after the Italian mathematician Leonard Fibonacci of Pisa (1170–1250). The simplest way to form this sequence is to define the first two terms to be $x_1 = 1$ and $x_2 = 1$, and then define the nth term as the sum of its two immediate predecessors. That is,

$$x_n = x_{n-1} + x_{n-2}.$$

Therefore, the third term is $2 = 1 + 1$, the fourth term is $3 = 2 + 1$, and so on. The formula $x_n = x_{n-1} + x_{n-2}$ is called *recursive* because the first $n - 1$ terms must be calculated before we can calculate the nth term. Is it possible to find an *explicit* formula for the nth term of the Fibonacci sequence? In this project, you will use eigenvalues and diagonalization to derive such a formula.

1. Use the formula $x_n = x_{n-1} + x_{n-2}$ to calculate the first 12 terms in the Fibonacci sequence.

2. Explain how the matrix equation
$$\begin{bmatrix} 1 & 1 \\ 1 & 0 \end{bmatrix} \begin{bmatrix} x_{n-1} \\ x_{n-2} \end{bmatrix} = \begin{bmatrix} x_{n-1} + x_{n-2} \\ x_{n-1} \end{bmatrix}$$
   can be used to recursively generate the Fibonacci sequence.

3. Show that $A^{n-2} \begin{bmatrix} 1 \\ 1 \end{bmatrix} = \begin{bmatrix} x_n \\ x_{n-1} \end{bmatrix}$, where $A = \begin{bmatrix} 1 & 1 \\ 1 & 0 \end{bmatrix}$.

4. Find a matrix P that diagonalizes A.

5. Derive an explicit formula for the nth term of the Fibonacci sequence. Use this formula to calculate x_1, x_2, and x_3.

6. Use the explicit formula for the nth term of the Fibonacci sequence together with a computer or calculator to find x_{10} and x_{20}.

7. Calculate the quotient x_n/x_{n-1} for various large values of n. Does the quotient appear to be approaching a fixed number as n tends to infinity?

8. Determine the limit of x_n/x_{n-1} as n approaches infinity. Do you recognize this number?

For Further Reference You can learn more about Fibonacci numbers in most books on number theory. You might find it interesting to look at the *Fibonacci Quarterly*, the official journal of the Fibonacci Association.

CHAPTER 7   ☐   MATLAB EXERCISES

1. The MATLAB command **poly(A)** produces the coefficients of the characteristic polynomial of the square matrix A, beginning with the highest degree term. Find the characteristic polynomial of the following matrices.

   (a) $A = \begin{bmatrix} 2 & 3 \\ 1 & 4 \end{bmatrix}$

(b) $A = \begin{bmatrix} 1 & 2 & -2 \\ -2 & 5 & -2 \\ -6 & 6 & -3 \end{bmatrix}$

(c) $A = \begin{bmatrix} 1 & 2 & 3 & 4 \\ 5 & 6 & 7 & 8 \\ 9 & 10 & 11 & 12 \\ 13 & 14 & 15 & 16 \end{bmatrix}$

2. If we set **p = poly(A)**, then the command **roots(p)** calculates the roots of the characteristic polynomial of the matrix A. Use this sequence of commands to find the eigenvalues of the matrices in Exercise 1.

3. The MATLAB command **[V, D] = eig(A)** produces a diagonal matrix D containing the eigenvalues of A on the diagonal, and a matrix V whose columns are the corresponding eigenvectors. Use this command to find the eigenvalues and corresponding eigenvectors of the three matrices in Exercise 1.

4. Let

$$A = \begin{bmatrix} -2 & 2 & -3 \\ 2 & 1 & -6 \\ -1 & -2 & 0 \end{bmatrix}.$$

Use MATLAB to find the eigenvalues and corresponding eigenvectors of A, A^T, and A^{-1}. What do you observe?

5. Let

$$A = \begin{bmatrix} 4 & -5 \\ 2 & -3 \end{bmatrix}.$$

We can use MATLAB to diagonalize A as follows. First compute the eigenvalues and eigenvectors of A, using the command **[P, D] = eig(A).** The diagonal matrix D contains the eigenvalues of A, and the corresponding eigenvectors form the columns of P. Verify that P diagonalizes A by showing that $P^{-1}AP = D$.

6. Follow the procedure outlined in Exercise 5 to show that the matrix

$$A = \begin{bmatrix} 1 & 2 \\ 0 & 1 \end{bmatrix}$$

is *not* diagonalizable.

7. Follow the procedure outlined in Exercise 5 to diagonalize (if possible) the following matrices.

(a) $A = \begin{bmatrix} 2 & 3 \\ 1 & 4 \end{bmatrix}$

(b) $A = \begin{bmatrix} 1 & 2 & -2 \\ -2 & 5 & -2 \\ -6 & 6 & -3 \end{bmatrix}$

(c) $A = \begin{bmatrix} 1 & 2 & 3 & 4 \\ 5 & 6 & 7 & 8 \\ 9 & 10 & 11 & 12 \\ 13 & 14 & 15 & 16 \end{bmatrix}$

8. For a symmetric matrix A, the MATLAB command **[P, D] = eig(A)** will produce a diagonal matrix D containing the eigenvalues of A, and an *orthogonal* matrix P containing the corresponding eigenvectors. For instance, if

$$A = \begin{bmatrix} -2 & 2 \\ 2 & 1 \end{bmatrix}$$

is the matrix from Example 8, then the command **[P, D] = eig(A)** yields

$$P = \begin{bmatrix} 0.8944 & 0.4472 \\ -0.4472 & 0.8944 \end{bmatrix} \text{ and } D = \begin{bmatrix} -3 & 0 \\ 0 & 2 \end{bmatrix},$$

which is equivalent to the solution given in the text.

Use this procedure to orthogonally diagonalize the following symmetric matrices.

(a) $A = \begin{bmatrix} 2 & 3 \\ 3 & 4 \end{bmatrix}$

(b) $A = \begin{bmatrix} 1 & 2 & -2 \\ 2 & 5 & 0 \\ -2 & 0 & -3 \end{bmatrix}$

CUMULATIVE TEST FOR CHAPTERS 6 AND 7

Take this test as you would take a test in class. After you are done, check your work against the answers at the back of the book.

1. Determine whether the function $T: R^3 \to R^2$, $T(x, y, z) = (2x, y - x)$ is a linear transformation.

2. Determine whether the function $T: M_{2,2} \to R$, $T(A) = |A + A^T|$ is a linear transformation.

3. Let $T: R^2 \to R^3$ be the linear transformation defined by $T(\mathbf{v}) = A\mathbf{v}$, where

$$A = \begin{bmatrix} 1 & 0 \\ -1 & 0 \\ 0 & 0 \end{bmatrix}.$$

Find (a) $T(1, -2)$ and (b) the preimage of $(1, 3, 0)$.

4. Find the kernel of the linear transformation $T: R^4 \to R^4$, $T(x_1, x_2, x_3, x_4) = (x_1 - x_2, x_2 - x_1, 0, x_3 + x_4)$.

5. Let $T: R^4 \to R^2$ be the linear transformation given by $T(\mathbf{v}) = A\mathbf{v}$, where

$$A = \begin{bmatrix} 1 & 0 & 1 & 0 \\ 0 & -1 & 0 & -1 \end{bmatrix}.$$

Find a basis for (a) the kernel of T and (b) the range of T. (c) Determine the rank and nullity of T.

6. Find the standard matrix for the linear transformation given by

$$T(x, y, z) = (y - x, z - y, x - z).$$

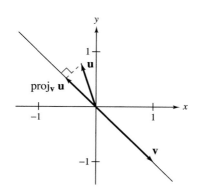

7. Find the standard matrix A of the linear transformation $\text{proj}_v\mathbf{u}: R^2 \to R^2$ that projects an arbitrary vector $\mathbf{u}$ onto the vector
$$\mathbf{v} = \begin{bmatrix} 1 \\ -1 \end{bmatrix}.$$
Use this matrix to find the images of the vectors $(1, 1)$ and $(-2, 2)$.

8. Find the inverse of the linear transformation $T: R^2 \to R^2$ given by $T(x, y) = (x - y, 2x + y)$. Verify that $(T^{-1} \circ T)(3, -2) = (3, -2)$.

9. Find the matrix of the linear transformation $T(x, y) = (y, 2x, x + y)$ relative to the bases $B = \{(1, 1), (1, 0)\}$ for R^2 and $B' = \{(1, 0, 0), (1, 1, 0), (1, 1, 1)\}$ for R^3. Use this matrix to find the image of the vector $(0, 1)$.

10. Let $B = \{(1, 0), (0, 1)\}$ and $B' = \{(1, 1), (1, 2)\}$ be bases for R^2.
    (a) Find the matrix A of $T: R^2 \to R^2$, $T(x, y) = (x - 2y, x + 4y)$ relative to the basis B.
    (b) Find the transition matrix P from B' to B.
    (c) Find the matrix A' of T relative to the basis B'.
    (d) Find $[T(\mathbf{v})]_{B'}$ if $[\mathbf{v}]_{B'} = \begin{bmatrix} 3 \\ -2 \end{bmatrix}$.
    (e) Verify your answer in (d) by finding $[\mathbf{v}]_B$ and $[T(\mathbf{v})]_B$.

11. Find the characteristic polynomial and the eigenvalues of the matrix.
$$A = \begin{bmatrix} 3 & 0 & 0 \\ 0 & 2 & 1 \\ 0 & 0 & 2 \end{bmatrix}$$

12. Find the eigenvalues and the corresponding eigenvectors of the matrix.
$$A = \begin{bmatrix} 1 & 2 & 1 \\ 0 & 3 & 1 \\ 0 & -3 & -1 \end{bmatrix}$$

13. Find the eigenvalues and the corresponding eigenvectors of the matrix.
$$A = \begin{bmatrix} 1 & -1 & 1 \\ 0 & 1 & 2 \\ 0 & 0 & 1 \end{bmatrix}$$

14. Find a nonsingular matrix P such that $P^{-1}AP$ is diagonal if
$$A = \begin{bmatrix} 1 & 3 \\ -1 & 5 \end{bmatrix}.$$

15. Find a basis B for R^3 such that the matrix for $T: R^3 \to R^3$, $T(x, y, z) = (2x - 2z, 2y - 2z, 3x - 3z)$ relative to B is diagonal.

16. Find an orthogonal matrix P such that P^TAP diagonalizes the symmetric matrix A,
$$A = \begin{bmatrix} 1 & 3 \\ 3 & 1 \end{bmatrix}.$$

17. Use the Gram-Schmidt orthonormalization process to find an orthogonal matrix P such that $P^T A P$ diagonalizes the symmetric matrix A,

$$A = \begin{bmatrix} 0 & 1 & 1 \\ 1 & 0 & 1 \\ 1 & 1 & 0 \end{bmatrix}.$$

18. Let A be an $n \times n$ matrix. Define the terms **eigenvalue** and **eigenvector** of A. How many eigenvalues can A have?

19. Define **orthogonal matrix** and determine the possible values of its determinant.

20. Prove that if A is similar to B and A is diagonalizable, then B is diagonalizable.

21. Prove that if 0 is an eigenvalue of A, then A is singular.

22. Prove that the eigenvectors corresponding to distinct eigenvalues of a symmetric matrix are orthogonal.

23. Prove that the range of a linear transformation $T: V \rightarrow W$ is a subspace of W.

24. Prove that a linear transformation is one-to-one if and only if its kernel is $\{0\}$.

25. Find all eigenvalues of A if $A^2 = 0$.

8 COMPLEX VECTOR SPACES

Charles
Hermite
1 8 2 2 – 1 9 0 1

*C*harles Hermite was born on Christmas Eve in Dieuze, France—the sixth of seven children. His father was a cloth merchant who had studied engineering. Although much of his early education occurred at home, he went to Paris to study when he was eighteen.

At the age of 20, Hermite published a paper titled *Considerations on the Algebraic Solution of the Equation of the Fifth Degree.* (Later in his life, Hermite showed how to solve a general fifth-degree equation by means of elliptic modular functions—such equations cannot be solved generally by algebraic means.) That same year, Hermite was admitted to the École Polytechnique, but he was dismissed from the school after one year. While at the Polytechnique, Hermite became acquainted with Joseph Liouville, who in turn introduced Hermite to Carl Jacobi. Hermite's

correspondence with Jacobi reveals Hermite's early understanding of abstract mathematics.

In 1848, Hermite gained a position at the Polytechnique (the same institution that had dismissed him five years earlier). With this appointment, Hermite's career finally began to take shape. In 1856 he was appointed to the Academy of Sciences, in 1869 to the École Normale, and finally in 1870 to a professorship at the Sorbonne, a position he held until his retirement in 1897.

Hermite is best known for his work with elliptic functions, for his proof that *e* is a transcendental number, and for his introduction of what are today called Hermite polynomials. Hermite was the first to use the term *orthogonal matrices*, and was the first to prove that if a matrix is equal to its own conjugate transpose, then its eigenvalues must be real.

8.1 COMPLEX NUMBERS

Thus far in the text, the scalar quantities we have used have been *real numbers*. In this chapter, we expand the set of scalars to include **complex numbers.**

In algebra we often need to solve quadratic equations such as $x^2 - 3x + 2 = 0$. The general quadratic equation is $ax^2 + bx + c = 0$ and its solutions are

$$x = \frac{-b \pm \sqrt{b^2 - 4ac}}{2a}$$

where the quantity in the radical $b^2 - 4ac$ is called the **discriminant.** If $b^2 - 4ac \geq 0$, then the solutions are ordinary real numbers. But what can we conclude about the solutions of a quadratic equation whose discriminant is negative? For example, the equation

$x^2 + 4 = 0$ has a discriminant of $b^2 - 4ac = -16$. From our experience with ordinary algebra, it is clear that there is no real number whose square is -16. However, by writing

$$\sqrt{-16} = \sqrt{16(-1)} = \sqrt{16}\sqrt{-1} = 4\sqrt{-1}$$

we see that the essence of the problem is that there is no real number whose square is -1. To solve the problem, mathematicians invented the **imaginary unit i,** which has the property that $i^2 = -1$. In terms of this imaginary unit, we can write

$$\sqrt{-16} = 4\sqrt{-1} = 4i.$$

We define the imaginary unit i as follows.

Definition of Imaginary Unit i

The number i is called the **imaginary unit** and is defined by

$$i = \sqrt{-1}$$

where $i^2 = -1$.

REMARK: When working with products involving square roots of negative numbers, be sure to convert to a multiple of i *before* multiplying. For instance, consider the following.

$$\sqrt{-1}\sqrt{-1} = i \cdot i = i^2 = -1 \qquad \text{Correct}$$

$$\sqrt{-1}\sqrt{-1} = \sqrt{(-1)(-1)} = \sqrt{1} = 1 \qquad \text{Incorrect}$$

With this single addition to the real number system, we can develop the system of **complex numbers.**

Definition of a Complex Number

If a and b are real numbers, then the number

$$a + bi$$

is a **complex number,** where a is the **real part** and bi is the **imaginary part** of the number. The form $a + bi$ is the **standard form** of a complex number.

Some examples of complex numbers written in standard form are $2 = 2 + 0i, 4 + 3i$, and $-6i = 0 - 6i$. The set of real numbers is a subset of the set of complex numbers. To see this, note that every real number a can be written as a complex number using $b = 0$. That is, for every real number,

$$a = a + 0i.$$

A complex number is uniquely determined by its real and imaginary parts. Thus, we say that two complex numbers are equal if and only if their real and imaginary parts are equal. That is, if $a + bi$ and $c + di$ are two complex numbers written in standard form, then

$$a + bi = c + di$$

if and only if $a = c$ and $b = d$.

The Complex Plane

Since a complex number is uniquely determined by its real and imaginary parts, it is natural to associate the number $a + bi$ with the ordered pair (a, b). With this association, we can graphically represent complex numbers as points in a coordinate plane that we call the **complex plane.** This plane is an adaptation of the rectangular coordinate plane. Specifically, we call the horizontal axis the **real axis** and the vertical axis the **imaginary axis.** For instance, Figure 8.1 shows the graph of two complex numbers, $3 + 2i$ and $-2 - i$. The number $3 + 2i$ is associated with the point $(3, 2)$ and the number $-2 - i$ is associated with the point $(-2, -1)$.

Another way to represent the complex number $a + bi$ is as a vector whose *horizontal* component is a and *vertical* component is b. (See Figure 8.2.) (Note that the use of the letter i to represent the imaginary unit is unrelated to the use of **i** to represent a unit vector.)

Figure 8.1

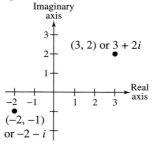

The Complex Plane

Figure 8.2

Vector Representation of a
Complex Number

Addition and Scalar Multiplication of Complex Numbers

Since a complex number consists of a real part added to a multiple of i, we define the operations of addition and multiplication in a manner consistent with the rules for operating with real numbers. For instance, to add (or subtract) two complex numbers, we add (or subtract) the real and imaginary parts separately.

Definition of Addition and Subtraction of Complex Numbers	The **sum** and **difference** of $a + bi$ and $c + di$ are defined as follows.
	$(a + bi) + (c + di) = (a + c) + (b + d)i$ **Sum**
	$(a + bi) - (c + di) = (a - c) + (b - d)i$ **Difference**

EXAMPLE 1   *Adding and Subtracting Complex Numbers*

(a) $(2 - 4i) + (3 + 4i) = (2 + 3) + (-4 + 4)i = 5$
(b) $(1 - 3i) - (3 + i) = (1 - 3) + (-3 - 1)i = -2 - 4i$

REMARK: Note in part (a) of Example 1 that the sum of two complex numbers can be a real number.

Using the vector representation of complex numbers, we can add or subtract two complex numbers geometrically using the parallelogram rule for vector addition, as shown in Figure 8.3.

Figure 8.3

Addition of Complex Numbers

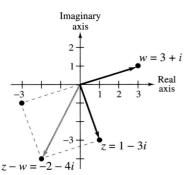

Subtraction of Complex Numbers

Many of the properties of addition of real numbers are valid for complex numbers as well. For instance, addition of complex numbers is both *associative* and *commutative*. Moreover, to find the sum of three or more complex numbers, we extend the definition of addition in the natural way. For example,

$$(2 + i) + (3 - 2i) + (-2 + 4i) = (2 + 3 - 2) + (1 - 2 + 4)i$$
$$= 3 + 3i.$$

To multiply a complex number by a *real* scalar, we use the following definition.

Definition of Scalar Multiplication	If c is a real number and $a + bi$ is a complex number, then the **scalar multiple** of c and $a + bi$ is defined to be $$c(a + bi) = ca + cbi.$$

Geometrically, multiplication of a complex number by a real scalar corresponds to the multiplication of a vector by a scalar, as shown in Figure 8.4.

EXAMPLE 2   *Operations with Complex Numbers*

(a) $3(2 + 7i) + 4(8 - i) = 6 + 21i + 32 - 4i$
$$= 38 + 17i$$

(b) $-4(1 + i) + 2(3 - i) - 3(1 - 4i) = -4 - 4i + 6 - 2i - 3 + 12i$
$$= -1 + 6i$$

Figure 8.4

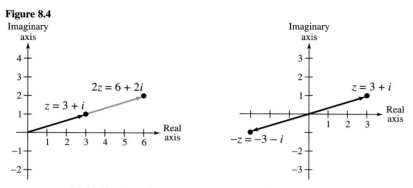

Multiplication of a Complex Number by a Real Number

With addition and scalar multiplication, the set of complex numbers forms a vector space of dimension two (where the scalars are the real numbers). You are asked to verify this in Exercise 55.

Multiplication of Complex Numbers

The operations of addition, subtraction, and multiplication by a real number have exact counterparts with the corresponding vector operations. By contrast, there is no direct counterpart for the multiplication of two complex numbers.

Definition of Multiplication of Complex Numbers	The **product** of the complex numbers $a + bi$ and $c + di$ is defined to be $$(a + bi)(c + di) = (ac - bd) + (ad + bc)i.$$

Rather than try to memorize this definition of the product of two complex numbers, you should simply apply the distributive law as follows.

$$(a + bi)(c + di) = a(c + di) + bi(c + di) \qquad \text{Distributive law}$$
$$= ac + (ad)i + (bc)i + (bd)i^2 \qquad \text{Distributive law}$$
$$= ac + (ad)i + (bc)i + (bd)(-1) \qquad \text{Use } i^2 = -1$$
$$= ac - bd + (ad)i + (bc)i \qquad \text{Commutative law}$$
$$= (ac - bd) + (ad + bc)i \qquad \text{Distributive law}$$

This is demonstrated in the following example.

EXAMPLE 3   *Multiplying Complex Numbers*

(a) $(-2)(1 - 3i) = -2 + 6i$

(b) $(2 - i)(4 + 3i) = 8 + 6i - 4i - 3i^2 = 8 + 6i - 4i - 3(-1)$
$$= 8 + 3 + 6i - 4i = 11 + 2i$$

Many computers and graphing calculators are capable of calculating with complex numbers. For example, on the TI-85 or the HP 48G, you express a complex number $a + bi$ as an ordered pair (a, b). Try verifying the result of Example 3(b) by multiplying $(2, -1)$ and $(4, 3)$. You should obtain the ordered pair $(11, 2)$.

EXAMPLE 4   *Complex Zeros of a Polynomial*

Use the Quadratic Formula to find the zeros of the polynomial

$$p(x) = x^2 - 6x + 13$$

and verify that $p(x) = 0$ for each zero.

Solution   Using the Quadratic Formula, we have

$$x = \frac{-b \pm \sqrt{b^2 - 4ac}}{2a} = \frac{6 \pm \sqrt{36 - 52}}{2}$$

$$= \frac{6 \pm \sqrt{-16}}{2} = \frac{6 \pm 4i}{2} = 3 \pm 2i.$$

Substituting these values of x into the polynomial $p(x)$, we have

$$p(3 + 2i) = (3 + 2i)^2 - 6(3 + 2i) + 13$$
$$= 9 + 12i - 4 - 18 - 12i + 13 = 0$$

and

$$p(3 - 2i) = (3 - 2i)^2 - 6(3 - 2i) + 13$$
$$= 9 - 12i - 4 - 18 + 12i + 13 = 0.$$

In Example 4, the two complex numbers $3 + 2i$ and $3 - 2i$ are **complex conjugates** of each other (together they are a **conjugate pair**). A well known result from algebra states that the complex zeros of a polynomial with real coefficients must occur in conjugate pairs. (See Review Exercise 72.) We will say more about complex conjugates in Section 8.2.

Complex Matrices

Now that we are able to add, subtract, and multiply complex numbers, we can apply these operations to matrices whose entries are complex numbers. We call such a matrix **complex.**

Definition of a Complex Matrix

A matrix whose entries are complex numbers is called a **complex matrix.**

All of the ordinary operations for matrices work for complex matrices, as demonstrated in the next two examples.

EXAMPLE 5   *Operations with Complex Matrices*

Let A and B be the complex matrices given by

$$A = \begin{bmatrix} i & 1+i \\ 2-3i & 4 \end{bmatrix} \quad \text{and} \quad B = \begin{bmatrix} 2i & 0 \\ i & 1+2i \end{bmatrix}$$

and determine the following matrices.

(a) $3A$ (b) $(2-i)B$ (c) $A + B$ (d) BA

Solution

(a) $3A = 3 \begin{bmatrix} i & 1+i \\ 2-3i & 4 \end{bmatrix} = \begin{bmatrix} 3i & 3+3i \\ 6-9i & 12 \end{bmatrix}$

(b) $(2-i)B = (2-i) \begin{bmatrix} 2i & 0 \\ i & 1+2i \end{bmatrix} = \begin{bmatrix} 2+4i & 0 \\ 1+2i & 4+3i \end{bmatrix}$

(c) $A + B = \begin{bmatrix} i & 1+i \\ 2-3i & 4 \end{bmatrix} + \begin{bmatrix} 2i & 0 \\ i & 1+2i \end{bmatrix} = \begin{bmatrix} 3i & 1+i \\ 2-2i & 5+2i \end{bmatrix}$

(d) $BA = \begin{bmatrix} 2i & 0 \\ i & 1+2i \end{bmatrix} \begin{bmatrix} i & 1+i \\ 2-3i & 4 \end{bmatrix} = \begin{bmatrix} -2 & -2+2i \\ 7+i & 3+9i \end{bmatrix}$

EXAMPLE 6   *Finding the Determinant of a Complex Matrix*

Find the determinant of the matrix

$$A = \begin{bmatrix} 2-4i & 2 \\ 3 & 5-3i \end{bmatrix}.$$

Solution

$$\det(A) = \begin{vmatrix} 2-4i & 2 \\ 3 & 5-3i \end{vmatrix} = (2-4i)(5-3i) - (2)(3)$$

$$= 10 - 20i - 6i - 12 - 6$$
$$= -8 - 26i.$$

TECHNOLOGY NOTE

Many computers and graphing calculators are capable of performing matrix operations on complex matrices. Try verifying the determinant calculation of the matrix from Example 6. You should obtain the same answer, $(-8, -26)$.

SECTION 8.1 ☐ EXERCISES

In Exercises 1–6, determine the value of the given expression.

1. $\sqrt{-2}\sqrt{-3}$ **2.** $\sqrt{8}\sqrt{-8}$

3. $\sqrt{-4}\sqrt{-4}$ **4.** i^3

5. i^4 **6.** $(-i)^7$

In Exercises 7–12, plot the given complex number.

7. $z = 6 - 2i$ **8.** $z = 3i$

9. $z = -5 + 5i$ **10.** $z = 7$

11. $z = 1 + 5i$ **12.** $z = 1 - 5i$

In Exercises 13 and 14, use vectors to illustrate graphically the given operation.

13. $-u$ and $2u$, where $u = 3 - i$

14. $3u$ and $-\frac{3}{2}u$, where $u = 2 + i$

In Exercises 15–18, determine x so that the complex numbers in each pair are equal.

15. $x + 3i, 6 + 3i$

16. $(2x - 8) + (x - 1)i, 2 + 4i$

17. $(x^2 + 6) + (2x)i, 15 + 6i$

18. $(-x + 4) + (x + 1)i, x + 3i$

In Exercises 19–26, find the sum and difference of the given complex numbers. Use vectors to illustrate your answers graphically.

19. $2 + 6i, 3 - 3i$ **20.** $1 + \sqrt{2}i, 2 - \sqrt{2}i$

21. $5 + i, 5 - i$ **22.** $i, 3 + i$

23. $6, -2i$ **24.** $12 - 7i, 3 + 4i$

25. $2 + i, 2 + i$ **26.** $2 + i, 2 - i$

In Exercises 27–36, find the product.

27. $(5 - 5i)(1 + 3i)$ **28.** $(3 + i)(\frac{2}{3} + i)$

29. $(\sqrt{7} - i)(\sqrt{7} + i)$ **30.** $(4 + \sqrt{2}i)(4 - \sqrt{2}i)$

31. $(a + bi)^2$ **32.** $(a + bi)(a - bi)$

33. $(1 + i)^3$ **34.** $(2 - i)(2 + 2i)(4 + i)$

35. $(a + bi)^3$ **36.** $(1 + i)^2(1 - i)^2$

In Exercises 37–44, determine the zeros of the given polynomial.

37. $2x^2 + 2x + 5$ **38.** $x^2 + x + 1$

39. $x^2 - 5x + 6$ **40.** $x^2 - 4x + 5$

41. $x^3 - 3x^2 + 4x - 2$ **42.** $x^3 - 2x^2 - 11x + 52$

43. $x^4 - 16$ **44.** $x^4 + 10x^2 + 9$

In Exercises 45–54, perform the indicated matrix operation using the following complex matrices.

$$A = \begin{bmatrix} 1 + i & 1 \\ 2 - 2i & -3i \end{bmatrix} \quad \text{and} \quad B = \begin{bmatrix} 1 - i & 3i \\ -3 & -i \end{bmatrix}$$

45. $A + B$ **46.** $B - A$

47. $2A$ **48.** $\frac{1}{2}B$

49. $2iA$ **50.** $\frac{1}{4}iB$

51. $\det(A + B)$ **52.** $\det(B)$

53. $5AB$ **54.** BA

55. Prove that the set of complex numbers, with the operations of addition and scalar multiplication (with *real* scalars), is a vector space of dimension two.

56. (a) Evaluate i^n for $n = 1, 2, 3, 4,$ and 5.

   (b) Calculate i^{57} and i^{1995}.

   (c) Find a general formula for i^n for any positive integer n.

57. Let $A = \begin{bmatrix} 0 & i \\ i & 0 \end{bmatrix}$.

   (a) Calculate A^n for $n = 1, 2, 3, 4,$ and 5.

   (b) Calculate A^{57} and A^{1995}.

   (c) Find a general formula for A^n for any positive integer n.

58. Prove that if the product of two complex numbers is zero, then at least one of the numbers must be zero.

8.2 CONJUGATES AND DIVISION OF COMPLEX NUMBERS

In Section 8.1, we mentioned that the complex zeros of a polynomial with real coefficients occur in conjugate pairs. For instance, we saw that the zeros of $p(x) = x^2 - 6x + 13$ are $3 + 2i$ and $3 - 2i$.

In this section, we examine some additional properties of complex conjugates. We begin with the definition of the conjugate of a complex number.

Definition of the Conjugate of a Complex Number	The **conjugate** of the complex number $z = a + bi$, is denoted by $\bar{z}$ and is given by $$\bar{z} = a - bi.$$

From this definition, we can see that the conjugate of a complex number is found by changing the sign of the imaginary part of the number, as demonstrated in the following example.

EXAMPLE 1   *Finding the Conjugate of a Complex Number*

Complex Number
(a) $z = -2 + 3i$
(b) $z = 4 - 5i$
(c) $z = -2i$
(d) $z = 5$

Conjugate
$\bar{z} = -2 - 3i$
$\bar{z} = 4 + 5i$
$\bar{z} = 2i$
$\bar{z} = 5$

REMARK: In part (d) of Example 1, note that 5 is its own complex conjugate. In general, it can be shown that a number is its own complex conjugate if and only if the number is real. (See Exercise 29.)

Geometrically, two points in the complex plane are conjugates if and only if they are reflections about the real (horizontal) axis, as shown in Figure 8.5.

Figure 8.5

Conjugate of a Complex Number

Complex conjugates have many useful properties. Some of these are given in Theorem 8.1.

Theorem 8.1

Properties of Complex Conjugates

For a complex number $z = a + bi$, the following properties are true.

1. $z\bar{z} = a^2 + b^2$
2. $z\bar{z} \geq 0$
3. $z\bar{z} = 0$ if and only if $z = 0$.
4. $\overline{(\bar{z})} = z$

Proof   To prove the first property, we let $z = a + bi$. Then $\bar{z} = a - bi$ and

$$z\bar{z} = (a + bi)(a - bi) = a^2 + abi - abi - b^2i^2 = a^2 + b^2.$$

The second and third properties follow directly from the first. Finally, the fourth property follows the definition of complex conjugate. That is,

$$\overline{(\bar{z})} = \overline{(a + bi)} = \overline{a - bi} = a + bi = z.$$

EXAMPLE 2   *Finding the Product of Complex Conjugates*

Find the product of $z = 1 - 2i$ and its complex conjugate.

Solution   Since $\bar{z} = 1 + 2i$ we have

$$z\bar{z} = (1 - 2i)(1 + 2i) = 1^2 + 2^2 = 1 + 4 = 5.$$

The Modulus of a Complex Number

Since a complex number can be represented by a vector in the complex plane, it makes sense to talk about the *length* of a complex number. We call this length the modulus of the complex number.

Definition of the Modulus of a Complex Number

The **modulus** of the complex number $z = a + bi$ is denoted by $|z|$ and is given by

$$|z| = \sqrt{a^2 + b^2}.$$

REMARK: The modulus of a complex number is also called the **absolute value** of the number. In fact, when $z = a + 0i$ is a real number, we have

$$|z| = \sqrt{a^2 + 0^2} = |a|.$$

EXAMPLE 3   *Finding the Modulus of a Complex Number*

For $z = 2 + 3i$ and $w = 6 - i$, determine the following.

  (a) $|z|$ (b) $|w|$ (c) $|zw|$

Solution   (a) $|z| = \sqrt{2^2 + 3^2} = \sqrt{13}$

(b) $|w| = \sqrt{6^2 + (-1)^2} = \sqrt{37}$

(c) Since $zw = (2 + 3i)(6 - i) = 15 + 16i$, we have

$$|zw| = \sqrt{15^2 + 16^2} = \sqrt{481}.$$

Note that in Example 3, $|zw| = |z|\,|w|$. In Exercise 30, you are asked to show that this multiplicative property of the modulus always holds. The modulus of a complex number is related to its conjugate in the following way.

Theorem 8.2

The Modulus of a Complex Number

For a complex number z,

$$|z|^2 = z\bar{z}.$$

Proof   Let $z = a + bi$, then $\bar{z} = a - bi$ and we have

$$z\bar{z} = (a + bi)(a - bi) = a^2 + b^2 = |z|^2.$$

Division of Complex Numbers

One of the most important uses of the conjugate of a complex number is in performing division in the complex number system. To define division of complex numbers, let us consider $z = a + bi$ and $w = c + di$ and assume that c and d are not both 0. If the quotient

$$\frac{z}{w} = x + yi$$

is to make sense, it would have to be true that

$$z = w(x + yi) = (c + di)(x + yi) = (cx - dy) + (dx + cy)i.$$

But, since $z = a + bi$, we can form the following linear system.

$$cx - dy = a$$
$$dx + cy = b$$

Solving this system of linear equations for x and y we get

$$x = \frac{ac + bd}{w\overline{w}} \quad \text{and} \quad y = \frac{bc - ad}{w\overline{w}}.$$

Now, since $z\overline{w} = (a + bi)(c - di) = (ac + bd) + (bc - ad)i$, we obtain the following definition.

Definition of Division of Complex Numbers

The **quotient** of the complex numbers $z = a + bi$ and $w = c + di$ is defined to be

$$\frac{z}{w} = \frac{a + bi}{c + di} = \frac{ac + bd}{c^2 + d^2} + \frac{bc - ad}{c^2 + d^2}i = \frac{1}{|w|^2}(z\overline{w})$$

provided $c^2 + d^2 \neq 0$.

REMARK: If $c^2 + d^2 = 0$, then $c = d = 0$, and therefore $w = 0$. In other words, just as is the case with real numbers, division of complex numbers by zero is not defined.

In practice, the quotient of two complex numbers can be found by multiplying the numerator and the denominator by the conjugate of the denominator, as follows.

$$\frac{a + bi}{c + di} = \frac{a + bi}{c + di}\left(\frac{c - di}{c - di}\right) = \frac{(a + bi)(c - di)}{(c + di)(c - di)}$$

$$= \frac{(ac + bd) + (bc - ad)i}{c^2 + d^2}$$

$$= \frac{ac + bd}{c^2 + d^2} + \frac{bc - ad}{c^2 + d^2}i$$

EXAMPLE 4   *Division of Complex Numbers*

(a) $\dfrac{1}{1 + i} = \dfrac{1}{1 + i}\left(\dfrac{1 - i}{1 - i}\right) = \dfrac{1 - i}{1^2 - i^2} = \dfrac{1 - i}{2} = \dfrac{1}{2} - \dfrac{1}{2}i$

(b) $\dfrac{2 - i}{3 + 4i} = \dfrac{2 - i}{3 + 4i}\left(\dfrac{3 - 4i}{3 - 4i}\right) = \dfrac{2 - 11i}{9 + 16} = \dfrac{2}{25} - \dfrac{11}{25}i$

Now that we are able to divide complex numbers, we can find the (multiplicative) inverse of a complex matrix, as demonstrated in Example 5.

EXAMPLE 5   *Finding the Inverse of a Complex Matrix*

Find the inverse of the matrix

$$A = \begin{bmatrix} 2 - i & -5 + 2i \\ 3 - i & -6 + 2i \end{bmatrix}$$

and verify your solution by showing that $AA^{-1} = I_2$.

Solution   Using the formula for the inverse of a 2×2 matrix given in Section 2.3, we have

$$A^{-1} = \frac{1}{|A|} \begin{bmatrix} -6 + 2i & 5 - 2i \\ -3 + i & 2 - i \end{bmatrix}.$$

Furthermore, because

$$\begin{aligned} |A| &= (2 - i)(-6 + 2i) - (-5 + 2i)(3 - i) \\ &= (-12 + 6i + 4i + 2) - (-15 + 6i + 5i + 2) \\ &= 3 - i \end{aligned}$$

we can write

$$\begin{aligned} A^{-1} &= \frac{1}{3 - i} \begin{bmatrix} -6 + 2i & 5 - 2i \\ -3 + i & 2 - i \end{bmatrix} \\ &= \frac{1}{3 - i} \left(\frac{1}{3 + i} \right) \begin{bmatrix} (-6 + 2i)(3 + i) & (5 - 2i)(3 + i) \\ (-3 + i)(3 + i) & (2 - i)(3 + i) \end{bmatrix} \\ &= \frac{1}{10} \begin{bmatrix} -20 & 17 - i \\ -10 & 7 - i \end{bmatrix}. \end{aligned}$$

To verify our solution, we multiply A and A^{-1} as follows.

$$\begin{aligned} AA^{-1} &= \begin{bmatrix} 2 - i & -5 + 2i \\ 3 - i & -6 + 2i \end{bmatrix} \frac{1}{10} \begin{bmatrix} -20 & 17 - i \\ -10 & 7 - i \end{bmatrix} \\ &= \frac{1}{10} \begin{bmatrix} 10 & 0 \\ 0 & 10 \end{bmatrix} \\ &= \begin{bmatrix} 1 & 0 \\ 0 & 1 \end{bmatrix} \end{aligned}$$

TECHNOLOGY NOTE

If your computer or graphing utility can perform operations with complex matrices, then you can verify the result of Example 5. For instance, on the HP 48G, you would enter the matrix A on the stack and then press the $1/x$ key. On the TI-85, if you have stored the matrix A, then you should evaluate A^{-1}.

The last theorem in this section summarizes some useful properties of complex conjugates.

Theorem 8.3

Properties of Complex Conjugates

For the complex numbers z and w, the following properties are true.
1. $\overline{z + w} = \overline{z} + \overline{w}$
2. $\overline{z - w} = \overline{z} - \overline{w}$
3. $\overline{zw} = \overline{z}\,\overline{w}$
4. $\overline{z/w} = \overline{z}/\overline{w}$

Proof   To prove the first property, let $z = a + bi$ and $w = c + di$. Then

$$\overline{z + w} = \overline{(a + c) + (b + d)i}$$
$$= (a + c) - (b + d)i$$
$$= (a - bi) + (c - di)$$
$$= \overline{z} + \overline{w}.$$

The proof of the second property is similar. The proofs of the other two properties are left to you.

SECTION 8.2   □   EXERCISES

In Exercises 1–4, find the complex conjugate $\overline{z}$ and graphically represent both z and $\overline{z}$.

1. $z = 6 - 3i$ **2.** $z = 2 + 5i$

3. $z = -8i$ **4.** $z = 4$

In Exercises 5–10, find the indicated modulus, where $z = 2 + i$, $w = -3 + 2i$, and $v = -5i$.

5. $|z|$ **6.** $|z^2|$ **7.** $|zw|$

8. $|wz|$ **9.** $|v|$ **10.** $|zv^2|$

11. Verify that $|wz| = |w|\,|z| = |zw|$, where $z = 1 + i$ and $w = -1 + 2i$.

12. Verify that $|zv^2| = |z|\,|v^2| = |z|\,|v|^2$, where $z = 1 + 2i$ and $v = -2 - 3i$.

In Exercises 13–18, perform the indicated operations.

13. $\dfrac{2 + i}{i}$ **14.** $\dfrac{1}{6 + 3i}$

15. $\dfrac{3 - \sqrt{2}i}{3 + \sqrt{2}i}$ **16.** $\dfrac{5 + i}{4 + i}$

17. $\dfrac{(2 + i)(3 - i)}{4 - 2i}$ **18.** $\dfrac{3 - i}{(2 - i)(5 + 2i)}$

In Exercises 19 and 20, find the following powers of the complex number z.

(a) z^2 (b) z^3 (c) z^{-1} (d) z^{-2}

19. $z = 2 - i$ **20.** $z = 1 + i$

In Exercises 21–26, determine whether the complex matrix A has an inverse. If A is invertible, find its inverse and verify that $AA^{-1} = I$.

21. $A = \begin{bmatrix} 6 & 3i \\ 2 - i & i \end{bmatrix}$ **22.** $A = \begin{bmatrix} 2i & -2 - i \\ 3 & 3i \end{bmatrix}$

23. $A = \begin{bmatrix} 1 - i & 2 \\ 1 & 1 + i \end{bmatrix}$ **24.** $A = \begin{bmatrix} 1 - i & 2 \\ 0 & 1 + i \end{bmatrix}$

25. $A = \begin{bmatrix} 1 & 0 & 0 \\ 0 & 1 - i & 0 \\ 0 & 0 & 1 + i \end{bmatrix}$ **26.** $A = \begin{bmatrix} i & 0 & 0 \\ 0 & i & 0 \\ 0 & 0 & i \end{bmatrix}$

In Exercises 27 and 28, determine all values of the complex number z for which A is singular. (Hint: Set $\det(A) = 0$ and solve for z.)

27. $A = \begin{bmatrix} 5 & z \\ 3i & 2 - i \end{bmatrix}$ **28.** $A = \begin{bmatrix} 2 & 2i & 1 + i \\ 1 - i & -1 + i & z \\ 1 & 0 & 0 \end{bmatrix}$

29. Prove that $z = \overline{z}$ if and only if z is real.

30. Prove that for any two complex numbers z and w, the following are true.

(a) $|zw| = |z|\,|w|$

(b) If $w \neq 0$, then $|z/w| = |z|/|w|$.

31. Describe the set of points in the complex plane that satisfy the following.

(a) $|z| = 3$ (b) $|z - 1 + i| = 5$

(c) $|z - i| \leq 2$ (d) $2 \leq |z| \leq 5$

32. Describe the set of points in the complex plane that satisfy the following.

(a) $|z| = 4$ (b) $|z - i| = 2$

(c) $|z + 1| \leq 1$ (d) $|z| > 3$

33. (a) Evaluate $(1/i)^n$ for $n = 1, 2, 3, 4,$ and 5.

(b) Calculate $(1/i)^{57}$ and $(1/i)^{1995}$.

(c) Find a general formula for $(1/i)^n$ for any positive integer n.

34. (a) Verify that $\left(\dfrac{1 + i}{\sqrt{2}} \right)^2 = i$.

(b) Find the two square roots of i.

(c) Find all zeros of the polynomial $x^4 + 1$.

8.3 POLAR FORM AND DEMOIVRE'S THEOREM

Figure 8.6

Complex Number: $a + bi$
Rectangular Form: (a, b)
Polar Form: (r, θ)

At this point we can add, subtract, multiply, and divide complex numbers. However, there is still one basic procedure that is missing from our algebra of complex numbers. To see this, consider the problem of finding the square root of a complex number such as i. When we use the four basic operations (addition, subtraction, multiplication, and division), there seems to be no reason to guess that

$$\sqrt{i} = \frac{1 + i}{\sqrt{2}}. \quad \text{That is,} \quad \left(\frac{1 + i}{\sqrt{2}} \right)^2 = i.$$

To work effectively with *powers* and *roots* of complex numbers, it is helpful to use a polar representation for complex numbers, as shown in Figure 8.6. Specifically, if $a + bi$ is a nonzero complex number, then we let θ be the angle from the positive x-axis to the radial line passing through the point (a, b) and we let r be the modulus of $a + bi$. Thus,

$$a = r \cos \theta, \qquad b = r \sin \theta, \qquad \text{and} \qquad r = \sqrt{a^2 + b^2}$$

and we have $a + bi = (r \cos \theta) + (r \sin \theta)i$ from which we obtain the following **polar form** of a complex number.

Definition of Polar Form of a Complex Number

The **polar form** of the nonzero complex number $z = a + bi$ is given by

$$z = r(\cos \theta + i \sin \theta)$$

where $a = r \cos \theta$, $b = r \sin \theta$, $r = \sqrt{a^2 + b^2}$, and $\tan \theta = b/a$. The number r is the **modulus** of z and θ is called the **argument** of z.

REMARK: The polar form of $z = 0$ is given by $z = 0(\cos\theta + i\sin\theta)$ where θ is any angle.

Because there are infinitely many choices for the argument, the polar form of a complex number is not unique. Normally, we use values of θ that lie between $-\pi$ and π, though on occasion it is convenient to use other values. The value of θ that satisfies the inequality

$$-\pi < \theta \leq \pi \qquad \text{Principal argument}$$

is called the **principal argument** and is denoted by $\text{Arg}(z)$. Two nonzero complex numbers in polar form are equal if and only if they have the same modulus and the same principal argument.

EXAMPLE 1   *Finding the Polar Form of a Complex Number*

Find the polar form of the following complex numbers. (Use the principal argument.)
(a) $1 - i$ (b) $2 + 3i$ (c) i

Solution   (a) We have $a = 1$ and $b = -1$, so $r^2 = 1^2 + (-1)^2 = 2$, which implies that $r = \sqrt{2}$. From $a = r\cos\theta$ and $b = r\sin\theta$, we have

$$\cos\theta = \frac{a}{r} = \frac{1}{\sqrt{2}} = \frac{\sqrt{2}}{2} \qquad \text{and} \qquad \sin\theta = \frac{b}{r} = -\frac{1}{\sqrt{2}} = -\frac{\sqrt{2}}{2}.$$

Thus, $\theta = -\pi/4$ and

$$z = \sqrt{2}\left[\cos\left(-\frac{\pi}{4}\right) + i\sin\left(-\frac{\pi}{4}\right)\right].$$

(b) Since $a = 2$ and $b = 3$, we have $r^2 = 2^2 + 3^2 = 13$, which implies that $r = \sqrt{13}$. Therefore,

$$\cos\theta = \frac{a}{r} = \frac{2}{\sqrt{13}} \qquad \text{and} \qquad \sin\theta = \frac{b}{r} = \frac{3}{\sqrt{13}}$$

and it follows that $\theta = \arctan(3/2)$. Therefore, the polar form is

$$z = \sqrt{13}\left[\cos\left(\arctan\frac{3}{2}\right) + i\sin\left(\arctan\frac{3}{2}\right)\right]$$

$$\approx \sqrt{13}\left[\cos(0.98) + i\sin(0.98)\right].$$

(c) Since $a = 0$ and $b = 1$, it follows that $r = 1$ and $\theta = \pi/2$, so we have

$$z = 1\left(\cos\frac{\pi}{2} + i\sin\frac{\pi}{2}\right).$$

The polar forms derived in parts (a), (b), and (c) are depicted graphically in Figure 8.7.

Figure 8.7

(a) $z = \sqrt{2}\left[\cos\left(-\frac{\pi}{4}\right) + i \sin\left(-\frac{\pi}{4}\right)\right]$

(b) $z = \sqrt{13}[\cos(0.98)$ $+ i \sin(0.98)]$

(c) $z = 1\left(\cos\frac{\pi}{2} + i \sin\frac{\pi}{2}\right)$

EXAMPLE 2   *Converting from Polar to Standard Form*

Express the following complex number in standard form.

$$z = 8\left[\cos\left(-\frac{\pi}{3}\right) + i \sin\left(-\frac{\pi}{3}\right)\right]$$

Solution   Since $\cos(-\pi/3) = 1/2$ and $\sin(-\pi/3) = -\sqrt{3}/2$, we obtain the standard form

$$z = 8\left[\cos\left(-\frac{\pi}{3}\right) + i \sin\left(-\frac{\pi}{3}\right)\right] = 8\left[\frac{1}{2} - i\frac{\sqrt{3}}{2}\right] = 4 - 4\sqrt{3}i.$$

The polar form adapts nicely to multiplication and division of complex numbers. Suppose we are given two complex numbers in polar form

$$z_1 = r_1(\cos\theta_1 + i \sin\theta_1) \quad \text{and} \quad z_2 = r_2(\cos\theta_2 + i \sin\theta_2).$$

Then the product of z_1 and z_2 is given by

$$z_1 z_2 = r_1 r_2(\cos\theta_1 + i \sin\theta_1)(\cos\theta_2 + i \sin\theta_2)$$
$$= r_1 r_2[(\cos\theta_1 \cos\theta_2 - \sin\theta_1 \sin\theta_2) + i(\cos\theta_1 \sin\theta_2 + \sin\theta_1 \cos\theta_2)].$$

Using the trigonometric identities

$$\cos(\theta_1 + \theta_2) = \cos\theta_1 \cos\theta_2 - \sin\theta_1 \sin\theta_2$$

and

$$\sin(\theta_1 + \theta_2) = \sin\theta_1 \cos\theta_2 + \cos\theta_1 \sin\theta_2$$

we have

$$z_1 z_2 = r_1 r_2[\cos(\theta_1 + \theta_2) + i \sin(\theta_1 + \theta_2)].$$

This establishes the first part of the following theorem. The proof of the second part is left to you. (See Exercise 63.)

Theorem 8.4

Product and Quotient of Two Complex Numbers

Given two complex numbers in polar form

$$z_1 = r_1(\cos \theta_1 + i \sin \theta_1) \quad \text{and} \quad z_2 = r_2(\cos \theta_2 + i \sin \theta_2)$$

the product and quotient of the numbers are as follows.

$$z_1 z_2 = r_1 r_2 [\cos(\theta_1 + \theta_2) + i \sin(\theta_1 + \theta_2)] \qquad \text{Product}$$

$$\frac{z_1}{z_2} = \frac{r_1}{r_2} [\cos(\theta_1 - \theta_2) + i \sin(\theta_1 - \theta_2)], \ z_2 \neq 0 \qquad \text{Quotient}$$

This theorem says that to multiply two complex numbers in polar form, we multiply moduli and add arguments, and to divide two complex numbers, we divide moduli and subtract arguments. (See Figure 8.8.)

Figure 8.8

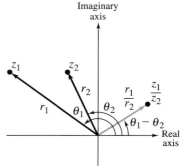

To multiply z_1 and z_2:
Multiply moduli and add arguments.

To divide z_1 by z_2:
Divide moduli and add arguments.

EXAMPLE 3 *Multiplying and Dividing in Polar Form*

Determine $z_1 z_2$ and z_1/z_2 for the complex numbers

$$z_1 = 5\left(\cos \frac{\pi}{4} + i \sin \frac{\pi}{4}\right) \quad \text{and} \quad z_2 = \frac{1}{3}\left(\cos \frac{\pi}{6} + i \sin \frac{\pi}{6}\right).$$

Solution   Since we are given the polar forms of z_1 and z_2, we can apply Theorem 8.4 as follows.

$$z_1 z_2 = \overbrace{(5)\left(\frac{1}{3}\right)}^{multiply}\left[\cos\left(\underbrace{\frac{\pi}{4} + \frac{\pi}{6}}_{add}\right) + i \sin\left(\underbrace{\frac{\pi}{4} + \frac{\pi}{6}}_{add}\right)\right] = \frac{5}{3}\left(\cos \frac{5\pi}{12} + i \sin \frac{5\pi}{12}\right)$$

$$\frac{z_1}{z_2} = \overbrace{\frac{5}{1/3}}^{divide}\left[\cos\left(\underbrace{\frac{\pi}{4} - \frac{\pi}{6}}_{subtract}\right) + i \sin\left(\underbrace{\frac{\pi}{4} - \frac{\pi}{6}}_{subtract}\right)\right] = 15\left(\cos \frac{\pi}{12} + i \sin \frac{\pi}{12}\right)$$

REMARK: Try performing the multiplication and division in Example 3 using the standard forms

$$z_1 = \frac{5\sqrt{2}}{2} + \frac{5\sqrt{2}}{2}i \quad \text{and} \quad z_2 = \frac{\sqrt{3}}{6} + \frac{1}{6}i.$$

DeMoivre's Theorem

Our final topic in this section involves procedures for finding powers and roots of complex numbers. Repeated use of multiplication in the polar form yields

$$z = r(\cos\theta + i\sin\theta)$$
$$z^2 = r(\cos\theta + i\sin\theta)\,r(\cos\theta + i\sin\theta) = r^2(\cos 2\theta + i\sin 2\theta)$$
$$z^3 = r(\cos\theta + i\sin\theta)\,r^2(\cos 2\theta + i\sin 2\theta) = r^3(\cos 3\theta + i\sin 3\theta).$$

Similarly,

$$z^4 = r^4(\cos 4\theta + i\sin 4\theta)$$

$$z^5 = r^5(\cos 5\theta + i\sin 5\theta).$$

This pattern leads to the following important theorem, named after the French mathematician Abraham DeMoivre (1667–1754). You are asked to prove this theorem in Chapter Review Exercise 71.

Theorem 8.5 DeMoivre's Theorem	If $z = r(\cos\theta + i\sin\theta)$ and n is any positive integer, then $z^n = r^n(\cos n\theta + i\sin n\theta).$

EXAMPLE 4   ***Raising a Complex Number to an Integer Power***

Find $(-1 + \sqrt{3}i)^{12}$ and write the result in standard form.

Solution   We first convert to polar form. For $-1 + \sqrt{3}i$, we have

$$r = \sqrt{(-1)^2 + (\sqrt{3})^2} = 2 \quad \text{and} \quad \tan\theta = \frac{\sqrt{3}}{-1} = -\sqrt{3}$$

which implies that $\theta = 2\pi/3$. Therefore,

$$-1 + \sqrt{3}i = 2\left(\cos\frac{2\pi}{3} + i\sin\frac{2\pi}{3}\right).$$

By DeMoivre's Theorem, we have

$$(-1 + \sqrt{3}i)^{12} = \left[2\left(\cos\frac{2\pi}{3} + i\sin\frac{2\pi}{3}\right)\right]^{12}$$

$$= 2^{12}\left[\cos\frac{12(2\pi)}{3} + i\sin\frac{12(2\pi)}{3}\right]$$

$$= 4096(\cos 8\pi + i \sin 8\pi)$$

$$= 4096[1 + i(0)] = 4096.$$

Recall that a consequence of the Fundamental Theorem of Algebra is that a polynomial of degree n has n zeros in the complex number system. Hence, a polynomial like $p(x) = x^6 - 1$ has six zeros, and in this case we can find the six zeros by factoring and using the quadratic formula.

$$x^6 - 1 = (x^3 - 1)(x^3 + 1) = (x - 1)(x^2 + x + 1)(x + 1)(x^2 - x + 1)$$

Consequently, the zeros are

$$x = \pm 1, \quad x = \frac{-1 \pm \sqrt{3}i}{2}, \quad \text{and} \quad x = \frac{1 \pm \sqrt{3}i}{2}.$$

Each of these numbers is called a sixth root of 1. In general, we define the nth root of a complex number as follows.

Definition of nth Root of a Complex Number	The complex number $w = a + bi$ is an **nth root** of the complex number z if $$z = w^n = (a + bi)^n.$$

DeMoivre's Theorem is useful in determining roots of complex numbers. To see how this is done, let w be an nth root of z, where

$$w = s(\cos \beta + i \sin \beta) \quad \text{and} \quad z = r(\cos \theta + i \cos \theta).$$

Then, by DeMoivre's Theorem we have $w^n = s^n (\cos n\beta + i \sin n\beta)$ and since $w^n = z$, it follows that

$$s^n (\cos n\beta + i \sin n\beta) = r(\cos \theta + i \sin\theta).$$

Now, since the right and left sides of this equation represent equal complex numbers, we can equate moduli to obtain $s^n = r$ which implies that $s = \sqrt[n]{r}$ and equate principal arguments to conclude that θ and $n\beta$ must differ by a multiple of 2π. Note that r is a positive real number and hence $s = \sqrt[n]{r}$ is also a positive real number. Consequently, for some integer k, $n\beta = \theta + 2\pi k$, which implies that

$$\beta = \frac{\theta + 2\pi k}{n}.$$

Finally, substituting this value for β into the polar form of w, we obtain the result stated in the following theorem.

Theorem 8.6

nth Roots of a Complex Number

For any positive integer n, the complex number

$$z = r(\cos\theta + i\sin\theta)$$

has exactly n distinct roots. These n roots are given by

$$\sqrt[n]{r}\left[\cos\left(\frac{\theta + 2\pi k}{n}\right) + i\sin\left(\frac{\theta + 2\pi k}{n}\right)\right]$$

where $k = 0, 1, 2, \ldots, n-1$.

Figure 8.9

nth Roots of a Complex Number

REMARK: Note that when k exceeds $n-1$, the roots begin to repeat. For instance, if $k = n$, the angle is

$$\frac{\theta + 2\pi n}{n} = \frac{\theta}{n} + 2\pi$$

which yields the same value for the sine and cosine as $k = 0$.

The formula for the nth roots of a complex number has a nice geometric interpretation, as shown in Figure 8.9. Note that because the nth roots all have the same modulus (length) $\sqrt[n]{r}$, they will lie on a circle of radius $\sqrt[n]{r}$ with center at the origin. Furthermore, the n roots are equally spaced along the circle, since successive nth roots have arguments that differ by $2\pi/n$.

We have already found the sixth roots of 1 by factoring and the quadratic formula. Try solving the same problem using Theorem 8.6 to see if you get the roots shown in Figure 8.10. When Theorem 8.6 is applied to the real number 1, we give the nth roots a special name—the **nth roots of unity**.

Figure 8.10

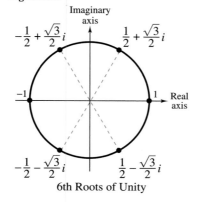

6th Roots of Unity

EXAMPLE 5   *Finding the nth Roots of a Complex Number*

Determine the fourth roots of i.

Solution   In polar form, we can write i as

$$i = 1\left(\cos\frac{\pi}{2} + i \sin\frac{\pi}{2}\right)$$

so that $r = 1$, $\theta = \pi/2$. Then, by applying Theorem 8.6, we have

$$i^{1/4} = \sqrt[4]{1}\left[\cos\left(\frac{\pi/2}{4} + \frac{2k\pi}{4}\right) + i \sin\left(\frac{\pi/2}{4} + \frac{2k\pi}{4}\right)\right]$$

$$= \cos\left(\frac{\pi}{8} + \frac{k\pi}{2}\right) + i \sin\left(\frac{\pi}{8} + \frac{k\pi}{2}\right).$$

Setting $k = 0$, 1, 2, and 3 we obtain the four roots

$$z_1 = \cos\frac{\pi}{8} + i \sin\frac{\pi}{8}$$

$$z_2 = \cos\frac{5\pi}{8} + i \sin\frac{5\pi}{8}$$

$$z_3 = \cos\frac{9\pi}{8} + i \sin\frac{9\pi}{8}$$

$$z_4 = \cos\frac{13\pi}{8} + i \sin\frac{13\pi}{8}$$

as shown in Figure 8.11.

REMARK: In Figure 8.11 note that when each of the four angles, $\pi/8, 5\pi/8, 9\pi/8$, and $13\pi/8$ is multiplied by 4, the result is of the form $(\pi/2) + 2k\pi$.

Figure 8.11

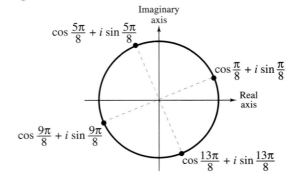

SECTION 8.3 ☐ EXERCISES

In Exercises 1–4, express the complex number in polar form.

1.

2.

3.

4.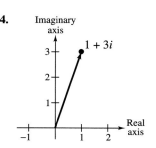

In Exercises 5–16, represent the complex number graphically, and give the polar form of the number.

5. $-2 - 2i$

6. $\sqrt{3} + i$

7. $-2(1 + \sqrt{3}\, i)$

8. $\frac{5}{2}(\sqrt{3} - i)$

9. $6i$

10. 4

11. 7

12. $-2i$

13. $1 + 6i$

14. $2\sqrt{2} - i$

15. $-3 - i$

16. $-4 + 2i$

In Exercises 17–26, represent the complex number graphically, and give the standard form of the number.

17. $2\left(\cos\dfrac{\pi}{2} + i\sin\dfrac{\pi}{2}\right)$

18. $5\left(\cos\dfrac{3\pi}{4} + i\sin\dfrac{3\pi}{4}\right)$

19. $\dfrac{3}{2}\left(\cos\dfrac{5\pi}{3} + i\sin\dfrac{5\pi}{3}\right)$

20. $\dfrac{3}{4}\left(\cos\dfrac{7\pi}{4} + i\sin\dfrac{7\pi}{4}\right)$

21. $3.75\left(\cos\dfrac{\pi}{4} + i\sin\dfrac{\pi}{4}\right)$

22. $8\left(\cos\dfrac{\pi}{6} + i\sin\dfrac{\pi}{6}\right)$

23. $4\left(\cos\dfrac{3\pi}{2} + i\sin\dfrac{3\pi}{2}\right)$

24. $6\left(\cos\dfrac{5\pi}{6} + i\sin\dfrac{5\pi}{6}\right)$

25. $7(\cos 0 + i\sin 0)$

26. $6(\cos\pi + i\sin\pi)$

In Exercises 27–34, perform the indicated operation and leave the result in polar form.

27. $\left[3\left(\cos\dfrac{\pi}{3} + i\sin\dfrac{\pi}{3}\right)\right]\left[4\left(\cos\dfrac{\pi}{6} + i\sin\dfrac{\pi}{6}\right)\right]$

28. $\left[\dfrac{3}{4}\left(\cos\dfrac{\pi}{2} + i\sin\dfrac{\pi}{2}\right)\right]\left[6\left(\cos\dfrac{\pi}{4} + i\sin\dfrac{\pi}{4}\right)\right]$

29. $[0.5(\cos\pi + i\sin\pi)][\,0.5(\cos[-\pi] + i\sin[-\pi])]$

30. $\left[3\left(\cos\dfrac{\pi}{3} + i\sin\dfrac{\pi}{3}\right)\right]\left[\dfrac{1}{3}\left(\cos\dfrac{2\pi}{3} + i\sin\dfrac{2\pi}{3}\right)\right]$

31. $\dfrac{2[\cos(2\pi/3) + i\sin(2\pi/3)]}{4[\cos(2\pi/9) + i\sin(2\pi/9)]}$

32. $\dfrac{\cos(5\pi/3) + i\sin(5\pi/3)}{\cos\pi + i\sin\pi}$

33. $\dfrac{12[\cos(\pi/3) + i\sin(\pi/3)]}{3[\cos(\pi/6) + i\sin(\pi/6)]}$

34. $\dfrac{9[\cos(3\pi/4) + i\sin(3\pi/4)]}{5[\cos(-\pi/4) + i\sin(-\pi/4)]}$

In Exercises 35–44, use DeMoivre's Theorem to find the indicated powers of the given complex number. Express the result in standard form.

35. $(1 + i)^4$

36. $(2 + 2i)^6$

37. $(-1 + i)^{10}$

38. $(\sqrt{3} + i)^7$

39. $(1 - \sqrt{3}i)^3$

40. $\left[5\left(\cos\dfrac{\pi}{9} + i\sin\dfrac{\pi}{9}\right)\right]^3$

41. $\left[3\left(\cos\dfrac{5\pi}{6} + i\sin\dfrac{5\pi}{6}\right)\right]^4$

42. $\left(\cos\dfrac{5\pi}{4} + i\sin\dfrac{5\pi}{4}\right)^{10}$

43. $\left[2\left(\cos\dfrac{\pi}{2} + i\sin\dfrac{\pi}{2}\right)\right]^8$

44. $\left[5\left(\cos\dfrac{3\pi}{2} + i\sin\dfrac{3\pi}{2}\right)\right]^4$

In Exercises 45–56, (a) use DeMoivre's Theorem to find the indicated roots, (b) represent each of the roots graphically, and (c) express each of the roots in standard form.

45. Square roots: $16\left(\cos\dfrac{\pi}{3} + i\sin\dfrac{\pi}{3}\right)$

46. Square roots: $9\left(\cos\dfrac{2\pi}{3} + i\sin\dfrac{2\pi}{3}\right)$

47. Fourth roots: $16\left(\cos\dfrac{4\pi}{3} + i\sin\dfrac{4\pi}{3}\right)$

48. Fifth roots: $32\left(\cos\dfrac{5\pi}{6} + i\sin\dfrac{5\pi}{6}\right)$

49. Square roots: $-25i$ **50.** Fourth roots: $625i$

51. Cube roots: $-\dfrac{125}{2}(1 + \sqrt{3}i)$

52. Cube roots: $-4\sqrt{2}\,(1 - i)$

53. Cube roots: 8   **54.** Fourth roots: i

55. Fourth roots: 1   **56.** Cube roots: 1000

In Exercises 57–62, find all the solutions to the given equation and represent your solutions graphically.

57. $x^4 - i = 0$ **58.** $x^3 + 1 = 0$

59. $x^5 + 243 = 0$ **60.** $x^4 - 81 = 0$

61. $x^3 + 64i = 0$ **62.** $x^4 + i = 0$

63. Given two complex numbers $z_1 = r_1(\cos\theta_1 + i\sin\theta_1)$ and $z_2 = r_2(\cos\theta_2 + i\sin\theta_2)$ with $z_2 \neq 0$ prove that
$$\frac{z_1}{z_2} = \frac{r_1}{r_2}[\cos(\theta_1 - \theta_2) + i\sin(\theta_1 - \theta_2)].$$

64. Show that the complex conjugate of $z = r(\cos\theta + i\sin\theta)$ is
$$\bar{z} = r[\cos(-\theta) + i\sin(-\theta)].$$

65. Use the polar form of z and $\bar{z}$ in Exercise 64 to find the following.

(a) $z\bar{z}$ (b) $z/\bar{z},\ \bar{z} \neq 0$

66. Show that the negative of $z = r(\cos\theta + i\sin\theta)$ is
$$-z = r[\cos(\theta + \pi) + i\sin(\theta + \pi)].$$

67. (a) Let $z = r(\cos\theta + i\sin\theta) = 2\left(\cos\dfrac{\pi}{6} + i\sin\dfrac{\pi}{6}\right)$. Sketch z, iz, and z/i in the complex plane.

(b) What is the geometric effect of multiplying a complex number z by i? What is the geometric effect of dividing z by i?

68. (Calculus) Recall that the Maclaurin series for e^x, $\sin x$, and $\cos x$ are
$$e^x = 1 + x + \frac{x^2}{2!} + \frac{x^3}{3!} + \frac{x^4}{4!} + \cdots$$
$$\sin x = x - \frac{x^3}{3!} + \frac{x^5}{5!} - \frac{x^7}{7!} + \cdots$$
$$\cos x = 1 - \frac{x^2}{2!} + \frac{x^4}{4!} - \frac{x^6}{6!} + \cdots.$$

(a) Substitute $x = i\theta$ into the series for e^x and show that
$$e^{i\theta} = \cos\theta + i\sin\theta.$$

(b) Show that any complex number $z = a + bi$ can be expressed in polar form as $z = re^{i\theta}$.

(c) Prove that if $z = re^{i\theta}$, then $\bar{z} = re^{-i\theta}$.

(d) Prove the amazing formula $e^{i\pi} = -1$.

8.4 COMPLEX VECTOR SPACES AND INNER PRODUCTS

All the vector spaces we have studied thus far in the text are *real vector spaces* since the scalars are real numbers. A **complex vector space** is one in which the scalars are complex numbers. Thus, if $\mathbf{v}_1, \mathbf{v}_2, \ldots, \mathbf{v}_m$ are vectors in a complex vector space, then a linear combination is of the form

$$c_1\mathbf{v}_1 + c_2\mathbf{v}_2 + \cdots + c_m\mathbf{v}_m$$

where the scalars $c_1, c_2, \ldots, c_m$ are complex numbers. The complex version of R^n is the complex vector space C^n consisting of ordered n-tuples of complex numbers. Thus, a vector in C^n has the form

$$\mathbf{v} = (a_1 + b_1i, a_2 + b_2i, \ldots, a_n + b_ni).$$

It is also convenient to represent vectors in C^n by column matrices of the form

$$\mathbf{v} = \begin{bmatrix} a_1 + b_1i \\ a_2 + b_2i \\ \vdots \\ a_n + b_ni \end{bmatrix}.$$

As with R^n, the operations of addition and scalar multiplication in C^n are performed component by component.

EXAMPLE 1   *Vector Operations in C^n*

Let

$$\mathbf{v} = (1 + 2i, 3 - i) \quad \text{and} \quad \mathbf{u} = (-2 + i, 4)$$

be vectors in the complex vector space C^2, and determine the following vectors.

(a) $\mathbf{v} + \mathbf{u}$ (b) $(2 + i)\mathbf{v}$ (c) $3\mathbf{v} - (5 - i)\mathbf{u}$

Solution   (a) In column matrix form, the sum $\mathbf{v} + \mathbf{u}$ is

$$\mathbf{v} + \mathbf{u} = \begin{bmatrix} 1 + 2i \\ 3 - i \end{bmatrix} + \begin{bmatrix} -2 + i \\ 4 \end{bmatrix} = \begin{bmatrix} -1 + 3i \\ 7 - i \end{bmatrix}.$$

(b) Since $(2 + i)(1 + 2i) = 5i$ and $(2 + i)(3 - i) = 7 + i$, we have
$$(2 + i)\mathbf{v} = (2 + i)(1 + 2i, 3 - i) = (5i, 7 + i).$$

(c) $3\mathbf{v} - (5 - i)\mathbf{u} = 3(1 + 2i, 3 - i) - (5 - i)(-2 + i, 4)$
$$= (3 + 6i, 9 - 3i) - (-9 + 7i, 20 - 4i)$$
$$= (12 - i, -11 + i)$$

Many of the properties of R^n are shared by C^n. For instance, the scalar multiplicative identity is the scalar 1 and the additive identity in C^n is $\mathbf{0} = (0, 0, 0, \ldots, 0)$. The **standard basis** for C^n is simply

$$\mathbf{e}_1 = (1, 0, 0, \ldots, 0)$$
$$\mathbf{e}_2 = (0, 1, 0, \ldots, 0)$$
$$\vdots$$
$$\mathbf{e}_n = (0, 0, 0, \ldots, 1)$$

which is the standard basis for R^n. Since this basis contains n vectors, it follows that the dimension of C^n is n. Other bases exist; in fact, any linearly independent set of n vectors in C^n can be used, as we demonstrate in Example 2.

EXAMPLE 2   *Verifying a Basis*

Show that

$$S = \{\overbrace{(i, 0, 0)}^{\mathbf{v}_1}, \overbrace{(i, i, 0)}^{\mathbf{v}_2}, \overbrace{(0, 0, i)}^{\mathbf{v}_3}\}$$

is a basis for C^3.

Solution   Since C^3 has a dimension of 3, the set $\{\mathbf{v}_1, \mathbf{v}_2, \mathbf{v}_3\}$ will be a basis if it is linearly independent. To check for linear independence, we set a linear combination of the vectors in S equal to $\mathbf{0}$ as follows.

$$c_1\mathbf{v}_1 + c_2\mathbf{v}_2 + c_3\mathbf{v}_3 = (0, 0, 0)$$
$$(c_1i, 0, 0) + (c_2i, c_2i, 0) + (0, 0, c_3i) = (0, 0, 0)$$
$$((c_1 + c_2)i, c_2i, c_3i) = (0, 0, 0)$$

This implies that

$$(c_1 + c_2)i = 0$$
$$c_2i = 0$$
$$c_3i = 0.$$

Therefore, $c_1 = c_2 = c_3 = 0$, and we conclude that $\{\mathbf{v}_1, \mathbf{v}_2, \mathbf{v}_3\}$ is linearly independent.

EXAMPLE 3   *Representing a Vector in C^n by a Basis*

Use the basis S in Example 2 to represent the vector

$$\mathbf{v} = (2, i, 2 - i).$$

Solution   By writing

$$\mathbf{v} = c_1\mathbf{v}_1 + c_2\mathbf{v}_2 + c_3\mathbf{v}_3$$
$$= ((c_1 + c_2)i, c_2i, c_3i)$$
$$= (2, i, 2 - i)$$

we obtain

$$(c_1 + c_2)i = 2$$
$$c_2i = i$$
$$c_3i = 2 - i$$

which implies that $c_2 = 1$ and

$$c_1 = \frac{2 - i}{i} = -1 - 2i \quad \text{and} \quad c_3 = \frac{2 - i}{i} = -1 - 2i.$$

Therefore,

$$\mathbf{v} = (-1 - 2i)\mathbf{v}_1 + \mathbf{v}_2 + (-1 - 2i)\mathbf{v}_3.$$

Try verifying that this linear combination yields $(2, i, 2 - i)$.

Other than C^n, there are several additional examples of complex vector spaces. For instance, the set of $m \times n$ complex matrices with matrix addition and scalar multiplication forms a complex vector space. Example 4 describes a complex vector space in which the vectors are functions.

EXAMPLE 4   *The Space of Complex-Valued Functions*

Consider the set S of *complex-valued* functions of the form

$$\mathbf{f}(x) = \mathbf{f}_1(x) + i\mathbf{f}_2(x)$$

where $\mathbf{f}_1$ and $\mathbf{f}_2$ are real-valued functions of a real variable. The set of complex numbers form the scalars for S and vector addition is defined by

$$\mathbf{f}(x) + \mathbf{g}(x) = [\mathbf{f}_1(x) + i\mathbf{f}_2(x)] + [\mathbf{g}_1(x) + i\mathbf{g}_2(x)]$$
$$= [\mathbf{f}_1(x) + \mathbf{g}_1(x)] + i[\mathbf{f}_2(x) + \mathbf{g}_2(x)].$$

It can be shown that S, scalar multiplication, and vector addition form a complex vector space. For instance, to show that S is closed under scalar multiplication, we let $c = a + bi$ be a complex number. Then

$$c\mathbf{f}(x) = (a + bi)[\mathbf{f}_1(x) + i\mathbf{f}_2(x)]$$
$$= [a\mathbf{f}_1(x) - b\mathbf{f}_2(x)] + i[b\mathbf{f}_1(x) + a\mathbf{f}_2(x)]$$

is in S.

The definition of the Euclidean inner product in C^n is similar to that of the standard dot product in R^n, except that here the second factor in each term is a complex conjugate.

Definition of Euclidean Inner Product in C^n

Let $\mathbf{u}$ and $\mathbf{v}$ be vectors in C^n. The **Euclidean inner product** of $\mathbf{u}$ and $\mathbf{v}$ is given by

$$\mathbf{u} \cdot \mathbf{v} = u_1 \overline{v_1} + u_2 \overline{v_2} + \cdots + u_n \overline{v_n}.$$

REMARK: Note that if $\mathbf{u}$ and $\mathbf{v}$ happen to be "real," then this definition agrees with the standard inner (or dot) product in R^n.

EXAMPLE 5   ***Finding the Euclidean Inner Product in C^3***

Determine the Euclidean inner product of the vectors

$$\mathbf{u} = (2 + i, 0, 4 - 5i) \quad \text{and} \quad \mathbf{v} = (1 + i, 2 + i, 0).$$

Solution

$$
\begin{aligned}
\mathbf{u} \cdot \mathbf{v} &= u_1 \overline{v_1} + u_2 \overline{v_2} + u_3 \overline{v_3} \\
&= (2 + i)(1 - i) + 0(2 - i) + (4 - 5i)(0) \\
&= 3 - i
\end{aligned}
$$

Several properties of the Euclidean inner product C^n are stated in the following theorem.

Theorem 8.7

Properties of the Euclidean Inner Product

Let $\mathbf{u}$, $\mathbf{v}$, and $\mathbf{w}$ be vectors in C^n and let k be a complex number. Then the following properties are true.

1. $\mathbf{u} \cdot \mathbf{v} = \overline{\mathbf{v} \cdot \mathbf{u}}$
2. $(\mathbf{u} + \mathbf{v}) \cdot \mathbf{w} = \mathbf{u} \cdot \mathbf{w} + \mathbf{v} \cdot \mathbf{w}$
3. $(k\mathbf{u}) \cdot \mathbf{v} = k(\mathbf{u} \cdot \mathbf{v})$
4. $\mathbf{u} \cdot (k\mathbf{v}) = \overline{k}(\mathbf{u} \cdot \mathbf{v})$
5. $\mathbf{u} \cdot \mathbf{u} \geq 0$
6. $\mathbf{u} \cdot \mathbf{u} = 0$ if and only if $\mathbf{u} = \mathbf{0}$.

Proof   We prove the first property and leave the proofs of the remaining properties to you. Let

$$\mathbf{u} = (u_1, u_2, \ldots, u_n) \quad \text{and} \quad \mathbf{v} = (v_1, v_2, \ldots, v_n).$$

Then

$$
\begin{aligned}
\overline{\mathbf{v} \cdot \mathbf{u}} &= \overline{v_1 \overline{u_1} + v_2 \overline{u_2} + \cdots + v_n \overline{u_n}} \\
&= \overline{v_1 \overline{u_1}} + \overline{v_2 \overline{u_2}} + \cdots + \overline{v_n \overline{u_n}} \\
&= \overline{v_1} u_1 + \overline{v_2} u_2 + \cdots + \overline{v_n} u_n
\end{aligned}
$$

$$= u_1\overline{v_1} + u_2\overline{v_2} + \cdots + u_n\overline{v_n}$$

$$= \mathbf{u} \cdot \mathbf{v}.$$

We now use the Euclidean inner product in C^n to define the Euclidean norm (or length) of a vector in C^n and the Euclidean distance between two vectors in C^n.

Definition of Norm and Distance in C^n

The **Euclidean norm** (or **length**) of $\mathbf{u}$ in C^n is denoted by $\|\mathbf{u}\|$ and is

$$\|\mathbf{u}\| = (\mathbf{u} \cdot \mathbf{u})^{1/2}.$$

The **Euclidean distance** between $\mathbf{u}$ and $\mathbf{v}$ is

$$d(\mathbf{u}, \mathbf{v}) = \|\mathbf{u} - \mathbf{v}\|.$$

The Euclidean norm and distance may be expressed in terms of components as

$$\|\mathbf{u}\| = (|u_1|^2 + |u_2|^2 + \cdots + |u_n|^2)^{1/2}$$

$$d(\mathbf{u}, \mathbf{v}) = (|u_1 - v_1|^2 + |u_2 - v_2|^2 + \cdots + |u_n - v_n|^2)^{1/2}.$$

EXAMPLE 6   *Finding the Euclidean Norm and Distance in C^n*

Determine the norms of the vectors

$$\mathbf{u} = (2 + i, 0, 4 - 5i) \qquad \text{and} \qquad \mathbf{v} = (1 + i, 2 + i, 0)$$

and find the distance between $\mathbf{u}$ and $\mathbf{v}$.

Solution   The norms of $\mathbf{u}$ and $\mathbf{v}$ are given as follows.

$$\|\mathbf{u}\| = (|u_1|^2 + |u_2|^2 + |u_3|^2)^{1/2}$$

$$= [(2^2 + 1^2) + (0^2 + 0^2) + (4^2 + 5^2)]^{1/2}$$

$$= (5 + 0 + 41)^{1/2} = \sqrt{46}$$

$$\|\mathbf{v}\| = (|v_1|^2 + |v_2|^2 + |v_3|^2)^{1/2}$$

$$= [(1^2 + 1^2) + (2^2 + 1^2) + (0^2 + 0^2)]^{1/2}$$

$$= (2 + 5 + 0)^{1/2} = \sqrt{7}$$

The distance between $\mathbf{u}$ and $\mathbf{v}$ is given by

$$d(\mathbf{u}, \mathbf{v}) = \|\mathbf{u} - \mathbf{v}\|$$

$$= \|(1, -2 - i, 4 - 5i)\|$$

$$= [(1^2 + 0^2) + ((-2)^2 + (-1)^2) + (4^2 + 5^2)]^{1/2}$$

$$= (1 + 5 + 41)^{1/2} = \sqrt{47}.$$

Complex Inner Product Spaces

The Euclidean inner product is the most commonly used inner product in C^n. However, on occasion it is useful to consider other inner products. To generalize the notion of an inner product, we use the properties listed in Theorem 8.7.

Definition of a Complex Inner Product	Let $\mathbf{u}$ and $\mathbf{v}$ be vectors in a complex vector space. A function that associates with $\mathbf{u}$ and $\mathbf{v}$ the complex number $\langle \mathbf{u}, \mathbf{v} \rangle$ is called a **complex inner product** if it satisfies the following properties.
	1. $\langle \mathbf{u}, \mathbf{v} \rangle = \overline{\langle \mathbf{v}, \mathbf{u} \rangle}$
	2. $\langle \mathbf{u} + \mathbf{v}, \mathbf{w} \rangle = \langle \mathbf{u}, \mathbf{w} \rangle + \langle \mathbf{v}, \mathbf{w} \rangle$
	3. $\langle k\mathbf{u}, \mathbf{v} \rangle = k \langle \mathbf{u}, \mathbf{v} \rangle$
	4. $\langle \mathbf{u}, \mathbf{u} \rangle \geq 0$ and $\langle \mathbf{u}, \mathbf{u} \rangle = 0$ if and only if $\mathbf{u} = \mathbf{0}.$

A complex vector space with a complex inner product is called a **complex inner product space** or **unitary space.**

EXAMPLE 7   *A Complex Inner Product Space*

Let $\mathbf{u} = (u_1, u_2)$ and $\mathbf{v} = (v_1, v_2)$ be vectors in the complex space C^2. Show that the function defined by

$$\langle \mathbf{u}, \mathbf{v} \rangle = u_1 \overline{v_1} + 2u_2 \overline{v_2}$$

is a complex inner product.

Solution   We verify the four properties of a complex inner product as follows.

1. $\overline{\langle \mathbf{v}, \mathbf{u} \rangle} = \overline{v_1 \overline{u_1} + 2v_2 \overline{u_2}} = u_1 \overline{v_1} + 2u_2 \overline{v_2} = \langle \mathbf{u}, \mathbf{v} \rangle$

2. $\langle \mathbf{u} + \mathbf{v}, \mathbf{w} \rangle = (u_1 + v_1)\overline{w_1} + 2(u_2 + v_2)\overline{w_2}$

   $\qquad = (u_1 \overline{w_1} + 2u_2 \overline{w_2}) + (v_1 \overline{w_1} + 2v_2 \overline{w_2})$

   $\qquad = \langle \mathbf{u}, \mathbf{w} \rangle + \langle \mathbf{v}, \mathbf{w} \rangle$

3. $\langle k\mathbf{u}, \mathbf{v} \rangle = (ku_1)\overline{v_1} + 2(ku_2)\overline{v_2} = k(u_1 \overline{v_1} + 2u_2 \overline{v_2}) = k \langle \mathbf{u}, \mathbf{v} \rangle$

4. $\langle \mathbf{u}, \mathbf{u} \rangle = u_1 \overline{u_1} + 2u_2 \overline{u_2} = |u_1|^2 + 2|u_2|^2 \geq 0$

   Moreover, $\langle \mathbf{u}, \mathbf{u} \rangle = 0$ if and only if $u_1 = u_2 = 0.$

Since all properties hold, $\langle \mathbf{u}, \mathbf{v} \rangle$ is a complex inner product.

SECTION 8.4 ☐ EXERCISES

In Exercises 1–8, perform the indicated operation using
$\mathbf{u} = (i, 3 - i)$, $\mathbf{v} = (2 + i, 3 + i)$, and $\mathbf{w} = (4i, 6)$.

1. $3\mathbf{u}$

2. $4i\mathbf{w}$

3. $(1 + 2i)\mathbf{w}$

4. $i\mathbf{v} + 3\mathbf{w}$

5. $\mathbf{u} - (2 - i)\mathbf{v}$

6. $(6 + 3i)\mathbf{v} - (2 + 2i)\mathbf{w}$

7. $\mathbf{u} + i\mathbf{v} + 2i\mathbf{w}$

8. $2i\mathbf{v} - (3 - i)\mathbf{w} + \mathbf{u}$

In Exercises 9–12, determine whether S is a basis for C^n.

9. $S = \{(1, i), (i, -1)\}$

10. $S = \{(1, i), (i, 1)\}$

11. $S = \{(i, 0, 0), (0, i, i), (0, 0, 1)\}$

12. $S = \{(1 - i, 0, 1), (2, i, 1 + i), (1 - i, 1, 1)\}$

In Exercises 13–16, express $\mathbf{v}$ as a linear combination of the following basis vectors.

    (a) $\{(i, 0, 0), (i, i, 0), (i, i, i)\}$

    (b) $\{(1, 0, 0), (1, 1, 0), (0, 0, 1 + i)\}$

13. $\mathbf{v} = (1, 2, 0)$

14. $\mathbf{v} = (1 - i, 1 + i, -3)$

15. $\mathbf{v} = (-i, 2 + i, -1)$

16. $\mathbf{v} = (i, i, i)$

In Exercises 17–24, determine the Euclidean norm of $\mathbf{v}$.

17. $\mathbf{v} = (i, -i)$

18. $\mathbf{v} = (1, 0)$

19. $\mathbf{v} = 3(6 + i, 2 - i)$

20. $\mathbf{v} = (2 + 3i, 2 - 3i)$

21. $\mathbf{v} = (1, 2 + i, -i)$

22. $\mathbf{v} = (0, 0, 0)$

23. $\mathbf{v} = (1 - 2i, i, 3i, 1 + i)$

24. $\mathbf{v} = (2, -1 + i, 2 - i, 4i)$

In Exercises 25–30, determine the Euclidean distance between $\mathbf{u}$ and $\mathbf{v}$.

25. $\mathbf{u} = (1, 0), \mathbf{v} = (i, i)$

26. $\mathbf{u} = (2 + i, 4, -i), \mathbf{v} = (2 + i, 4, -i)$

27. $\mathbf{u} = (i, 2i, 3i), \mathbf{v} = (0, 1, 0)$

28. $\mathbf{u} = (\sqrt{2}, 2i, -i), \mathbf{v} = (i, i, i)$

29. $\mathbf{u} = (1, 0), \mathbf{v} = (0, 1)$

30. $\mathbf{u} = (1, 2, 1, -2i), \mathbf{v} = (i, 2i, i, 2)$

In Exercises 31–34, determine whether the set of vectors is linearly independent or linearly dependent.

31. $\{(1, i), (i, -1)\}$

32. $\{(1 + i, 1 - i, 1), (i, 0, 1), (-2, -1 + i, 0)\}$

33. $\{(1, i, 1 + i), (0, i, -i), (0, 0, 1)\}$

34. $\{(1 + i, 1 - i, 0), (1 - i, 0, 0), (0, 1, 1)\}$

In Exercises 35–38, determine whether the given function is a complex inner product, where $\mathbf{u} = (u_1, u_2)$ and $\mathbf{v} = (v_1, v_2)$.

35. $\langle \mathbf{u}, \mathbf{v} \rangle = u_1 + u_2 v_2$

36. $\langle \mathbf{u}, \mathbf{v} \rangle = (u_1 + v_1) + 2(u_2 + v_2)$

37. $\langle \mathbf{u}, \mathbf{v} \rangle = 4u_1\overline{v_1} + 6u_2\overline{v_2}$

38. $\langle \mathbf{u}, \mathbf{v} \rangle = u_1 v_1 - u_2 v_2$

39. Let $\mathbf{v}_1 = (i, 0, 0)$ and $\mathbf{v}_2 = (i, i, 0)$. If $\mathbf{v}_3 = (z_1, z_2, z_3)$ and the set $\{\mathbf{v}_1, \mathbf{v}_2, \mathbf{v}_3\}$ is *not* a basis for C^3, what does this imply about z_1, z_2, and z_3?

40. Let $\mathbf{v}_1 = (i, i, i)$ and $\mathbf{v}_2 = (1, 0, 1)$. Determine a vector $\mathbf{v}_3$ such that $\{\mathbf{v}_1, \mathbf{v}_2, \mathbf{v}_3\}$ is a basis for C^3.

In Exercises 41–45, prove the given property where $\mathbf{u}, \mathbf{v}$, and $\mathbf{w}$ are vectors in C^n and k is a complex number.

41. $(\mathbf{u} + \mathbf{v}) \cdot \mathbf{w} = \mathbf{u} \cdot \mathbf{w} + \mathbf{v} \cdot \mathbf{w}$

42. $(k\mathbf{u}) \cdot \mathbf{v} = k(\mathbf{u} \cdot \mathbf{v})$

43. $\mathbf{u} \cdot (k\mathbf{v}) = \overline{k}(\mathbf{u} \cdot \mathbf{v})$

44. $\mathbf{u} \cdot \mathbf{u} \geq 0$

45. $\mathbf{u} \cdot \mathbf{u} = 0$ if and only if $\mathbf{u} = \mathbf{0}$.

▶ **46.** Let $\langle \mathbf{u}, \mathbf{v} \rangle$ be a complex inner product and k a complex number. How are $\langle \mathbf{u}, \mathbf{v} \rangle$ and $\langle \mathbf{u}, k\mathbf{v} \rangle$ related?

In Exercises 47 and 48, determine the linear transformation $T: C^m \to C^n$ that has the given characteristics.

47. $T(1, 0) = (2 + i, 1), T(0, 1) = (0, -i)$

48. $T(i, 0) = (2 + i, 1), T(0, i) = (0, -i)$

In Exercises 49–52, the linear transformation $T: C^m \to C^n$ is given by $T(\mathbf{v}) = A\mathbf{v}$. Find the image of $\mathbf{v}$ and the preimage of $\mathbf{w}$.

49. $A = \begin{bmatrix} 1 & 0 \\ i & i \end{bmatrix}, \mathbf{v} = \begin{bmatrix} 1 + i \\ 1 - i \end{bmatrix}, \mathbf{w} = \begin{bmatrix} 0 \\ 0 \end{bmatrix}$

50. $A = \begin{bmatrix} 0 & i & 1 \\ i & 0 & 0 \end{bmatrix}, \mathbf{v} = \begin{bmatrix} i \\ 0 \\ 1 + i \end{bmatrix}, \mathbf{w} = \begin{bmatrix} 1 \\ 1 \end{bmatrix}$

51. $A = \begin{bmatrix} 1 & 0 \\ i & 0 \\ i & i \end{bmatrix}, \mathbf{v} = \begin{bmatrix} 2 - i \\ 3 + 2i \end{bmatrix}, \mathbf{w} = \begin{bmatrix} 2 \\ 2i \\ 3i \end{bmatrix}$

52. $A = \begin{bmatrix} 0 & 1 & 1 \\ i & i & -1 \\ 0 & i & 0 \end{bmatrix}, \mathbf{v} = \begin{bmatrix} 2 \\ 5 \\ 0 \end{bmatrix}, \mathbf{w} = \begin{bmatrix} 1 - i \\ 1 + i \\ i \end{bmatrix}$

53. Find the kernel of the linear transformation given in Exercise 49.

54. Find the kernel of the linear transformation given in Exercise 50.

In Exercises 55 and 56, find the image of $\mathbf{v} = (i, i)$ for the indicated composition, where T_1 and T_2 are given by the following matrices.

$$A_1 = \begin{bmatrix} 0 & i \\ i & 0 \end{bmatrix} \quad \text{and} \quad A_2 = \begin{bmatrix} -i & i \\ i & -i \end{bmatrix}$$

55. $T_2 \circ T_1$ **56.** $T_1 \circ T_2$

57. Determine which of the following sets are subspaces of the vector space of 2×2 complex matrices.

(a) The set of 2×2 symmetric matrices.

(b) The set of 2×2 matrices A satisfying $(\overline{A})^T = A$.

(c) The set of 2×2 matrices in which all entries are real.

(d) The set of 2×2 diagonal matrices.

58. Determine which of the following sets are subspaces of the vector space of complex-valued functions (see Example 4).

(a) The set of all functions f satisfying $f(i) = 0$.

(b) The set of all functions f satisfying $f(0) = 1$.

(c) The set of all functions f satisfying $f(i) = f(-i)$.

8.5 UNITARY AND HERMITIAN MATRICES

Problems involving diagonalization of complex matrices, and the associated eigenvalue problems, require the concept of **unitary** and **Hermitian** matrices. These matrices roughly correspond to orthogonal and symmetric real matrices. In order to define unitary and Hermitian matrices, we first introduce the concept of the **conjugate transpose** of a complex matrix.

Definition of the Conjugate Transpose of a Complex Matrix	The **conjugate transpose** of a complex matrix A, denoted by A^*, is given by $$A^* = \overline{A}^T$$ where the entries of $\overline{A}$ are the complex conjugates of the corresponding entries of A.

Note that if A is a matrix with real entries, then $A^* = A^T$. To find the conjugate transpose of a matrix, we first calculate the complex conjugate of each entry and then take the transpose of the matrix, as shown in the following example.

EXAMPLE 1   *Finding the Conjugate Transpose of a Complex Matrix*

Determine A^* for the matrix

$$A = \begin{bmatrix} 3 + 7i & 0 \\ 2i & 4 - i \end{bmatrix}.$$

Solution

$$\overline{A} = \begin{bmatrix} \overline{3 + 7i} & \overline{0} \\ \overline{2i} & \overline{4 - i} \end{bmatrix} = \begin{bmatrix} 3 - 7i & 0 \\ -2i & 4 + i \end{bmatrix}$$

$$A^* = \overline{A}^T = \begin{bmatrix} 3 - 7i & -2i \\ 0 & 4 + i \end{bmatrix}$$

We list several properties of the conjugate transpose of a matrix in the following theorem. The proofs of these properties are straightforward and are left for you to supply in Exercises 49–52.

Theorem 8.8	If A and B are complex matrices and k is a complex number, then the following properties are true.
Properties of Conjugate Transpose	1. $(A^*)^* = A$ 2. $(A + B)^* = A^* + B^*$ 3. $(kA)^* = \overline{k}A^*$ 4. $(AB)^* = B^*A^*$

Unitary Matrices

Recall that a real matrix A is *orthogonal* if and only if $A^{-1} = A^T$. In the complex system, matrices having the property that $A^{-1} = A^*$ are more useful and we call such matrices **unitary.**

Definition of a Unitary Matrix	A complex matrix A is called **unitary** if $$A^{-1} = A^*.$$

EXAMPLE 2   *A Unitary Matrix*

Show that the following matrix is unitary.

$$A = \frac{1}{2}\begin{bmatrix} 1 + i & 1 - i \\ 1 - i & 1 + i \end{bmatrix}$$

Solution   Since

$$AA^* = \frac{1}{2}\begin{bmatrix} 1 + i & 1 - i \\ 1 - i & 1 + i \end{bmatrix} \frac{1}{2}\begin{bmatrix} 1 - i & 1 + i \\ 1 + i & 1 - i \end{bmatrix} = \frac{1}{4}\begin{bmatrix} 4 & 0 \\ 0 & 4 \end{bmatrix} = I_2$$

we conclude that $A^* = A^{-1}$. Therefore, A is a unitary matrix.

In Section 7.3, we showed that a real matrix is orthogonal if and only if its row (or column) vectors form an orthonormal set. For complex matrices, this property characterizes matrices that are unitary. Note that we call a set of vectors

$$\{\mathbf{v}_1, \mathbf{v}_2, \ldots, \mathbf{v}_m\}$$

in C^n (complex Euclidean space) orthonormal if the following are true.

1. $\|\mathbf{v}_i\| = 1, i = 1, 2, \ldots, m$
2. $\mathbf{v}_i \cdot \mathbf{v}_j = 0, \ i \neq j$

The proof of the following theorem is similar to the proof of Theorem 7.8 given in Section 7.3.

Theorem 8.9	An $n \times n$ complex matrix A is unitary if and only if its row (or column) vectors form an orthonormal set in C^n.
Unitary Matrices	

EXAMPLE 3   *The Row Vectors of a Unitary Matrix*

Show that the following complex matrix is unitary by showing that its set of row vectors form an orthonormal set in C^3.

$$A = \begin{bmatrix} \dfrac{1}{2} & \dfrac{1+i}{2} & -\dfrac{1}{2} \\[2mm] -\dfrac{i}{\sqrt{3}} & \dfrac{i}{\sqrt{3}} & \dfrac{1}{\sqrt{3}} \\[2mm] \dfrac{5i}{2\sqrt{15}} & \dfrac{3+i}{2\sqrt{15}} & \dfrac{4+3i}{2\sqrt{15}} \end{bmatrix}$$

Solution   We let $\mathbf{r}_1$, $\mathbf{r}_2$, and $\mathbf{r}_3$ be defined as follows.

$$\mathbf{r}_1 = \left(\frac{1}{2}, \frac{1+i}{2}, -\frac{1}{2}\right)$$

$$\mathbf{r}_2 = \left(-\frac{i}{\sqrt{3}}, \frac{i}{\sqrt{3}}, \frac{1}{\sqrt{3}}\right)$$

$$\mathbf{r}_3 = \left(\frac{5i}{2\sqrt{15}}, \frac{3+i}{2\sqrt{15}}, \frac{4+3i}{2\sqrt{15}}\right)$$

The length of $\mathbf{r}_1$ is

$$\|\mathbf{r}_1\| = (\mathbf{r}_1 \cdot \mathbf{r}_1)^{1/2}$$

$$= \left[\left(\frac{1}{2}\right)\overline{\left(\frac{1}{2}\right)} + \left(\frac{1+i}{2}\right)\overline{\left(\frac{1+i}{2}\right)} + \left(\frac{-1}{2}\right)\overline{\left(\frac{-1}{2}\right)}\right]^{1/2}$$

$$= \left[\frac{1}{4} + \frac{2}{4} + \frac{1}{4}\right]^{1/2} = 1.$$

The vectors $\mathbf{r}_2$ and $\mathbf{r}_3$ can also be shown to be unit vectors. The inner product of $\mathbf{r}_1$ and $\mathbf{r}_2$ is given by

$$\mathbf{r}_1 \cdot \mathbf{r}_2 = \left(\frac{1}{2}\right)\overline{\left(\frac{-i}{\sqrt{3}}\right)} + \left(\frac{1+i}{2}\right)\overline{\left(\frac{i}{\sqrt{3}}\right)} + \left(\frac{-1}{2}\right)\overline{\left(\frac{1}{\sqrt{3}}\right)}$$

$$= \left(\frac{1}{2}\right)\left(\frac{i}{\sqrt{3}}\right) + \left(\frac{1+i}{2}\right)\left(\frac{-i}{\sqrt{3}}\right) + \left(\frac{-1}{2}\right)\left(\frac{1}{\sqrt{3}}\right)$$

$$= \frac{i}{2\sqrt{3}} - \frac{i}{2\sqrt{3}} + \frac{1}{2\sqrt{3}} - \frac{1}{2\sqrt{3}}$$

$$= 0.$$

Similarly, $\mathbf{r}_1 \cdot \mathbf{r}_3 = 0$ and $\mathbf{r}_2 \cdot \mathbf{r}_3 = 0$ and we can conclude that $\{\mathbf{r}_1, \mathbf{r}_2, \mathbf{r}_3\}$ is an orthonormal set. (Try showing that the column vectors of A also form an orthonormal set in C^3.)

Hermitian Matrices

A real matrix is called symmetric if it is equal to its own transpose. In the complex system, the more useful type of matrix is one that is equal to its own *conjugate* transpose. We call such a matrix **Hermitian** after the French mathematician Charles Hermite (1822–1901).

Definition of a Hermitian Matrix	A square matrix A is **Hermitian** if $$A = A^*.$$

As with symmetric matrices, we can easily recognize Hermitian matrices by inspection. To see this, consider the 2×2 matrix.

$$A = \begin{bmatrix} a_1 + a_2i & b_1 + b_2i \\ c_1 + c_2i & d_1 + d_2i \end{bmatrix}.$$

The conjugate transpose of A has the form

$$A^* = \overline{A}^T$$

$$= \begin{bmatrix} \overline{a_1 + a_2i} & \overline{c_1 + c_2i} \\ \overline{b_1 + b_2i} & \overline{d_1 + d_2i} \end{bmatrix}$$

$$= \begin{bmatrix} a_1 - a_2i & c_1 - c_2i \\ b_1 - b_2i & d_1 - d_2i \end{bmatrix}.$$

If A is Hermitian, then $A = A^*$ and we can conclude that A must be of the form

$$A = \begin{bmatrix} a_1 & b_1 + b_2i \\ b_1 - b_2i & d_1 \end{bmatrix}.$$

Similar results can be obtained for Hermitian matrices of order $n \times n$. In other words, a square matrix A is Hermitian if and only if the following two conditions are met.
1. The entries on the main diagonal of A are real.
2. The entry a_{ij} in the ith row and the jth column is the complex conjugate of the entry a_{ji} in the jth row and ith column.

EXAMPLE 4   *Hermitian Matrices*

Which of the following matrices are Hermitian?

(a) $\begin{bmatrix} 1 & 3 - i \\ 3 + i & i \end{bmatrix}$

(b) $\begin{bmatrix} 0 & 3 - 2i \\ 3 - 2i & 4 \end{bmatrix}$

(c) $\begin{bmatrix} 3 & 2 - i & -3i \\ 2 + i & 0 & 1 - i \\ 3i & 1 + i & 0 \end{bmatrix}$

(d) $\begin{bmatrix} -1 & 2 & 3 \\ 2 & 0 & -1 \\ 3 & -1 & 4 \end{bmatrix}$

Solution   (a) This matrix is not Hermitian because it has an imaginary entry on its main diagonal.
(b) This matrix is symmetric but not Hermitian because the entry in the first row and second column is not the complex conjugate of the entry in the second row and first column.
(c) This matrix is Hermitian.
(d) This matrix is Hermitian, because all real symmetric matrices are Hermitian.

One of the most important characteristics of Hermitian matrices is that their eigenvalues are real. This is formally stated in the next theorem.

Theorem 8.10
The Eigenvalues of a Hermitian Matrix

If A is a Hermitian matrix, then its eigenvalues are real numbers.

Proof   Let λ be an eigenvalue of A and

$$\mathbf{v} = \begin{bmatrix} a_1 + b_1 i \\ a_2 + b_2 i \\ \vdots \\ a_n + b_n i \end{bmatrix}$$

be its corresponding eigenvector. If we multiply both sides of the equation $A\mathbf{v} = \lambda\mathbf{v}$ by the row vector $\mathbf{v}^*$, we obtain

$$\mathbf{v}^*A\mathbf{v} = \mathbf{v}^*(\lambda\mathbf{v}) = \lambda(\mathbf{v}^*\mathbf{v}) = \lambda(a_1^2 + b_1^2 + a_2^2 + b_2^2 + \cdots + a_n^2 + b_n^2).$$

Furthermore, since

$$(\mathbf{v}^*A\mathbf{v})^* = \mathbf{v}^*A^*(\mathbf{v}^*)^* = \mathbf{v}^*A\mathbf{v}$$

it follows that $\mathbf{v}^*A\mathbf{v}$ is a Hermitian 1×1 matrix. This implies that $\mathbf{v}^*A\mathbf{v}$ is a real number, and we may conclude that λ is real.

REMARK: Note that this theorem implies that the eigenvalues of a *real symmetric matrix* are real, as stated in Theorem 7.7.

To find the eigenvalues of complex matrices, we follow the same procedure as for real matrices.

EXAMPLE 5   *Finding the Eigenvalues of a Hermitian Matrix*

Find the eigenvalues of the following matrix.

$$A = \begin{bmatrix} 3 & 2-i & -3i \\ 2+i & 0 & 1-i \\ 3i & 1+i & 0 \end{bmatrix}$$

Solution   The characteristic polynomial of A is

$$|\lambda I - A| = \begin{bmatrix} \lambda-3 & -2+i & 3i \\ -2-i & \lambda & -1+i \\ -3i & -1-i & \lambda \end{bmatrix}$$

$$= (\lambda-3)(\lambda^2-2) - (-2+i)[(-2-i)\lambda - (3i+3)]$$
$$+ 3i[(1+3i) + 3\lambda i]$$

$$= (\lambda^3 - 3\lambda^2 - 2\lambda + 6) - (5\lambda + 9 + 3i) + (3i - 9 - 9\lambda)$$

$$= \lambda^3 - 3\lambda^2 - 16\lambda - 12$$

$$= (\lambda+1)(\lambda-6)(\lambda+2)$$

which implies that the eigenvalues of A are $-1, 6,$ and -2.

To find the eigenvectors of a complex matrix, we use a similar procedure to that used for a real matrix. For instance, in Example 5, the eigenvector corresponding to the eigenvalue $\lambda = -1$ is obtained by solving the following equation.

$$\begin{bmatrix} \lambda-3 & -2+i & 3i \\ -2-i & \lambda & -1+i \\ -3i & -1-i & \lambda \end{bmatrix} \begin{bmatrix} v_1 \\ v_2 \\ v_3 \end{bmatrix} = \begin{bmatrix} 0 \\ 0 \\ 0 \end{bmatrix}$$

$$\begin{bmatrix} -4 & -2+i & 3i \\ -2-i & -1 & -1+i \\ -3i & -1-i & -1 \end{bmatrix} \begin{bmatrix} v_1 \\ v_2 \\ v_3 \end{bmatrix} = \begin{bmatrix} 0 \\ 0 \\ 0 \end{bmatrix}$$

Using Gauss-Jordan elimination, or a computer or calculator, we obtain the following eigenvector corresponding to $\lambda_1 = -1$.

$$\mathbf{v}_1 = \begin{bmatrix} -1 \\ 1 + 2i \\ 1 \end{bmatrix} \quad (\lambda_1 = -1)$$

Eigenvectors for $\lambda_2 = 6$ and $\lambda_3 = -2$ can be found in a similar manner. They are

$$\begin{bmatrix} 1 - 21i \\ 6 - 9i \\ 13 \end{bmatrix} \quad (\lambda_2 = 6); \quad \begin{bmatrix} 1 + 3i \\ -2 - i \\ 5 \end{bmatrix} \quad (\lambda_3 = -2)$$

TECHNOLOGY NOTE

Some computers and calculators have built-in programs for finding the eigenvalues and corresponding eigenvectors of complex matrices. For example, on the TI-85, the eigVl key on the MATRX MATH menu calculates the eigenvalues of the matrix A, and the eigVc key gives the corresponding eigenvectors.

Just as we saw in Section 7.3 that real symmetric matrices were orthogonally diagonalizable, we will show now that Hermitian matrices are **unitarily diagonalizable.** A square matrix A is unitarily diagonalizable if there exists a unitary matrix P such that

$$P^{-1}AP$$

is a diagonal matrix. Since P is unitary, $P^{-1} = P*$, so an equivalent statement is that A is unitarily diagonalizable if there exists a unitary matrix P such that $P*AP$ is a diagonal matrix. The next theorem tells us that Hermitian matrices are unitarily diagonalizable.

Theorem 8.11

Hermitian Matrices and Diagonalization

If A is an $n \times n$ Hermitian matrix, then
1. eigenvectors corresponding to distinct eigenvalues are orthogonal.
2. A is unitarily diagonalizable.

Proof

To prove part 1, let $\mathbf{v}_1$ and $\mathbf{v}_2$ be two eigenvectors corresponding to the distinct (and real) eigenvalues λ_1 and λ_2. Because $A\mathbf{v}_1 = \lambda_1\mathbf{v}_1$ and $A\mathbf{v}_2 = \lambda_2\mathbf{v}_2$, we have the following equations for the matrix product $(A\mathbf{v}_1)*\mathbf{v}_2$.

$$(A\mathbf{v}_1)*\mathbf{v}_2 = \mathbf{v}_1*A*\mathbf{v}_2 = \mathbf{v}_1*A\mathbf{v}_2 = \mathbf{v}_1*\lambda_2\mathbf{v}_2 = \lambda_2\mathbf{v}_1*\mathbf{v}_2$$
$$(A\mathbf{v}_1)*\mathbf{v}_2 = (\lambda_1\mathbf{v}_1)*\mathbf{v}_2 = \mathbf{v}_1*\lambda_1\mathbf{v}_2 = \lambda_1\mathbf{v}_1*\mathbf{v}_2$$

Therefore,

$$\lambda_2\mathbf{v}_1*\mathbf{v}_2 - \lambda_1\mathbf{v}_1*\mathbf{v}_2 = 0$$
$$(\lambda_2 - \lambda_1)\mathbf{v}_1*\mathbf{v}_2 = 0$$
$$\mathbf{v}_1*\mathbf{v}_2 = 0 \qquad \text{since } \lambda_1 \neq \lambda_2,$$

and we have shown that $\mathbf{v}_1$ and $\mathbf{v}_2$ are orthogonal. Part 2 of Theorem 8.11 is often called the **Spectral Theorem,** and its proof is omitted.

EXAMPLE 6   *The Eigenvectors of a Hermitian Matrix*

The eigenvectors of the Hermitian matrix given in Example 5 are mutually orthogonal because the eigenvalues are distinct. We can verify this by calculating the Euclidean inner products $\mathbf{v}_1 \cdot \mathbf{v}_2$, $\mathbf{v}_1 \cdot \mathbf{v}_3$ and $\mathbf{v}_2 \cdot \mathbf{v}_3$. For example,

$$\mathbf{v}_1 \cdot \mathbf{v}_2 = (-1)\overline{(1 - 21i)} + (1 + 2i)\overline{(6 - 9i)} + (1)\overline{(13)}$$

$$= (-1)(1 + 21i) + (1 + 2i)(6 + 9i) + 13$$

$$= -1 - 21i + 6 + 12i + 9i - 18 + 13$$

$$= 0.$$

The other two inner products $\mathbf{v}_1 \cdot \mathbf{v}_3$ and $\mathbf{v}_2 \cdot \mathbf{v}_3$ can be shown to equal zero in a similar manner.

The three eigenvectors in Example 6 are mutually orthogonal because they correspond to distinct eigenvalues of the Hermitian matrix A. Two or more eigenvectors corresponding to the same eigenvector may not be orthogonal. However, once we obtain any set of linearly independent eigenvectors for a given eigenvalue, we can use the Gram-Schmidt orthonormalization process to obtain an orthogonal set.

EXAMPLE 7   *Diagonalization of a Hermitian Matrix*

Find a unitary matrix P such that P^*AP is a diagonal matrix where

$$A = \begin{bmatrix} 3 & 2 - i & -3i \\ 2 + i & 0 & 1 - i \\ 3i & 1 + i & 0 \end{bmatrix}.$$

Solution   The eigenvectors of A are given after Example 5. We form the matrix P by normalizing these three eigenvectors and using the results to create the columns of P. Thus, since

$$\|\mathbf{v}_1\| = \|(-1, 1 + 2i, 1)\| = \sqrt{1 + 5 + 1} = \sqrt{7}$$

$$\|\mathbf{v}_2\| = \|(1 - 21i, 6 - 9i, 13)\| = \sqrt{442 + 117 + 169} = \sqrt{728}$$

$$\|\mathbf{v}_3\| = \|(1 + 3i, -2 - i, 5)\| = \sqrt{10 + 5 + 25} = \sqrt{40}$$

we obtain the unitary matrix P,

$$P = \begin{bmatrix} -\dfrac{1}{\sqrt{7}} & \dfrac{1 - 21i}{\sqrt{728}} & \dfrac{1 + 3i}{\sqrt{40}} \\ \dfrac{1 + 2i}{\sqrt{7}} & \dfrac{6 - 9i}{\sqrt{728}} & \dfrac{-2 - i}{\sqrt{40}} \\ \dfrac{1}{\sqrt{7}} & \dfrac{13}{\sqrt{728}} & \dfrac{5}{\sqrt{40}} \end{bmatrix}.$$

Try computing the product $P*AP$ for the matrices A and P in Example 7 to see that you obtain

$$P^*AP = \begin{bmatrix} -1 & 0 & 0 \\ 0 & 6 & 0 \\ 0 & 0 & -2 \end{bmatrix}$$

where $-1, 6,$ and -2 are the eigenvalues of A.

We have seen that Hermitian matrices are unitarily diagonalizable. However, it turns out that there is a larger class of matrices, called **normal** matrices, which are also unitarily diagonalizable. A square complex matrix A is **normal** if it commutes with its conjugate transpose: $AA* = A*A$. The main theorem of normal matrices says that a complex matrix A is normal if and only if it is unitarily diagonalizable. You are asked to explore normal matrices further in Exercise 59.

The properties of complex matrices described in this section are comparable to the properties of real matrices discussed in Chapter 7. The following summary indicates the correspondence between unitary and Hermitian complex matrices when compared with orthogonal and symmetric real matrices.

Comparison of Hermitian and Symmetric Matrices	*A is a symmetric matrix* *(Real)*	*A is a Hermitian matrix* *(Complex)*
	1. Eigenvalues of A are real.	1. Eigenvalues of A are real.
	2. Eigenvectors corresponding to distinct eigenvalues are orthogonal.	2. Eigenvectors corresponding to distinct eigenvalues are orthogonal.
	3. There exists an orthogonal matrix P such that $$P^TAP$$ is diagonal.	3. There exists a unitary matrix P such that $$P^*AP$$ is diagonal.

SECTION 8.5 ☐ EXERCISES

In Exercises 1–8, determine the conjugate transpose of the given matrix.

1. $A = \begin{bmatrix} i & -i \\ 2 & 3i \end{bmatrix}$

2. $A = \begin{bmatrix} 1 + 2i & 2 - i \\ 1 & 1 \end{bmatrix}$

3. $A = \begin{bmatrix} 0 & 1 \\ 2 & 0 \end{bmatrix}$

4. $A = \begin{bmatrix} 4 + 3i & 2 + i \\ 2 - i & 6i \end{bmatrix}$

5. $A = \begin{bmatrix} 0 & 5 + i & \sqrt{2}i \\ 5 - i & 6 & 4 \\ -\sqrt{2}i & 4 & 3 \end{bmatrix}$

6. $A = \begin{bmatrix} 2 + i & 3 - i & 4 + 5i \\ 3 - i & 2 & 6 - 2i \end{bmatrix}$

7. $A = \begin{bmatrix} 7 + 5i \\ 2i \\ 4 \end{bmatrix}$

8. $A = \begin{bmatrix} 2 & i \\ 5 & 3i \\ 0 & 6 - i \end{bmatrix}$

In Exercises 9–12, explain why the given matrix is *not* unitary.

9. $A = \begin{bmatrix} i & 0 \\ 0 & 0 \end{bmatrix}$

10. $A = \begin{bmatrix} 1 & i \\ i & -1 \end{bmatrix}$

11. $A = \begin{bmatrix} \dfrac{1 + i}{\sqrt{2}} & 0 & -\dfrac{i}{\sqrt{2}} \\ 0 & 1 & 0 \end{bmatrix}$

12. $A = \begin{bmatrix} \dfrac{1}{2} & -\dfrac{1}{2} & \dfrac{1 + i}{2} \\ -\dfrac{i}{\sqrt{3}} & \dfrac{1}{\sqrt{3}} & \dfrac{i}{\sqrt{3}} \\ -\dfrac{1}{2} & \dfrac{1}{2} & -\dfrac{1 + i}{2} \end{bmatrix}$

In Exercises 13–18, determine whether A is unitary by calculating AA^*.

13. $A = \begin{bmatrix} 1 + i & 1 + i \\ 1 - i & 1 - i \end{bmatrix}$

14. $A = \begin{bmatrix} 1 + i & 1 - i \\ 1 - i & 1 + i \end{bmatrix}$

15. $A = I_n$

16. $A = \begin{bmatrix} \dfrac{i}{\sqrt{2}} & \dfrac{i}{\sqrt{2}} \\ \dfrac{i}{\sqrt{2}} & -\dfrac{i}{\sqrt{2}} \end{bmatrix}$

17. $A = \begin{bmatrix} -\dfrac{i}{\sqrt{2}} & \dfrac{i}{\sqrt{3}} & \dfrac{i}{\sqrt{6}} \\ \dfrac{i}{\sqrt{2}} & \dfrac{i}{\sqrt{3}} & \dfrac{i}{\sqrt{6}} \\ 0 & \dfrac{i}{\sqrt{3}} & -\dfrac{i}{\sqrt{6}} \end{bmatrix}$

18. $A = \begin{bmatrix} \dfrac{4}{5} & \dfrac{3}{5} \\ \dfrac{3}{5}i & \dfrac{4}{5}i \end{bmatrix}$

In Exercises 19–22. (a) verify that A is unitary by showing that its rows are orthonormal, and (b) determine the inverse of A.

19. $A = \begin{bmatrix} \dfrac{4}{5} & \dfrac{3}{5}i \\ \dfrac{3}{5} & \dfrac{4}{5}i \end{bmatrix}$

20. $A = \begin{bmatrix} \dfrac{1 + i}{2} & -\dfrac{1 + i}{2} \\ \dfrac{1}{\sqrt{2}} & \dfrac{1}{\sqrt{2}} \end{bmatrix}$

21. $A = \dfrac{1}{2\sqrt{2}} \begin{bmatrix} \sqrt{3} - i & 1 + \sqrt{3}i \\ \sqrt{3} + i & 1 - \sqrt{3}i \end{bmatrix}$

22. $A = \begin{bmatrix} 0 & 1 & 0 \\ \dfrac{-1 + i}{\sqrt{6}} & 0 & \dfrac{1 - i}{\sqrt{3}} \\ \dfrac{2}{\sqrt{6}} & 0 & \dfrac{1}{\sqrt{3}} \end{bmatrix}$

In Exercises 23–28, determine whether the matrix A is Hermitian.

23. $A = \begin{bmatrix} 0 & 2 + i & 1 \\ 2 - i & i & 0 \\ 1 & 0 & 1 \end{bmatrix}$

24. $A = \begin{bmatrix} 1 & 0 \\ 0 & 1 \end{bmatrix}$

25. $A = \begin{bmatrix} 0 & i \\ -i & 0 \end{bmatrix}$

26. $A = \begin{bmatrix} 1 & 2 + i & 3 - i \\ 2 - i & 2 & 3 + i \end{bmatrix}$

27. $A = \begin{bmatrix} 0 & 0 \\ 0 & 0 \end{bmatrix}$

28. $A = \begin{bmatrix} 1 & \sqrt{2} + i & 5 \\ \sqrt{2} - i & 2 & 3 + i \\ 5 & 3 - i & 6 \end{bmatrix}$

In Exercises 29–34, determine the eigenvalues of the matrix A.

29. $A = \begin{bmatrix} 0 & i \\ -i & 0 \end{bmatrix}$

30. $A = \begin{bmatrix} 0 & 2 + i \\ 2 - i & 4 \end{bmatrix}$

31. $A = \begin{bmatrix} 3 & 1 - i \\ 1 + i & 2 \end{bmatrix}$

32. $A = \begin{bmatrix} 3 & i \\ -i & 3 \end{bmatrix}$

33. $A = \begin{bmatrix} 2 & -\dfrac{i}{\sqrt{2}} & \dfrac{i}{\sqrt{2}} \\ \dfrac{i}{\sqrt{2}} & 2 & 0 \\ -\dfrac{i}{\sqrt{2}} & 0 & 2 \end{bmatrix}$

34. $A = \begin{bmatrix} 1 & 4 & 1 - i \\ 0 & i & 3i \\ 0 & 0 & 2 + i \end{bmatrix}$

In Exercises 35–38, determine the eigenvectors of the given matrix.

35. The matrix in Exercise 29.

36. The matrix in Exercise 30.

37. The matrix in Exercise 33.

38. The matrix in Exercise 32.

In Exercises 39–43, find a unitary matrix P that diagonalizes the given matrix A.

39. $A = \begin{bmatrix} 0 & i \\ -i & 0 \end{bmatrix}$

40. $A = \begin{bmatrix} 0 & 2 + i \\ 2 - i & 4 \end{bmatrix}$

41. $A = \begin{bmatrix} 2 & -\dfrac{i}{\sqrt{2}} & \dfrac{i}{\sqrt{2}} \\ \dfrac{i}{\sqrt{2}} & 2 & 0 \\ -\dfrac{i}{\sqrt{2}} & 0 & 2 \end{bmatrix}$

42. $A = \begin{bmatrix} 4 & 2 + 2i \\ 2 - 2i & 6 \end{bmatrix}$

43. $A = \begin{bmatrix} -1 & 0 & 0 \\ 0 & -1 & -1 + i \\ 0 & -1 - i & 0 \end{bmatrix}$

44. Let z be a complex number with modulus 1. Show that the following matrix is unitary.

$$A = \frac{1}{\sqrt{2}} \begin{bmatrix} z & \bar{z} \\ iz & -i\bar{z} \end{bmatrix}$$

In Exercises 45–48, use the result of Exercise 44 to determine a, b, and c so that A is unitary.

45. $A = \dfrac{1}{\sqrt{2}} \begin{bmatrix} -1 & a \\ b & c \end{bmatrix}$

46. $A = \dfrac{1}{\sqrt{2}} \begin{bmatrix} \dfrac{3 - 4i}{5} & a \\ b & c \end{bmatrix}$

47. $A = \dfrac{1}{\sqrt{2}} \begin{bmatrix} i & a \\ b & c \end{bmatrix}$

48. $A = \dfrac{1}{\sqrt{2}} \begin{bmatrix} a & \dfrac{6 + 3i}{\sqrt{45}} \\ b & c \end{bmatrix}$

In Exercises 49–52, prove the given formula, where A and B are $n \times n$ complex matrices.

49. $(A^*)^* = A$

50. $(A + B)^* = A^* + B^*$

51. $(kA)^* = \bar{k}A^*$

52. $(AB)^* = B^*A^*$

53. Let A be a matrix such that $A^* + A = O$. Prove that iA is Hermitian.

54. Show that $\det(\bar{A}) = \overline{\det(A)}$, where A is a 2×2 matrix.

In Exercises 55–56, assume that the result of Exercise 54 is true for matrices of any size.

55. Show that $\det(A^*) = \overline{\det(A)}$.

56. Prove that if A is unitary, then $|\det(A)| = 1$.

57. (a) Prove that every Hermitian matrix A can be written as the sum $A = B + iC$, where B is a real symmetric matrix and C is real and skew-symmetric.

(b) Use part (a) to write the matrix

$$A = \begin{bmatrix} 2 & 1 + i \\ 1 - i & 3 \end{bmatrix}$$

as a sum $A = B + iC$, where B is a real symmetric matrix and C is real and skew-symmetric.

(c) Prove that every $n \times n$ complex matrix A can be written as $A = B + iC$, where B and C are Hermitian.

(d) Use part (c) to write the complex matrix

$$A = \begin{bmatrix} i & 2 \\ 2 + i & 1 - 2i \end{bmatrix}$$

as a sum $A = B + iC$, where B and C are Hermitian.

58. Determine which of the following sets are subspaces of the vector space of $n \times n$ complex matrices.

  (a) The set of $n \times n$ Hermitian matrices.

  (b) The set of $n \times n$ unitary matrices.

  (c) The set of $n \times n$ normal matrices.

59. (a) Prove that every Hermitian matrix is normal.

  (b) Prove that every unitary matrix is normal.

  (c) Find a 2×2 matrix that is Hermitian, but not unitary.

  (d) Find a 2×2 matrix that is unitary, but not Hermitian.

  (e) Find a 2×2 matrix that is normal, but neither Hermitian nor unitary.

  (f) Find the eigenvalues and corresponding eigenvectors of your matrix from part (e).

  (g) Show that the complex matrix

$$\begin{bmatrix} i & 1 \\ 0 & i \end{bmatrix}$$

  is not diagonalizable. Is this matrix normal?

CHAPTER 8 ☐ REVIEW EXERCISES

In Exercises 1–6, perform the given operation.

1. Find $u + z: u = 2 - 4i, z = 4i$

2. Find $u - z: u = 4, z = 8i$

3. Find $uz: u = 4 - 2i, z = 4 + 2i$

4. Find $uz: u = 2i, z = 1 - 2i$

5. Find $\dfrac{u}{z}: u = 6 - 2i, z = 3 - 3i$

6. Find $\dfrac{u}{z}: u = 7 + i, z = i$

In Exercises 7–10, find all zeros of the given polynomial.

7. $x^2 - 4x + 8$

8. $x^2 - 4x + 7$

9. $3x^2 + 3x + 3$

10. $x^3 + 2x^2 + 2x + 1$

In Exercises 11–14, perform the given operation using

$A = \begin{bmatrix} 4 - i & 2 \\ 3 & 3 + i \end{bmatrix}$ and $B = \begin{bmatrix} 1 + i & i \\ 2i & 2 + i \end{bmatrix}$.

11. $A + B$

12. $2iB$

13. $\det(A - B)$

14. $3BA$

In Exercises 15–20, perform the given operation using $w = 2 - 2i, v = 3 + i,$ and $z = -1 + 2i.$

15. $\bar{z}$

16. $\bar{v}$

17. $|w|$

18. $|v\bar{z}|$

19. $\overline{wv}$

20. $|\bar{z}w|$

In Exercises 21–24, perform the indicated operation.

21. $\dfrac{2 + i}{2 - i}$

22. $\dfrac{1 + i}{-1 + 2i}$

23. $\dfrac{(1 - 2i)(1 + 2i)}{3 - 3i}$

24. $\dfrac{5 + 2i}{(-2 + 2i)(2 - 3i)}$

In Exercises 25 and 26, find A^{-1} (if it exists).

25. $A = \begin{bmatrix} 3 - i & -1 - 2i \\ -\dfrac{23}{5} + \dfrac{11}{5}i & 2 + 3i \end{bmatrix}$

26. $A = \begin{bmatrix} 5 & 1 - i \\ 0 & i \end{bmatrix}$

In Exercises 27–30, determine the polar form of the complex number.

27. $4 + 4i$

28. $3 + 2i$

29. $7 - 4i$

30. $\sqrt{3} + i$

In Exercises 31–34, find the standard form of the given complex number.

31. $5\left[\cos\left(-\dfrac{\pi}{6}\right) + i \sin\left(-\dfrac{\pi}{6}\right)\right]$

32. $4\left(\cos\dfrac{5\pi}{4} + i \sin\dfrac{5\pi}{4}\right)$

33. $6\left(\cos\dfrac{2\pi}{3} + i \sin\dfrac{2\pi}{3}\right)$

34. $7\left(\cos\dfrac{3\pi}{2} + i \sin\dfrac{3\pi}{2}\right)$

In Exercises 35–38, perform the indicated operation. Leave the result in polar form.

35. $\left[4\left(\cos\dfrac{\pi}{2} + i \sin\dfrac{\pi}{2}\right)\right]\left[3\left(\cos\dfrac{\pi}{6} + i \sin\dfrac{\pi}{6}\right)\right]$

36. $\left[\frac{1}{2}\left(\cos\frac{\pi}{2} + i\sin\frac{\pi}{2}\right)\right]\left[2\left(\cos\left(-\frac{\pi}{2}\right) + i\sin\left(-\frac{\pi}{2}\right)\right)\right]$

37. $\dfrac{9[\cos(\pi/2) + i\sin(\pi/2)]}{6[\cos(2\pi/3) + i\sin(2\pi/3)]}$

38. $\dfrac{4[\cos(\pi/4) + i\sin(\pi/4)]}{7[\cos(\pi/3) + i\sin(\pi/3)]}$

In Exercises 39– 42, find the indicated power of the given number and express the result in polar form.

39. $(-1 - i)^4$

40. $(2i)^3$

41. $\left[\sqrt{2}\left(\cos\frac{\pi}{6} + i\sin\frac{\pi}{6}\right)\right]^7$

42. $\left[5\left(\cos\frac{\pi}{3} + i\sin\frac{\pi}{3}\right)\right]^4$

In Exercises 43–46, express the given roots in standard form.

43. Square roots: $25\left(\cos\dfrac{2\pi}{3} + i\sin\dfrac{2\pi}{3}\right)$

44. Cube roots: $27\left(\cos\dfrac{\pi}{6} + i\sin\dfrac{\pi}{6}\right)$

45. Cube roots: i

46. Fourth roots: $16\left(\cos\dfrac{\pi}{4} + i\sin\dfrac{\pi}{4}\right)$

In Exercises 47 and 48, determine the conjugate transpose of the given matrix.

47. $A = \begin{bmatrix} -1 + 4i & 3 + i \\ 3 - i & 2 + i \end{bmatrix}$

48. $A = \begin{bmatrix} 5 & 2 - i & 3 + 2i \\ 2 + 2i & 3 - 2i & i \\ 3i & 2 + i & -1 - 2i \end{bmatrix}$

In Exercises 49–52, find the indicated vector using $\mathbf{u} = (4i, 2 + i)$, $\mathbf{v} = (3, -i)$, and $\mathbf{w} = (3 - i, 4 + i)$.

49. $7\mathbf{u} - \mathbf{v}$

50. $3i\mathbf{w} + (4 - i)\mathbf{v}$

51. $i\mathbf{u} + i\mathbf{v} - i\mathbf{w}$

52. $(3 + 2i)\mathbf{u} - (-2i)\mathbf{w}$

In Exercises 53 and 54, determine the Euclidean norm of the given vector.

53. $\mathbf{v} = (3 - 5i, 2i)$

54. $\mathbf{v} = (3i, -1 - 5i, 3 + 2i)$

In Exercises 55 and 56, find the Euclidean distance between the given vectors.

55. $\mathbf{v} = (2 - i, i)$, $\mathbf{u} = (i, 2 - i)$

56. $\mathbf{v} = (2 + i, -1 + 2i, 3i)$, $\mathbf{u} = (4 - 2i, 3 + 2i, 4)$

In Exercises 57–60, determine whether the given matrix is unitary.

57. $\begin{bmatrix} \dfrac{i}{\sqrt{2}} & -\dfrac{1}{\sqrt{2}} \\ \dfrac{i}{\sqrt{2}} & \dfrac{1}{\sqrt{2}} \end{bmatrix}$

58. $\begin{bmatrix} \dfrac{2 + i}{4} & \dfrac{1 + i}{4} \\ \dfrac{1}{\sqrt{3}} & \dfrac{\sqrt{2}}{\sqrt{3}} \end{bmatrix}$

59. $\begin{bmatrix} 1 & 0 \\ i & -i \end{bmatrix}$

60. $\begin{bmatrix} \dfrac{1}{\sqrt{2}} & 0 & \dfrac{1}{\sqrt{2}} \\ 0 & i & 0 \\ \dfrac{1 + i}{2} & 0 & \dfrac{-1 - i}{2} \end{bmatrix}$

In Exercises 61 and 62, determine whether the given matrix is Hermitian.

61. $\begin{bmatrix} 1 & -1 + i & 2 - i \\ 1 - i & 3 & i \\ 2 + i & -i & 4 \end{bmatrix}$

62. $\begin{bmatrix} 9 & 2 - i & 2 \\ 2 + i & 0 & -1 - i \\ 2 & -1 + i & 3 \end{bmatrix}$

In Exercises 63 and 64, find the eigenvalues and corresponding eigenvectors of the given matrix.

63. $\begin{bmatrix} 4 & 2 - i \\ 2 + i & 0 \end{bmatrix}$

64. $\begin{bmatrix} 2 & 0 & -i \\ 0 & 3 & 0 \\ i & 0 & 2 \end{bmatrix}$

65. Prove that if A is an invertible matrix, then $A*$ is also invertible.

66. Determine all complex numbers z such that $z = -\bar{z}$

67. Prove that if the product of two complex numbers is zero, then one of the numbers must be zero.

68. (a) Find the determinant of the following Hermitian matrix.

$$\begin{bmatrix} 3 & 2 - i & -3i \\ 2 + i & 0 & 1 - i \\ 3i & 1 + i & 0 \end{bmatrix}$$

(b) Prove that the determinant of any Hermitian matrix is real.

69. Let A and B be Hermitian matrices. Prove that $AB = BA$ if and only if AB is Hermitian.

70. Let $\mathbf{u}$ be a unit vector in C^n. Define $H = I - 2\mathbf{u}\mathbf{u}*$. Prove that H is an $n \times n$ Hermitian and unitary matrix.

71. Use mathematical induction to prove DeMoivre's Theorem.

72. Prove that if z is a zero of a polynomial equation with real coefficients, then the conjugate of z is also a zero.

73. Show that if $z_1 + z_2$ and $z_1 \overline{z_2}$ are both nonzero real numbers, then z_1 and z_2 are both real numbers.

74. Prove that if z and w are complex numbers, then $|z + w| \le |z| + |w|$.

75. Prove that for all vectors $\mathbf{u}$ and $\mathbf{v}$ in a complex inner product space,

$$\langle \mathbf{u}, \mathbf{v} \rangle = \tfrac{1}{4}\big[\|\mathbf{u} + \mathbf{v}\|^2 - \|\mathbf{u} - \mathbf{v}\|^2 + i\|\mathbf{u} + i\mathbf{v}\|^2 - i\|\mathbf{u} - i\mathbf{v}\|^2\big].$$

CHAPTER 8   PROJECTS

1 Population Growth and Dynamical Systems - II

In the projects for Chapter 7, you were asked to model the population of two species using a system of differential equations of the form

$$y'_1(t) = ay_1(t) + by_2(t)$$
$$y'_2(t) = cy_1(t) + dy_2(t).$$

The constants a, b, c, and d depend on the particular species being studied. In Chapter 7, we looked at an example of a predator–prey relationship, in which $a = 0.5$, $b = 0.6$, $c = -0.4$, and $d = 3.0$. Suppose we now consider a slightly different model.

$$y'_1(t) = 0.6y_1(t) + 0.8y_2(t), \quad y_1(0) = 36$$
$$y'_2(t) = -0.8y_1(t) + 0.6y_2(t), \quad y_2(0) = 121$$

1. Use the diagonalization technique to find the general solutions $y_1(t)$ and $y_2(t)$ at any time $t > 0$. Although the eigenvalues and eigenvectors of the matrix
   $$A = \begin{bmatrix} 0.6 & 0.8 \\ -0.8 & 0.6 \end{bmatrix}$$
   are complex, the same principles apply, and you can obtain complex exponential solutions.

2. Convert your complex solutions to real solutions by observing that if $\lambda = a + bi$ is a (complex) eigenvalue of A with (complex) eigenvector $\mathbf{v}$, then the real and imaginary parts of $e^{\lambda t}\mathbf{v}$ form a linearly independent pair of (real) solutions. You will need to use the formula $e^{i\theta} = \cos\theta + i\sin\theta$.

3. Use the initial conditions to find the explicit form of the (real) solutions to the original equations.

4. If you have access to a computer or graphing calculator, graph the solutions obtained in part (3) over the domain $0 \le t \le 3$. At what moment are the two populations equal?

5. Interpret the solution in terms of the long-term population trend for the two species. Does one species ultimately disappear? Why or why not? Contrast this solution to that obtained for the model in Chapter 7.

6. If you have access to a computer or graphing calculator that can numerically solve differential equations, use it to graph the solutions to the original system of equations. Does this numerical approximation appear to be accurate?

CHAPTER 8 ☐ MATLAB EXERCISES

1. MATLAB handles complex numbers and matrices in much the same way as real ones. The imaginary unit $i = \sqrt{-1}$ is a built-in constant. For instance, the complex number $2 - 3i$ would be represented as $2 - 3 * i$ in MATLAB. You can verify the result of Example 5, Section 8.2, by entering the matrix A,

$$A = [2 - i \quad -5 + 2 * i \; ; \; 3 - i \quad -6 + 2 * i]$$

and then typing **inv(A).**

Use MATLAB to perform the following matrix operations, given

$$A = \begin{bmatrix} 1 & 2 - i \\ 2 + i & i \end{bmatrix}, \; B = \begin{bmatrix} 3i & 4 \\ -4 & -i \end{bmatrix}, \; \text{and} \; C = \begin{bmatrix} i & -i & 0 \\ 2 & 0 & 2 + 3i \end{bmatrix}.$$

(a) AB (b) $3iC$ (c) A^{-1}

(d) $C^T C$ (e) $|A + B|$ (f) $iAB^2 + (1 - i)CC^T$

2. Use MATLAB to solve the system of linear equations $Ax = \mathbf{b}$.

(a) $A = \begin{bmatrix} i & 2 - i \\ 3 - 2i & 0 \end{bmatrix}, \quad \mathbf{b} = \begin{bmatrix} 1 + i \\ 6 - 4i \end{bmatrix}$

(b) $A = \begin{bmatrix} 1 & 0 & i \\ -2 & i + 1 & -i \\ 1 - i & 0 & -1 \end{bmatrix}, \quad \mathbf{b} = \begin{bmatrix} i \\ 0 \\ 2 - i \end{bmatrix}$

3. For a complex matrix A, the MATLAB command $\mathbf{A}'$ produces the complex conjugate transpose A^* of A. Use this command to determine which of the following matrices are Hermitian and which are normal.

(a) $\begin{bmatrix} i & 1 \\ 1 & -i \end{bmatrix}$ (b) $\begin{bmatrix} 1 & 1 \\ -1 & 1 \end{bmatrix}$

(c) $\begin{bmatrix} 3 - 4i & 2 \\ 1 + i & 4 - i \end{bmatrix}$ (d) $\begin{bmatrix} 1 & 0 & 0 \\ 0 & 2 & i \\ 0 & i & 2 \end{bmatrix}$

4. The MATLAB command $[\mathbf{P,D}] = \mathbf{eig(A)}$ will produce a diagonal matrix D containing the eigenvalues of the complex matrix A, and a matrix P containing the corresponding eigenvectors. For instance, if

$$A = \begin{bmatrix} 3 & 2 - i & -3i \\ 2 + i & 0 & 1 - i \\ 3i & 1 + i & 0 \end{bmatrix}$$

is the matrix from Example 7, Section 8.5, then the command $[\mathbf{P,D}] = \mathbf{eig(A)}$ yields

$$
P = \begin{bmatrix} 0.7792 + 0.0000i & -0.4472 + 0.2236i & -0.2870 - 0.2460i \\ 0.3438 + 0.2063i & 0.1118 - 0.3354i & -0.2050 + 0.8199i \\ 0.0229 + 0.4813i & 0.1118 + 0.7826i & 0.2870 + 0.2460i \end{bmatrix}
$$

and

$$
D = \begin{bmatrix} 6.0000 + 0.0000i & 0 & 0 \\ 0 & -2.0000 + 0.0000i & 0 \\ 0 & 0 & -1.0000 - 0.0000i \end{bmatrix},
$$

which is equivalent to the solution given in the text. Use this procedure to diagonalize the following matrices.

(a) $A = \begin{bmatrix} 1 & i \\ i & 1 \end{bmatrix}$ (b) $A = \begin{bmatrix} 1 & 0 & 0 \\ 0 & 2 & i \\ 0 & i & 2 \end{bmatrix}$ (c) $\begin{bmatrix} 1 & 1+i & 1-i \\ 1-i & 0 & i \\ 1+i & -i & 0 \end{bmatrix}$

9 LINEAR PROGRAMMING

John
von
Neumann

1 9 0 3 – 1 9 5 7

ohn von Neumann was born in Budapest, Hungary, where his father was a successful banker. John's genius was recognized at an early age. By the age of ten, his mathematical knowledge was so great that instead of attending regular classes he studied privately under the direction of leading Hungarian mathematicians.

At the age of twenty-one, he acquired two degrees, one in chemical engineering at Zurich, and the other a Ph.D. in mathematics from the University of Budapest. He spent some time teaching at the University of Berlin, and then, in 1930, accepted a visiting professorship at Princeton University. In 1933, John von Neumann and Albert Einstein were among the first full professors to be appointed to the newly organized Institute for Advanced Study at Princeton.

During World War II, von Neumann was a consultant at Los Alamos, and his research helped in the development of the atomic bomb. In 1954, President Eisenhower appointed him to the Atomic Energy Commission.

von Neumann is considered to be the father of modern game theory—a branch of mathematics that deals with strategies and decision making. Much of his results concerning game theory were published in a lengthy paper in 1944 titled *Theory of Games and Economic Behavior*, written with Oskar Morgenstern.

In 1955, John von Neumann was diagnosed with cancer—he died in 1957 at the age of 53. Many stories are told of his mental abilities. Even during the final months of his life, as his brother read to him in German from Goethe's *Faust,* each time a page was turned John would recite from memory the continuation of the passage on the following page.

9.1 SYSTEMS OF LINEAR INEQUALITIES

The following statements are inequalities in two variables.

$$3x - 2y < 6 \quad \text{and} \quad x + y \geq 6$$

An ordered pair (a, b) is a **solution of an inequality** in x and y if the inequality is true when a and b are substituted for x and y, respectively. For instance, $(1, 1)$ is a solution of the inequality $3x - 2y < 6$ because $3(1) - 2(1) = 1 < 6$. The **graph** of an inequality is the collection of all solutions of the inequality. To sketch the graph of an inequality such as

$$3x - 2y < 6$$

we begin by sketching the graph of the *corresponding equation*

$$3x - 2y = 6.$$

The graph of the equation will normally separate the plane into two or more regions. In each such region, one of the following must be true. (1) All points in the region are solutions of the inequality. (2) No points in the region are solutions of the inequality. Thus, we can determine whether the points in an entire region satisfy the inequality by simply testing *one* point in the region.

Sketching the Graph of an Inequality in Two Variables	1. Replace the inequality sign by an equal sign, and sketch the graph of the resulting equation. (We use a dashed line for < or > and a solid line for ≤ or ≥.) 2. Test one point in each of the regions formed by the graph in Step 1. If the point satisfies the inequality, then shade the entire region to denote that every point in the region satisfies the inequality.

In this section, we will work with **linear inequalities** of the form

$$ax + by < c \qquad ax + by \le c$$

$$ax + by > c \qquad ax + by \ge c.$$

The graph of each of these linear inequalities is a half-plane lying on one side of the line $ax + by = c$. The simplest linear inequalities are those corresponding to horizontal or vertical lines, as shown in Example 1.

EXAMPLE 1   *Sketching the Graph of a Linear Inequality*

Sketch the graphs of (a) $x > -2$ and (b) $y \le 3$.

Solution   (a) The graph of the corresponding equation $x = -2$ is a vertical line. The points that satisfy the inequality $x > -2$ are those lying to the right of this line, as shown in Figure 9.1.

(b) The graph of the corresponding equation $y = 3$ is a horizontal line. The points that satisfy the inequality $y \le 3$ are those lying below (or on) this line, as shown in Figure 9.2.

Figure 9.1

Figure 9.2

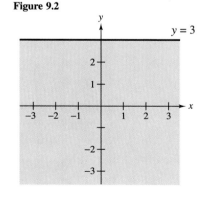

EXAMPLE 2   *Sketching the Graph of a Linear Inequality*

Sketch the graph of $x - y < 2$.

Solution   The graph of the corresponding equation $x - y = 2$ is a line, as shown in Figure 9.3. Since the origin $(0, 0)$ satisfies the inequality, the graph consists of the half-plane lying above the line. (Try checking a point below the line. Regardless of which point you choose, you will see that it does not satisfy the inequality.)

Figure 9.3

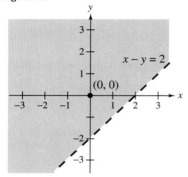

For a linear inequality in two variables, we can sometimes simplify the graphing procedure by writing the inequality in *slope-intercept* form. For instance, by writing $x - y < 2$ in the form

$$y > x - 2$$

we can see that the solution points lie *above* the line $y = x - 2$, as shown in Figure 9.3. Similarly, by writing the inequality $3x - 2y > 5$ in the form

$$y < \frac{3}{2}x - \frac{5}{2}$$

we see that the solutions lie *below* the line $y = \frac{3}{2}x - \frac{5}{2}$.

Systems of Inequalities

Many practical problems in business, science, and engineering involve systems of linear inequalities. Here is an example of such a system.

$$
\begin{aligned}
x + y &\leq 12 \\
3x - 4y &\leq 15 \\
x &\geq 0 \\
y &\geq 0
\end{aligned}
$$

A **solution** of a system of inequalities in x and y is a point (x, y) that satisfies each inequality in the system. For instance, $(2, 4)$ is a solution of this system because $x = 2$ and $y = 4$ satisfy each of the four inequalities in the system. The **graph** of a system of inequalities in two variables is the collection of all points that are solutions of the system. For instance, the graph of the system above is the region shown in Figure 9.4. Note that the point $(2, 4)$ lies in the region because it is a solution of the system of inequalities.

To sketch the graph of a system of inequalities in two variables, we first sketch the graph of each individual inequality (on the same coordinate system) and then find the region that is *common* to every graph in the system. For systems of linear inequalities, it is helpful to find the *vertices* of the solution region, as shown in the following example.

Figure 9.4

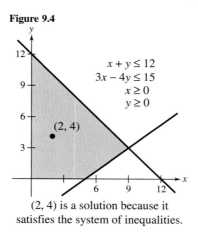

$$x + y \leq 12$$
$$3x - 4y \leq 15$$
$$x \geq 0$$
$$y \geq 0$$

$(2, 4)$ is a solution because it
satisfies the system of inequalities.

EXAMPLE 3   *Solving a System of Inequalities*

Sketch the graph (and label the vertices) of the solution set of the following system.

$$x - y < 2$$
$$x > -2$$
$$y \leq 3$$

Solution   We have already sketched the graph of each inequality in Examples 1 and 2. The triangular region common to all three graphs can be found by superimposing the graphs on the same coordinate plane, as shown in Figure 9.5. To find the vertices of the region, we find the points of intersection of the boundaries of the region.

Vertex A: $(-2, -4)$	*Vertex B :* $(5, 3)$	*Vertex C :* $(-2, 3)$
Obtained by finding the point of intersection of	Obtained by finding the point of intersection of	Obtained by finding the point of intersection of
$x - y = 2$	$x - y = 2$	$x = -2$
$x = -2.$	$y = 3.$	$y = 3.$

Figure 9.5

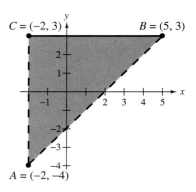

For the triangular region shown in Figure 9.5, each point of intersection of a pair of boundary lines corresponds to a vertex. With more complicated regions, two border lines can sometimes intersect at a point that is not a vertex of the region, as shown in Figure 9.6. In order to keep track of which points of intersection are actually vertices of the region, we suggest that you make a careful sketch of the region and refer to your sketch as you find each point of intersection.

When solving a system of inequalities, you should be aware that the system might have no solution. For instance, the system

$$x + y > 3$$
$$x + y < -1$$

has no solution points because the quantity $(x + y)$ cannot be both less than -1 and greater than 3, as shown in Figure 9.7.

Figure 9.6

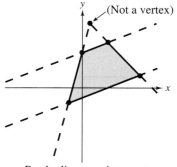

Border lines can intersect
at a point that is not a vertex.

Figure 9.7

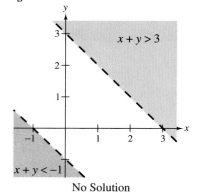

No Solution

Another possibility is that the solution set of a system of inequalities can be unbounded. For instance, the solution set of

$$x + y < 3$$
$$x + 2y > 3$$

forms an *infinite wedge*, as shown in Figure 9.8.

Figure 9.8

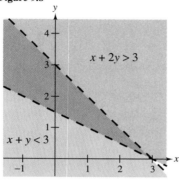

Unbounded Region

Applications

Our last example in this section shows how a system of linear inequalities can arise in an applied problem.

EXAMPLE 4   *An Application of a System of Inequalities*

The liquid portion of a diet is to provide at least 300 calories, 36 units of vitamin A, and 90 units of vitamin C daily. A cup of dietary drink X provides 60 calories, 12 units of vitamin A, and 10 units of vitamin C. A cup of dietary drink Y provides 60 calories, 6 units of vitamin A, and 30 units of vitamin C. Set up a system of linear inequalities that describes the minimum daily requirements for calories and vitamins.

Solution   We let

$$x = \text{number of cups of dietary drink X}$$
$$y = \text{number of cups of dietary drink Y.}$$

Then, to meet the minimum daily requirements, the following inequalities must be satisfied.

For calories: $60x + 60y \geq 300$
For vitamin A: $12x + 6y \geq 36$
For vitamin C: $10x + 30y \geq 90$
$$x \geq 0$$
$$y \geq 0$$

The last two inequalities are included because x and y cannot be negative. The graph of this system of linear inequalities is shown in Figure 9.9.

Figure 9.9

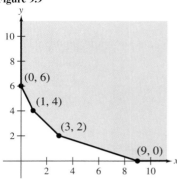

Any point inside the region shown in Figure 9.9 (or on its boundary) meets the minimum daily requirements for calories and vitamins. For instance, 3 cups of dietary drink X and 2 cups of dietary drink Y supply 300 calories, 48 units of vitamin A, and 90 units of vitamin C.

SECTION 9.1 EXERCISES

In Exercises 1–6, match the linear inequality with its graph. [The graphs are labeled (a)–(f).]

1. $x > 3$ **2.** $y \leq 2$ **3.** $2x + 3y \leq 6$

4. $2x - y \geq -2$ **5.** $x \geq \dfrac{y}{2}$ **6.** $y > 3x$

(a)

(b)

(c)

(d)

(e)

(f)

In Exercises 7–22, sketch the graph of the given linear inequality.

7. $x \geq 2$ **8.** $x \leq 4$ **9.** $y \geq -1$

10. $y \leq 3$ **11.** $y < 2 - x$ **12.** $y > 2x - 4$

13. $2y - x \geq 4$ **14.** $5x + 3y \geq -15$

15. $y \leq x$ **16.** $3x > y$ **17.** $y \geq 4 - 2x$

18. $y \leq 3 + x$ **19.** $3y + 4 \geq x$ **20.** $6 - 2y < x$

21. $4x - 2y \leq 12$ **22.** $y + 3x > 6$

In Exercises 23–32, sketch the graph of the solution of the given system of linear inequalities.

23. $x \geq 0$ **24.** $x \geq -1$ **25.** $x + y \leq 1$

  $y \geq 0$ $y \geq -1$ $-x + y \leq 1$

  $x \leq 2$ $x \leq 1$ $y \geq 0$

  $y \leq 4$ $y \leq 2$

26. $3x + 2y < 6$
$\quad x \qquad > 0$
$\quad \qquad y > 0$

27. $x + y \le 5$
$\quad x \qquad \ge 2$
$\quad \qquad y \ge 0$

28. $2x + y \ge 2$
$\quad x \qquad \le 2$
$\quad \qquad y \le 1$

29. $-3x + 2y < \quad 6$
$\quad x + 4y > -2$
$\quad 2x + \ y < \quad 3$

30. $x - 7y > -36$
$\quad 5x + 2y > \quad 5$
$\quad 6x - 5y > \quad 6$

31. $x \qquad \ge 1$
$\quad x - 2y \le 3$
$\quad 3x + 2y \ge 9$
$\quad x + \ y \le 6$

32. $x + y < 10$
$\quad 2x + y > 10$
$\quad \quad x - y < \ 2$

In Exercises 33–36, derive a set of inequalities to describe the given region.

33. Rectangular region with vertices at $(2, 1)$, $(5, 1)$, $(5, 7)$, and $(2, 7)$.

34. Parallelogram with vertices at $(0, 0)$, $(4, 0)$, $(1, 4)$, and $(5, 4)$.

35. Triangular region with vertices at $(0, 0)$, $(5, 0)$, and $(2, 3)$.

36. Triangular region with vertices at $(-1, 0)$, $(1, 0)$, and $(0, 1)$.

37. A furniture company can sell all the tables and chairs it produces. Each table requires 1 hour in the assembly center and $1\frac{1}{3}$ hours in the finishing center. Each chair requires $1\frac{1}{2}$ hours in the assembly center and $1\frac{1}{2}$ hours in the finishing center. The company's assembly center is available 12 hours per day, and its finishing center is available 15 hours per day. If x is the number of tables produced per day and y is the number of chairs, find a system of inequalities describing all possible production levels. Sketch the graph of the system.

38. A store sells two models of a certain brand of computer. Because of the demand, it is necessary to stock at least twice as many units of model A as units of model B. The cost to the store for the two models is $800 and $1200, respectively. The management does not want more than $20,000 in computer inventory at any one time, and it wants at least four model A computers and two model B computers in inventory at all times. Devise a system of inequalities describing all possible inventory levels, and sketch the graph of the system.

39. A person plans to invest no more than $20,000 in two different interest-bearing accounts. Each account is to contain at least $5000. Moreover, one account should have at least twice the amount that is in the other account. Find a system of inequalities to describe the various amounts that can be deposited in each account, and sketch the graph of the system.

40. Two types of tickets are to be sold for a concert. One type costs $15 per ticket and the other type costs $25 per ticket. The promoter of the concert must sell at least 15,000 tickets including 8000 of the $15 tickets and 4000 of the $25 tickets. Moreover, the gross receipts must total at least $275,000 in order for the concert to be held. Find a system of inequalities describing the different numbers of tickets that can be sold, and sketch the graph of the system.

41. A dietitian is asked to design a special diet supplement using two different foods. Each ounce of food X contains 20 units of calcium, 15 units of iron, and 10 units of vitamin B. Each ounce of food Y contains 10 units of calcium, 10 units of iron, and 20 units of vitamin B. The minimum daily requirements in the diet are 300 units of calcium, 150 units of iron, and 200 units of vitamin B. Find a system of inequalities describing the different amounts of food X and food Y that can be used in the diet, and sketch the graph of the system.

42. Rework Exercise 41 using minimum daily requirements of 280 units of calcium, 160 units of iron, and 180 units of vitamin B.

9.2 LINEAR PROGRAMMING INVOLVING TWO VARIABLES

Many applications in business and economics involve a process called **optimization,** in which we are required to find the minimum cost, the maximum profit, or the minimum use of resources. In this section we discuss one type of optimization problem called **linear programming.**

A two-dimensional linear programming problem consists of a linear **objective function** and a system of linear inequalities called **constraints.** The objective function gives the quantity that is to be maximized (or minimized), and the constraints determine the set of **feasible solutions.**

For example, consider a linear programming problem in which we are asked to maximize the value of

$$z = ax + by \qquad \text{Objective function}$$

subject to a set of constraints that determine the region indicated in Figure 9.10. Because every point in the region satisfies each constraint, it is not clear how we should go about finding the point that yields a maximum value of z. Fortunately, it can be shown that if there is an optimal solution, it must occur at one of the vertices of the region. In other words, *we can find the maximum value by testing z at each of the vertices*, as illustrated in Example 1.

Figure 9.10

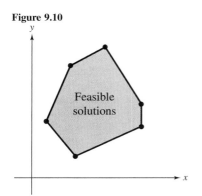

The objective function has its optimal value at one of the vertices of the region determined by the constraints.

Theorem 9.1

Optimal Solution of a Linear Programming Problem

If a linear programming problem has a solution, it must occur at a vertex of the set of feasible solutions. If the problem has more than one solution, then at least one of them must occur at a vertex of the set of feasible solutions. In either case, the value of the objective function is unique.

EXAMPLE 1   *Solving a Linear Programming Problem*

Find the maximum value of

$$z = 3x + 2y \qquad \text{Objective function}$$

subject to the following constraints.

$$\left. \begin{array}{r} x \geq 0 \\ y \geq 0 \\ x + 2y \leq 4 \\ x - y \leq 1 \end{array} \right\} \quad \text{Constraints}$$

Solution   The constraints form the region shown in Figure 9.11. At the four vertices of this region, the objective function has the following values.

At $(0, 0)$: $z = 3(0) + 2(0) = 0$
At $(1, 0)$: $z = 3(1) + 2(0) = 3$
At $(2, 1)$: $z = 3(2) + 2(1) = 8$ **(Maximum value of z)**
At $(0, 2)$: $z = 3(0) + 2(2) = 4$

Thus, the maximum value of z is 8, and this occurs when $x = 2$ and $y = 1$.

Figure 9.11

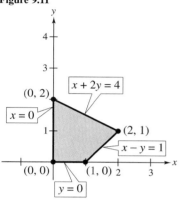

REMARK: In Example 1, try testing some of the interior points in the region. You will see that the corresponding values of z are less than 8.

To see why the maximum value of the objective function in Example 1 must occur at a vertex, consider writing the objective function in the form

$$y = -\frac{3}{2}x + \frac{z}{2}.$$

This equation represents a family of lines, each of slope $-3/2$. Of these infinitely many lines, we want the one that has the largest z-value, while still intersecting the region determined by the constraints. In other words, of all the lines whose slope is $-3/2$, we want the one that has the largest y-intercept *and* intersects the given region, as shown in Figure 9.12. It should be clear that such a line will pass through one (or more) of the vertices of the region.

Figure 9.12

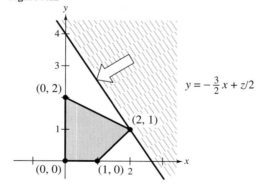

We outline the graphical method for solving a linear programming problem as follows.

Graphical Method of Solving a Linear Programming Problem

To solve a linear programming problem involving two variables by the graphical method, use the following steps.
1. Sketch the region corresponding to the system of constraints. (The points inside or on the boundary of the region are called *feasible solutions*.)
2. Find the vertices of the region.
3. Test the objective function at each of the vertices and select the values of the variables that optimize the objective function. For a bounded region, both a minimum and maximum value will exist. (For an unbounded region, *if* an optimal solution exists, then it will occur at a vertex.)

These guidelines will work regardless of whether the objective function is to be maximized *or* minimized. For instance, in Example 1 the same test used to find the maximum value of z can be used to conclude that the minimum value of z is 0, and this occurs at the vertex $(0, 0)$.

EXAMPLE 2   *Solving a Linear Programming Problem*

Find the maximum value of the objective function

$$z = 4x + 6y \qquad \text{Objective function}$$

where $x \geq 0$ and $y \geq 0$, subject to the constraints

$$\left.\begin{array}{r} -x + y \leq 11 \\ x + y \leq 27 \\ 2x + 5y \leq 90. \end{array}\right\} \quad \text{Constraints}$$

Solution   The region bounded by the constraints is shown in Figure 9.13. By testing the objective function at each vertex, we obtain the following.

$$
\begin{aligned}
\text{At} \quad (0, 0)&: z = 4(0) + 6(0) = 0 \\
\text{At} \quad (0, 11)&: z = 4(0) + 6(11) = 66 \\
\text{At} \quad (5, 16)&: z = 4(5) + 6(16) = 116 \\
\text{At} \quad (15, 12)&: z = 4(15) + 6(12) = 132 \qquad \text{(Maximum value of } z\text{)} \\
\text{At} \quad (27, 0)&: z = 4(27) + 6(0) = 108
\end{aligned}
$$

Thus, the maximum value of z is 132, and this occurs when $x = 15$ and $y = 12$.

In the next example, we show that the same basic procedure can be used to solve a linear programming problem in which the objective function is to be *minimized*.

Figure 9.13

$-x + y = 11$

$2x + 5y = 90$

(5, 16)

(15, 12)

$x + y = 27$

(0, 11)

(0, 0)

(27, 0)

Figure 9.14

(1, 5)

(0, 4)

(6, 3)

(0, 2)

(3, 0)   (5, 0)

EXAMPLE 3   *Minimizing an Objective Function*

Find the minimum value of the objective function

$$z = 5x + 7y \qquad \text{Objective function}$$

where $x \geq 0$ and $y \geq 0$, subject to the constraints

$$\left.\begin{array}{r} 2x + 3y \geq 6 \\ 3x - y \leq 15 \\ -x + y \leq 4 \\ 2x + 5y \leq 27. \end{array}\right\} \quad \text{Constraints}$$

Solution   The region bounded by the constraints is shown in Figure 9.14. By testing the objective function at each vertex, we obtain the following.

$$
\begin{aligned}
&\text{At } (0, 2): z = 5(0) + 7(2) &&= 14 \qquad \text{(Minimum value of } z\text{)}\\
&\text{At } (0, 4): z = 5(0) + 7(4) &&= 28\\
&\text{At } (1, 5): z = 5(1) + 7(5) &&= 40\\
&\text{At } (6, 3): z = 5(6) + 7(3) &&= 51\\
&\text{At } (5, 0): z = 5(5) + 7(0) &&= 25\\
&\text{At } (3, 0): z = 5(3) + 7(0) &&= 15
\end{aligned}
$$

Thus, the minimum value of z is 14, and this occurs when $x = 0$ and $y = 2$.

REMARK: In Example 3, note that the steps used to find the minimum value are precisely the same ones we would use to find the maximum value. In other words, once we have evaluated the objective function at the vertices of the feasible region, we simply choose the largest value as the maximum and the smallest value as the minimum.

When solving a linear programming problem, it is possible that the maximum (or minimum) value occurs at *two* different vertices. For instance, at the vertices of the region shown in Figure 9.15, the objective function

$$z = 2x + 2y \qquad \text{Objective function}$$

Figure 9.15

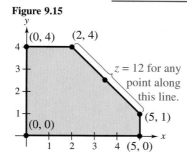

(0, 4)   (2, 4)

$z = 12$ for any point along this line.

(0, 0)

(5, 1)

(5, 0)

has the following values.

$$\text{At } (0, 0): z = 2(0) + 2(0) = 0$$
$$\text{At } (0, 4): z = 2(0) + 2(4) = 8$$
$$\text{At } (2, 4): z = 2(2) + 2(4) = 12 \quad \text{(Maximum value of } z\text{)}$$
$$\text{At } (5, 1): z = 2(5) + 2(1) = 12 \quad \text{(Maximum value of } z\text{)}$$
$$\text{At } (5, 0): z = 2(5) + 2(0) = 10$$

In this case, we can conclude that the objective function has a maximum value not only at the vertices (2, 4) and (5, 1), it also has a maximum value (of 12) at *any point on the line segment connecting these two vertices.*

Some linear programming problems have no optimal solution. This can occur if the region determined by the constraints is *unbounded*. Example 4 illustrates such a problem.

EXAMPLE 4   *An Unbounded Region*

Find the maximum value of

$$z = 4x + 2y \qquad \text{Objective function}$$

where $x \geq 0$ and $y \geq 0$, subject to the constraints

$$\left. \begin{array}{r} x + 2y \geq 4 \\ 3x + y \geq 7 \\ -x + 2y \leq 7. \end{array} \right\} \quad \text{Constraints}$$

Solution   The region determined by the constraints is shown in Figure 9.16. For this unbounded region, there is no maximum value of z. To see this, note that the point $(x, 0)$ lies in the region for all values of $x \geq 4$. By choosing x to be large, we can obtain values of $z = 4(x) + 2(0) = 4x$ that are as large as we want. Thus, there is no maximum value of z.

Figure 9.16

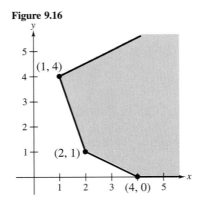

Applications

EXAMPLE 5   *An Application: Minimum Cost*

In Example 4 in Section 9.1, we set up a system of linear equations for the following problem. The liquid portion of a diet is to provide at least 300 calories, 36 units of vitamin A, and 90 units of vitamin C daily. A cup of dietary drink X provides 60 calories, 12 units of vitamin A, and 10 units of vitamin C. A cup of dietary drink Y provides 60 calories, 6 units of vitamin A, and 30 units of vitamin C. Now, suppose that dietary drink X costs $0.12 per cup and drink Y costs $0.15 per cup. How many cups of each drink should be consumed each day to minimize the cost and still meet the stated daily requirements?

Solution   We begin by letting x be the number of cups of dietary drink X and y be the number of cups of dietary drink Y. Moreover, to meet the minimum daily requirements, the following inequalities must be satisfied.

$$\left. \begin{array}{ll} \text{For calories:} & 60x + 60y \geq 300 \\ \text{For vitamin A:} & 12x + 6y \geq 36 \\ \text{For vitamin C:} & 10x + 30y \geq 90 \\ & x \geq 0 \\ & y \geq 0 \end{array} \right\} \quad \textbf{Constraints}$$

The cost C is given by

$$C = 0.12x + 0.15y. \qquad \textbf{Objective function}$$

The graph of the region corresponding to the constraints is shown in Figure 9.17. To determine the minimum cost, we test C at each vertex of the region as follows.

At $(0, 6)$: $C = 0.12(0) + 0.15(6) = 0.90$

At $(1, 4)$: $C = 0.12(1) + 0.15(4) = 0.72$

At $(3, 2)$: $C = 0.12(3) + 0.15(2) = 0.66$ (Minimum value of C)

At $(9, 0)$: $C = 0.12(9) + 0.15(0) = 1.08$

Thus, the minimum cost is $0.66 per day, and this occurs when three cups of drink X and two cups of drink Y are consumed each day.

Figure 9.17

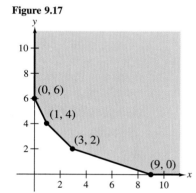

SECTION 9.2 ☐ EXERCISES

In Exercises 1–16, find the minimum and maximum values of the given objective function, subject to the indicated constraints.

1. Objective function:

$z = 3x + 2y$

Constraints:

$$x \geq 0$$
$$y \geq 0$$
$$x + 3y \leq 15$$
$$4x + y \leq 16$$

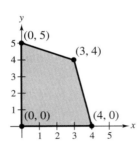

2. Objective function:

$z = 4x + 3y$

Constraints:

$$x \geq 0$$
$$y \geq 0$$
$$2x + 3y \geq 6$$
$$3x - 2y \leq 9$$
$$x + 5y \leq 20$$

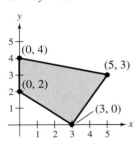

3. Objective function:

$z = 5x + 0.5y$

Constraints:

(See Exercise 1.)

4. Objective function:

$z = x + 6y$

Constraints:

(See Exercise 2.)

5. Objective function:

$z = 10x + 7y$

Constraints:

$$0 \leq x \leq 60$$
$$0 \leq y \leq 45$$
$$5x + 6y \leq 420$$

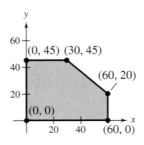

6. Objective function:

$z = 50x + 35y$

Constraints:

$$x \geq 0$$
$$y \geq 0$$
$$8x + 9y \leq 7200$$
$$8x + 9y \geq 5400$$

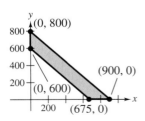

7. Objective function:

$z = 25x + 30y$

Constraints:

(See Exercise 5.)

8. Objective function:

$z = 16x + 18y$

Constraints:

(See Exercise 6.)

9. Objective function:

$z = 4x + 5y$

Constraints:

$$x \geq 0$$
$$y \geq 0$$
$$4x + 3y \geq 27$$
$$x + y \geq 8$$
$$3x + 5y \geq 30$$

10. Objective function:

$z = 4x + 5y$

Constraints:

$$x \geq 0$$
$$y \geq 0$$
$$2x + 2y \leq 10$$
$$x + 2y \leq 6$$

11. Objective function:

$z = 2x + 7y$

Constraints:

(See Exercise 9.)

12. Objective function:

$z = 2x - y$

Constraints:

(See Exercise 10.)

13. Objective function:

$z = 4x + y$

Constraints:

$$x \geq 0$$
$$y \geq 0$$
$$x + 2y \leq 40$$
$$x + y \geq 30$$
$$2x + 3y \geq 72$$

14. Objective function:

$z = x$

Constraints:

$$x \geq 0$$
$$y \geq 0$$
$$2x + 3y \leq 60$$
$$2x + y \leq 28$$
$$4x + y \leq 48$$

15. Objective function:

$z = x + 4y$

Constraints:

(See Exercise 13.)

16. Objective function:

$z = y$

Constraints:

(See Exercise 14.)

In Exercises 17–20, maximize the given objective function subject to the constraints $3x_1 + x_2 \leq 15$ and $4x_1 + 3x_2 \leq 30$ where $x_1, x_2 \geq 0$.

17. $z = 2x_1 + x_2$

18. $z = 5x_1 + x_2$

19. $z = x_1 + x_2$

20. $z = 3x_1 + x_2$

21. A merchant plans to sell two models of home computers at costs of $250 and $400, respectively. The $250 model yields a profit of $45 and the $400 model yields a profit of $50. The merchant estimates that the total monthly demand will not exceed 250 units. Find the number of units of each model that should be stocked in order to maximize profit. Assume that the merchant does not want to invest more than $70,000 in computer inventory.

22. A fruit grower has 150 acres of land available to raise two crops, A and B. It takes one day to trim an acre of crop A and two days to trim an acre of crop B, and there are 240 days per year available for trimming. It takes 0.3 day to pick an acre of crop A and 0.1 day to pick an acre of crop B, and there are 30 days per year available for picking. Find the number of acres of each fruit that should be planted to maximize profit, assuming that the profit is $140 per acre for crop A and $235 per acre for crop B.

23. A farming cooperative mixes two brands of cattle feed. Brand X costs $25 per bag and contains 2 units of nutritional element A, 2 units of element B, and 2 units of element C. Brand Y costs $20 per bag and contains 1 unit of nutritional element A, 9 units of element B, and 3 units of element C. Find the number of bags of each brand that should be mixed to produce a mixture having a minimum cost per bag. The minimum requirements of nutrients A, B, and C are 12 units, 36 units, and 24 units, respectively.

24. Two gasolines, type A and type B, have octane ratings of 80 and 92, respectively. Type A costs $0.83 per liter and type B costs $0.98 per liter. Determine the blend of minimum cost with an octane rating of at least 90. [Hint: Let x be the fraction of each liter that is type A and y be the fraction that is type B.]

In Exercises 25–30, the given linear programming problem has an unusual characteristic. Sketch a graph of the solution region for the problem and describe the unusual characteristic. (In each problem, the objective function is to be maximized.)

25. Objective function:
$$z = 2.5x + y$$
Constraints:
$$x \geq 0$$
$$y \geq 0$$
$$3x + 5y \leq 15$$
$$5x + 2y \leq 10$$

26. Objective function:
$$z = x + y$$
Constraints:
$$x \geq 0$$
$$y \geq 0$$
$$-x + y \leq 1$$
$$-x + 2y \leq 4$$

27. Objective function:
$$z = -x + 2y$$
Constraints:
$$x \geq 0$$
$$y \geq 0$$
$$x \leq 10$$
$$x + y \leq 7$$

28. Objective function:
$$z = x + y$$
Constraints:
$$x \geq 0$$
$$y \geq 0$$
$$-x + y \leq 0$$
$$-3x + y \geq 3$$

29. Objective function:
$$z = 3x + 4y$$
Constraints:
$$x \geq 0$$
$$y \geq 0$$
$$x + y \leq 1$$
$$2x + y \geq 4$$

30. Objective function:
$$z = x + 2y$$
Constraints:
$$x \geq 0$$
$$y \geq 0$$
$$x + 2y \leq 4$$
$$2x + y \leq 4$$

In Exercises 31 and 32, determine t-values such that the given objective function has a maximum value at the indicated vertex.

31. Objective function:
$$z = x + ty$$
Constraints:
$$x \geq 0$$
$$y \geq 0$$
$$x \leq 1$$
$$y \leq 1$$

(a) $(0, 0)$ (b) $(1, 0)$

(c) $(1, 1)$ (d) $(0, 1)$

32. Objective function:
$$z = 3x + ty$$
Constraints:
$$x \geq 0$$
$$y \geq 0$$
$$x + 2y \leq 4$$
$$x - y \leq 1$$

(a) $(0, 0)$ (b) $(1, 0)$

(c) $(2, 1)$ (d) $(0, 2)$

[Note: For $t = 2$, this problem is equivalent to that given in Example 1.]

9.3 THE SIMPLEX METHOD: MAXIMIZATION

For linear programming problems involving two variables, the graphical solution method introduced in Section 9.2 is convenient. However, for problems involving more than two variables or problems involving a large number of constraints, it is better to use solution methods that are adaptable to computers. One such method is called the **simplex method,** developed by George Dantzig in 1946. It provides us with a systematic way of examining the vertices of the feasible region to determine the optimal value of the objective function. We introduce this method with an example.

Suppose we want to find the maximum value of $z = 4x_1 + 6x_2$, where $x_1 \geq 0$ and $x_2 \geq 0$, subject to the following constraints.

$$-x_1 + x_2 \leq 11$$
$$x_1 + x_2 \leq 27$$
$$2x_1 + 5x_2 \leq 90$$

Since the left-hand side of each *inequality* is less than or equal to the right-hand side, there must exist nonnegative numbers s_1, s_2 and s_3 that can be added to the left side of each equation to produce the following system of linear *equations*.

$$-x_1 + x_2 + s_1 \qquad\qquad = 11$$
$$x_1 + x_2 \qquad + s_2 \qquad = 27$$
$$2x_1 + 5x_2 \qquad\qquad + s_3 = 90$$

The numbers s_1, s_2 and s_3 are called **slack variables** because they take up the "slack" in each inequality.

Standard Form of a Linear Programming Problem

A linear programming problem is in **standard form** if it seeks to *maximize* the objective function $z = c_1x_1 + c_2x_2 + \cdots + c_nx_n$ subject to the constraints

$$a_{11}x_1 + a_{12}x_2 + \cdots + a_{1n}x_n \leq b_1$$
$$a_{21}x_1 + a_{22}x_2 + \cdots + a_{2n}x_n \leq b_2$$
$$\vdots$$
$$a_{m1}x_1 + a_{m2}x_2 + \cdots + a_{mn}x_n \leq b_m$$

where $x_i \geq 0$ and $b_i \geq 0$. After adding slack variables, the corresponding system of **constraint equations** is

$$a_{11}x_1 + a_{12}x_2 + \cdots + a_{1n}x_n + s_1 \qquad\qquad = b_1$$
$$a_{21}x_1 + a_{22}x_2 + \cdots + a_{2n}x_n \qquad + s_2 \qquad = b_2$$
$$\vdots$$
$$a_{m1}x_1 + a_{m2}x_2 + \cdots + a_{mn}x_n \qquad\qquad + s_m = b_m$$

where $s_i \geq 0$.

REMARK: Note that for a linear programming problem in standard form, the objective function is to be maximized, not minimized. (Minimization problems will be discussed in Sections 9.4 and 9.5.)

A **basic solution** of a linear programming problem in standard form is a solution $(x_1, x_2, \ldots, x_n, s_1, s_2, \ldots, s_m)$ of the constraint equations in which *at most m* variables are nonzero—the variables that are nonzero are called **basic variables.** A basic solution for which all variables are nonnegative is called a **basic feasible solution.**

The Simplex Tableau

The simplex method is carried out by performing elementary row operations on a matrix that we call the **simplex tableau.** This tableau consists of the augmented matrix corresponding to the constraint equations together with the coefficients of the objective function written in the form

$$-c_1x_1 - c_2x_2 - \cdots - c_nx_n + (0)s_1 + (0)s_2 + \cdots + (0)\, s_m + z = 0.$$

In the tableau, it is customary to omit the coefficient of z. For instance, the simplex tableau for the linear programming problem

$$z = 4x_1 + 6x_2 \qquad\qquad \text{Objective function}$$

$$\left. \begin{array}{l} -x_1 + x_2 + s_1 \qquad\qquad = 11 \\ x_1 + x_2 \qquad + s_2 \qquad = 27 \\ 2x_1 + 5x_2 \qquad\qquad + s_3 = 90 \end{array} \right\} \qquad \text{Constraints}$$

is as follows.

x_1	x_2	s_1	s_2	s_3	b	Basic Variables
-1	1	1	0	0	11	s_1
1	1	0	1	0	27	s_2
2	5	0	0	1	90	s_3
-4	-6	0	0	0	0	

$$\uparrow$$
$$\text{\textit{Current z–value}}$$

For this **initial simplex tableau,** the **basic variables** are $s_1, s_2,$ and s_3, and the **nonbasic variables** (which have a value of zero) are x_1 and x_2. Hence, from the two columns that are farthest to the right, we see that the current solution is

$$x_1 = 0, \quad x_2 = 0, \quad s_1 = 11, \quad s_2 = 27, \quad \text{and} \quad s_3 = 90.$$

This solution is a basic feasible solution and is often written as

$$(x_1, x_2, s_1, s_2, s_3) = (0, 0, 11, 27, 90).$$

The entry in the lower–right corner of the simplex tableau is the current value of z. Note that the bottom–row entries under x_1 and x_2 are the negatives of the coefficients of x_1 and x_2 in the objective function

$$z = 4x_1 + 6x_2.$$

To perform an **optimality check** for a solution represented by a simplex tableau, we look at the entries in the bottom row of the tableau. If any of these entries are negative (as above), then the current solution is *not* optimal.

Pivoting

Once we have set up the initial simplex tableau for a linear programming problem, the simplex method consists of checking for optimality and then, if the current solution is not optimal, improving the current solution. (An improved solution is one that has a larger z-value than the current solution.) To improve the current solution, we bring a new basic variable into the solution—we call this variable the **entering variable.** This implies that one of the current basic variables must leave, otherwise we would have too many variables for a basic solution—we call this variable the **departing variable.** We choose the entering and departing variables as follows.

1. The **entering variable** corresponds to the smallest (the most negative) entry in the bottom row of the tableau.
2. The **departing variable** corresponds to the smallest nonnegative ratio of b_i/a_{ij}, in the column determined by the entering variable.
3. The entry in the simplex tableau in the entering variable's column and the departing variable's row is called the **pivot.**

Finally, to form the improved solution, we apply Gauss-Jordan elimination to the column that contains the pivot, as illustrated in the following example. (This process is called **pivoting.)**

EXAMPLE 1   *Pivoting to Find an Improved Solution*

Use the simplex method to find an improved solution for the linear programming problem represented by the following tableau.

x_1	x_2	s_1	s_2	s_3	b	Basic Variables
−1	1	1	0	0	11	s_1
1	1	0	1	0	27	s_2
2	5	0	0	1	90	s_3
−4	−6	0	0	0	0	

The objective function for this problem is $z = 4x_1 + 6x_2$.

Solution   Note that the current solution ($x_1 = 0, x_2 = 0, s_1 = 11, s_2 = 27, s_3 = 90$) corresponds to a z–value of 0. To improve this solution, we determine that x_2 is the entering variable, because -6 is the smallest entry in the bottom row.

x_1	x_2	s_1	s_2	s_3	b	Basic Variables
-1	1	1	0	0	11	s_1
1	1	0	1	0	27	s_2
2	5	0	0	1	90	s_3
-4	-6	0	0	0	0	

$\uparrow$ Entering

To see *why* we choose x_2 as the entering variable, remember that $z = 4x_1 + 6x_2$. Hence, it appears that a unit change in x_2 produces a change of 6 in z, whereas a unit change in x_1 produces a change of only 4 in z.

To find the departing variable, we locate the b_i's that have corresponding positive elements in the entering variables column and form the following ratios.

$$\frac{11}{1} = 11, \quad \frac{27}{1} = 27, \quad \frac{90}{5} = 18$$

Here the smallest positive ratio is 11, so we choose s_1 as the departing variable.

x_1	x_2	s_1	s_2	s_3	b	Basic Variables
-1	$\langle 1 \rangle$	1	0	0	11	s_1 $\leftarrow$ *Departing*
1	1	0	1	0	27	s_2
2	5	0	0	1	90	s_3
-4	-6	0	0	0	0	

$\uparrow$ Entering

Note that the pivot is the entry in the first row and second column. Now, we use Gauss-Jordan elimination to obtain the following improved solution.

Before Pivoting

$$\begin{bmatrix} -1 & 1 & 1 & 0 & 0 & 11 \\ 1 & 1 & 0 & 1 & 0 & 27 \\ 2 & 5 & 0 & 0 & 1 & 90 \\ -4 & -6 & 0 & 0 & 0 & 0 \end{bmatrix} \longrightarrow$$

After Pivoting

$$\begin{bmatrix} -1 & 1 & 1 & 0 & 0 & 11 \\ 2 & 0 & -1 & 1 & 0 & 16 \\ 7 & 0 & -5 & 0 & 1 & 35 \\ -10 & 0 & 6 & 0 & 0 & 66 \end{bmatrix}$$

The new tableau now appears as follows.

	x_1	x_2	s_1	s_2	s_3	b	Basic Variables
	-1	1	1	0	0	11	x_2
	2	0	-1	1	0	16	s_2
	7	0	-5	0	1	35	s_3
	-10	0	6	0	0	66	

Note that x_2 has replaced s_1 in the basis column and the improved solution

$$(x_1, x_2, s_1, s_2, s_3) = (0, 11, 0, 16, 35)$$

has a z-value of

$$z = 4x_1 + 6x_2 = 4(0) + 6(11) = 66.$$

In Example 1 the improved solution is not yet optimal since the bottom row still has a negative entry. Thus, we can apply another iteration of the simplex method to further improve our solution as follows. We choose x_1 as the entering variable. Moreover, the smallest nonnegative ratio of $11/(-1)$, $16/2 = 8$, and $35/7 = 5$ is 5, so s_3 is the departing variable. Gauss-Jordan elimination produces the following.

$$\begin{bmatrix} -1 & 1 & 1 & 0 & 0 & 11 \\ 2 & 0 & -1 & 1 & 0 & 16 \\ 7 & 0 & -5 & 0 & 1 & 35 \\ -10 & 0 & 6 & 0 & 0 & 66 \end{bmatrix} \longrightarrow \begin{bmatrix} -1 & 1 & 1 & 0 & 0 & 11 \\ 2 & 0 & -1 & 1 & 0 & 16 \\ 1 & 0 & -\frac{5}{7} & 0 & \frac{1}{7} & 5 \\ -10 & 0 & 6 & 0 & 0 & 66 \end{bmatrix}$$

$$\longrightarrow \begin{bmatrix} 0 & 1 & \frac{2}{7} & 0 & \frac{1}{7} & 16 \\ 0 & 0 & \frac{3}{7} & 1 & -\frac{2}{7} & 6 \\ 1 & 0 & -\frac{5}{7} & 0 & \frac{1}{7} & 5 \\ 0 & 0 & -\frac{8}{7} & 0 & \frac{10}{7} & 116 \end{bmatrix}$$

Thus, the new simplex tableau is as follows.

	x_1	x_2	s_1	s_2	s_3	b	Basic Variables
	0	1	$\frac{2}{7}$	0	$\frac{1}{7}$	16	x_2
	0	0	$\frac{3}{7}$	1	$-\frac{2}{7}$	6	s_2
	1	0	$-\frac{5}{7}$	0	$\frac{1}{7}$	5	x_1
	0	0	$-\frac{8}{7}$	0	$\frac{10}{7}$	116	

In this tableau, there is still a negative entry in the bottom row. Thus, we choose s_1 as the entering variable and s_2 as the departing variable, as shown in the following tableau.

x_1	x_2	s_1	s_2	s_3	b	Basic Variables	
0	1	$\frac{2}{7}$	0	$\frac{1}{7}$	16	x_2	
0	0	$\left(\frac{3}{7}\right)$	1	$-\frac{2}{7}$	6	s_2	← *Departing*
1	0	$-\frac{5}{7}$	0	$\frac{1}{7}$	5	x_1	
0	0	$-\frac{8}{7}$	0	$\frac{10}{7}$	116		

↑
Entering

By performing one more iteration of the simplex method, we obtain the following tableau. (Try checking this.)

x_1	x_2	s_1	s_2	s_3	b	Basic Variables	
0	1	0	$-\frac{2}{3}$	$\frac{1}{3}$	12	x_2	
0	0	1	$\frac{7}{3}$	$-\frac{2}{3}$	14	s_1	
1	0	0	$\frac{5}{3}$	$-\frac{1}{3}$	15	x_1	
0	0	0	$\frac{8}{3}$	$\frac{2}{3}$	132		← *Maximum z-value*

In this tableau, there are no negative elements in the bottom row. We have therefore determined the optimal solution to be

$$(x_1, x_2, s_1, s_2, s_3) = (15, 12, 14, 0, 0)$$

with

$$z = 4x_1 + 6x_2 = 4(15) + 6(12) = 132.$$

REMARK: Ties may occur in choosing entering and/or departing variables. Should this happen, any choice among the tied variables may be made.

Because the linear programming problem in Example 1 involved only two decision variables, we could have used a graphical solution technique, as we did in Example 2, Section 9.2. Notice in Figure 9.18 that each iteration in the simplex method corresponds to moving from a given vertex to an adjacent vertex with an improved z-value.

(0, 0)	→	(0, 11)	→	(5, 16)	→	(15, 12)
$z = 0$		$z = 66$		$z = 116$		$z = 132$

Figure 9.18

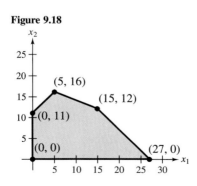

The Simplex Method

We summarize the steps involved in the simplex method as follows.

The Simplex Method (Standard Form)

To solve a linear programming problem in standard form, use the following steps.

1. Convert each inequality in the set of constraints to an equation by adding slack variables.
2. Create the initial simplex tableau.
3. Locate the most negative entry in the bottom row. The column for this entry is called the **entering column.** (If ties occur, any of the tied entries can be used to determine the entering column.)
4. Form the ratios of the entries in the "b-column" with their corresponding positive entries in the entering column. The **departing row** corresponds to the smallest non-negative ratio b_i/a_{ij}. (If all entries in the entering column are 0 or negative, then there is no maximum solution. For ties, choose either entry.) The entry in the departing row and the entering column is called the **pivot.**
5. Use elementary row operations so that the pivot is 1, and all other entries in the entering column are 0. This process is called **pivoting.**
6. If all entries in the bottom row are zero or positive, this is the final tableau. If not, go back to Step 3.
7. If you obtain a final tableau, then the linear programming problem has a maximum solution, which is given by the entry in the lower-right corner of the tableau.

Note that the basic feasible solution of an initial simplex tableau is

$$(x_1, x_2, \ldots, x_n, s_1, s_2, \ldots, s_m) = (0, 0, \ldots, 0, b_1, b_2, \ldots, b_m).$$

This solution is basic because at most m variables are nonzero (namely the slack variables). It is feasible because each variable is nonnegative.

In the next two examples, we illustrate the use of the simplex method to solve a problem involving three decision variables.

EXAMPLE 2   ***The Simplex Method with Three Decision Variables***

Use the simplex method to find the maximum value of

$$z = 2x_1 - x_2 + 2x_3 \qquad \textbf{Objective function}$$

subject to the constraints

$$\begin{aligned} 2x_1 + x_2 \quad\quad\; &\le 10 \\ x_1 + 2x_2 - 2x_3 &\le 20 \\ x_2 + 2x_3 &\le 5 \end{aligned}$$

where $x_1 \ge 0$, $x_2 \ge 0$, and $x_3 \ge 0$.

Solution   Using the basic feasible solution

$$(x_1, x_2, x_3, s_1, s_2, s_3) = (0, 0, 0, 10, 20, 5)$$

the initial simplex tableau for this problem is as follows. (Try checking these computations, and note the "tie" that occurs when choosing the first entering variable.)

x_1	x_2	x_3	s_1	s_2	s_3	b	Basic Variables	
2	1	0	1	0	0	10	s_1	
1	2	-2	0	1	0	20	s_2	
0	1	$\langle\widehat{2}\rangle$	0	0	1	5	s_3	$\leftarrow$ Departing
-2	1	-2	0	0	0	0		

$$\uparrow$$
Entering

x_1	x_2	x_3	s_1	s_2	s_3	b	Basic Variables	
$\langle\widehat{2}\rangle$	1	0	1	0	0	10	s_1	$\leftarrow$ Departing
1	3	0	0	1	1	25	s_2	
0	$\frac{1}{2}$	1	0	0	$\frac{1}{2}$	$\frac{5}{2}$	x_3	
-2	2	0	0	0	1	5		

$$\uparrow$$
Entering

x_1	x_2	x_3	s_1	s_2	s_3	b	Basic Variables
1	$\frac{1}{2}$	0	$\frac{1}{2}$	0	0	5	x_1
0	$\frac{5}{2}$	0	$-\frac{1}{2}$	1	1	20	s_2
0	$\frac{1}{2}$	1	0	0	$\frac{1}{2}$	$\frac{5}{2}$	x_3
0	3	0	1	0	1	15	

This implies that the optimal solution is

$$(x_1, x_2, x_3, s_1, s_2, s_3) = (5, 0, \tfrac{5}{2}, 0, 20, 0)$$

and the maximum value of z is 15.

Occasionally, the constraints in a linear programming problem will include an equation. In such cases, we still add a "slack variable" called an **artificial variable** to form the initial simplex tableau. Technically, this new variable is not a slack variable (because there is no slack to be taken). Once you have determined an optimal solution in such a problem, you should check to see that any equations given in the original constraints are satisfied. Example 3 illustrates such a case.

EXAMPLE 3   *The Simplex Method with Three Decision Variables*

Use the simplex method to find the maximum value of

$$z = 3x_1 + 2x_2 + x_3 \qquad \text{**Objective function**}$$

subject to the constraints

$$4x_1 + x_2 + x_3 = 30$$
$$2x_1 + 3x_2 + x_3 \leq 60$$
$$x_1 + 2x_2 + 3x_3 \leq 40$$

where $x_1 \geq 0$, $x_2 \geq 0$, and $x_3 \geq 0$.

Solution   Using the basic feasible solution

$$(x_1, x_2, x_3, s_1, s_2, s_3) = (0, 0, 0, 30, 60, 40)$$

the initial simplex tableau for this problem is as follows. (Note that s_1 is an artificial variable, rather than a slack variable.)

x_1	x_2	x_3	s_1	s_2	s_3	b	Basic Variables	
④	1	1	1	0	0	30	s_1	← Departing
2	3	1	0	1	0	60	s_2	
1	2	3	0	0	1	40	s_3	
-3	-2	-1	0	0	0	0		

↑
Entering

x_1	x_2	x_3	s_1	s_2	s_3	b	Basic Variables	
1	$\frac{1}{4}$	$\frac{1}{4}$	$\frac{1}{4}$	0	0	$\frac{15}{2}$	x_1	
0	$\frac{5}{2}$	$\frac{1}{2}$	$-\frac{1}{2}$	1	0	45	s_2	← Departing
0	$\frac{7}{4}$	$\frac{11}{4}$	$-\frac{1}{4}$	0	1	$\frac{65}{2}$	s_3	
0	$-\frac{5}{4}$	$-\frac{1}{4}$	$\frac{3}{4}$	0	0	$\frac{45}{2}$		

↑
Entering

x_1	x_2	x_3	s_1	s_2	s_3	b	Basic Variables
1	0	$\frac{1}{5}$	$\frac{3}{10}$	$-\frac{1}{10}$	0	3	x_1
0	1	$\frac{1}{5}$	$-\frac{1}{5}$	$\frac{2}{5}$	0	18	x_2
0	0	$\frac{12}{5}$	$\frac{1}{10}$	$-\frac{7}{10}$	1	1	s_3
0	0	0	$\frac{1}{2}$	$\frac{1}{2}$	0	45	

This implies that the optimal solution is

$$(x_1, x_2, x_3, s_1, s_2, s_3) = (3, 18, 0, 0, 0, 1)$$

and the maximum value of z is 45. (This solution satisfies the equation given in the constraints because $4(3) + 1(18) + 1(0) = 30$.)

Applications

EXAMPLE 4   *A Business Application: Maximum Profit*

A manufacturer produces three types of plastic fixtures. The time required for molding, trimming, and packaging is given in Table 9.1. (Times are given in hours per dozen fixtures.)

TABLE 9.1

Process	Type A	Type B	Type C	Total time available
Molding	1	2	$\frac{3}{2}$	12,000
Trimming	$\frac{2}{3}$	$\frac{2}{3}$	1	4,600
Packaging	$\frac{1}{2}$	$\frac{1}{3}$	$\frac{1}{2}$	2,400
Profit	$11	$16	$15	—

How many dozen of each type of fixture should be produced to obtain a maximum profit?

Solution   Letting x_1, x_2, and x_3 represent the number of dozen units of Types A, B, and C, respectively, the objective function is given by

$$\text{Profit} = P = 11x_1 + 16x_2 + 15x_3.$$

Moreover, using the information in the table, we construct the following constraints.

$$x_1 + 2x_2 + \tfrac{3}{2}x_3 \leq 12{,}000$$
$$\tfrac{2}{3}x_1 + \tfrac{2}{3}x_2 + x_3 \leq 4{,}600$$
$$\tfrac{1}{2}x_1 + \tfrac{1}{3}x_2 + \tfrac{1}{2}x_3 \leq 2{,}400$$

(We also assume that $x_1 \geq 0$, $x_2 \geq 0$, and $x_3 \geq 0$.) Now, applying the simplex method with the basic feasible solution

$$(x_1, x_2, x_3, s_1, s_2, s_3) = (0, 0, 0, 12{,}000, 4{,}600, 2{,}400)$$

we obtain the following tableaus.

x_1	x_2	x_3	s_1	s_2	s_3	b	Basic Variables	
1	$\widehat{2}$	$\frac{3}{2}$	1	0	0	12,000	s_1	← *Departing*
$\frac{2}{3}$	$\frac{2}{3}$	1	0	1	0	4,600	s_2	
$\frac{1}{2}$	$\frac{1}{3}$	$\frac{1}{2}$	0	0	1	2,400	s_3	
-11	-16	-15	0	0	0	0		

↑
Entering

x_1	x_2	x_3	s_1	s_2	s_3	b	Basic Variables
$\frac{1}{2}$	1	$\frac{3}{4}$	$\frac{1}{2}$	0	0	6,000	x_2
$\frac{1}{3}$	0	$\frac{1}{2}$	$-\frac{1}{3}$	1	0	600	s_2
$\left(\frac{1}{3}\right)$	0	$\frac{1}{4}$	$-\frac{1}{6}$	0	1	400	s_3 ← Departing
-3	0	-3	8	0	0	96,000	

↑
Entering

x_1	x_2	x_3	s_1	s_2	s_3	b	Basic Variables
0	1	$\frac{3}{8}$	$\frac{3}{4}$	0	$-\frac{3}{2}$	5,400	x_2
0	0	$\left(\frac{1}{4}\right)$	$-\frac{1}{6}$	1	-1	200	s_2 ← Departing
1	0	$\frac{3}{4}$	$-\frac{1}{2}$	0	3	1,200	x_1
0	0	$-\frac{3}{4}$	$\frac{13}{2}$	0	9	99,600	

↑
Entering

x_1	x_2	x_3	s_1	s_2	s_3	b	Basic Variables
0	1	0	1	$-\frac{3}{2}$	0	5,100	x_2
0	0	1	$-\frac{2}{3}$	4	-4	800	x_3
1	0	0	0	-3	6	600	x_1
0	0	0	6	3	6	100,200	

From this final simplex tableau, we see that the maximum profit is $100,200, and this is obtained by the following production levels.

Type A:	600 dozen units
Type B:	5,100 dozen units
Type C:	800 dozen units

REMARK: In Example 4, note that the second simplex tableau contains a "tie" for the minimum entry in the bottom row. (Both the first and third entries in the bottom row are -3.) Although we chose the first column to represent the departing variable, we could have chosen the third column. Try reworking the problem with this choice to see that you obtain the same solution.

EXAMPLE 5   *A Business Application: Media Selection*

The advertising alternatives for a company include television, radio, and newspaper advertisements. The costs and estimates for audience coverage are given in Table 9.2

TABLE 9.2

	Television	Newspaper	Radio
Cost per advertisement	$ 2,000	$ 600	$ 300
Audience per advertisement	100,000	40,000	18,000

The local newspaper limits the number of weekly advertisements from a single company to ten. Moreover, in order to balance the advertising among the three types of media, no more than half of the total number of advertisements should occur on the radio, and at least 10% should occur on television. The weekly advertising budget is $18,200. How many advertisements should be run in each of the three types of media to maximize the total audience?

Solution

To begin, we let x_1, x_2, and x_3 represent the number of advertisements in television, newspaper, and radio, respectively. The objective function (to be maximized) is therefore

$$z = 100,000x_1 + 40,000x_2 + 18,000x_3 \qquad \textbf{Objective function}$$

where $x_1 \geq 0$, $x_2 \geq 0$, and $x_3 \geq 0$. The constraints for this problem are as follows.

$$2000x_1 + 600x_2 + 300x_3 \leq 18,200$$
$$x_2 \leq 10$$
$$x_3 \leq 0.5(x_1 + x_2 + x_3)$$
$$x_1 \geq 0.1(x_1 + x_2 + x_3)$$

A more manageable form of this system of constraints is as follows.

$$\left. \begin{array}{r} 20x_1 + 6x_2 + 3x_3 \leq 182 \\ x_2 \leq 10 \\ -x_1 - x_2 + x_3 \leq 0 \\ -9x_1 + x_2 + x_3 \leq 0 \end{array} \right\} \qquad \textbf{Constraints}$$

Thus, the initial simplex tableau is as follows.

x_1	x_2	x_3	s_1	s_2	s_3	s_4	b	Basic Variables	
(20)	6	3	1	0	0	0	182	s_1	← Departing
0	1	0	0	1	0	0	10	s_2	
−1	−1	1	0	0	1	0	0	s_3	
−9	1	1	0	0	0	1	0	s_4	
−100,000	−40,000	−18,000	0	0	0	0	0		

↑
Entering

Now, to this initial tableau, we apply the simplex method as follows.

x_1	x_2	x_3	s_1	s_2	s_3	s_4	b	Basic Variables
1	$\frac{3}{10}$	$\frac{3}{20}$	$\frac{1}{20}$	0	0	0	$\frac{91}{10}$	x_1
0	(1)	0	0	1	0	0	10	$s_2 \leftarrow$ Departing
0	$-\frac{7}{10}$	$\frac{23}{20}$	$\frac{1}{20}$	0	1	0	$\frac{91}{10}$	s_3
0	$\frac{37}{10}$	$\frac{47}{20}$	$\frac{9}{20}$	0	0	1	$\frac{819}{10}$	s_4
0	$-10,000$	$-3,000$	$5,000$	0	0	0	$910,000$	

$\uparrow$

Entering

x_1	x_2	x_3	s_1	s_2	s_3	s_4	b	Basic Variables
1	0	$\frac{3}{20}$	$\frac{1}{20}$	$-\frac{3}{10}$	0	0	$\frac{61}{10}$	x_1
0	1	0	0	1	0	0	10	x_2
0	0	$(\frac{23}{20})$	$\frac{1}{20}$	$\frac{7}{10}$	1	0	$\frac{161}{10}$	$s_3 \leftarrow$ Departing
0	0	$\frac{47}{20}$	$\frac{9}{20}$	$-\frac{37}{10}$	0	1	$\frac{449}{10}$	s_4
0	0	$-3,000$	$5,000$	$10,000$	0	0	$1,010,000$	

$\uparrow$

Entering

x_1	x_2	x_3	s_1	s_2	s_3	s_4	b	Basic Variables
1	0	0	$\frac{1}{23}$	$-\frac{9}{23}$	$-\frac{3}{23}$	0	4	x_1
0	1	0	0	1	0	0	10	x_2
0	0	1	$\frac{1}{23}$	$\frac{14}{23}$	$\frac{20}{23}$	0	14	x_3
0	0	0	$\frac{8}{23}$	$-\frac{118}{23}$	$-\frac{47}{23}$	1	12	s_4
0	0	0	$\frac{118,000}{23}$	$\frac{272,000}{23}$	$\frac{60,000}{23}$	0	$1,052,000$	

From this tableau, we see that the maximum weekly audience for an advertising budget of $18,200 is

$$z = 1,052,000 \qquad \text{Maximum weekly audience}$$

and this occurs when $x_1 = 4$, $x_2 = 10$, and $x_3 = 14$. We sum up the results here.

Media	Number of Advertisements	Cost	Audience
Television	4	$ 8,000	400,000
Newspaper	10	$ 6,000	400,000
Radio	14	$ 4,200	252,000
Total	28	$18,200	1,052,000

SECTION 9.3 ☐ EXERCISES

In Exercises 1–4, write the simplex tableau for the given linear programming problem. You do not need to solve the problem. (In each case the objective function is to be maximized.)

1. Objective function:

$z = x_1 + 2x_2$

Constraints:

$2x_1 + x_2 \leq 8$

$x_1 + x_2 \leq 5$

$x_1, x_2 \geq 0$

2. Objective function:

$z = x_1 + 3x_2$

Constraints:

$x_1 + x_2 \leq 4$

$x_1 - x_2 \leq 1$

$x_1, x_2 \geq 0$

3. Objective function:

$z = 2x_1 + 3x_2 + 4x_3$

Constraints:

$x_1 + 2x_2 \qquad \leq 12$

$x_1 \qquad + x_3 \leq 8$

$x_1, x_2, x_3 \geq 0$

4. Objective function:

$z = 6x_1 - 9x_2$

Constraints:

$2x_1 - 3x_2 \leq 6$

$x_1 + x_2 \leq 20$

$x_1, x_2 \geq 0$

In Exercises 5–8, explain why the linear programming problem is *not* in standard form as given.

5. (Minimize)

Objective function:

$z = x_1 + x_2$

Constraints:

$x_1 + 2x_2 \leq 4$

$x_1, x_2 \geq 0$

6. (Maximize)

Objective function:

$z = x_1 + x_2$

Constraints:

$x_1 + 2x_2 \leq 6$

$2x_1 - x_2 \leq -1$

$x_1, x_2 \geq 0$

7. (Maximize)

Objective function:

$z = x_1 + x_2$

Constraints:

$x_1 + x_2 + 3x_3 \leq 5$

$2x_1 \qquad - 2x_3 \geq 1$

$x_2 + x_3 \leq 0$

$x_1, x_2, x_3 \geq 0$

8. (Maximize)

Objective function:

$z = x_1 + x_2$

Constraints:

$x_1 + x_2 \geq 4$

$2x_1 + x_2 \geq 6$

$x_1, x_2 \geq 0$

In Exercises 9–20, use the simplex method to solve the given linear programming problem. (In each case the objective function is to be maximized.)

9. Objective function:

$z = x_1 + 2x_2$

Constraints:

$x_1 + 4x_2 \leq 8$

$x_1 + x_2 \leq 12$

$x_1, x_2 \geq 0$

10. Objective function:

$z = x_1 + x_2$

Constraints:

$x_1 + 2x_2 \leq 6$

$3x_1 + 2x_2 \leq 12$

$x_1, x_2 \geq 0$

11. Objective function:

$z = 5x_1 + 2x_2 + 8x_3$

Constraints:

$2x_1 - 4x_2 + x_3 \leq 42$

$2x_1 + 3x_2 - x_3 \leq 42$

$6x_1 - x_2 + 3x_3 \leq 42$

$x_1, x_2, x_3 \geq 0$

12. Objective function:

$z = x_1 - x_2 + 2x_3$

Constraints:

$2x_1 + 2x_2 \leq 8$

$x_3 \leq 5$

$x_1, x_2, x_3 \geq 0$

13. Objective function:

$z = 4x_1 + 5x_2$

Constraints:

$x_1 + x_2 \leq 10$

$3x_1 + 7x_2 \leq 42$

$x_1, x_2 \geq 0$

14. Objective function:

$z = x_1 + 2x_2$

Constraints:

$x_1 + 3x_2 \leq 15$

$2x_1 - x_2 \leq 12$

$x_1, x_2 \geq 0$

15. Objective function:

$z = 3x_1 + 4x_2 + x_3 + 7x_4$

Constraints:

$8x_1 + 3x_2 + 4x_3 + x_4 \leq 7$

$2x_1 + 6x_2 + x_3 + 5x_4 \leq 3$

$x_1 + 4x_2 + 5x_3 + 2x_4 \leq 8$

$x_1, x_2, x_3, x_4 \geq 0$

16. Objective function:

$z = x_1$

Constraints:

$3x_1 + 2x_2 \leq 60$

$x_1 + 2x_2 \leq 28$

$x_1 + 4x_2 \leq 48$

$x_1, x_2 \geq 0$

17. Objective function:

$z = x_1 - x_2 + x_3$

Constraints:

$2x_1 + x_2 - 3x_3 \leq 40$

$x_1 \qquad + x_3 \leq 25$

$2x_2 + 3x_3 \leq 32$

$x_1, x_2, x_3 \geq 0$

18. Objective function:

$z = 2x_1 + x_2 + 3x_3$

Constraints:

$x_1 + x_2 + x_3 \leq 59$

$2x_1 \qquad + 3x_3 \leq 75$

$x_2 + 6x_3 \leq 54$

$x_1, x_2, x_3 \geq 0$

19. Objective function:

$z = x_1 + 2x_2 - x_4$

Constraints:

$x_1 + 2x_2 + 3x_3 \qquad \leq 24$

$3x_2 + 7x_3 + x_4 \leq 42$

$x_1, x_2, x_3, x_4 \geq 0$

20. Objective function:

$z = x_1 + 2x_2 + x_3 - x_4$

Constraints:

$x_1 + x_2 + 3x_3 + 4x_4 \leq 60$

$x_2 + 2x_3 + 5x_4 \leq 50$

$2x_1 + 3x_2 \qquad + 6x_4 \leq 72$

$x_1, x_2, x_3, x_4 \geq 0$

21. A merchant plans to sell two models of home computers at costs of $250 and $400, respectively. The $250 model yields a profit of $45 and the $400 model yields a profit of $50. The merchant estimates that the total monthly demand will not exceed 250 units. Find the number of units of each model that should be stocked in order to maximize profit. Assume that the merchant does not want to invest more than $70,000 in computer inventory. (See Exercise 21 in Section 9.2.)

22. A fruit grower has 150 acres of land available to raise two crops, A and B. It takes one day to trim an acre of crop A and two days to trim an acre of crop B, and there are 240 days per year available for trimming. It takes 0.3 day to pick an acre of crop A and 0.1 day to pick an acre of crop B, and there are 30 days per year available for picking. Find the number of acres of each fruit that should be planted to maximize profit, assuming that the profit is $140 per acre for crop A and $235 per acre for B. (See Exercise 22 in Section 9.2.)

23. A grower has 50 acres of land for which she plans to raise three crops. It costs $200 to produce an acre of carrots and the profit is $60 per acre. It costs $80 to produce an acre of celery and the profit is $20 per acre. Finally, it costs $140 to produce an acre of lettuce and the profit is $30 per acre. Use the simplex method to find the number of acres of each crop she should plant in order to maximize her profit. Assume that her cost cannot exceed $10,000.

24. A fruit juice company makes two special drinks by blending apple and pineapple juices. The first drink uses 30% apple juice and 70% pineapple, while the second drink uses 60% apple and 40% pineapple. There are 1000 liters of apple and 1500 liters of pineapple juice available. If the profit for the first drink is $0.60 per liter and that for the second drink is $0.50, use the simplex method to find the number of liters of each drink that should be produced in order to maximize the profit.

25. A manufacturer produces three models of bicycles. The time (in hours) required for assembling, painting, and packaging each model is as follows.

	Model A	Model B	Model C
Assembling	2	2.5	3
Painting	1.5	2	1
Packaging	1	0.75	1.25

The total time available for assembling, painting, and packaging is 4006 hours, 2495 hours and 1500 hours, respectively. The profit per unit for each model is $45 (Model A), $50 (Model B), and $55 (Model C). How many of each type should be produced to obtain a maximum profit?

26. Suppose in Exercise 25 the total time available for assembling, painting, and packaging is 4000 hours, 2500 hours, and 1500 hours, respectively, and that the profit per unit is $48 (Model A), $50 (Model B), and $52 (Model C). How many of each type should be produced to obtain a maximum profit?

27. A company has budgeted a maximum of $600,000 for advertising a certain product nationally. Each minute of television time costs $60,000 and each one-page newspaper ad costs $15,000. Each television ad is expected to be viewed by 15 million viewers, and each newspaper ad is expected to be seen by 3 million readers. The company's market research department advises the company to use at most 90% of the advertising budget on television ads. How should the advertising budget be allocated to maximize the total audience?

28. Rework Exercise 27 assuming that each one-page newspaper ad costs $30,000.

29. An investor has up to $250,000 to invest in three types of investments. Type A pays 8% annually and has a risk factor of 0. Type B pays 10% annually and has a risk factor of 0.06. Type C pays 14% annually and has a risk factor of 0.10. To have a well-balanced portfolio, the investor imposes the following conditions. The average risk factor should be no greater than 0.05. Moreover, at least one-fourth of the total portfolio is to be allocated to Type A investments and at least one-fourth of the portfolio is to be allocated to Type B investments. How much should be allocated to each type of investment to obtain a maximum return?

30. An investor has up to $450,000 to invest in three types of investments. Type A pays 6% annually and has a risk factor of 0. Type B pays 10% annually and has a risk factor of 0.06. Type C pays 12% annually and has a risk factor of 0.08. To have a well-balanced portfolio, the investor imposes the following conditions. The average risk factor should be no greater than 0.05. Moreover, at least one-half of the total portfolio is to be allocated to Type A investments and at least one-fourth of the portfolio is to be allocated to Type B investments. How much should be allocated to each type of investment to obtain a maximum return?

31. An accounting firm has 900 hours of staff time and 100 hours of reviewing time available each week. The firm charges $2000 for an audit and $300 for a tax return. Each audit requires 100 hours of staff time and 10 hours of review time, and each tax return requires 12.5 hours of staff time and 2.5 hours of review time. What number of audits and tax returns will bring in a maximum revenue?

32. The accounting firm in Exercise 31 raises its charge for an audit to $2500. What number of audits and tax returns will bring in a maximum revenue?

In the simplex method, it may happen that in selecting the departing variable all the calculated ratios are negative. This indicates an *unbounded solution*. Demonstrate this in Exercises 33 and 34.

33. (Maximize)
Objective function:
$$z = x_1 + 2x_2$$
Constraints:
$$x_1 - 3x_2 \le 1$$
$$-x_1 + 2x_2 \le 4$$
$$x_1, x_2 \ge 0$$

34. (Maximize)
Objective function:
$$z = x_1 + 3x_2$$
Constraints:
$$-x_1 + x_2 \le 20$$
$$-2x_1 + x_2 \le 50$$
$$x_1, x_2 \ge 0$$

If the simplex method terminates and one or more variables *not in the final basis* have bottom-row entries of zero, bringing these variables into the basis will determine other optimal solutions. Demonstrate this in Exercises 35 and 36.

35. (Maximize)
Objective function:
$$z = 2.5x_1 + x_2$$
Constraints:
$$3x_1 + 5x_2 \le 15$$
$$5x_1 + 2x_2 \le 10$$
$$x_1, x_2 \ge 0$$

36. (Maximize)
Objective function:
$$z = x_1 + \tfrac{1}{2}x_2$$
Constraints:
$$2x_1 + x_2 \le 20$$
$$x_1 + 3x_2 \le 35$$
$$x_1, x_2 \ge 0$$

C 37. Use a computer to maximize the objective function
$$z = 2x_1 + 7x_2 + 6x_3 + 4x_4$$
subject to the constraints
$$x_1 + x_2 + 0.83x_3 + 0.5x_4 \le 65$$
$$1.2x_1 + x_2 + x_3 + 1.2x_4 \le 96$$
$$0.5x_1 + 0.7x_2 + 1.2x_3 + 0.4x_4 \le 80$$
where $x_1, x_2, x_3, x_4 \ge 0$.

C 38. Use a computer to maximize the objective function
$$z = 1.2x_1 + x_2 + x_3 + x_4$$
subject to the same set of constraints given in Exercise 37.

9.4 THE SIMPLEX METHOD: MINIMIZATION

In Section 9.3, we applied the simplex method only to linear programming problems in standard form where the objective function was to be *maximized*. In this section, we extend this procedure to linear programming problems in which the objective function is to be *minimized*.

A minimization problem is in **standard form** if the objective function $w = c_1x_1 + c_2x_2 + \cdots + c_nx_n$ is to be minimized, subject to the constraints

$$a_{11}x_1 + a_{12}x_2 + \cdots + a_{1n}x_n \ge b_1$$

$$a_{21}x_1 + a_{22}x_2 + \cdots + a_{2n}x_n \ge b_2$$

$$\vdots$$

$$a_{m1}x_1 + a_{m2}x_2 + \cdots + a_{mn}x_n \ge b_m$$

where $x_i \ge 0$ and $b_i \ge 0$. The basic procedure used to solve such a problem is to convert it to a *maximization problem* in standard form, and then apply the simplex method as discussed in Section 9.3.

In Example 5 in Section 9.2, we used geometric methods to solve the following minimization problem.

Minimization Problem: Find the minimum value of

$$w = 0.12x_1 + 0.15x_2 \qquad \textbf{Objective function}$$

subject to the following constraints

$$\left.\begin{array}{r} 60x_1 + 60x_2 \geq 300 \\ 12x_1 + 6x_2 \geq 36 \\ 10x_1 + 30x_2 \geq 90 \end{array}\right\} \qquad \textbf{Constraints}$$

where $x_1 \geq 0$ and $x_2 \geq 0$. The first step in converting this problem to a maximization problem is to form the augmented matrix for this system of inequalities. To this augmented matrix we add a last row that represents the coefficients of the objective function, as follows.

$$\begin{bmatrix} 60 & 60 & \vdots & 300 \\ 12 & 6 & \vdots & 36 \\ 10 & 30 & \vdots & 90 \\ \cdots & \cdots & \cdots & \cdots \\ 0.12 & 0.15 & \vdots & 0 \end{bmatrix}$$

Next, we form the **transpose** of this matrix by interchanging its rows and columns.

$$\begin{bmatrix} 60 & 12 & 10 & \vdots & 0.12 \\ 60 & 6 & 30 & \vdots & 0.15 \\ \cdots & \cdots & \cdots & \cdots & \cdots \\ 300 & 36 & 90 & \vdots & 0 \end{bmatrix}$$

Note that the rows of this matrix are the columns of the first matrix, and vice versa. Finally, we interpret the new matrix as a *maximization* problem as follows. (To do this, we introduce new variables, y_1, y_2, and y_3.) We call this corresponding maximization problem the **dual** of the original minimization problem.

Dual Maximization Problem: Find the maximum value of

$$z = 300y_1 + 36y_2 + 90y_3 \qquad \textbf{Dual objective function}$$

subject to the constraints

$$\left.\begin{array}{r} 60y_1 + 12y_2 + 10y_3 \leq 0.12 \\ 60y_1 + 6y_2 + 30y_3 \leq 0.15 \end{array}\right\} \qquad \textbf{Dual constraints}$$

where $y_1 \geq 0$, $y_2 \geq 0$, and $y_3 \geq 0$.

As it turns out, the solution of the original minimization problem can be found by applying the simplex method to the new dual problem, as follows.

y_1	y_2	y_3	s_1	s_2	b	Basic Variables	
60	12	10	1	0	0.12	s_1	← Departing
60	6	30	0	1	0.15	s_2	
−300	−36	−90	0	0	0		

↑
Entering

y_1	y_2	y_3	s_1	s_2	b	Basic Variables	
1	$\frac{1}{5}$	$\frac{1}{6}$	$\frac{1}{60}$	0	$\frac{1}{500}$	y_1	
0	−6	20	−1	1	$\frac{3}{100}$	s_2	← Departing
0	24	−40	5	0	$\frac{3}{5}$		

↑
Entering

y_1	y_2	y_3	s_1	s_2	b	Basic Variables
1	$\frac{1}{4}$	0	$\frac{1}{40}$	$-\frac{1}{120}$	$\frac{7}{4000}$	y_1
0	$-\frac{3}{10}$	1	$-\frac{1}{20}$	$\frac{1}{20}$	$\frac{3}{2000}$	y_3
0	12	0	3	2	$\frac{33}{50}$	

↑ ↑
x_1 x_2

Thus, the solution of the dual maximization problem is $z = \frac{33}{50} = 0.66$. This is the same value we obtained in the minimization problem given in Example 5, in Section 9.2. The x-values corresponding to this optimal solution are obtained from the entries in the bottom row corresponding to slack variable columns. In other words, the optimal solution occurs when $x_1 = 3$ and $x_2 = 2$.

The fact that a dual maximization problem has the same solution as its original minimization problem is stated formally in a result called the **von Neumann Duality Principle,** after the American mathematician John von Neumann (1903–1957).

Theorem 9.2 The von Neumann Duality Principle	The objective value w of a minimization problem in standard form has a minimum value if and only if the objective value z of the dual maximization problem has a maximum value. Moreover, the minimum value of w is equal to the maximum value of z.

Solving a Minimization Problem

We summarize the steps used to solve a minimization problem as follows.

Solving a Minimization Problem

A minimization problem is in standard form if the objective function $w = c_1 x_1 + c_2 x_2 + \cdots + c_n x_n$ is to be minimized, subject to the constraints

$$a_{11} x_1 + a_{12} x_2 + \cdots + a_{1n} x_n \geq b_1$$
$$a_{21} x_1 + a_{22} x_2 + \cdots + a_{2n} x_n \geq b_2$$
$$\vdots$$
$$a_{m1} x_1 + a_{m2} x_2 + \cdots + a_{mn} x_n \geq b_m$$

where $x_i \geq 0$ and $b_i \geq 0$. To solve this problem we use the following steps.

1. Form the **augmented matrix** for the given system of inequalities, and add a bottom row consisting of the coefficients of the objective function.

$$\begin{bmatrix} a_{11} & a_{12} & \cdots & a_{1n} & \vdots & b_1 \\ a_{21} & a_{22} & \cdots & a_{2n} & \vdots & b_2 \\ & & & & \vdots & \\ a_{m1} & a_{m2} & \cdots & a_{mn} & \vdots & b_m \\ \cdots & \cdots & \cdots & \cdots & & \cdots \\ c_1 & c_2 & \cdots & c_n & \vdots & 0 \end{bmatrix}$$

2. Form the **transpose** of this matrix.

$$\begin{bmatrix} a_{11} & a_{21} & \cdots & a_{m1} & \vdots & c_1 \\ a_{12} & a_{22} & \cdots & a_{m2} & \vdots & c_2 \\ & & & & \vdots & \\ a_{1n} & a_{2n} & \cdots & a_{mn} & \vdots & c_n \\ \cdots & \cdots & \cdots & \cdots & & \cdots \\ b_1 & b_2 & \cdots & b_m & \vdots & 0 \end{bmatrix}$$

3. Form the **dual maximization problem** corresponding to this transposed matrix. That is, find the maximum of the objective function given by $z = b_1 y_1 + b_2 y_2 + \cdots + b_m y_m$ subject to the constraints

$$a_{11} y_1 + a_{21} y_2 + \cdots + a_{m1} y_m \leq c_1$$
$$a_{12} y_1 + a_{22} y_2 + \cdots + a_{m2} y_m \leq c_2$$
$$\vdots$$
$$a_{1n} y_1 + a_{2n} y_2 + \cdots + a_{mn} y_m \leq c_n$$

where $y_1 \geq 0, y_2 \geq 0, \ldots,$ and $y_m \geq 0$.

4. Apply the **simplex method** to the dual maximization problem. The maximum value of z will be the minimum value of w. Moreover, the values of $x_1, x_2, \ldots,$ and x_n will occur in the bottom row of the final simplex tableau, in the columns corresponding to the slack variables.

We illustrate the steps used to solve a minimization problem in Examples 1 and 2.

EXAMPLE 1   *Solving a Minimization Problem*

Find the minimum value of

$$w = 3x_1 + 2x_2 \qquad \text{Objective function}$$

subject to the constraints

$$\left.\begin{array}{r} 2x_1 + x_2 \geq 6 \\ x_1 + x_2 \geq 4 \end{array}\right\} \qquad \text{Constraints}$$

where $x_1 \geq 0$ and $x_2 \geq 0$.

Solution   The augmented matrix corresponding to this minimization problem is

$$\begin{bmatrix} 2 & 1 & \vdots & 6 \\ 1 & 1 & \vdots & 4 \\ \cdots & \cdots & \vdots & \cdots \\ 3 & 2 & \vdots & 0 \end{bmatrix}.$$

Thus, the matrix corresponding to the dual maximization problem is given by the following transpose.

$$\begin{bmatrix} 2 & 1 & \vdots & 3 \\ 1 & 1 & \vdots & 2 \\ \cdots & \cdots & \vdots & \cdots \\ 6 & 4 & \vdots & 0 \end{bmatrix}.$$

This implies that the dual maximization problem is as follows.
  Dual Maximization Problem: Find the maximum value of

$$z = 6y_1 + 4y_2 \qquad \text{Dual objective function}$$

subject to the constraints

$$\left.\begin{array}{r} 2y_1 + y_2 \leq 3 \\ y_1 + y_2 \leq 2 \end{array}\right\} \qquad \text{Dual constraints}$$

where $y_1 \geq 0$ and $y_2 \geq 0$. We now apply the simplex method to the dual problem as follows.

y_1	y_2	s_1	s_2	b	Basic Variables	
⟨2⟩	1	1	0	3	s_1	← *Departing*
1	1	0	1	2	s_2	
−6	−4	0	0	0		

$\uparrow$
Entering

					Basic Variables
y_1	y_2	s_1	s_2	b	
1	$\frac{1}{2}$	$\frac{1}{2}$	0	$\frac{3}{2}$	y_1
0	$\left(\frac{1}{2}\right)$	$-\frac{1}{2}$	1	$\frac{1}{2}$	s_2 ← *Departing*
0	-1	3	0	9	

$$\underset{\text{*Entering*}}{\uparrow}$$

					Basic Variables
y_1	y_2	s_1	s_2	b	
1	0	1	-1	1	y_1
0	1	-1	2	1	y_2
0	0	2	2	10	

$$\underset{x_1}{\uparrow} \quad \underset{x_2}{\uparrow}$$

From this final simplex tableau, we see that the maximum value of z is 10. Therefore, the solution of the original minimization problem is

$$w = 10 \qquad\qquad \textbf{Minimum Value}$$

and this occurs when

$$x_1 = 2 \quad \text{and} \quad x_2 = 2.$$

Both the minimization and the maximization linear programming problems in Example 1 could have been solved with a graphical method, as indicated in Figure 9.19. Note in Figure 9.19 (a) that the maximum value of $z = 6y_1 - 4y_2$ is the same as the minimum value of $w = 3x_1 + 2x_2$, as shown in Figure 9.19 (b). (See page 515.)

EXAMPLE 2   *Solving a Minimization Problem*

Find the minimum value of

$$w = 2x_1 + 10x_2 + 8x_3 \qquad \textbf{Objective function}$$

subject to the constraints

$$\left.\begin{array}{r} x_1 + x_2 + x_3 \ge 6 \\ x_2 + 2x_3 \ge 8 \\ -x_1 + 2x_2 + 2x_3 \ge 4 \end{array}\right\} \quad \textbf{Constraints}$$

where $x_1 \ge 0$, $x_2 \ge 0$, and $x_3 \ge 0$.

Solution The augmented matrix corresponding to this minimization problem is

$$\begin{bmatrix} 1 & 1 & 1 & \vdots & 6 \\ 0 & 1 & 2 & \vdots & 8 \\ -1 & 2 & 2 & \vdots & 4 \\ \cdots & \cdots & \cdots & \vdots & \cdots \\ 2 & 10 & 8 & \vdots & 0 \end{bmatrix}.$$

Thus, the matrix corresponding to the dual maximization problem is given by the following transpose.

$$\begin{bmatrix} 1 & 0 & -1 & \vdots & 2 \\ 1 & 1 & 2 & \vdots & 10 \\ 1 & 2 & 2 & \vdots & 8 \\ \cdots & \cdots & \cdots & \vdots & \cdots \\ 6 & 8 & 4 & \vdots & 0 \end{bmatrix}$$

This implies that the dual maximization problem is as follows.

Dual Maximization Problem: Find the maximum value of

$$z = 6y_1 + 8y_2 + 4y_3 \qquad \text{Dual objective function}$$

subject to the constraints

$$\left. \begin{aligned} y_1 \quad\quad - \ y_3 &\le 2 \\ y_1 + \ y_2 + 2y_3 &\le 10 \\ y_1 + 2y_2 + 2y_3 &\le 8 \end{aligned} \right\} \qquad \text{Dual constraints}$$

where $y_1 \ge 0$, $y_2 \ge 0$, and $y_3 \ge 0$. We now apply the simplex method to the dual problem as follows.

y_1	y_2	y_3	s_1	s_2	s_3	b	Basic Variables	
1	0	−1	1	0	0	2	s_1	
1	1	2	0	1	0	10	s_2	
⟨1⟩	2	2	0	0	1	8	s_3	← *Departing*
−6	−8	−4	0	0	0	0		

$\uparrow$
Entering

y_1	y_2	y_3	s_1	s_2	s_3	b	Basic Variables	
⟨1⟩	0	−1	1	0	0	2	s_1	← *Departing*
$\frac{1}{2}$	0	1	0	1	$-\frac{1}{2}$	6	s_2	
$\frac{1}{2}$	1	1	0	0	$\frac{1}{2}$	4	y_2	
−2	0	4	0	0	4	32		

$\uparrow$
Entering

Figure 9.19

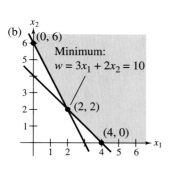

(a)

Maximum:
$z = 6y_1 + 4y_2 = 10$

(0, 2)

(1, 1)

(0, 0) $\left(\frac{3}{2}, 0\right)$

(b)   (0, 6)

Minimum:
$w = 3x_1 + 2x_2 = 10$

(2, 2)

(4, 0)

| | | | | | | | Basic |
y_1	y_2	y_3	s_1	s_2	s_3	b	Variables
1	0	-1	1	0	0	2	y_1
0	0	$\frac{3}{2}$	$-\frac{1}{2}$	1	$-\frac{1}{2}$	5	s_2
0	1	$\frac{3}{2}$	$-\frac{1}{2}$	0	$\frac{1}{2}$	3	y_2
0	0	2	2	0	4	36	

$$\uparrow \quad \uparrow \quad \uparrow$$
$$x_1 \quad x_2 \quad x_3$$

From this final simplex tableau, we see that the maximum value of z is 36. Therefore, the solution of the original minimization problem is

$$w = 36 \qquad \textbf{Minimum Value}$$

and this occurs when

$$x_1 = 2, \ x_2 = 0, \text{ and } x_3 = 4.$$

Applications

EXAMPLE 3 **A Business Application: Minimum Cost**

A small petroleum company owns two refineries. Refinery 1 costs $20,000 per day to operate, and it can produce 400 barrels of high-grade oil, 300 barrels of medium-grade oil, and 200 barrels of low-grade oil each day. Refinery 2 is newer and more modern. It costs $25,000 per day to operate, and it can produce 300 barrels of high-grade oil, 400 barrels of medium-grade oil, and 500 barrels of low-grade oil each day.

   The company has orders totaling 25,000 barrels of high-grade oil, 27,000 barrels of medium-grade oil, and 30,000 barrels of low-grade oil. How many days should it run each refinery to minimize its costs and still refine enough oil to meet its orders?

Solution   To begin, we let x_1 and x_2 represent the number of days the two refineries are operated. Then the total cost is given by

$$C = 20{,}000x_1 + 25{,}000x_2. \qquad \textbf{Objective function}$$

The constraints are given by

$$\begin{array}{lll} \text{(High-grade)} & 400x_1 + 300x_2 \geq 25{,}000 & \\ \text{(Medium-grade)} & 300x_1 + 400x_2 \geq 27{,}000 & \textbf{Constraints} \\ \text{(Low-grade)} & 200x_1 + 500x_2 \geq 30{,}000 & \end{array}$$

where $x_1 \geq 0$ and $x_2 \geq 0$. The augmented matrix corresponding to this minimization problem is

$$\begin{bmatrix} 400 & 300 & \vdots & 25{,}000 \\ 300 & 400 & \vdots & 27{,}000 \\ 200 & 500 & \vdots & 30{,}000 \\ \cdots & \cdots & \vdots & \cdots \\ 20{,}000 & 25{,}000 & \vdots & 0 \end{bmatrix}.$$

The matrix corresponding to the dual maximization problem is

$$\begin{bmatrix} 400 & 300 & 200 & \vdots & 20{,}000 \\ 300 & 400 & 500 & \vdots & 25{,}000 \\ \cdots & \cdots & \cdots & \vdots & \cdots \\ 25{,}000 & 27{,}000 & 30{,}000 & \vdots & 0 \end{bmatrix}.$$

We now apply the simplex method to the dual problem as follows.

y_1	y_2	y_3	s_1	s_2	b	Basic Variables
400	300	200	1	0	20,000	s_1
300	400	(500)	0	1	25,000	s_2 ← *Departing*
$-25{,}000$	$-27{,}000$	$-30{,}000$	0	0	0	

↑
Entering

y_1	y_2	y_3	s_1	s_2	b	Basic Variables
(280)	140	0	1	$-\frac{2}{5}$	10,000	s_1 ← *Departing*
$\frac{3}{5}$	$\frac{4}{5}$	1	0	$\frac{1}{500}$	50	y_3
$-7{,}000$	$-3{,}000$	0	0	60	1,500,000	

↑
Entering

y_1	y_2	y_3	s_1	s_2	b	Basic Variables
1	$\frac{1}{2}$	0	$\frac{1}{280}$	$-\frac{1}{700}$	$\frac{250}{7}$	y_1
0	$\frac{1}{2}$	1	$-\frac{3}{1400}$	$\frac{1}{350}$	$\frac{200}{7}$	y_3
0	500	0	25	50	1,750,000	

$\qquad\qquad\qquad\qquad$ ↑ $\quad$ ↑

$\qquad\qquad\qquad\qquad x_1 \quad x_2$

From the third simplex tableau, we see that the solution to the original minimization problem is

$$C = \$1,750,000 \qquad \text{Minimum cost}$$

and this occurs when $x_1 = 25$ and $x_2 = 50$. Thus, the two refineries should be operated for the following number of days.

Refinery 1: 25 days

Refinery 2: 50 days

Note that by operating the two refineries for this number of days, the company will have produced the following amounts of oil.

High-grade oil:	$25(400) + 50(300) = 25,000$ barrels
Medium-grade oil:	$25(300) + 50(400) = 27,500$ barrels
Low-grade oil:	$25(200) + 50(500) = 30,000$ barrels

Thus, the original production level has been met (with a surplus of 500 barrels of medium-grade oil).

SECTION 9.4 ☐ EXERCISES

In Exercises 1–6, determine the dual of the given minimization problem.

1. Objective function:

$w = 3x_1 + 3x_2$

Constraints:

$2x_1 + x_2 \geq 4$
$x_1 + 2x_2 \geq 4$
$x_1, x_2 \geq 0$

2. Objective function:

$w = 2x_1 + x_2$

Constraints:

$5x_1 + x_2 \geq 9$
$2x_1 + 2x_2 \geq 10$
$x_1, x_2 \geq 0$

3. Objective function:

$w = 4x_1 + x_2 + x_3$

Constraints:

$3x_1 + 2x_2 + x_3 \geq 23$
$x_1 \quad\quad + x_3 \geq 10$
$8x_1 + x_2 + 2x_3 \geq 40$
$x_1, x_2, x_3 \geq 0$

4. Objective function:

$w = 9x_1 + 6x_2$

Constraints:

$x_1 + 2x_2 \geq 5$
$2x_1 + 2x_2 \geq 8$
$2x_1 + x_2 \geq 6$
$x_1, x_2 \geq 0$

5. Objective function:

$w = 14x_1 + 20x_2 + 24x_3$

Constraints:

$x_1 + x_2 + 2x_3 \geq 7$
$x_1 + 2x_2 + x_3 \geq 4$
$x_1, x_2, x_3 \geq 0$

6. Objective function:

$w = 9x_1 + 4x_2 + 10x_3$

Constraints:

$2x_1 + x_2 + 3x_3 \geq 6$
$6x_1 + x_2 + x_3 \geq 9$
$x_1, x_2, x_3 \geq 0$

In Exercises 7–12, (a) solve the given minimization problem by the graphical method, (b) formulate the dual problem, and (c) solve the dual problem by the graphical method.

7. Objective function:

$w = 2x_1 + 2x_2$

Constraints:

$x_1 + 2x_2 \geq 3$
$3x_1 + 2x_2 \geq 5$
$x_1, x_2 \geq 0$

8. Objective function:

$w = 14x_1 + 20x_2$

Constraints:

$x_1 + 2x_2 \geq 4$
$7x_1 + 6x_2 \geq 20$
$x_1, x_2 \geq 0$

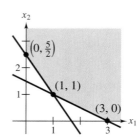

9. Objective function:

$w = x_1 + 4x_2$

Constraints:

$$x_1 + x_2 \geq 3$$
$$-x_1 + 2x_2 \geq 2$$
$$x_1, x_2 \geq 0$$

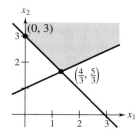

10. Objective function:

$w = 2x_1 + 6x_2$

Constraints:

$$-2x_1 + 3x_2 \geq 0$$
$$x_1 + 3x_2 \geq 9$$
$$x_1, x_2 \geq 0$$

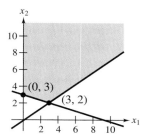

11. Objective function:

$w = 6x_1 + 3x_2$

Constraints:

$$4x_1 + x_2 \geq 4$$
$$x_2 \geq 2$$
$$x_1, x_2 \geq 0$$

12. Objective function:

$w = x_1 + 6x_2$

Constraints:

$$2x_1 + 3x_2 \geq 15$$
$$-x_1 + 2x_2 \geq 3$$
$$x_1, x_2 \geq 0$$

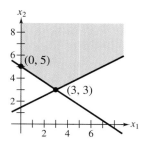

In Exercises 13–20, solve the given minimization problem by solving the dual maximization problem with the simplex method.

13. Objective function:

$w = x_2$

Constraints:

$$x_1 + 5x_2 \geq 10$$
$$-6x_1 + 5x_2 \geq 3$$
$$x_1, x_2 \geq 0$$

14. Objective function:

$w = 3x_1 + 8x_2$

Constraints:

$$2x_1 + 7x_2 \geq 9$$
$$x_1 + 2x_2 \geq 4$$
$$x_1, x_2 \geq 0$$

15. Objective function:

$w = 2x_1 + x_2$

Constraints:

$$5x_1 + x_2 \geq 9$$
$$2x_1 + 2x_2 \geq 10$$
$$x_1, x_2 \geq 0$$

16. Objective function:

$w = 2x_1 + 2x_2$

Constraints:

$$3x_1 + x_2 \geq 6$$
$$-4x_1 + 2x_2 \geq 2$$
$$x_1, x_2 \geq 0$$

17. Objective function:

$w = 8x_1 + 4x_2 + 6x_3$

Constraints:

$$3x_1 + 2x_2 + x_3 \geq 6$$
$$4x_1 + x_2 + 3x_3 \geq 7$$
$$2x_1 + x_2 + 4x_3 \geq 8$$
$$x_1, x_2, x_3 \geq 0$$

18. Objective function:

$w = 8x_1 + 16x_2 + 18x_3$

Constraints:

$$2x_1 + 2x_2 - 2x_3 \geq 4$$
$$-4x_1 + 3x_2 - x_3 \geq 1$$
$$x_1 - x_2 + 3x_3 \geq 8$$
$$x_1, x_2, x_3 \geq 0$$

19. Objective function:

$w = 6x_1 + 2x_2 + 3x_3$

Constraints:

$$3x_1 + 2x_2 + x_3 \geq 28$$
$$6x_1 + x_3 \geq 24$$
$$3x_1 + x_2 + 2x_3 \geq 40$$
$$x_1, x_2, x_3 \geq 0$$

20. Objective function:

$w = 42x_1 + 5x_2 + 17x_3$

Constraints:

$$3x_1 - x_2 + 7x_3 \geq 5$$
$$-3x_1 - x_2 + 3x_3 \geq 8$$
$$6x_1 + x_2 + x_3 \geq 16$$
$$x_1, x_2, x_3 \geq 0$$

In Exercises 21–24, two dietary drinks are used to supply protein and carbohydrates. The first drink provides 1 unit of protein and 3 units of carbohydrates in each liter. The second drink supplies 2 units of protein and 2 units of carbohydrates in each liter. An athlete requires 3 units of protein and 5 units of carbohydrates. Find the amount of each drink the athlete should consume to minimize the cost and still meet the minimum dietary requirements.

21. The first drink costs $2 per liter and the second costs $3 per liter.

22. The first drink costs $4 per liter and the second costs $2 per liter.

23. The first drink costs $1 per liter and the second costs $3 per liter.

24. The first drink costs $1 per liter and the second costs $2 per liter.

In Exercises 25–28, an athlete uses two dietary drinks that provide the nutritional elements listed in the following table.

Drink	Protein	Carbohydrates	Vitamin D
I	4	2	1
II	1	5	1

Find the combination of drinks of minimum cost that will meet the minimum requirements of 4 units of protein, 10 units of carbohydrates, and 3 units of vitamin D.

25. Drink I costs $5 per liter and drink II costs $8 per liter.

26. Drink I costs $7 per liter and drink II costs $4 per liter.

27. Drink I costs $1 per liter and drink II costs $5 per liter.

28. Drink I costs $8 per liter and drink II costs $1 per liter.

29. A company has three production plants, each of which produces three different models of a particular product. The daily capacities (in thousands of units) of the three plants are as follows.

	Model 1	Model 2	Model 3
Plant 1	8	4	8
Plant 2	6	6	3
Plant 3	12	4	8

The total demand for Model 1 is 300,000 units, for Model 2 is 172,000 units, and for Model 3 is 249,500 units. Moreover, the daily operating cost for Plant 1 is $55,000, for Plant 2 is $60,000, and for Plant 3 is $60,000. How many days should each plant be operated in order to fill the total demand, and keep the operating cost at a minimum?

30. The company in Exercise 29 has lowered the daily operating cost for Plant 3 to $50,000. How many days should each plant be operated in order to fill the total demand, and keep the operating cost at a minimum?

31. A small petroleum company owns two refineries. Refinery 1 costs $25,000 per day to operate, and it can produce 300 barrels of high-grade oil, 200 barrels of medium-grade oil, and 150 barrels of low-grade oil each day. Refinery 2 is newer and more modern. It costs $30,000 per day to operate, and it can produce 300 barrels of high-grade oil, 250 barrels of medium-grade oil, and 400 barrels of low-grade oil each day. The company has orders totaling 35,000 barrels of high-grade oil, 30,000 barrels of medium-grade oil, and 40,000 barrels of low-grade oil. How many days should the company run each refinery to minimize its costs and still meet its orders?

32. A steel company has two mills. Mill 1 costs $70,000 per day to operate, and it can produce 400 tons of high-grade steel, 500 tons of medium-grade steel, and 450 tons of low-grade steel each day. Mill 2 costs $60,000 per day to operate, and it can produce 350 tons of high-grade steel, 600 tons of medium-grade steel, and 400 tons of low-grade steel each day. The company has orders totaling 100,000 tons of high-grade steel, 150,000 tons of medium-grade steel, and 124,500 tons of low-grade steel. How many days should the company run each mill to minimize its costs and still fill the orders?

C **33.** Use a computer to minimize the objective function

$$w = x_1 + 0.5x_2 + 2.5x_3 + 3x_4$$

subject to the constraints

$$1.5x_1 + x_2 \qquad\quad + \quad 2x_4 \geq 35$$
$$2x_2 + 6x_3 + 4x_4 \geq 120$$
$$x_1 + x_2 + x_3 + x_4 \geq 50$$
$$0.5x_1 \qquad + 2.5x_3 + 1.5x_4 \geq 75$$

where $x_1, x_2, x_3, x_4 \geq 0$.

C **34.** Use a computer to minimize the objective function

$$w = 1.5x_1 + x_2 + 0.5x_3 + 2x_4$$

subject to the same set of constraints given in Exercise 33.

9.5   THE SIMPLEX METHOD: MIXED CONSTRAINTS

In Sections 9.3 and 9.4, we looked at linear programming problems that occurred in *standard form*. The constraints for the maximization problems all involved $\leq$ inequalities, and the constraints for the minimization problems all involved $\geq$ inequalities.

Linear programming problems for which the constraints involve *both* types of inequalities are called **mixed-constraint** problems. For instance, consider the following linear programming problem.

Mixed-Constraint Problem: Find the maximum value of

$$z = x_1 + x_2 + 2x_3 \qquad \text{Objective function}$$

subject to the constraints

$$\left.\begin{array}{r} 2x_1 + x_2 + x_3 \leq 50 \\ 2x_1 + x_2 \qquad \geq 36 \\ x_1 \qquad + x_3 \geq 10 \end{array}\right\} \qquad \text{Constraints}$$

where $x_1 \geq 0, x_2 \geq 0$, and $x_3 \geq 0$. Since this is a maximization problem, we would expect each of the inequalities in the set of constraints to involve $\leq$. Moreover, since the first inequality does involve $\leq$, we can add a slack variable to form the following equation.

$$2x_1 + x_2 + x_3 + s_1 = 50$$

For the other two inequalities, we must introduce a new type of variable, called a **surplus variable,** as follows.

$$\begin{array}{r} 2x_1 + x_2 \qquad - s_2 \qquad = 36 \\ x_1 \qquad + x_3 \qquad - s_3 = 10 \end{array}$$

Notice that surplus variables are *subtracted from* (not added to) their inequalities. We call s_2 and s_3 surplus variables because they represent the amount that the left side of the inequality exceeds the right side. Surplus variables must be nonnegative.

Now, to solve the linear programming problem, we form an initial simplex tableau as follows.

x_1	x_2	x_3	s_1	s_2	s_3	b	Basic Variables
2	1	1	1	0	0	50	s_1
2	1	0	0	−1	0	36	s_2
1	0	⟨1⟩	0	0	−1	10	s_3 ← Departing
−1	−1	−2	0	0	0	0	

$$\underset{\text{Entering}}{\uparrow}$$

You will soon discover that solving mixed-constraint problems can be difficult. One reason for this is that we do not have a convenient feasible solution to begin the simplex method. Note that the solution represented by the initial tableau above.

$$(x_1, x_2, x_3, s_1, s_2, s_3) = (0, 0, 0, 50, -36, -10)$$

is not a feasible solution because the values of the two surplus variables are negative. In fact, the values $x_1 = x_2 = x_3 = 0$ do not even satisfy the constraint equations. In order to eliminate the surplus variables from the current solution, we basically use "trial and error." That is, in an effort to find a feasible solution, we arbitrarily choose new entering variables. For instance, in this tableau, it seems reasonable to select x_3 as the entering variable. After pivoting, the new simplex tableau becomes

| | | | | | | | Basic | |
x_1	x_2	x_3	s_1	s_2	s_3	b	Variables	
1	1	0	1	0	1	40	s_1	
2	⟨1⟩	0	0	−1	0	36	s_2	← Departing
1	0	1	0	0	−1	10	x_3	
1	−1	0	0	0	−2	20		

Entering

The current solution $(x_1, x_2, x_3, s_1, s_2, s_3) = (0, 0, 10, 40, -36, 0)$ is still not feasible, so we choose x_2 as the entering variable and pivot to obtain the following simplex tableau.

| | | | | | | | Basic | |
x_1	x_2	x_3	s_1	s_2	s_3	b	Variables	
−1	0	0	1	1	⟨1⟩	4	s_1	← Departing
2	1	0	0	−1	0	36	x_2	
1	0	1	0	0	−1	10	x_3	
3	0	0	0	−1	−2	56		

Entering

At this point, we finally obtained a feasible solution

$$(x_1, x_2, x_3, s_1, s_2, s_3) = (0, 36, 10, 4, 0, 0).$$

From here on, we apply the simplex method as usual. Note that the entering variable here is s_3 because its column has the most negative entry in the bottom row. After pivoting one more time, we obtain the following final simplex tableau.

| | | | | | | | Basic |
x_1	x_2	x_3	s_1	s_2	s_3	b	Variables
−1	0	0	1	1	1	4	s_3
2	1	0	0	−1	0	36	x_2
0	0	1	1	1	0	14	x_3
1	0	0	2	1	0	64	

Note that this tableau is final because it represents a feasible solution *and* there are no negative entries in the bottom row. Thus, we conclude that the maximum value of the objective function is

$$z = 64 \qquad \text{Maximum value}$$

and this occurs when

$$x_1 = 0, \ x_2 = 36, \ \text{and} \ x_3 = 14.$$

EXAMPLE 1   *A Maximization Problem with Mixed Constraints*

Find the maximum value of

$$z = 3x_1 + 2x_2 + 4x_3 \qquad \text{Objective function}$$

subject to the constraints

$$
\left.
\begin{aligned}
3x_1 + 2x_2 + 5x_3 &\le 18 \\
4x_1 + 2x_2 + 3x_3 &\le 16 \\
2x_1 + \ x_2 + \ x_3 &\ge 4
\end{aligned}
\right\} \qquad \text{Constraints}
$$

where $x_1 \ge 0$, $x_2 \ge 0$, and $x_3 \ge 0$.

Solution   To begin, we add a slack variable to each of the first two inequalities and subtract a surplus variable from the third inequality to produce the following initial simplex tableau.

x_1	x_2	x_3	s_1	s_2	s_3	b	Basic Variables
3	2	5	1	0	0	18	s_1
4	2	3	0	1	0	16	s_2
2	⟨1⟩	1	0	0	−1	4	s_3 ← *Departing*
−3	−2	−4	0	0	0	0	

↑ *Entering* (under x_2)

As it stands, this tableau does not represent a feasible solution (because the value of s_3 is negative). Thus, we want s_3 to be the departing variable. We have no real guidelines as to which variable should enter the solution, but by trial and error, we discover that using x_2 as the entering variable produces the following tableau (which does represent a feasible solution).

x_1	x_2	x_3	s_1	s_2	s_3	b	Basic Variables
−1	0	3	1	0	2	10	s_1 ← *Departing*
0	0	1	0	1	2	8	s_2
2	1	1	0	0	−1	4	x_2
1	0	−2	0	0	−2	8	

Now, because this simplex tableau does represent a feasible solution, we proceed as usual, choosing the most negative entry in the bottom row to be the entering variable. (In this case, we have a tie, so we arbitrarily choose x_3 to be the entering variable.)

x_1	x_2	x_3	s_1	s_2	s_3	b	Basic Variables
-1	0	$\widehat{3}$	1	0	2	10	s_1 ← Departing
0	0	1	0	1	2	8	s_2
2	1	1	0	0	-1	4	x_2
1	0	-2	0	0	-2	8	

Entering (x_3)

x_1	x_2	x_3	s_1	s_2	s_3	b	Basic Variables
$-\frac{1}{3}$	0	1	$\frac{1}{3}$	0	$\frac{2}{3}$	$\frac{10}{3}$	x_3
$\frac{1}{3}$	0	0	$-\frac{1}{3}$	1	$\widehat{\frac{4}{3}}$	$\frac{14}{3}$	s_2 ← Departing
$\frac{7}{3}$	1	0	$-\frac{1}{3}$	0	$-\frac{5}{3}$	$\frac{2}{3}$	x_2
$\frac{1}{3}$	0	0	$\frac{2}{3}$	0	$-\frac{2}{3}$	$\frac{44}{3}$	

Entering (s_3)

x_1	x_2	x_3	s_1	s_2	s_3	b	Basic Variables
$-\frac{1}{2}$	0	1	$\frac{1}{2}$	$-\frac{1}{2}$	0	1	x_3
$\frac{1}{4}$	0	0	$-\frac{1}{4}$	$\frac{3}{4}$	1	$\frac{7}{2}$	s_3
$\frac{11}{4}$	1	0	$-\frac{3}{4}$	$\frac{5}{4}$	0	$\frac{13}{2}$	x_2
$\frac{1}{2}$	0	0	$\frac{1}{2}$	$\frac{1}{2}$	0	17	

Thus, the maximum value of the objective function is

$$z = 17$$

and this occurs when

$$x_1 = 0, \quad x_2 = \tfrac{13}{2}, \text{ and } x_3 = 1.$$

Mixed Constraints and Minimization

In Section 9.4, we discussed the solution of minimization problems in *standard form.* Minimization problems that are not in standard form are more difficult to solve. One technique that can be used is to change a mixed-constraint minimization problem to a mixed-constraint maximization problem by multiplying each coefficient in the objective function by -1. We demonstrate this technique in the following example.

EXAMPLE 2   *A Minimization Problem with Mixed Constraints*

Find the minimum value of

$$w = 4x_1 + 2x_2 + x_3 \qquad \text{Objective function}$$

subject to the constraints

$$\left. \begin{array}{r} 2x_1 + 3x_2 + 4x_3 \le 14 \\ 3x_1 + \ x_2 + 5x_3 \ge \ 4 \\ x_1 + 4x_2 + 3x_3 \ge \ 6 \end{array} \right\} \qquad \text{Constraints}$$

where $x_1 \ge 0$, $x_2 \ge 0$, and $x_3 \ge 0$.

Solution   First, we rewrite the objective function by multiplying each of its coefficients by -1, as follows.

$$z = -4x_1 - 2x_2 - x_3 \qquad \text{Revised objective function}$$

Maximizing this revised objective function is equivalent to minimizing the original objective function. Next, we add a slack variable to the first inequality and subtract surplus variables from the second and third inequalities to produce the following initial simplex tableau.

x_1	x_2	x_3	s_1	s_2	s_3	b	Basic Variables
2	3	4	1	0	0	14	s_1
3	⟨1⟩	5	0	−1	0	4	s_2 ← *Departing*
1	4	3	0	0	−1	6	s_3
4	2	1	0	0	0	0	

↑
Entering

Note that the bottom row has the negatives of the coefficients of the revised objective function. Another way of looking at this is that for minimization problems (in nonstandard form), the bottom row of the initial simplex consists of the coefficients of the original objective function.

As with maximization problems with mixed constraints, this initial simplex tableau does not represent a feasible solution. By trial and error, we discover that we can choose x_2 as the entering variable and s_2 as the departing variable. After pivoting, we obtain the following tableau.

x_1	x_2	x_3	s_1	s_2	s_3	b	Basic Variables
−7	0	−11	1	3	0	2	s_1
3	1	5	0	−1	0	4	x_2
−11	0	−17	0	4	−1	−10	s_3
−2	0	−9	0	2	0	−8	

From this tableau, we can see that the choice of x_2 as the entering variable was a good one. All we need to do to transform the tableau into one that represents a feasible solution is to multiply the third row by -1, as follows.

x_1	x_2	x_3	s_1	s_2	s_3	b	Basic Variables
-7	0	-11	1	3	0	2	s_1
3	1	5	0	-1	0	4	x_2
11	0	17	0	-4	1	10	s_3 ← Departing
-2	0	-9	0	2	0	-8	

↑
Entering

Now that we have obtained a simplex tableau that represents a feasible solution, we continue with our standard pivoting operations as follows.

x_1	x_2	x_3	s_1	s_2	s_3	b	Basic Variables
$\frac{2}{17}$	0	0	1	$\frac{7}{17}$	$\frac{11}{17}$	$\frac{144}{17}$	s_1
$-\frac{4}{17}$	1	0	0	$\frac{3}{17}$	$-\frac{5}{17}$	$\frac{18}{17}$	x_2 ← Departing
$\frac{11}{17}$	0	1	0	$-\frac{4}{17}$	$\frac{1}{17}$	$\frac{10}{17}$	x_3
$\frac{65}{17}$	0	0	0	$-\frac{2}{17}$	$\frac{9}{17}$	$-\frac{46}{17}$	

↑
Entering

x_1	x_2	x_3	s_1	s_2	s_3	b	Basic Variables
$\frac{2}{3}$	$-\frac{7}{3}$	0	1	0	$\frac{4}{3}$	6	s_1
$-\frac{4}{3}$	$\frac{17}{3}$	0	0	1	$-\frac{5}{3}$	6	s_2
$\frac{1}{3}$	$\frac{4}{3}$	1	0	0	$-\frac{1}{3}$	2	x_3
$\frac{11}{3}$	$\frac{2}{3}$	0	0	0	$\frac{1}{3}$	-2	

Finally, we conclude that the maximization value of the revised objective function is $z = -2$, and hence the minimum value of the original objective function is

$$w = 2$$

(the negative of the entry in the lower-right corner), and this occurs when

$$x_1 = 0, \quad x_2 = 0, \quad \text{and} \quad x_3 = 2.$$

Applications

EXAMPLE 3   **A Business Application: Minimum Shipment Cost**

An automobile company has two factories. One factory has 400 cars (of a certain model) in stock and the other factory has 300 cars (of the model) in stock. Two customers order this car model. The first customer needs 200 cars, and the second customer needs 300 cars. The cost of shipping cars from the two factories to the customers is shown in Table 9.3.

TABLE 9.3

	Customer 1	Customer 2
Factory 1	$ 30	$ 25
Factory 2	$ 36	$ 30

How should the company ship the cars in order to minimize the shipping cost?

Solution   To begin, we let x_1 and x_2 represent the number of cars shipped from Factory 1 to the first and second customers, respectively. (See Figure 9.20.) The total cost of shipping is then given by

$$C = 30x_1 + 25x_2 + 36(200 - x_1) + 30(300 - x_2) = 16{,}200 - 6x_1 - 5x_2.$$

The constraints for this minimization problem are as follows.

$$x_1 + x_2 \le 400$$
$$(200 - x_1) + (300 - x_2) \le 300 \quad \longrightarrow \quad x_1 + x_2 \ge 200$$
$$x_1 \le 200$$
$$x_2 \le 300$$

Figure 9.20

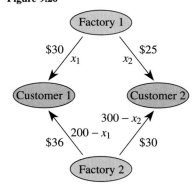

The corresponding maximization problem is to maximize $z = 6x_1 + 5x_2 - 16{,}200$. Thus, the initial simplex tableau is as follows.

x_1	x_2	s_1	s_2	s_3	s_4	b	Basic Variables	
1	1	1	0	0	0	400	s_1	
1	1	0	-1	0	0	200	s_2	← Departing
1	0	0	0	1	0	200	s_3	
0	1	0	0	0	1	300	s_4	
-6	-5	0	0	0	0	-16,200		

↑
Entering

Note that the current z-value is $-16,200$ because the initial solution is

$$(x_1, x_2, s_1, s_2, s_3, s_4) = (0, 0, 400, -200, 200, 300).$$

Now, to this initial tableau, we apply the simplex method as follows.

x_1	x_2	s_1	s_2	s_3	s_4	b	Basic Variables	
0	0	1	1	0	0	200	s_1	
1	1	0	-1	0	0	200	x_1	
0	-1	0	1	1	0	0	s_3	$\leftarrow$ Departing
0	1	0	0	0	1	300	s_4	
0	1	0	-6	0	0	$-15,000$		

↑
Entering

x_1	x_2	s_1	s_2	s_3	s_4	b	Basic Variables	
0	1	1	0	-1	0	200	s_1	$\leftarrow$ Departing
1	0	0	0	1	0	200	x_1	
0	-1	0	1	1	0	0	s_2	
0	1	0	0	0	1	300	s_4	
0	-5	0	0	6	0	$-15,000$		

↑
Entering

x_1	x_2	s_1	s_2	s_3	s_4	b	Basic Variables
0	1	1	0	-1	0	200	x_2
1	0	0	0	1	0	200	x_1
0	0	1	1	0	0	200	s_2
0	0	-1	0	1	1	100	s_4
0	0	5	0	1	0	$-14,000$	

From this tableau, we see that the minimum shipping cost is $14,000. Since $x_1 = 200$ and $x_2 = 200$, we conclude that the number of cars that should be shipped from each factory is as shown in Table 9.4.

TABLE 9.4

	Customer 1	Customer 2
Factory 1	200 cars	200 cars
Factory 2	0	100 cars

SECTION 9.5 ☐ EXERCISES

In Exercises 1–6, add the appropriate slack and surplus variables to the system and form the initial simplex tableau.

1. (Maximize)

Objective function:

$w = 10x_1 + 4x_2$

Constraints:

$2x_1 + x_2 \geq 4$
$x_1 + x_2 \leq 8$
$x_1, x_2 \geq 0$

2. (Maximize)

Objective function:

$w = 3x_1 + x_2 + x_3$

Constraints:

$x_1 + 2x_2 + x_3 \leq 10$
$x_2 + 5x_3 \geq 6$
$4x_1 - x_2 + x_3 \geq 16$
$x_1, x_2, x_3 \geq 0$

3. (Minimize)

Objective function:

$w = x_1 + x_2$

Constraints:

$2x_1 + x_2 \leq 4$
$x_1 + 3x_2 \geq 2$
$x_1, x_2 \geq 0$

4. (Minimize)

Objective function:

$w = 2x_1 + 3x_2$

Constraints:

$3x_1 + x_2 \geq 4$
$4x_1 + 2x_2 \leq 3$
$x_1, x_2 \geq 0$

5. (Maximize)

Objective function:

$w = x_1 + x_3$

Constraints:

$4x_1 + x_2 \geq 10$
$x_1 + x_2 + 3x_3 \leq 30$
$2x_1 + x_2 + 4x_3 \geq 16$
$x_1, x_2, x_3 \geq 0$

6. (Maximize)

Objective function:

$w = 4x_1 + x_2 + x_3$

Constraints:

$2x_1 + x_2 + 4x_3 \leq 60$
$x_2 + x_3 \geq 40$
$x_1, x_2, x_3 \geq 0$

In Exercises 7–12, use the given entering and departing variables to solve the given mixed constraint problem.

7. (Maximize)

Objective function:

$w = -x_1 + 2x_2$

Constraints:

$x_1 + x_2 \geq 3$
$x_1 + x_2 \leq 6$
$x_1, x_2 \geq 0$

Entering x_2, departing s_1.

8. (Maximize)

Objective function:

$w = 2x_1 + x_2$

Constraints:

$x_1 + x_2 \geq 4$
$x_1 + x_2 \leq 8$
$x_1, x_2 \geq 0$

Entering x_1, departing s_1.

9. (Minimize)

Objective function:

$w = x_1 + 2x_2$

Constraints:

$2x_1 + 3x_2 \leq 25$
$x_1 + 2x_2 \geq 16$
$x_1, x_2 \geq 0$

Entering x_2, departing s_2.

10. (Minimize)

Objective function:

$w = 3x_1 + 2x_2$

Constraints:

$x_1 + x_2 \geq 20$
$3x_1 + 4x_2 \leq 70$
$x_1, x_2 \geq 0$

Entering x_1, departing s_1.

11. (Maximize)

Objective function:

$w = x_1 + x_2$

Constraints:

$-4x_1 + 3x_2 + x_3 \leq 40$
$-2x_1 + x_2 + x_3 \geq 10$
$x_2 + x_3 \leq 20$
$x_1, x_2, x_3 \geq 0$

Entering x_2, departing s_2.

12. (Maximize)

Objective function:

$w = x_1 + 2x_2 + 2x_3$

Constraints:

$x_1 + x_2 \geq 50$
$2x_1 + x_2 + x_3 \leq 70$
$x_2 + 3x_3 \geq 40$
$x_1, x_2, x_3 \geq 0$

Entering x_2, departing s_1.

In Exercises 13–20, use the simplex method to solve the given problem.

13. (Maximize)

Objective function:

$w = 2x_1 + 5x_2$

Constraints:

$x_1 + 2x_2 \geq 4$
$x_1 + x_2 \leq 8$
$x_1, x_2 \geq 0$

14. (Maximize)

Objective function:

$w = -x_1 + 3x_2$

Constraints:

$2x_1 + x_2 \leq 4$
$x_1 + 5x_2 \geq 5$
$x_1, x_2 \geq 0$

15. (Maximize)

Objective function:

$w = 2x_1 + x_2 + 3x_3$

Constraints:

$x_1 + 4x_2 + 2x_3 \leq 85$
$x_2 - 5x_3 \geq 20$
$3x_1 + 2x_2 + 11x_3 \geq 49$
$x_1, x_2, x_3 \geq 0$

16. (Maximize)

Objective function:

$w = 3x_1 + 5x_2 + 2x_3$

Constraints:

$9x_1 + 4x_2 + x_3 \leq 70$
$5x_1 + 2x_2 + x_3 \leq 40$
$4x_1 + x_2 \geq 16$
$x_1, x_2, x_3 \geq 0$

17. (Minimize)

Objective function:

$w = x_1 + x_2$

Constraints:

$x_1 + 2x_2 \geq 25$

$2x_1 + 5x_2 \leq 60$

$x_1, x_2 \geq 0$

18. (Minimize)

Objective function:

$w = 2x_1 + 3x_2$

Constraints:

$3x_1 + 2x_2 \leq 22$

$x_1 + x_2 \geq 10$

$x_1, x_2 \geq 0$

19. (Minimize)

Objective function:

$w = -2x_1 + 4x_2 - x_3$

Constraints:

$3x_1 - 6x_2 + 4x_3 \leq 30$

$2x_1 - 8x_2 + 10x_3 \geq 18$

$x_1, x_2, x_3 \geq 0$

20. (Minimize)

Objective function:

$w = x_1 + x_2 + x_3$

Constraints:

$x_1 + 2x_2 + x_3 \geq 30$

$6x_2 + x_3 \leq 54$

$x_1 + x_2 + 3x_3 \geq 20$

$x_1, x_2, x_3 \geq 0$

In Exercises 21–24, maximize the given objective function subject to the following constraints.

$x_1 + x_2 \leq 5$

$-x_1 + x_2 \leq 3$

$x_2 \geq 1$

$x_1, x_2 \geq 0$

21. $w = 2x_1 + x_2$

22. $w = x_1 + 2x_2$

23. $w = x_2$

24. $w = -x_1 - x_2$

In Exercises 25–28, maximize the given objective function subject to the following constraints.

$3x_1 + 2x_2 \geq 6$

$x_1 - x_2 \leq 2$

$-x_1 + 2x_2 \leq 6$

$x_1 \leq 4$

$x_1, x_2 \geq 0$

25. $w = x_1 + x_2$

26. $w = x_1 - 2x_2$

27. $w = -4x_1 + x_2$

28. $w = 4x_1 - x_2$

In Exercises 29–32, a tire company has two suppliers, S_1 and S_2. S_1 has 900 tires on hand and S_2 has 800 tires on hand. Customer C_1 needs 500 tires and customer C_2 needs 600 tires. Minimize the cost of filling the orders subject to the given table (showing the shipping cost per tire).

29.

	C_1	C_2
S_1	0.60	1.20
S_2	1.00	1.80

30.

	C_1	C_2
S_1	0.80	1.00
S_2	1.00	1.20

31.

	C_1	C_2
S_1	1.20	1.00
S_2	1.00	1.20

32.

	C_1	C_2
S_1	0.80	1.00
S_2	1.00	0.80

33. An automobile company has two factories. One factory has 400 cars (of a certain model) in stock and the other factory has 300 cars (of the model) in stock. Two customers order this car model. The first customer needs 200 cars, and the second customer needs 300 cars. The cost of shipping cars from the two factories to the two customers is as follows.

	Customer 1	Customer 2
Factory 1	$36	$30
Factory 2	$30	$25

How should the company ship the cars in order to minimize the shipping cost?

34. Suppose in Exercise 33 that the shipping costs for each of the two factories are as follows.

	Customer 1	Customer 2
Factory 1	$25	$30
Factory 2	$35	$30

How should the company ship the cars in order to minimize the shipping cost?

35. A company has budgeted a maximum of $600,000 for advertising a certain product nationally. Each minute of television time costs $60,000 and each one-page newspaper ad costs $15,000. Each television ad is expected to be viewed by 15 million viewers, and each newspaper ad is expected to be seen by 3 million readers. The company's market research department advises the company to use at least 6 television ads and at least 4 newspaper ads. How should the advertising budget be allocated to maximize the total audience?

36. Rework Exercise 35 assuming that each one-page newspaper ad costs $30,000.

In Exercises 37 and 38, use the following information. A computer company has two assembly plants, Plant A and Plant B, and two distribution outlets, Outlet I and Outlet II. Plant A can assemble 5000 computers in a year and Plant B can assemble 4000 computers in a year. Outlet I must have 3000 computers per year and Outlet II must have 5000 computers per year. The transportation costs from each plant to each outlet are indicated in the given table. Find the shipping schedule that will produce the minimum cost. What is the minimum cost?

37.

	Outlet I	Outlet II
Plant A	$4	$5
Plant B	$5	$6

38.

	Outlet I	Outlet II
Plant A	$4	$5
Plant B	$6	$4

CHAPTER 9 ☐ REVIEW EXERCISES

In Exercises 1–6, sketch a graph of the solution of the system of inequalities.

1. $x + 2y \le 160$
$3x + y \le 180$
$x \ge 0$
$y \ge 0$

2. $2x + 3y \le 24$
$2x + y \le 16$
$x \ge 0$
$y \ge 0$

3. $3x + 2y \ge 24$
$x + 2y \ge 12$
$2 \le x \le 15$
$y \le 15$

4. $2x + y \ge 16$
$x + 3y \ge 18$
$0 \le x \le 25$
$0 \le y \le 15$

5. $2x - 3y \ge 0$
$2x - y \le 8$
$y \ge 0$

6. $x - y \le 10$
$x \ge 0$
$y \ge 0$

In Exercises 7 and 8, determine a system of inequalities that models the given description, and sketch a graph of the solution of the system.

7. A Pennsylvania fruit grower has 1500 bushels of apples that are to be divided between markets in Harrisburg and Philadelphia. These two markets need at least 400 bushels and 600 bushels, respectively.

8. A warehouse operator has 24,000 square meters of floor space in which to store two products. Each unit of product I requires 20 square meters of floor space and costs $12 per day to store. Each unit of product II requires 30 square meters of floor space and costs $8 per day to store. The total storage cost per day cannot exceed $12,400.

In Exercises 9–14, find the minimum and/or maximum values of the given objective function by the graphical method.

9. Maximize: $z = 3x + 4y$

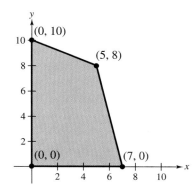

10. Minimize: $z = 10x + 7y$

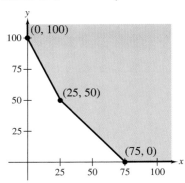

11. Objective function:

$z = x + 3y$

Constraints:

$$x \geq 0$$
$$y \geq 0$$
$$x \leq 5$$
$$x + y \geq 3$$
$$x - y \leq 3$$
$$-x + y \leq 3$$

12. Objective function:

$z = 4x - y$

Constraints:

$$x \geq 0$$
$$y \geq 0$$
$$x \leq 6$$
$$x + y \geq 2$$
$$x \geq y$$
$$3x - y \leq 12$$

13. Objective function:

$z = 3x - y$

Constraints:

$$x \geq 0$$
$$y \geq 0$$
$$x \leq 3y$$
$$-x + 2y \leq 12$$
$$4x + 3y \leq 40$$
$$x + 2y \leq 15$$

14. Objective function:

$z = x - 2y$

Constraints:

$$x \geq 0$$
$$y \geq 0$$
$$x + y \leq 12$$
$$5x + y \leq 36$$
$$5x - 2y \geq 4$$
$$2x + 5y \geq 19$$

In Exercises 15–22, use the simplex method to maximize the given objective function, subject to the given constraints.

15. Objective function:

$z = x_1 + 2x_2$

Constraints:

$$2x_1 + x_2 \leq 31$$
$$x_1 + 4x_2 \leq 40$$
$$x_1, x_2 \geq 0$$

16. Objective function:

$z = 5x_1 + 4x_2$

Constraints:

$$x_1 - x_2 \leq 22$$
$$x_1 + 2x_2 \leq 43$$
$$x_1, x_2 \geq 0$$

17. Objective function:

$z = x_1 + 2x_2 + x_3$

Constraints:

$$2x_1 + 2x_2 + x_3 \leq 20$$
$$x_1 + x_2 - 2x_3 \leq 23$$
$$-2x_1 + x_2 - 2x_3 \leq 8$$
$$x_1, x_2, x_3 \geq 0$$

18. Objective function:

$z = 4x_1 + 5x_2 + 6x_3$

Constraints:

$$4x_1 + 2x_2 + x_3 \leq 30$$
$$x_1 + 3x_2 + 2x_3 \leq 54$$
$$x_1 + x_2 + 2x_3 \leq 24$$
$$x_1, x_2, x_3 \geq 0$$

19. Objective function:

$z = x_1 + x_2$

Constraints:

$$3x_1 + x_2 \leq 432$$
$$x_1 + 4x_2 \leq 628$$
$$x_1, x_2 \geq 0$$

20. Objective function:

$z = 6x_1 + 8x_2$

Constraints:

$$20x_1 + 40x_2 \leq 200$$
$$30x_1 + 42x_2 \leq 228$$
$$x_1, x_2 \geq 0$$

21. Objective function:

$z = 3x_1 + 5x_2 + 4x_3$

Constraints:

$$6x_1 - 2x_2 + 3x_3 \leq 24$$
$$3x_1 - 3x_2 + 9x_3 \leq 33$$
$$-2x_1 + x_2 - 2x_3 \leq 25$$
$$x_1, x_2, x_3 \geq 0$$

22. Objective function:

$z = 2x_1 + 5x_2 - x_3$

Constraints:

$$-x_1 + 3x_2 + 2x_3 \leq 92$$
$$-2x_1 + 2x_2 + 12x_3 \leq 76$$
$$3x_1 + x_2 - 6x_3 \leq 24$$
$$x_1, x_2, x_3 \geq 0$$

In Exercises 23 and 24, determine the dual of the given minimization problem.

23. Objective function:

$w = 7x_1 + 3x_2 + x_3$

Constraints:

$$x_1 + x_2 + 2x_3 \geq 30$$
$$3x_1 + 6x_2 + 4x_3 \geq 75$$
$$x_1, x_2, x_3 \geq 0$$

24. Objective function:

$w = 2x_1 + 3x_2 + 4x_3$

Constraints:

$$x_1 + 5x_2 + 3x_3 \geq 90$$
$$2x_1 + x_2 + 3x_3 \geq 60$$
$$3x_1 + 2x_2 + x_3 \geq 56$$
$$x_1, x_2, x_3 \geq 0$$

In Exercises 25–30, solve the given minimization problem by solving the dual maximization problem with the simplex method.

25. Objective function:

$w = 9x_1 + 15x_2$

Constraints:

$$x_1 + 5x_2 \geq 15$$
$$4x_1 - 10x_2 \geq 0$$
$$x_1, x_2 \geq 0$$

26. Objective function:

$w = 16x_1 + 18x_2$

Constraints:

$$2x_1 - 3x_2 \geq 14$$
$$-4x_1 + 9x_2 \geq 8$$
$$x_1, x_2 \geq 0$$

27. Objective function:

$w = 24x_1 + 22x_2 + 18x_3$

Constraints:

$$2x_1 + 2x_2 - 3x_3 \geq 24$$
$$6x_1 \qquad - 2x_3 \geq 21$$
$$-8x_1 - 4x_2 + 8x_3 \geq 12$$
$$x_1, x_2, x_3 \geq 0$$

28. Objective function:

$w = 32x_1 + 36x_2 + 4x_3$

Constraints:

$$4x_1 + 3x_2 - x_3 \geq 8$$
$$-8x_1 + 6x_2 - 6x_3 \geq 0$$
$$-4x_1 \qquad + 9x_3 \geq 4$$
$$x_1, x_2, x_3 \geq 0$$

29. Objective function:

$w = 16x_1 + 54x_2 + 48x_3$

Constraints:

$$x_1 + 2x_2 + 3x_3 \geq 2$$
$$2x_1 + 7x_2 + 4x_3 \geq 5$$
$$x_1 + 3x_2 + 4x_3 \geq 1$$
$$x_1, x_2, x_3 \geq 0$$

30. Objective function:

$w = 22x_1 + 27x_2 + 18x_3$

Constraints:

$$-2x_1 - 3x_2 + 6x_3 \geq 0$$
$$-2x_1 + 7x_2 + 3x_3 \geq 4$$
$$2x_1 + x_2 - 3x_3 \geq 12$$
$$x_1, x_2, x_3 \geq 0$$

In Exercises 31–36, use the simplex method to solve the mixed constraints problem.

31. (Maximize)

Objective function:

$z = x_1 + 2x_2$

Constraints:

$$-4x_1 + 2x_2 \leq 26$$
$$-3x_1 + x_2 \geq 12$$
$$x_1, x_2 \geq 0$$

32. (Maximize)

Objective function:

$z = 2x_1 + 3x_2$

Constraints:

$$-x_1 + x_2 \geq 40$$
$$x_2 \leq 61$$
$$x_1, x_2 \geq 0$$

33. (Maximize)

Objective function:

$z = 2x_1 + x_2 + x_3$

Constraints:

$$x_1 + x_2 + x_3 \leq 60$$
$$-4x_1 + 2x_2 + x_3 \geq 52$$
$$2x_1 + x_3 \geq 40$$
$$x_1, x_2, x_3 \geq 0$$

34. (Maximize)

Objective function:

$z = 3x_1 + 2x_2 + x_3$

Constraints:

$$2x_1 + x_2 + 3x_3 \leq 52$$
$$x_1 + x_2 + 2x_3 \geq 24$$
$$2x_2 + x_3 \leq 52$$
$$x_1, x_2, x_3 \geq 0$$

35. (Minimize)

Objective function:

$z = 9x_1 + 4x_2 + 10x_3$

Constraints:

$$32x_1 + 16x_2 + 8x_3 \leq 344$$
$$20x_1 - 40x_2 + 20x_3 \geq 200$$
$$-45x_1 + 15x_2 + 30x_3 \leq 525$$
$$x_1, x_2, x_3 \geq 0$$

36. (Minimize)

Objective function:

$z = 4x_1 - 2x_2 - x_3$

Constraints:

$$2x_1 - x_2 - x_3 \leq 41$$
$$x_1 - 2x_2 - x_3 \geq 10$$
$$-x_1 - 7x_2 + 5x_3 \leq 11$$
$$x_1, x_2, x_3 \geq 0$$

37. A tailor has 12 square feet of cotton, 21 square feet of silk, and 11 square feet of wool. A vest requires 1 square foot of cotton, 2 square feet of silk, and 3 square feet of wool. A purse requires 2 square feet of cotton, 1 square foot of silk, and 1 square foot of wool. If the purse sells for $80 and the vest sells for $50, how many purses and vests should be made to maximize the tailor's profit? What is the maximum revenue?

38. A carpenter has 400 board feet of plywood, 487 board feet of birch, and 795 board feet of pine. Product A requires 1 board foot of plywood, 2 board feet of birch, and 1 board foot of pine. Product B requires 1 board foot of plywood, 1 board foot of birch, and 3 board feet of pine. Product C requires 2 board feet of plywood, 1 board foot of birch, and 1 board foot of pine. If product A sells for $22, product B sells for $42, and product C sells for $29, what combination of products would yield the maximum gross income?

39. A company owns three mines that have the following daily production (in metric tons).

Mine	Grade of Ore		
	High	Medium	Low
A	1	2	3
B	1	2	2
C	2	1	1

The company needs 60 metric tons of high-grade ore, 48 metric tons of medium-grade ore, and 55 metric tons of low-grade ore. Minimize the cost of meeting this production level if the daily operating costs are $200 for mine A, $200 for mine B, and $100 for mine C.

40. Rework Exercise 39 given the following daily production schedule.

Mine	Grade of Ore		
	High	Medium	Low
A	2	1	2
B	1	1	1
C	4	2	1

The company needs 190 metric tons of high-grade ore, 120 metric tons of medium-grade ore, and 200 tons of low-grade ore. The daily operating costs are $200 for mine A, $150 for mine B, and $125 for mine C.

10 NUMERICAL METHODS

Carl Gustav Jacob
Jacobi
1 8 0 4 – 1 8 5 1

Carl Gustav Jacob Jacobi was the second son of a successful banker in Potsdam, Germany. After completing his secondary schooling in Potsdam in 1821, he entered the University of Berlin. In 1825, having been granted a doctorate in mathematics, Jacobi served as a lecturer at the University of Berlin. Then he accepted a position in mathematics at the University of Königsberg.

Jacobi's mathematical writings encompassed a wide variety of topics, including elliptic functions, functions of a complex variable, functional determinants (called Jacobians), differential equations, and Abelian functions. Jacobi was the first to apply elliptic functions to the theory of numbers, and he was able to prove a longstanding conjecture by Fermat that every positive integer can be written as the sum of four perfect squares. (For instance, $10 = 1^2 + 1^2 + 2^2 + 2^2$.) He also contributed to several branches of mathematical physics, including dynamics, celestial mechanics, and fluid dynamics.

In spite of his contributions to applied mathematics, Jacobi did not believe that mathematical research needed to be justified by its applicability. He stated that the sole end of science and mathematics is "the honor of the human mind" and that "a question about numbers is worth as much as a question about the system of the world."

Jacobi was such an incessant worker that in 1842 his health failed and he retired to Berlin. By the time of his death in 1851, he had become one of the most famous mathematicians in Europe.

10.1 GAUSSIAN ELIMINATION WITH PARTIAL PIVOTING

In Chapter 1 two methods for solving a system of n linear equations in n variables were discussed. When either of these methods (Gaussian elimination and Gauss-Jordan elimination) is used with a digital computer, the computer introduces a problem that we have not dealt with yet—**rounding error.**

Digital computers store real numbers in **floating point form,**

$$\pm M \times 10^k,$$

where k is an integer and the **mantissa** M satisfies the inequality $0.1 \leq M < 1$. For instance, the floating point forms of some real numbers are as follows.

Real Number	Floating Point Form
527	0.527×10^3
−3.81623	$−0.381623 \times 10^1$
0.00045	0.45×10^{-3}

The number of decimal places that can be stored in the mantissa depends on the computer. If n places are stored, then we say that the computer stores **n significant digits.** Additional digits are either truncated or rounded off. When a number is **truncated** to n significant digits, all digits after the first n significant digits are simply omitted. For instance, truncated to two significant digits, the number 0.1251 becomes 0.12.

When a number is **rounded** to n significant digits, the last retained digit is increased by one if the discarded portion is greater than half a digit, and the last retained digit is not changed if the discarded portion is less than half a digit. For instance, rounded to two significant digits, 0.1251 becomes 0.13 and 0.1249 becomes 0.12. For the special case in which the discarded portion is precisely half a digit, we round so that the last retained digit is even. Thus, rounded to two significant digits, 0.125 becomes 0.12 and 0.135 becomes 0.14.

Whenever the computer truncates or rounds, a rounding error that can affect subsequent calculations is introduced. The result after rounding or truncating is called the **stored value.**

EXAMPLE 1   ***Finding the Stored Value of Number***

Determine the stored value of each of the following real numbers in a computer that rounds to three significant digits.

    (a) 54.7   (b) 0.1134   (c) –8.2256

    (d) 0.08335   (e) 0.08345

Solution

Number	Floating Point Form	Stored Value
(a) 54.7	0.547×10^2	0.547×10^2
(b) 0.1134	0.1134×10^0	0.113×10^0
(c) –8.2256	-0.82256×10^1	-0.823×10^1
(d) 0.08335	0.8335×10^{-1}	0.834×10^{-1}
(e) 0.08345	0.8345×10^{-1}	0.834×10^{-1}

Note in parts (d) and (e) that when the discarded portion of a decimal is precisely half a digit, the number is rounded so that the stored value ends in an even digit.

REMARK: Most computers store numbers in binary form (base two) rather than decimal form (base ten). Because rounding occurs in both systems, however, we will restrict our discussion to the more familiar base ten.

Rounding error tends to propagate as the number of arithmetic operations increases. This phenomenon is illustrated in the following example.

EXAMPLE 2   ***Propagation of Rounding Error***

Evaluate the determinant of the matrix

$$A = \begin{bmatrix} 0.12 & 0.23 \\ 0.12 & 0.12 \end{bmatrix},$$

rounding each intermediate calculation to two significant digits. Then find the exact solution and compare the two results.

Solution   Rounding each intermediate calculation to two significant digits, we obtain the following.

$$|A| = (0.12)(0.12) - (0.12)(0.23)$$

$$= 0.0144 - 0.0276$$

$$\approx 0.014 - 0.028 \qquad \text{Round to two significant digits}$$

$$= -0.014$$

On the other hand, the exact solution is

$$|A| = 0.0144 - 0.0276$$

$$= -0.0132.$$

Thus, to two significant digits, the correct solution is -0.013. Note that the rounded solution is not correct to two significant digits, even though each arithmetic operation was performed with two significant digits of accuracy. This is what we mean when we say that arithmetic operations tend to propagate rounding error.

In Example 2, by rounding at the intermediate steps we introduced a rounding error of

$$-0.0132 - (-0.014) = 0.0008. \qquad \text{Rounding error}$$

Although this error may seem slight, it represents a **percentage error** of

$$\frac{0.0008}{0.0132} \approx 0.061 = 6.1\%. \qquad \text{Percentage error}$$

In most practical applications, a percentage error of this magnitude would be intolerable. Keep in mind that this particular percentage error arose with only a few arithmetic steps. When the number of arithmetic steps increases, the likelihood of a large percentage error also increases.

Gaussian Elimination with Partial Pivoting

For large systems of linear equations, Gaussian elimination can involve hundreds of arithmetic computations, each of which can produce rounding error. The following straightforward example illustrates the potential magnitude of the problem.

TECHNOLOGY NOTE

You can see the effect of rounding on a calculator. For example, the determinant of

$$A = \begin{bmatrix} 3 & 11 \\ 2 & 6 \end{bmatrix}$$

is -4. However, the TI-85 calculates the greatest integer of the determinant of A to be -5: **int det A** $= -5$. Do you see what happened?

EXAMPLE 3   *Gaussian Elimination and Rounding Error*

Use Gaussian elimination to solve the following system.

$$\begin{aligned} 0.143x_1 + 0.357x_2 + 2.01x_3 &= -5.173 \\ -1.31x_1 + 0.911x_2 + 1.99x_3 &= -5.458 \\ 11.2x_1 - 4.30x_2 - 0.605x_3 &= 4.415 \end{aligned}$$

After *each* intermediate calculation, round the result to three significant digits.

Solution   Applying Gaussian elimination to the augmented matrix for this system produces the following.

$$\begin{bmatrix} 0.143 & 0.357 & 2.01 & -5.17 \\ -1.31 & 0.911 & 1.99 & -5.46 \\ 11.2 & -4.30 & -0.605 & 4.42 \end{bmatrix}$$

$$\begin{bmatrix} 1.00 & 2.50 & 14.1 & -36.2 \\ -1.31 & 0.911 & 1.99 & -5.46 \\ 11.2 & -4.30 & -0.605 & 4.42 \end{bmatrix}$$ ← Dividing the first row by 0.143 produces a new first row.

$$\begin{bmatrix} 1.00 & 2.50 & 14.1 & -36.2 \\ 0.00 & 4.19 & 20.5 & -52.9 \\ 11.2 & -4.30 & -0.605 & 4.42 \end{bmatrix}$$ ← Adding 1.31 times the first row to the second row produces a new second row.

$$\begin{bmatrix} 1.00 & 2.50 & 14.1 & -36.2 \\ 0.00 & 4.19 & 20.5 & -52.9 \\ 0.00 & -32.3 & -159. & 409. \end{bmatrix}$$ ← Adding –11.2 times the first row to the third row produces a new third row.

$$\begin{bmatrix} 1.00 & 2.50 & 14.1 & -36.2 \\ 0.00 & 1.00 & 4.89 & -12.6 \\ 0.00 & -32.3 & -159. & 409. \end{bmatrix}$$ ← Dividing the second row by 4.19 produces a new second row.

$$\begin{bmatrix} 1.00 & 2.50 & 14.1 & -36.2 \\ 0.00 & 1.00 & 4.89 & -12.6 \\ 0.00 & 0.00 & -1.00 & 2.00 \end{bmatrix}$$ ← Adding 32.3 times the second row to the third row produces a new third row.

$$\begin{bmatrix} 1.00 & 2.50 & 14.1 & -36.2 \\ 0.00 & 1.00 & 4.89 & -12.6 \\ 0.00 & 0.00 & 1.00 & -2.00 \end{bmatrix}$$ ← Multiplying the third row by –1 produces a new third row.

Thus $x_3 = -2.00$, and using back-substitution we obtain $x_2 = -2.82$ and $x_1 = -0.950$. Try checking this "solution" in the original system of equations to see that it is not correct. (The correct solution is $x_1 = 1$, $x_2 = 2$, and $x_3 = -3$.)

What went wrong with the Gaussian elimination procedure used in Example 3? Clearly, rounding error propagated to such an extent that the final "solution" became hopelessly inaccurate.

Part of the problem is that the original augmented matrix contains entries that differ in orders of magnitude. For instance, the first column of the matrix

$$\begin{bmatrix} 0.143 & 0.357 & 2.01 & -5.17 \\ -1.31 & 0.911 & 1.99 & -5.46 \\ 11.2 & -4.30 & -0.605 & 4.42 \end{bmatrix}$$

has entries that increase roughly by powers of ten as one moves down the column. In subsequent elementary row operations, the first row was multiplied by 1.31 and –11.2 and the second row was multiplied by 32.3. When floating point arithmetic is used, such large row multipliers tend to propagate rounding error. This type of error propagation can be lessened by appropriate row interchanges that produce smaller multipliers. One method for restricting the size of the multipliers is called **Gaussian elimination with partial pivoting.**

Gaussian Elimination with Partial Pivoting

1. Find the entry in the left column with the largest absolute value. This entry is called the **pivot.**
2. Perform a row interchange, if necessary, so that the pivot is in the first row.
3. Divide the first row by the pivot. (This step is unnecessary if the pivot is 1.)
4. Use elementary row operations to reduce the remaining entries in the first column to zero.

The completion of these four steps is called a **pass.** After performing the first pass, ignore the first row and first column and repeat the four steps on the remaining submatrix. Continue this process until the matrix is in row-echelon form.

Example 4 shows what happens when this partial pivoting technique is used on the system of linear equations given in Example 3.

EXAMPLE 4   *Gaussian Elimination with Partial Pivoting*

Use Gaussian elimination with partial pivoting to solve the system of linear equations given in Example 3. After *each* intermediate calculation, round the result to three significant digits.

Solution   As in Example 3, the augmented matrix for this system is

$$
\begin{bmatrix}
0.143 & 0.357 & 2.01 & -5.17 \\
-1.31 & 0.911 & 1.99 & -5.46 \\
11.2 & -4.30 & -0.605 & 4.42
\end{bmatrix}.
$$

$\uparrow$
Pivot

In the left column 11.2 is the pivot because it is the entry that has the largest absolute value. Therefore we interchange the first and third rows and apply elementary row operations as follows.

$$
\begin{bmatrix}
11.2 & -4.30 & -0.605 & 4.42 \\
-1.31 & 0.911 & 1.99 & -5.46 \\
0.143 & 0.357 & 2.01 & -5.17
\end{bmatrix}
$$
⟵ Interchange the first and third rows.

$$
\begin{bmatrix}
1.00 & -0.384 & -0.0540 & 0.395 \\
-1.31 & 0.911 & 1.99 & -5.46 \\
0.143 & 0.357 & 2.01 & -5.17
\end{bmatrix}
$$
⟵ Dividing the first row by 11.2 produces a new first row.

$$\begin{bmatrix} 1.00 & -0.384 & -0.0540 & 0.395 \\ 0.00 & 0.408 & 1.92 & -4.94 \\ 0.143 & 0.357 & 2.01 & -5.17 \end{bmatrix}$$ ← Adding 1.31 times the first row to the second row produces a new second row.

$$\begin{bmatrix} 1.00 & -0.384 & -0.0540 & 0.395 \\ 0.00 & 0.408 & 1.92 & -4.94 \\ 0.00 & 0.412 & 2.02 & -5.23 \end{bmatrix}$$ ← Adding −0.143 times the first row to the third row produces a new third row.

This completes the first pass. For the second pass we consider the submatrix formed by deleting the first row and first column. In this matrix the pivot is 0.412, which means that the second and third rows should be interchanged. Then we proceed with Gaussian elimination as follows.

Pivot

$$\begin{bmatrix} 1.00 & -0.384 & -0.0540 & 0.395 \\ 0.00 & 0.412 & 2.02 & -5.23 \\ 0.00 & 0.408 & 1.92 & -4.94 \end{bmatrix}$$ ← Interchange the second and third rows.

$$\begin{bmatrix} 1.00 & -0.384 & -0.0540 & 0.395 \\ 0.00 & 1.00 & 4.90 & -12.7 \\ 0.00 & 0.408 & 1.92 & -4.94 \end{bmatrix}$$ ← Dividing the second row by 0.412 produces a new second row.

$$\begin{bmatrix} 1.00 & -0.384 & -0.0540 & 0.395 \\ 0.00 & 1.00 & 4.90 & -12.7 \\ 0.00 & 0.00 & -0.0800 & 0.240 \end{bmatrix}$$ ← Adding −0.408 times the second row to the third row produces a new third row.

This completes the second pass, and we can complete the entire procedure by dividing the third row by −0.0800 as follows.

$$\begin{bmatrix} 1.00 & -0.384 & -0.0540 & 0.395 \\ 0.00 & 1.00 & 4.90 & -12.7 \\ 0.00 & 0.00 & 1.00 & -3.00 \end{bmatrix}$$ ← Dividing the third row by −0.0800 produces a new third row.

Thus $x_3 = -3.00$, and using back-substitution we have $x_2 = 2.00$ and $x_1 = 1.00$, which agrees with the exact solution of $x_1 = 1$, $x_2 = 2$, and $x_3 = -3$ when rounded to three significant digits.

REMARK: Note that the row multipliers used in Example 4 are 1.31, −0.143, and −0.408, as contrasted with the multipliers of 1.31, 11.2, and 32.3 encountered in Example 3.

The term *partial* in partial pivoting refers to the fact that in each pivot search only entries in the left column of the matrix or submatrix are considered. This search can be extended to include every entry in the coefficient matrix or submatrix; the resulting technique is called **Gaussian elimination with complete pivoting.** Unfortunately, neither complete pivoting nor partial pivoting solves all problems of rounding error. Some systems of linear equations, called **ill-conditioned** systems, are extremely sensitive to numerical errors. For such systems, pivoting is not much help. A common type of system of linear equations that tends to be ill-conditioned is one for which the determinant of the coefficient matrix is nearly zero. The next example illustrates this problem.

EXAMPLE 5   *An Ill-Conditioned System of Linear Equations*

Use Gaussian elimination to solve the following system of linear equations.

$$x + \quad y = \quad 0$$

$$x + \frac{401}{400}y = 20$$

Round each intermediate calculation to four significant digits.

Solution   Using Gaussian elimination with rational arithmetic, we find the exact solution to be $y = 8000$ and $x = -8000$. But rounding $401/400 = 1.0025$ to four significant digits introduces a large rounding error, as follows.

$$\begin{bmatrix} 1 & 1 & 0 \\ 1 & 1.002 & 20 \end{bmatrix}$$

$$\begin{bmatrix} 1 & 1 & 0 \\ 0 & 0.002 & 20 \end{bmatrix}$$

$$\begin{bmatrix} 1 & 1 & 0 \\ 0 & 1.00 & 10,000 \end{bmatrix}$$

Thus $y = 10,000$ and back-substitution produces

$$x = -y$$

$$= -10,000.$$

This "solution" represents a percentage error of 25% for both the x-value and the y-value. Note that this error was caused by a rounding error of only 0.0005 (when we rounded 1.0025 to 1.002).

SECTION 10.1 ☐ EXERCISES

In Exercises 1–8, express the given real number in floating point form.

1. 4281   **2.** 321.61   **3.** −2.62   **4.** −21.001

5. −0.00121   **6.** 0.00026   **7.** $\frac{1}{8}$ **8.** $16\frac{1}{2}$

In Exercises 9–16, determine the stored value of the given real number in a computer that rounds to (a) three significant digits and (b) four significant digits.

9. 331   **10.** 21.4   **11.** −92.646   **12.** 216.964

13. $\frac{7}{16}$ **14.** $\frac{5}{32}$ **15.** $\frac{1}{7}$ **16.** $\frac{1}{6}$

In Exercises 17 and 18, evaluate the determinant of the given matrix, rounding each intermediate calculation to three significant digits. Then compare the rounded value with the exact solution.

17. $\begin{bmatrix} 1.24 & 56.00 \\ 66.00 & 1.02 \end{bmatrix}$

18. $\begin{bmatrix} 2.12 & 4.22 \\ 1.07 & 2.12 \end{bmatrix}$

In Exercises 19 and 20, use Gaussian elimination to solve the given system of linear equations. After each intermediate calculation, round the result to three significant digits. Then compare this solution with the exact solution.

19. $1.21x + 16.7y = 28.8$
$4.66x + 64.4y = 111.0$

20. $14.4x − 17.1y = 31.5$
$81.6x − 97.4y = 179.0$

C In Exercises 21–24, use Gaussian elimination without partial pivoting to solve the system of linear equations, rounding to three significant digits after each intermediate calculation. Then use partial pivoting to solve the same system, again rounding to three significant digits after each intermediate calculation. Finally, compare both solutions with the given exact solution.

21. $x + 1.04y = 2.04$
$6x + 6.20y = 12.20$
(Exact: $x = 1, y = 1$)

22. $0.51x + 92.6y = 97.7$
$99.00x − 449.0y = 541.0$
(Exact: $x = 10, y = 1$)

23. $x + 4.01y + 0.00445z = 0.00$
$−x − 4.00y + 0.00600z = 0.21$
$2x − 4.05y + 0.05000z = −0.385$
(Exact: $x = −0.49, y = 0.1, z = 20$)

24. $0.007x + 61.20y + 0.093z = 61.3$
$4.810x − 5.92y + 1.110z = 0.0$
$81.400x + 1.12y + 1.180z = 83.7$
(Exact: $x = 1, y = 1, z = 1$)

In Exercises 25 and 26, use Gaussian elimination to solve the ill-conditioned system of linear equations, rounding each intermediate calculation to three significant digits. Then compare this solution with the given exact solution.

25. $x + y = 2$
$x + \frac{600}{601}y = 20$
(Exact: $x = 10,820$,
$y = −10,818$)

26. $x − \frac{800}{801}y = 10$
$−x + y = 50$
(Exact: $x = 48,010$,
$y = 48,060$)

27. Consider the ill-conditioned systems
$x + y = 2$ and $x + y = 2$
$x + 1.0001y = 2$ $x + 1.0001y = 2.0001$.

Calculate the solution to each system. Notice that although the systems are almost the same, their solutions differ greatly.

28. Repeat Exercise 27 for the systems
$x − y = 0$ and $x − y = 0$
$−1.001x + y = 0.001$ $−1.001x + y = 0$.

29. The **Hilbert matrix** of size $n \times n$ is the $n \times n$ symmetric matrix $H_n = [a_{ij}]$, where $a_{ij} = 1/(i + j − 1)$. As n increases, the Hilbert matrix becomes more and more ill-conditioned. Use Gaussian elimination to solve the following system of linear equations, rounding to two significant digits after each intermediate calculation. Compare this solution with the exact solution ($x_1 = 3, x_2 = −24$, and $x_3 = 30$).

$x_1 + \frac{1}{2}x_2 + \frac{1}{3}x_3 = 1$
$\frac{1}{2}x_1 + \frac{1}{3}x_2 + \frac{1}{4}x_3 = 1$
$\frac{1}{3}x_1 + \frac{1}{4}x_2 + \frac{1}{5}x_3 = 1$

30. Repeat Exercise 29 for $H_4\mathbf{x} = \mathbf{b}$, where $\mathbf{b} = (1, 1, 1, 1)^T$, rounding to four significant digits. Compare this solution with the exact solution ($x_1 = −4, x_2 = 60, x_3 = −180$, and $x_4 = 140$).

C **31.** The inverse of the $n \times n$ Hilbert matrix H_n has integer entries. Use your computer of graphing calculator to calculate the inverses of the Hilbert matrices H_n for $n = 4, 5, 6$, and 7. For what values of n do the inverses appear to be accurate?

10.2 ITERATIVE METHODS FOR SOLVING LINEAR SYSTEMS

As a numerical technique, Gaussian elimination is rather unusual because it is *direct*. That is, a solution is obtained after a single application of Gaussian elimination. Once a "solution" has been obtained, Gaussian elimination offers no method of refinement. The lack of refinements can be a problem because, as the previous section shows, Gaussian elimination is sensitive to rounding error.

Numerical techniques more commonly involve an iterative method. For example, in calculus you probably studied Newton's iterative method for approximating the zeros of a differentiable function. In this section we look at two iterative methods for approximating the solution of a system of n linear equations in n variables.

The Jacobi Method

The first iterative technique is called the **Jacobi method,** after Carl Gustav Jacob Jacobi (1804–1851). This method makes two assumptions: (1) that the system given by

$$a_{11}x_1 + a_{12}x_2 + \cdots + a_{1n}x_n = b_1$$
$$a_{21}x_1 + a_{22}x_2 + \cdots + a_{2n}x_n = b_2$$
$$\vdots \qquad \vdots \qquad \qquad \vdots \qquad \vdots$$
$$a_{n1}x_1 + a_{n2}x_2 + \cdots + a_{nn}x_n = b_n$$

has a unique solution and (2) that the coefficient matrix A has no zeros on its main diagonal. If any of the diagonal entries $a_{11}, a_{22}, \ldots, a_{nn}$ are zero, then rows or columns must be interchanged to obtain a coefficient matrix that has nonzero entries on the main diagonal.

To begin the Jacobi method, we solve the first equation for x_1, the second equation for x_2, and so on, as follows.

$$x_1 = \frac{1}{a_{11}}(b_1 - a_{12}x_2 - a_{13}x_3 - \cdots - a_{1n}x_n)$$

$$x_2 = \frac{1}{a_{22}}(b_2 - a_{21}x_1 - a_{23}x_3 - \cdots - a_{2n}x_n)$$

$$\vdots$$

$$x_n = \frac{1}{a_{nn}}(b_n - a_{n1}x_1 - a_{n2}x_2 - \cdots - a_{n,n-1}x_{n-1})$$

Then we make an *initial approximation* of the solution,

$$(x_1, x_2, x_3, \ldots, x_n), \qquad \textbf{Initial approximation}$$

and substitute these values of x_i into the right-hand side of the rewritten equations to obtain the *first approximation*. After this procedure has been completed, we say that one **iteration** has been performed. In the same way, the second approximation is formed by substituting the first approximation's x-values into the right-hand side of the rewritten equations. By repeated iterations, we form a sequence of approximations that often **converges** to the actual solution. This procedure is illustrated in the following example.

EXAMPLE 1   *Applying the Jacobi Method*

Use the Jacobi method to approximate the solution of the following system of linear equations.

$$5x_1 - 2x_2 + 3x_3 = -1$$
$$-3x_1 + 9x_2 + x_3 = 2$$
$$2x_1 - x_2 - 7x_3 = 3$$

Continue the iterations until two successive approximations are identical when rounded to three significant digits.

Solution   To begin, we write the system in the form

$$x_1 = -\tfrac{1}{5} + \tfrac{2}{5}x_2 - \tfrac{3}{5}x_3$$
$$x_2 = \tfrac{2}{9} + \tfrac{3}{9}x_1 - \tfrac{1}{9}x_3$$
$$x_3 = -\tfrac{3}{7} + \tfrac{2}{7}x_1 - \tfrac{1}{7}x_2.$$

Since we have no idea of the actual solution, we choose

$$x_1 = 0, \qquad x_2 = 0, \qquad x_3 = 0 \qquad \text{Initial approximation}$$

as a convenient initial approximation. This means that the first approximation is

$$x_1 = -\tfrac{1}{5} + \tfrac{2}{5}(0) - \tfrac{3}{5}(0) = -0.200$$
$$x_2 = \tfrac{2}{9} + \tfrac{3}{9}(0) - \tfrac{1}{9}(0) \approx 0.222$$
$$x_3 = -\tfrac{3}{7} + \tfrac{2}{7}(0) - \tfrac{1}{7}(0) \approx -0.429.$$

Continuing this procedure, we obtain the sequence of approximations shown in Table 10.1.

TABLE 10.1

n	0	1	2	3	4	5	6	7
x_1	0.000	−0.200	0.146	0.192	0.181	0.185	0.186	0.186
x_2	0.000	0.222	0.203	0.328	0.332	0.329	0.331	0.331
x_3	0.000	−0.429	−0.517	−0.416	−0.421	−0.424	−0.423	−0.423

Because the last two columns in Table 10.1 are identical, we conclude that to three significant digits the solution is

$$x_1 = 0.186, \qquad x_2 = 0.331, \qquad x_3 = -0.423.$$

For the system of linear equations given in Example 1, the Jacobi method is said to **converge.** That is, repeated iterations succeed in producing an approximation that is correct to three significant digits. As is generally true for iterative methods, greater accuracy would require more iterations.

The Gauss-Seidel Method

We now look at a modification of the Jacobi method called the Gauss-Seidel method, named after Carl Friedrich Gauss (1777–1855) and Philipp L. Seidel (1821–1896). This modification is no more difficult to use than the Jacobi method, and it often requires fewer iterations to produce the same degree of accuracy.

With the Jacobi method, the values of x_i obtained in the nth approximation remain unchanged until the entire $(n + 1)$th approximation has been calculated. With the Gauss-Seidel method, on the other hand, we use the new values of each x_i as soon as they are known. That is, once we have determined x_1 from the first equation, its value is then used in the second equation to obtain the new x_2. Similarly, the new x_1 and x_2 are used in the third equation to obtain the new x_3, and so on. This procedure is demonstrated in Example 2.

EXAMPLE 2   *Applying the Gauss-Seidel Method*

Use the Gauss-Seidel iteration method to approximate the solution to the system of equations given in Example 1.

Solution   The first computation is identical to that given in Example 1. That is, using $(x_1, x_2, x_3) = (0, 0, 0)$ as the initial approximation, we obtain the following new value for x_1.

$$x_1 = -\tfrac{1}{5} + \tfrac{2}{5}(0) - \tfrac{3}{5}(0) = -0.200$$

Now that we have a new value for x_1, however, we use it to compute a new value for x_2. That is,

$$x_2 = \tfrac{2}{9} + \tfrac{3}{9}(-0.200) - \tfrac{1}{9}(0) \approx 0.156.$$

Similarly, we use $x_1 = -0.200$ and $x_2 = 0.156$ to compute a new value for x_3.

$$x_3 = -\tfrac{3}{7} + \tfrac{2}{7}(-0.200) - \tfrac{1}{7}(0.156) \approx -0.508$$

Thus the first approximation is $x_1 = -0.200$, $x_2 = 0.156$, and $x_3 = -0.508$. Continued iterations produce the sequence of approximations shown in Table 10.2.

TABLE 10.2

n	0	1	2	3	4	5
x_1	0.000	-0.200	0.167	0.191	0.186	0.186
x_2	0.000	0.156	0.334	0.333	0.331	0.331
x_3	0.000	-0.508	-0.429	-0.422	-0.423	-0.423

Note that after only five iterations of the Gauss-Seidel method, we achieved the same accuracy as was obtained with seven iterations of the Jacobi method in Example 1.

Neither of the iterative methods presented in this section always converges. That is, it is possible to apply the Jacobi method or the Gauss-Seidel method to a system of linear equations and obtain a divergent sequence of approximations. In such cases, we say that the method **diverges.**

EXAMPLE 3   *An Example of Divergence*

Apply the Jacobi method to the system

$$x_1 - 5x_2 = -4$$
$$7x_1 - x_2 = 6,$$

using the initial approximation $(x_1, x_2) = (0, 0)$, and show that the method diverges.

Solution   As usual, we begin by rewriting the given system in the form

$$x_1 = -4 + 5x_2$$
$$x_2 = -6 + 7x_1.$$

Then the initial approximation (0, 0) produces

$$x_1 = -4 + 5(0) = -4$$
$$x_2 = -6 + 7(0) = -6$$

as the first approximation. Repeated iterations produce the sequence of approximations shown in Table 10.3.

TABLE 10.3

n	0	1	2	3	4	5	6	7
x_1	0	-4	-34	-174	$-1,244$	$-6,124$	$-42,874$	$-214,374$
x_2	0	-6	-34	-244	$-1,244$	$-8,574$	$-42,874$	$-300,124$

For this particular system of linear equations we can determine that the actual solution is $x_1 = 1$ and $x_2 = 1$. Thus we see from Table 10.3 that the approximations given by the Jacobi method become progressively *worse* instead of better, and we conclude that the method diverges.

The problem of divergence in Example 3 is not resolved by using the Gauss-Seidel method rather than the Jacobi method. In fact, for this particular system the Gauss-Seidel method diverges more rapidly, as shown in Table 10.4.

TABLE 10.4

n	0	1	2	3	4	5
x_1	0	-4	-174	$-6{,}124$	$-214{,}374$	$-7{,}503{,}124$
x_2	0	-34	$-1{,}224$	$-42{,}874$	$-1{,}500{,}624$	$-52{,}521{,}874$

With an initial approximation of $(x_1, x_2) = (0, 0)$, neither the Jacobi method nor the Gauss-Seidel method converges to the solution of the system of linear equations given in Example 3. We now look at a special type of coefficient matrix A, called a **strictly diagonally dominant matrix,** for which we are guaranteed that both methods will converge.

Definition of Strictly Diagonally Dominant Matrix	An $n \times n$ matrix A is **strictly diagonally dominant** if the absolute value of each entry on the main diagonal is greater than the sum of the absolute values of the other entries in the same row. That is, $$|a_{11}| > |a_{12}| + |a_{13}| + \cdots + |a_{1n}|$$ $$|a_{22}| > |a_{21}| + |a_{23}| + \cdots + |a_{2n}|$$ $$\vdots$$ $$|a_{nn}| > |a_{n1}| + |a_{n2}| + \cdots + |a_{n,n-1}|.$$

EXAMPLE 4   *Strictly Diagonally Dominant Matrices*

Which of the following systems of linear equations has a strictly diagonally dominant coefficient matrix?

(a) $3x_1 - x_2 = -4$
    $2x_1 + 5x_2 = 2$

(b) $4x_1 + 2x_2 - x_3 = -1$
    $x_1 \qquad + 2x_3 = -4$
    $3x_1 - 5x_2 + x_3 = 3$

Solution   (a) The coefficient matrix

$$A = \begin{bmatrix} 3 & -1 \\ 2 & 5 \end{bmatrix}$$

is strictly diagonally dominant because $|3| > |-1|$ and $|5| > |2|$.

(b) The coefficient matrix

$$A = \begin{bmatrix} 4 & 2 & -1 \\ 1 & 0 & 2 \\ 3 & -5 & 1 \end{bmatrix}$$

is not strictly diagonally dominant because the entries in the second and third rows do not conform to the definition. For instance, in the second row $a_{21} = 1$, $a_{22} = 0$, $a_{23} = 2$, and it is not true that $|a_{22}| > |a_{21}| + |a_{23}|$. If we interchange the second and third rows in the original system of linear equations, however, then the coefficient matrix becomes

$$A' = \begin{bmatrix} 4 & 2 & -1 \\ 3 & -5 & 1 \\ 1 & 0 & 2 \end{bmatrix},$$

and this matrix is strictly diagonally dominant.

The following theorem, which we list without proof, states that strict diagonal dominance is sufficient for the convergence of either the Jacobi method or the Gauss-Seidel method.

Theorem 10.1

Convergence of the Jacobi and Gauss-Seidel Methods

If A is strictly diagonally dominant, then the system of linear equations given by $A\mathbf{x} = \mathbf{b}$ has a unique solution to which the Jacobi method and the Gauss-Seidel method will converge for any initial approximation.

In Example 3 we looked at a system of linear equations for which the Jacobi and Gauss-Seidel methods diverged. In the following example we see that by interchanging the rows of the system given in Example 3, we can obtain a coefficient matrix that is strictly diagonally dominant. After this interchange, we are assured of convergence.

EXAMPLE 5   *Interchanging Rows to Obtain Convergence*

Interchange the rows of the system

$$\begin{array}{rcl} x_1 - 5x_2 &=& -4 \\ 7x_1 - x_2 &=& 6 \end{array}$$

to obtain one with a strictly diagonally dominant coefficient matrix. Then apply the Gauss-Seidel method to approximate the solution to four significant digits.

Solution   We begin by interchanging the two rows of the given system to obtain

$$7x_1 - x_2 = 6$$
$$x_1 - 5x_2 = -4.$$

Note that the coefficient matrix of this system is strictly diagonally dominant. Then we solve for x_1 and x_2 as follows.

$$x_1 = \tfrac{6}{7} + \tfrac{1}{7}x_2$$
$$x_2 = \tfrac{4}{5} + \tfrac{1}{5}x_1$$

Using the initial approximation $(x_1, x_2) = (0, 0)$, we obtain the sequence of approximations shown in Table 10.5.

TABLE 10.5

n	0	1	2	3	4	5
x_1	0.0000	0.8571	0.9959	0.9999	1.000	1.000
x_2	0.0000	0.9714	0.9992	1.000	1.000	1.000

Thus we conclude that the solution is $x_1 = 1$ and $x_2 = 1$.

Do not conclude from Theorem 10.1 that strict diagonal dominance is a necessary condition for convergence of the Jacobi or Gauss-Seidel methods. For instance, the coefficient matrix of the system

$$-4x_1 + 5x_2 = 1$$
$$x_1 + 2x_2 = 3$$

is not a strictly diagonally dominant matrix, and yet both methods converge to the solution $x_1 = 1$ and $x_2 = 1$ when we use an initial approximation of $(x_1, x_2) = (0, 0)$. (See Exercise 21.)

SECTION 10.2 □ EXERCISES

In Exercises 1–4, apply the Jacobi method to the given system of linear equations, using the initial approximation $(x_1, x_2, \ldots, x_n) = (0, 0, \ldots, 0)$. Continue performing iterations until two successive approximations are identical when rounded to three significant digits.

1. $3x_1 - x_2 = 2$
$x_1 + 4x_2 = 5$

2. $-4x_1 + 2x_2 = -6$
$3x_1 - 5x_2 = 1$

3. $2x_1 - x_2 \quad= 2$
$x_1 - 3x_2 + x_3 = -2$
$-x_1 + x_2 - 3x_3 = -6$

4. $4x_1 + x_2 + x_3 = 7$
$x_1 - 7x_2 + 2x_3 = -2$
$3x_1 \quad+ 4x_3 = 11$

5. Apply the Gauss-Seidel method to Exercise 1.

6. Apply the Gauss-Seidel method to Exercise 2.

7. Apply the Gauss-Seidel method to Exercise 3.

8. Apply the Gauss-Seidel method to Exercise 4.

In Exercises 9–12, show that the Gauss-Seidel method diverges for the given system using the initial approximation $(x_1, x_2, \ldots, x_n) = (0, 0, \ldots, 0)$.

9. $x_1 - 2x_2 = -1$
$2x_1 + x_2 = 3$

10. $-x_1 + 4x_2 = 1$
$3x_1 - 2x_2 = 2$

11. $2x_1 - 3x_2 \quad= -7$
$x_1 + 3x_2 - 10x_3 = 9$
$3x_1 \quad+ x_3 = 13$

12. $x_1 + 3x_2 - x_3 = 5$
$3x_1 - x_2 \quad= 5$
$x_2 + 2x_3 = 1$

In Exercises 13–16, determine whether the given matrix is strictly diagonally dominant.

13. $\begin{bmatrix} 2 & 1 \\ 3 & 5 \end{bmatrix}$

14. $\begin{bmatrix} -1 & -2 \\ 0 & 1 \end{bmatrix}$

15. $\begin{bmatrix} 12 & 6 & 0 \\ 2 & -3 & 2 \\ 0 & 6 & 13 \end{bmatrix}$

16. $\begin{bmatrix} 7 & 5 & -1 \\ 1 & -4 & 1 \\ 0 & 2 & -3 \end{bmatrix}$

17. Interchange the rows of the system of linear equations in Exercise 9 to obtain a system with a strictly diagonally dominant coefficient matrix. Then apply the Gauss-Seidel method to approximate the solution to two significant digits.

18. Interchange the rows of the system of linear equations in Exercise 10 to obtain a system with a strictly diagonally dominant coefficient matrix. Then apply the Gauss-Seidel method to approximate the solution to two significant digits.

19. Interchange the rows of the system of linear equations in Exercise 11 to obtain a system with a strictly diagonally dominant coefficient matrix. Then apply the Gauss-Seidel method to approximate the solution to two significant digits.

20. Interchange the rows of the system of linear equations in Exercise 12 to obtain a system with a strictly diagonally dominant coefficient matrix. Then apply the Gauss-Seidel method to approximate the solution to two significant digits.

In Exercises 21 and 22, the coefficient matrix of the given system of linear equations is not strictly diagonally dominant. Show that the Jacobi and Gauss-Seidel methods converge using an initial approximation of $(x_1, x_2, \ldots, x_n) = (0, 0, \ldots, 0)$.

21. $-4x_1 + 5x_2 = 1$
$x_1 + 2x_2 = 3$

22. $4x_1 + 2x_2 - 2x_3 = 0$
$x_1 - 3x_2 - x_3 = 7$
$3x_1 - x_2 + 4x_3 = 5$

C In Exercises 23 and 24, write a computer program that applies the Gauss-Siedel method to solve the given system of linear equations.

23. $4x_1 + x_2 - x_3 \qquad\qquad\qquad= 3$
$x_1 + 6x_2 - 2x_3 + x_4 - x_5 \qquad\qquad= -6$
$x_2 + 5x_3 \quad- x_5 + x_6 \qquad= -5$
$2x_2 \quad+ 5x_4 - x_5 \quad- x_7 - x_8 = 0$
$-x_3 - x_4 + 6x_5 - x_6 \quad- x_8 = 12$
$-x_3 \quad- x_5 + 5x_6 \qquad= -12$
$-x_4 \qquad+ 4x_7 - x_8 = -2$
$-x_4 - x_5 \qquad- x_7 + 5x_8 = 2$

24. $4x_1 - x_2 - x_3 \qquad\qquad\qquad= 18$
$-x_1 + 4x_2 - x_3 - x_4 \qquad\qquad= 18$
$-x_2 + 4x_3 - x_4 - x_5 \qquad\qquad= 4$
$-x_3 + 4x_4 - x_5 - x_6 \qquad= 4$
$-x_4 + 4x_5 - x_6 - x_7 \qquad= 26$
$-x_5 + 4x_6 - x_7 - x_8 = 16$
$-x_6 + 4x_7 - x_8 = 10$
$-x_7 + 4x_8 = 32$

10.3 POWER METHOD FOR APPROXIMATING EIGENVALUES

In Chapter 7 we saw that the eigenvalues of an $n \times n$ matrix A are obtained by solving its characteristic equation

$$\lambda^n + c_{n-1}\lambda^{n-1} + c_{n-2}\lambda^{n-2} + \cdots + c_0 = 0.$$

For large values of n, polynomial equations like this one are difficult and time-consuming to solve. Moreover, numerical techniques for approximating roots of polynomial equations of high degree are sensitive to rounding errors. In this section we look at an alternative method for approximating eigenvalues. As presented here, the method can be used only to find the eigenvalue of A that is largest in absolute value—we call this eigenvalue the **dominant eigenvalue** of A. Although this restriction may seem severe, dominant eigenvalues are of primary interest in many physical applications.

Definition of Dominant Eigenvalue and Dominant Eigenvector

Let $\lambda_1, \lambda_2, \ldots,$ and λ_n be the eigenvalues of an $n \times n$ matrix A. λ_1 is called the **dominant eigenvalue** of A if

$$|\lambda_1| > |\lambda_i|, \quad i = 2, \ldots, n.$$

The eigenvectors corresponding to λ_1 are called **dominant eigenvectors** of A.

Not every matrix has a dominant eigenvalue. For instance, the matrix

$$A = \begin{bmatrix} 1 & 0 \\ 0 & -1 \end{bmatrix}$$

(with eigenvalues of $\lambda_1 = 1$ and $\lambda_2 = -1$) has no dominant eigenvalue. Similarly, the matrix

$$A = \begin{bmatrix} 2 & 0 & 0 \\ 0 & 2 & 0 \\ 0 & 0 & 1 \end{bmatrix}$$

(with eigenvalues of $\lambda_1 = 2$, $\lambda_2 = 2$, and $\lambda_3 = 1$) has no dominant eigenvalue.

EXAMPLE 1   *Finding a Dominant Eigenvalue*

Find the dominant eigenvalue and corresponding eigenvectors of the matrix

$$A = \begin{bmatrix} 2 & -12 \\ 1 & -5 \end{bmatrix}.$$

Solution   From Example 4 of Section 7.1 we know that the characteristic polynomial of A is $\lambda^2 + 3\lambda + 2 = (\lambda + 1)(\lambda + 2)$. Therefore the eigenvalues of A are $\lambda_1 = -1$ and $\lambda_2 = -2$, of which the dominant one is $\lambda_2 = -2$. From the same example we know that the dominant eigenvectors of A (those corresponding to $\lambda_2 = -2$) are of the form

$$\mathbf{x} = t\begin{bmatrix} 3 \\ 1 \end{bmatrix}, \quad t \neq 0.$$

The Power Method

Like the Jacobi and Gauss-Seidel methods, the power method for approximating eigenvalues is iterative. First we assume that the matrix A has a dominant eigenvalue with corresponding dominant eigenvectors. Then we choose an initial approximation $\mathbf{x}_0$ of one of the dominant eigen*vectors* of A. This initial approximation must be a *nonzero* vector in R^n. Finally we form the sequence given by

$$\mathbf{x}_1 = A\mathbf{x}_0$$
$$\mathbf{x}_2 = A\mathbf{x}_1 = A(A\mathbf{x}_0) = A^2\mathbf{x}_0$$
$$\mathbf{x}_3 = A\mathbf{x}_2 = A(A^2\mathbf{x}_0) = A^3\mathbf{x}_0$$
$$\vdots$$
$$\mathbf{x}_k = A\mathbf{x}_{k-1} = A(A^{k-1}\mathbf{x}_0) = A^k\mathbf{x}_0.$$

For large powers of k, and by properly scaling this sequence, we will see that we obtain a good approximation of the dominant eigenvector of A. This procedure is illustrated in Example 2.

EXAMPLE 2   *Approximating a Dominant Eigenvector by the Power Method*

Complete six iterations of the power method to approximate a dominant eigenvector of

$$A = \begin{bmatrix} 2 & -12 \\ 1 & -5 \end{bmatrix}.$$

Solution   We begin with an initial nonzero approximation of

$$\mathbf{x}_0 = \begin{bmatrix} 1 \\ 1 \end{bmatrix}.$$

We then obtain the following approximations.

Iteration	*Approximation*

$$\mathbf{x}_1 = A\mathbf{x}_0 = \begin{bmatrix} 2 & -12 \\ 1 & -5 \end{bmatrix}\begin{bmatrix} 1 \\ 1 \end{bmatrix} = \begin{bmatrix} -10 \\ -4 \end{bmatrix} \longrightarrow -4\begin{bmatrix} 2.50 \\ 1.00 \end{bmatrix}$$

$$\mathbf{x}_2 = A\mathbf{x}_1 = \begin{bmatrix} 2 & -12 \\ 1 & -5 \end{bmatrix}\begin{bmatrix} -10 \\ -4 \end{bmatrix} = \begin{bmatrix} 28 \\ 10 \end{bmatrix} \longrightarrow 10\begin{bmatrix} 2.80 \\ 1.00 \end{bmatrix}$$

$$\mathbf{x}_3 = A\mathbf{x}_2 = \begin{bmatrix} 2 & -12 \\ 1 & -5 \end{bmatrix}\begin{bmatrix} 28 \\ 10 \end{bmatrix} = \begin{bmatrix} -64 \\ -22 \end{bmatrix} \longrightarrow -22\begin{bmatrix} 2.91 \\ 1.00 \end{bmatrix}$$

$$\mathbf{x}_4 = A\mathbf{x}_3 = \begin{bmatrix} 2 & -12 \\ 1 & -5 \end{bmatrix}\begin{bmatrix} -64 \\ -22 \end{bmatrix} = \begin{bmatrix} 136 \\ 46 \end{bmatrix} \longrightarrow 46\begin{bmatrix} 2.96 \\ 1.00 \end{bmatrix}$$

$$\mathbf{x}_5 = A\mathbf{x}_4 = \begin{bmatrix} 2 & -12 \\ 1 & -5 \end{bmatrix}\begin{bmatrix} 136 \\ 46 \end{bmatrix} = \begin{bmatrix} -280 \\ -94 \end{bmatrix} \longrightarrow -94\begin{bmatrix} 2.98 \\ 1.00 \end{bmatrix}$$

$$\mathbf{x}_6 = A\mathbf{x}_5 = \begin{bmatrix} 2 & -12 \\ 1 & -5 \end{bmatrix}\begin{bmatrix} -280 \\ -94 \end{bmatrix} = \begin{bmatrix} 568 \\ 190 \end{bmatrix} \longrightarrow 190\begin{bmatrix} 2.99 \\ 1.00 \end{bmatrix}$$

Note that the approximations in Example 2 appear to be approaching scalar multiples of

$$\begin{bmatrix} 3 \\ 1 \end{bmatrix},$$

which we know from Example 1 is a dominant eigenvector of the matrix

$$A = \begin{bmatrix} 2 & -12 \\ 1 & -5 \end{bmatrix}.$$

In Example 2 the power method was used to approximate a dominant eigenvector of the matrix A. In that example we already knew that the dominant eigenvalue of A was $\lambda = -2$. For the sake of demonstration, however, let us assume that we do not know the dominant eigenvalue of A. The following theorem provides a formula for determining the eigenvalue corresponding to a given eigenvector. This theorem is credited to the English physicist John William Rayleigh (1842–1919).

Theorem 10.2

Determining an Eigenvalue from an Eigenvector

If $\mathbf{x}$ is an eigenvector of a matrix A, then its corresponding eigenvalue is given by

$$\lambda = \frac{A\mathbf{x} \cdot \mathbf{x}}{\mathbf{x} \cdot \mathbf{x}}.$$

This quotient is called the **Rayleigh quotient.**

Proof   Since $\mathbf{x}$ is an eigenvector of A, we know that $A\mathbf{x} = \lambda\mathbf{x}$, and we can write

$$\frac{A\mathbf{x} \cdot \mathbf{x}}{\mathbf{x} \cdot \mathbf{x}} = \frac{\lambda\mathbf{x} \cdot \mathbf{x}}{\mathbf{x} \cdot \mathbf{x}} = \frac{\lambda(\mathbf{x} \cdot \mathbf{x})}{\mathbf{x} \cdot \mathbf{x}} = \lambda.$$

In cases for which the power method generates a good approximation of a dominant eigenvector, the Rayleigh quotient provides a correspondingly good approximation of the dominant eigenvalue. The use of the Rayleigh quotient is demonstrated in Example 3.

EXAMPLE 3   *Approximating a Dominant Eigenvalue*

Use the result of Example 2 to approximate the dominant eigenvalue of the matrix

$$A = \begin{bmatrix} 2 & -12 \\ 1 & -5 \end{bmatrix}.$$

Solution   After the sixth iteration of the power method in Example 2, we had obtained.

$$\mathbf{x}_6 = \begin{bmatrix} 568 \\ 190 \end{bmatrix} \approx 190 \begin{bmatrix} 2.99 \\ 1.00 \end{bmatrix}.$$

With $\mathbf{x} = (2.99, 1)$ as our approximation of a dominant eigenvector of A, we use the Rayleigh quotient to obtain an approximation of the dominant eigenvalue of A. First we compute the product $A\mathbf{x}.$

$$Ax = \begin{bmatrix} 2 & -12 \\ 1 & -5 \end{bmatrix} \begin{bmatrix} 2.99 \\ 1.00 \end{bmatrix} = \begin{bmatrix} -6.02 \\ -2.01 \end{bmatrix}$$

Then, since

$$Ax \cdot x = (-6.02)(2.99) + (-2.01)(1) \approx -20.0$$

and

$$x \cdot x = (2.99)(2.99) + (1)(1) \approx 9.94,$$

we compute the Rayleigh quotient to be

$$\lambda = \frac{Ax \cdot x}{x \cdot x} \approx \frac{-20.0}{9.94} \approx -2.01,$$

which is a good approximation of the dominant eigenvalue $\lambda = -2$.

From Example 2 we can see that the power method tends to produce approximations with large entries. In practice it is best to "scale down" each approximation before proceeding to the next iteration. One way to accomplish this **scaling** is to determine the component of Ax_i that has the largest absolute value and multiply the vector Ax_i by the reciprocal of this component. The resulting vector will then have components whose absolute values are less than or equal to 1. (Other scaling techniques are possible. For examples, see Exercises 27 and 28.)

EXAMPLE 4   *The Power Method with Scaling*

Calculate seven iterations of the power method with *scaling* to approximate a dominant eigenvector of the matrix

$$A = \begin{bmatrix} 1 & 2 & 0 \\ -2 & 1 & 2 \\ 1 & 3 & 1 \end{bmatrix}.$$

Use $x_0 = (1, 1, 1)$ as the initial approximation.

Solution   One iteration of the power method produces

$$Ax_0 = \begin{bmatrix} 1 & 2 & 0 \\ -2 & 1 & 2 \\ 1 & 3 & 1 \end{bmatrix} \begin{bmatrix} 1 \\ 1 \\ 1 \end{bmatrix} = \begin{bmatrix} 3 \\ 1 \\ 5 \end{bmatrix},$$

and by scaling we obtain the approximation

$$x_1 = \frac{1}{5} \begin{bmatrix} 3 \\ 1 \\ 5 \end{bmatrix} = \begin{bmatrix} 0.60 \\ 0.20 \\ 1.00 \end{bmatrix}.$$

A second iteration yields

$$A\mathbf{x}_1 = \begin{bmatrix} 1 & 2 & 0 \\ -2 & 1 & 2 \\ 1 & 3 & 1 \end{bmatrix} \begin{bmatrix} 0.60 \\ 0.20 \\ 1.00 \end{bmatrix} = \begin{bmatrix} 1.00 \\ 1.00 \\ 2.20 \end{bmatrix}$$

and

$$\mathbf{x}_2 = \frac{1}{2.20} \begin{bmatrix} 1.00 \\ 1.00 \\ 2.20 \end{bmatrix} = \begin{bmatrix} 0.45 \\ 0.45 \\ 1.00 \end{bmatrix}.$$

Continuing this process, we obtain the sequence of approximations shown in Table 10.6.

TABLE 10.6

$\mathbf{x}_0$	$\mathbf{x}_1$	$\mathbf{x}_2$	$\mathbf{x}_3$	$\mathbf{x}_4$	$\mathbf{x}_5$	$\mathbf{x}_6$	$\mathbf{x}_7$
$\begin{bmatrix} 1.00 \\ 1.00 \\ 1.00 \end{bmatrix}$	$\begin{bmatrix} 0.60 \\ 0.20 \\ 1.00 \end{bmatrix}$	$\begin{bmatrix} 0.45 \\ 0.45 \\ 1.00 \end{bmatrix}$	$\begin{bmatrix} 0.48 \\ 0.55 \\ 1.00 \end{bmatrix}$	$\begin{bmatrix} 0.51 \\ 0.51 \\ 1.00 \end{bmatrix}$	$\begin{bmatrix} 0.50 \\ 0.49 \\ 1.00 \end{bmatrix}$	$\begin{bmatrix} 0.50 \\ 0.50 \\ 1.00 \end{bmatrix}$	$\begin{bmatrix} 0.50 \\ 0.50 \\ 1.00 \end{bmatrix}$

From Table 10.6 we approximate a dominant eigenvector of A to be

$$\mathbf{x} = \begin{bmatrix} 0.50 \\ 0.50 \\ 1.00 \end{bmatrix}.$$

Using the Rayleigh quotient, we approximate the dominant eigenvalue of A to be $\lambda = 3$. (For this example you can check that the approximations of $\mathbf{x}$ and λ are exact.)

REMARK: Note that the *scaling factors* used to obtain the vectors in Table 10.6,

$\mathbf{x}_1$	$\mathbf{x}_2$	$\mathbf{x}_3$	$\mathbf{x}_4$	$\mathbf{x}_5$	$\mathbf{x}_6$	$\mathbf{x}_7$
↓	↓	↓	↓	↓	↓	↓
5.00	2.20	2.82	3.13	3.02	2.99	3.00,

are approaching the dominant eigenvalue $\lambda = 3$.

In Example 4 the power method with scaling converges to a dominant eigenvector. The following theorem tells us that a sufficient condition for convergence of the power method is that the matrix A be diagonalizable (and have a dominant eigenvalue).

Theorem 10.3

Convergence of the
Power Method

If A is an $n \times n$ diagonalizable matrix with a dominant eigenvalue, then there exists a nonzero vector $\mathbf{x}_0$ such that the sequence of vectors given by

$$A\mathbf{x}_0, \quad A^2\mathbf{x}_0, \quad A^3\mathbf{x}_0, \quad A^4\mathbf{x}_0, \quad \dots, \quad A^k\mathbf{x}_0, \quad \dots$$

approaches a multiple of the dominant eigenvector of A.

Proof   Since A is diagonalizable, we know from Theorem 7.5 that it has n linearly independent eigenvectors $x_1, x_2, \ldots, x_n$ with corresponding eigenvalues of $\lambda_1, \lambda_2, \ldots, \lambda_n$. We assume that these eigenvalues are ordered so that λ_1 is the dominant eigenvalue (with a corresponding eigenvector of x_1). Because the n eigenvectors $x_1, x_2, \ldots, x_n$ are linearly independent, they must form a basis for R^n. For the initial approximation x_0, we choose a nonzero vector such that the linear combination

$$x_0 = c_1 x_1 + c_2 x_2 + \cdots + c_n x_n$$

has nonzero leading coefficients. (If $c_1 = 0$, the power method may not converge, and a different x_0 must be used as the initial approximation. See Exercises 21 and 22.) Now, multiplying both sides of this equation by A produces

$$
\begin{aligned}
A x_0 &= A(c_1 x_1 + c_2 x_2 + \cdots + c_n x_n) \\
&= c_1(A x_1) + c_2(A x_2) + \cdots + c_n(A x_n) \\
&= c_1(\lambda_1 x_1) + c_2(\lambda_2 x_2) + \cdots + c_n(\lambda_n x_n).
\end{aligned}
$$

Repeated multiplication of both sides of this equation by A produces

$$A^k x_0 = c_1(\lambda_1{}^k x_1) + c_2(\lambda_2{}^k x_2) + \cdots + c_n(\lambda_n{}^k x_n),$$

which implies that

$$A^k x_0 = \lambda_1{}^k \left[c_1 x_1 + c_2 \left(\frac{\lambda_2}{\lambda_1} \right)^k x_2 + \cdots + c_n \left(\frac{\lambda_n}{\lambda_1} \right)^k x_n \right].$$

Now, from our original assumption that λ_1 is larger in absolute value than the other eigenvalues it follows that each of the fractions

$$\frac{\lambda_2}{\lambda_1}, \quad \frac{\lambda_3}{\lambda_1}, \quad \ldots, \quad \frac{\lambda_n}{\lambda_1}$$

is less than 1 in absolute value. Therefore each of the factors

$$\left(\frac{\lambda_2}{\lambda_1} \right)^k, \quad \left(\frac{\lambda_3}{\lambda_1} \right)^k, \quad \ldots, \quad \left(\frac{\lambda_n}{\lambda_1} \right)^k$$

must approach 0 as k approaches infinity. This implies that the approximation

$$A^k x_0 \approx \lambda_1{}^k c_1 x_1, \quad c_1 \neq 0$$

improves as k increases. Since x_1 is a dominant eigenvector, it follows that any scalar multiple of x_1 is also a dominant eigenvector. Thus we have shown that $A^k x_0$ approaches a multiple of the dominant eigenvector of A.

The proof of Theorem 10.3 provides some insight into the rate of convergence of the power method. That is, if the eigenvalues of A are ordered so that

$$|\lambda_1| > |\lambda_2| \geq |\lambda_3| \geq \ldots \geq |\lambda_n|,$$

then the power method will converge quickly if $|\lambda_2| / |\lambda_1|$ is small, and slowly if $|\lambda_2| / |\lambda_1|$ is close to 1. This principle is illustrated in Example 5.

EXAMPLE 5   *The Rate of Convergence of the Power Method*

(a) The matrix

$$A = \begin{bmatrix} 4 & 5 \\ 6 & 5 \end{bmatrix}$$

has eigenvalues of $\lambda_1 = 10$ and $\lambda_2 = -1$. Thus the ratio $|\lambda_2| / |\lambda_1|$ is 0.1. For this matrix, only four iterations are required to obtain successive approximations that agree when rounded to three significant digits. (See Table 10.7.)

TABLE 10.7

x_0	x_1	x_2	x_3	x_4
$\begin{bmatrix} 1.000 \\ 1.000 \end{bmatrix}$	$\begin{bmatrix} 0.818 \\ 1.000 \end{bmatrix}$	$\begin{bmatrix} 0.835 \\ 1.000 \end{bmatrix}$	$\begin{bmatrix} 0.833 \\ 1.000 \end{bmatrix}$	$\begin{bmatrix} 0.833 \\ 1.000 \end{bmatrix}$

(b) The matrix

$$A = \begin{bmatrix} -4 & 10 \\ 7 & 5 \end{bmatrix}$$

has eigenvalues of $\lambda_1 = 10$ and $\lambda_2 = -9$. For this matrix, the ratio $|\lambda_2| / |\lambda_1|$ is 0.9, and the power method does not produce successive approximations that agree to three significant digits until sixty-eight iterations have been performed, as shown in Table 10.8.

TABLE 10.8

x_0	x_1	x_2		x_{66}	x_{67}	x_{68}
$\begin{bmatrix} 1.000 \\ 1.000 \end{bmatrix}$	$\begin{bmatrix} 0.500 \\ 1.000 \end{bmatrix}$	$\begin{bmatrix} 0.941 \\ 1.000 \end{bmatrix}$	$\cdots$ $\cdots$	$\begin{bmatrix} 0.715 \\ 1.000 \end{bmatrix}$	$\begin{bmatrix} 0.714 \\ 1.000 \end{bmatrix}$	$\begin{bmatrix} 0.714 \\ 1.000 \end{bmatrix}$

In this section we have discussed the use of the power method to approximate the *dominant* eigenvalue of a matrix. This method can be modified to approximate other eigenvalues through use of a procedure called **deflation.** Moreover, the power method is only one of several techniques that can be used to approximate the eigenvalues of a matrix. Another popular method is called the **QR algorithm.**

This is the method used in most computer programs and calculators for finding eigenvalues and eigenvectors. The algorithm uses the *QR*–factorization of the matrix, as presented in Chapter 5. Discussions of the deflation method and the *QR* algorithm can be found in most texts on numerical methods.

SECTION 10.3 ☐ EXERCISES

In Exercises 1–6, use the techniques presented in Chapter 7 to find the eigenvalues of the given matrix A. If A has a dominant eigenvalue, find a corresponding dominant eigenvector.

1. $A = \begin{bmatrix} 2 & 1 \\ 0 & -4 \end{bmatrix}$

2. $A = \begin{bmatrix} -3 & 0 \\ 1 & 3 \end{bmatrix}$

3. $A = \begin{bmatrix} 1 & -5 \\ -3 & -1 \end{bmatrix}$

4. $A = \begin{bmatrix} 4 & -5 \\ 2 & -3 \end{bmatrix}$

5. $A = \begin{bmatrix} 2 & 3 & 1 \\ 0 & -1 & 2 \\ 0 & 0 & 3 \end{bmatrix}$

6. $A = \begin{bmatrix} -5 & 0 & 0 \\ 3 & 7 & 0 \\ 4 & -2 & 3 \end{bmatrix}$

In Exercises 7–10, use the Rayleigh quotient to compute the eigenvalue λ of A corresponding to the given eigenvector $\mathbf{x}$.

7. $A = \begin{bmatrix} 4 & -5 \\ 2 & -3 \end{bmatrix}, \mathbf{x} = \begin{bmatrix} 5 \\ 2 \end{bmatrix}$

8. $A = \begin{bmatrix} 2 & 3 \\ 1 & 4 \end{bmatrix}, \mathbf{x} = \begin{bmatrix} -3 \\ 1 \end{bmatrix}$

9. $A = \begin{bmatrix} 1 & 2 & -2 \\ -2 & 5 & -2 \\ -6 & 6 & -3 \end{bmatrix}, \mathbf{x} = \begin{bmatrix} 1 \\ 1 \\ 3 \end{bmatrix}$

10. $A = \begin{bmatrix} 3 & 2 & -3 \\ -3 & -4 & 9 \\ -1 & -2 & 5 \end{bmatrix}, \mathbf{x} = \begin{bmatrix} 3 \\ 0 \\ 1 \end{bmatrix}$

C In Exercises 11–14, use the power method with scaling to approximate a dominant eigenvector of the matrix A. Start with $\mathbf{x}_0 = (1, 1)$ and calculate five iterations. Then use $\mathbf{x}_5$ to approximate the dominant eigenvalue of A.

11. $A = \begin{bmatrix} 2 & 1 \\ 0 & -7 \end{bmatrix}$

12. $A = \begin{bmatrix} -1 & 0 \\ 1 & 6 \end{bmatrix}$

13. $A = \begin{bmatrix} 1 & -4 \\ -2 & 8 \end{bmatrix}$

14. $A = \begin{bmatrix} 6 & -3 \\ -2 & 1 \end{bmatrix}$

C In Exercises 15–18, use the power method with scaling to approximate a dominant eigenvector of the matrix A. Start with $\mathbf{x}_0 = (1, 1, 1)$ and calculate four iterations. Then use $\mathbf{x}_4$ to approximate the dominant eigenvalue of A.

15. $A = \begin{bmatrix} 3 & 0 & 0 \\ 1 & -1 & 0 \\ 0 & 2 & 8 \end{bmatrix}$

16. $A = \begin{bmatrix} 1 & 2 & 0 \\ 0 & -7 & 1 \\ 0 & 0 & 0 \end{bmatrix}$

17. $A = \begin{bmatrix} -1 & -6 & 0 \\ 2 & 7 & 0 \\ 1 & 2 & -1 \end{bmatrix}$

18. $A = \begin{bmatrix} 0 & 6 & 0 \\ 0 & -4 & 0 \\ 2 & 1 & 1 \end{bmatrix}$

C In Exercises 19 and 20, the given matrix A does not have a dominant eigenvalue. Apply the power method with scaling, starting with $\mathbf{x}_0 = (1, 1, 1)$, and observe the results of the first four iterations.

19. $A = \begin{bmatrix} 1 & 1 & 0 \\ 3 & -1 & 0 \\ 0 & 0 & -2 \end{bmatrix}$

20. $A = \begin{bmatrix} 1 & 2 & -2 \\ -2 & 5 & -2 \\ -6 & 6 & -3 \end{bmatrix}$

▷ 21. (a) Find the eigenvalues and corresponding eigenvectors of

$$A = \begin{bmatrix} 3 & -1 \\ -2 & 4 \end{bmatrix}.$$

(b) Calculate two iterations of the power method with scaling, starting with $\mathbf{x}_0 = (1, 1)$.

(c) Explain why the method does not seem to converge to a dominant eigenvector.

▷ 22. Repeat Exercise 21 using $\mathbf{x}_0 = (1, 1, 1)$, for the matrix

$$A = \begin{bmatrix} -3 & 0 & 2 \\ 0 & -1 & 0 \\ 0 & 1 & -2 \end{bmatrix}.$$

C 23. The matrix

$$A = \begin{bmatrix} 2 & -12 \\ 1 & -5 \end{bmatrix}$$

has a dominant eigenvalue of $\lambda = -2$. Observe that $A\mathbf{x} = \lambda\mathbf{x}$ implies that

$$A^{-1}\mathbf{x} = \frac{1}{\lambda}\mathbf{x}.$$

Apply five iterations of the power method (with scaling) on A^{-1} to compute the eigenvalue of A with the smallest magnitude.

C 24. Repeat Exercise 23 for the matrix

$$A = \begin{bmatrix} 2 & 3 & 1 \\ 0 & -1 & 2 \\ 0 & 0 & 3 \end{bmatrix}.$$

C **25.** (a) Compute the eigenvalues of

$$A = \begin{bmatrix} 2 & 1 \\ 1 & 2 \end{bmatrix} \text{ and } B = \begin{bmatrix} 2 & 3 \\ 1 & 4 \end{bmatrix}.$$

  (b) Apply four iterations of the power method with scaling to each matrix in part (a), starting with $\mathbf{x}_0 = (-1, 2)$.

  (c) Compute the ratios λ_2/λ_1 for A and B. For which do you expect faster convergence?

26. Use the proof of Theorem 10.3 to show that

$$A(A^k\mathbf{x}_0) \approx \lambda_1(A^k\mathbf{x}_0)$$

for large values of k. That is, show that the scale factors obtained in the power method approach the dominant eigenvalue.

C In Exercises 27 and 28, apply four iterations of the power method (with scaling) to approximate the dominant eigenvalue of the given matrix. After each iteration, scale the approximation by dividing by its length so that the resulting approximation will be a unit vector.

27. $A = \begin{bmatrix} 5 & 6 \\ 4 & 3 \end{bmatrix}$

28. $A = \begin{bmatrix} 7 & -4 & 2 \\ 16 & -9 & 6 \\ 8 & -4 & 5 \end{bmatrix}$

10.4 APPLICATIONS OF NUMERICAL METHODS

Applications of Gaussian Elimination with Pivoting

In Section 2.5 we used least squares regression analysis to find *linear* mathematical models that best fit a set of n points in the plane. This procedure can be extended to cover polynomial models of any degree as follows.

Regression Analysis for Polynomials

The least squares regression polynomial of degree m for the points $\{(x_1, y_1), (x_2, y_2), \ldots, (x_n, y_n)\}$ is given by

$$y = a_m x^m + a_{m-1} x^{m-1} + \cdots + a_2 x^2 + a_1 x + a_0,$$

where the coefficients are determined by the following system of $m + 1$ linear equations.

$$na_0 + \left(\Sigma x_i\right)a_1 + \left(\Sigma x_i^2\right)a_2 + \cdots + \left(\Sigma x_i^m\right)a_m = \Sigma y_i$$
$$\left(\Sigma x_i\right)a_0 + \left(\Sigma x_i^2\right)a_1 + \left(\Sigma x_i^3\right)a_2 + \cdots + \left(\Sigma x_i^{m+1}\right)a_m = \Sigma x_i y_i$$
$$\left(\Sigma x_i^2\right)a_0 + \left(\Sigma x_i^3\right)a_1 + \left(\Sigma x_i^4\right)a_2 + \cdots + \left(\Sigma x_i^{m+2}\right)a_m = \Sigma x_i^2 y_i$$
$$\vdots$$
$$\left(\Sigma x_i^m\right)a_0 + \left(\Sigma x_i^{m+1}\right)a_1 + \left(\Sigma x_i^{m+2}\right)a_2 + \cdots + \left(\Sigma x_i^{2m}\right)a_m = \Sigma x_i^m y_i$$

Note that if $m = 1$ this system of equations reduces to

$$na_0 + \left(\Sigma x_i\right)a_1 = \Sigma y_i$$
$$\left(\Sigma x_i\right)a_0 + \left(\Sigma x_i^2\right)a_1 = \Sigma x_i y_i,$$

which has a solution of

$$a_1 = \frac{n\Sigma\, x_i y_i - (\Sigma\, x_i)(\Sigma\, y_i)}{n\Sigma\, x_i^2 - (\Sigma\, x_i)^2} \quad \text{and} \quad a_0 = \frac{\Sigma\, y_i}{n} - a_1\frac{\Sigma\, x_i}{n}.$$

Exercise 16 asks you to show that this formula is equivalent to the matrix formula for linear regression that was presented in Section 2.5.

Example 1 illustrates the use of regression analysis to find a second-degree polynomial model.

EXAMPLE 1   *Least Squares Regression Analysis*

The world population in billions for the years between 1950 and 1985, as given by the *Statistical Abstract of the United States*, is shown in the following table.

Year	1950	1955	1960	1965	1970	1975	1980	1985
Population	2.53	2.77	3.05	3.36	3.72	4.10	4.47	4.87

Find the second-degree least squares regression polynomial for these data and use the resulting model to predict the world population for 1990 and 1995.

Solution   We begin by letting $x = -4$ represent 1950, $x = -3$ represent 1955, and so on. Thus the collection of points is given by $\{(-4, 2.53), (-3, 2.77), (-2, 3.05), (-1, 3.36), (0, 3.72), (1, 4.10), (2, 4.47), (3, 4.87)\}$, which yields

$$n = 8, \qquad \sum_{i=1}^{8} x_i = -4, \qquad \sum_{i=1}^{8} x_i^2 = 44, \qquad \sum_{i=1}^{8} x_i^3 = -64,$$

$$\sum_{i=1}^{8} x_i^4 = 452, \qquad \sum_{i=1}^{8} y_i = 28.87, \qquad \sum_{i=1}^{8} x_i y_i = -0.24, \qquad \sum_{i=1}^{8} x_i^2 y_i = 146.78.$$

Therefore the system of linear equations giving the coefficients of the quadratic model $y = a_2 x^2 + a_1 x + a_0$ is

$$8a_0 - 4a_1 + 44a_2 = 28.87$$
$$-4a_0 + 44a_1 - 64a_2 = {-0.24}$$
$$44a_0 - 64a_1 + 452a_2 = 146.78.$$

Gaussian elimination with pivoting on the matrix

$$\begin{bmatrix} 8 & -4 & 44 & 28.87 \\ -4 & 44 & -64 & -0.24 \\ 44 & -64 & 452 & 146.78 \end{bmatrix}$$

produces

$$\begin{bmatrix} 1 & -1.4545 & 10.2727 & 3.3359 \\ 0 & 1 & -0.6000 & 0.3432 \\ 0 & 0 & 1 & 0.0130 \end{bmatrix}.$$

Thus by back substitution we find the solution to be

$$a_2 = 0.0130, \quad a_1 = 0.3510, \quad a_0 = 3.7126,$$

and the regression quadratic is

$$y = 0.0130x^2 + 0.3510x + 3.7126.$$

Figure 10.1

Figure 10.1 compares this model with the given points. To predict the world population for 1990, we let $x = 4$, obtaining

$$y = 0.0130(4^2) + 0.3510(4) + 3.7126 = 5.32 \text{ billion.}$$

Similarly, the prediction for 1995 ($x = 5$) is

$$y = 0.0130(5^2) + 0.3510(5) + 3.7126 = 5.79 \text{ billion.}$$

EXAMPLE 2   **Least Squares Regression Analysis**

Find the third-degree least squares regression polynomial

$$y = a_3x^3 + a_2x^2 + a_1x + a_0$$

for the points

$$\{(0, 0), (1, 2), (2, 3), (3, 2), (4, 1), (5, 2), (6, 4)\}.$$

Solution   For this set of points the linear system

$$na_0 + (\Sigma x_i)a_1 + (\Sigma x_i^2)a_2 + (\Sigma x_i^3)a_3 = \Sigma y_i$$
$$(\Sigma x_i)a_0 + (\Sigma x_i^2)a_1 + (\Sigma x_i^3)a_2 + (\Sigma x_i^4)a_3 = \Sigma x_i y_i$$
$$(\Sigma x_i^2)a_0 + (\Sigma x_i^3)a_1 + (\Sigma x_i^4)a_2 + (\Sigma x_i^5)a_3 = \Sigma x_i^2 y_i$$
$$(\Sigma x_i^3)a_0 + (\Sigma x_i^4)a_1 + (\Sigma x_i^5)a_2 + (\Sigma x_i^6)a_3 = \Sigma x_i^3 y_i$$

becomes

$$7a_0 + 21a_1 + 91a_2 + 441a_3 = 14$$
$$21a_0 + 91a_1 + 441a_2 + 2{,}275a_3 = 52$$
$$91a_0 + 441a_1 + 2{,}275a_2 + 12{,}201a_3 = 242$$
$$441a_0 + 2{,}275a_1 + 12{,}201a_2 + 67{,}171a_3 = 1{,}258.$$

Using Gaussian elimination with pivoting on the matrix

$$\begin{bmatrix} 7 & 21 & 91 & 441 & 14 \\ 21 & 91 & 441 & 2{,}275 & 52 \\ 91 & 441 & 2{,}275 & 12{,}201 & 242 \\ 441 & 2{,}275 & 12{,}201 & 67{,}171 & 1{,}258 \end{bmatrix}$$

produces

$$\begin{bmatrix} 1.0000 & 5.1587 & 27.6667 & 152.3150 & 2.8526 \\ 0.0000 & 1.0000 & 8.5312 & 58.3482 & 0.6183 \\ 0.0000 & 0.0000 & 1.0000 & 9.7714 & 0.1286 \\ 0.0000 & 0.0000 & 0.0000 & 1.0000 & 0.1667 \end{bmatrix},$$

Figure 10.2

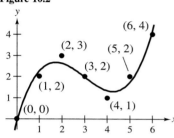

which implies that

$$a_3 = 0.1667, \quad a_2 = -1.5000, \quad a_1 = 3.6905, \quad a_0 = -0.0714.$$

Therefore the cubic model is

$$y = 0.1667x^3 - 1.5000x^2 + 3.6905x - 0.0714.$$

Figure 10.2 compares this model with the given points.

Applications of the Gauss-Seidel Method

EXAMPLE 3   *An Application to Probability*

Figure 10.3 is a diagram of a maze used in a laboratory experiment. The experiment is begun by placing a mouse at one of the ten interior intersections of the maze. Once the mouse emerges in the outer corridor, it cannot return to the maze. When the mouse is at an interior intersection, its choice of paths is assumed to be random. What is the probability that the mouse will emerge in the "food corridor" when it begins at the ith intersection?

Solution   We let the probability of winning (getting food) by starting at the ith intersection be represented by p_i. Then we form a linear equation involving p_i and the probabilities associated with the intersections bordering the ith intersection. For instance, at the first intersection the mouse has a probability of $\frac{1}{4}$ of choosing the upper right path and losing, a probability of $\frac{1}{4}$ of choosing the upper left path and losing, a probability of $\frac{1}{4}$ of choosing the lower right path (at which point it has a probability of p_3 of winning), and a probability of $\frac{1}{4}$ of choosing the lower left path (at which point it has a probability of p_2 of winning). Thus we have

Figure 10.3

$$p_1 = \tfrac{1}{4}(0) + \tfrac{1}{4}(0) + \tfrac{1}{4}p_2 + \tfrac{1}{4}p_3.$$

$$\underbrace{\phantom{\tfrac{1}{4}(0)}}_{\substack{Upper \\ right}} \quad \underbrace{\phantom{\tfrac{1}{4}(0)}}_{\substack{Upper \\ left}} \quad \underbrace{\phantom{\tfrac{1}{4}p_2}}_{\substack{Lower \\ left}} \quad \underbrace{\phantom{\tfrac{1}{4}p_3}}_{\substack{Lower \\ right}}$$

Using similar reasoning, we find the other nine probabilities to be represented by the following equations.

$$p_2 = \tfrac{1}{5}(0) + \tfrac{1}{5}p_1 + \tfrac{1}{5}p_3 + \tfrac{1}{5}p_4 + \tfrac{1}{5}p_5$$

$$p_3 = \tfrac{1}{5}(0) + \tfrac{1}{5}p_1 + \tfrac{1}{5}p_2 + \tfrac{1}{5}p_5 + \tfrac{1}{5}p_6$$

$$p_4 = \tfrac{1}{5}(0) + \tfrac{1}{5}p_2 + \tfrac{1}{5}p_5 + \tfrac{1}{5}p_7 + \tfrac{1}{5}p_8$$

$$p_5 = \tfrac{1}{6}p_2 + \tfrac{1}{6}p_3 + \tfrac{1}{6}p_4 + \tfrac{1}{6}p_6 + \tfrac{1}{6}p_8 + \tfrac{1}{6}p_9$$

$$p_6 = \tfrac{1}{5}(0) + \tfrac{1}{5}p_3 + \tfrac{1}{5}p_5 + \tfrac{1}{5}p_9 + \tfrac{1}{5}p_{10}$$

$$p_7 = \tfrac{1}{4}(0) + \tfrac{1}{4}(1) + \tfrac{1}{4}p_4 + \tfrac{1}{4}p_8$$

$$p_8 = \tfrac{1}{5}(1) + \tfrac{1}{5}p_4 + \tfrac{1}{5}p_5 + \tfrac{1}{5}p_7 + \tfrac{1}{5}p_9$$

$$p_9 = \tfrac{1}{5}(1) + \tfrac{1}{5}p_5 + \tfrac{1}{5}p_6 + \tfrac{1}{5}p_8 + \tfrac{1}{5}p_{10}$$

$$p_{10} = \tfrac{1}{4}(0) + \tfrac{1}{4}(1) + \tfrac{1}{4}p_6 + \tfrac{1}{4}p_9$$

Rewriting these equations in standard form produces the following system of ten linear equations in ten variables.

$$
\begin{array}{rrrrrrrrrrr}
4p_1 & - p_2 & - p_3 & & & & & & & & = 0 \\
-p_1 & + 5p_2 & - p_3 & - p_4 & - p_5 & & & & & & = 0 \\
-p_1 & - p_2 & + 5p_3 & & - p_5 & - p_6 & & & & & = 0 \\
& - p_2 & & + 5p_4 & - p_5 & & - p_7 & - p_8 & & & = 0 \\
& - p_2 & - p_3 & - p_4 & + 6p_5 & - p_6 & & - p_8 & - p_9 & & = 0 \\
& & - p_3 & & - p_5 & + 5p_6 & & & - p_9 & - p_{10} & = 0 \\
& & & - p_4 & & & + 4p_7 & - p_8 & & & = 1 \\
& & & - p_4 & - p_5 & & - p_7 & + 5p_8 & - p_9 & & = 1 \\
& & & & - p_5 & - p_6 & & - p_8 & + 5p_9 & - p_{10} & = 1 \\
& & & & & - p_6 & & & - p_9 & + 4p_{10} & = 1
\end{array}
$$

The augmented matrix for this system is

$$
\begin{bmatrix}
4 & -1 & -1 & 0 & 0 & 0 & 0 & 0 & 0 & 0 & 0 \\
-1 & 5 & -1 & -1 & -1 & 0 & 0 & 0 & 0 & 0 & 0 \\
-1 & -1 & 5 & 0 & -1 & -1 & 0 & 0 & 0 & 0 & 0 \\
0 & -1 & 0 & 5 & -1 & 0 & -1 & -1 & 0 & 0 & 0 \\
0 & -1 & -1 & -1 & 6 & -1 & 0 & -1 & -1 & 0 & 0 \\
0 & 0 & -1 & 0 & -1 & 5 & 0 & 0 & -1 & -1 & 0 \\
0 & 0 & 0 & -1 & 0 & 0 & 4 & -1 & 0 & 0 & 1 \\
0 & 0 & 0 & -1 & -1 & 0 & -1 & 5 & -1 & 0 & 1 \\
0 & 0 & 0 & 0 & -1 & -1 & 0 & -1 & 5 & -1 & 1 \\
0 & 0 & 0 & 0 & 0 & -1 & 0 & 0 & -1 & 4 & 1
\end{bmatrix}.
$$

Using the Gauss-Seidel method with an initial approximation of $p_1 = p_2 = \ldots = p_{10} = 0$ produces (after 18 iterations) an approximation of

$$p_1 = 0.090, \qquad p_2 = 0.180$$
$$p_3 = 0.180, \qquad p_4 = 0.298$$
$$p_5 = 0.333, \qquad p_6 = 0.298$$
$$p_7 = 0.455, \qquad p_8 = 0.522$$
$$p_9 = 0.522, \qquad p_{10} = 0.455.$$

The structure of the probability problem described in Example 3 is related to a technique called **finite element analysis,** which is used in many engineering problems.

Note that the matrix developed in Example 3 has mostly zero entries. We call such matrices **sparse.** For solving systems of equations with sparse coefficient matrices, the Jacobi and Gauss-Seidel methods are much more efficient than Gaussian elimination.

Applications of the Power Method

Section 7.4 introduced the idea of an *age transition matrix* as a model for population growth. Recall that this model was developed by grouping the population into n age classes of equal duration. Thus for a maximum life span of L years, the age classes are given by the following intervals.

$$\overbrace{\left[0, \frac{L}{n}\right)}^{\substack{\text{First age} \\ \text{class}}}, \quad \overbrace{\left[\frac{L}{n}, \frac{2L}{n}\right)}^{\substack{\text{Second age} \\ \text{class}}}, \quad \ldots, \quad \overbrace{\left[\frac{(n-1)L}{n}, L\right]}^{\substack{n\text{th age} \\ \text{class}}}$$

The number of population members in each age class is then represented by the age distribution vector

$$\mathbf{x} = \begin{bmatrix} x_1 \\ x_2 \\ \vdots \\ x_n \end{bmatrix}. \qquad \begin{array}{l} \textbf{Number in first age class} \\[4pt] \textbf{Number in second age class} \\[12pt] \textbf{Number in } n\textbf{th age class} \end{array}$$

Over a period of L/n years, the *probability* that a member of the ith age class will survive to become a member of the $(i + 1)$th age class is given by p_i, where $0 \le p_i \le 1$, $i = 1, 2, \ldots, n - 1$. The *average number* of offspring produced by a member of the ith age class is given by b_i, where $0 \le b_i$, $i = 1, 2, \ldots, n$. These numbers can be written in matrix form:

$$A = \begin{bmatrix} b_1 & b_2 & b_3 & \cdots & b_{n-1} & b_n \\ p_1 & 0 & 0 & \cdots & 0 & 0 \\ 0 & p_2 & 0 & \cdots & 0 & 0 \\ \vdots & \vdots & \vdots & & \vdots & \vdots \\ 0 & 0 & 0 & \cdots & p_{n-1} & 0 \end{bmatrix}$$

Multiplying this age transition matrix by the age distribution vector for a given period of time produces the age distribution vector for the next period of time. That is,

$$A\mathbf{x}_i = \mathbf{x}_{i+1}.$$

In Section 7.4 we saw that the growth pattern for a population is *stable* if the same percentage of the total population is in each age class each year. That is,

$$A\mathbf{x}_i = \mathbf{x}_{i+1} = \lambda\mathbf{x}_i.$$

For populations with many age classes, the solution to this eigenvalue problem can be found with the power method, as illustrated in Example 4.

EXAMPLE 4   *A Population Growth Model*

Assume that a population of human females has the following characteristics.

Age Class (in years)	Average Number of Female Children During Ten-Year Period	Probability of Surviving to Next Age Class
$0 \le$ age $< \ 10$	0.000	0.985
$10 \le$ age $< \ 20$	0.174	0.996
$20 \le$ age $< \ 30$	0.782	0.994
$30 \le$ age $< \ 40$	0.263	0.990
$40 \le$ age $< \ 50$	0.022	0.975
$50 \le$ age $< \ 60$	0.000	0.940
$60 \le$ age $< \ 70$	0.000	0.866
$70 \le$ age $< \ 80$	0.000	0.680
$80 \le$ age $< \ 90$	0.000	0.361
$90 \le$ age < 100	0.000	0.000

Find a stable age distribution for this population.

Solution   The age transition matrix for this population is

$$A = \begin{bmatrix} 0.000 & 0.174 & 0.782 & 0.263 & 0.022 & 0.000 & 0.000 & 0.000 & 0.000 & 0.000 \\ 0.985 & 0 & 0 & 0 & 0 & 0 & 0 & 0 & 0 & 0 \\ 0 & 0.996 & 0 & 0 & 0 & 0 & 0 & 0 & 0 & 0 \\ 0 & 0 & 0.994 & 0 & 0 & 0 & 0 & 0 & 0 & 0 \\ 0 & 0 & 0 & 0.990 & 0 & 0 & 0 & 0 & 0 & 0 \\ 0 & 0 & 0 & 0 & 0.975 & 0 & 0 & 0 & 0 & 0 \\ 0 & 0 & 0 & 0 & 0 & 0.940 & 0 & 0 & 0 & 0 \\ 0 & 0 & 0 & 0 & 0 & 0 & 0.866 & 0 & 0 & 0 \\ 0 & 0 & 0 & 0 & 0 & 0 & 0 & 0.680 & 0 & 0 \\ 0 & 0 & 0 & 0 & 0 & 0 & 0 & 0 & 0.361 & 0 \end{bmatrix}.$$

To apply the power method with scaling to find an eigenvector for this matrix, we use an initial approximation of $\mathbf{x}_0 = (1, 1, 1, 1, 1, 1, 1, 1, 1, 1)$. The following is an approximation for an eigenvector of A, with the percentage of each age in the total population.

Eigenvector	Age Class	Percentage in Age Class
1.000	$0 \leq$ age < 10	15.27
0.925	$10 \leq$ age < 20	14.13
0.864	$20 \leq$ age < 30	13.20
0.806	$30 \leq$ age < 40	12.31
0.749	$40 \leq$ age < 50	11.44
0.686	$50 \leq$ age < 60	10.48
0.605	$60 \leq$ age < 70	9.24
0.492	$70 \leq$ age < 80	7.51
0.314	$80 \leq$ age < 90	4.80
0.106	$90 \leq$ age < 100	1.62

$\mathbf{x} =$ (the above eigenvector column)

The eigenvalue corresponding to the eigenvector $\mathbf{x}$ in Example 4 is $\lambda \approx 1.065$. That is,

$$A\mathbf{x} = A \begin{bmatrix} 1.000 \\ 0.925 \\ 0.864 \\ 0.806 \\ 0.749 \\ 0.686 \\ 0.605 \\ 0.492 \\ 0.314 \\ 0.106 \end{bmatrix} \approx \begin{bmatrix} 1.065 \\ 0.985 \\ 0.921 \\ 0.859 \\ 0.798 \\ 0.731 \\ 0.645 \\ 0.524 \\ 0.334 \\ 0.113 \end{bmatrix} \approx 1.065 \begin{bmatrix} 1.000 \\ 0.925 \\ 0.864 \\ 0.806 \\ 0.749 \\ 0.686 \\ 0.605 \\ 0.492 \\ 0.314 \\ 0.106 \end{bmatrix}.$$

This means that the population in Example 4 increases by 6.5% every ten years.

REMARK: Should you try duplicating the results of Example 4, you would notice that the convergence of the power method for this problem is very slow. The reason is that the dominant eigenvalue of $\lambda \approx 1.065$ is only slightly larger in absolute value than the next largest eigenvalue.

SECTION 10.4 ☐ EXERCISES

Applications of Gaussian Elimination with Pivoting

C In Exercises 1–4, find the second-degree least squares regression polynomial for the given data. Then graphically compare the model to the given points.

1. $(-2, 1), (-1, 0), (0, 0), (1, 1), (3, 2)$
2. $(0, 4), (1, 2), (2, -1), (3, 0), (4, 1), (5, 4)$
3. $(-2, 1), (-1, 2), (0, 6), (1, 3), (2, 0), (3, -1)$
4. $(1, 1), (2, 1), (3, 0), (4, -1), (5, -4)$

C In Exercises 5–8, find the third-degree least squares regression polynomial for the given data. Then graphically compare the model to the given points.

5. $(0, 0), (1, 2), (2, 4), (3, 1), (4, 0), (5, 1)$
6. $(1, 1), (2, 4), (3, 4), (5, 1), (6, 2)$
7. $(-3, 4), (-1, 1), (0, 0), (1, 2), (2, 5)$
8. $(-7, 2), (-3, 0), (1, -1), (2, 3), (4, 6)$

C 9. Find the second-degree least squares regression polynomial for the points

$$\left(-\frac{\pi}{2}, 0\right), \left(-\frac{\pi}{3}, \frac{1}{2}\right), (0, 1), \left(\frac{\pi}{3}, \frac{1}{2}\right), \left(\frac{\pi}{2}, 0\right).$$

Then use the results to approximate $\cos(\pi/4)$. Compare the approximation with the exact value.

C 10. Find the third-degree least squares regression polynomial for the points

$$\left(-\frac{\pi}{4}, -1\right), \left(-\frac{\pi}{3}, -\sqrt{3}\right), (0, 0), \left(\frac{\pi}{3}, \sqrt{3}\right), \left(\frac{\pi}{4}, 1\right).$$

Then use the result to approximate $\tan(\pi/6)$. Compare the approximation with the exact value.

C 11. The number of minutes a scuba diver can stay at a particular depth without acquiring decompression sickness, as given by the United States Navy's Standard Air Decompression Tables, is shown in the following table.

Depth (in feet)	35	40	50	60	70
Time (in minutes)	310	200	100	60	50

Depth (in feet)	80	90	100	110
Time (in minutes)	40	30	25	20

(a) Find the least squares regression line for these data.
(b) Find the second-degree least squares regression polynomial for these data.
(c) Sketch the graphs of the models found in parts (a) and (b).
(d) Use the models found in parts (a) and (b) to approximate the maximum number of minutes a diver should stay at a depth of 120 feet. (The value given in the Navy's tables is 15 minutes.)

C 12. The life expectancy for *additional* years of life for females in the United States is given in the following table.

Current Age	10	20	30	40
Life Expectancy	69.7	59.9	50.2	40.6

Current Age	50	60	70	80
Life Expectancy	31.3	22.8	15.3	9.0

Find the second-degree least squares regression polynomial for these data.

C 13. Total federal payments (in billions of dollars) for Medicare from 1970 to 1984 are given in the following table.

Year	1970	1972	1974	1976
Medicare	7.5	9.1	13.1	19.3

Year	1978	1980	1982	1984
Medicare	25.9	36.8	52.4	64.8

Find the second-degree least squares regression polynomial for these data. Then use the result to predict the Medicare payments for 1986 and 1988.

C 14. Rework Exercise 13 using the data in the following table, in which Medicare payments have been adjusted for inflation.

Year	1970	1972	1974	1976
Medicare	7.5	8.4	10.3	13.2

Year	1978	1980	1982	1984
Medicare	15.4	17.3	21.1	24.2

C 15. Find the least squares regression line for the population data given in Example 1. Then use the model to predict the world population in 1990 and 1995, and compare the results with the predictions obtained in Example 1.

16. Show that the formula for the least squares regression line presented in Section 2.5 is equivalent to the formula presented in this section. That is, if

$$Y = \begin{bmatrix} y_1 \\ y_2 \\ \vdots \\ y_n \end{bmatrix}, \quad X = \begin{bmatrix} 1 & x_1 \\ 1 & x_2 \\ \vdots & \vdots \\ 1 & x_n \end{bmatrix}, \quad A = \begin{bmatrix} a_0 \\ a_1 \end{bmatrix},$$

then the matrix equation $A = (X^T X)^{-1} X^T Y$ is equivalent to

$$a_1 = \frac{n\Sigma x_i y_i - (\Sigma x_i)(\Sigma y_i)}{n\Sigma x_i^2 - (\Sigma x_i)^2} \quad \text{and} \quad a_0 = \frac{\Sigma y_i}{n} - a_1 \frac{\Sigma x_i}{n}.$$

Applications of the Gauss-Seidel Method

C 17. Suppose that the experiment in Example 3 is performed with the maze shown in Figure 10.4. Find the probability that the mouse will emerge in the food corridor when it begins in the ith intersection.

Figure 10.4

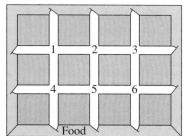

C 18. Suppose that the experiment in Example 3 is performed with the maze shown in Figure 10.5. Find the probability that the mouse will emerge in the food corridor when it begins in the ith intersection.

Figure 10.5

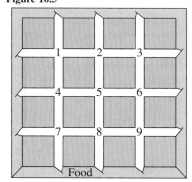

C 19. A square metal plate has a constant temperature on each of its four boundaries, as shown in Figure 10.6. Use a 4×4 grid to approximate the temperature distribution in the interior of the plate. Assume that the temperature at each interior point is the average of the temperatures at the four closest neighboring points.

Figure 10.6

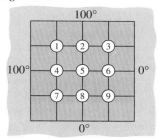

C 20. A rectangular metal plate has a constant temperature on each of its four boundaries, as shown in Figure 10.7. Use a 4×5 grid to approximate the temperature distribution in the interior of the plate. Assume that the temperature at each interior point is the average of the temperatures at the four closest neighboring points.

Figure 10.7

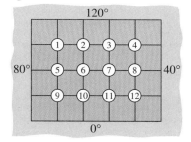

Applications of the Power Method

In Exercises 21–24, the given matrix represents the age transition matrix for a population. Use the power method with scaling to find a stable age distribution.

21. $A = \begin{bmatrix} 1 & 4 \\ \frac{1}{2} & 0 \end{bmatrix}$

22. $A = \begin{bmatrix} 1 & 2 \\ \frac{1}{4} & 0 \end{bmatrix}$

C 23. $A = \begin{bmatrix} 0 & 1 & 2 \\ \frac{1}{2} & 0 & 0 \\ 0 & \frac{1}{4} & 0 \end{bmatrix}$

C 24. $A = \begin{bmatrix} 1 & 2 & 2 \\ \frac{1}{3} & 0 & 0 \\ 0 & \frac{1}{3} & 0 \end{bmatrix}$

C **25.** In Example 1 of Section 7.4, a laboratory population of rabbits is described. The age transition matrix for the population is

$$A = \begin{bmatrix} 0 & 6 & 8 \\ 0.5 & 0 & 0 \\ 0 & 0.5 & 0 \end{bmatrix}.$$

Find a stable age distribution for this population.

C **26.** A population has the following characteristics.

(a) A total of 75% of the population survives its first year. Of that 75%, 25% survives its second year. The maximum life span is three years.

(b) The average number of offspring for each member of the population is 2 the first year, 4 the second year, and 2 the third year.

Find a stable age distribution for this population. (See Exercise 9, Section 7.4.)

27. Apply the power method to the matrix

$$A = \begin{bmatrix} 1 & 1 \\ 1 & 0 \end{bmatrix}$$

discussed in Chapter 7 (Fibonacci sequence). Use the power method to approximate the dominant eigenvalue of A. (The dominant eigenvalue is $\lambda = (1 + \sqrt{5})/2$.)

28. In Example 2 of Section 2.5, the stochastic matrix

$$P = \begin{bmatrix} 0.70 & 0.15 & 0.15 \\ 0.20 & 0.80 & 0.15 \\ 0.10 & 0.05 & 0.70 \end{bmatrix}$$

represents the transition probabilities for a consumer preference model. Use the power method to approximate a dominant eigenvector for this matrix. How does the approximation relate to the steady-state matrix described in the discussion following Example 3 in Section 2.5?

C **29.** In Exercise 9 of Section 2.5, a population of 10,000 is divided into nonsmokers, moderate smokers, and heavy smokers. Use the power method to approximate a dominant eigenvector for this matrix.

APPENDIX A

PROOFS OF SELECTED THEOREMS

This appendix contains proofs of several theorems that are omitted from the text.

Theorem 2.3

Properties of Matrix Multiplication

If A, B, and C are matrices (with sizes such that the given matrix products are defined) and c is a scalar, then the following properties are true.

1. $A(BC) = (AB)C$ **Associative property of multiplication**
2. $A(B + C) = AB + AC$ **Distributive property**
3. $(A + B)C = AC + BC$ **Distributive property**
4. $c(AB) = (cA)B = A(cB)$

Proof

To prove property 1, we compute the entry in the ith row and jth column of both $A(BC)$ and $(AB)C$. To begin, we assume that A has size $m \times n$, B has size $n \times p$, and C has size $p \times q$. Then the jth column of BC is

$$\begin{bmatrix} b_{11}c_{1j} + \cdots + b_{1p}c_{pj} \\ \vdots \qquad\qquad \vdots \\ b_{n1}c_{1j} + \cdots + b_{np}c_{pj} \end{bmatrix},$$

which implies that the ith entry of the jth column of $A(BC)$ is

$$a_{i1}(b_{11}c_{1j} + \cdots + b_{1p}c_{pj}) + \cdots + a_{in}(b_{n1}c_{1j} + \cdots + b_{np}c_{pj}).$$

On the other hand, the ith row of AB is

$$(a_{i1}b_{11} + \cdots + a_{in}b_{n1}), \ldots, (a_{i1}b_{1p} + \cdots + a_{in}b_{np}),$$

which implies that the ith entry of the jth column of $(AB)C$ is

$$(a_{i1}b_{11} + \cdots + a_{in}b_{n1})c_{1j} + \cdots + (a_{i1}b_{1p} + \cdots + a_{in}b_{np})c_{pj}.$$

By distributing and regrouping, we can see these two ijth entries are equal and we conclude that

$$A(BC) = (AB)C.$$

To prove property 2, we find the entry in the ith row and jth column of $A(B + C)$ to be

$$a_{i1}(b_{1j} + c_{1j}) + \cdots + a_{in}(b_{nj} + c_{nj}).$$

Moreover, the entry in the ith row and jth column of $AB + AC$ is

$$(a_{i1}b_{1j} + \cdots + a_{in}b_{nj}) + (a_{i1}c_{1j} + \cdots + a_{in}c_{nj}).$$

Again, by distributing and regrouping, we can see that these two ijth entries are equal and we conclude that

$$A(B + C) = AB + AC.$$

Theorem 3.3

Elementary Row Operations and Determinants

Let A and B be square matrices.
1. If B is obtained from A by interchanging two rows of A, then

$$\det(B) = -\det(A).$$

2. If B is obtained from A by adding a multiple of a row of A to another row of A, then

$$\det(B) = \det(A).$$

3. If B is obtained from A by multiplying a row of A by a nonzero constant c, then

$$\det(B) = c \det(A).$$

Proof To prove the first property, we use mathematical induction as follows. Assume that A and B are 2×2 matrices such that

$$A = \begin{bmatrix} a_{11} & a_{12} \\ a_{21} & a_{22} \end{bmatrix}$$

and

$$B = \begin{bmatrix} a_{21} & a_{22} \\ a_{11} & a_{12} \end{bmatrix}.$$

Then, we have

$$|A| = a_{11}a_{22} - a_{12}a_{21}$$

and

$$|B| = a_{21}a_{12} - a_{11}a_{22}.$$

Thus, $|B| = -|A|$. Now assume that the property is true for matrices of order $(n - 1) \times (n - 1)$. Let A be an $n \times n$ matrix such that B is obtained from A by interchanging two rows of A. Then to find $|A|$ and $|B|$, we expand along a row other than the two interchanged rows. By our induction assumption, the cofactors of B will be the negatives of the cofactors of A because the corresponding $(n - 1) \times (n - 1)$ matrices have two rows interchanged. Thus, it follows that

$$|B| = -|A|$$

and the proof is complete.

Theorem 3.5

Determinant of a Matrix Product

If A and B are square matrices of order n, then

$$\det(AB) = \det(A)\det(B).$$

Proof To begin, we observe that if E is an elementary matrix, then by Theorem 3.3, the following statements are true. If E is obtained from I by interchanging two rows, then $|E| = -1$. If E is obtained by multiplying a row of I by a nonzero constant c, then $|E| = c$. If E is obtained by adding a multiple of one row of I to another row of I, then $|E| = 1$. In any case, it follows that

$$|EB| = |E|\,|B|.$$

This can be generalized to conclude that

$$|E_k \cdots E_2 E_1 B| = |E_k| \cdots |E_2|\,|E_1|\,|B|,$$

where E_i is an elementary matrix. Now, let's consider the matrix AB. If A is *nonsingular*, then by Theorem 2.14 it can be written as the product of elementary matrices $A = E_k \cdots E_2 E_1$ and we can write

$$|AB| = |E_k \cdots E_2 E_1 B|$$
$$= |E_k| \cdots |E_2|\,|E_1|\,|B| = |E_k \cdots E_2 E_1|\,|B| = |A|\,|B|.$$

If A is *singular*, then A is row equivalent to a matrix with an entire row of zeros. Thus, from Theorem 3.4, we can conclude that $|A| = 0$. Moreover, because A is singular it follows that AB is also singular. [If AB were nonsingular, then $A[B(AB)^{-1}] = I$ would imply that A is nonsingular.] Thus, $|AB| = 0$, and we can conclude that $|AB| = |A|\,|B|$.

Theorem 4.17

Dimension of the Solution Space

If A is an $m \times n$ matrix of rank r, then the dimension of the solution space of $A\mathbf{x} = \mathbf{0}$ is $n - r$. That is,

$$n = \text{rank}(A) + \text{nullity}(A).$$

Proof Since A has rank r, we know that it is row equivalent to a reduced row-echelon matrix B with r nonzero rows. No generality is lost by assuming that the upper left corner of B has the form of the $r \times r$ identity matrix I_r. Moreover, because the zero rows of B contribute nothing to the solution, we can discard them to form the $r \times n$ matrix B', where $B' = [I_r \vdots C]$. The matrix C has $n - r$ columns corresponding to the variables $x_{r+1}, x_{r+2}, \ldots, x_n$. Thus the solution space of $A\mathbf{x} = \mathbf{0}$ can be represented by the system

$$x_1 + \qquad\qquad c_{11}x_{r+1} + c_{12}x_{r+2} + \cdots + c_{1,n-r}x_n = 0$$
$$x_2 + \qquad\qquad c_{21}x_{r+1} + c_{22}x_{r+2} + \cdots + c_{2,n-r}x_n = 0$$
$$\vdots \qquad\qquad \vdots \qquad\quad \vdots \qquad\qquad \vdots$$
$$x_r + c_{r1}x_{r+1} + c_{r2}x_{r+2} + \cdots + c_{r,n-r}x_n = 0.$$

Solving for the first r variables in terms of the last $n - r$ variables produces $n - r$ vectors in the basis of the solution space. Consequently, the solution space has dimension $n - r$.

Before giving a proof of Theorem 4.20, we prove a preliminary lemma.

Lemma A.1

Let $B = \{v_1, v_2, \ldots, v_n\}$ and $B' = \{u_1, u_2, \ldots, u_n\}$ be two bases for a vector space V. If

$$v_1 = c_{11}u_1 + c_{21}u_2 + \cdots + c_{n1}u_n$$
$$v_2 = c_{12}u_1 + c_{22}u_2 + \cdots + c_{n2}u_n$$
$$\vdots$$
$$v_n = c_{1n}u_1 + c_{2n}u_2 + \cdots + c_{nn}u_n$$

then the transition matrix from B to B' is

$$Q = \begin{bmatrix} c_{11} & c_{12} & \cdots & c_{1n} \\ c_{21} & c_{22} & \cdots & c_{2n} \\ \vdots & \vdots & & \vdots \\ c_{n1} & c_{n2} & \cdots & c_{nn} \end{bmatrix}.$$

Proof   Let $v = d_1v_1 + d_2v_2 + \cdots + d_nv_n$ be an arbitrary vector in V. The coordinate matrix of v with respect to the basis B is therefore

$$[v]_B = \begin{bmatrix} d_1 \\ d_2 \\ \vdots \\ d_n \end{bmatrix}.$$

Then we have

$$Q[v]_B = \begin{bmatrix} c_{11} & c_{12} & \cdots & c_{1n} \\ c_{21} & c_{22} & \cdots & c_{2n} \\ \vdots & \vdots & & \vdots \\ c_{n1} & c_{n2} & \cdots & c_{nn} \end{bmatrix} \begin{bmatrix} d_1 \\ d_2 \\ \vdots \\ d_n \end{bmatrix}$$

$$= \begin{bmatrix} c_{11}d_1 + c_{12}d_2 + \cdots + c_{1n}d_n \\ c_{21}d_1 + c_{22}d_2 + \cdots + c_{2n}d_n \\ \vdots & \vdots & & \vdots \\ c_{n1}d_1 + c_{n2}d_2 + \cdots + c_{nn}d_n \end{bmatrix}.$$

On the other hand, we can write

$$\mathbf{v} = d_1\mathbf{v}_1 + d_2\mathbf{v}_2 + \cdots + d_n\mathbf{v}_n$$
$$= d_1(c_{11}\mathbf{u}_1 + \cdots + c_{n1}\mathbf{u}_n) + \cdots + d_n(c_{1n}\mathbf{u}_1 + \cdots + c_{nn}\mathbf{u}_n)$$
$$= (d_1c_{11} + \cdots + d_nc_{1n})\mathbf{u}_1 + \cdots + (d_1c_{n1} + \cdots + d_nc_{nn})\mathbf{u}_n$$

which implies that

$$[\mathbf{v}]_{B'} = \begin{bmatrix} c_{11}d_1 + c_{12}d_2 + \cdots + c_{1n}d_n \\ c_{21}d_1 + c_{22}d_2 + \cdots + c_{2n}d_n \\ \vdots \qquad \vdots \qquad\qquad \vdots \\ c_{n1}d_1 + c_{n2}d_2 + \cdots + c_{nn}d_n \end{bmatrix}.$$

Therefore, $Q[\mathbf{v}]_B = [\mathbf{v}]_{B'}$ and we conclude that Q is the transition matrix from B to B'.

Theorem 4.20

The Inverse of a Transition Matrix

If P is the transition matrix from a basis B' to a basis B in R^n, then P is invertible and the transition matrix from B to B' is given by P^{-1}.

Proof From Lemma A.1, let Q be the transition matrix from B to B'. Then

$$[\mathbf{v}]_B = P[\mathbf{v}]_{B'} \qquad \text{and} \qquad [\mathbf{v}]_{B'} = Q[\mathbf{v}]_B$$

which implies that $[\mathbf{v}]_B = PQ[\mathbf{v}]_B$ for every vector $\mathbf{v}$ in R^n. From this it follows that $PQ = I$. Therefore, P is invertible and P^{-1} is equal to Q, the transition matrix from B to B'.

Theorem 4.21

Transition Matrix from B to B'

Let $B = \{\mathbf{v}_1, \mathbf{v}_2, \ldots, \mathbf{v}_n\}$ and $B' = \{\mathbf{u}_1, \mathbf{u}_2, \ldots, \mathbf{u}_n\}$ be two bases for R^n. Then the transition matrix P^{-1} from B to B' can be found by using Gauss-Jordan elimination on the $n \times 2n$ matrix $[B' \vdots B]$ as follows.

$$[B' \vdots B] \longrightarrow [I_n \vdots P^{-1}]$$

Proof To begin, we let

$$\mathbf{v}_1 = c_{11}\mathbf{u}_1 + c_{21}\mathbf{u}_2 + \cdots + c_{n1}\mathbf{u}_n$$
$$\mathbf{v}_2 = c_{12}\mathbf{u}_1 + c_{22}\mathbf{u}_2 + \cdots + c_{n2}\mathbf{u}_n$$
$$\vdots$$
$$\mathbf{v}_n = c_{1n}\mathbf{u}_1 + c_{2n}\mathbf{u}_2 + \cdots + c_{nn}\mathbf{u}_n$$

which implies that

$$c_{1i}\begin{bmatrix} u_{11} \\ u_{12} \\ \vdots \\ u_{1n} \end{bmatrix} + c_{2i}\begin{bmatrix} u_{21} \\ u_{22} \\ \vdots \\ u_{2n} \end{bmatrix} + \cdots + c_{ni}\begin{bmatrix} u_{n1} \\ u_{n2} \\ \vdots \\ u_{nn} \end{bmatrix} = \begin{bmatrix} v_{i1} \\ v_{i2} \\ \vdots \\ v_{in} \end{bmatrix}$$

for $i = 1, 2, \ldots, n$. From these vector equations we can write the following n systems of linear equations

$$u_{11}c_{1i} + u_{21}c_{2i} + \cdots + u_{n1}c_{ni} = v_{i1}$$
$$u_{12}c_{1i} + u_{22}c_{2i} + \cdots + u_{n2}c_{ni} = v_{i2}$$
$$\vdots$$
$$u_{1n}c_{1i} + u_{2n}c_{2i} + \cdots + u_{nn}c_{ni} = v_{in}$$

for $i = 1, 2, \ldots, n$. Because each of the n systems has the same coefficient matrix we can reduce all n systems simultaneously using the following augmented matrix.

$$\left[\begin{array}{cccc:cccc} u_{11} & u_{21} & \cdots & u_{n1} & v_{11} & v_{21} & \cdots & v_{n1} \\ u_{12} & u_{22} & \cdots & u_{n2} & v_{12} & v_{22} & \cdots & v_{n2} \\ \vdots & \vdots & & \vdots & \vdots & \vdots & & \vdots \\ u_{1n} & u_{2n} & \cdots & u_{nn} & v_{1n} & v_{2n} & \cdots & v_{nn} \end{array}\right]$$

$$\underbrace{\qquad\qquad}_{B'} \qquad\qquad \underbrace{\qquad\qquad}_{B}$$

Applying Gauss-Jordan elimination to this matrix produces

$$\left[\begin{array}{cccc:cccc} 1 & 0 & \cdots & 0 & c_{11} & c_{12} & \cdots & c_{1n} \\ 0 & 1 & \cdots & 0 & c_{21} & c_{22} & \cdots & c_{2n} \\ \vdots & \vdots & & \vdots & \vdots & \vdots & & \vdots \\ 0 & 0 & \cdots & 1 & c_{n1} & c_{n2} & \cdots & c_{nn} \end{array}\right].$$

However, by Lemma A.1, the right hand side of this matrix is $Q = P^{-1}$, which implies that the matrix has the form

$$[I : P^{-1}],$$

which proves the theorem.

Theorem 5.13

Properties of Orthogonal Subspaces

Let S be a subspace of R^n. Then the following properties are true.

1. $\dim(S) + \dim(S^{\perp}) = n$
2. $R^n = S \oplus S^{\perp}$
3. $(S^{\perp})^{\perp} = S$

Proof
1. If $S = R^n$ or $S = \{0\}$ then the property 1 is trivial. So let $\{v_1, v_2, \ldots, v_t\}$ be a basis for S, $0 < t < n$. Let A be the $n \times t$ matrix whose columns are the basis vectors v_i. Then $S = R(A)$ which implies that $S^\perp = N(A^T)$, where A^T is a $t \times n$ matrix of rank t (see Section 5.3, Exercise 59). Since the dimension of $N(A^T)$ is $n - t$, we have shown that

$$\dim(S) + \dim(S^\perp) = t + (n - t) = n.$$

2. If $S = R^n$ or $S = \{0\}$ then property 2 is trivial. So let $\{v_1, v_2, \ldots, v_t\}$ be a basis for S and let $\{v_{t+1}, v_{t+2}, \ldots, v_n\}$ be a basis for $S^\perp$. It is easy to show that the set $\{v_1, v_2, \ldots, v_t, v_{t+1}, \ldots, v_n\}$ is linearly independent, and hence forms a basis for R^n. Let $x \in R^n$, $x = c_1v_1 + \cdots + c_tv_t + c_{t+1}v_{t+1} + \cdots + c_nv_n$. If we write $v = c_1v_1 + \cdots + c_tv_t$ and $w = c_{t+1}v_{t+1} + \cdots + c_nv_n$, then we have expressed an arbitrary vector x as the sum of a vector from S and a vector from $S^\perp$, $x = v + w$.

To show the uniqueness of this representation, assume that $x = v + w = \hat{v} + \hat{w}$. This implies that $\hat{v} - v = w - \hat{w}$. Thus the two vectors $\hat{v} - v$ and $w - \hat{w}$ are in both S and $S^\perp$. Since $S \cap S^\perp = \{0\}$, we must have $\hat{v} = v$ and $w = \hat{w}$.

3. Let $v \in S$. Then $v \cdot u = 0$ for all $u \in S^\perp$, which implies that $v \in (S^\perp)^\perp$. On the other hand, if $v \in (S^\perp)^\perp$, then since $R^n = S \oplus S^\perp$, we can write v as the unique sum of the vector from S and a vector from $S^\perp$, $v = s + w$, $s \in S$, $w \in S^\perp$. Since w is in $S^\perp$, it is orthogonal to every vector in S, and in particular to v. Thus,

$$\begin{aligned} 0 = w \cdot v &= w \cdot (s + w) \\ &= w \cdot s + w \cdot w \\ &= w \cdot w. \end{aligned}$$

This implies that $w = 0$ and $v = s + w = s \in S$.

In this appendix we will study a form of mathematical proof called the principle of **mathematical induction.** It is important to clearly see the logical need for it, so let us look at a typical problem situation.

EXAMPLE 1   *Sum of Odd Integers*

Use the following pattern to conjecture a formula for the sum of the first n odd integers.

$$1 = 1$$
$$1 + 3 = 4$$
$$1 + 3 + 5 = 9$$
$$1 + 3 + 5 + 7 = 16$$
$$1 + 3 + 5 + 7 + 9 = 25$$

Solution   Notice that the sums on the left are equal to the squares $1^2, 2^2, 3^2, 4^2$, and 5^2. Judging from this pattern, we can *conjecture* that the sum of the first n odd integers is n^2,

$$1 + 3 + 5 + 7 + \cdots + (2n - 1) = n^2.$$

Although this formula is valid, it is important to see that recognizing a pattern and then simply *jumping to the conclusion* that the pattern must be true for all values of n is not a logically valid method of proof. There are many examples in which a pattern appears to be developing for small values of n and then at some point the pattern fails. One of the most famous cases of this was the conjecture by the French mathematician Pierre de Fermat (1601–1655), who speculated that all numbers of the form

$$F_n = 2^{2^n} + 1, \quad n = 0, 1, 2, \ldots$$

are prime. For $n = 0, 1, 2, 3$, and 4, the conjecture is true.

$$F_0 = 3$$
$$F_1 = 5$$
$$F_2 = 17$$
$$F_3 = 257$$
$$F_4 = 65,537$$

The size of the next Fermat number ($F_5 = 4{,}294{,}967{,}297$) is so great it was difficult for Fermat to determine whether it was prime or not. However, another well-known mathematician, Leonhard Euler (1707–1783), later found the factorization

$$F_5 = 4{,}294{,}967{,}297 = (641)(6{,}700{,}417),$$

which proved that F_5 is *not* prime, and therefore Fermat's conjecture was false.

Just because a rule, pattern, or formula seems to work for several values of n, we cannot simply decide that it is valid for all values of n without proving it so. One legitimate method of proof for such conjectures is the **Principle of Mathematical Induction.**

Principle of Mathematical Induction

Let P_n be a statement involving the positive integer n. If
1. P_1 is true, and
2. the truth of P_k implies the truth of P_{k+1} for every positive integer k, then P_n must be true for all positive integers n.

In the next example we use the Principle of Mathematical Induction to prove the conjecture from Example 1.

EXAMPLE 2   *Using Mathematical Induction*

Use mathematical induction to prove that the following formula is valid for all positive integers n.

$$S_n = 1 + 3 + 5 + 7 + \cdots + (2n - 1) = n^2$$

Solution   Mathematical induction consists of two distinct parts. First, you must show that the formula is true when $n = 1$.

1. When $n = 1$, the formula is valid, because

$$S_1 = 1 = 1^2.$$

The second part of mathematical induction has two steps. The first step is to assume that the formula is valid for some integer k (the **induction hypothesis**). The second step is to use this assumption to prove that the formula is valid for the next integer, $k + 1$.

2. Assuming that the formula

$$S_k = 1 + 3 + 5 + 7 + \cdots + (2k - 1) = k^2$$

is true, we must show that the formula

$$S_{k+1} = (k + 1)^2$$

is true. Notice in the following steps that since $(2k - 1)$ is the kth term of the sum, then $[2(k + 1) - 1]$ is the $(k + 1)$st term.

$$S_{k+1} = 1 + 3 + 5 + 7 + \cdots + (2k - 1) + [2(k + 1) - 1]$$
$$= [1 + 3 + 5 + 7 + \cdots + (2k - 1)] + [2k + 1]$$
$$= S_k + (2k + 1)$$
$$= k^2 + 2k + 1 \qquad\qquad S_k = k^2 \text{ from induction hypothesis.}$$
$$= (k + 1)^2$$

Combining the results of parts (1) and (2), we can conclude by mathematical induction that the formula is valid for *all* positive integers n.

A well-known illustration used to explain why mathematical induction works is the unending line of dominoes shown in Figure A.1. If the line actually contains infinitely many dominoes, then it is clear that we could not knock the entire line down by knocking down only *one domino* at a time. However, suppose it were true that each domino would knock down the next one as it fell. Then you could knock them all down simply by pushing the first one and starting a chain reaction.

The first domino knocks over the second which knocks over
the third which knocks over the fourth and so on.

Mathematical induction works in the same way. If the truth of P_k implies the truth of P_{k+1} and if P_1 is true, then the chain reaction proceeds as follows.

P_1 implies P_2

P_2 implies P_3

P_3 implies P_4

and so on.

In the next example we prove a formula that is often used in calculus.

EXAMPLE 3   *Using Mathematical Induction*

Use mathematical induction to prove the following formula for the sum of the first n squares.

$$S_n = 1^2 + 2^2 + 3^2 + 4^2 + \cdots + n^2 = \frac{n(n + 1)(2n + 1)}{6}$$

Solution   1. The formula is valid when $n = 1$ because

$$S_n = 1^2 = \frac{1(1 + 1)(2(1) + 1)}{6} = \frac{1(2)(3)}{6} = 1.$$

2. Assuming that the formula is true for k,

$$S_k = 1^2 + 2^2 + 3^2 + 4^2 + \cdots + k^2 = \frac{k(k + 1)(2k + 1)}{6},$$

we must show that it is true for $k + 1$,

$$S_{k+1} = \frac{(k + 1)[(k + 1) + 1][2(k + 1) + 1]}{6} = \frac{(k + 1)(k + 2)(2k + 3)}{6}.$$

To do this, we write S_{k+1} as the sum of S_k and the $(k + 1)$st term, $(k + 1)^2$, as follows.

$$
\begin{aligned}
S_{k+1} &= 1^2 + 2^2 + 3^2 + 4^2 + \cdots + k^2 + (k + 1)^2 \\
&= [1^2 + 2^2 + 3^2 + 4^2 + \cdots + k^2] + (k + 1)^2 \\
&= \frac{k(k + 1)(2k + 1)}{6} + (k + 1)^2 && \text{Induction hypothesis} \\
&= \frac{k(k + 1)(2k + 1) + 6(k + 1)^2}{6} \\
&= \frac{(k + 1)[k(2k + 1) + 6(k + 1)]}{6} \\
&= \frac{(k + 1)[2k^2 + 7k + 6]}{6} \\
&= \frac{(k + 1)(k + 2)(2k + 3)}{6}
\end{aligned}
$$

Combining the results of parts (1) and (2), we can conclude by mathematical induction that the formula is valid for *all* positive integers n.

Many of the proofs in linear algebra use mathematical induction. Here is an example from Chapter 2.

EXAMPLE 4   *Using Mathematical Induction in Linear Algebra*

If $A_1, A_2, \ldots, A_n$ are invertible matrices, prove the following generalization of Theorem 2.9.

$$(A_1 A_2 A_3 \cdots A_n)^{-1} = A_n^{-1} \cdots A_3^{-1} A_2^{-1} A_1^{-1}$$

Solution   1. The formula is valid trivially when $n = 1$ because $A_1^{-1} = A_1^{-1}$.
2. Assuming that the formula is valid for k,

$$(A_1 A_2 A_3 \cdots A_k)^{-1} = A_k^{-1} \cdots A_3^{-1} A_2^{-1} A_1^{-1},$$

we must show that it is valid for $k + 1$. To do this we will use Theorem 2.9 which says that the inverse of a product of two invertible matrices is the product of their inverses in reverse order.

$$(A_1A_2A_3 \cdots A_kA_{k+1})^{-1} = [(A_1A_2A_3 \cdots A_k)A_{k+1}]^{-1}$$
$$= A_{k+1}^{-1}(A_1A_2A_3 \cdots A_k)^{-1} \qquad \text{Theorem 2.9}$$
$$= A_{k+1}^{-1}(A_k^{-1} \cdots A_3^{-1}A_2^{-1}A_1^{-1}) \qquad \text{Induction hypothesis}$$
$$= A_{k+1}^{-1}A_k^{-1} \cdots A_3^{-1}A_2^{-1}A_1^{-1}$$

Hence we have shown that the formula is valid for $k + 1$.

Combining the results of parts (1) and (2), we can conclude by mathematical induction that the formula is valid for *all* positive integers n.

Mathematical Induction—Exercises

In Exercises 1–4, use mathematical induction to prove that the formula is valid for all positive integers n.

1. $1 + 2 + 3 + \cdots + n = \dfrac{n(n + 1)}{2}$

2. $1^3 + 2^3 + 3^3 + \cdots + n^3 = \dfrac{n^2(n + 1)^2}{4}$

3. $3 + 7 + 11 + 15 + \cdots + (4n - 1) = n(2n + 1)$

4. $\left(1 + \dfrac{1}{1}\right)\left(1 + \dfrac{1}{2}\right)\left(1 + \dfrac{1}{3}\right) \cdots \left(1 + \dfrac{1}{n}\right) = n + 1$

In Exercises 5 and 6, conjecture a formula for the sum of the first n terms of the sequence. Then use mathematical induction to prove that the formula is valid.

5. $2^1, 2^2, 2^3, 2^4, \ldots$

6. $\dfrac{1}{1 \cdot 2}, \dfrac{1}{2 \cdot 3}, \dfrac{1}{3 \cdot 4}, \dfrac{1}{4 \cdot 5}, \ldots$

In Exercises 7 and 8 use mathematical induction to prove the given inequality for the indicated integer values of n.

7. $n! > 2^n, \quad n \geq 4$.

8. $\dfrac{1}{\sqrt{1}} + \dfrac{1}{\sqrt{2}} + \dfrac{1}{\sqrt{3}} + \cdots + \dfrac{1}{\sqrt{n}} > \sqrt{n}, \quad n \geq 2$.

9. Prove that for all integers $n > 0$,

$$a^0 + a^1 + a^2 + a^3 + \cdots + a^n = \dfrac{1 - a^{n+1}}{1 - a}, \quad (a \neq 1)$$

10. (From Chapter 2) Use mathematical induction to prove that

$$(A_1A_2A_3 \cdots A_n)^T = A_n^T \cdots A_3^TA_2^TA_1^T,$$

assuming that $A_1, A_2, A_3, \ldots, A_n$ are matrices with sizes such that the multiplications are defined.

11. (From Chapter 3) Use mathematical induction to prove that

$$|A_1A_2A_3 \cdots A_n| = |A_1| \, |A_2| \, |A_3| \cdots |A_n|,$$

where $A_1, A_2, A_3, \ldots, A_n$ are square matrices of the same size.

COMPUTER ALGEBRA SYSTEMS AND GRAPHING
CALCULATORS

To help you become acquainted with the rudiments of using a Computer Algebra System (CAS) or graphing calculator, the following pages contain certain introductory instructions for the following popular systems: MATLAB, MAPLE, MATHEMATICA, DERIVE, and MATRIXPAD, as well as information about various graphing calculator models.

Introduction to MATLAB

The purpose of this introduction is to illustrate some basic MATLAB commands for linear algebra. We suggest that you complete the following series of simple examples while actually working at the computer terminal. Once you have signed on to MATLAB, you should type in your commands to the right of the prompt >.

1. Enter the matrix

$$a = \begin{bmatrix} 1 & 2 & 3 \\ 4 & 5 & 6 \\ 7 & 8 & 0 \end{bmatrix}$$

by typing **a = [1 2 3; 4 5 6; 7 8 0]** and hitting the **return** or **enter** key. Be sure to separate the entries in each row by spaces and to terminate the rows with semicolons. MATLAB should return the following matrix.

$$a = \begin{matrix} 1 & 2 & 3 \\ 4 & 5 & 6 \\ 7 & 8 & 0 \end{matrix}$$

2. Perform the following elementary commands on your matrix a. You should obtain the results indicated at the right.

(a) **inv(a)**

$$\text{ans} = \begin{matrix} -1.7778 & 0.8889 & -0.1111 \\ 1.5556 & -0.7778 & 0.2222 \\ -0.1111 & 0.2222 & -0.1111 \end{matrix}$$

(b) **a**′

$$\text{ans} = \begin{matrix} 1 & 4 & 7 \\ 2 & 5 & 8 \\ 3 & 6 & 0 \end{matrix}$$

(c) a***inv(a)**

$$\text{ans} = \begin{matrix} 1.0000 & 0 & -0.0000 \\ -0.0000 & 1.0000 & 0 \\ 0.0000 & -0.0000 & 1.0000 \end{matrix}$$

(d) **2*a**

$$\text{ans} = \begin{matrix} 2 & 4 & 6 \\ 8 & 10 & 12 \\ 14 & 16 & 0 \end{matrix}$$

(e) **rref(a)**

$$\text{ans} = \begin{matrix} 1 & 0 & 0 \\ 0 & 1 & 0 \\ 0 & 0 & 1 \end{matrix}$$

(f) **det(a)**

ans = 27

(g) **rank(a)**

ans = 3

(h) **diag(a)**

$$\text{ans} = \begin{matrix} 1 \\ 5 \\ 0 \end{matrix}$$

3. Enter the matrix **b** = [**7; 16; 7**]. You can solve the system of linear equations $a\mathbf{x} = \mathbf{b}$ in several ways:

(a) **a\b**

$$\text{ans} = \begin{matrix} 1 \\ 0 \\ 2 \end{matrix}$$

(b) $\mathbf{c} = [\mathbf{a} \ \mathbf{b}]$ and then **rref(c)**

$$c = \begin{array}{cccc} 1 & 2 & 3 & 7 \\ 4 & 5 & 6 & 16 \\ 7 & 8 & 0 & 7 \end{array}$$

$>>$ **rref(c)**

$$\text{ans} = \begin{array}{cccc} 1 & 0 & 0 & 1 \\ 0 & 1 & 0 & 0 \\ 0 & 0 & 1 & 2 \end{array}$$

4. Enter the matrices $\mathbf{A} = [\mathbf{1} \ \mathbf{2}; \ \mathbf{3} \ \mathbf{4}]$ and $\mathbf{B} = [\mathbf{2} \ \mathbf{0}; \ -\mathbf{3} \ \mathbf{5}]$ and perform the following matrix operations. Notice that MATLAB distinguishes between upper and lower case letters; using the letter B for labeling the matrix above is not the same as lower case b.

(a) $\mathbf{A} + \mathbf{B}$

$$\text{ans} = \begin{array}{cc} 3 & 2 \\ 0 & 9 \end{array}$$

(b) $\mathbf{A} - \mathbf{B}$

$$\text{ans} = \begin{array}{cc} -1 & 2 \\ 6 & -1 \end{array}$$

(c) $\mathbf{A} * \mathbf{B}$

$$\text{ans} = \begin{array}{cc} -4 & 10 \\ -6 & 20 \end{array}$$

5. What do the following commands do?
   (a) **zeros(3, 5)**
   (b) **eye(5)**
   (c) **rand(6)**
   (d) **hilb(6)**

6. Describe the effect of the following commands on the matrix $\mathbf{a} = [\mathbf{1 \ 2 \ 3; \ 4 \ 5 \ 6; \ 7 \ 8 \ 0}]$.
   (a) **a(2, 3)**
   (b) **a(2, :)**
   (c) **a(:, 3)**

7. You can obtain more information about MATLAB by typing **help.**

8. You can exit MATLAB by typing **exit.**

Introduction to MATRIXPAD

The purpose of this introduction is to illustrate some basic MATRIXPAD commands for linear algebra. We suggest you complete the following series of simple examples while actually working at the computer terminal. Once you have signed on to MATRIXPAD by typing **matrix** to the right of the prompt >, you will obtain the following screen:

| T-register | 3   3 \| 0 |
| Z-register | 3   3 \| 0 |

===

| Y-register | 3   3 \| 0 |

0	0	0
0	0	0
0	0	0

===

| X-register | 3   3 \| 0 |

0	0	0
0	0	0
0	0	0

===

Press <H> for Help   <Q> to Quit Program

1. Enter the matrix

$$A = \begin{bmatrix} 1 & 2 & 3 \\ 4 & 5 & 6 \\ 7 & 8 & 0 \end{bmatrix}$$

in the X register by typing each entry and then hitting the **Tab** key, the **Return** key, or one of the cursor keys to move to the next entry. You will need to experiment with the use of these keys to see what sort of cursor movement they cause. After entering all of the elements, the X register will look like the following:

| X-register | 3   3 \| 0 |

1	2	3
4	5	6
7	8	0

All operations must be performed on the X register and all results appear in the X register.

2. Perform the following elementary commands on your matrix A. To save yourself the time of re-inputting this matrix for each operation, save it now with the name A by typing the letter **S** (for save) and then **A** and the **Return** key. The result for each procedure is shown below.

(a) Hit the function key **F7** to find the inverse. (If the entries in the resulting matrix appear as fractions, you can change them to their decimal form by hitting **Alt A.**)

X-register   3   3 | 0

−1.77778	.88889	−.11111
1.55556	−.77778	.22222
−.11111	.22222	−.11111

(b) Recall the original matrix A to the X register by hitting **R** (for recall), and then at the prompt, **A** and **Return.** Hit the key **F1** to find the transpose of A.

X-register   3   3 | 0

1	4	7
2	5	8
3	6	0

(c) Recall the original matrix A to the X register as you did in part (b). Then copy it to the Y register by typing **U** (for upstack). Hit the key **F7** to find the inverse of A again, and then hit **F8** to multiply the matrix in the Y register by the matrix in the X register (that is, to multiply AA^{-1}).

X-register   3   3 | 0

1	0	0
0	1	0
0	0	1

(d) Recall matrix A to the X register. Hit **Shift F10** and then the number **2** and **Return** at the prompt at the bottom of the screen to multiply A by the scalar 2.

A   3   3 | 0

2	4	6
8	10	12
14	16	0

(e) Recall matrix A to the X register. Hit the key **F6** to row-reduce the matrix.

X-register   3   3 | 0

1	0	0
0	1	0
0	0	1

(f) Recall matrix A to the X register. Hit the key **F5** to find the determinant of A. This number will appear in the first line of the X register, and this register will still contain the matrix A.

A   3   3 | 0   DET = 27

        1   2   3
        4   5   6
        7   8   0

3. To solve the system $A\mathbf{x} = \mathbf{b}$ where $\mathbf{b} = \begin{bmatrix} 7 \\ 16 \\ 7 \end{bmatrix}$, you must first change the shape of the X register so that it can receive the augmented matrix that represents the system. Type the letter **F** in order to move the cursor to the first line of the X register. The three values on this line indicate the number of rows of the coefficient matrix, the number of columns of the coefficient matrix, and the number of columns of constants, respectively. Since the default values for the first two entries are both 3 (which is what we want), you can tab over them to the last entry. In this last position, type the number **1** to indicate that there is one column of constant values. Then hit **Return.**

Now input the entries for the last column of the augmented matrix

$$\begin{bmatrix} 1 & 2 & 3 & | & 7 \\ 4 & 5 & 6 & | & 16 \\ 7 & 8 & 0 & | & 7 \end{bmatrix}$$

into the X register and then hit the key **F6** to row-reduce. Now you can read off the solution from the resulting matrix, which is in the X register.

X-register   3   3 | 1

        1   0   0   1
        0   1   0   0
        0   0   1   2

4. Enter the matrix $P = \begin{bmatrix} 1 & 2 \\ 3 & 4 \end{bmatrix}$ into the X register, save it, and then move it to the Y register. Then enter the matrix $Q = \begin{bmatrix} 2 & 0 \\ -3 & 5 \end{bmatrix}$ into the X register and save it.

(a) Hit the key **F10** to find the sum $P + Q$.

Q   2   2 | 0

        3   2
        0   9

(b) Recall matrix Q to the X register. (Note that matrix P is still in the Y register.) Hit the key **F9** to find the difference $P - Q$.

$$
\begin{array}{ll}
Q & 2 \quad 2 \mid 0 \\
\quad -1 & \quad\quad 2 \\
\quad 6 & \quad\quad -1
\end{array}
$$

(c) Recall matrix Q to the X register. Hit the key **F8** to find the matrix product PQ.

$$
\begin{array}{ll}
\text{X-register} & 2 \quad 2 \mid 0 \\
\quad -4 & \quad\quad 10 \\
\quad -6 & \quad\quad 20
\end{array}
$$

5. Input any square matrix into the X register. What do the following keystrokes do to this matrix?
   (a) **F2**
   (b) **Shift F2**
6. Describe the effect of the following steps on matrix A from question 1.
   (a) Hit **Shift F5** followed by **R.** At the prompt at the bottom of the screen, type **2** and then hit **Return.**
   (b) Hit **Shift F5** followed by **C.** At the prompt at the bottom of the screen, type **3** and then hit **Return.**
7. You can obtain more information about MATRIXPAD by typing the letter **H.**
8. To quit MATRIXPAD, type the letter **Q** and then hit **Return.**

Introduction to MAPLE

The purpose of this introduction is to illustrate some basic MAPLE commands for linear algebra. We suggest that you complete the following series of simple examples while actually working at the computer terminal. Once you have signed on to MAPLE, you should type in your commands to the right of the prompt >.

Begin by loading the linear algebra package that comes with MAPLE by typing **with(linalg);** and hitting the **return** or **enter** key. Notice that all commands in MAPLE terminate with a semicolon ;.

1. Enter the matrix

$$
a = \begin{bmatrix} 1 & 2 & 3 \\ 4 & 5 & 6 \\ 7 & 8 & 0 \end{bmatrix}
$$

by typing **a: = matrix ([[1, 2, 3], [4, 5, 6], [7, 8, 0]]);** and hitting the **return** or **enter** key. Be sure to separate the entries in each row by commas and place each row of the matrix within brackets. MAPLE should return the following matrix.

$$
a : = \begin{bmatrix} 1 & 2 & 3 \\ 4 & 5 & 6 \\ 7 & 8 & 0 \end{bmatrix}
$$

2. Perform the following elementary commands on your matrix a. You should obtain the results indicated at the right.

   (a) **inverse(a);**

   $$\begin{bmatrix} -\frac{16}{9} & \frac{8}{9} & -\frac{1}{9} \\ \frac{14}{9} & -\frac{7}{9} & \frac{2}{9} \\ -\frac{1}{9} & \frac{2}{9} & -\frac{1}{9} \end{bmatrix}$$

   (b) **transpose(a);**

   $$\begin{bmatrix} 1 & 4 & 7 \\ 2 & 5 & 8 \\ 3 & 6 & 0 \end{bmatrix}$$

   (c) **multiply(a, inverse(a));**

   $$\begin{bmatrix} 1 & 0 & 0 \\ 0 & 1 & 0 \\ 0 & 0 & 1 \end{bmatrix}$$

   (d) **scalarmul(a, 2);**

   $$\begin{bmatrix} 2 & 4 & 6 \\ 8 & 10 & 12 \\ 14 & 16 & 0 \end{bmatrix}$$

   (e) **rref(a);**

   $$\begin{bmatrix} 1 & 0 & 0 \\ 0 & 1 & 0 \\ 0 & 0 & 1 \end{bmatrix}$$

   (f) **det(a);**

   $$27$$

   (g) **rank(a);**

   $$3$$

   (h) **diag(a, inverse(a));**

   $$\begin{bmatrix} 1 & 2 & 3 & 0 & 0 & 0 \\ 4 & 5 & 6 & 0 & 0 & 0 \\ 7 & 8 & 0 & 0 & 0 & 0 \\ 0 & 0 & 0 & -\frac{16}{9} & \frac{8}{9} & -\frac{1}{9} \\ 0 & 0 & 0 & \frac{14}{9} & -\frac{7}{9} & \frac{2}{9} \\ 0 & 0 & 0 & -\frac{1}{9} & \frac{2}{9} & -\frac{1}{9} \end{bmatrix}$$

3. Enter the column matrix **b: = transpose(matrix([[7, 16, 7]]));**. You can solve the system of linear equations $a\mathbf{x} = \mathbf{b}$ in several ways:

(a) **linsolve(a, b);**

$$\begin{bmatrix} 1 \\ 0 \\ 2 \end{bmatrix}$$

(b) **c: = augment(a, b);** and then **rref(c);**

$$c := \begin{bmatrix} 1 & 2 & 3 & 7 \\ 4 & 5 & 6 & 16 \\ 7 & 8 & 0 & 7 \end{bmatrix}$$

$$\begin{bmatrix} 1 & 0 & 0 & 1 \\ 0 & 1 & 0 & 0 \\ 0 & 0 & 1 & 2 \end{bmatrix}$$

4. Enter the matrices **A: = matrix([[1, 2],[3, 4]]);** and **B: = matrix([[2, 0],[−3, 5]]);** and perform the following matrix operations. Notice that MAPLE distinguishes between upper and lower case letters; using the letter B for labeling the matrix above is not the same as lower case b.

(a) **add(A, B);**

$$\begin{bmatrix} 3 & 2 \\ 0 & 9 \end{bmatrix}$$

(b) **add(A, B, 1, −1);**

$$\begin{bmatrix} -1 & 2 \\ 6 & -1 \end{bmatrix}$$

(c) **multiply(A, B);**

$$\begin{bmatrix} -4 & 10 \\ -6 & 20 \end{bmatrix}$$

5. What do the following commands do?

(a) **matrix(3, 5, 0);**
(b) **band([1], 5);**
(c) **randmatrix(4, 6);**
(d) **hilbert(6);**

6. Describe the effect of the following commands on the matrix **a: = matrix([[1, 2, 3],[4, 5, 6],[7, 8, 0]]);**

(a) **submatrix(a, 2..2, 3..3);**
(b) **submatrix(a, 2..2, 1..3);**
(c) **submatrix(a, 1..3, 3..3);**

7. You can obtain more information about a particular topic, such as eigenvalues, by typing **?eigenvalues**.

8. You can exit MAPLE by typing **quit;**.

Introduction to MATHEMATICA

The purpose of this introduction is to illustrate some basic MATHEMATICA commands for linear algebra. We suggest that you complete the following series of simple examples while actually working at the computer terminal. Once you have signed on to MATHEMATICA, you should type in your commands to the right of the prompt.

1. Enter the matrix

$$a = \begin{bmatrix} 1 & 2 & 3 \\ 4 & 5 & 6 \\ 7 & 8 & 0 \end{bmatrix}$$

by typing **a = {{1, 2, 3}, {4, 5, 6}, {7, 8, 0}}** and evaluating the expression (cell). Be sure to separate the entries in each row by commas and place each row of the matix within braces. MATHEMATICA should return the following matrix. You can obtain the more natural matrix display by typing **%/ /MatrixForm.**

> *Out[1]* =
>> {{1, 2, 3}, {4, 5, 6}, {7, 8, 0}}
>
> *In[2]* =
>> %//MatrixForm
>
> *Out[2]//MatrixForm* =
>> 1   2   3
>> 4   5   6
>> 7   8   0

2. Perform the following elementary commands on your matrix *a*. You should obtain the results indicated at the right.

(a) **Inverse[a] //MatrixForm**

> *Out[3]//MatrixForm* =
>> $-(\frac{16}{9})$ $\frac{8}{9}$ $-(\frac{1}{9})$
>> $\frac{14}{9}$ $-(\frac{7}{9})$ $\frac{2}{9}$
>> $-(\frac{1}{9})$ $\frac{2}{9}$ $-(\frac{1}{9})$

(b) **Transpose[a]**

> *Out[4]* =
>> {{1, 4, 7}, {2, 5, 8}, {3, 6, 0}}

(c) **a.Inverse[a]**

> *Out[5]* =
>> {{1, 0, 0}, {0, 1, 0}, {0, 0, 1}}

(d) **2∗a**

> *Out[6]* =
>> {{2, 4, 6}, {8, 10, 12}, {14, 16, 0}}

(e) **RowReduce[a]**

$Out[7] =$

$$\{\{1, 0, 0\}, \{0, 1, 0\}, \{0, 0, 1\}\}$$

(f) **Det[a]**

$Out[8] =$

27

3. Enter the matrix $\mathbf{b} = \{7, 16, 7\}$. You can solve the system of linear equations $a\mathbf{x} = \mathbf{b}$ in several ways:

(a) **LinearSolve[a, b]**

$Out[10] =$

$$\{1, 0, 2\}$$

(b) $\mathbf{c} =$ **Table[Append[a[[i]], b[[i]]], {i, 1, 3}]** and then **RowReduce[c]**

$Out[11] =$

$$\{\{1, 2, 3, 7\}, \{4, 5, 6, 16\}, \{7, 8, 0, 7\}\}$$

$In[12] =$

RowReduce[c]//MatrixForm

$Out[12]$ //MatrixForm$=$

1	0	0	1
0	1	0	0
0	0	1	2

4. Enter the matrices $\mathbf{A} = \{\{1, 2\}, \{3, 4\}\}$ and $\mathbf{B} = \{\{2, 0\}, \{-3, 5\}\}$ and perform the following matrix operations. Notice that MATHEMATICA distinguishes between upper and lower case letters; using the letter B for labeling the matrix above is not the same as lower case b.

(a) $\mathbf{A} + \mathbf{B}$

$Out[15] =$

$$\{\{3, 2\}, \{0, 9\}\}$$

(b) $\mathbf{A} - \mathbf{B}$

$Out[16] =$

$$\{\{-1, 2\}, \{6, -1\}\}$$

(c) **A.B** (matrix multiplication is not $A * B$)

$Out[17] =$

$$\{\{-4, 10\}, \{-6, 20\}\}$$

5. What do the following commands do?

(a) **Table[0, {i, 1, 3}, {j, 1, 5}]**

(b) **IdentityMatrix[5]**

(c) **Table[Random[Integer,{-100, 100}], {4}, {6}]//MatrixForm**

(d) **Table[1/(i + j - 1), {i, 1, 6}, {j, 1, 6}]**

6. Describe the effect of the following commands on the matrix $\mathbf{a} = [\mathbf{1\ 2\ 3;\ 4\ 5\ 6;\ 7\ 8\ 0}]$.
   (a) **a[[2, 3]]**
   (b) **a[[2]]**
   (c) **Transpose[a][[3]]**
7. You can obtain more information about a particular topic, such as determinants, by typing **?Det.**
8. You can exit MATHEMATICA by choosing **Close** from the file menu.

Introduction to DERIVE

The purpose of this introduction is to illustrate some basic DERIVE commands for linear algebra. We suggest that you complete the following series of simple examples while actually working at the computer terminal.
1. Enter the matrix
$$a = \begin{bmatrix} 1 & 2 & 3 \\ 4 & 5 & 6 \\ 7 & 8 & 0 \end{bmatrix}$$

   by using the **Author** feature, i.e. **a: = [[1, 2, 3], [4, 5, 6],[7, 8, 0]]** and hitting the **return** or **enter** key. Be sure to separate the entries in each row by commas and place each row of the matrix within brackets. DERIVE should return the following matrix.
$$a := \begin{bmatrix} 1 & 2 & 3 \\ 4 & 5 & 6 \\ 7 & 8 & 0 \end{bmatrix}$$

2. Perform the following elementary operations on your matrix a by typing the expression and **Simplifying** it. You should obtain the results indicated at the right.
   (a) $\mathbf{a^{-1}}$
$$\begin{bmatrix} -\frac{16}{9} & \frac{8}{9} & -\frac{1}{9} \\ \frac{14}{9} & -\frac{7}{9} & \frac{2}{9} \\ -\frac{1}{9} & \frac{2}{9} & -\frac{1}{9} \end{bmatrix}$$

   (b) $\mathbf{a`}$
$$\begin{bmatrix} 1 & 4 & 7 \\ 2 & 5 & 8 \\ 3 & 6 & 0 \end{bmatrix}$$

   (c) $\mathbf{a \star a^{-1}}$
$$\begin{bmatrix} 1 & 0 & 0 \\ 0 & 1 & 0 \\ 0 & 0 & 1 \end{bmatrix}$$

(d) **a ⋆ 2**

$$\begin{bmatrix} 2 & 4 & 6 \\ 8 & 10 & 12 \\ 14 & 16 & 0 \end{bmatrix}$$

(e) **Row_Reduce(a)**

$$\begin{bmatrix} 1 & 0 & 0 \\ 0 & 1 & 0 \\ 0 & 0 & 1 \end{bmatrix}$$

(f) **det(a)**

27

3. Enter the column matrix **b: = [[7],[16],[7]]**. You can solve the system of linear equations $a\mathbf{x} = \mathbf{b}$ in several ways.

(a) You can row-reduce the augmented matrix [a, b].

   Row_Reduce(a, b)

$$\begin{bmatrix} 1 & 0 & 0 & 1 \\ 0 & 1 & 0 & 0 \\ 0 & 0 & 1 & 2 \end{bmatrix}$$

(b) You can **Simplify** the expression $\begin{bmatrix} x \\ y \\ z \end{bmatrix} = a^{-1} \star b.$

$$\begin{bmatrix} x = 1 \\ y = 0 \\ z = 2 \end{bmatrix}$$

(c) You can **Solve** the equation $a\begin{bmatrix} x \\ y \\ z \end{bmatrix} = b.$

$$[x = 1, \ y = 0, \ z = 2]$$

4. Enter the matrices **A: = [[1, 2], [3, 4]]** and **B: = [[2, 0], [−3, 5]]** and perform the following matrix operations.

(a) **"A + B"**

$$\begin{bmatrix} 3 & 2 \\ 0 & 9 \end{bmatrix}$$

(b) **"A − B"**

$$\begin{bmatrix} -1 & 2 \\ 6 & -1 \end{bmatrix}$$

(c) **"A ⋆ B"**

$$\begin{bmatrix} -4 & 10 \\ -6 & 20 \end{bmatrix}$$

5. What do the following commands do?
    (a) **Vector(Vector(0, j, 1, 5), k, 1, 3)**
    (b) **Identity_Matrix(5)**
    (c) **Vector(Vector(Random(100), j, 1, 6), k, 1, 4)**
    (d) **Vector(Vector(1/(j + k − 1), j, 1, 6), k, 1, 6)**

6. Describe the effect of the following commands on the matrix
    a: = [[1, 2, 3], [4, 5, 6], [7, 8, 0]].
    (a) **Element(Element(a, 2), 3)**
    (b) **Element(a, 2)**
    (c) **Element(a` , 3)`**

7. You can obtain more information about a particular topic by typing **H** for help.

8. You can exit DERIVE by typing **q** for quit.

Graphing Calculators

The following chart lists various graphing calculators* and their built-in matrix capabilities. For example, the first row indicates that all the calculators can perform matrix addition. Further down the chart you see that only the *TI-85* and *HP-48G* are able to find the norm of a matrix.

matrix operation	TI–85	TI–82	TI–81	HP–48G	Casio cfx-9800G and fx-9700GE	SharpEL-9200/9300
addition	x	x	x	x	x	x
scalar multiplication	x	x	x	x	x	x
multiplication	x	x	x	x	x	x
elementary row operations	x	x	x	x	x	x
reduced row echelon form	x			x		
determinant	x	x	x	x	x	x
inverse	x	x	x	x	x	x
transpose	x	x	x	x	x	x
norm	x			x		
power	x	x		x		
eigenvalues	x			x		
LU decomposition	x			x		
identity matrix	x	x		x		
random matrix	x	x		x		
concatenate matrices	x	x		x		
condition number	x			x		
complex matrices	x			x		
vectors	x			x		

* For other calculator models, see your user's manual.

Technology Pitfalls

Many matrix computations in linear algebra can be performed by modern graphing calculators and computer software. However, you should be aware that these devices are not perfect because of roundoff error. That is, the calculator or computer must approximate fractions by decimals either by rounding off the last digit or truncating.

For example, evaluate $\frac{1}{6}$ using your calculator. On the *TI*-85 and *HP*-48G you will get .166666666667, which is not correct, since the calculator has rounded up the last digit. To analyze this more closely, evaluate $[(\frac{1}{6}) \cdot 3] - 0.5$. Do you get the expected answer of 0? Normally this kind of rounding will not cause much effect in your answers to problems in linear algebra, but it can happen. Here are a couple of simple examples.

1. Calculate the row reduced echelon form of the matrix $\begin{bmatrix} \frac{1}{6} & 1 \\ 1 & 6 \end{bmatrix}$. The correct answer is $\begin{bmatrix} 1 & 6 \\ 0 & 0 \end{bmatrix}$, but on the *HP*-48G we obtained the identity matrix because of roundoff error.

2. Calculate the determinant of the matrix $A = \begin{bmatrix} 3 & 11 \\ 2 & 6 \end{bmatrix}$ on the *TI*-85. Then calculate the greatest integer of the determinant, int det A. Again, roundoff error has produced an error.

3. The Hilbert matrix of order six is

$$H = \begin{bmatrix} 1 & \frac{1}{2} & \frac{1}{3} & \frac{1}{4} & \frac{1}{5} & \frac{1}{6} \\ \frac{1}{2} & \frac{1}{3} & \frac{1}{4} & \frac{1}{5} & \frac{1}{6} & \frac{1}{7} \\ \frac{1}{3} & \frac{1}{4} & \frac{1}{5} & \frac{1}{6} & \frac{1}{7} & \frac{1}{8} \\ \frac{1}{4} & \frac{1}{5} & \frac{1}{6} & \frac{1}{7} & \frac{1}{8} & \frac{1}{9} \\ \frac{1}{5} & \frac{1}{6} & \frac{1}{7} & \frac{1}{8} & \frac{1}{9} & \frac{1}{10} \\ \frac{1}{6} & \frac{1}{7} & \frac{1}{8} & \frac{1}{9} & \frac{1}{10} & \frac{1}{11} \end{bmatrix}.$$

This matrix is notorious for causing poor results in matrix computations. Try calculating $\mathrm{inv}(H) \cdot H$ to see if you obtain the identity matrix.

You might find it interesting to discover other examples for which your calculator gives erroneous results. In general, you should always be aware that such errors are possible, and accept your calculator output with some skepticism. You should read Section 10.1 for further discussion of roundoff error in the solution of systems of linear equations.

ANSWERS TO ODD-NUMBERED EXERCISES

Chapter 1

SECTION 1.1 (*page 11*)

1. Linear   **3.** Not linear   **5.** Not Linear

7. $x = 2t$
    $y = t$

9. $x = 1 - s - t$
    $y = s$
    $z = t$

11. $x_1 = 1 + 2s - 3t$
    $x_2 = s$
    $x_3 = t$

13. $x_1 = 5$
    $x_2 = 3$

15. $x = \frac{3}{2}$
    $y = \frac{3}{2}$
    $z = 0$

17. $x = 0$
    $y = 0$

19. $x = 2$
    $y = 0$

21. No solution

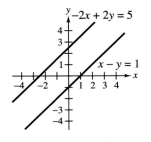

23. $x_1 = -1$
    $x_2 = -1$

25. $u = 40$
    $v = 40$

27. $x_1 = \frac{3}{5} + \frac{6}{5}t$
    $x_2 = t$

29. $x = -\frac{1}{3}$
    $y = -\frac{2}{3}$

31. $x = 7$
    $y = 1$

33. $x_1 = 8$
    $x_2 = 7$

35. $x = 1$
    $y = 2$
    $z = 3$

37. No solution

39. $x_1 = 10 - 3t$
    $x_2 = -7 + 5t$
    $x_3 = t$

41. $x_1 = 13 - 4t$
    $x_2 = \frac{45}{2} - \frac{15}{2}t$
    $x_3 = t$

43. No solution

45. $x = 1$
    $y = 0$
    $z = 3$
    $w = 2$

47. $x_1 = 11.2415$
    $x_2 = -60.9029$
    $x_3 = 40.7674$
    $x_4 = 27.4267$

49. $x_1 = 8.1124$
    $x_2 = -4.5588$
    $x_3 = -9.0448$

51. $x = 0$
    $y = 0$
    $z = 0$

53. $x = -\frac{3}{5}t$
    $y = \frac{4}{5}t$
    $z = t$

55. $3x_1 - x_2 = 4$
      $-3x_1 + x_2 = -4$
      (The answer is not unique.)

57. $x = 3$
    $y = -4$

59. $x = \cos \theta$
    $y = \sin \theta$

61. All $k \neq \pm 2$ **63.** All $k \neq \pm 1$

65. $k = \frac{8}{3}$ **67.** $k = 1, -2$

69. (a) Three lines intersecting at one point
    (b) Three coincident lines
    (c) Three lines having no common point

73. $x - 4y = -3$
      $5x - 6y = 13$

$x - 4y = -3$
$14y = 28$

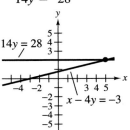

$x - 4y = -3$
    $y = 2$

$x = 5$
    $y = 2$

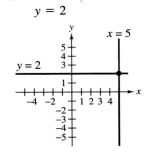

SECTION 1.2 (*page 24*)

1. 3×2 **3.** 1×5 **5.** 4×1

7. Reduced row-echelon form

9. Not in row-echelon form

11. Reduced row-echelon form

13. Reduced row-echelon form

15. $x_1 = 0$
$x_2 = 2$

17. $x_1 = \quad 2$
$x_2 = -1$
$x_3 = -1$

19. $x_1 = -26$
$x_2 = \quad 13$
$x_3 = \quad -7$
$x_4 = \quad 4$

21. $x = 3$
$y = 2$

23. $x = 5 + 3t$
$y = t$

25. No solution

27. $x = \quad 4$
$y = -2$

29. $x_1 = \quad 4$
$x_2 = -3$
$x_3 = \quad 2$

31. $x_1 = 1 + 2t$
$x_2 = 2 + 3t$
$x_3 = t$

33. No solution

35. $x = 0$
$y = 2 - 4t$
$z = t$

37. $x_1 = 23.5361 + 0.5278t$
$x_2 = 18.5444 + 4.1111t$
$x_3 = 7.4306 + 2.1389t$
$x_4 = t$

39. $x_1 = 2$
$x_2 = -2$
$x_3 = 3$
$x_4 = -5$
$x_5 = 1$

41. $x_1 = 0$
$x_2 = -t$
$x_3 = t$

43. $x_1 = -t$
$x_2 = s$
$x_3 = 0$
$x_4 = t$

45. (a) $a + b + c = 0$
(b) $a + b + c \neq 0$
(c) Not possible

47. (a) $x = \frac{8}{3} - \frac{5}{6}t$
$y = -\frac{8}{3} + \frac{5}{6}t$
$z = t$

(b) $x = \frac{18}{7} - \frac{11}{14}t$
$y = -\frac{20}{7} + \frac{13}{14}t$
$z = t$

(c) $x = 3 - t$
$y = -3 + t$
$z = t$

(d) Each system has an infinite number of solutions.

49. $\begin{bmatrix} 1 & 0 \\ 0 & 1 \end{bmatrix}$

51. $\begin{bmatrix} 1 & 0 \\ 0 & 1 \end{bmatrix}, \begin{bmatrix} 1 & k \\ 0 & 0 \end{bmatrix}, \begin{bmatrix} 0 & 1 \\ 0 & 0 \end{bmatrix}, \begin{bmatrix} 0 & 0 \\ 0 & 0 \end{bmatrix}$

53. $ad - bc \neq 0$ **55.** $\lambda = 1, 3$

57. Yes, it is possible:
$x_1 + x_2 + x_3 = 0$
$x_1 + x_2 + x_3 = 1$

59. $\alpha = \pi/3, 5\pi/3, \beta = \pi/2$

61. The rows have been interchanged.

SECTION 1.3 (*page 34*)

1. (a) $p(x) = 29 - 18x + 3x^2$
(b)
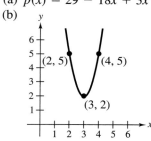

3. (a) $p(x) = 2x$
(b)

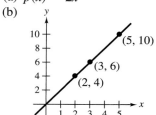

5. (a) $p(z) = 7 + \frac{7}{2}z + \frac{3}{2}z^2$
$p(x) = 7 + \frac{7}{2}(x - 1987)$
$+ \frac{3}{2}(x - 1987)^2$
(b)

7. y is not a function of x because the x-value of 3 is repeated.

9. $p(x) = 1 + x$

$y = \dfrac{1}{1+x}$

$y = \dfrac{x^2}{15} - \dfrac{7x}{15} + 1$

$(0, 1)$ $\left(2, \dfrac{1}{3}\right)$ $\left(4, \dfrac{1}{5}\right)$

11. $p(x) = -3x + x^3$

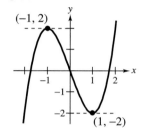

$(-1, 2)$

$(1, -2)$

13. $p(x) = 179.3 + 28.13x - 4.13x^2$

1985: $x = 3.5 \longrightarrow p = 227.1$

1990: $x = 4 \longrightarrow p = 225.1$

15. $p(x) = -\dfrac{4}{\pi^2}x^2 + \dfrac{4}{\pi}x$

$\sin\dfrac{\pi}{3} \approx \dfrac{8}{9} \approx 0.889$

(Actual value is $\sqrt{3}/2 \approx 0.866$.)

19. (a) $x_1 = s$ (b) $x_1 = 0$ (c) $x_1 = 0$

$x_2 = t$ $x_2 = 0$ $x_2 = -500$

$x_3 = 600 - s$ $x_3 = 600$ $x_3 = 600$

$x_4 = s - t$ $x_4 = 0$ $x_4 = 500$

$x_5 = 500 - t$ $x_5 = 500$ $x_5 = 1000$

$x_6 = s$ $x_6 = 0$ $x_6 = 0$

$x_7 = t$ $x_7 = 0$ $x_7 = -500$

21. (a) $x_1 = 100 + t$ (b) $x_1 = 100$ (c) $x_1 = 200$

$x_2 = -100 + t$ $x_2 = -100$ $x_2 = 0$

$x_3 = 200 + t$ $x_3 = 200$ $x_3 = 300$

$x_4 = t$ $x_4 = 0$ $x_4 = 100$

23. $I_1 = 0$

$I_2 = 1$

$I_3 = 1$

25. (a) $I_1 = 1$ (b) $I_1 = 0$

$I_2 = 2$ $I_2 = 1$

$I_3 = 1$ $I_3 = 1$

Review Exercises – Chapter 1 (*page 36*)

1. $x = -\dfrac{1}{4} + \dfrac{1}{2}s - \dfrac{3}{2}t$

$y = s$

$z = t$

3. Row-echelon form (not reduced)

5. Not in row-echelon form   **7.** $x_1 = -2t$

$x_2 = t$

$x_3 = 0$

9. $x = 1$ **11.** $x = 4$ **13.** $x = 0$

$y = 1$ $y = 8$ $y = 0$

15. No solution   **17.** $x_1 = -\dfrac{1}{2}$ **19.** $x = 0$

$x_2 = \dfrac{4}{5}$ $y = 0$

21. $x = 2$ **23.** $x = \dfrac{1}{2}$ **25.** $x = 4 + 3t$

$y = -3$ $y = -\dfrac{1}{3}$ $y = 5 + 2t$

$z = 3$ $z = 1$ $z = t$

27. $x = \dfrac{3}{2} - 2t$ **29.** $x_1 = 1$

$y = 1 + 2t$ $x_2 = 4$

$z = t$ $x_3 = -3$

$x_4 = -2$

31. $x_1 = 0$ **33.** $x_1 = -4t$ **35.** $k = \pm 1$

$x_2 = 0$ $x_2 = -\dfrac{1}{2}t$

$x_3 = 0$ $x_3 = t$

37. (a) $b = 2a$ and $a \neq -3$

(b) $b \neq 2a$

(c) $a = -3$ and $b = -6$

39. The two matrices are row-equivalent because each is row-equivalent to

$$\begin{bmatrix} 1 & 0 & 0 \\ 0 & 1 & 0 \\ 0 & 0 & 1 \end{bmatrix}.$$

41.
$$\begin{bmatrix} 1 & 0 & -1 & -2 & \cdots & 2-n \\ 0 & 1 & 2 & 3 & \cdots & n-1 \\ 0 & 0 & 0 & 0 & \cdots & 0 \\ \vdots & & & & & \vdots \\ 0 & 0 & 0 & 0 & \cdots & 0 \end{bmatrix}$$

43. (a) $p(x) = 90 - \frac{135}{2}x + \frac{25}{2}x^2$

(b)

45. $p(x) = 50 + \frac{15}{2}x + \frac{5}{2}x^2$

(First year is represented by $x = 0$.)

Fourth-year sales: $p(3) = 95$

47. (a) $x_1 = 100 - r + t$ (b) $x_1 = 50$

$x_2 = 300 - r + s$ $x_2 = 250$

$x_3 = r$ $x_3 = 100$

$x_4 = -s + t$ $x_4 = 0$

$x_5 = s$ $x_5 = 50$

$x_6 = t$ $x_6 = 50$

CHAPTER 1 MATLAB (*page 39*)

1. $x = 1$ **3.** $x = 1.00000000000012$

$y = -1$ $y = 1.00000000000009$

$z = 2$ $z = 1.00000000000007$

$w = 1.00000000000006$

5. $x = 0$

$y = 2 - 4t$

$z = t$

7. $p(x) = 0.8667x^2 + 3.4x - 6.2667$

9. 4.84 billion

Chapter 2

SECTION 2.1 (*page 51*)

1. (a) $\begin{bmatrix} 3 & -2 \\ 1 & 7 \end{bmatrix}$ (b) $\begin{bmatrix} -1 & 0 \\ 3 & -9 \end{bmatrix}$

(c) $\begin{bmatrix} 2 & -2 \\ 4 & -2 \end{bmatrix}$ (d) $\begin{bmatrix} 0 & -1 \\ 5 & -10 \end{bmatrix}$

3. (a) $\begin{bmatrix} 7 & 3 \\ 1 & 9 \\ -2 & 15 \end{bmatrix}$ (b) $\begin{bmatrix} 5 & -5 \\ 3 & -1 \\ -4 & -5 \end{bmatrix}$

(c) $\begin{bmatrix} 12 & -2 \\ 4 & 8 \\ -6 & 10 \end{bmatrix}$ (d) $\begin{bmatrix} 11 & -6 \\ 5 & 3 \\ -7 & 0 \end{bmatrix}$

5. (a) $\begin{bmatrix} 3 & 3 & -2 & 1 & 1 \\ -2 & 5 & 7 & -6 & -8 \end{bmatrix}$

(b) $\begin{bmatrix} 1 & 1 & 0 & -1 & 1 \\ 4 & -3 & -11 & 6 & 6 \end{bmatrix}$

(c) $\begin{bmatrix} 4 & 4 & -2 & 0 & 2 \\ 2 & 2 & -4 & 0 & -2 \end{bmatrix}$

(d) $\begin{bmatrix} 3 & 3 & -1 & -1 & 2 \\ 5 & -2 & -13 & 6 & 5 \end{bmatrix}$

7. (a) $c_{21} = -6$ **9.** $x = 3, y = 2, z = 1$

(b) $c_{13} = 29$

11. (a) $\begin{bmatrix} 0 & 15 \\ 6 & 12 \end{bmatrix}$ (b) $\begin{bmatrix} -2 & 2 \\ 31 & 14 \end{bmatrix}$

13. (a) $\begin{bmatrix} 0 & -10 \\ 10 & 0 \end{bmatrix}$ (b) $\begin{bmatrix} 0 & -10 \\ 10 & 0 \end{bmatrix}$

15. (a) $\begin{bmatrix} 6 & -21 & 15 \\ 8 & -23 & 19 \\ 4 & 7 & 5 \end{bmatrix}$ (b) $\begin{bmatrix} 9 & 0 & 13 \\ 7 & -2 & 21 \\ 1 & 4 & -19 \end{bmatrix}$

17. (a) Not defined   (b) $\begin{bmatrix} 3 & -4 \\ 10 & 16 \\ 26 & 46 \end{bmatrix}$

19. (a) $\begin{bmatrix} -1 & 19 \\ 4 & -27 \\ 0 & 14 \end{bmatrix}$ (b) Not defined

21. (a) $\begin{bmatrix} 1 & 0 & 0 \\ 0 & 1 & 0 \\ 0 & 0 & 1 \end{bmatrix}$ (b) $\begin{bmatrix} 1 & 0 & 0 \\ 0 & 1 & 0 \\ 0 & 0 & 1 \end{bmatrix}$

23. (a) $\begin{bmatrix} 60 & 72 \\ -20 & -24 \\ 10 & 12 \\ 60 & 72 \end{bmatrix}$ (b) Not defined

25. $\begin{bmatrix} 1 & 3 \\ 2 & -1 \end{bmatrix}\begin{bmatrix} x_1 \\ x_2 \end{bmatrix} = \begin{bmatrix} -1 \\ 3 \end{bmatrix}$

$\begin{bmatrix} x_1 \\ x_2 \end{bmatrix} = \begin{bmatrix} \frac{8}{7} \\ -\frac{5}{7} \end{bmatrix}$

27. $\begin{bmatrix} 8 & -8 \\ -3 & 2 \end{bmatrix}\begin{bmatrix} x_1 \\ x_2 \end{bmatrix} = \begin{bmatrix} 0 \\ 0 \end{bmatrix}$

$\begin{bmatrix} x_1 \\ x_2 \end{bmatrix} = \begin{bmatrix} 0 \\ 0 \end{bmatrix}$

29. $\begin{bmatrix} 1 & 0 & 2 \\ 3 & -2 & 1 \\ -2 & 2 & -1 \end{bmatrix}\begin{bmatrix} x_1 \\ x_2 \\ x_3 \end{bmatrix} = \begin{bmatrix} 5 \\ 8 \\ -3 \end{bmatrix}$

$\begin{bmatrix} x_1 \\ x_2 \\ x_3 \end{bmatrix} = \begin{bmatrix} 5 \\ \frac{7}{2} \\ 0 \end{bmatrix}$

31. $\begin{bmatrix} -5 & 2 \\ 3 & -1 \end{bmatrix}$

33. $a = -2 - t$
$b = -1 - t$
$c = 5 + 2t$
$d = t$

35. $w = z, \quad x = -y$

37. $\begin{bmatrix} 1 & 0 & 0 \\ 0 & 4 & 0 \\ 0 & 0 & 9 \end{bmatrix}$

41. 2

43. (a) $\text{Tr}(A + B) = \text{Tr}[a_{ij} + b_{ij}] = \sum_{i=1}^{n}(a_{ii} + b_{ii})$

$= \sum_{i=1}^{n}a_{ii} + \sum_{i=1}^{n}b_{ii}$

$= \text{Tr}(A) + \text{Tr}(B)$

(b) $\text{Tr}(cA) = \sum_{i=1}^{n}(ca_{ii}) = c\sum_{i=1}^{n}a_{ii} = c\,\text{Tr}(A)$

47. Assume that A is an $m \times n$ matrix and B is a $p \times q$ matrix. Since the product AB is defined, we know that $n = p$. Moreover, since AB is square, we know that $m = q$. Therefore, B must be of order $n \times m$, which implies that the product BA is defined.

51. $\begin{bmatrix} 110 & 99 & 77 & 33 \\ 44 & 22 & 66 & 66 \end{bmatrix}$

53. $[1250 \quad 1331.25 \quad 981.25]$
This row matrix represents the profits at each of the three outlets.

55. $\left[\begin{array}{cc|c} -1 & 4 & 0 \\ -1 & 1 & 0 \\ 0 & 0 & 5 \end{array}\right]$

57. $\mathbf{b} = 3\begin{bmatrix} 1 \\ 3 \end{bmatrix} + 0\begin{bmatrix} -1 \\ -3 \end{bmatrix} - 2\begin{bmatrix} 2 \\ 1 \end{bmatrix}$
(The answer is not unique.)

SECTION 2.2 (*page 62*)

1. $\begin{bmatrix} 3 & 2 \\ 13 & 4 \end{bmatrix}$ **3.** $\begin{bmatrix} 0 & -12 \\ 12 & -24 \end{bmatrix}$ **5.** $\begin{bmatrix} 7 & 7 \\ 28 & 14 \end{bmatrix}$

7. $\begin{bmatrix} 3 & \frac{2}{3} \\ -\frac{4}{3} & \frac{11}{3} \\ \frac{10}{3} & 0 \end{bmatrix}$ **9.** $\begin{bmatrix} -14 & -4 \\ 7 & -17 \\ -17 & -2 \end{bmatrix}$

11. $\begin{bmatrix} -3 & -5 & -10 \\ -2 & -5 & -5 \end{bmatrix}$ **13.** $\begin{bmatrix} 1 & 6 & -1 \\ -2 & -2 & -8 \end{bmatrix}$

15. $\begin{bmatrix} 12 & -4 \\ 8 & 4 \end{bmatrix}$ **17.** $AC = BC = \begin{bmatrix} 12 & -6 & 9 \\ 16 & -8 & 12 \\ 4 & -2 & 3 \end{bmatrix}$

19. $\begin{bmatrix} 1 & 0 \\ 0 & 1 \end{bmatrix}$ **21.** $\begin{bmatrix} 2 & 2 \\ 0 & 0 \end{bmatrix}$

23. (a) $\begin{bmatrix} 2 & 4 \\ -1 & 3 \\ 3 & -5 \end{bmatrix}$ (b) $\begin{bmatrix} 20 & 10 & -14 \\ 10 & 10 & -18 \\ -14 & -18 & 34 \end{bmatrix}$

(c) $\begin{bmatrix} 14 & -10 \\ -10 & 50 \end{bmatrix}$

25. (a) $\begin{bmatrix} 6 & 0 & 7 \\ 0 & -4 & 5 \end{bmatrix}$ (b) $\begin{bmatrix} 85 & 35 \\ 35 & 41 \end{bmatrix}$

(c) $\begin{bmatrix} 36 & 0 & 42 \\ 0 & 16 & -20 \\ 42 & -20 & 74 \end{bmatrix}$

27. $(A + B)(A - B) = A^2 + BA - AB - B^2$, which is not necessarily equal to $A^2 - B^2$ because AB is not necessarily equal to BA.

29. $(AB)^T = B^T A^T = \begin{bmatrix} 2 & -5 \\ 4 & -1 \end{bmatrix}$

31. $a = 2, \quad b = -1$

35. $\begin{bmatrix} 1 & 0 & 0 \\ 0 & -1 & 0 \\ 0 & 0 & 1 \end{bmatrix}$ **37.** $\begin{bmatrix} \pm 3 & 0 \\ 0 & \pm 2 \end{bmatrix}$

39. $\begin{bmatrix} -4 & 0 \\ 8 & 2 \end{bmatrix}$ **41.** $\begin{bmatrix} 0 & 0 & 0 \\ 0 & 0 & 0 \\ 0 & 0 & 0 \end{bmatrix}$

53. Skew-symmetric   **55.** Symmetric

59. $A = \frac{1}{2}(A - A^T) + \frac{1}{2}(A + A^T) =$

$\begin{bmatrix} 0 & 4 & -\frac{1}{2} \\ -4 & 0 & -\frac{1}{2} \\ \frac{1}{2} & \frac{1}{2} & 0 \end{bmatrix} + \begin{bmatrix} 2 & 1 & \frac{7}{2} \\ 1 & 6 & \frac{1}{2} \\ \frac{7}{2} & \frac{1}{2} & 1 \end{bmatrix}$

Skew-symmetric   Symmetric

61. (a) $A = \begin{bmatrix} 0 & 1 \\ 1 & 0 \end{bmatrix}, \quad B = \begin{bmatrix} -1 & 1 \\ 1 & 0 \end{bmatrix}$

(The answer is not unique.)

SECTION 2.3 (*page 75*)

1. $AB = \begin{bmatrix} 1 & 0 \\ 0 & 1 \end{bmatrix} = BA$

3. $AB = \begin{bmatrix} 1 & 0 & 0 \\ 0 & 1 & 0 \\ 0 & 0 & 1 \end{bmatrix} = BA$

5. $AB = \begin{bmatrix} 1 & 0 & 0 \\ 0 & 1 & 0 \\ 0 & 0 & 1 \end{bmatrix} = BA$ **7.** $\begin{bmatrix} 7 & -2 \\ -3 & 1 \end{bmatrix}$

9. $\begin{bmatrix} -19 & -33 \\ -4 & -7 \end{bmatrix}$ **11.** Singular

13. $\begin{bmatrix} \frac{4}{5} & -\frac{3}{5} \\ -\frac{1}{5} & \frac{2}{5} \end{bmatrix}$ **15.** $\begin{bmatrix} 1 & 1 & -1 \\ -3 & 2 & -1 \\ 3 & -3 & 2 \end{bmatrix}$

17. Singular   **19.** $\begin{bmatrix} -24 & 7 & 1 & -2 \\ -10 & 3 & 0 & -1 \\ -29 & 7 & 3 & -2 \\ 12 & -3 & -1 & 1 \end{bmatrix}$

21. $\begin{bmatrix} -\frac{3}{2} & \frac{3}{2} & 1 \\ \frac{9}{2} & -\frac{7}{2} & -3 \\ -1 & 1 & 1 \end{bmatrix}$ **23.** $\begin{bmatrix} 0 & -2 & 0.8 \\ -10 & 4 & 4.4 \\ 10 & -2 & -3.2 \end{bmatrix}$

25. Singular   **27.** $\begin{bmatrix} 1 & 0 & 0 \\ -\frac{3}{4} & \frac{1}{4} & 0 \\ \frac{7}{20} & -\frac{1}{4} & \frac{1}{5} \end{bmatrix}$

29. Singular

31. (a) $x = 4$ (b) $x = -8$ (c) $x = 0$
          $y = 8$ $y = -11$ $y = 0$

33. (a) $x = -5$ (b) $x = -3$ (c) $x = 0$
          $y = -40.5$ $y = -24$ $y = 0$
          $z = 48$ $z = 28$ $z = 0$

35. (a) $\begin{bmatrix} 35 & 17 \\ 4 & 10 \end{bmatrix}$ (b) $\begin{bmatrix} 2 & -7 \\ 5 & 6 \end{bmatrix}$

(c) $\begin{bmatrix} -31 & 40 \\ -56 & 1 \end{bmatrix}$ (d) $\begin{bmatrix} 1 & \frac{5}{2} \\ -\frac{7}{2} & 3 \end{bmatrix}$

37. (a) $\frac{1}{16}\begin{bmatrix} 138 & 56 & -84 \\ 37 & 26 & -71 \\ 24 & 34 & 3 \end{bmatrix}$ **(b)** $\frac{1}{4}\begin{bmatrix} 4 & 6 & 1 \\ -2 & 2 & 4 \\ 3 & -8 & 2 \end{bmatrix}$

(c) $\frac{1}{16}\begin{bmatrix} 7 & 0 & 34 \\ 28 & -40 & -14 \\ 30 & 14 & -25 \end{bmatrix}$ **(d)** $\frac{1}{8}\begin{bmatrix} 4 & -2 & 3 \\ 6 & 2 & -8 \\ 1 & 4 & 2 \end{bmatrix}$

39. $x = 4$ **41.** $\begin{bmatrix} -1 & \frac{1}{2} \\ \frac{3}{4} & -\frac{1}{4} \end{bmatrix}$

45. Assume that A is nonsingular and symmetric, $A^T = A$. Then
$$(A^{-1})^T = (A^T)^{-1}$$
$$= A^{-1}$$
(Exercise 44.)
which implies that A^{-1} is symmetric.

49. Because $AB = 0$, $A^{-1}(AB) = A^{-1}0 = 0$, you have $(A^{-1}A)B = IB = B = 0$.

51. The sum of two invertible matrices is not necessarily invertible. For example, let
$$A = \begin{bmatrix} 1 & 0 \\ 0 & 1 \end{bmatrix} \quad \text{and} \quad B = \begin{bmatrix} -1 & 0 \\ 0 & -1 \end{bmatrix}.$$

53. (a) $\begin{bmatrix} -1 & 0 & 0 \\ 0 & \frac{1}{3} & 0 \\ 0 & 0 & \frac{1}{2} \end{bmatrix}$ **(b)** $\begin{bmatrix} 2 & 0 & 0 \\ 0 & 3 & 0 \\ 0 & 0 & 4 \end{bmatrix}$

55. Let $H = I - 2\mathbf{u}\mathbf{u}^T$, where $\mathbf{u}^T\mathbf{u} = 1$. Then $H^T = (I - 2\mathbf{u}\mathbf{u}^T)^T = I - 2(\mathbf{u}\mathbf{u}^T)^T = I - 2\mathbf{u}\mathbf{u}^T = H$.
Furthermore, $HH = (I - 2\mathbf{u}\mathbf{u}^T)(I - 2\mathbf{u}\mathbf{u}^T) = I - 4\mathbf{u}\mathbf{u}^T + 4\mathbf{u}\mathbf{u}^T\mathbf{u}\mathbf{u}^T = I - 4\mathbf{u}\mathbf{u}^T + 4\mathbf{u}\mathbf{u}^T = I$, and hence $H^{-1} = H$.

SECTION 2.4 (*page 85*)

1. Elementary, multiply Row 2 by 2

3. Elementary, add 2 times Row 1 to Row 2

5. Not elementary   **7.** Not elementary

9. Elementary, add -5 times Row 2 to Row 3

11. $\begin{bmatrix} 0 & 0 & 1 \\ 0 & 1 & 0 \\ 1 & 0 & 0 \end{bmatrix}$ **13.** $\begin{bmatrix} 0 & 0 & 1 \\ 0 & 1 & 0 \\ 1 & 0 & 0 \end{bmatrix}$

15. $\begin{bmatrix} 0 & 1 \\ 1 & 0 \end{bmatrix}$ **17.** $\begin{bmatrix} 1 & 0 \\ -4 & 1 \end{bmatrix}$

19. $\begin{bmatrix} 0 & 0 & 1 \\ 0 & 1 & 0 \\ 1 & 0 & 0 \end{bmatrix}$ **21.** $\begin{bmatrix} \frac{1}{k} & 0 & 0 \\ 0 & 1 & 0 \\ 0 & 0 & 1 \end{bmatrix}$

23. $\begin{bmatrix} 1 & 0 & 0 & 0 \\ 0 & 1 & -k & 0 \\ 0 & 0 & 1 & 0 \\ 0 & 0 & 0 & 1 \end{bmatrix}$

25. $\begin{bmatrix} 1 & 0 \\ 1 & 1 \end{bmatrix}\begin{bmatrix} 1 & -1 \\ 0 & 1 \end{bmatrix}\begin{bmatrix} 1 & 0 \\ 0 & -2 \end{bmatrix}$
(The answer is not unique.)

27. $\begin{bmatrix} 1 & 1 \\ 0 & 1 \end{bmatrix}\begin{bmatrix} 1 & 0 \\ 3 & 1 \end{bmatrix}\begin{bmatrix} 1 & 0 \\ 0 & -1 \end{bmatrix}$
(The answer is not unique.)

29. $\begin{bmatrix} 1 & 0 & 0 \\ -1 & 1 & 0 \\ 0 & 0 & 1 \end{bmatrix}\begin{bmatrix} 1 & -2 & 0 \\ 0 & 1 & 0 \\ 0 & 0 & 1 \end{bmatrix}$
(The answer is not unique.)

31. $\begin{bmatrix} 1 & 0 & 0 \\ 1 & 1 & 0 \\ 0 & 0 & 1 \end{bmatrix}\begin{bmatrix} 2 & 0 & 0 \\ 0 & 1 & 0 \\ 0 & 0 & 1 \end{bmatrix}\begin{bmatrix} 1 & 0 & 0 \\ 0 & 2 & 0 \\ 0 & 0 & 1 \end{bmatrix}$

$\begin{bmatrix} 1 & 0 & 0 \\ 0 & 1 & 0 \\ 0 & 2 & 1 \end{bmatrix}\begin{bmatrix} 1 & 0 & 0 \\ 0 & 1 & 0 \\ 0 & 0 & -3 \end{bmatrix}\begin{bmatrix} 1 & 0 & -4 \\ 0 & 1 & 0 \\ 0 & 0 & 1 \end{bmatrix}$

$\begin{bmatrix} 1 & 0 & 0 \\ 0 & 1 & 5 \\ 0 & 0 & 1 \end{bmatrix}$ (The answer is not unique.)

33. (a) EA will have two rows interchanged. (The same rows are interchanged in E.)
(b) $E^2 = I_n$

35. $A^{-1} = \begin{bmatrix} 1 & -a & 0 \\ -b & ab + 1 & 0 \\ 0 & 0 & \frac{1}{c} \end{bmatrix}$

37. No. For example, $\begin{bmatrix} 1 & 0 \\ 2 & 1 \end{bmatrix}\begin{bmatrix} 1 & 1 \\ 0 & 1 \end{bmatrix} = \begin{bmatrix} 1 & 1 \\ 2 & 3 \end{bmatrix}$.

39. $\begin{bmatrix} 1 & 0 \\ -2 & 1 \end{bmatrix}\begin{bmatrix} 1 & 0 \\ 0 & 1 \end{bmatrix}$

(The answer is not unique.)

41. $\begin{bmatrix} 1 & 0 & 0 \\ 2 & 1 & 0 \\ -1 & 1 & 1 \end{bmatrix}\begin{bmatrix} 3 & 0 & 1 \\ 0 & 1 & -1 \\ 0 & 0 & 2 \end{bmatrix}$

(The answer is not unique.)

43. (a) $\begin{bmatrix} 1 & 0 & 0 \\ 0 & 1 & 0 \\ -1 & 2 & 1 \end{bmatrix}\begin{bmatrix} 2 & 1 & 0 \\ 0 & 1 & -1 \\ 0 & 0 & 3 \end{bmatrix}$

(The answer is not unique.)

(b) $\mathbf{y} = \begin{bmatrix} 1 \\ 2 \\ -5 \end{bmatrix}$

(c) $\mathbf{x} = \begin{bmatrix} \frac{1}{3} \\ \frac{1}{3} \\ -\frac{5}{3} \end{bmatrix}$

47. Idempotent   **49.** Not idempotent

51. Not idempotent

53. *Case 1.* $b = 1, a = 0$
Case 2. $b = 0, a =$ any real

55. Since A is idempotent, it follows that $A^2 = A$. Moreover, since A is invertible we can use the result of Exercise 50 in Section 2.3 to conclude that $A = I$.

57. Assume that $A^2 = A$ and $B^2 = B$. Since $AB = BA$, it follows that

$$(AB)^2 = ABAB = AABB = A^2B^2 = AB.$$

Therefore, AB is idempotent.

SECTION 2.5 (*page 100*)

1. Not stochastic   **3.** Stochastic

5. Stochastic

7. Next month: 350 people
In two months: 475 people

9.

	In one month	In two months
Nonsmokers	5025	5047
Smokers of less than one pack/day	2500	2499
Smokers of more than one pack/day	2475	2454

11. Tomorrow: 25 students
In two days: 44 students
In thirty days: 40 students

15. Uncoded: $[19 \ \ 5 \ \ 12], [12 \ \ 0 \ \ 3], [15 \ \ 14 \ \ 19],$
$[15 \ \ 12 \ \ 9], [4 \ \ 1 \ \ 20], [5 \ \ 4 \ \ 0]$
Encoded: $-48, 5, 31, \ -6, -6, 9, \ -85, 23, 43,$
$-27, 3, 15, \ -115, 36, 59, 9, -5, -4$

17. Uncoded: $[3 \ \ 15], [13 \ \ 5], [0 \ \ 8], [15 \ \ 13], [5 \ \ 0],$
$[19 \ \ 15], [15 \ \ 14]$
Encoded: $48, 81, \ 28, 51, \ 24, 40, \ 54, 95, \ 5, 10$
$64, 113, \ 57, 100$

19. HAPPY_NEW_YEAR   **21.** FILM_AT_ELEVEN

23. MEET_ME_TONIGHT_RON

25. $D = \begin{bmatrix} 0.1 & 0.2 \\ 0.8 & 0.1 \end{bmatrix}\begin{matrix} \text{Coal} \\ \text{Steel} \end{matrix}$ $X = \begin{bmatrix} 20{,}000 \\ 40{,}000 \end{bmatrix}\begin{matrix} \text{Coal} \\ \text{Steel} \end{matrix}$

(with column labels Coal   Steel above D)

27. $X = \begin{bmatrix} 8622.0 \\ 4685.0 \\ 3661.4 \end{bmatrix}\begin{matrix} \text{Farmer} \\ \text{Baker} \\ \text{Grocer} \end{matrix}$

29. (a)

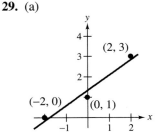

(b) $y = \frac{4}{3} + \frac{3}{4}x$
(c) $\frac{1}{6}$

31. (a)

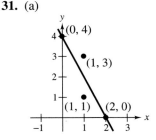

(b) $y = 4 - 2x$
(c) 2

33. $y = 1.3 + 0.6x$

35. $y = \frac{10}{3} + \frac{8}{7}x$

37. $y = 1.75 - 0.65x$

39. $y = -\frac{1}{3} + 2x$

41. $y = \frac{945}{148} - \frac{175}{148}x$

43. (a) $y = 685 - 240x$
(b) 349

REVIEW EXERCISES – CHAPTER 2 (*page 103*)

1. $\begin{bmatrix} -13 & -8 & 18 \\ 0 & 11 & -19 \end{bmatrix}$

3. $\begin{bmatrix} 14 & -2 & 8 \\ 14 & -10 & 40 \\ 36 & -12 & 48 \end{bmatrix}$

5. $\begin{bmatrix} 4 & 6 & 3 \\ 0 & 6 & -10 \\ 0 & 0 & 6 \end{bmatrix}$

7. $\begin{aligned} 5x + 4y &= 2 \\ -x + y &= -22 \end{aligned}$

9. $\begin{bmatrix} 2 & 3 & 1 \\ 2 & -3 & -3 \\ 4 & -2 & 3 \end{bmatrix} \begin{bmatrix} x_1 \\ x_2 \\ x_3 \end{bmatrix} = \begin{bmatrix} 10 \\ 22 \\ -2 \end{bmatrix}$

11. $A^t = \begin{bmatrix} 1 & 0 \\ 2 & 1 \\ -3 & 2 \end{bmatrix}$, $A^t A = \begin{bmatrix} 1 & 2 & -3 \\ 2 & 5 & -4 \\ -3 & -4 & 13 \end{bmatrix}$,

$AA^t = \begin{bmatrix} 14 & -4 \\ -4 & 5 \end{bmatrix}$

13. $\begin{bmatrix} 1 & -1 \\ 2 & -3 \end{bmatrix}$

15. $\begin{bmatrix} \frac{3}{20} & \frac{3}{20} & \frac{1}{10} \\ \frac{3}{10} & -\frac{1}{30} & -\frac{2}{15} \\ -\frac{1}{5} & -\frac{1}{5} & \frac{1}{5} \end{bmatrix}$

17. $\begin{bmatrix} 5 & 4 \\ -1 & 1 \end{bmatrix} \begin{bmatrix} x_1 \\ x_2 \end{bmatrix} = \begin{bmatrix} 2 \\ -22 \end{bmatrix}$

$A^{-1} = \begin{bmatrix} \frac{1}{9} & -\frac{4}{9} \\ \frac{1}{9} & \frac{5}{9} \end{bmatrix}$

$\begin{bmatrix} x_1 \\ x_2 \end{bmatrix} = \begin{bmatrix} 10 \\ -12 \end{bmatrix}$

19. $\begin{bmatrix} \frac{1}{14} & \frac{1}{42} \\ -\frac{1}{21} & \frac{2}{21} \end{bmatrix}$

21. $\begin{bmatrix} 1 & 0 & -4 \\ 0 & 1 & 0 \\ 0 & 0 & 1 \end{bmatrix}$

23. $\begin{bmatrix} 1 & 3 \\ 0 & 1 \end{bmatrix} \begin{bmatrix} 2 & 0 \\ 0 & 1 \end{bmatrix}$
(The answer is not unique.)

25. $\begin{bmatrix} 1 & 0 & 0 \\ 0 & 1 & 0 \\ 0 & 0 & 4 \end{bmatrix} \begin{bmatrix} 1 & 0 & 0 \\ 0 & 1 & -2 \\ 0 & 0 & 1 \end{bmatrix} \begin{bmatrix} 1 & 0 & 1 \\ 0 & 1 & 0 \\ 0 & 0 & 1 \end{bmatrix}$
(The answer is not unique.)

27. $\begin{bmatrix} -1 & 0 \\ 0 & -1 \end{bmatrix}$ and $\begin{bmatrix} 1 & 0 \\ 0 & 1 \end{bmatrix}$
(The answer is not unique.)

29. $\begin{bmatrix} 0 & 0 \\ 0 & 0 \end{bmatrix}, \begin{bmatrix} 1 & 0 \\ 0 & 1 \end{bmatrix}$, and $\begin{bmatrix} 1 & 0 \\ 0 & 0 \end{bmatrix}$
(The answer is not unique.)

31. $\begin{aligned} a &= -1 \\ b &= -1 \\ c &= 1 \end{aligned}$

35. $\begin{bmatrix} 1 & 0 \\ 3 & 1 \end{bmatrix} \begin{bmatrix} 2 & 5 \\ 0 & -1 \end{bmatrix}$
(The answer is not unique.)

37. $x = 4$, $y = 1$, $z = -1$

39. Not stochastic

41. $PX = \begin{bmatrix} 80 \\ 112 \end{bmatrix}$, $P^2 X = \begin{bmatrix} 68 \\ 124 \end{bmatrix}$, $P^3 X = \begin{bmatrix} 65 \\ 127 \end{bmatrix}$

43. (a) $\begin{bmatrix} 110,000 \\ 100,000 \\ 90,000 \end{bmatrix} \begin{matrix} \text{Region 1} \\ \text{Region 2} \\ \text{Region 3} \end{matrix}$ (b) $\begin{bmatrix} 123,125 \\ 100,000 \\ 76,875 \end{bmatrix}$

45. Uncoded: $[15 \ \ 14], [5 \ \ 0], [9 \ \ 6], [0 \ \ 2], [25 \ \ 0],$
$[12 \ \ 1], [14 \ \ 4]$
Encoded: 103, 44, 25, 10, 57, 24, 4, 2, 125, 50, 62, 25, 78, 32

47. $A^{-1} = \begin{bmatrix} 3 & 2 \\ 4 & 3 \end{bmatrix}$,   ALL_SYSTEMS_GO

49. $D = \begin{bmatrix} 0.20 & 0.50 \\ 0.30 & 0.10 \end{bmatrix}$, $X = \begin{bmatrix} 133,333 \\ 133,333 \end{bmatrix}$

51. $y = \frac{20}{3} - \frac{3}{2}x$

53. $y = \frac{2}{5} - \frac{9}{5}x$

55. (a) $y = 19 + 14x$
(b) $y(1.6) = 41.4$ bushels per acre

CHAPTER 2 MATLAB (*page 106*)

1. (a) $\begin{bmatrix} -5 & 2 & 12 \\ 3 & 0 & 0 \\ 6 & 1 & 1 \end{bmatrix}$ (b) $\begin{bmatrix} -5 & 18 & -8 \\ -9 & -4 & 8 \\ -2 & -3 & -15 \end{bmatrix}$

(c) $\begin{bmatrix} 20 & 4 & -23 \\ -23 & 17 & 29 \\ 6 & 11 & 4 \end{bmatrix}$ (d) $\begin{bmatrix} 32 & 33 & -9 \\ 1 & 1 & 10 \\ -6 & -19 & 8 \end{bmatrix}$

3. $\begin{bmatrix} 1 \\ 1 \\ -1 \end{bmatrix}$ **5.** $D^4 = \begin{bmatrix} 0 & 0 & 0 & 0 & 0 \\ 0 & 1 & 0 & 0 & 0 \\ 0 & 0 & 16 & 0 & 0 \\ 0 & 0 & 0 & 81 & 0 \\ 0 & 0 & 0 & 0 & 256 \end{bmatrix}$

7. $A^2 = \begin{bmatrix} 1 & 0.4167 \\ 0 & 0.0625 \end{bmatrix}$, $A^3 = \begin{bmatrix} 1 & 0.4375 \\ 0 & 0.0156 \end{bmatrix}$,

$A^8 = \begin{bmatrix} 1 & 0.4444 \\ 0 & 0 \end{bmatrix}$, $A^n \approx \begin{bmatrix} 1 & 0.4444 \\ 0 & 0 \end{bmatrix}$ for large n.

9. $\text{inv}(A) \approx 10^{15} \begin{bmatrix} -2.0910 & -4.1819 & 2.0910 \\ 1.1259 & 2.2518 & -1.1259 \\ 0.1608 & 0.3217 & -0.1608 \end{bmatrix}$

(The answers will vary.)

$\text{rref}([A \ \ I]) = \begin{bmatrix} 1 & 0 & 13 & 0 & -16 & 7 \\ 0 & 1 & -7 & 0 & 7 & -3 \\ 0 & 0 & 0 & 1 & 2 & -1 \end{bmatrix}$

which shows that A is in fact singular.

11. $y = 1.2x - 0.2$

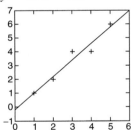

Chapter 3

Section 3.1 (*page 117*)

1. 1   **3.** 5   **5.** 27   **7.** -24

9. 6   **11.** $\lambda^2 - 4\lambda - 5$

13. (a) $M_{11} = 4$ $M_{12} = 3$ (b) $C_{11} = 4$ $C_{12} = -3$
        $M_{21} = 2$ $M_{22} = 1$ $C_{21} = -2$ $C_{22} = 1$

15. (a) $M_{11} = 23$ $M_{12} = -8$ $M_{13} = -22$
        $M_{21} = 5$ $M_{22} = -5$ $M_{23} = 5$
        $M_{31} = 7$ $M_{32} = -22$ $M_{33} = -23$

(b) $C_{11} = 23$ $C_{12} = 8$ $C_{13} = -22$
    $C_{21} = -5$ $C_{22} = -5$ $C_{23} = -5$
    $C_{31} = 7$ $C_{32} = 22$ $C_{33} = -23$

17. (a) $4(-5) + 5(-5) + 6(-5) = -75$
    (b) $2(8) + 5(-5) - 3(22) = -75$

19. -58 **21.** -30 **23.** 0

25. -0.022 **27.** $4x - 2y - 2$

29. -108 **31.** 0   **33.** 0

35. -100 **37.** -24 **39.** 0

41. -30 **43.** $\lambda = \pm 3$

51. Expand along the row consisting of zeros.

Section 3.2 (*page 125*)

1. The first row is 2 times the second row. If one row of a matrix is a multiple of another row, then the determinant of the matrix is zero.

3. The second row consists entirely of zeros. If one row of a matrix consists entirely of zeros, then the determinant of the matrix is zero.

5. The second and third columns are interchanged. If two columns of a matrix are interchanged, then the determinant of the matrix changes signs.

7. The first row of the matrix is multiplied by 5. If a row in a matrix is multiplied by a scalar, then the determinant of the matrix is multiplied by that scalar.

9. The matrix is multiplied by 5. If an $n \times n$ matrix is multiplied by a scalar c, then the determinant of the matrix is multiplied by c^n.

11. -4 times the first row has been added to the second row. If a scalar multiple of one row of a matrix is added to another row, then the determinant of the matrix is unchanged.

13. -5 times the second column has been added to the third column. If a scalar multiple of one column of a matrix is added to another column, then the determinant of the matrix is unchanged.

15. 28   **17.** 17   **19.** -60

21. 223   **23.** -1344 **25.** 136

27. -1100 **29.** k **31.** -1

33. 1   **37.** $\cos^2\theta + \sin^2\theta = 1$

41. The cost for cofactor expansion would be

$3,628,799 \times 0.001 + 6,235,300 \times 0.003 \approx$
$22,334.70$ dollars

The cost for row reduction would be

$285 \times 0.001 + 339 \times 0.003 \approx 1.302$ dollars.

Clearly, row reduction is more efficient than cofactor expansion.

SECTION 3.3 (*page 135*)

1. (a) -3 (b) -2

(c) $\begin{bmatrix} -2 & 0 \\ 0 & -3 \end{bmatrix}$ (d) 6

3. (a) 0 (b) -1

(c) $\begin{bmatrix} -2 & -3 \\ 4 & 6 \end{bmatrix}$ (d) 0

5. (a) 2 (b) -6

(c) $\begin{bmatrix} 1 & 4 & 3 \\ -1 & 0 & 3 \\ 0 & 2 & 0 \end{bmatrix}$ (d) -12

7. -44 **9.** 54

11. (a) -2 (b) -2 (c) 0

13. (a) 14 (b) 196 (c) 196
(d) 56 (e) $\frac{1}{14}$

15. (a) 29 (b) 841 (c) 841
(d) 232 (e) $\frac{1}{29}$

17. (a) -15 (b) -125 (c) 243
(d) -15 (e) $-\frac{1}{5}$

19. Singular   **21.** Nonsingular   **23.** Nonsingular

25. Singular

27. The solution is not unique because the determinant of the coefficient matrix is zero.

29. The solution is unique because the determinant of the coefficient matrix is nonzero.

31. $k = -1, 4$

33. Assume that A and B are $n \times n$ matrices such that $AB = I$. Then we know that $|AB| = 1$. If $|A| = 0$, then it follows that $|AB| = |A||B| = 0|B| = 0$, which is a contradiction. Therefore, we can conclude that $|A| \neq 0$. If $|B| = 0$, we obtain a similar contradiction.

35. $\begin{bmatrix} 0 & 1 \\ 0 & 0 \end{bmatrix}$ and $\begin{bmatrix} 1 & 0 \\ 0 & 0 \end{bmatrix}$
(The answer is not unique.)

37. 0

41. No, in general $P^{-1}AP \neq A$. For example, let

$P = \begin{bmatrix} 1 & 2 \\ 3 & 5 \end{bmatrix}$, $P^{-1} = \begin{bmatrix} -5 & 2 \\ 3 & -1 \end{bmatrix}$,

and $A = \begin{bmatrix} 2 & 1 \\ -1 & 0 \end{bmatrix}$.

Then you have

$P^{-1}AP = \begin{bmatrix} -27 & -49 \\ 16 & 29 \end{bmatrix} \neq A$.

However, the equation $|P^{-1}AP| = |A|$ is true in general because

$|P^{-1}AP| = |P^{-1}||A||P| = |P^{-1}||P||A| =$

$\dfrac{1}{|P|}|P||A| = |A|$.

43. Assume that A is an $n \times n$ matrix such that $A^T = -A$. Then it follows that

$$|A| = |A^T| = |-A| = (-1)^n|A|.$$

45. Orthogonal   **47.** Not orthogonal

49. Orthogonal

51. Assume that A is orthogonal. That is, $A^{-1} = A^T$. Then it follows that $|A^T| = |A^{-1}|$, which implies that

$$|AA^{-1}| = |A||A^{-1}| = |A||A^T| = |A|^2 = 1.$$

Therefore, we can conclude that $|A| = \pm 1$.

55. $\begin{bmatrix} 1 & 2 \\ 0 & -3 \end{bmatrix}\begin{bmatrix} 1 \\ 0 \end{bmatrix} = 1\begin{bmatrix} 1 \\ 0 \end{bmatrix}$;

$\begin{bmatrix} 1 & 2 \\ 0 & -3 \end{bmatrix}\begin{bmatrix} -1 \\ 2 \end{bmatrix} = \begin{bmatrix} 3 \\ -6 \end{bmatrix} = -3\begin{bmatrix} -1 \\ 2 \end{bmatrix}$

57. $\begin{bmatrix} 1 & 1 & 1 \\ 0 & 1 & 0 \\ 1 & 1 & 1 \end{bmatrix}\begin{bmatrix} 1 \\ 0 \\ 1 \end{bmatrix} = \begin{bmatrix} 2 \\ 0 \\ 2 \end{bmatrix} = 2\begin{bmatrix} 1 \\ 0 \\ 1 \end{bmatrix}$

$\begin{bmatrix} 1 & 1 & 1 \\ 0 & 1 & 0 \\ 1 & 1 & 1 \end{bmatrix}\begin{bmatrix} -1 \\ 0 \\ 1 \end{bmatrix} = \begin{bmatrix} 0 \\ 0 \\ 0 \end{bmatrix} = 0\begin{bmatrix} -1 \\ 0 \\ 1 \end{bmatrix}$

$\begin{bmatrix} 1 & 1 & 1 \\ 0 & 1 & 0 \\ 1 & 1 & 1 \end{bmatrix}\begin{bmatrix} -1 \\ 1 \\ -1 \end{bmatrix} = \begin{bmatrix} -1 \\ 1 \\ -1 \end{bmatrix} = 1\begin{bmatrix} -1 \\ 1 \\ -1 \end{bmatrix}$

59. (a) $\lambda^2 - \lambda - 2$
(b) $2, -1$

(c) $\lambda = 2 : \mathbf{x} = \begin{bmatrix} 5 \\ 2 \end{bmatrix}$; $\lambda = -1 : \mathbf{x} = \begin{bmatrix} 1 \\ 1 \end{bmatrix}$

61. (a) $\lambda^3 - 3\lambda^2 - 4\lambda + 12$
(b) $2, 3, -2$

(c) $\lambda = 2 : \mathbf{x} = \begin{bmatrix} -1 \\ 0 \\ 1 \end{bmatrix}$; $\lambda = 3 : \mathbf{x} = \begin{bmatrix} -1 \\ 1 \\ 1 \end{bmatrix}$;

$\lambda = -2 : \mathbf{x} = \begin{bmatrix} 1 \\ -1 \\ 4 \end{bmatrix}$

SECTION 3.4 (*page 148*)

1. $\text{adj}(A) = \begin{bmatrix} 4 & -2 \\ -3 & 1 \end{bmatrix}$, $A^{-1} = \begin{bmatrix} -2 & 1 \\ \frac{3}{2} & -\frac{1}{2} \end{bmatrix}$

3. $\text{adj}(A) = \begin{bmatrix} 0 & 0 & 0 \\ 0 & -12 & -6 \\ 0 & 4 & 2 \end{bmatrix}$, A^{-1} does not exist.

5. $\text{adj}(A) = \begin{bmatrix} -7 & -12 & 13 \\ 2 & 3 & -5 \\ 2 & 3 & -2 \end{bmatrix}$, $A^{-1} = \begin{bmatrix} \frac{7}{3} & 4 & -\frac{13}{3} \\ -\frac{2}{3} & -1 & \frac{5}{3} \\ -\frac{2}{3} & -1 & \frac{2}{3} \end{bmatrix}$

7. $\text{adj}(A) = \begin{bmatrix} 7 & 1 & 9 & -13 \\ 7 & 1 & 0 & -4 \\ -4 & 2 & -9 & 10 \\ 2 & -1 & 9 & -5 \end{bmatrix}$,

$A^{-1} = \begin{bmatrix} \frac{7}{9} & \frac{1}{9} & 1 & -\frac{13}{9} \\ \frac{7}{9} & \frac{1}{9} & 0 & -\frac{4}{9} \\ -\frac{4}{9} & \frac{2}{9} & -1 & \frac{10}{9} \\ \frac{2}{9} & -\frac{1}{9} & 1 & -\frac{5}{9} \end{bmatrix}$

9. Assume that $|A| = 1$ and that all the entries of A are integers. This implies that all the entries of $\text{adj}(A)$ must be integers. Moreover, since

$$A^{-1} = \frac{1}{|A|}\,\text{adj}(A) = \text{adj}(A)$$

we can conclude that all the entries of A^{-1} must be integers.

11. Assume that A is an $n \times n$ matrix. Since $\text{adj}(A) = A^{-1}|A|$, it follows that

$$|\text{adj}(A)| = \left||A|A^{-1}\right| = |A|^n|A^{-1}| = |A|^{n-1}.$$

13. $|\text{adj}(A)| = \begin{vmatrix} -2 & 0 \\ -1 & 1 \end{vmatrix} = -2$, $|A|^{2-1} =$

$\begin{vmatrix} 1 & 0 \\ 1 & -2 \end{vmatrix}^{2-1} = -2$

15. Assume that A *is* an invertible $n \times n$ matrix. Since $\text{adj}(A^{-1}) = |A^{-1}|A$ and

$$[\text{adj}(A)]^{-1}(|A|A^{-1})^{-1} = \frac{1}{|A|}A = |A^{-1}|A$$

it follows that $\text{adj}(A^{-1}) = [\text{adj}(A)]^{-1}$.

17. $x_1 = 1$
$x_2 = 2$

19. $x_1 = 2$
$x_2 = -2$

21. $x_1 = \frac{3}{4}$
$x_2 = -\frac{1}{2}$

23. Cramer's Rule does not apply because the coefficient matrix has a determinant of zero.

25. Cramer's Rule does not apply because the coefficient matrix has a determinant of zero.

27. $x_1 = 1$
$x_2 = 1$
$x_3 = 2$

29. $x_1 = 1$
$x_2 = \frac{1}{2}$
$x_3 = \frac{3}{2}$

31. $x_1 = 0$
$x_2 = -\frac{1}{2}$
$x_3 = \frac{1}{2}$

33. 5   **35.** 1

37. $x = \dfrac{4k - 3}{2k - 1}, \ y = \dfrac{4k - 1}{2k - 1}$

The system will be inconsistent if $k = \frac{1}{2}$.

39. 3   **41.** 3   **43.** Collinear

45. Not collinear   **47.** $3y - 4x = 0$

49. $x = -2$ **51.** $\frac{1}{3}$ **53.** 2

55. Not coplanar   **57.** Coplanar

59. $4x - 10y + 3z = 27$

61. $x + y + z = 0$

REVIEW EXERCISES – CHAPTER 3 (*page 149*)

1. 10   **3.** 0   **5.** 0

7. -6 **9.** 1620   **11.** 82

13. -64 **15.** -1 **17.** -1

19. (a) -1 (b) -5

 (c) $\begin{bmatrix} 1 & -2 \\ 2 & 1 \end{bmatrix}$ (d) 5

21. (a) -12 (b) -1728
 (c) 144   (d) -300

23. (a) -20 (b) $-\frac{1}{20}$

25. Unique solution   **27.** Unique solution

29. Not unique solution   **31.** 128   **35.** 0

37. $\lambda = 7, \begin{bmatrix} 1 \\ 1 \end{bmatrix}$ and $\lambda = -8, \begin{bmatrix} -2 \\ 1 \end{bmatrix}$

39. $-\frac{1}{2}$ **41.** $-uv$

45. $\begin{bmatrix} 1 & 0 & 0 \\ -2 & 1 & 0 \\ -4 & 1 & 1 \end{bmatrix}$

47. Unique solution: $x_1 = 0.6$
$x_2 = 0.5$

49. Unique solution: $x_1 = \frac{1}{2}$
$x_2 = -\frac{1}{3}$
$x_3 = 1$

51. 16   **53.** $x - 2y = -4$

55. $9x + 4y - 3z = 0$

CHAPTER 3 MATLAB (*page 153*)

1. (a) 0   (b) 61
 (c) 1   (d) $2.7371 \times 10^{-33} \approx 0$

3. In general, $\det(A)\det(B) = \det(AB)$, whereas
$\det(A) + \det(B) \neq \det(A + B)$

5. (a) -26 (b) -2 (c) -0.5

7. $x = 1, \ y = 1, \ z = -1$

CUMULATIVE TEST CHAPTERS 1–3 (*page 154*)

1. $x_1 = 4, \ x_2 = \frac{1}{2}$

2. $x_1 = 2, \ x_2 = -3, \ x_3 = -2$

3. $x_1 = s - 2t, \ x_2 = 2 + t, \ x_3 = t, \ x_4 = s$

4. $x_1 = -2s, \ x_2 = s, \ x_3 = 2t, \ x_4 = t$ **5.** $k = 12$

6. $A + B = \begin{bmatrix} 1 & 1 & 1 \\ 7 & 3 & -3 \end{bmatrix},$

$2A - 3B = \begin{bmatrix} 2 & 7 & -8 \\ -6 & -9 & 19 \end{bmatrix}$

7. $AB = \begin{bmatrix} 1 & 2 \\ 1 & 1 \\ 1 & 0 \end{bmatrix}, \quad BA$ is not defined.

8. $BA = [13{,}275.00 \quad 15{,}500.00];$
The entries represent the value of the models sent to
each of the warehouses.

9. $x = -3, \ y = 4$ **10.** $A^T A = \begin{bmatrix} 17 & 22 & 27 \\ 22 & 29 & 36 \\ 27 & 36 & 45 \end{bmatrix}$

11. Does not exist; $\begin{bmatrix} -\frac{2}{7} & \frac{1}{7} \\ \frac{1}{7} & \frac{2}{21} \end{bmatrix}$

12. $\begin{bmatrix} 1 & 0 & -1 \\ 0 & 0 & 1 \\ \frac{3}{5} & \frac{1}{5} & -\frac{9}{5} \end{bmatrix}$

13. $\begin{bmatrix} 0 & 1 \\ 1 & 0 \end{bmatrix}\begin{bmatrix} 1 & 0 \\ 2 & 1 \end{bmatrix}\begin{bmatrix} 1 & 0 \\ 0 & -4 \end{bmatrix}$ **14.** 53

(The answer is not unique.)

15. (a) 14   (b) -10

(c) -140 (d) $\frac{1}{14}$

16. (a) 567   (b) 7

(c) $\frac{1}{7}$ (d) 343

17. $y = \frac{7}{6}x^2 + \frac{1}{6}x + 1$

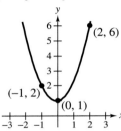

18. $a = 1, \; b = 0, \; c = 2$

19. No, C could be singular.

20. $(B^TB)^T = B^T(B^T)^T = B^TB$

21. Let B and C be inverses of A. Then $B = IB = (CA)B = C(AB) = CI = C$

22. (a) A is row equivalent to B if there exist elementary matrices $E_1, \ldots, E_k$ such that $A = E_k \cdots E_1B$.

(b) $A = E_k \cdots E_1B$ and $B = F_l \cdots F_1C$ implies that $A = E_k \cdots E_1(F_l \cdots F_1C) = E_k \cdots E_1F_l \cdots F_1C$, which implies that A is row equivalent to C.

23. $\det(AA^T) = \det(A^2)$ and $\det(A(-A)) = (-1)^n\det(A^2)$, where n is the (odd) order of A. Thus, $\det(A^2) = -\det(A^2)$, which implies that $\det(A) = 0$.

24. (a) $\begin{bmatrix} 0 & 0 \\ 0 & 0 \end{bmatrix}, \begin{bmatrix} 1 & 0 \\ 0 & 1 \end{bmatrix}, \begin{bmatrix} 1 & 0 \\ 0 & 0 \end{bmatrix}$ (b) 0 or 1

(The answer is not unique.)

25. (a) The sum is not necessarily nonsingular.

(b) The product is nonsingular.

26. $\begin{bmatrix} 0 & 0 \\ 0 & 0 \end{bmatrix}, \begin{bmatrix} 0 & 1 \\ 0 & 0 \end{bmatrix}, \begin{bmatrix} 1 & a \\ 0 & 0 \end{bmatrix}, \begin{bmatrix} 1 & 0 \\ 0 & 1 \end{bmatrix}$

Chapter 4

SECTION 4.1 (*page 165*)

1. $\mathbf{v} = \left(3, -\frac{3}{2}\right)$

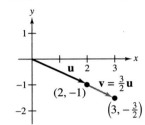

3. $\mathbf{v} = (4, 3)$

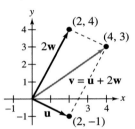

5. $\mathbf{v} = \left(\frac{7}{2}, -\frac{1}{2}\right)$

7. (a)   (b)

(c)

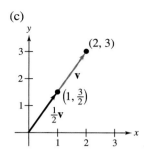

9. $\mathbf{u} - \mathbf{v} = (-1, 0, 4)$ **11.** $(6, 12, 6)$
    $\mathbf{v} - \mathbf{u} = (1, 0, -4)$

13. $\left(\frac{7}{2}, 3, \frac{5}{2}\right)$

15. (a)   (b)

(c)

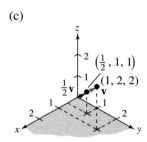

17. (a) and (b)   **19.** (a) $(4, -2, -8, 1)$
                                  (b) $(8, 12, 24, 34)$

21. (a) $(-9, 3, 2, -3, 6)$
    (b) $(-2, -18, -12, 18, 36)$

23. $\left(\frac{1}{2}, -\frac{7}{2}, -\frac{9}{2}, 2\right)$ **25.** $\mathbf{v} = \mathbf{u} + \mathbf{w}$

27. $\mathbf{v} = \mathbf{u} + 2\mathbf{w}$ **29.** $\left(-1, \frac{5}{3}, 6, \frac{2}{3}\right)$

31. $\mathbf{v} = \mathbf{u}_1 + 2\mathbf{u}_2 - 3\mathbf{u}_3$

33. It is not possible to write $\mathbf{v}$ as a linear combination of $\mathbf{u}_1, \mathbf{u}_2,$ and $\mathbf{u}_3$.

35. No

SECTION 4.2 (*page 172*)

1. $(0, 0, 0, 0)$ **3.** $\begin{bmatrix} 0 & 0 & 0 \\ 0 & 0 & 0 \end{bmatrix}$

5. $0 + 0x + 0x^2 + 0x^3$

7. $-(v_1, v_2, v_3, v_4) = (-v_1, -v_2, -v_3, -v_4)$

9. $-\begin{bmatrix} a_{11} & a_{12} & a_{13} \\ a_{21} & a_{22} & a_{23} \end{bmatrix} = \begin{bmatrix} -a_{11} & -a_{12} & -a_{13} \\ -a_{21} & -a_{22} & -a_{23} \end{bmatrix}$

11. $-(a_0 + a_1x + a_2x^2 + a_3x^3) = -a_0 - a_1x - a_2x^2 - a_3x^3$

13. The set is a vector space.

15. The set is not a vector space. Axiom 1 fails since $x^5 + (-x^5 + x) = x$, which is not a 5th degree polynomial. (Axioms 4, 5, and 6 also fail.)

17. The set is a vector space.

19. The set is a vector space.

21. The set is not a vector space. Axiom 1 fails since

$$\begin{bmatrix} 1 & 0 \\ 0 & 0 \end{bmatrix} + \begin{bmatrix} 0 & 0 \\ 0 & 1 \end{bmatrix} = \begin{bmatrix} 1 & 0 \\ 0 & 1 \end{bmatrix}$$

which is not singular.

23. The set is a vector space.

25. (a) The set is not a vector space because Axiom 8 fails.
$$(1 + 2)(1, 1) = \quad 3(1, 1) \quad = (3, 1)$$
$$1(1, 1) + 2(1, 1) = (1, 1) + (2, 1) = (3, 2)$$

(b) The set is not a vector space because Axiom 2 fails.
$$(1, 2) + (2, 1) = (1, 0)$$
$$(2, 1) + (1, 2) = (2, 0)$$
(Axioms 4, 5, and 8 also fail.)

(c) The set is not a vector space. Axiom 6 fails since $(-1)(1, 1) = (\sqrt{-1}, \sqrt{-1})$, which is not in R^2. (Axioms 8 and 9 also fail.)

29. The set is not a vector space because Axiom 5 fails. Since $(1, 1)$ is the additive identity, $(0, 0)$ has no additive inverse. (Axioms 7 and 8 also fail.)

SECTION 4.3 (*page 179*)

7. Not closed under addition:
$(0, 0, -1) + (0, 0, -1) = (0, 0, -2)$
Not closed under scalar multiplication:
$2(0, 0, -1) = (0, 0, -2)$

9. Not closed under scalar multiplication: $(-1) e^x = -e^x$

11. Not closed under addition:
$$\begin{bmatrix} 1 & 0 \\ 0 & 0 \end{bmatrix} + \begin{bmatrix} 0 & 0 \\ 0 & 1 \end{bmatrix} = \begin{bmatrix} 1 & 0 \\ 0 & 1 \end{bmatrix}$$

13. (b), (c), (d), and (e)

15. W is a subspace of R^3. (W is nonempty and closed under addition and scalar multiplication.)

17. W is a subspace of R^3. (W is nonempty and closed under addition and scalar multiplication.)

19. W is not a subspace of R^3.
Not closed under addition:
$(1, 1, 1) + (1, 1, 1) = (2, 2, 2)$ which is not in W.
Not closed under scalar multiplication:
$2(1, 1, 1) = (2, 2, 2)$ which is not in W.

27. Assume A is a fixed 2×2 matrix, and let X and Y be 2×2 matrices such that $AX = XA$ and $AY = YA$. Then
$$A(X + Y) = AX + AY = XA + YA = (X + Y)A$$
and
$$A(cX) = c(AX) = c(XA) = (cX)A$$
which implies that the set $W = \{X: XA = AX\}$ is closed under addition and scalar multiplication. Since W is nonempty, W is a subspace of $M_{2,2}$.

SECTION 4.4 (*page 190*)

1. (a) $\mathbf{u} = 5(2, -1, 3) - 2(5, 0, 4)$
   (b) $\mathbf{v} = \frac{1}{2}(2, -1, 3) + 3(5, 0, 4)$
   (c) $\mathbf{w}$ cannot be written as a linear combination of the given vectors.

3. (a) $\mathbf{u} = 7(2, 0, 7) - 5(2, 4, 5) + 0(2, -12, 13)$
   (b) $\mathbf{v}$ cannot be written as a linear combination of the given vectors.
   (c) $\mathbf{w} = -3(2, 0, 7) + 6(2, 4, 5) + 0(2, -12, 13)$

5. S spans R^2.

7. S does not span R^2. (It spans a line in R^2.)

9. S does not span R^2. (It spans a line in R^2.)

11. S spans R^3.

13. S does not span R^3. (It spans a plane in R^3.)

15. S does not span R^3. (It spans a plane in R^3.)

17. Linearly independent   19. Linearly dependent

21. Linearly independent   23. Linearly dependent

25. Linearly independent   27. Linearly independent

29. $(3, 4) - 4(-1, 1) - \frac{7}{2}(2, 0) = (0, 0)$, $(3, 4) = 4(-1, 1) + \frac{7}{2}(2, 0)$
(The answer is not unique.)

31. $(1, 1, 1) - (1, 1, 0) - (0, 0, 1) - 0(0, 1, 1) = (0, 0, 0)$
$(1, 1, 1) = (1, 1, 0) + (0, 0, 1) - 0(0, 1, 1)$
(The answer is not unique.)

33. (a) All $t \neq 1, -2$ (b) All $t \neq \frac{1}{2}$

35. (a) $\begin{bmatrix} 6 & -19 \\ 10 & 7 \end{bmatrix} = 3A - 2B$
    (b) Not a linear combination of A and B
    (c) $\begin{bmatrix} -2 & 28 \\ 1 & -11 \end{bmatrix} = -A + 5B$
    (d) $\begin{bmatrix} 0 & 0 \\ 0 & 0 \end{bmatrix} = 0A + 0B$

37. (a) Linearly dependent
    (b) Linearly independent
    (c) Linearly independent

39. (a) Any set of three vectors in R^2 must be linearly dependent.
    (b) The second vector is a scalar multiple of the first vector.
    (c) The first vector is the zero vector.

41. S_1 and S_2 span the same subspace.

43. Linearly dependent

49. Let $S = \{\mathbf{0}, \mathbf{v}_1, \mathbf{v}_2, \ldots, \mathbf{v}_n\}$. Then $1(\mathbf{0}) + 0\mathbf{v}_1 + 0\mathbf{v}_2 + \ldots + 0\mathbf{v}_n = \mathbf{0}$, which implies that S is linearly dependent.

53. The theorem requires that only one of the vectors be a linear combination of the others. Since $(-1, 0, 2) = 0(1, 2, 3) - (1, 0, -2)$, there is no contradiction.

55. Assume $S = \{\mathbf{u}, \mathbf{v}\}$ is linearly independent. If there exist nonzero scalars c_1 and c_2, such that $c_1(\mathbf{u} + \mathbf{v}) + c_2(\mathbf{u} - \mathbf{v}) = \mathbf{0}$, then it follows that $(c_1 + c_2)\mathbf{u} + (c_1 - c_2)\mathbf{v} = \mathbf{0}$. Thus $c_1 + c_2 = 0$ and $c_1 - c_2 = 0$, which implies that $c_1 = 0$ and $c_2 = 0$. Thus, the set $\{(\mathbf{u} + \mathbf{v}), (\mathbf{u} - \mathbf{v})\}$ is linearly independent.

SECTION 4.5 (*page 200*)

1. R^6: $\{(1, 0, 0, 0, 0, 0), (0, 1, 0, 0, 0, 0), (0, 0, 1, 0, 0, 0), (0, 0, 0, 1, 0, 0), (0, 0, 0, 0, 1, 0), (0, 0, 0, 0, 0, 1)\}$

3. $M_{2,4}$:
$$\left\{ \begin{bmatrix} 1 & 0 & 0 & 0 \\ 0 & 0 & 0 & 0 \end{bmatrix}, \begin{bmatrix} 0 & 1 & 0 & 0 \\ 0 & 0 & 0 & 0 \end{bmatrix}, \begin{bmatrix} 0 & 0 & 1 & 0 \\ 0 & 0 & 0 & 0 \end{bmatrix}, \begin{bmatrix} 0 & 0 & 0 & 1 \\ 0 & 0 & 0 & 0 \end{bmatrix}, \begin{bmatrix} 0 & 0 & 0 & 0 \\ 1 & 0 & 0 & 0 \end{bmatrix}, \begin{bmatrix} 0 & 0 & 0 & 0 \\ 0 & 1 & 0 & 0 \end{bmatrix}, \begin{bmatrix} 0 & 0 & 0 & 0 \\ 0 & 0 & 1 & 0 \end{bmatrix}, \begin{bmatrix} 0 & 0 & 0 & 0 \\ 0 & 0 & 0 & 1 \end{bmatrix} \right\}$$

5. S is linearly dependent. (S does span R^2.)

7. S is linearly dependent and does not span R^2.

9. S is linearly dependent and does not span R^3.

11. S is linearly dependent and does not span R^3.

13. S is linearly dependent (S does span P_2.)

15. S does not span $M_{2,2}$. (S is linearly independent.)

17. The set is a basis for R^2.

19. The set is not a basis for R^2.

21. S is a basis for R^2.   **23.** S is not a basis for R^3.

25. S is a basis for R^4.   **27.** S is a basis for $M_{2,2}$.

29. S is a basis for P_3.

31. S is a basis for R^3.
$(8, 3, 8) = 2(4, 3, 2) - (0, 3, 2) + 3(0, 0, 2)$

33. S is not a basis for R^3.   **35.** 6   **37.** 8

39. $\begin{bmatrix} 1 & 0 & 0 \\ 0 & 0 & 0 \\ 0 & 0 & 0 \end{bmatrix}, \begin{bmatrix} 0 & 0 & 0 \\ 0 & 1 & 0 \\ 0 & 0 & 0 \end{bmatrix}, \begin{bmatrix} 0 & 0 & 0 \\ 0 & 0 & 0 \\ 0 & 0 & 1 \end{bmatrix}$,

$\dim(D_{3,3}) = 3$

41. $\{(1, 0), (0, 1)\}, \{(1, 0), (1, 1)\}, \{(0, 1), (1, 1)\}$

43. $\{(1, 1), (1, 0)\}$ (The answer is not unique.)

45. (a) Line through the origin
(b) $\{(2, 1)\}$
(c) 1

47. (a) Line through the origin
(b) $\{(2, 1, -1)\}$
(c) 1

49. (a) $\{(2, 1, 0, 1), (-1, 0, 1, 0)\}$
(b) 2

51. (a) $\{(0, 6, 1, -1)\}$
(b) 1

53. False, if the dimension of V is n, then every spanning set of V must have at least n vectors.

55. True

61. (a) Basis for S_1: $\{(1, 0, 0), (1, 1, 0)\}$, dimension $= 2$
Basis for S_2: $\{(0, 0, 1), (0, 1, 0)\}$, dimension $= 2$
Basis for $S_1 \cap S_2$: $\{(0, 1, 0)\}$, dimension $= 1$
Basis for $S_1 + S_2$: $\{(1, 0, 0), (0, 1, 0), (0, 0, 1)\}$, dimension $= 3$
(b) No, it is not possible.

Section 4.6 (*page 214*)

1. (a) 2
(b) $\{(1, 0), (0, 1)\}$
(c) $\left\{ \begin{bmatrix} 1 \\ 0 \end{bmatrix}, \begin{bmatrix} 0 \\ 1 \end{bmatrix} \right\}$

3. (a) 2
(b) $\{(1, 2), (0, 1)\}$
(c) $\left\{ \begin{bmatrix} 1 \\ \frac{1}{2} \end{bmatrix}, \begin{bmatrix} 0 \\ 1 \end{bmatrix} \right\}$

5. (a) 2
(b) $\left\{ (1, 0, \frac{1}{4}), (0, 1, \frac{3}{2}) \right\}$
(c) $\left\{ \begin{bmatrix} 1 \\ 0 \\ -\frac{2}{5} \end{bmatrix}, \begin{bmatrix} 0 \\ 1 \\ \frac{3}{5} \end{bmatrix} \right\}$

7. (a) 2
(b) $\{(1, 2, -2, 0), (0, 0, 0, 1)\}$
(c) $\left\{ \begin{bmatrix} 1 \\ 0 \\ \frac{19}{7} \end{bmatrix}, \begin{bmatrix} 0 \\ 1 \\ \frac{8}{7} \end{bmatrix} \right\}$

9. $\{(1, 0, -1, 0), (0, 1, 0, 0), (0, 0, 0, 1)\}$

11. $\{(1, 0, 0, 0), (0, 1, 0, 0), (0, 0, 1, 0), (0, 0, 0, 1)\}$

13. Solution space is $\{(0, 0)\}$, dim $= 0$

15. $\{(-2, 1, 0), (-3, 0, 1)\}$, dim $= 2$

17. $\{(-1, 2, 1)\}$, dim $= 1$

19. (a) $\{(-1, -3, 2)\}$
   (b) 1

21. (a) $\{(-3, 0, 1), (2, 1, 0)\}$
   (b) 2

23. (a) $\{(8, -9, -6, 6)\}$
   (b) 1

25. (a) Consistent
   (b) $\mathbf{x} = t(2, -4, 1) + (3, 5, 0)$

27. (a) Inconsistent

29. (a) Consistent
   (b) $\mathbf{x} = t(5, 0, -6, -4, 1) + s(-2, 1, 0, 0, 0) +$
   $(1, 0, 2, -3, 0)$

31. $\begin{bmatrix} -1 \\ 4 \end{bmatrix} + 2\begin{bmatrix} 2 \\ 0 \end{bmatrix} = \begin{bmatrix} 3 \\ 4 \end{bmatrix}$

33. $-\frac{5}{4}\begin{bmatrix} 1 \\ -1 \\ 2 \end{bmatrix} + \frac{3}{4}\begin{bmatrix} 3 \\ 1 \\ 0 \end{bmatrix} - \frac{1}{2}\begin{bmatrix} 0 \\ 0 \\ 1 \end{bmatrix} = \begin{bmatrix} 1 \\ 2 \\ -3 \end{bmatrix}$

35. Four vectors in R^3 must be linearly dependent.

37. Assume that A is an $m \times n$ matrix where $n > m$. Then the set of n column vectors of A are vectors in R^m and must be linearly dependent. On the other hand, if $m > n$, then the set of m row vectors of A are vectors in R^n and must be linearly dependent.

39. (a) $\begin{bmatrix} 1 & 0 \\ 0 & 1 \end{bmatrix}, \begin{bmatrix} 0 & 1 \\ 1 & 0 \end{bmatrix}$ (b) $\begin{bmatrix} 1 & 0 \\ 0 & 0 \end{bmatrix}, \begin{bmatrix} 0 & 1 \\ 0 & 0 \end{bmatrix}$
   (c) $\begin{bmatrix} 1 & 0 \\ 0 & 0 \end{bmatrix}, \begin{bmatrix} 0 & 0 \\ 0 & 1 \end{bmatrix}$

41. (a) m (b) r (c) r
   (d) R^n (e) R^m

Section 4.7 (*page 223*)

1. $\begin{bmatrix} 8 \\ -3 \end{bmatrix}$ **3.** $\begin{bmatrix} 5 \\ 4 \\ 3 \end{bmatrix}$ **5.** $\begin{bmatrix} -1 \\ 2 \\ 0 \\ 1 \end{bmatrix}$

7. $\begin{bmatrix} 3 \\ 2 \end{bmatrix}$ **9.** $\begin{bmatrix} 1 \\ -1 \\ 2 \end{bmatrix}$ **11.** $\begin{bmatrix} 0 \\ -1 \\ 2 \end{bmatrix}$

13. $\begin{bmatrix} \frac{3}{2} & -\frac{1}{2} \\ -2 & 1 \end{bmatrix}$ **15.** $\begin{bmatrix} 2 & -1 \\ 4 & 3 \end{bmatrix}$

17. $\begin{bmatrix} 1 & 2 & -\frac{1}{2} \\ 0 & \frac{1}{2} & 0 \\ 0 & -\frac{1}{3} & \frac{1}{12} \end{bmatrix}$ **19.** $\begin{bmatrix} 1 & 1 & 1 \\ 3 & 5 & 4 \\ 3 & 6 & 5 \end{bmatrix}$

21. $\begin{bmatrix} -24 & 7 & 1 & -2 \\ -10 & 3 & 0 & -1 \\ -29 & 7 & 3 & -2 \\ 12 & -3 & -1 & 1 \end{bmatrix}$

23. (a) $\begin{bmatrix} -\frac{1}{3} & \frac{1}{3} \\ \frac{3}{4} & -\frac{1}{2} \end{bmatrix}$ (b) $\begin{bmatrix} 6 & 4 \\ 9 & 4 \end{bmatrix}$ (c) $\begin{bmatrix} 6 \\ 3 \end{bmatrix}$

25. (a) $\begin{bmatrix} 4 & 5 & 1 \\ -7 & -10 & -1 \\ -2 & -2 & 0 \end{bmatrix}$ (b) $\begin{bmatrix} \frac{1}{2} & \frac{1}{2} & -\frac{5}{4} \\ -\frac{1}{2} & -\frac{1}{2} & \frac{3}{4} \\ \frac{3}{2} & \frac{1}{2} & \frac{5}{4} \end{bmatrix}$

   (c) $\begin{bmatrix} \frac{11}{4} \\ -\frac{9}{4} \\ \frac{5}{4} \end{bmatrix}$

27. $\begin{bmatrix} 4 \\ 11 \\ 1 \end{bmatrix}$ **29.** $\begin{bmatrix} 0 \\ 3 \\ 2 \end{bmatrix}$ **31.** QP

Section 4.8 (*page 232*)

1. (b), (c), and (d)   **3.** (a), (b), and (d)

5. -2 **7.** 0   **9.** Linearly independent

11. Linearly dependent   **13.** Linearly dependent

15. Linearly dependent   **17.** $y = C_1 \sin x + C_2 \cos x$

19. $y = C_1 + C_2 \sin x + C_3 \cos x$

25. No. For instance, consider $y'' = 1$. Two solutions are
$y = \dfrac{x^2}{2}$ and $y = \dfrac{x^2}{2} + 1$. Their sum is not a solution.

27. Parabola

$y^2 + x = 0$

29. Hyperbola

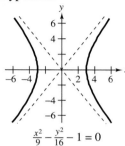

$\dfrac{x^2}{9} - \dfrac{y^2}{16} - 1 = 0$

31. Point

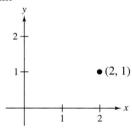

$9x^2 + 25y^2 - 36x - 50y + 61 = 0$

33. Ellipse

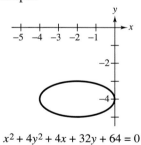

$x^2 + 4y^2 + 4x + 32y + 64 = 0$

35. Parabola

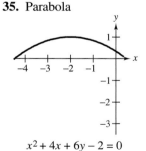

$x^2 + 4x + 6y - 2 = 0$

37. $\dfrac{(y')^2}{2} - \dfrac{(x')^2}{2} = 1$

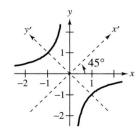

39. $\dfrac{(x')^2}{6} + \dfrac{(y')^2}{4} = 1$

41. $(x')^2 + \dfrac{(y')^2}{4} = 1$

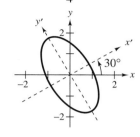

43. $y' + 4 = -(x')^2$

45. $y' = 0$

REVIEW EXERCISES – CHAPTER 4 (*page 233*)

1. (a) $(0, 2, 5)$
   (b) $(2, 0, 4)$
   (c) $(-2, 2, 1)$
   (d) $(-5, 6, 5)$

3. (a) $(3, 1, 4, 4)$
   (b) $(0, 4, 4, 2)$
   (c) $(3, -3, 0, 2)$
   (d) $(9, -7, 2, 7)$

5. $\left(\dfrac{1}{2}, -4, -4\right)$

7. $\mathbf{v} = \dfrac{9}{8}\mathbf{u}_1 + \dfrac{1}{8}\mathbf{u}_2 + 0\mathbf{u}_3$

9. $O_{3,4} = \begin{bmatrix} 0 & 0 & 0 & 0 \\ 0 & 0 & 0 & 0 \\ 0 & 0 & 0 & 0 \end{bmatrix}$,

$-A = \begin{bmatrix} -a_{11} & -a_{12} & -a_{13} & -a_{14} \\ -a_{21} & -a_{22} & -a_{23} & -a_{24} \\ -a_{31} & -a_{32} & -a_{33} & -a_{34} \end{bmatrix}$

11. W is a subspace of R^2.

13. W is a subspace of R^3.

15. W is not a subspace of $C[-1, 1]$.

17. (a) W is a subspace of R^3.
   (b) W is not a subspace of R^3.

Does S span R^3?	Is S linearly independent?	Is S a basis for R^3?
19. (a) Yes	(b) No	(c) No
21. (a) Yes	(b) Yes	(c) Yes
23. (a) No	(b) No	(c) No

25. S is a basis for P_3.

27. (a) $\{(-3, 0, 4, 1), (-2, 1, 0, 0)\}$
    (b) 2

29. $\{(8, 5)\}$
    Rank(A) and nullity(A) $= 1 + 1 = 2$

31. $\{(3, 0, 1, 0), (-1, -2, 0, 1)\}$
    Rank(A) and nullity(A) $= 2 + 2 = 4$

33. (a) 2
    (b) $\{(1, 0), (0, 1)\}$

35. (a) 3
    (b) $\{(1, 0, 0), (0, 1, 0), (0, 0, 1)\}$

37. $\begin{bmatrix} -2 \\ 8 \end{bmatrix}$ **39.** $\begin{bmatrix} 2 \\ -1 \\ -1 \end{bmatrix}$ **41.** $\begin{bmatrix} \frac{2}{5} \\ -\frac{1}{4} \end{bmatrix}$

43. $\begin{bmatrix} 3 \\ 1 \\ 0 \\ 1 \end{bmatrix}$ **45.** $\begin{bmatrix} -12 \\ 6 \end{bmatrix}$ **47.** $\begin{bmatrix} 1 & 3 \\ -1 & 1 \end{bmatrix}$

49. $\begin{bmatrix} -\frac{1}{2} & \frac{1}{2} \\ -\frac{3}{2} & -\frac{5}{2} \end{bmatrix}$

51. Basis for W: $\{x, x^2, x^3\}$
    Basis for U: $\{(x - 1), (x - 1)^2, (x - 1)^3\}$
    Basis for $W \cap U$: $\{(x(x - 1), x^2(x - 1)\}$

55. Yes, W is a subspace of V.   **61.** (a) and (d)

63. e^x **65.** Linearly independent

67. Linearly dependent

69. Circle

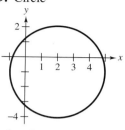

$x^2 + y^2 - 4x + 2y - 4 = 0$

71. Parabola

(5, −4)
$2x^2 - 20x - y + 46 = 0$

73. $\dfrac{(x')^2}{6} - \dfrac{(y')^2}{6} = 1$

CHAPTER 4 MATLAB (*page 237*)

1. (a) Not possible   (b) $\mathbf{v} = \mathbf{u}_1 + \mathbf{u}_2 - 2\mathbf{u}_3$

3. (a) Independent   (b) Independent

5. (a) $\{\mathbf{v}_1, \mathbf{v}_2, \mathbf{e}_1, \mathbf{e}_4, \mathbf{e}_5\}$ (b) $\{\mathbf{v}_1, \mathbf{v}_2, \mathbf{v}_3, \mathbf{e}_1, \mathbf{e}_4\}$

7. (a) $\{(1, 0, 3, 0, 0), (0, 1, 1.5, 0, 1.5), (0, 0, 0, 1, 1)\}$

    (b) $\left\{ \begin{bmatrix} -1 \\ 0 \\ -1 \\ 2 \\ 0 \end{bmatrix}, \begin{bmatrix} 2 \\ 2 \\ 4 \\ -4 \\ 0 \end{bmatrix}, \begin{bmatrix} 0 \\ -1 \\ -1 \\ 0 \\ 1 \end{bmatrix} \right\}$

    (c) 3

9. $[\mathbf{x}]_B = \begin{bmatrix} 5 \\ -8 \\ -2 \end{bmatrix}$

Chapter 5

SECTION 5.1 (*page 250*)

1. 5

3. 1

5. 0

7. $5\sqrt{2}$

9. (a) 5

11. (a) $\sqrt{6}$

    (b) $\sqrt{6}$

    (b) $\sqrt{11}$

    (c) $\sqrt{21}$

    (c) $\sqrt{13}$

13. (a) $\left(-\frac{5}{13}, \frac{12}{13}\right)$

15. (a) $\left(\frac{3}{\sqrt{38}}, \frac{2}{\sqrt{38}}, -\frac{5}{\sqrt{38}}\right)$

    (b) $\left(\frac{5}{13}, -\frac{12}{13}\right)$

    (b) $\left(-\frac{3}{\sqrt{38}}, -\frac{2}{\sqrt{38}}, \frac{5}{\sqrt{38}}\right)$

17. $\pm\dfrac{1}{\sqrt{14}}$

19. $\left(2\sqrt{2}, 2\sqrt{2}\right)$

21. $\left(1, \sqrt{3}, 0\right)$

23. (a) $(4, 4, 3)$

    (b) $\left(-2, -2, -\frac{3}{2}\right)$

25. $2\sqrt{2}$

27. $2\sqrt{3}$

29. (a) -6

31. (a) 1

    (b) 25

    (b) 6

    (c) 25

    (c) 6

    (d) $(-12, 18)$

    (d) $(1, 0, -1)$

    (e) -12

    (e) 2

33. (a) 5

35. -7

    (b) 50

    (c) 50

    (d) $(0, 10, 25, 20)$

    (e) 10

37. $|(3, 4) \cdot (2, -3)| \leq \|(3, 4)\| \, \|(2, -3)\|$
$$6 \leq 5\sqrt{13}$$

39. $\dfrac{\pi}{2}$

41. 1.713 radians
(98.13°)

43. 1.080 radians
(61.87°)

45. $\dfrac{\pi}{4}$

47. $\mathbf{v} = (t, 0)$

49. $\mathbf{v} = (2t, 3t)$

51. $\mathbf{v} = (t, 4t, s)$

53. Neither

55. Orthogonal   **57.** Neither   **59.** Orthogonal

63. $\|(5, 1)\| \leq \|(4, 0)\| + \|(1, 1)\|$
$$\sqrt{26} \leq 4 + \sqrt{2}$$

65. $\|(2, 0)\|^2 = \|(1, -1)\|^2 + \|(1, 1)\|^2$
$$4 = \left(\sqrt{2}\right)^2 + \left(\sqrt{2}\right)^2$$

67. (a) $\theta = \dfrac{\pi}{2}$ provided $\mathbf{u} \neq \mathbf{0}$ and $\mathbf{v} \neq \mathbf{0}$

    (b) $0 \leq \theta < \dfrac{\pi}{2}$ (c) $\dfrac{\pi}{2} < \theta \leq \pi$

69. $\theta = \arccos\left(\dfrac{1}{\sqrt{3}}\right) \approx 54.7°$

75. Let $\mathbf{u} = (\cos\theta)\mathbf{i} - (\sin\theta)\mathbf{j}$ and $\mathbf{v} = (\sin\theta)\mathbf{i} + (\cos\theta)\mathbf{j}$.
Then
$$\|\mathbf{u}\| = \sqrt{\cos^2\theta + \sin^2\theta} = 1$$
and
$$\|\mathbf{v}\| = \sqrt{\sin^2\theta + \cos^2\theta} = 1.$$

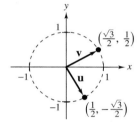

77. $\mathbf{u} \cdot \mathbf{v} = 17{,}139.05$, which represents the total amount for the three crops.

SECTION 5.2 (*page 262*)

1. (a) -33

3. (a) 15

5. (a) -34

    (b) 5

    (b) $\sqrt{57}$

    (b) $\sqrt{97}$

    (c) $2\sqrt{65}$

    (c) $2\sqrt{13}$

    (c) $\sqrt{266}$

7. (a) 0

9. (a) -73

11. (a) $\dfrac{16}{15}$

    (b) $8\sqrt{3}$

    (b) $\sqrt{83}$

    (c) $3\sqrt{67}$

    (c) $\sqrt{367}$

    (b) $\dfrac{\sqrt{10}}{5}$

    (c) $\sqrt{2}$

13. (a) $\dfrac{2}{e} \approx 0.736$

    (b) $\dfrac{\sqrt{6}}{3} \approx 0.816$

    (c) $\sqrt{\dfrac{e^2}{2} + \dfrac{2}{3} - \dfrac{1}{2e^2} - \dfrac{4}{e}} \approx 1.680$

15. (a) -6

(b) $\sqrt{35}$

(c) $3\sqrt{6}$

17. (a) -4

(b) $\sqrt{11}$

(c) $\sqrt{21}$

23. Axiom 4 fails.
$\langle(0, 1), (0, 1)\rangle = 0$, but $(0, 1) \neq 0$.

25. Axiom 2 fails.

$$\langle(1, 0), (1, 0) + (1, 0)\rangle = \langle(1, 0), (2, 0)\rangle = 4$$
$$\langle(1, 0), (1, 0)\rangle + \langle(1, 0), (1, 0)\rangle = 1 + 1 \qquad = 2$$

27. 2.103 radians
(120.5°)

29. $\dfrac{\pi}{2}$

31. $\dfrac{\pi}{2}$

33. (a) $|\langle(5, 12), (3, 4)\rangle| \leq \|(5, 12)\| \, \|(3, 4)\|$
$$63 \leq (13)(5)$$

(b) $\|(5, 12) + (3, 4)\| \leq \|(5, 12)\| + \|(3, 4)\|$
$$8\sqrt{5} \leq 13 + 5$$

35. (a) $|\langle 2x, 3x^2 + 1\rangle| \leq \|2x\| \, \|3x^2 + 1\|$
$$0 \leq (2)(\sqrt{10})$$

(b) $\|2x + 3x^2 + 1\| \leq \|2x\| + \|3x^2 + 1\|$
$$\sqrt{14} \leq 2 + \sqrt{10}$$

37. (a) $|\langle \sin x, \cos x\rangle| \leq \|\sin x\| \, \|\cos x\|$
$$0 \leq (\sqrt{\pi} \, ((\sqrt{\pi})$$

(b) $\|\sin x + \cos x\| \leq \|\sin x\| + \|\cos x\|$
$$\sqrt{2\pi} \leq \sqrt{\pi} + \sqrt{\pi}$$

43. (a) $\left(\frac{8}{5}, \frac{4}{5}\right)$

(b) $\left(\frac{4}{5}, \frac{8}{5}\right)$

(c)

45. (a) $\left(0, \frac{5}{2}, -\frac{5}{2}\right)$

(b) $\left(-\frac{5}{14}, -\frac{15}{14}, \frac{10}{14}\right)$

47. $\mathrm{proj}_g \, \mathbf{f} = 0$

49. $\mathrm{proj}_g \, \mathbf{f} = \dfrac{2e^x}{e^2 - 1}$

51. $\mathrm{proj}_g \, \mathbf{f} = 0$

53. (b) Not orthogonal in the Euclidean sense

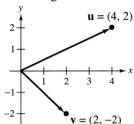

59. (b) $W^{\perp} = \mathrm{span}\{(-2, 1, 0), (-3, 0, 1)\}$

Section 5.3 *(page 275)*

1. Neither

3. Orthonormal

5. Orthogonal

7. Neither

9. Orthonormal

13. $\begin{bmatrix} \dfrac{4\sqrt{13}}{13} \\ \dfrac{7\sqrt{13}}{13} \end{bmatrix}$

15. $\begin{bmatrix} \dfrac{\sqrt{10}}{2} \\ -2 \\ -\dfrac{\sqrt{10}}{2} \end{bmatrix}$

17. $\begin{bmatrix} 11 \\ 2 \\ 15 \end{bmatrix}$

19. $\left\{\left(\frac{3}{5}, \frac{4}{5}\right), \left(\frac{4}{5}, -\frac{3}{5}\right)\right\}$

21. $\left\{\left(\dfrac{\sqrt{2}}{2}, -\dfrac{\sqrt{2}}{2}\right), \left(\dfrac{\sqrt{2}}{2}, \dfrac{\sqrt{2}}{2}\right)\right\}$

23. $\left\{\left(\frac{4}{5}, -\frac{3}{5}, 0\right), \left(\frac{3}{5}, \frac{4}{5}, 0\right), (0, 0, 1)\right\}$

25. $\left\{\left(0, \dfrac{\sqrt{2}}{2}, \dfrac{\sqrt{2}}{2}\right), \left(\dfrac{\sqrt{6}}{3}, \dfrac{\sqrt{6}}{6}, -\dfrac{\sqrt{6}}{6}\right), \right.$
$\left. \left(\dfrac{\sqrt{3}}{3}, -\dfrac{\sqrt{3}}{3}, \dfrac{\sqrt{3}}{3}\right)\right\}$

27. $\left\{\left(-\dfrac{4\sqrt{2}}{7}, \dfrac{3\sqrt{2}}{14}, \dfrac{5\sqrt{2}}{14}\right)\right\}$

29. $\left\{\left(\frac{3}{5}, \frac{4}{5}, 0\right), \left(\frac{4}{5}, -\frac{3}{5}, 0\right)\right\}$

31. $\left\{\left(\dfrac{\sqrt{6}}{6}, \dfrac{\sqrt{6}}{3}, -\dfrac{\sqrt{6}}{6}, 0\right), \left(\dfrac{\sqrt{3}}{3}, 0, \dfrac{\sqrt{3}}{3}, \dfrac{\sqrt{3}}{3}\right)\right\}$

33. $\langle x, 1 \rangle = \displaystyle\int_{-1}^{1} x \, dx = \dfrac{x^2}{2}\Big]_{-1}^{1} = 0$

35. $\langle x^2, 1 \rangle = \displaystyle\int_{-1}^{1} x^2 \, dx = \dfrac{x^3}{3}\Big]_{-1}^{1} = \dfrac{2}{3}$

37. $\left\{\left(\dfrac{3\sqrt{10}}{10}, 0, \dfrac{\sqrt{10}}{10}, 0\right), \left(0, -\dfrac{2\sqrt{5}}{5}, 0, \dfrac{\sqrt{5}}{5}\right)\right\}$

39. $\left\{\left(\dfrac{\sqrt{2}}{2}, 0, \dfrac{\sqrt{2}}{2}, 0\right), \left(\dfrac{\sqrt{6}}{6}, 0, -\dfrac{\sqrt{6}}{6}, \dfrac{\sqrt{6}}{3}\right)\right\}$

41. Orthonormal   **43.** $\{x^2, x, 1\}$

45. $\left\{\dfrac{1}{\sqrt{2}}\left(x^2 - 1\right), -\dfrac{1}{\sqrt{6}}\left(x^2 - 2x + 1\right)\right\}$

47. $\left\{\left(\dfrac{2}{3}, -\dfrac{1}{3}\right), \left(\dfrac{\sqrt{2}}{6}, \dfrac{2\sqrt{2}}{3}\right)\right\}$

49. Assume that **w** is orthogonal to each vector in $\{\mathbf{v}_1, \mathbf{v}_2, \ldots, \mathbf{v}_n\}$. Then

$\mathbf{w} \cdot (c_1\mathbf{v}_1 + c_2\mathbf{v}_2 + \cdots + c_n\mathbf{v}_n)$

$\qquad = \mathbf{w} \cdot c_1\mathbf{v}_1 + \mathbf{w} \cdot c_2\mathbf{v}_2 + \cdots + \mathbf{w} \cdot c_n\mathbf{v}_n$

$\qquad = c_1\mathbf{w} \cdot \mathbf{v}_1 + c_2\mathbf{w} \cdot \mathbf{v}_2 + \cdots + c_n\mathbf{w} \cdot \mathbf{v}_n$

$\qquad = c_1(0) + c_2(0) + \cdots + c_n(0)$

$\qquad = 0.$

53. $\left\{\left(\dfrac{1}{\sqrt{2}}, 0, \dfrac{1}{\sqrt{2}}, 0\right), \left(0, -\dfrac{1}{\sqrt{2}}, 0, \dfrac{1}{\sqrt{2}}\right),\right.$

$\qquad \left. \left(\dfrac{1}{\sqrt{2}}, 0, -\dfrac{1}{\sqrt{2}}, 0\right), \left(0, \dfrac{1}{\sqrt{2}}, 0, \dfrac{1}{\sqrt{2}}\right)\right\}$

55. $N(A) = \text{span}\{(3, -1, 2)\}$
$N(A^T) = \text{span}\{(-1, -1, 1)\}$
$R(A) = \text{span}\{(1, 0, 1), (1, 2, 3)\}$
$R(A^T) = \text{span}\{(1, 1, -1), (0, 2, 1)\}$

57. $N(A) = \text{span}\{(1, 0, -1)\}$
$N(A^T) = \{(0, 0, 0)\}$
$R(A) = \mathbf{R}^2$
$R(A^T) = \text{span}\{(1, 0, 1), (0, 1, 0)\}$

SECTION 5.4 *(page 289)*

1. Not orthogonal   **3.** Orthogonal

5. $\text{span}\left\{\begin{bmatrix} 0 \\ 1 \\ 0 \end{bmatrix}\right\}$ **7.** $\text{span}\left\{\begin{bmatrix} 0 \\ 0 \\ 1 \\ 0 \end{bmatrix}, \begin{bmatrix} 2 \\ -1 \\ 0 \\ 1 \end{bmatrix}\right\}$

9. $\text{span}\left\{\begin{bmatrix} 1 \\ 2 \\ 0 \\ 0 \end{bmatrix}, \begin{bmatrix} 0 \\ 1 \\ 0 \\ 1 \end{bmatrix}\right\}$ **11.** $\begin{bmatrix} 0 \\ \frac{2}{3} \\ \frac{2}{3} \\ \frac{2}{3} \end{bmatrix}$

13. $\begin{bmatrix} \frac{5}{3} \\ \frac{8}{3} \\ \frac{13}{3} \end{bmatrix}$ **15.** $\begin{bmatrix} 1 \\ -1 \\ 2 \end{bmatrix}$

17. $R(A) = \text{span}\left\{\begin{bmatrix} 1 \\ 0 \end{bmatrix}, \begin{bmatrix} 0 \\ 1 \end{bmatrix}\right\} = \mathbf{R}^2$

$N(A^T) = \left\{\begin{bmatrix} 0 \\ 0 \end{bmatrix}\right\}$

$N(A) = \text{span}\left\{\begin{bmatrix} -3 \\ 0 \\ 1 \end{bmatrix}\right\}$

$R(A^T) = \text{span}\left\{\begin{bmatrix} 1 \\ 0 \\ 3 \end{bmatrix}, \begin{bmatrix} 0 \\ 1 \\ 0 \end{bmatrix}\right\}$

19. $R(A) = \text{span}\left\{\begin{bmatrix} 1 \\ 0 \\ 1 \\ 1 \end{bmatrix}, \begin{bmatrix} 0 \\ 1 \\ 1 \\ 2 \end{bmatrix}\right\}$

$N(A^T) = \text{span}\left\{\begin{bmatrix} -1 \\ -1 \\ 1 \\ 0 \end{bmatrix}, \begin{bmatrix} -1 \\ -2 \\ 0 \\ 1 \end{bmatrix}\right\}$

$N(A) = \text{span}\left\{\begin{bmatrix} -1 \\ -1 \\ 0 \\ 1 \end{bmatrix}, \begin{bmatrix} 0 \\ -1 \\ 1 \\ 0 \end{bmatrix}\right\}$

$$R(A^T) = \text{span}\left\{ \begin{bmatrix} 1 \\ 0 \\ 0 \\ 1 \end{bmatrix}, \begin{bmatrix} 0 \\ 1 \\ 1 \\ 1 \end{bmatrix} \right\}$$

21. $x = \begin{bmatrix} 1 \\ -1 \end{bmatrix}$ **23.** $x = \begin{bmatrix} 2 \\ -2 \\ 1 \end{bmatrix}$

25. $y = -x + \frac{1}{3}$

27. $y = 1.2x + 0.45$

29. $y = \frac{3}{7}x^2 + \frac{6}{5}x + \frac{26}{35}$

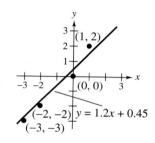

31. Many models are possible. For example,

$R = 131.8t^2 - 67.9t + 19{,}494.6$
(*K-Mart*, $t = 5$ is 1985)

$R = 749.0t^2 - 6248.4t + 21{,}918.3$
(*Wal-Mart*, $t = 5$ is 1985)

For 1993, $t = 13$ yields $R \approx \$40{,}866$ (*K-Mart*) and $R \approx \$62{,}270$ (*Wal-Mart*).

SECTION 5.5 *(page 305)*

1. $(0, 0, 1)$ **3.** $(1, 0, 0)$ **5.** $(-2, 3, -1)$

7. 1   **9.** $6\sqrt{5}$ **11.** 1

13. 6   **15.** 3

27. (a) $g(x) = -\frac{1}{6} + x$

(b)

29. (a) $g(x) \approx 0.1945 + 6x$

(b)

31. (a) $g(x) \approx 0.1148 + 0.6644x$

(b)

33. (a) $g(x) = 1.5x^2 - 0.6x + 0.05$

(b)

35. (a) $g(x) \approx -0.0505 + 1.3122x - 0.4177x^2$

(b)

37. $g(x) = 2 \sin x + \sin 2x + \frac{2}{3} \sin 3x$

39. $g(x) = \frac{\pi^2}{3} + 4 \cos x + \cos 2x + \frac{4}{9} \cos 3x$

41. $g(x) = \frac{1}{2\pi}(1 - e^{-2\pi})(1 + \cos x + \sin x)$

43. $g(x) = (1 + \pi) - 2 \sin x - \sin 2x - \dfrac{2}{3} \sin 3x$

45. $g(x) = \sin 2x$

47. $g(x) = 2\left(\sin x + \dfrac{\sin 2x}{2} + \dfrac{\sin 3x}{3} + \cdots + \dfrac{\sin nx}{n} \right)$

REVIEW EXERCISES – CHAPTER 5 *(page 306)*

1. (a) $\sqrt{5}$ **3.** (a) $\sqrt{6}$ **5.** (a) 3

(b) $\sqrt{17}$ (b) $\sqrt{14}$ (b) 3

(c) 6 (c) 1 (c) 4

(d) $\sqrt{10}$ (d) $3\sqrt{2}$ (d) $\sqrt{10}$

7. $\|\mathbf{v}\| = \sqrt{38}$

$$\mathbf{u} = \left(\dfrac{5}{\sqrt{38}}, \dfrac{3}{\sqrt{38}}, -\dfrac{2}{\sqrt{38}} \right)$$

9. 0.2663 radians   **11.** $\dfrac{\pi}{2}$
$(15.26°)$

13. π **15.** $\left(-\dfrac{9}{13}, \dfrac{45}{13} \right)$ **17.** $\left(\dfrac{18}{29}, \dfrac{12}{29}, \dfrac{24}{29} \right)$

19. (a) -2 (b) $\dfrac{3\sqrt{11}}{2}$

21. Triangle Inequality:

$$\left\| \left(2, -\dfrac{1}{2}, 1 \right) + \left(\dfrac{3}{2}, 2, -1 \right) \right\|$$

$$\leq \left\| \left(2, -\dfrac{1}{2}, 1 \right) \right\| + \left\| \left(\dfrac{3}{2}, 2, -1 \right) \right\|$$

$$\dfrac{\sqrt{67}}{2} \leq \sqrt{\dfrac{15}{2}} + \sqrt{\dfrac{53}{4}}$$

$$4.093 \leq 6.379$$

Cauchy–Schwarz Inequality:

$$\left| \left\langle \left(2, -\dfrac{1}{2}, 1 \right), \left(\dfrac{3}{2}, 2, -1 \right) \right\rangle \right|$$

$$\leq \left\| \left(2, -\dfrac{1}{2}, 1 \right) \right\| \left\| \left(\dfrac{3}{2}, 2, -1 \right) \right\|$$

$$2 \leq \sqrt{\dfrac{15}{2}} \sqrt{\dfrac{53}{4}} \approx 9.969$$

23. $(s, 3t, 4t)$

25. $\left\{ \left(\dfrac{1}{\sqrt{2}}, \dfrac{1}{\sqrt{2}} \right), \left(-\dfrac{1}{\sqrt{2}}, \dfrac{1}{\sqrt{2}} \right) \right\}$

27. $\left\{ \left(0, \dfrac{3}{5}, \dfrac{4}{5} \right), (1, 0, 0), \left(0, \dfrac{4}{5}, -\dfrac{3}{5} \right) \right\}$

29. (a) $(-1, 4, -2) = 2(0, 2, -2) - (1, 0, -2)$

(b) $\left\{ \left(0, \dfrac{1}{\sqrt{2}}, -\dfrac{1}{\sqrt{2}} \right), \left(\dfrac{1}{\sqrt{3}}, -\dfrac{1}{\sqrt{3}}, -\dfrac{1}{\sqrt{3}} \right) \right\}$

(c) $(-1, 4, -2) = 3\sqrt{2} \left(0, \dfrac{1}{\sqrt{2}}, -\dfrac{1}{\sqrt{2}} \right)$

$$- \sqrt{3} \left(\dfrac{1}{\sqrt{3}}, -\dfrac{1}{\sqrt{3}}, -\dfrac{1}{\sqrt{3}} \right)$$

31. (a) $\dfrac{1}{4}$ (b) $\dfrac{1}{\sqrt{5}}$

(c) $\dfrac{1}{\sqrt{30}}$ (d) $\{ \sqrt{3}x, \sqrt{5}x(4x^2 - 3x) \}$

33. Let $f(x) = \sqrt{1 - x^2}$ and $g(x) = 2x\sqrt{1 - x^2}$.

$$\langle \mathbf{f}, \mathbf{g} \rangle = \int_{-1}^{1} \sqrt{1 - x^2}\, 2x\sqrt{1 - x^2}\, dx$$

$$= \int_{-1}^{1} 2x(1 - x^2)\, dx = 2 \int_{-1}^{1} (x - x^3)\, dx$$

$$= 2 \left[\dfrac{x^2}{2} - \dfrac{x^4}{4} \right]_{-1}^{1} = 0$$

35. $\left\{ \left(-\dfrac{1}{\sqrt{2}}, 0, \dfrac{1}{\sqrt{2}} \right), \left(-\dfrac{1}{\sqrt{6}}, \dfrac{2}{\sqrt{6}}, -\dfrac{1}{\sqrt{6}} \right) \right\}$

(The answer is not unique.)

37. (a) 0

(b) Orthogonal

(c) Since $\langle \mathbf{f}, \mathbf{g} \rangle = 0$, it follows that $|\langle \mathbf{f}, \mathbf{g} \rangle| \leq \|\mathbf{f}\| \, \|\mathbf{g}\|$.

39. Assume that $\|\mathbf{u}\| \leq 1$ and $\|\mathbf{v}\| \leq 1$. Then, by the Cauchy–Schwarz Inequality it follows that $|\langle \mathbf{u}, \mathbf{v} \rangle| \leq \|\mathbf{u}\| \, \|\mathbf{v}\| \leq (1)(1) = 1$.

47. $\text{span} \left\{ \begin{bmatrix} 2 \\ -1 \\ 3 \end{bmatrix} \right\}$

49. $R(A) = \text{span}\left\{\begin{bmatrix} 0 \\ 0 \\ 1 \end{bmatrix}, \begin{bmatrix} 1 \\ -3 \\ 0 \end{bmatrix}\right\}$

$N(A^T) = \text{span}\left\{\begin{bmatrix} 3 \\ 1 \\ 0 \end{bmatrix}\right\}$

$N(A) = \text{span}\left\{\begin{bmatrix} 1 \\ 0 \\ -1 \end{bmatrix}\right\}$

$R(A^T) = \text{span}\left\{\begin{bmatrix} 0 \\ 1 \\ 0 \end{bmatrix}, \begin{bmatrix} 1 \\ 0 \\ 1 \end{bmatrix}\right\}$

51. $(0, 1, -1)$ **53.** 7   **55.** 1

57. $g(x) = \dfrac{3}{5}x$ **59.** $g(x) = \dfrac{2}{\pi}$

61. $g(x) = \dfrac{2}{35}(-10x^2 + 24x + 3)$

63. $g(x) = \dfrac{\pi^2}{3} - 4\cos x$

CHAPTER 5 MATLAB *(page 311)*

1. (a) 5   (b) $\frac{1}{7.4162}(-3, 2, 4, -5, 0, 1)$
   (c) 11

3. 1.5236 radians

5. (a) $(3, 5, 7)$ (b) $(34, 10, 5)$

7. (a) $\begin{bmatrix} 0.0 \\ 0.3333 \end{bmatrix}$ (b) $\begin{bmatrix} -2.3333 \\ 1.0000 \end{bmatrix}$ (c) $\begin{bmatrix} 2.0588 \\ -0.8824 \\ -0.4118 \end{bmatrix}$

CUMULATIVE TEST CHAPTERS 4 AND 5 *(page 313)*

1. (a) $(2, 1)$

(b) $(-3, 6)$

(c) $(-14, 8)$

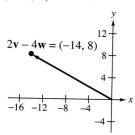

2. $\mathbf{w} = 4\mathbf{v}_1 + \mathbf{v}_2 - 2\mathbf{v}_3$

3. The set of singular 2×2 matrices is not closed under addition. For example, the sum of the singular matrices

$\begin{bmatrix} 1 & 0 \\ 0 & 0 \end{bmatrix}$ and $\begin{bmatrix} 0 & 0 \\ 0 & 1 \end{bmatrix}$ is the nonsingular matrix

$\begin{bmatrix} 1 & 0 \\ 0 & 1 \end{bmatrix}$.

4. Yes   **5.** No   **6.** Yes

7. (a) A set of vectors $\{\mathbf{v}_1, \ldots, \mathbf{v}_n\}$ is linearly independent if the vector equation $c_1\mathbf{v}_1 + \cdots + c_n\mathbf{v}_n = \mathbf{0}$
has only the trivial solution.

   (b) Linearly dependent

8. The dimension is 6. One basis is

$$\left\{ \begin{bmatrix} 1 & 0 & 0 \\ 0 & 0 & 0 \\ 0 & 0 & 0 \end{bmatrix}, \begin{bmatrix} 0 & 1 & 0 \\ 1 & 0 & 0 \\ 0 & 0 & 0 \end{bmatrix}, \begin{bmatrix} 0 & 0 & 1 \\ 0 & 0 & 0 \\ 1 & 0 & 0 \end{bmatrix}, \right.$$

$$\left. \begin{bmatrix} 0 & 0 & 0 \\ 0 & 1 & 0 \\ 0 & 0 & 0 \end{bmatrix}, \begin{bmatrix} 0 & 0 & 0 \\ 0 & 0 & 1 \\ 0 & 1 & 0 \end{bmatrix}, \begin{bmatrix} 0 & 0 & 0 \\ 0 & 0 & 0 \\ 0 & 0 & 1 \end{bmatrix} \right\}$$

9. (a) A set of vectors $\{\mathbf{v}_1, \ldots, \mathbf{v}_n\}$ in a vector space V is a
basis for V if the set is linearly independent and
spans V.

   (b) Yes

10. (a) 2

   (b) $\{(1, 0, -2), (0, 1, 2)\}$

   (c) $\left\{ \begin{bmatrix} 1 \\ 0 \end{bmatrix}, \begin{bmatrix} 0 \\ 1 \end{bmatrix} \right\}$

11. $\left\{ \begin{bmatrix} -1 \\ 1 \\ 0 \\ 0 \end{bmatrix}, \begin{bmatrix} 0 \\ 0 \\ -1 \\ 1 \end{bmatrix} \right\}$ **12.** $\begin{bmatrix} -1 \\ 3 \\ -2 \end{bmatrix}$

13. $\begin{bmatrix} -2 & 0 & -2 \\ 5 & 1 & 4 \\ 2 & 1 & 3 \end{bmatrix}$

14. (a) $\sqrt{5}$ **15.** $\frac{-5}{12}$

   (b) $\sqrt{11}$

   (c) 4

16. $\left\{ (1, 0, 0), \left(0, \frac{\sqrt{2}}{2}, \frac{\sqrt{2}}{2} \right), \left(0, -\frac{\sqrt{2}}{2}, \frac{\sqrt{2}}{2} \right) \right\}$

17. $\frac{1}{13}(-3, 2)$

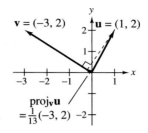

18. $R(A) = \mathbf{R}^3$

$$N(A^T) = \left\{ \begin{bmatrix} 0 \\ 0 \\ 0 \end{bmatrix} \right\}$$

$$N(A) = \text{span} \left\{ \begin{bmatrix} 0 \\ 1 \\ -1 \\ 0 \end{bmatrix} \right\}$$

$$R(A^T) = \left\{ \begin{bmatrix} 0 \\ 1 \\ 1 \\ 0 \end{bmatrix}, \begin{bmatrix} -1 \\ 0 \\ 0 \\ 1 \end{bmatrix}, \begin{bmatrix} 1 \\ 1 \\ 1 \\ 1 \end{bmatrix} \right\}$$

19. $\text{span} \left\{ \begin{bmatrix} -1 \\ -1 \\ 1 \end{bmatrix} \right\}$

20.
$$0\mathbf{v} = (0 + 0)\mathbf{v} = 0\mathbf{v} + 0\mathbf{v}$$
$$-0\mathbf{v} + 0\mathbf{v} = -0\mathbf{v} + (0\mathbf{v} + 0\mathbf{v}) = (-0\mathbf{v} + 0\mathbf{v}) + 0\mathbf{v}$$
$$\mathbf{0} = 0\mathbf{v}$$

21. Suppose $c_1\mathbf{x}_1 + \cdots c_n\mathbf{x}_n + c\mathbf{y} = \mathbf{0}$. Notice that $c = 0$,
for otherwise you could solve for $\mathbf{y}$, $\mathbf{y} = \frac{c_1}{c}\mathbf{x}_1 + \frac{c_n}{c}\mathbf{x}_n$,
which would imply that $\mathbf{y}$ is in the span of $\mathbf{x}_1, \ldots, \mathbf{x}_n$.
Hence, $c = 0$, and $c_1\mathbf{x}_1 + \ldots c_n\mathbf{x}_n = \mathbf{0}$. But since the
$\mathbf{x}_i$ are linearly independent, the c_i must all be zero.
Therefore, the vectors $\mathbf{x}_1, \ldots, \mathbf{x}_n, \mathbf{y}$ are linearly
independent.

22. The set $W^\perp$ is nonempty since it contains the zero vector. Let $\mathbf{v}_1$ and $\mathbf{v}_2$ be vectors in $W^\perp$. Then $\langle \mathbf{v}_1, \mathbf{w} \rangle = 0$ and $\langle \mathbf{v}_2, \mathbf{w} \rangle = 0$. Thus, $\langle \mathbf{v}_1 + \mathbf{v}_2, \mathbf{w} \rangle = 0$ and $W^\perp$ is closed under addition.

Similarly, let $\mathbf{v}$ be a vector in $W^\perp$ and c a scalar. Then $\langle \mathbf{v}, \mathbf{w} \rangle = 0$ which implies that $c\langle \mathbf{v}, \mathbf{w} \rangle = \langle c\mathbf{v}, \mathbf{w} \rangle = 0$, which shows that $W^\perp$ is also closed under scalar multiplication.

23. $y = \frac{7}{3} - x$

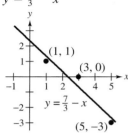

24. (a) 3

(b) One basis consists of the first three rows of A.

(c) One basis consists of columns 1, 3, 4 and 5 of A.

(d) $\left\{ \begin{bmatrix} 2 \\ 1 \\ 0 \\ 0 \\ 0 \\ 0 \end{bmatrix}, \begin{bmatrix} -3 \\ 0 \\ 5 \\ -1 \\ 1 \\ 0 \end{bmatrix}, \begin{bmatrix} -2 \\ 0 \\ 3 \\ -7 \\ 0 \\ 1 \end{bmatrix} \right\}$ (e) No

(f) No   (g) Yes   (h) No

25. $\|\mathbf{u} + \mathbf{v}\| = \|\mathbf{u} - \mathbf{v}\|$

if and only if $\|\mathbf{u} + \mathbf{v}\|^2 = \|\mathbf{u} - \mathbf{v}\|^2$

if and only if $(\mathbf{u} + \mathbf{v}) \cdot (\mathbf{u} + \mathbf{v}) = (\mathbf{u} - \mathbf{v}) \cdot (\mathbf{u} - \mathbf{v})$

if and only if $\mathbf{u} \cdot \mathbf{u} + 2\mathbf{u} \cdot \mathbf{v} + \mathbf{v} \cdot \mathbf{v} = \mathbf{u} \cdot \mathbf{u} - 2\mathbf{u} \cdot \mathbf{v} + \mathbf{v} \cdot \mathbf{v}$

if and only if $2\mathbf{u} \cdot \mathbf{v} = -2\mathbf{u} \cdot \mathbf{v}$

if and only if $\mathbf{u} \cdot \mathbf{v} = 0$

Chapter 6

SECTION 6.1 *(page 325)*

1. (a) $(-1, 7)$ **3.** (a) $(1, 5, 4)$ **5.** (a) $(-14, -7)$
    (b) $(11, -8)$ (b) $(5, -6, t)$ (b) $(1, 1, t)$

7. Not linear   **9.** Not linear   **11.** Not linear

13. Linear   **15.** Linear   **17.** $T: R^4 \rightarrow R^3$

19. $T: R^2 \rightarrow R^3$ **21.** $T: R^4 \rightarrow R^4$

23. (a) $(-1, 9, 3)$ (b) $(6t, -t, 2t, 5t)$

25. (a) $(10, 12, 4)$ (b) $(-1, 0)$

(c) The system represented by

$$\begin{bmatrix} 1 & 2 \\ -2 & 4 \\ -2 & 2 \end{bmatrix} \begin{bmatrix} x_1 \\ x_2 \end{bmatrix} = \begin{bmatrix} 1 \\ 1 \\ 1 \end{bmatrix}$$

is inconsistent.

27. (a) $(-1, 1, 2, 1)$ (b) $(-1, 1, \frac{1}{2}, 1)$

29. (a) $(0, 4\sqrt{2})$ (b) $(2\sqrt{3} - 2, 2\sqrt{3} + 2)$

(c) $\left(-\frac{5}{2}, \frac{5\sqrt{3}}{2} \right)$

31. (a) True   **33.** (a) -1
    (b) True   (b) $\frac{1}{12}$
    (c) False   (c) -4

35. $T(1, 0) = \left(\frac{1}{2}, \frac{1}{2} \right)$ **37.** $x^2 - 3x - 5$
    $T(0, 2) = (1, -1)$

39. (a) $(x, 0)$ **41.** $\left(\frac{1}{2}(x + y), \frac{1}{2}(x + y) \right)$
    (b) Projection onto
        the x-axis.

45. $T(3, 4) = \left(\frac{7}{2}, \frac{7}{2} \right)$

$T(T(3, 4)) = \left(\frac{7}{2}, \frac{7}{2} \right)$

T is a projection onto the line $y = x$.

47. For any linear transformation $T: V \rightarrow V$, the zero vector is a fixed point since $T(\mathbf{0}) = \mathbf{0}$.

49. $(t, 0)$

51. Assume that h and k are not both zero. Since

$$T(0, 0) = (0 - h, 0 - k) = (-h, -k) \neq (0, 0)$$

it follows that T is not a linear transformation.

53. If $T(x, y) = (x - h, y - k) = (x, y)$, then $h = 0$ and $k = 0$, which contradicts the assumption that h and k are not both zero. Therefore, T has no fixed points.

55. Let $T: R^3 \to R^3$ be given by $T(x, y, z) = (0, 0, 0)$. Then if $\{\mathbf{v}_1, \mathbf{v}_2, \mathbf{v}_3\}$ is any set of vectors in R^3, the set $\{T(\mathbf{v}_1), T(\mathbf{v}_2), T(\mathbf{v}_3)\} = \{\mathbf{0}, \mathbf{0}, \mathbf{0}\}$ is linearly dependent.

57. Let $T: V \to V$ be given by $T(\mathbf{v}) = \mathbf{v}$. Then $T(\mathbf{u} + \mathbf{v}) = \mathbf{u} + \mathbf{v} = T(\mathbf{u}) + T(\mathbf{v})$, and $T(c\mathbf{u}) = c\mathbf{u} = cT(\mathbf{u})$, which implies that T is a linear transformation.

SECTION 6.2 *(page 339)*

1. R^3

3. $\{a_1 x + a_2 x^2 + a_3 x^3: a_1, a_2, a_3 \text{ are real}\}$

5. $\{(0, 0)\}$

7. (a) $\{(0, 0)\}$ **9.** (a) $\{(-4, -2, 1)\}$
    (b) $\{(1, 0), (0, 1)\}$ (b) $\{(1, 0), (0, 1)\}$

11. (a) $\{(-1, 1, 1, 0)\}$
    (b) $\{(1, 0, -1, 0), (0, 1, -1, 0), (0, 0, 0, 1)\}$

13. (a) $\{(0, 0)\}$ (b) 0
    (c) R^2 (d) 2

15. (a) $\{(0, 0)\}$ (b) 0
    (c) $\{(4s, 4t, s - t): s \text{ and } t \text{ are real}\}$
    (d) 2

17. (a) $\{(-11t, 6t, 4t): t \text{ is real}\}$
    (b) 1
    (c) R^2
    (d) 2

19. (a) $\{(t, -3t): t \text{ is real}\}$
    (b) 1
    (c) $\{(3t, t): t \text{ is real}\}$
    (d) 1

21. (a) $\{(2s - t, t, 4s, -5s, s): s \text{ and } t \text{ are real}\}$
    (b) 2
    (c) $\{(7r, 7s, 7t, 8r + 20s + 2t): r, s, \text{ and } t \text{ are real}\}$
    (d) 3

23. (a) $\{(s + t, s, -2t): s \text{ and } t \text{ are real}\}$
    (b) 2
    (c) $\{(2t, -2t, t): t \text{ is real}\}$
    (d) 1

25. Nullity $= 1$ **27.** Nullity $= 3$

Kernel: a line   Kernel: R^3
Range: a plane   Range: $\{(0, 0, 0)\}$

29. Nullity $= 0$
Kernel: $\{(0, 0, 0)\}$
Range: R^3

31. Nullity $= 2$
Kernel: $\{(x, y, z): x + 2y + 2z = 0\}$ (plane)
Range: $\{(t, 2t, 2t), t \text{ is real}\}$ (line)

33. 3 **35.** 5

37.

	Zero	Standard Basis
(a)	$(0, 0, 0, 0)$	$\{(1, 0, 0, 0), (0, 1, 0, 0),$ $(0, 0, 1, 0), (0, 0, 0, 1)\}$

(b) $\begin{bmatrix} 0 \\ 0 \\ 0 \\ 0 \end{bmatrix}$ $\left\{ \begin{bmatrix} 1 \\ 0 \\ 0 \\ 0 \end{bmatrix}, \begin{bmatrix} 0 \\ 1 \\ 0 \\ 0 \end{bmatrix}, \begin{bmatrix} 0 \\ 0 \\ 1 \\ 0 \end{bmatrix}, \begin{bmatrix} 0 \\ 0 \\ 0 \\ 1 \end{bmatrix} \right\}$

(c) $\begin{bmatrix} 0 & 0 \\ 0 & 0 \end{bmatrix}$ $\left\{ \begin{bmatrix} 1 & 0 \\ 0 & 0 \end{bmatrix}, \begin{bmatrix} 0 & 1 \\ 0 & 0 \end{bmatrix}, \begin{bmatrix} 0 & 0 \\ 1 & 0 \end{bmatrix}, \begin{bmatrix} 0 & 0 \\ 0 & 1 \end{bmatrix} \right\}$

(d) $p(x) = 0$ $\{1, x, x^2, x^3\}$

(e) $(0, 0, 0, 0, 0)$ $\{(1, 0, 0, 0, 0), (0, 1, 0, 0, 0),$ $(0, 0, 1, 0, 0), (0, 0, 0, 1, 0)\}$

39. The set of constant functions: $p(x) = a_0$.

41. (a) Rank $= 1$, nullity $= 2$
    (b) $\{(1, 0, -2), (1, 2, 0)\}$

47. (a) Rank $= n$ **49.** $mn = jk$
    (b) Rank $< n$

SECTION 6.3 *(page 350)*

1. $\begin{bmatrix} 1 & 1 \\ 1 & -1 \end{bmatrix}$ **3.** $\begin{bmatrix} 5 & -3 \\ 1 & 1 \\ -4 & 1 \end{bmatrix}$

5. $\begin{bmatrix} 1 & 1 & 0 \\ 1 & -1 & 0 \\ 0 & 0 & 1 \end{bmatrix}$ **7.** $\begin{bmatrix} 0 & -2 & 3 \\ 4 & 0 & 11 \end{bmatrix}$

9. $\begin{bmatrix} 35 \\ -7 \end{bmatrix}$ **11.** $\begin{bmatrix} 0 \\ 0 \end{bmatrix}$

13. (a) $\begin{bmatrix} -1 & 0 \\ 0 & -1 \end{bmatrix}$ (b) $(-3, -4)$

(c)

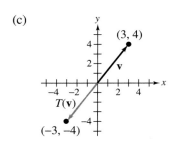

15. (a) $\begin{bmatrix} -\dfrac{\sqrt{2}}{2} & -\dfrac{\sqrt{2}}{2} \\ \dfrac{\sqrt{2}}{2} & -\dfrac{\sqrt{2}}{2} \end{bmatrix}$ (b) $(-4\sqrt{2}, 0)$

(c)

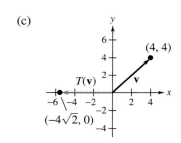

17. (a) $\begin{bmatrix} 1 & 0 & 0 \\ 0 & 1 & 0 \\ 0 & 0 & -1 \end{bmatrix}$ (b) $(3, 2, -2)$

(c)

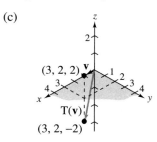

19. (a) $\begin{bmatrix} -1 & 0 \\ 0 & -1 \end{bmatrix}$ (b) $(-1, -2)$

(c)

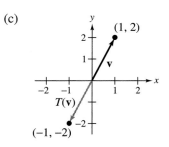

21. (a) $\begin{bmatrix} \dfrac{9}{10} & \dfrac{3}{10} \\ \dfrac{3}{10} & \dfrac{1}{10} \end{bmatrix}$ (b) $\left(\dfrac{21}{10}, \dfrac{7}{10}\right)$

(c)

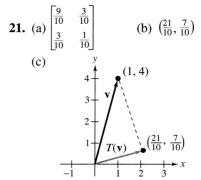

23. (a) $\begin{bmatrix} \dfrac{4}{5} & \dfrac{3}{5} \\ \dfrac{3}{5} & -\dfrac{4}{5} \end{bmatrix}$ (b) $\left(\dfrac{16}{5}, -\dfrac{13}{5}\right)$

(c)

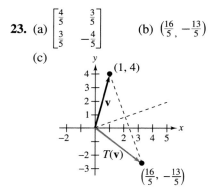

25. $A = \begin{bmatrix} 2 & -4 \\ -1 & -5 \end{bmatrix}, A' = \begin{bmatrix} 0 & 2 \\ 7 & -3 \end{bmatrix}$

27. $A = \begin{bmatrix} 0 & 0 & 0 \\ 1 & 0 & 0 \\ 0 & 0 & 0 \end{bmatrix}, A' = \begin{bmatrix} 0 & 0 & 0 \\ 1 & 0 & 0 \\ 0 & 0 & 0 \end{bmatrix}$

29. $A = \begin{bmatrix} -4 & -1 \\ -2 & 5 \end{bmatrix}, A' = \begin{bmatrix} 5 & 3 & 2 \\ 4 & -3 & 1 \\ -2 & -3 & -1 \end{bmatrix}$

31. $T^{-1}(x, y) = \left(\dfrac{x + y}{2}, \dfrac{x - y}{2}\right)$

33. T is not invertible

35. $T^{-1}(x, y) = \left(\dfrac{x}{5}, \dfrac{y}{5}\right)$

37. $(9, 5, 4)$

39. $(-1, 5)$

41. $(2, -4, -3, 3)$

43. $(9, 16, -20)$

45. $\begin{bmatrix} 0 & 0 & 0 \\ 1 & 0 & 0 \\ 0 & 1 & 0 \\ 0 & 0 & 1 \end{bmatrix}$

47. $\begin{bmatrix} 0 & 1 & 0 & 0 \\ 0 & 0 & 0 & 0 \\ 0 & 0 & 1 & 1 \\ 0 & 0 & 0 & 1 \end{bmatrix}$

49. $3 - 2e^x - 2xe^x$

51. (a) $\begin{bmatrix} 0 & 0 & 0 & 0 \\ 1 & 0 & 0 & 0 \\ 0 & \frac{1}{2} & 0 & 0 \\ 0 & 0 & \frac{1}{3} & 0 \\ 0 & 0 & 0 & \frac{1}{4} \end{bmatrix}$ (b) $6x - x^2 + \frac{3}{4}x^4$

53. $\begin{bmatrix} 1 & 0 & 0 & 0 & 0 & 0 \\ 0 & 0 & 0 & 1 & 0 & 0 \\ 0 & 1 & 0 & 0 & 0 & 0 \\ 0 & 0 & 0 & 0 & 1 & 0 \\ 0 & 0 & 1 & 0 & 0 & 0 \\ 0 & 0 & 0 & 0 & 0 & 1 \end{bmatrix}$

SECTION 6.4 *(page 357)*

1. (a) $A' = \begin{bmatrix} 4 & -3 \\ \frac{5}{3} & -1 \end{bmatrix}$

(b) $A' = \begin{bmatrix} 1 & 0 \\ \frac{2}{3} & \frac{1}{3} \end{bmatrix} \begin{bmatrix} 2 & -1 \\ -1 & 1 \end{bmatrix} \begin{bmatrix} 1 & 0 \\ -2 & 3 \end{bmatrix}$

3. (a) $A' = \begin{bmatrix} -1 & 0 \\ 0 & 1 \end{bmatrix}$

(b) $A' = \begin{bmatrix} \frac{1}{2} & -\frac{1}{2} \\ \frac{1}{2} & \frac{1}{2} \end{bmatrix} \begin{bmatrix} 0 & 1 \\ 1 & 0 \end{bmatrix} \begin{bmatrix} 1 & 1 \\ -1 & 1 \end{bmatrix}$

5. (a) $A' = \begin{bmatrix} 1 & 0 & 0 \\ 0 & 1 & 0 \\ 0 & 0 & 1 \end{bmatrix}$

(b) $A' = \begin{bmatrix} \frac{1}{2} & \frac{1}{2} & -\frac{1}{2} \\ \frac{1}{2} & -\frac{1}{2} & \frac{1}{2} \\ -\frac{1}{2} & \frac{1}{2} & \frac{1}{2} \end{bmatrix} \begin{bmatrix} 1 & 0 & 0 \\ 0 & 1 & 0 \\ 0 & 0 & 1 \end{bmatrix}$

$\begin{bmatrix} 1 & 1 & 0 \\ 1 & 0 & 1 \\ 0 & 1 & 1 \end{bmatrix}$

7. (a) $A' = \begin{bmatrix} \frac{7}{3} & \frac{10}{3} & -\frac{1}{3} \\ -\frac{1}{6} & \frac{4}{3} & \frac{8}{3} \\ \frac{2}{3} & -\frac{4}{3} & -\frac{2}{3} \end{bmatrix}$

(b) $A' = \begin{bmatrix} \frac{2}{3} & -\frac{1}{3} & \frac{1}{3} \\ -\frac{1}{3} & \frac{1}{6} & \frac{1}{3} \\ \frac{1}{3} & \frac{1}{3} & -\frac{1}{3} \end{bmatrix} \begin{bmatrix} 1 & -1 & 2 \\ 2 & 1 & -1 \\ 1 & 2 & 1 \end{bmatrix}$

$\begin{bmatrix} 1 & 0 & 1 \\ 0 & 2 & 2 \\ 1 & 2 & 0 \end{bmatrix}$

9. (a) $\begin{bmatrix} 6 & 4 \\ 9 & 4 \end{bmatrix}$

(b) $[\mathbf{v}]_B = \begin{bmatrix} 2 \\ -1 \end{bmatrix}, [T(\mathbf{v})]_B = \begin{bmatrix} 4 \\ -4 \end{bmatrix}$

(c) $A' = \begin{bmatrix} 0 & -\frac{4}{3} \\ 9 & 7 \end{bmatrix}, P^{-1} = \begin{bmatrix} -\frac{1}{3} & \frac{1}{3} \\ \frac{3}{4} & -\frac{1}{2} \end{bmatrix}$

(d) $\begin{bmatrix} -\frac{8}{3} \\ 5 \end{bmatrix}$

11. (a) $\begin{bmatrix} \frac{1}{2} & \frac{1}{2} & -\frac{1}{2} \\ \frac{1}{2} & -\frac{1}{2} & \frac{1}{2} \\ -\frac{1}{2} & \frac{1}{2} & \frac{1}{2} \end{bmatrix}$

(b) $[\mathbf{v}]_B = \begin{bmatrix} 1 \\ 0 \\ -1 \end{bmatrix}$, $[T(\mathbf{v})]_B = \begin{bmatrix} 2 \\ -1 \\ -2 \end{bmatrix}$

(c) $A' = \begin{bmatrix} 1 & 0 & 0 \\ 0 & 2 & 0 \\ 0 & 0 & 3 \end{bmatrix}$, $P^{-1} = \begin{bmatrix} 1 & 1 & 0 \\ 1 & 0 & 1 \\ 0 & 1 & 1 \end{bmatrix}$

(d) $\begin{bmatrix} 1 \\ 0 \\ -3 \end{bmatrix}$

13. Assume that A and B are similar. Then,

$$|B| = |P^{-1}AP| = |P^{-1}|\,|A|\,|P| = \frac{1}{|P|}|A|\,|P|$$
$$= |A|. \text{ No.}$$

17. I_n

19. Assume that $A^2 = O$ and that $B = P^{-1}AP$. Then
$B^2 = P^{-1}APP^{-1}AP = P^{-1}A^2P = P^{-1}OP = O.$

23. Assume A and B are similar. Then $B^2 = P^{-1}APP^{-1}AP$
$= P^{-1}A^2P$, which implies that A^2 is similar to B^2.

25. Assume that $A = CD$, where C is invertible. Then
$C^{-1}A = D$ and we have $DC = C^{-1}AC$ which implies
that DC is similar to A.

SECTION 6.5 *(page 365)*

1. (a) $(3, -5)$ (b) $(2, 1)$
(c) $(a, 0)$ (d) $(0, -b)$

3. (a) (y, x) (b) Reflection in the line $y = x$.

5. (a) Vertical contraction
(b)

7. (a) Horizontal shear
(b)

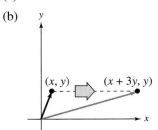

9. $\{(0, t): t \text{ is real}\}$ **11.** $\{(t, 0): t \text{ is real}\}$

13.

15.

17.

19.

21.

23.

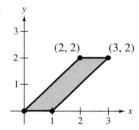

25. $T(1, 0) = (2, 0)$, $T(0, 1) = (0, 3)$, $T(2, 2) = (4, 6)$

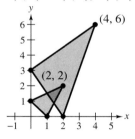

27. Horizontal expansion

29. Reflection in the line $y = x$.

31. Vertical shear followed by a horizontal expansion.

33. $\begin{bmatrix} \dfrac{\sqrt{3}}{2} & -\dfrac{1}{2} & 0 \\ \dfrac{1}{2} & \dfrac{\sqrt{3}}{2} & 0 \\ 0 & 0 & 1 \end{bmatrix}$

35. $\begin{bmatrix} \dfrac{1}{2} & 0 & \dfrac{\sqrt{3}}{2} \\ 0 & 1 & 0 \\ -\dfrac{\sqrt{3}}{2} & 0 & \dfrac{1}{2} \end{bmatrix}$

37. $\left(\dfrac{\sqrt{3} - 1}{2}, \dfrac{\sqrt{3} + 1}{2}, 1 \right)$

39. $\left(\dfrac{1 + \sqrt{3}}{2}, 1, \dfrac{1 - \sqrt{3}}{2} \right)$

41. 90° about the x-axis   **43.** 180° about the y-axis
45. 90° about the z-axis

47. $\begin{bmatrix} 0 & 1 & 0 \\ 0 & 0 & -1 \\ -1 & 0 & 0 \end{bmatrix}$,

Line segment from $(0, 0, 0)$ to $(1, -1, -1)$

49. $\begin{bmatrix} \dfrac{\sqrt{3}}{4} & -\dfrac{1}{4} & \dfrac{\sqrt{3}}{2} \\ \dfrac{1}{2} & \dfrac{\sqrt{3}}{2} & 0 \\ -\dfrac{3}{4} & \dfrac{\sqrt{3}}{4} & \dfrac{1}{2} \end{bmatrix}$

Line segment from $(0, 0, 0)$ to

$\left(\dfrac{3\sqrt{3} - 1}{4}, \dfrac{1 + \sqrt{3}}{2}, \dfrac{\sqrt{3} - 1}{4} \right)$

REVIEW EXERCISES – CHAPTER 6 *(page 366)*

1. (a) $(2, -4)$ **3.** (a) $(1, 1, 1)$
    (b) $(4, 4)$ (b) $(0, 4, 4)$

5. Linear, $\begin{bmatrix} 1 & 2 \\ -1 & -1 \end{bmatrix}$ **7.** Not linear

9. Linear, $\begin{bmatrix} 0 & 1 \\ 0 & 1 \\ 1 & 0 \end{bmatrix}$ **11.** Linear, $\begin{bmatrix} 1 & -1 & 0 \\ 0 & 1 & -1 \\ -1 & 0 & 1 \end{bmatrix}$

13. $T(1, 1) = \left(\dfrac{3}{2}, \dfrac{3}{2} \right)$ **15.** $A^2 = I$
    $T(0, 1) = (1, 1)$

17. $A^3 = \begin{bmatrix} \cos 3\theta & -\sin 3\theta \\ \sin 3\theta & \cos 3\theta \end{bmatrix}$

19. (a) $T: R^3 \rightarrow R^2$
    (b) $(3, -12)$
    (c) $\{(-\tfrac{5}{2}, 3 - 2t, t): t \text{ is real}\}$

21. (a) $T: R^3 \rightarrow R^3$
    (b) $(-2, -4, -5)$
    (c) $(2, 2, 2)$

23. (a) $\{(2, -1, 0, 0), (2, 0, 1, -2)\}$
    (b) $\{(5, 0, 4), (0, 5, 8)\}$

25. (a) $\{(0, 0)\}$
    (b) $\{(1, 0, \frac{1}{2}), (0, 1, -\frac{1}{2})\}$
    (c) Rank = 2, Nullity = 0

27. 3   **29.** 1

31. $A = \begin{bmatrix} 0 & 1 \\ 1 & 0 \end{bmatrix}, A^{-1} = \begin{bmatrix} 0 & 1 \\ 1 & 0 \end{bmatrix}$

33. $A = \begin{bmatrix} 1 & 0 \\ k & 1 \end{bmatrix}, A^{-1} = \begin{bmatrix} 1 & 0 \\ -k & 1 \end{bmatrix}$

35. T has no inverse.

37. $T = \begin{bmatrix} 0 & 0 & 0 \\ 0 & 1 & 0 \\ 0 & 1 & 0 \end{bmatrix}, T' = \begin{bmatrix} 0 & 0 \\ 1 & 1 \end{bmatrix}$

39.

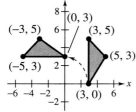

41. (a) One-to-one
    (b) Onto
    (c) Invertible

43. (a) One-to-one
    (b) Onto
    (c) Invertible

45. (a) $(0, 1, 1)$
    (b) $(0, 1, 1)$

47. $A' = \begin{bmatrix} 3 & -1 \\ 1 & -1 \end{bmatrix}, A' = P^{-1}AP = \begin{bmatrix} \frac{1}{2} & -\frac{1}{2} \\ \frac{1}{2} & \frac{1}{2} \end{bmatrix}\begin{bmatrix} 1 & -3 \\ -1 & 1 \end{bmatrix}$
$\begin{bmatrix} 1 & 1 \\ -1 & 1 \end{bmatrix}$

49. (a) $\begin{bmatrix} 0 & 0 & 0 \\ 0 & \frac{1}{5} & \frac{2}{5} \\ 0 & \frac{2}{5} & \frac{4}{5} \end{bmatrix}$

55. (b) Nullity = 3, rank = 1
    (c) $\{1 - x, 1 - x^2, 1 - x^3\}$

57. $\text{Ker}(T) = \{\mathbf{v}: \langle \mathbf{v}, \mathbf{v}_0 \rangle = 0\}$
    Range = R
    Rank = 1
    Nullity = dim $(V) - 1$

59. $mn = pq$

61. (a) Vertical expansion
    (b)

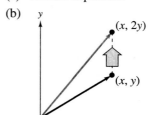

63. (a) Vertical shear
    (b)

65.

67.

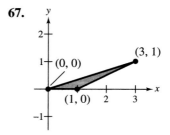

69. Reflection in the line $y = x$ followed by a horizontal expansion.

71. $\begin{bmatrix} \dfrac{\sqrt{2}}{2} & -\dfrac{\sqrt{2}}{2} & 0 \\ \dfrac{\sqrt{2}}{2} & \dfrac{\sqrt{2}}{2} & 0 \\ 0 & 0 & 1 \end{bmatrix}, (\sqrt{2}, 0, 1)$

73. $\begin{bmatrix} \dfrac{\sqrt{3}}{2} & -\dfrac{1}{4} & \dfrac{\sqrt{3}}{4} \\ \dfrac{1}{2} & \dfrac{\sqrt{3}}{4} & -\dfrac{3}{4} \\ 0 & \dfrac{\sqrt{3}}{2} & \dfrac{1}{2} \end{bmatrix}$

75. $(0, 0, 0), \left(\dfrac{\sqrt{2}}{2}, \dfrac{\sqrt{2}}{2}, 0\right), (0, \sqrt{2}, 0),$

$\left(-\dfrac{\sqrt{2}}{2}, \dfrac{\sqrt{2}}{2}, 0\right), (0, 0, 1), \left(\dfrac{\sqrt{2}}{2}, \dfrac{\sqrt{2}}{2}, 1\right),$

$(0, \sqrt{2}, 1), \left(-\dfrac{\sqrt{2}}{2}, \dfrac{\sqrt{2}}{2}, 1\right)$

CHAPTER 6 MATLAB *(page 370)*

1. (a) kernel $= \{(0, 0, 0)\}$, range $=$ span$\{(1, 1, -1, -2),$
$(0, 1, -1, 0), (0, 0, 1, -2)\}$

(b) kernel $=$ span$\{(1, 0, 1, 1)\}$, range $= \mathbf{R}^3$

(c) kernel $=$ span$\{(1, -2, 1, 0), (2, -3, 0, 1)\}$,
range $=$ span$\{(1, 9, 5, -13), (2, 10, 6, -14)\}$

3. (b) and (c) are one-to one; (b) and (c) are onto.

5. (a) $(9, 5, 4)$ (b) $(-7, -5)$ (c) $(2, -4, -3, 3)$

7. (a) $\begin{bmatrix} 1 & 1 & 0 \\ 1 & -1 & 0 \\ 0 & 0 & 1 \end{bmatrix}$ (b) $\begin{bmatrix} \frac{1}{2} & \frac{1}{2} & 0 \\ \frac{1}{2} & -\frac{1}{2} & 0 \\ 0 & 0 & 1 \end{bmatrix}$

(c) $\begin{bmatrix} 4 & 0 & 0 \\ 0 & -2 & 0 \\ 0 & 0 & -2 \end{bmatrix}$ (d) $\begin{bmatrix} 3 \\ -1 \\ 3 \end{bmatrix}, \begin{bmatrix} 0 \\ 8 \\ -6 \end{bmatrix}$

(e) $\begin{bmatrix} 4 \\ -4 \\ -6 \end{bmatrix}$

Chapter 7
Section 7.1 *(page 383)*

1. $\begin{bmatrix} 0 & 1 \\ 1 & 0 \end{bmatrix}\begin{bmatrix} 1 \\ 1 \end{bmatrix} = 1\begin{bmatrix} 1 \\ 1 \end{bmatrix}, \begin{bmatrix} 0 & 1 \\ 1 & 0 \end{bmatrix}\begin{bmatrix} 1 \\ -1 \end{bmatrix} = -1\begin{bmatrix} 1 \\ -1 \end{bmatrix}$

3. $\begin{bmatrix} 1 & k \\ 0 & -1 \end{bmatrix}\begin{bmatrix} 1 \\ 0 \end{bmatrix} = 1\begin{bmatrix} 1 \\ 0 \end{bmatrix}$

5. $\begin{bmatrix} 1 & 1 \\ 1 & 1 \end{bmatrix}\begin{bmatrix} 1 \\ -1 \end{bmatrix} = 0\begin{bmatrix} 1 \\ -1 \end{bmatrix}, \begin{bmatrix} 1 & 1 \\ 1 & 1 \end{bmatrix}\begin{bmatrix} 1 \\ 1 \end{bmatrix} = 2\begin{bmatrix} 1 \\ 1 \end{bmatrix}$

7. $\begin{bmatrix} -2 & 2 & -3 \\ 2 & 1 & -6 \\ -1 & -2 & 0 \end{bmatrix}\begin{bmatrix} 1 \\ 2 \\ -1 \end{bmatrix} = 5\begin{bmatrix} 1 \\ 2 \\ -1 \end{bmatrix},$

$\begin{bmatrix} -2 & 2 & -3 \\ 2 & 1 & -6 \\ -1 & -2 & 0 \end{bmatrix}\begin{bmatrix} -2 \\ 1 \\ 0 \end{bmatrix} = -3\begin{bmatrix} -2 \\ 1 \\ 0 \end{bmatrix},$

$\begin{bmatrix} -2 & 2 & -3 \\ 2 & 1 & -6 \\ -1 & -2 & 0 \end{bmatrix}\begin{bmatrix} 3 \\ 0 \\ 1 \end{bmatrix} = -3\begin{bmatrix} 3 \\ 0 \\ 1 \end{bmatrix}$

9. (a) $\begin{bmatrix} 1 & 1 \\ 1 & 1 \end{bmatrix}\begin{bmatrix} c \\ -c \end{bmatrix} = 0\begin{bmatrix} c \\ -c \end{bmatrix}$

(b) $\begin{bmatrix} 1 & 1 \\ 1 & 1 \end{bmatrix}\begin{bmatrix} 2c \\ 2c \end{bmatrix} = 2\begin{bmatrix} 2c \\ 2c \end{bmatrix}$

11. (a) No   **13.** (a) Yes
(b) Yes   (b) No
(c) Yes   (c) Yes
(d) No   (d) Yes

15. (a) $\lambda^2 - 5\lambda + 6 = 0$ **17.** (a) $\lambda^2 - 7\lambda = 0$
(b) $\lambda = 2, (1, 0)$ (b) $\lambda = 0, (1, 2)$
$\lambda = 3, (1, 1)$ $\lambda = 7, (3, -1)$

19. (a) $\lambda^2 - 6\lambda + 5 = 0$
(b) $\lambda = 1, (3, -1)$
$\lambda = 5, (1, 1)$

21. (a) $\lambda^3 - 6\lambda^2 + 11\lambda - 6 = 0$
(b) $\lambda = 1, (1, 2, -1)$
$\lambda = 2, (1, 0, 0)$
$\lambda = 3, (0, 1, 0)$

23. (a) $\lambda^3 - 3\lambda^2 - 9\lambda + 27 = 0$
   (b) $\lambda = -3, (1, 1, 3)$
     $\lambda = 3, (1, 0, -1), (1, 1, 0)$

25. (a) $\lambda^3 - 4\lambda^2 + 5\lambda - 2 = 0$
   (b) $\lambda = 1, (1, 0, 0)$
     $\lambda = 2, (7, -4, -1)$

27. (a) $\lambda^3 - 8\lambda^2 + 4\lambda + 48 = 0$
   (b) $\lambda = -2, (3, 2, 0)$
     $\lambda = 4, (5, -10, -2)$
     $\lambda = 6, (1, -2, 0)$

29. (a) $\lambda^4 - 6\lambda^3 + 9\lambda^2 = 0$
   (b) $\lambda = 0, (1, 0, 1, 0), (1, 1, 0, -1)$
     $\lambda = 3, (1, 0, -2, 0)$

31. $p(\lambda) = \lambda^2 - 6\lambda + 8, p(A) = \begin{bmatrix} 0 & 0 \\ 0 & 0 \end{bmatrix}$

33. $p(\lambda) = \lambda^3 - 5\lambda^2 + 15\lambda - 27, p(A) = \begin{bmatrix} 0 & 0 & 0 \\ 0 & 0 & 0 \\ 0 & 0 & 0 \end{bmatrix}$

37. Assume that λ is an eigenvalue of A, with corresponding eigenvector $\mathbf{x}$. Because A is invertible, we know (from Exercise 36) that $\lambda \neq 0$. Then, $A\mathbf{x} = \lambda\mathbf{x}$ implies that $\mathbf{x} = A^{-1}A\mathbf{x} = A^{-1}\lambda\mathbf{x} = \lambda A^{-1}\mathbf{x}$, which in turn implies that $(1/\lambda)\mathbf{x} = A^{-1}\mathbf{x}$. Thus, $\mathbf{x}$ is an eigenvector of A^{-1}, and its corresponding eigenvalue is $1/\lambda$.

39. The characteristic polynomial of A is $p(\lambda) = |\lambda I - A|$. Thus, the constant term of $p(\lambda)$ is given by $p(0) = |-A| = \pm |A|$.

41. Assume that A is a (real) triangular matrix with $\lambda_1, \lambda_2, \ldots, \lambda_n$ as its main diagonal entries. From Theorem 7.3, we know that the eigenvalues of A are $\lambda_1, \lambda_2, \ldots \lambda_n$. Thus, A has real eigenvalues. Moreover, because the determinant of A is $|A| = \lambda_1 \cdot \lambda_2 \cdots \lambda_n$, it follows that A is nonsingular if and only if each λ_i is nonzero.

43. $a = 0, d = 1$ or $a = 1, d = 0$ 45. dim $= 3$

47. dim $= 1$ 49. $T(e^x) = \dfrac{d}{dx}[e^x] = e^x = 1(e^x)$

51. $\lambda = -2, 3 + 2x$
   $\lambda = 4, -5 + 10x + 2x^2$
   $\lambda = 6, -1 + 2x$

53. $\lambda = 0, \begin{bmatrix} 1 & 0 \\ 1 & 0 \end{bmatrix}, \begin{bmatrix} 1 & 1 \\ 0 & -1 \end{bmatrix}$

   $\lambda = 3, \begin{bmatrix} 1 & 0 \\ -2 & 0 \end{bmatrix}$

55. The only possible eigenvalue is 0.

SECTION 7.2 *(page 394)*

1. $P^{-1} = \begin{bmatrix} 1 & -4 \\ -1 & 3 \end{bmatrix}, P^{-1}AP = \begin{bmatrix} 1 & 0 \\ 0 & -2 \end{bmatrix}$

3. $P^{-1} = \begin{bmatrix} \frac{2}{3} & -\frac{2}{3} & 1 \\ 0 & \frac{1}{4} & 0 \\ -\frac{1}{3} & \frac{1}{12} & 0 \end{bmatrix}, P^{-1}AP = \begin{bmatrix} 5 & 0 & 0 \\ 0 & 3 & 0 \\ 0 & 0 & -1 \end{bmatrix}$

5. There is only one eigenvalue, $\lambda = 0$, and the dimension of its eigenspace is 1.

7. There are two eigenvalues, 1 and 2. The dimension of the eigenspace for the repeated eigenvalue 1 is 1. Therefore, the matrix is not diagonalizable.

9. There are two repeated eigenvalues, 0 and 3. The eigenspace associated with 3 is of dimension 1. Therefore, the matrix is not diagonalizable.

11. $\lambda = 0, 2$ Matrix is diagonalizable.

13. $\lambda = 0, 2$ Insufficient number of eigenvalues to guarantee diagonalizability.

15. $P = \begin{bmatrix} 1 & 1 \\ -1 & 1 \end{bmatrix}$
(The answer is not unique.)

17. $P = \begin{bmatrix} -3 & 1 \\ 1 & 1 \end{bmatrix}$
(The answer is not unique.)

19. $P = \begin{bmatrix} 1 & 0 & -1 \\ 0 & 1 & -2 \\ 0 & 0 & 1 \end{bmatrix}$
(The answer is not unique.)

21. $P = \begin{bmatrix} 1 & -1 & 1 \\ 1 & 0 & 1 \\ 3 & 1 & 0 \end{bmatrix}$

(The answer is not unique.)

23. $P = \begin{bmatrix} 3 & -1 & -5 \\ 2 & 2 & 10 \\ 0 & 0 & 2 \end{bmatrix}$

(The answer is not unique.)

25. A is not diagonalizable.

27. $P = \begin{bmatrix} 4 & 0 & 0 & 0 \\ 4 & 0 & -2 & 0 \\ 4 & 3 & 1 & 0 \\ 1 & 1 & 1 & 1 \end{bmatrix}$

(The answer is not unique.)

29. $\{(1, -1), (1, 1)\}$ **31.** $\{(-1 + x), x\}$

33. (a) $B^k = (P^{-1}AP)^k = (P^{-1}AP)(P^{-1}AP)(P^{-1}AP) \cdots$
$(P^{-1}AP) = P^{-1}A^kP$

(b) $A^k = (PBP^{-1})^k = (PBP^{-1})(PBP^{-1})(PBP^{-1}) \cdots$
$(PBP^{-1}) = PB^kP^{-1}$

35. $\begin{bmatrix} -188 & -378 \\ 126 & 253 \end{bmatrix}$

37. $\begin{bmatrix} 384 & 256 & -384 \\ -384 & -512 & 1152 \\ -128 & -256 & 640 \end{bmatrix}$

39. Yes, the order of elements on the main diagonal may change.

41. Assume that A is diagonalizable. Then $P^{-1}AP = D$ is diagonal and
$$D^T = (P^{-1}AP)^T = P^TA^T(P^{-1})^T = P^TA^T(P^T)^{-1}$$
is diagonal. Therefore, A^T is diagonalizable.

43. Assume that A is diagonalizable with real eigenvalues $\lambda_1, \lambda_2, \ldots, \lambda_n$. Then,
$$|A| = |P^{-1}AP| = \begin{vmatrix} \lambda_1 & 0 & \cdots & 0 \\ 0 & \lambda_2 & \cdots & 0 \\ \vdots & \vdots & & \vdots \\ 0 & 0 & \cdots & \lambda_n \end{vmatrix}$$
$$= \lambda_1\lambda_2 \cdots \lambda_n.$$

Section 7.3 (*page 405*)

1. Symmetric   **3.** Not symmetric

5. Symmetric   **7.** $\lambda = -1$, dim $= 1$
$\lambda = 3$, dim $= 1$

9. $\lambda = 2$, dim $= 2$ **11.** $\lambda = -2$, dim $= 2$
$\lambda = 3$, dim $= 1$ $\lambda = 4$, dim $= 1$

13. Orthogonal   **15.** Not orthogonal

17. Orthogonal   **19.** Orthogonal

21. $P = \begin{bmatrix} \dfrac{\sqrt{2}}{2} & \dfrac{\sqrt{2}}{2} \\ -\dfrac{\sqrt{2}}{2} & \dfrac{\sqrt{2}}{2} \end{bmatrix}$

(The answer is not unique.)

23. $P = \begin{bmatrix} \dfrac{\sqrt{3}}{3} & \dfrac{\sqrt{6}}{3} \\ -\dfrac{\sqrt{6}}{3} & \dfrac{\sqrt{3}}{3} \end{bmatrix}$

(The answer is not unique.)

25. $P = \begin{bmatrix} -\dfrac{2}{3} & -\dfrac{1}{3} & \dfrac{2}{3} \\ \dfrac{1}{3} & \dfrac{2}{3} & \dfrac{2}{3} \\ \dfrac{2}{3} & -\dfrac{2}{3} & \dfrac{1}{3} \end{bmatrix}$

(The answer is not unique.)

27. $P = \begin{bmatrix} \dfrac{\sqrt{2}}{2} & 0 & \dfrac{\sqrt{2}}{2} & 0 \\ -\dfrac{\sqrt{2}}{2} & 0 & \dfrac{\sqrt{2}}{2} & 0 \\ 0 & \dfrac{\sqrt{2}}{2} & 0 & \dfrac{\sqrt{2}}{2} \\ 0 & -\dfrac{\sqrt{2}}{2} & 0 & \dfrac{\sqrt{2}}{2} \end{bmatrix}$

(The answer is not unique.)

29. A^TA is symmetric because $(A^TA)^T = A^T(A^T)^T = A^TA$.
AA^T is symmetric because $(AA^T)^T = (A^T)^TA^T = AA^T$.

31. Assume that A is orthogonal. Then, $A^{-1} = A^T$, and we have $|A^T| = |A^{-1}|$, which implies that

$$|AA^{-1}| = |A|\,|A^{-1}| = |A|\,|A^T| = |A|^2 = 1.$$

Thus, $|A| = \pm 1$.

33. $A^{-1} = \left(\dfrac{1}{\cos^2\theta + \sin^2\theta}\right)\begin{bmatrix} \cos\theta & \sin\theta \\ -\sin\theta & \cos\theta \end{bmatrix} =$

$$\begin{bmatrix} \cos\theta & \sin\theta \\ -\sin\theta & \cos\theta \end{bmatrix} = A^T$$

SECTION 7.4 (*page 421*)

1. $\mathbf{x}_2 = \begin{bmatrix} 20 \\ 5 \end{bmatrix}$, $\mathbf{x}_3 = \begin{bmatrix} 10 \\ 10 \end{bmatrix}$

3. $\mathbf{x}_2 = \begin{bmatrix} 84 \\ 12 \\ 6 \end{bmatrix}$, $\mathbf{x}_3 = \begin{bmatrix} 60 \\ 84 \\ 6 \end{bmatrix}$ **5.** $\mathbf{x} = t\begin{bmatrix} 2 \\ 1 \end{bmatrix}$

7. $\mathbf{x} = t\begin{bmatrix} 8 \\ 4 \\ 1 \end{bmatrix}$ **9.** $\mathbf{x}_2 = \begin{bmatrix} 960 \\ 90 \\ 30 \end{bmatrix}$, $\mathbf{x}_3 = \begin{bmatrix} 2340 \\ 720 \\ \frac{45}{2} \end{bmatrix}$

11. $y_1 = C_1 e^{2t}$
$y_2 = C_2 e^t$

13. $y_1 = C_1 e^{-t}$
$y_2 = C_2 e^{6t}$
$y_3 = C_3 e^t$

15. $y_1 = C_1 e^t - 4C_2 e^{2t}$
$y_2 = C_2 e^{2t}$

17. $y_1 = C_1 e^{-t} + C_2 e^{3t}$
$y_2 = -C_1 e^{-t} + C_2 e^{3t}$

19. $y_1 = 3C_1 e^{-2t} - 5C_2 e^{4t} - C_3 e^{6t}$
$y_2 = 2C_1 e^{-2t} + 10C_2 e^{4t} + 2C_3 e^{6t}$
$y_3 = \qquad\qquad 2C_2 e^{4t}$

21. $y_1 = C_1 e^t - 2C_2 e^{2t} - 7C_3 e^{3t}$
$y_2 = \qquad\quad C_2 e^{2t} + 8C_3 e^{3t}$
$y_3 = \qquad\qquad\quad 2C_3 e^{3t}$

23. $y_1' = y_1 + y_2$
$y_2' = \qquad y_2$

25. $y_1' = y_2$
$y_2' = y_3$
$y_3' = -4y_2$

27. $\begin{bmatrix} 1 & 0 \\ 0 & 1 \end{bmatrix}$ **29.** $\begin{bmatrix} 9 & 5 \\ 5 & -4 \end{bmatrix}$ **31.** $\begin{bmatrix} 0 & 5 \\ 5 & -10 \end{bmatrix}$

33. $A = \begin{bmatrix} 2 & -\frac{3}{2} \\ -\frac{3}{2} & -2 \end{bmatrix}$, $P = \begin{bmatrix} \dfrac{1}{\sqrt{10}} & -\dfrac{3}{\sqrt{10}} \\ \dfrac{3}{\sqrt{10}} & \dfrac{1}{\sqrt{10}} \end{bmatrix}$,

$\lambda_1 = -\frac{5}{2}$, $\lambda_2 = \frac{5}{2}$

35. $A = \begin{bmatrix} 13 & 3\sqrt{3} \\ 3\sqrt{3} & 7 \end{bmatrix}$, $P = \begin{bmatrix} \dfrac{1}{2} & \dfrac{\sqrt{3}}{2} \\ -\dfrac{\sqrt{3}}{2} & \dfrac{1}{2} \end{bmatrix}$,

$\lambda_1 = 4$, $\lambda_2 = 16$

37. $A = \begin{bmatrix} 16 & -12 \\ -12 & 9 \end{bmatrix}$, $P = \begin{bmatrix} \dfrac{3}{5} & -\dfrac{4}{5} \\ \dfrac{4}{5} & \dfrac{3}{5} \end{bmatrix}$, $\lambda_1 = 0$, $\lambda_2 = 25$

39. Ellipse, $5(x')^2 + 15(y')^2 - 45 = 0$
41. Hyperbola, $-25(x')^2 + 15(y')^2 - 50 = 0$
43. Parabola, $4(y')^2 + 4x' + 8y' + 4 = 0$
45. Hyperbola,
$\frac{1}{2}[-(x')^2 + (y')^2 - 3\sqrt{2}x' - \sqrt{2}y' + 6] = 0$

47. $A = \begin{bmatrix} 3 & -1 & 0 \\ -1 & 3 & 0 \\ 0 & 0 & 8 \end{bmatrix}$,

$2(x')^2 + 4(y')^2 + 8(z')^2 - 16 = 0$

REVIEW EXERCISES – CHAPTER 7 (*page 422*)

1. (a) $\lambda^2 - 9 = 0$
(b) $\lambda = -3$, $(1, -5)$
$\lambda = 3$, $(1, 1)$

3. (a) $\lambda^3 - 20\lambda^2 + 128\lambda - 256 = 0$
(b) $\lambda = 4$, $(1, -2, -1)$
$\lambda = 8$, $(4, -1, 0)$, $(3, 0, 1)$

5. (a) $\lambda^3 - 6\lambda^2 + 11\lambda - 6 = 0$
(b) $\lambda = 1$, $(1, 2, -1)$
$\lambda = 2$, $(1, 0, 0)$
$\lambda = 3$, $(0, 1, 0)$

7. Not diagonalizable

9. $P = \begin{bmatrix} 1 & 0 & 1 \\ 0 & 1 & 0 \\ 1 & 0 & -1 \end{bmatrix}$

(The answer is not unique.)

11. The characteristic equation of
$$A = \begin{bmatrix} \cos\theta & -\sin\theta \\ \sin\theta & \cos\theta \end{bmatrix}$$
is $\lambda^2 - (2\cos\theta)\lambda + 1 = 0$. The roots of this equation are $\lambda = \cos\theta \pm \sqrt{\cos^2\theta - 1}$. If $0 < \theta < \pi$, then $-1 < \cos\theta < 1$, which implies that $\sqrt{\cos^2\theta - 1}$ is imaginary.

13. A has only one eigenvalue, $\lambda = 3$, and the dimension of its eigenspace is 2.

15. $P = \begin{bmatrix} 0 & 1 \\ 1 & 0 \end{bmatrix}$

17. Both orthogonal and symmetric   **19.** Symmetric

21. $P = \begin{bmatrix} \dfrac{2}{\sqrt{5}} & -\dfrac{1}{\sqrt{5}} \\ \dfrac{1}{\sqrt{5}} & \dfrac{2}{\sqrt{5}} \end{bmatrix}$

(The answer is not unique.)

23. $P = \begin{bmatrix} \dfrac{1}{\sqrt{2}} & 0 & \dfrac{1}{\sqrt{2}} \\ 0 & 1 & 0 \\ -\dfrac{1}{\sqrt{2}} & 0 & \dfrac{1}{\sqrt{2}} \end{bmatrix}$

(The answer is not unique.)

25. $\left(\frac{3}{5}, \frac{2}{5}\right)$ **27.** $\left(\frac{1}{4}, \frac{1}{2}, \frac{1}{4}\right)$ **29.** $\left(\frac{4}{16}, \frac{5}{16}, \frac{7}{16}\right)$

33. $A = \begin{bmatrix} 0 & 1 \\ 0 & \frac{9}{4} \end{bmatrix}$, $\lambda_1 = 0$, $\lambda_2 = \frac{9}{4}$

35. $A^2 = \begin{bmatrix} 56 & -40 \\ 20 & -4 \end{bmatrix}$, $A^3 = \begin{bmatrix} 368 & -304 \\ 152 & -88 \end{bmatrix}$

37. (a) True. If $A\mathbf{x} = \lambda\mathbf{x}$, then $A^2\mathbf{x} = A(A\mathbf{x}) = A(\lambda\mathbf{x}) = \lambda A\mathbf{x} = \lambda^2\mathbf{x}$, which implies that $\mathbf{x}$ is an eigenvector of A^2.

(b) False. Let $A = \begin{bmatrix} 0 & 1 \\ 1 & 0 \end{bmatrix}$. Then $\mathbf{x} = (1, 0)$ is an eigenvector of A^2, but not of A.

39. Assume that A and B are $n \times n$ matrices with A non-singular. Then $A^{-1}(AB)A = BA$ which implies that AB is similar to BA.

41. $P = \begin{bmatrix} \dfrac{1}{\sqrt{2}} & -\dfrac{1}{\sqrt{2}} \\ \dfrac{1}{\sqrt{2}} & \dfrac{1}{\sqrt{2}} \end{bmatrix}$

43. (a) $a = b = c = 0$
(b) $\dim = 1$ if $a \neq 0$, $b \neq 0$, $c \neq 0$
$\dim = 2$ if exactly one is 0
$\dim = 3$ if exactly two are 0

45. $\mathbf{x}_2 = \begin{bmatrix} 100 \\ 25 \end{bmatrix}$, $\mathbf{x}_3 = \begin{bmatrix} 25 \\ 25 \end{bmatrix}$, $\mathbf{x} = t\begin{bmatrix} 2 \\ 1 \end{bmatrix}$

47. $\mathbf{x}_2 = \begin{bmatrix} 4500 \\ 300 \\ 50 \end{bmatrix}$, $\mathbf{x}_3 = \begin{bmatrix} 1500 \\ 4500 \\ 50 \end{bmatrix}$, $\mathbf{x} = t\begin{bmatrix} 24 \\ 12 \\ 1 \end{bmatrix}$

49. $y_1 = -2C_1 + C_2 e^t$
$y_2 = C_1$

51. $y_1 = C_1 e^t + C_2 e^{-t}$
$y_2 = C_1 e^t - C_2 e^{-t}$

53. $A = \begin{bmatrix} 1 & \frac{3}{2} \\ \frac{3}{2} & 1 \end{bmatrix}$

$P = \begin{bmatrix} \dfrac{1}{\sqrt{2}} & -\dfrac{1}{\sqrt{2}} \\ \dfrac{1}{\sqrt{2}} & \dfrac{1}{\sqrt{2}} \end{bmatrix}$

$5(x')^2 - (y')^2 = 6$

55. $A = \begin{bmatrix} 0 & \frac{1}{2} \\ \frac{1}{2} & 0 \end{bmatrix}$

$P = \begin{bmatrix} \dfrac{1}{\sqrt{2}} & -\dfrac{1}{\sqrt{2}} \\ \dfrac{1}{\sqrt{2}} & \dfrac{1}{\sqrt{2}} \end{bmatrix}$

$(x')^2 - (y')^2 = 4$

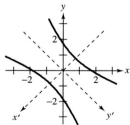

CHAPTER 7 MATLAB (*page 426*)

1. (a) $\lambda^2 - 6\lambda + 5$
(b) $\lambda^3 - 3\lambda^2 - 9\lambda + 27$
(c) $\lambda^4 - 34\lambda^3 - 80\lambda^2$

3. (a) $\lambda = 1, (-0.9487, 0.3162)$;
   $\lambda = 5, (-0.7071, -0.7071)$

(b) $\lambda = -3, (0.3015, 0.3015, 0.9045)$;
   $\lambda = 3$ (twice), $(0.7434, 0.0792, -0.6641)$,
   $(-0.4314, -0.8161, -0.3847)$

(c) $\lambda = 32.2094, (-0.1512, -0.3492, -0.5473,$
   $-0.7454)$;
   $\lambda = -2.2094, (0.7270, 0.2832, -0.1606,$
   $-0.6045)$;
   $\lambda = 0$ (twice), $(-0.5009, 0.5028, 0.4972, -0.4991)$,
   $(-0.1167, 0.5545, -0.7588, 0.3210)$

5. $P = \begin{bmatrix} 0.9285 & 0.7071 \\ 0.3714 & 0.7071 \end{bmatrix}, D = \begin{bmatrix} 2 & 0 \\ 0 & -1 \end{bmatrix}, P^{-1}AP = D$

7. (a) $P = \begin{bmatrix} -0.9487 & -0.7071 \\ 0.3162 & -0.7071 \end{bmatrix}, D = \begin{bmatrix} 1 & 0 \\ 0 & 5 \end{bmatrix} = P^{-1}AP$

(b) $P = \begin{bmatrix} 0.3015 & 0.7434 & -0.4314 \\ 0.3015 & 0.0792 & -0.8161 \\ 0.9045 & -0.6641 & -0.3847 \end{bmatrix}$,

$D = \begin{bmatrix} -3 & 0 & 0 \\ 0 & 3 & 0 \\ 0 & 0 & 3 \end{bmatrix} = P^{-1}AP$

(c) $P = \begin{bmatrix} -0.1512 & 0.7270 & -0.5009 & -0.1167 \\ -0.3492 & 0.2832 & 0.5028 & 0.5545 \\ -0.5473 & -0.1606 & 0.4972 & -0.7588 \\ -0.7454 & -0.6045 & -0.4991 & 0.3210 \end{bmatrix}$,

$D = \begin{bmatrix} 32.2094 & 0 & 0 & 0 \\ 0 & -2.2094 & 0 & 0 \\ 0 & 0 & 0 & 0 \\ 0 & 0 & 0 & 0 \end{bmatrix} = P^{-1}AP$

CUMULATIVE TEST CHAPTERS 6 AND 7 (*page 428*)

1. Yes, T is a linear transformation.

2. No, T is not a linear transformation.

3. (a) $(1, -1, 0)$ (b) $(1, -3)$

4. span$\{(1, 1, 0, 0), (0, 0, -1, 1)\}$

5. (a) span$\{(0, -1, 0, 1), (1, 0, -1, 0)\}$

(b) span$\{(1, 0), (0, 1)\}$

(c) rank $= 2$, nullity $= 2$

6. $\begin{bmatrix} -1 & 1 & 0 \\ 0 & -1 & 1 \\ 1 & 0 & -1 \end{bmatrix}$

7. $\begin{bmatrix} \frac{1}{2} & -\frac{1}{2} \\ -\frac{1}{2} & \frac{1}{2} \end{bmatrix}, T(1, 1) = (0, 0), T(-2, 2) = (-2, 2)$

8. $T^{-1}(x, y) = \left(\frac{1}{3}x + \frac{1}{3}y, -\frac{2}{3}x + \frac{1}{3}y\right)$

9. $\begin{bmatrix} -1 & -2 \\ 0 & 1 \\ 2 & 1 \end{bmatrix}, T(0, 1) = (1, 0, 1)$

10. (a) $A = \begin{bmatrix} 1 & -2 \\ 1 & 4 \end{bmatrix}$

(b) $P = \begin{bmatrix} 1 & 1 \\ 1 & 2 \end{bmatrix}$

(c) $A' = \begin{bmatrix} -7 & -15 \\ 6 & 12 \end{bmatrix}$

(d) $\begin{bmatrix} 9 \\ -6 \end{bmatrix}$

(e) $[\mathbf{v}]_B = \begin{bmatrix} 1 \\ -1 \end{bmatrix}, [T(\mathbf{v})]_B = \begin{bmatrix} 3 \\ -3 \end{bmatrix}$

11. $(\lambda - 3)(\lambda - 2)^2$, eigenvalues $= 2, 2, 3$

12. $\lambda = 1, \begin{bmatrix} 1 \\ 0 \\ 0 \end{bmatrix}; \lambda = 0, \begin{bmatrix} -1 \\ -1 \\ 3 \end{bmatrix}; \lambda = 2, \begin{bmatrix} 1 \\ 1 \\ -1 \end{bmatrix}$

13. $\lambda = 1$ (three times), $\begin{bmatrix} 1 \\ 0 \\ 0 \end{bmatrix}$

14. $P = \begin{bmatrix} 3 & 1 \\ 1 & 1 \end{bmatrix}$

(The answer is not unique.)

15. $\{(0, 1, 0), (1, 1, 1), (2, 2, 3)\}$

16. $\begin{bmatrix} \dfrac{1}{\sqrt{2}} & \dfrac{1}{\sqrt{2}} \\[2ex] -\dfrac{1}{\sqrt{2}} & \dfrac{1}{\sqrt{2}} \end{bmatrix}$

17. $\begin{bmatrix} \dfrac{1}{\sqrt{3}} & \dfrac{1}{\sqrt{2}} & \dfrac{1}{\sqrt{6}} \\[2ex] \dfrac{1}{\sqrt{3}} & 0 & -\dfrac{2}{\sqrt{6}} \\[2ex] \dfrac{1}{\sqrt{3}} & -\dfrac{1}{\sqrt{2}} & \dfrac{1}{\sqrt{6}} \end{bmatrix}$

18. λ is an eigenvalue of A if there exists a nonzero vector $\mathbf{x}$ such that $A\mathbf{x} = \lambda\mathbf{x}$. $\mathbf{x}$ is called an eigenvector of A. If A is an $n \times n$ matrix, then A can have n eigenvalues, possibly complex and possibly repeated.

19. P is orthogonal if $P^{-1} = P^{T}$. The possible eigenvalues of an orthogonal matrix are 1 and -1.

20. There exists P such that $P^{-1}AP = D$. A and B are similar implies that there exists Q such that $A = Q^{-1}BQ$. Then $D = P^{-1}AP = P^{-1}(Q^{-1}BQ)P = (QP)^{-1}A(QP)$.

21. If 0 is an eigenvalue of A, then $|A - \lambda I| = |A| = 0$, and hence A is singular.

22. Let λ_1 and λ_2 be distinct eigenvalues of A, with corresponding eigenvectors $\mathbf{x}_1$ and $\mathbf{x}_2$. Then we can write

$$\begin{aligned} \lambda_1(\mathbf{x}_1 \cdot \mathbf{x}_2) &= (\lambda_1\mathbf{x}_1) \cdot \mathbf{x}_2 \\ &= (A\mathbf{x}_1) \cdot \mathbf{x}_2 \\ &= (A\mathbf{x}_1)^T \mathbf{x}_2 \\ &= (\mathbf{x}_1^T A^T) \mathbf{x}_2 \\ &= (\mathbf{x}_1^T A) \mathbf{x}_2 \\ &= \mathbf{x}_1^T (A\mathbf{x}_2) \\ &= \mathbf{x}_1^T (\lambda_2\mathbf{x}_2) \\ &= \mathbf{x}_1 \cdot (\lambda_2\mathbf{x}_2) = \lambda_2(\mathbf{x}_1 \cdot \mathbf{x}_2) \end{aligned}$$

This implies that $(\lambda_1 - \lambda_2)(\mathbf{x}_1 \cdot \mathbf{x}_2) = 0$, and because $\lambda_1 \neq \lambda_2$, it follows that $\mathbf{x}_1 \cdot \mathbf{x}_2 = 0$. Therefore, $\mathbf{x}_1$ and $\mathbf{x}_2$ are orthogonal.

23. The range of T is nonempty because it contains $\mathbf{0}$. Let $T(\mathbf{u})$ and $T(\mathbf{v})$ be two vectors in the range of T. Then $T(\mathbf{u}) + T(\mathbf{v}) = T(\mathbf{u} + \mathbf{v})$. But since $\mathbf{u}$ and $\mathbf{v}$ are in V, it follows that $\mathbf{u} + \mathbf{v}$ is also in V, which in turn implies that $T(\mathbf{u} + \mathbf{v})$ is in the range.

Similarly, let $T(\mathbf{u})$ be in the range of T, and let c be a scalar. Then $cT(\mathbf{u}) = T(c\mathbf{u})$. But since $c\mathbf{u}$ is in V, this implies that $T(c\mathbf{u})$ is in the range.

24. If T is one-to-one and $\mathbf{v}$ is in the kernel, then $T(\mathbf{v}) = T(\mathbf{0}) = \mathbf{0}$, which implies that $\mathbf{v} = \mathbf{0}$. Conversely, if the kernel of T is $\{\mathbf{0}\}$ and $T(\mathbf{v}) = T(\mathbf{u})$, then $T(\mathbf{v} - \mathbf{u}) = \mathbf{0}$, which implies that $\mathbf{v} - \mathbf{u}$ is in the kernel. Since the kernel is trivial, $\mathbf{v} = \mathbf{u}$.

25. 0 is the only eigenvalue.

Chapter 8

SECTION 8.1 (*page 438*)

1. $-\sqrt{6}$ **3.** -4 **5.** 1

7.

9.

11.

13.

15. $x = 6$ **17.** $x = 3$

19. Sum: $5 + 3i$
Difference: $-1 + 9i$

21. Sum: 10
Difference: $2i$

23. Sum: $6 - 2i$
Difference: $6 + 2i$

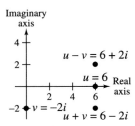

25. Sum: $4 + 2i$
Difference: 0

27. $20 + 10i$ **29.** 8

31. $(a^2 - b^2) + 2abi$ **33.** $-2 + 2i$

35. $(a^3 - 3ab^2) + (3a^2b - b^3)i$

37. $-\frac{1}{2} \pm \frac{3}{2}i$ **39.** 2, 3   **41.** $1, 1 \pm i$

43. $\pm 2, \pm 2i$ **45.** $\begin{bmatrix} 2 & 1 + 3i \\ -1 - 2i & -4i \end{bmatrix}$

47. $\begin{bmatrix} 2 + 2i & 2 \\ 4 - 4i & -6i \end{bmatrix}$ **49.** $\begin{bmatrix} -2 + 2i & 2i \\ 4 + 4i & 6 \end{bmatrix}$

51. $-5 - 3i$ **53.** $\begin{bmatrix} -5 & -15 + 10i \\ 25i & 15 + 30i \end{bmatrix}$

57. (a) $A^1 = A = \begin{bmatrix} 0 & i \\ i & 0 \end{bmatrix}$, $A^2 = \begin{bmatrix} -1 & 0 \\ 0 & -1 \end{bmatrix}$,

$A^3 = \begin{bmatrix} 0 & -i \\ -i & 0 \end{bmatrix}$, $A^4 = \begin{bmatrix} 1 & 0 \\ 0 & 1 \end{bmatrix}$,

$A^5 = A = \begin{bmatrix} 0 & i \\ i & 0 \end{bmatrix}$

(b) $A^{57} = A = \begin{bmatrix} 0 & i \\ i & 0 \end{bmatrix}$, $A^{1995} = A^3 = \begin{bmatrix} 0 & -i \\ -i & 0 \end{bmatrix}$

(c) $A^n = \begin{bmatrix} 0 & i \\ i & 0 \end{bmatrix}$, if $n = 1, 5, \ldots, 4k + 1$

$A^n = \begin{bmatrix} -1 & 0 \\ 0 & -1 \end{bmatrix}$, if $n = 2, 6, \ldots, 4k + 2$

$A^n = \begin{bmatrix} 0 & -i \\ -i & 0 \end{bmatrix}$, if $n = 3, 7, \ldots, 4k + 3$

$A^n = \begin{bmatrix} 1 & 0 \\ 0 & 1 \end{bmatrix}$, if $n = 4, 8, \ldots, 4k$

Section 8.2 (page 444)

1. $6 + 3i$

3. $8i$

5. $\sqrt{5}$ **7.** $\sqrt{65}$ **9.** 5

11. $|wz| = |-3 + i| = \sqrt{10}$
$|w|\,|z| = \sqrt{5}\sqrt{2} = \sqrt{10}$
$|zw| = |-3 + i| = \sqrt{10}$

13. $1 - 2i$ **15.** $\dfrac{7}{11} - \dfrac{6\sqrt{2}}{11}i$

17. $\dfrac{13}{10} + \dfrac{9}{10}i$

19. (a) $3 - 4i$ (b) $2 - 11i$
(c) $\dfrac{2}{5} + \dfrac{1}{5}i$ (d) $\dfrac{3}{25} + \dfrac{4}{25}i$

21. $A^{-1} = -\dfrac{1}{3}\begin{bmatrix} i & -3i \\ -2 + i & 6 \end{bmatrix}$ **23.** Not invertible

25. $A^{-1} = \dfrac{1}{2}\begin{bmatrix} 2 & 0 & 0 \\ 0 & 1 + i & 0 \\ 0 & 0 & 1 - i \end{bmatrix}$ **27** $-\dfrac{5}{3} - \dfrac{10}{3}i$

29. (a) Circle of radius 3 centered at origin.
(b) Circle of radius 5 centered at $1 - i$.
(c) Interior and boundary of circle of radius 2 centered at i.
(d) Closed region between the concentric circles of radii 2 and 5 centered at the origin.

33. (a) $(1/i)^1 = 1/i = -i$, $(1/i)^2 = -1$, $(1/i)^3 = i$,
$(1/i)^4 = 1$, $(1/i)^5 = -i$
(b) $(1/i)^{57} = -i$, $(1/i)^{1995} = i$
(c) $(1/i)^n = -i$, for $i = 1, 5, \ldots, 4k + 1$
$(1/i)^n = -1$, for $i = 2, 6, \ldots, 4k + 2$
$(1/i)^n = i$, for $i = 3, 7, \ldots, 4k + 3$
$(1/i)^n = 1$, for $i = 4, 8, \ldots, 4k$

Section 8.3 (page 453)

1. $\sqrt{8}\left[\cos\left(-\dfrac{\pi}{4}\right) + i\sin\left(-\dfrac{\pi}{4}\right)\right]$

3. $6(\cos\pi + i\sin\pi)$

5. $\sqrt{8}\left[\cos\left(-\dfrac{3\pi}{4}\right) + i\sin\left(-\dfrac{3\pi}{4}\right)\right]$

7. $4\left[\cos\left(-\dfrac{2\pi}{3}\right) + i\sin\left(-\dfrac{2\pi}{3}\right)\right]$

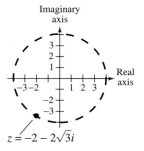

9. $6\left(\cos \dfrac{\pi}{2} + i \sin \dfrac{\pi}{2}\right)$

11. $7(\cos 0 + i \sin 0)$

13. $\sqrt{37}(\cos 1.4056 + i \sin 1.4056)$

15. $\sqrt{10}[\cos(-2.82) + i \sin(-2.82)]$

17. $2i$

19. $\dfrac{3}{4} - \dfrac{3\sqrt{3}}{4}i$

21. $\dfrac{15\sqrt{2}}{8} + \dfrac{15\sqrt{2}}{8}i$

23. $-4i$

25. 7

27. $12\left(\cos\dfrac{\pi}{2} + i\sin\dfrac{\pi}{2}\right)$ **29.** $0.25(\cos 0 + i\sin 0)$

31. $\dfrac{1}{2}\left(\cos\dfrac{4\pi}{9} + i\sin\dfrac{4\pi}{9}\right)$ **33.** $4\left(\cos\dfrac{\pi}{6} + i\sin\dfrac{\pi}{6}\right)$

35. -4 **37.** $-32i$ **39.** -8

41. $-\dfrac{81}{2} - \dfrac{81\sqrt{3}}{2}i$ **43.** 256

45. (a) $4\left(\cos\dfrac{\pi}{6} + i\sin\dfrac{\pi}{6}\right)$

$4\left(\cos\dfrac{7\pi}{6} + i\sin\dfrac{7\pi}{6}\right)$

(b)

(c) $2\sqrt{3} + 2i$
$-2\sqrt{3} - 2i$

47. (a) $2\left(\cos\dfrac{\pi}{3} + i\sin\dfrac{\pi}{3}\right)$

$2\left(\cos\dfrac{5\pi}{6} + i\sin\dfrac{5\pi}{6}\right)$

$2\left(\cos\dfrac{4\pi}{3} + i\sin\dfrac{4\pi}{3}\right)$

$2\left(\cos\dfrac{11\pi}{6} + i\sin\dfrac{11\pi}{6}\right)$

(b)

(c) $1 + \sqrt{3}i$
$-\sqrt{3} + i$
$-1 - \sqrt{3}i$
$\sqrt{3} - i$

49. (a) $5\left(\cos\dfrac{3\pi}{4} + i\sin\dfrac{3\pi}{4}\right)$

$5\left(\cos\dfrac{7\pi}{4} + i\sin\dfrac{7\pi}{4}\right)$

(b)

(c) $-\dfrac{5\sqrt{2}}{2} + \dfrac{5\sqrt{2}}{2}i$

$\dfrac{5\sqrt{2}}{2} - \dfrac{5\sqrt{2}}{2}i$

51. (a) $5\left(\cos\dfrac{4\pi}{9} + i\sin\dfrac{4\pi}{9}\right)$

$5\left(\cos\dfrac{10\pi}{9} + i\sin\dfrac{10\pi}{9}\right)$

$5\left(\cos\dfrac{16\pi}{9} + i\sin\dfrac{16\pi}{9}\right)$

(b)

(c) $0.868 + 4.92i$

$-4.70 - 1.71i$

$3.83 - 3.21i$

53. (a) $2(\cos 0 + i \sin 0)$

$2\left(\cos \dfrac{2\pi}{3} + i \sin \dfrac{2\pi}{3}\right)$

$2\left(\cos \dfrac{4\pi}{3} + i \sin \dfrac{4\pi}{3}\right)$

(b)

(c) 2

$-1 + \sqrt{3}\,i$

$-1 - \sqrt{3}\,i$

55. (a) $\cos 0 + i \sin 0$

$\cos \dfrac{\pi}{2} + i \sin \dfrac{\pi}{2}$

$\cos \pi + i \sin \pi$

$\cos \dfrac{3\pi}{2} + i \sin \dfrac{3\pi}{2}$

(b)

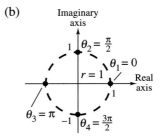

(c) 1

i

-1

$-i$

57. $\cos \dfrac{\pi}{8} + i \sin \dfrac{\pi}{8}$

$\cos \dfrac{5\pi}{8} + i \sin \dfrac{5\pi}{8}$

$\cos \dfrac{9\pi}{8} + i \sin \dfrac{9\pi}{8}$

$\cos \dfrac{13\pi}{8} + i \sin \dfrac{13\pi}{8}$

59. $3\left(\cos \dfrac{\pi}{5} + i \sin \dfrac{\pi}{5}\right)$

$3\left(\cos \dfrac{3\pi}{5} + i \sin \dfrac{3\pi}{5}\right)$

$3(\cos \pi + i \sin \pi)$

$3\left(\cos \dfrac{7\pi}{5} + i \sin \dfrac{7\pi}{5}\right)$

$3\left(\cos \dfrac{9\pi}{5} + i \sin \dfrac{9\pi}{5}\right)$

61. $4\left(\cos\dfrac{\pi}{2} + i\sin\dfrac{\pi}{2}\right)$

$4\left(\cos\dfrac{7\pi}{6} + i\sin\dfrac{7\pi}{6}\right)$

$4\left(\cos\dfrac{11\pi}{6} + i\sin\dfrac{11\pi}{6}\right)$

67.

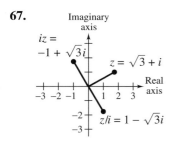

SECTION 8.4 (*page 461*)

1. $(3i, 9 - 3i)$ **3.** $(-8 + 4i, 6 + 12i)$

5. $(-5 + i, -4)$ **7.** $(-9 + 3i, 2 + 14i)$

9. S is *not* a basis for C^2 **11.** S *is* a basis for C^3

13. (a) $(1, 2, 0) = i(i, 0, 0) - 2i(i, i, 0) + 0(i, i, i)$

(b) $(1, 2, 0) = -(1, 0, 0) + 2(1, 1, 0) +$

$\qquad 0(0, 0, 1 + i)$

15. (a) $(-i, 2 + i, -1) = (-2 + 2i)(i, 0, 0) +$

$\qquad\qquad (1 - 3i)(i, i, 0) + i(i, i, i)$

(b) $(-i, 2 + i, -1) = (-2 - 2i)(1, 0, 0) +$

$\qquad\qquad (2 + i)(1, 1, 0) +$

$\qquad\qquad (-\tfrac{1}{2} + \tfrac{1}{2}i)(0, 0, 1 + i)$

17. $\sqrt{2}$ **19.** $3\sqrt{42}$ **21.** $\sqrt{7}$

23. $\sqrt{17}$ **25.** $\sqrt{3}$ **27.** $\sqrt{15}$

29. $\sqrt{2}$ **31.** Linearly dependent

33. Linearly independent

35. Not a complex inner product

37. Is a complex inner product

39. $z_3 = 0$, z_1 and z_2 can be any complex numbers.

47. $T\begin{bmatrix} u_1 \\ u_2 \end{bmatrix} = \begin{bmatrix} 2 + i & 0 \\ 1 & -i \end{bmatrix}\begin{bmatrix} u_1 \\ u_2 \end{bmatrix}$

49. $\begin{bmatrix} 1 + i \\ 2i \end{bmatrix}, \begin{bmatrix} 0 \\ 0 \end{bmatrix}$ **51.** $\begin{bmatrix} 2 - i \\ 1 + 2i \\ -1 + 5i \end{bmatrix}, \begin{bmatrix} 2 \\ 1 \end{bmatrix}$

53. ker $= \{(0, 0)\}$ **55.** $\begin{bmatrix} 0 \\ 0 \end{bmatrix}$

57. (a), (b), and (d) are subspaces.

SECTION 8.5 (*page 471*)

1. $A^* = \begin{bmatrix} -i & 2 \\ i & -3i \end{bmatrix}$ **3.** $A^* = \begin{bmatrix} 0 & 2 \\ 1 & 0 \end{bmatrix}$

5. $A^* = \begin{bmatrix} 0 & 5 + i & \sqrt{2}i \\ 5 - i & 6 & 4 \\ -\sqrt{2}i & 4 & 3 \end{bmatrix}$

7. $A^* = [7 - 5i \quad -2i \quad 4]$

9. A is not unitary because it is singular.

11. A is not unitary because it is not a square matrix.

13. $AA^* = \begin{bmatrix} 4 & 4i \\ -4i & 4 \end{bmatrix} \neq I_2$

Hence, A is not unitary.

15. $AA^* = I_n$

Hence, A is unitary.

17. $AA^* = \begin{bmatrix} 1 & 0 & \frac{1}{6} \\ 0 & 1 & \frac{1}{6} \\ \frac{1}{6} & \frac{1}{6} & \frac{1}{2} \end{bmatrix} \neq I_3$

Hence, A is not unitary.

19. (a) $r_1 = (-\frac{4}{5}, \frac{3}{5}i)$, $r_2 = (\frac{3}{5}, \frac{4}{5}i)$

$\|r_1\| = 1$, $\|r_2\| = 1$, $r_1 \cdot r_2 = 0$

(b) $A^{-1} = \begin{bmatrix} -\frac{4}{5} & \frac{3}{5} \\ -\frac{3}{5}i & -\frac{4}{5}i \end{bmatrix}$

21. (a) $r_1 = \dfrac{1}{2\sqrt{2}}(\sqrt{3} - i, 1 + \sqrt{3}i)$,

$r_2 = \dfrac{1}{2\sqrt{2}}(\sqrt{3} + i, 1 - \sqrt{3}i)$

$\|r_1\| = 1$, $\|r_2\| = 1$, $r_1 \cdot r_2 = 0$

(b) $A^{-1} = \dfrac{1}{2\sqrt{2}} \begin{bmatrix} \sqrt{3} + i & \sqrt{3} - i \\ 1 - \sqrt{3}i & 1 + \sqrt{3}i \end{bmatrix}$

23. A is not Hermitian because the entry a_{22}, on the main diagonal, is not a real number. Hence $A \neq A^*$.

25. A is Hermitian because $A = A^*$.

27. A is Hermitian because $A = A^*$.

29. $\lambda_1 = 1$ **31.** $\lambda_1 = 1$ **33.** $\lambda_1 = 1$
$\lambda_2 = -1$ $\lambda_2 = 4$ $\lambda_2 = 2$
                                         $\lambda_3 = 3$

35. $v_1 = (1, -i)$ **37.** $v_1 = (\sqrt{2}, -i, i)$
$v_2 = (1, i)$ $v_2 = (0, 1, 1)$
                         $v_3 = (\sqrt{2}, i, -i)$

39. $P = \dfrac{1}{\sqrt{2}} \begin{bmatrix} 1 & 1 \\ -i & i \end{bmatrix}$

41. $P = \dfrac{1}{2} \begin{bmatrix} \sqrt{2} & 0 & \sqrt{2} \\ -i\sqrt{2} & & i \\ i\sqrt{2} & & -i \end{bmatrix}$

43. $P = \dfrac{1}{\sqrt{6}} \begin{bmatrix} \sqrt{6} & 0 & 0 \\ 0 & -1+i & 2 \\ 0 & 2 & 1+i \end{bmatrix}$

45. $A = \dfrac{1}{\sqrt{2}} \begin{bmatrix} -1 & -1 \\ -i & i \end{bmatrix}$

47. $A = \dfrac{1}{\sqrt{2}} \begin{bmatrix} i & -i \\ -1 & -1 \end{bmatrix}$

57. (a) $A = \dfrac{A + \bar{A}}{2} + i\dfrac{A - \bar{A}}{2i}$

(b) $\begin{bmatrix} 2 & 1 \\ 1 & 3 \end{bmatrix} + i\begin{bmatrix} 0 & 1 \\ -1 & 0 \end{bmatrix}$

(c) $A = \dfrac{A + A^*}{2} + i\dfrac{A - A^*}{2i}$

(d) $\begin{bmatrix} 0 & 2 - \dfrac{i}{2} \\ 2 + \dfrac{i}{2} & 1 \end{bmatrix} + i\begin{bmatrix} 1 & \dfrac{1}{2} \\ \dfrac{1}{2} & -2 \end{bmatrix}$

REVIEW EXERCISES – CHAPTER 8 (*page 473*)

1. 2   **3.** 20   **5.** $\frac{4}{3} + \frac{2}{3}i$

7. $2 \pm 2i$ **9.** $-\dfrac{1}{2} \pm \dfrac{\sqrt{3}}{2}i$

11. $\begin{bmatrix} 5 & 2+i \\ 3+2i & 5+2i \end{bmatrix}$ **13.** $-1 + 5i$

15. $-1 - 2i$ **17.** $\sqrt{8}$

19. $8 + 4i$ **21.** $\frac{3}{5} + \frac{4}{5}i$ **23.** $\frac{5}{6} + \frac{5}{6}i$

25. A is singular.   **27.** $4\sqrt{2}\left(\cos\dfrac{\pi}{4} + i\sin\dfrac{\pi}{4}\right)$

29. $\sqrt{65}[\cos(-0.519) + i\sin(-0.519)]$

31. $\dfrac{5\sqrt{3}}{2} - \dfrac{5}{2}i$ **33.** $-3 + 3\sqrt{3}i$

35. $12\left(\cos\dfrac{2\pi}{3} + i\sin\dfrac{2\pi}{3}\right)$

37. $\dfrac{3}{2}\left[\cos\left(-\dfrac{\pi}{6}\right) + i\sin\left(-\dfrac{\pi}{6}\right)\right]$

39. $4(\cos\pi + i\sin\pi)$

41. $8\sqrt{2}\left[\cos\left(-\dfrac{5\pi}{6}\right) + i\sin\left(-\dfrac{5\pi}{6}\right)\right]$

43. $5\left(\cos\dfrac{\pi}{3} + i\sin\dfrac{\pi}{3}\right) = \dfrac{5}{2} + \dfrac{5\sqrt{3}}{2i}$

$5\left(\cos\dfrac{4\pi}{3} + i\sin\dfrac{4\pi}{3}\right) = -\dfrac{5}{2} - \dfrac{5\sqrt{3}}{2i}$

45. $\cos\dfrac{\pi}{6} + i\sin\dfrac{\pi}{6} = \dfrac{\sqrt{3}}{2} + \dfrac{1}{2}i$

$\cos\dfrac{5\pi}{6} + i\sin\dfrac{5\pi}{6} = -\dfrac{\sqrt{3}}{2} + \dfrac{1}{2}i$

$\cos\dfrac{3\pi}{2} + i\sin\dfrac{3\pi}{2} = i$

47. $A^* = \begin{bmatrix} -1 - 4i & 3 + i \\ 3 - i & 2 - i \end{bmatrix}$

49. $(-3 + 28i, 14 + 8i)$ **51.** $(-5, 1 - 2i)$

53. $\sqrt{38}$ **55.** 4   **57.** Unitary

59. Not unitary   **61.** Not Hermitian

63. $\lambda_1 = -1, \mathbf{v}_1 = (-2 + i, 5)$

$\lambda_2 = 5, \mathbf{v}_2 = (5, 2 + i)$

CHAPTER 8 MATLAB (*page 476*)

1. (a) $\begin{bmatrix} -8 + 7i & 3 - 2i \\ -3 + 2i & 9 + 4i \end{bmatrix}$

(b) $\begin{bmatrix} -3 & 3 & 0 \\ 6i & 0 & -9 + 6i \end{bmatrix}$

(c) $\begin{bmatrix} 0.0385 - 0.1923i & 0.4231 - 0.1154i \\ 0.3462 + 0.2692i & -0.1923 - 0.0385i \end{bmatrix}$

(d) $\begin{bmatrix} 5 & -1 & 4 + 6i \\ -1 & 1 & 0 \\ 4 - 6i & 0 & 13 \end{bmatrix}$

(e) $11 - 8i$

(f) $\begin{bmatrix} 18 - 35i & -23 - 32i \\ 23 - 44i & 18 - 25i \end{bmatrix}$

3. (a) Neither   (b) Normal
(c) Neither   (d) Normal

Chapter 9

SECTION 9.1 (*page 484*)

1. f   **3.** a   **5.** b

7.

9.

11.

13.

15.

17.

19.

21.

23.

25.

27.

29.

31.

33. $2 \leq x \leq 5$
$1 \leq y \leq 7$

35. $y \leq \frac{3}{2}x$
$y \leq -x + 5$
$y \geq 0$

37. $x + \frac{3}{2}y \leq 12$
$\frac{4}{3}x + \frac{3}{2}y \leq 15$
$x \geq 0$
$y \geq 0$

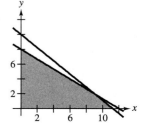

39. x = amount in one account
y = amount in other account
$x + y \leq 20{,}000$
$x \geq 5000$
$y \geq 5000$
$2x \leq y$

41. x = # of ounces of food X
y = # of ounces of food Y
$20x + 10y \geq 300$
$15x + 10y \geq 150$
$10x + 20y \geq 200$
$x, y \geq 0$

SECTION 9.2 (*page 492*)

1. Maximum is 17 at (3, 4)
Minimum is 0 at (0, 0)

3. Maximum is 20 at (4, 0)
Minimum is 0 at (0, 0)

5. Maximum is 740 at (60, 20)
Minimum is 0 at (0, 0)

7. Maximum is 2100 at any point on line segment between (30, 45) and (60, 20)
Minimum is 0 at (0, 0)

9. No maximum
Minimum is 35 at (5, 3)

11. No maximum
Minimum is 20 at (10, 0)

13. Maximum is 160 at (40, 0)
Minimum is 104 at (24, 8)

15. Maximum is 56 at (24, 8)
Minimum is 36 at (36, 0)

17. Maximum is 12 at (3, 6)

19. Maximum is 10 at (0, 10)

21. 200 units of model costing $250
50 units of model costing $400
Maximum profit: $11,500

23. 3 bags of brand X
6 bags of brand Y
Minimum cost: $195

25. z is maximum at any point on the line segment between points (2, 0) and $\left(\frac{20}{19}, \frac{45}{19}\right)$.

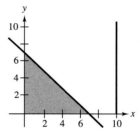

27. The constraint $x \leq 10$ is extraneous.

29. Feasible set is empty, no maximum

No solution points

31. (a) No value of t
(b) $t < 0$
(c) $t > 0$
(d) No value of t

SECTION 9.3 (*page 507*)

1.

x_1	x_2	s_1	s_2	b	Basic Variables
2	1	1	0	8	s_1
1	1	0	1	5	s_2
-1	-2	0	0	0	

3.

x_1	x_2	x_3	s_1	s_2	b	Basic Variables
1	2	0	1	0	12	s_1
1	0	1	0	1	8	s_2
-2	-3	-4	0	0	0	

5. Objective function should be maximized, not minimized.

7. All constraints must be $\leq$.

9. Maximum is 8 at $(8, 0)$

11. Maximum is 210 at $(0, 21, 21)$

13. Maximum is 43 at $(7, 3)$

15. Maximum is $\frac{83}{19}$ at $\left(\frac{16}{19}, 0, 0, \frac{5}{19}\right)$

17. Maximum is 25 at $(23, 0, 2)$ or $\left(\frac{43}{3}, 0, \frac{32}{3}\right)$

19. Maximum is 24 at $(0, 12, 0, 0)$

21. 200 units at \$250
50 units at \$400
Maximum profit: \$11,500

23. 50 acres of carrots
0 acres of celery and lettuce
Maximum profit: \$3000

25. 322 of Model A
764 of Model B
484 of Model C
Maximum profit: \$79,310

27. 9 television ads
4 newspaper ads
Maximum audience: 147,000,000

29. \$100,000 of type A
\$62,500 of type B
\$87,500 of type C
Maximum return: \$26,500

31. 8 audits, 8 tax returns
Maximum revenue: \$18,400

33. After one iteration, the simplex tableau is as follows.

x_1	x_2	s_1	s_2	b	Basic Variables
$-\frac{1}{2}$	0	1	$\frac{3}{2}$	7	s_1
$-\frac{1}{2}$	1	0	$\frac{1}{2}$	2	x_2
-2	0	0	1	4	

35. After one iteration, $x_1 = 2$, $x_2 = 0$, and $z = 5$.
Bringing x_2 in the basis after another iteration,
$x_1 = \frac{20}{19}$, $x_2 = \frac{45}{19}$, and z still equals 5.

37. Maximum is $\frac{85100}{177}$ at $\left(0, \frac{2740}{531}, \frac{28250}{531}, \frac{16655}{531}\right)$

SECTION 9.4 (*page 518*)

1. (Maximize)
Objective function:
$z = 4y_1 + 4y_2$
Constraints:
$2y_1 + y_2 \leq 3$
$y_1 + 2y_2 \leq 3$
$y_1, y_2 \geq 0$

3. (Maximize)
Objective function:
$z = 23y_1 + 10y_2 + 40y_3$
Constraints:
$3y_1 + y_2 + 8y_3 \leq 4$
$2y_1 + y_3 \leq 1$
$y_1 + y_2 + 2y_3 \leq 1$
$y_1, y_2, y_3 \geq 0$

5. (Maximize)
$z = 7y_1 + 4y_2$
Constraints:
$y_1 + y_2 \leq 14$
$y_1 + 2y_2 \leq 20$
$2y_1 + y_2 \leq 24$
$y_1, y_2 \geq 0$

7. (a) Minimum is 4 $(1, 1)$
(b) (Maximize)
Objective function:
$z = 3y_1 + 5y_2$
Constraints:
$y_1 + 3y_2 \leq 2$
$2y_1 + 2y_2 \leq 2$
$y_1, y_2 \geq 0$
(c) Maximum is 4 at $\left(\frac{1}{2}, \frac{1}{2}\right)$

9. (a) Minimum is 8 at $\left(\frac{4}{3}, \frac{5}{3}\right)$
(b) (Maximize)
Objective function:
$z = 3y_1 + 2y_2$
Constraints:
$y_1 - y_2 \leq 1$
$y_1 + 2y_2 \leq 4$
$y_1, y_2 \geq 0$
(c) Maximum is 8 at $(2, 1)$

11. (a) Minimum is 9 at $\left(\frac{1}{2}, 2\right)$
(b) (Maximize)
Objective function:
$z = 4y_1 + 2y_2$
Constraints:
$4y_1 \leq 6$
$y_1 + y_2 \leq 3$
$y_1, y_2 \geq 0$
(c) Maximum is 9 at $\left(\frac{3}{2}, \frac{3}{2}\right)$

13. Minimum is 1.8 at (1, 1.8)

15. Minimum is 6 at (1, 4)

17. Minimum is 18 at $\left(\frac{1}{5}, 2, \frac{7}{5}\right)$

19. Minimum is 64 at $\left(\frac{4}{3}, 4, 16\right)$

21. 1 liter of dietary drink I
1 liter of dietary drink II
Minimum cost: $5

23. 3 liters of dietary drink I
0 liters of dietary drink II
Minimum cost: $3

25. $\frac{5}{3}$ liters of dietary drink I
$\frac{4}{3}$ liters of dietary drink II
Minimum cost: $19

27. 5 liters of dietary drink I
0 liters of dietary drink II
Minimum cost: $5

29. 22.5 days for plant I
10.5 days for plant II
4.75 days for plant III
Minimum operating cost: $2,152,500

31. 0 days for refinery I
120 days for refinery II
Minimum operating cost: $3,600,000

33. Minimum is 87.14 at (21.43, 2.86, 25.71, 0)

SECTION 9.5 (*page 529*)

1.

x_1	x_2	s_1	s_2	b	Basic Variables
2	1	−1	0	4	s_1
1	1	0	1	8	s_2
−10	−4	0	0	0	

3.

x_1	x_2	s_1	s_2	b	Basic Variables
2	1	1	0	4	s_1
1	3	0	−1	2	s_2
1	1	0	0	0	

5.

x_1	x_2	x_3	s_1	s_2	s_3	b	Basic Variables
4	1	0	−1	0	0	10	s_1
1	1	3	0	1	0	30	s_2
2	1	4	0	0	0	16	s_3
−1	0	−1	0	0	0	0	

7. Maximum is 12 at (0, 6)

9. Minimum is 16 at any point on the line segment between (0, 8) and (2, 7)

11. Maximum is 25 at (5, 20, 0)

13. Maximum is 40 at (0, 8)

15. Maximum is 30 at (5, 20, 0)

17. Mimimum is 15 at (5, 10)

19. Mimimum is −20 at $\left(11, \frac{1}{2}, 0\right)$

21. Maximum is 9 at (4, 1)

23. Maximum is 4 at (1, 4)

25. Maximum is 9 at (4, 5)

27. Maximum is 3 at (0, 3)

29. 300 tires from S_1 to C_1
600 tires from S_1 to C_2
200 tires from S_2 to C_1
Minimum cost: $1100

31. 600 tires from S_1 to C_2
500 tires from S_2 to C_1
Minimum cost $1100

33.

	Customer 1	Customer 2
Factory 1	0	200
Factory 2	200	100

Minimum cost $14,500

35. 9 television ads
4 newspaper ads
Maximum audience: 147,000,000

37.

	Outlet I	Outlet II
Plant A	a	$5000 - a$
Plant B	$3000 - a$	a

Minimum cost: $40,000

REVIEW EXERCISES – CHAPTER 9 (*page 531*)

1.

3.

5.

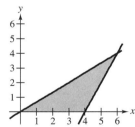

7. $x + y \le 1500, \ x \ge 400, \ y \ge 600$

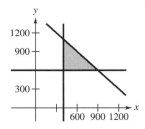

9. Maximum is 47 at (5, 8)

11. Minimum is 3 at (3, 0)
Maximum is 29 at (5, 8)

13. Minimum is -6 at (0, 6)
Maximum is $\frac{64}{3}$ at $\left(8, \frac{8}{3}\right)$

15. Maximum is 26 at (12, 7)

17. Maximum is 20 at (0, 9.6, 0.8)

19. Maximum is 232 at (100, 132)

21. Maximum is 3599 at (110, 537, 146)

23. (Maximize)
Objective function:
$z = 30y_1 + 75y_2$
Constraints:
$$y_1 + 3y_2 \le 7$$
$$y_1 + 6y_2 \le 3$$
$$2y_1 + 4y_2 \le 1$$
$$y_1, y_2 \ge 0$$

25. Minimum is 75 at (5, 2)

27. Minimum is 6006 at $\left(\frac{81}{2}, 138, 111\right)$

29. Minimum is $\frac{118}{3}$ at $\left(\frac{4}{3}, \frac{1}{3}, 0\right)$

31. Maximum is 31 at (1, 15)

33. Maximum is 67 at (7, 27, 26)

35. Minimum is 90 at (10, 0, 0)

37. Maximum is $500 for 2 vests and 5 purses.

39. Minimum is $4800 for 7 days on mine A, 5 days on mine B, and 24 days on mine C.

Chapter 10

SECTION 10.1 (*page 541*)

1. 0.4281×10^4

3. -0.262×10^1

5. -0.121×10^{-2}

7. 0.125×10^0

9. (a) 0.331×10^3
(b) 0.3310×10^3

11. (a) -0.926×10^2
(b) -0.9265×10^2

13. (a) 0.438×10^0
(b) 0.4375×10^0

15. (a) 0.143×10^0
(b) 0.1429×10^0

17. Approximate: -3700
Exact: -3694.7352

19. Approximate: $x = 23.8, y = 0$
Exact: $x = 10, \quad y = 1$

21.

Without Partial Pivoting	With Partial Pivoting
$x = 2.04$	$x = 1$
$y = 0$	$y = 1$

23.

Without Partial Pivoting	With Partial Pivoting
$x_1 = -0.0899$	$x_1 = -0.493$
$y_2 = 0$	$y_2 = 0.100$
$z_3 = 20.2$	$z_3 = 20.1$

25. $x = \quad 9000$

$\quad y = -9000$

27. $x = 2$ and $x = 1$

$\quad\quad\quad y = 0 \quad\quad y = 1$

29. $x_1 = -4.5$

$\quad x_2 = \quad 19$

$\quad x_3 = -12$

SECTION 10.2 (*page 549*)

1. $x_1 = 1.00$

$\quad x_2 = 1.00$

3. $x_1 = 2.00$

$\quad x_2 = 2.00$

$\quad x_3 = 2.00$

5. $x_1 = 1.00$

$\quad x_2 = 1.00$

7. $x_1 = 2.00$

$\quad x_2 = 2.00$

$\quad x_3 = 2.00$

9.

n	0	1	2	3	4	$\cdots$
x_1	0.000	-1.00	9.00	-31.0	129	$\cdots$
x_2	0.000	5.00	-15.00	65.0	-255	$\cdots$

11.

n	0	1	2	3	4	$\cdots$
x_1	0.000	-3.50	2.75	117.0	-33.8	$\cdots$
x_2	0.000	4.17	80.40	-20.2	-1114.0	$\cdots$
x_3	0.000	23.50	4.75	-338.0	114.0	$\cdots$

13. Strictly diagonally dominant

15. Not strictly diagonally dominant

17. $x_1 = 1.0$

$\quad x_2 = 1.0$

19. $x_1 = 4.00$

$\quad x_2 = 5.00$

$\quad x_3 = 1.00$

21. Jacobi Method

n	0	1	2	3	4	$\cdots$	31
x_1	0.00	-0.250	1.625	1.781	0.609	$\cdots$	1
x_2	0.00	1.500	1.625	0.688	0.609	$\cdots$	1

Gauss–Seidel Method

n	0	1	2	3	4	$\cdots$	19
x_1	0.00	-0.250	1.781	0.512	1.305	$\cdots$	1
x_2	0.00	1.625	0.609	1.244	0.847	$\cdots$	1

23.
```
10 REM  ———> Gauss–Seidel Method <———
15 LET X1 = 0
20 LET X2 = 0
25 LET X3 = 0
30 LET X4 = 0
35 LET X5 = 0
40 LET X6 = 0
45 LET X7 = 0
50 LET X8 = 0
55 LET E = 1
60 IF E < .001 THEN GOTO 195
65   LET T1 = X1
70   LET T2 = X2
75   LET T3 = X3
80   LET T4 = X4
85   LET T5 = X5
90   LET T6 = X6
95   LET T7 = X7
100 LET T8 = X8
105 LET X1 = 3/4 + (−X2 + X3)/4
110 LET X2 = −1 + (−X1 + 2*X3 − X4 + X5)/6
115 LET X3 = −1 + (−X2 + X5 − X6)/5
120 LET X4 = (−2*X2 + X5 + X7 + X8)/5
125 LET X5 = 2 + (X3 + X4 + X6 + X8)/6
130 LET X6 = −12/5(X3 + X5)/5
135 LET X7 = −1/2 + (X4 + X8)/4
140 LET X8 = 2/5 + (X4 + X5 + X7)/5
145 LET E = ABS (T1 − X1)
150 IF ABS(T2 − X2) > E THEN LET E =
     ABS(T2 − X2)
155 IF ABS(T3 − X3) > E THEN LET E =
     ABS(T3 − X3)
160 IF ABS(T4 − X4) > E THEN LET E =
     ABS(T4 − X4)
165 IF ABS(T5 − X5) > E THEN LET E =
     ABS(T5 − X5)
170 IF ABS(T6 − X6) > E THEN LET E =
     ABS(T6 − X6)
175 IF ABS(T7 − X7) > E THEN LET E =
     ABS(T7 − X7)
```

```
180  IF ABS(T8 − X8) > E THEN LET E =
        ABS(T8 − X8)
185  PRINT "*";
190      GOTO 60
195  PRINT
200  PRINT "The final solution is:"
205  PRINT "    X1 = ";: PRINT USING "##.###";X1
210  PRINT "    X2 = ";: PRINT USING "##.###";X2
215  PRINT "    X3 = ";: PRINT USING "##.###";X3
220  PRINT "    X4 = ";: PRINT USING "##.###";X4
225  PRINT "    X5 = ";: PRINT USING "##.###";X5
230  PRINT "    X6 = ";: PRINT USING "##.###";X6
235  PRINT "    X7 = ";: PRINT USING "##.###";X7
240  PRINT "    X8 = ";: PRINT USING "##.###";X8
245  END
```

****

```
The final solution is :
    X1 =    1.000
    X2 = −1.000
    X3 =    0.000
    X4 =    1.000
    X5 =    2.000
    X6 = −2.000
    X7 =    0.000
    X8 =    1.000
```

Section 10.3 (*page 557*)

1. $\lambda = -4, 2$

$$\begin{bmatrix} 1 \\ -6 \end{bmatrix}$$

3. $\lambda = -4, 4$

No dominant eigenvector

5. $\lambda = -1, 2, 3$

$$\begin{bmatrix} 5 \\ 1 \\ 2 \end{bmatrix}$$

7. $\lambda = 2$

9. $\lambda = -3$

11. $\mathbf{x}_5 = \begin{bmatrix} -0.1132 \\ 1.0000 \end{bmatrix}, \lambda \approx -6.998$

13. $\mathbf{x}_5 = \begin{bmatrix} -0.5 \\ 1.0 \end{bmatrix}, \lambda = 9$

15. $\mathbf{x}_4 = \begin{bmatrix} 0.0156 \\ 0.0041 \\ 1.0000 \end{bmatrix}, \lambda \approx 8.0068$

17. $\mathbf{x}_4 = \begin{bmatrix} -0.9984 \\ 1.0000 \\ 0.1673 \end{bmatrix}, \lambda \approx 5.0061$

19. $\mathbf{x}_0 = \begin{bmatrix} 1 \\ 1 \\ 1 \end{bmatrix}, \mathbf{x}_1 = \begin{bmatrix} 1 \\ 1 \\ -1 \end{bmatrix}, \mathbf{x}_2 = \begin{bmatrix} 1 \\ 1 \\ 1 \end{bmatrix}, \mathbf{x}_3 = \begin{bmatrix} 1 \\ 1 \\ -1 \end{bmatrix}, \mathbf{x}_4 = \begin{bmatrix} 1 \\ 1 \\ 1 \end{bmatrix}$

21. (a) Eigenvalues: 2, 5

Eigenvectors: $(1, 1), (-\frac{1}{2}, 1)$

(b) $\mathbf{x}_0 = \begin{bmatrix} 1 \\ 1 \end{bmatrix}, \mathbf{x}_1 = \begin{bmatrix} 1 \\ 1 \end{bmatrix}, \mathbf{x}_2 = \begin{bmatrix} 1 \\ 1 \end{bmatrix}$

(c) Because the initial guess was an eigenvector for $\lambda = 2$.

23. $\lambda \approx -0.982$ (Actual value is $\lambda = -1$.)

25. (a) $A: \lambda = 1, 3$

$B: \lambda = 1, 5$

(b) $A: \mathbf{x}_0 = \begin{bmatrix} -1 \\ 2 \end{bmatrix}, \mathbf{x}_1 = \begin{bmatrix} 0 \\ 1 \end{bmatrix}, \mathbf{x}_2 = \begin{bmatrix} 0.5 \\ 1 \end{bmatrix}, \mathbf{x}_3 = \begin{bmatrix} 0.8 \\ 1 \end{bmatrix},$

$$\mathbf{x}_4 = \begin{bmatrix} 0.929 \\ 1 \end{bmatrix}$$

$B: \mathbf{x}_0 = \begin{bmatrix} -1 \\ 2 \end{bmatrix}, \mathbf{x}_1 = \begin{bmatrix} 0.57 \\ 1 \end{bmatrix}, \mathbf{x}_2 = \begin{bmatrix} 0.906 \\ 1 \end{bmatrix},$

$$\mathbf{x}_3 = \begin{bmatrix} 0.981 \\ 1 \end{bmatrix}, \mathbf{x}_4 = \begin{bmatrix} 0.996 \\ 1 \end{bmatrix}$$

(c) $A: \dfrac{\lambda_2}{\lambda_1} = \dfrac{1}{3}$

$B: \dfrac{\lambda_2}{\lambda_1} = \dfrac{1}{5}$

B should converge faster.

27. $\lambda \approx 9.000$

Section 10.4 (*page 566*)

1. $y = 0.1760x^2 + 0.0935x + 0.2533$

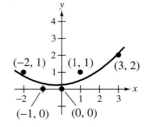

3. $y = -0.6786x^2 + 0.1357x + 3.9143$

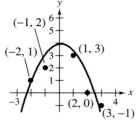

5. $y = 0.287x^3 - 2.456x^2 + 5.336x - 0.254$

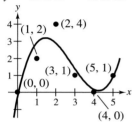

7. $y = 0.09434x^3 + 0.7922x^2 + 0.3518x + 0.4313$

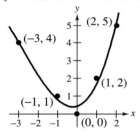

9. $y = -0.397x^2 + 0.966, y\left(\dfrac{\pi}{4}\right) = 0.721$ (Exact: 0.707)

11. (a) $p_1(x) = 310.7 - 3.088x$

(b) $p_2(x) = 0.08579x^2 - 15.37x + 696.8$

(c)

(d) $p_1(120) = -59.9, p_2(120) = 87.8$

13. Let $x = 0$ represent 1977.
$y = 0.2856x^2 + 4.139x + 22.62$
1986 ($x = 9$): 83.00
1988 ($x = 11$): 102.7

15. Let $x = 0$ represent 1970.
$y = 0.0676x + 3.778$
1990 ($x = 20$): 5.13
1995 ($x = 25$): 5.47

17. $p_1 = 0.1553$ $p_2 = 0.2050$
$p_3 = 0.1553$ $p_4 = 0.4162$
$p_5 = 0.5093$ $p_6 = 0.4162$

19. $t_1 = 85.7143$ $t_2 = 71.4286$
$t_3 = 50.0000$ $t_4 = 71.4286$
$t_5 = 50.0000$ $t_6 = 28.5714$
$t_7 = 50.0000$ $t_8 = 28.5714$
$t_9 = 14.2857$

21. $\mathbf{x} = t\begin{bmatrix} 4 \\ 1 \end{bmatrix}$

23. $\mathbf{x} \approx t\begin{bmatrix} 1.0000 \\ 0.5652 \\ 0.1597 \end{bmatrix}$

25. $\mathbf{x} = t\begin{bmatrix} 16 \\ 4 \\ 1 \end{bmatrix}$

29. $\mathbf{x} \approx t\begin{bmatrix} 1.0000 \\ 0.4750 \\ 0.4500 \end{bmatrix}$

INDEX